OPTICS

Seventh Edition

सूर्यस्य विविधवर्णाः पवनेन
विघट्टिताः कराः साभ्रे ।
वियति धनुः संस्थानाः
ये दृश्यन्ते तदिन्द्रधनुः ।।

Bruhatsamhita-chapter 35
(6th century CE)

The multicolored rays of the Sun, being dispersed
in a cloudy sky, are seen in the form of a bow,
which is called the Rainbow.

About the Author

Ajoy Ghatak is currently Meghnad Saha Distinguished Professor of The National Academy of Sciences India, Prayagraj. He received his B.Sc. from Agra College, M.Sc. from Delhi University and Ph.D. from Cornell University. He was a Research Associate at Brookhaven National Laboratory. He received D.Sc. (Honoris Causa) from University of Burdwan in 2007.

He joined IIT Delhi in 1966 where he became a Professor in 1974. His research interests are in Fiber Optics & Quantum Mechanics. He has authored several books including *Fiber Optics*, *Optical Electronics* & *LASERS* (all 3 coauthored with K. Thyagarajan), *Quantum Mechanics* (coauthored with S Lokanathan), *Mathematical Physics* (coauthored with I C Goyal & S J Chua) and a book on *Albert Einstein: The Story of a Genius.* He is recipient of the 2008 SPIE Educator award in recognition of "*his unparalleled global contributions to the field of fiber optics research, and his tireless dedication to optics education worldwide..*"; the 2003 Esther Hoffman Beller award (instituted by The Optical Society of America) in recognition of his "*outstanding contributions to optics education ...*" ; International Commission for Optics 1998 Galileo Galilei award and also the CSIR 1979 S.S. Bhatnagar award for "*outstanding contributions in physical sciences*". The photograph above is from his video lecture recorded by IIT Delhi in February 2017 for the IIT-PAL (Professor Assisted Learning) video lectures for Class XI and Class XII.

OPTICS

Seventh Edition

Ajoy Ghatak

Meghnad Saha Professor
The National Academy of Sciences India
(Former Professor of Physics at IIT Delhi)

McGraw Hill Education (India) Private Limited

Published by McGraw Hill Education (India) Private Limited
444/1, Sri Ekambara Naicker Industrial Estate, Alapakkam, Porur, Chennai - 600 116

Optics, 7e

Print Edition:
ISBN-13: 978-93-90113-59-0
ISBN-10: 93-90113-59-8

E-Book Edition:
ISBN-13: 978-93-90113-60-6
ISBN-10: 93-90113-60-1

1 2 3 4 5 6 7 8 9 D101417 24 23 22 21 20

Printed and bound in India

Managing Director: *Lalit Singh*

Business Head–Higher Education: *Ebi John Amos*
Senior Portfolio Manager–Higher Education: *Suman Sen*
Associate Portfolio Manager: *Jagriti Kundu*

Director–Content Development & Production Services: *Tanweer Ahmad*
Lead Content Developer: *Bhavna Malhotra*
Content Developer: *Shweta Pant*

Project Manager–Production Services: *Atul Gupta*
Asst. Manager–Production Services: *Anuj K Shriwastava*

General Manager–Production: *Rajender P Ghansela*
Senior Manager–Production: *Reji Kumar*

Typeset at The Composers, 260, C.A. Apt., Paschim Vihar, New Delhi 110 063 and printed at Rajkamal Electric Press, Kundli, Haryana.

Cover Image Source: Delphotos/Alamy Stock Photo

Cover Designer: Kapil Gupta

Cover Printer: Rajkamal Electric Press

RQBCRRYPLYQBD

Visit us at: www.mheducation.co.in

Write to us at: info.india@mheducation.com

CIN: U80302TN2010PTC111532
Toll Free Number: 1800 103 5875

I dedicate this book to my students
my continuous interactions with them have led to
a deeper understanding of optics

Contents

PART 4 Lasers & Fiber Optics

Preface

The keyword of the present civilization is science. In order to survive, we have to struggle with nature and to win this battle you must have science as a tool.

—Meghnad Saha

On 16th May 1960, Theodore Maiman, a physicist and engineer and at that time working at Hughes Research Laboratories in California, successfully operated the first laser. Since then, there has been a renaissance in the field of optics: from optical amplifiers to fiber lasers, fiber optics to optical communications, cutting through metals to eye surgery, optical data processing to holography, LIGO experiments to laser fusion, optical sensors to super continuum generation. Optics now finds extremely important applications in almost all branches of science, engineering and also medicine. Indeed in 2018, UNESCO declared that every year 16th May will be celebrated as the International Day of Light. On this day, throughout the world, numerous events are organized celebrating the International Day of Light. More details about the International Day of Light (and International Year of Light) are discussed in the PROLOGUE to the book. The PROLOGUE also gives the large number of Nobel Prizes that have been awarded in the general areas of Optics & Photonics demonstrating the tremendous importance of optics.

In addition to numerous practical applications of light, it is said that it was the quest to understand the "nature of light" that brought about the two revolutions in science: the development of quantum mechanics started with an attempt to understand the "light quantum", and the starting point of the special theory of relativity was Maxwell's equations which synthesized the laws of electricity and magnetism with those of light. Because of all this, an undergraduate course in optics has become a "must" not only for students of physics but also for students of engineering. Although it is impossible to cover all areas in a single book, this book attempts to give a comprehensive account of a large number of important topics in this exciting field and should meet the requirements of a course on optics meant for undergraduate students of science and engineering. This book attempts to give a balanced account of traditional optics as well as some of the recent developments in this field. The plan of the book is discussed in the PROLOGUE to the book.

Other Important Features of the book are

- A large number of figures correspond to actual numerical calculations which were generated using software such as GNUPLOT and Mathematica.
- Most chapters start with important milestones in the area. This gives a historical perspective of the subject matter discussed in the chapter.
- All important formulae have been derived from first principles so that the book can also be used for self-study.
- Numerous worked out examples are scattered throughout the book to help clarify difficult concepts.
- Each chapter ends with a summary of important results derived in the chapter.

Experiments in Fiber Optics

My own research interests are in the general area of fiber optics. I have found that there are many beautiful experiments in fiber optics, which are not very difficult to set up, that allow us not only to understand difficult concepts but also to find very important applications. For example,

- Chapter 11 discusses in great detail the dispersion of an optical pulse as it propagates through a dispersive medium. This is an extremely important concept. The chapter also discusses self phase modulation (usually abbreviated as SPM) that is probably the simplest nonlinear optical phenomenon which can be easily understood from first principles. Indeed, when a monochromatic laser pulse propagates through a special optical fiber, SPM (along with other phenomena) can lead to the awesome super continuum generation; we discuss this in Chapter 11.

- The working of a Fiber Bragg Grating (usually abbreviated as FBG) is a beautiful application of the interference phenomenon, and FBGs find very important applications in sensors and other optical devices. In Chapter 14, the basic physics of an FBG is discussed along with its very important application in temperature sensing at places where no other device would work.
- The experiment on Faraday rotation in optical fibers (discussed in Chapter 21) allows one to understand the concept of rotation of plane of polarization in the presence of a longitudinal magnetic field. This experiment finds important application in the industry for measuring very large currents (about 10,000 Amperes or more). The theory of Faraday rotation is also given from first principles. In Chapter 21, the change in the state of polarization (usually abbreviated as SOP) of a light beam as it propagates through an elliptic core single-mode optical fiber has been discussed; the experiment not only allows one to understand the changing SOP of a beam propagating through a birefringent fiber, but also helps one to understand the radiation pattern of an oscillating dipole.
- Erbium-doped fiber amplifier (usually abbreviated as EDFA) and fiber lasers are discussed in Chapter 27. The working of an EDFA allows one to easily understand the concept of optical amplification and therefore the working of a laser.
- Optical fibers with parabolic index variation are used in optical communication systems. Ray paths in such fibers and their dispersion characteristics are of great importance. This is discussed from first principles in Chapters 2 and 28.
- Chapters 28 through 30 are on waveguide theory and fiber optics, an area that has revolutionized communications and finds important applications in sensor technology. Optical fibers are now widely used in endoscopy, display illumination, and sensors, and of course the most important application is in the field of fiber-optic communication systems. We discuss all this in Chapter 28. Chapter 29 discusses basic waveguide theory (and concept of modes) with Maxwell's equations as the starting point. The chapter allows one to understand the transition from geometrical optics to wave optics, which happens to be similar to the transition from classical mechanics to quantum mechanics. Chapter 30 discusses the waveguiding properties of single-mode optical fibers, which are now extensively used in optical communication systems. The prism film coupling experiment (discussed in Chapter 29) allows one to understand the concept of quantization, an extremely important concept in physics and electrical engineering.

There are many such examples scattered throughout the book, and each example is unique and not usually found in other textbooks.

Online Resources for Instructors and Students

A number of supplementary resources—additional to the text—are available online as Instructor and Students resources.

Instructor Resources:

1. Solutions to end-of-chapter problems
2. Lecture PowerPoint presentations

Instructor resources can be accessed from https://connect.mheducation.com. Please see the inside front cover for more details.

Students Resources:

1. Additional Content on:
   - History of Optics
   - Fourier Integral Theorem
2. Additional Multiple Choice Questions with answers

Student resources can be accessed from *www.mheducation.co.in*. Search for Optics or ISBN of the book, and register using the steps and scratch code mentioned on back inner cover.

Acknowledgements

I was very fortunate to be born in a family which put great emphasis in the study of basic science. Then I had the great privilege of being taught by outstanding teachers like Mr J P Gupta (in a school in Agra); Dr V S Sinha and Dr L P Sharma (at Agra College); Professor D S Kothari and Professor R C Majumdar (at Delhi University) and Professor Mark Nelkin, Professor Hans Bethe and Professor W H J Fuchs (at Cornell University). And then after I joined IIT Delhi (in 1966), I was very fortunate to have the opportunity to interact with outstanding colleagues and also with outstanding students; it was always a pleasure and challenge to teach any course there. We had the opportunity and freedom to modify and develop any course and present it in a form, that would make the subject more interesting. That is how the present book evolved.

In the writing of various editions of this book, many have helped me and have also made very important suggestions. First I would like to mention the name of my very close friend and colleague Professor Ishwar Goyal, who used earlier Indian editions of this book many times while teaching Optics at IIT Delhi and offered numerous suggestions and many constructive criticisms; I am sure he would have been very happy to see this edition of the book, but unfortunately, he is no longer with us—I greatly miss my interactions with him. I am very grateful to Professor M S Sodha for his constant encouragement and support; he had motivated me to work in the general area of fiber optics. My sincere thanks to Professor K Thyagarajan for continuous collaboration and for letting me use some of his unpublished notes. My grateful thanks to Professor Arun Kumar, Professor Lalit Malhotra, Professor Bishnu Pal, Professor Anurag Sharma, Professor K Thyagarajan (from IIT Delhi); Dr Shyamal Bhadra, Dr Kamal Dasgupta and Dr Mrinmay Pal (from CGCRI, Kolkata); Professor Vengu Lakshminarayanan (from University of Waterloo, Canada) and Professor Enakshi Sharma (now at University of Delhi South Campus) for their help in writing some portions of the book. I am also grateful to Professor Anirban Pathak (from Jaypee Institute of Information Technology, Noida) for our recent collaboration and introducing me to new areas related to optics. I thank Dr Gouranga Bose, Dr Parthasarathi Palai (now at Tejas Networks in Bangalore), Professor Chandra Sakher, Professor R S Sirohi, Professor K Thyagarajan, and Professor Ravi Varshney (from IIT Delhi); Professor Govind Swarup (from GMRT, Pune); Dr Somnath Bandyopadhyay, Dr Shyamal Bhadra, Dr Kamal Dasgupta, Dr Tarun Gangopadhyay, Dr Atasi Pal, and Dr Mrinmay Pal (from CGCRI, Kolkata); Dr Brahmanand Upadhyay (from RRCAT, Indore), Dr Suresh Nair (from NeST, Cochin); Mr Avinash Pasricha (from the U.S. Information Service at New Delhi); Dr R E Bailey (from Australia), Dr Pekka Parviainen (from Finland), Dr David Monniaux (from France), Dr Ronald Koebler(from Germany), Dr Piotr Pieranski (from Poland), Dr Alan Reed and Dr Bob Tubbs (from UK), Dr J Alcoz, Professor R Boyd, Dr A G Chynoweth, Mr Marshall Dudley, Ms Theresa Knott, Professor Vengu Lakshminarayanan, Mr Justin Lebar, Dr Ramadas Pillai, Dr George Kaplan, Dr A Young, Professor R A Phillips, Dr R W Terhune (from USA), for allowing me to use photographs taken by them in this book. I also thank various publishers for their permission to use photographs from their publications. I would also like to thank my other colleagues, Professor B D Gupta, Professor Sunil Khijwania, Professor Vipul Rastogi, Professor M R Shenoy, Professor Kehar Singh and Mr Varghese Paulose for their help and many enlightening discussions.

I would also like to thank Mr Suman Sen, Ms Jagriti Kundu, Ms Shweta Pant and Mr Anuj Shriwastava (at McGraw Hill Education) for their great cooperation and help in bringing out this book.

Finally, I owe a lot to my family—particularly to my wife, Gopa—for allowing me to spend long hours in preparing this difficult manuscript and for her support all along.

I will be very grateful for suggestions for further improvement of the book. My e-mail address is ajoykghatak@gmail.com.

Ajoy Ghatak

Prologue

Considering that the applications of light science and technology are vital for existing and future advances in medicine, energy, information and communications, fibre optics, agriculture, mining, astronomy, architecture, archaeology, entertainment, art and culture, as well as many other industries and services, and that light-based technologies contribute to the fulfilment of internationally agreed development goals, including by providing access to information and increasing societal health and well-being. Considering also that technology and design can play an important role in the achievement of greater energy efficiency....

.......Part of Resolution No. 68/221 adopted by the United Nations General Assembly on 20 December 2013 proclaiming 2015 as International Year of Light and Light-based Technologies**

IYL, IDL & NOBEL Prizes in Optics: Why Study of Light is So Important*

The International Year of Light

On December 20, 2013, The United Nations General Assembly proclaimed 2015 as the International Year of Light and Light-based Technologies (IYL 2015) – see Figure 1.

(a)

(b)

Figure 1

(a) The UNESCO announcement and (b) the logo for the IYL (International Year of Light). adapted from http://en.unesco.org/

Above Image: Aurora Borealis photographed in the early hours of the morning in the Arctic Circle, with pine trees silhouetted against the colors. Photograph courtesy McGraw Hill Digital Access Library.

* IYL stands for International Year of Light & IDL stands for International Day of Light

** Adapted from https://undocs.org/en/A/RES/68/221

In proclaiming an International Year focusing on the topic of light science and its applications, the United Nations recognized that*

> *Light plays a vital role in our daily lives and is an imperative cross-cutting discipline of science in the 21st century. It has revolutionized medicine, opened up international communication via the Internet, and continues to be central to linking cultural, economic and political aspects of the global society*

According to UNESCO, the major goals of the International Year of Light 2015 were to:

> *improve the public understanding of how light and light-based technologies touch the daily lives of everybody, and are central to the future development of the global society.*

Choosing 2015 as the International Year of Light was primarily because exactly 1000 years back, Ibn Al-Haytham (also known as Alhazen) wrote the first book on Optics (see Figure 2); the original title of the book was *Kitab al Manazir* which was in 7 volumes. In addition to the great work of Ibn Al-Haytham, in 2015 the following anniversaries were also celebrated:

- 200th anniversary of Fresnel's theory of light (1815) – [discussed in Chapter 19].
- 150th anniversary of Maxwell's electromagnetic theory of light (1865) – [discussed in Chapter 22].
- 50th anniversary of Charles Kao's 1965 paper on optical fiber communication which got him the Nobel Prize – [discussed in Chapter 29].

As such, in 2015, there were numerous events (throughout the world) celebrating the Year of Light.

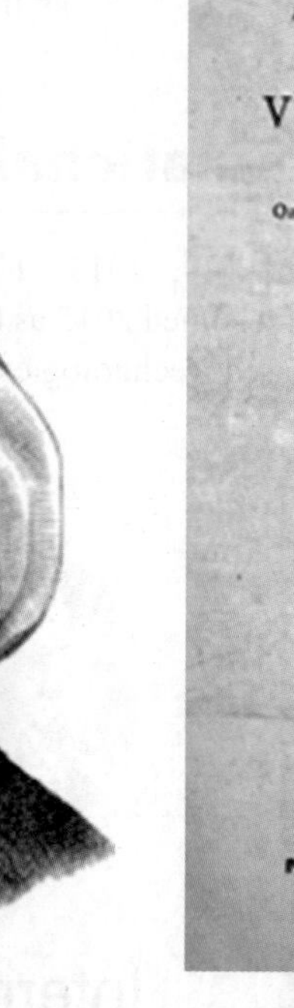

(a)

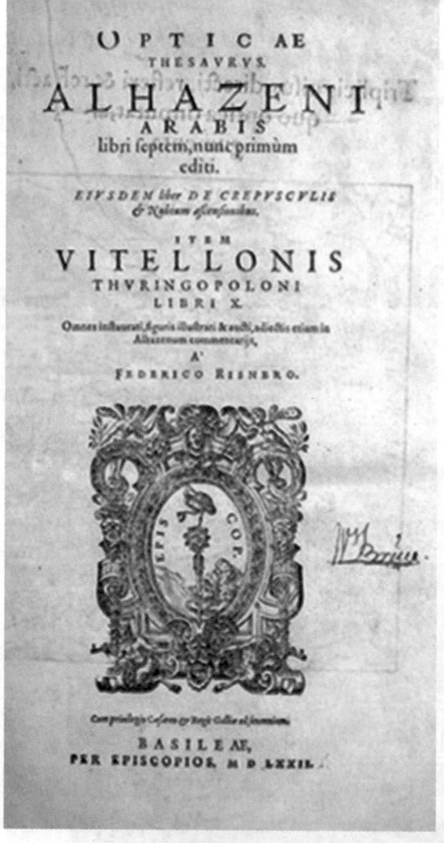

OPTICAE
THESAVRVS.
ALHAZENI
ARABIS
libri septem, nunc primùm
editi.
EIVSDEM liber DE CREPVSCVLIS
& Nubium ascensionibus.
ITEM
VITELLONIS
THVRINGOPOLONI
LIBRI X.
A
FEDERICO RISNERO.
BASILEAE,
PER EPISCOPIOS. M D LXXII.

(b)

The seven volumes of *Kitab al Manazir*:

Volume 1: *Theory of Vision, Light & Color. The Eye & its Anatomy.*

Volumes 2,3&4: *Visual perception & Reflection.*

Volumes 5&6: *Alhazens theories on reflection and experimental results.*

Volume 7: *Theory and experiments on Refraction.*

(c)

Figure 2

(a) In 1015 Alhazen wrote Kitab al Manazir which is the first book on Optics. (b) The cover page of a translated edition of Alhazen's book on Optics. (c) The 7 volumes of Alhazen's Optics

* Adapted from https://en.unesco.org/events/launch-international-year-light-and-light-based-technologies-2015

The International Day of Light

Then in 2018, UNESCO declared that every year 16th May will be celebrated as the International Day of Light (see Figure 3); this is because of the fact that May 16 marks the anniversary of the first successful operation of the laser. Theodore Maiman, a physicist and engineer (at that time working at Hughes Research Laboratories in California) successfully operated the first laser on 16th May 1960 (see Figure 3). Discovery of the laser has led to tremendous benefits to society in communications, healthcare and numerous other areas in which our industries and R&D laboratories are involved with. According to UNESCO:

> *IDL* (International Day of Light) *aims to raise awareness of the critical role light-based technologies play in our lives, elevating science, technology, art, and culture to help achieve the goals of UNESCO – education, equality, and peace.*

Why Study of Light has become Extremely Important

Lasers have indeed revolutionized our lives. Ever since the first laser was fabricated, there has been a renaissance in the field of optics and study of light has become extremely important. From optical amplifiers to laser physics, fiber optics to optical communications, optical data processing to holography, optical sensors to DVD technology, ultrashort

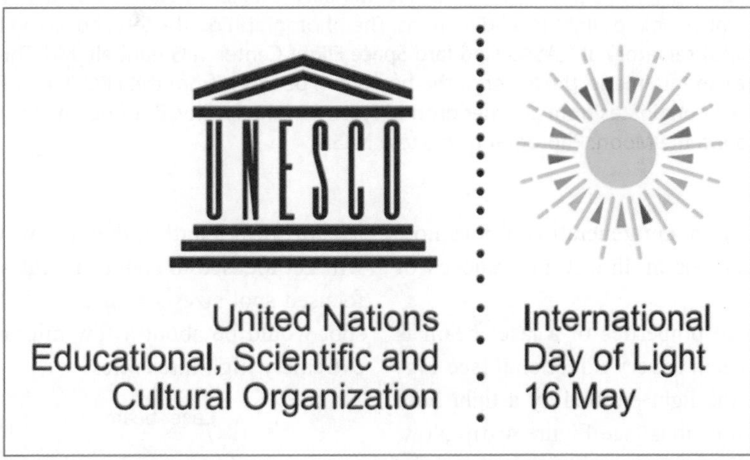

(a)

(b)

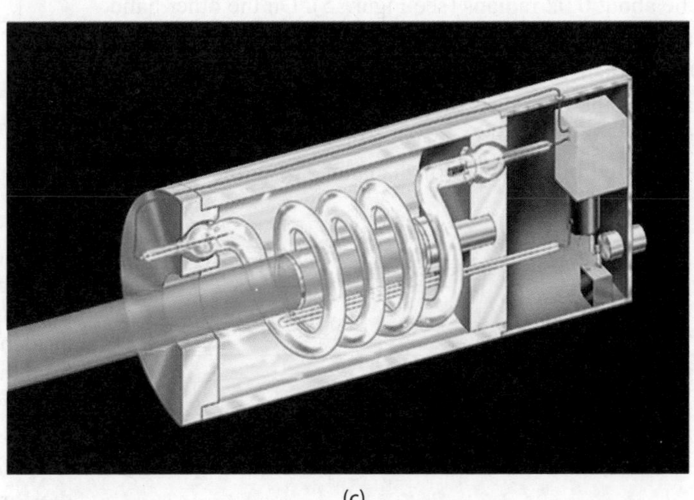

(c)

Figure 3
(a) UNESCO declared that every year 16th May will be celebrated as the International Day of Light. (b) Theodore Maiman (who successfully operated the first laser on 16th May 1960) holding the world's first (ruby) laser at the 25th anniversary of his invention. (c) A very directional beam coming out of a ruby laser. Photo credit: LLNL

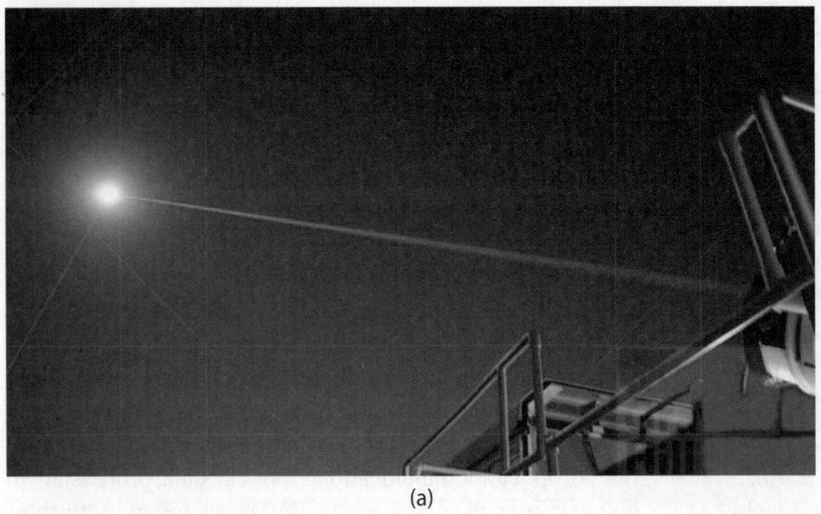

(a)

(b)

Figure 4

(a) One of the very important properties of a laser beam is its directionality; the laser beam is very directional in comparison to (b) light emitted by a light bulb which radiates light in all directions. The photograph on the left shows the Laser Ranging Facility at the Geophysical and Astronomical Observatory at NASA's Goddard Space Flight Center in Greenbelt, Md. The observatory helps NASA keep track of orbiting satellites. In this image, the lower of the two green beams is from the LRO (Lunar Reconnaissance Orbiter's) dedicated tracker. The other laser originates from another ground system at the facility. Both beams are pointed at the moon -- specifically at LRO in orbit around the Moon. Photograph courtesy NASA.

pulse generation to super continuum generation, optics now finds very important applications in almost all branches of science and engineering.

One of the very important properties of a laser beam is its directionality; the laser beam is very directional [see Figure 4(a)] in comparison to the light emitted by a light bulb which radiates light in all directions [see Figure 4(b)]. Now, if a small filament (of say 2 mm in length) is placed at the focal plane of a lens, the angular divergence of the beam $\Delta\theta$, will be about 0.02 radians (see Figure 5). On the other hand, the angular divergence of a laser beam can be as small as 0.00001 radians; we have discussed this in detail in Sec. 17.4. Because of the high directionality of a laser beam, it can be focused to a very small area. We will show in Sec. 17.4 that if a truncated plane wave (of diameter $2a$) is incident on a lens of focal length f, then the wave emerging from the lens will get focused to spot of radius $\approx \lambda_0 f/a$ and the area of the focused spot size is $\approx \pi(\lambda_0 f/a)^2$. Typically the radius of the spot would be about a few microns [see Figure 6] creating extremely high intensities.

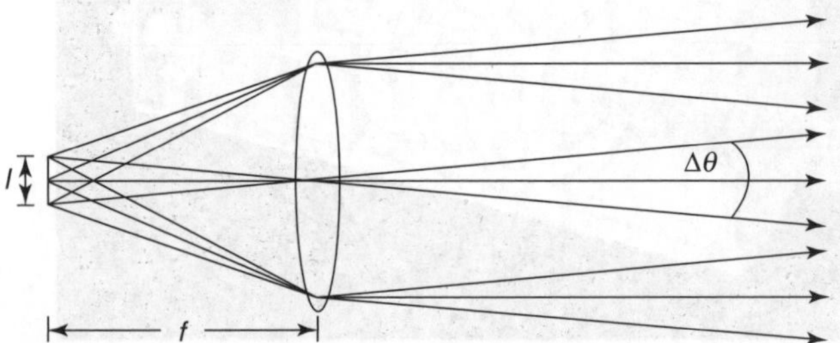

Figure 5

If a small filament (of say 2 mm in length) is placed at the focal plane of a lens, the angular divergence Δθ will be about 0.02 radians. On the other hand, the angular divergence of a laser beam [see Figure 4(a)] can be as small as 0.00001 radians.

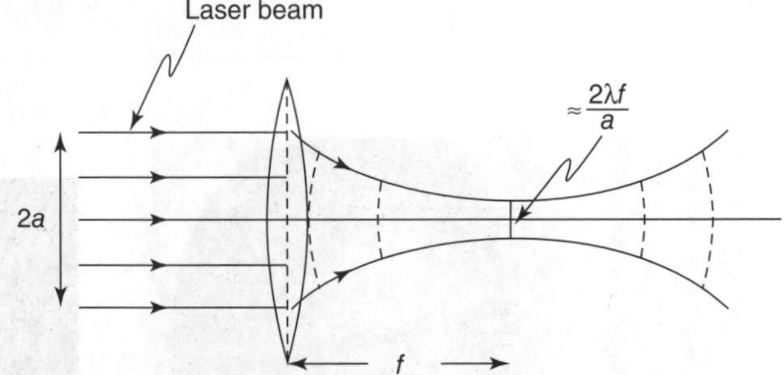

Figure 6

Because of the high directionality of a laser beam, it can be focused to a spot of radius about 1 micron creating extremely high intensities. If a truncated plane wave (of diameter $2a$) is incident on a lens of focal length f, then the wave emerging from the lens will get focused to spot of radius $\approx \lambda_0 f/a$ the area of the focused spot size is $\approx \pi(\lambda_0 f/a)^2$.

In fact, focused laser beams can cause retinal burns, but they are also extensively used to cure retinal detachment and other problems with the eye [see Figs. 7 and 8]. In December 1961, a hospital in the US used a laser on a human patient for the first time, destroying a retinal tumor; this was the first time a laser was used for medical treatments. Using focused

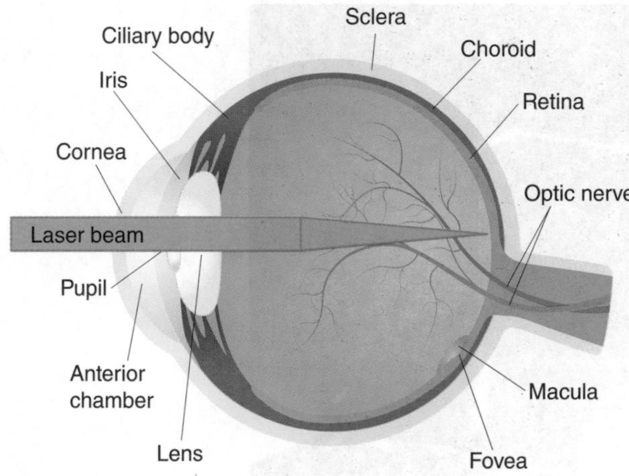

Figure 7

Focused laser beams can cause retinal burns, but they are also extensively used to cure retinal detachment; photograph courtesy shutterstock/wawritto

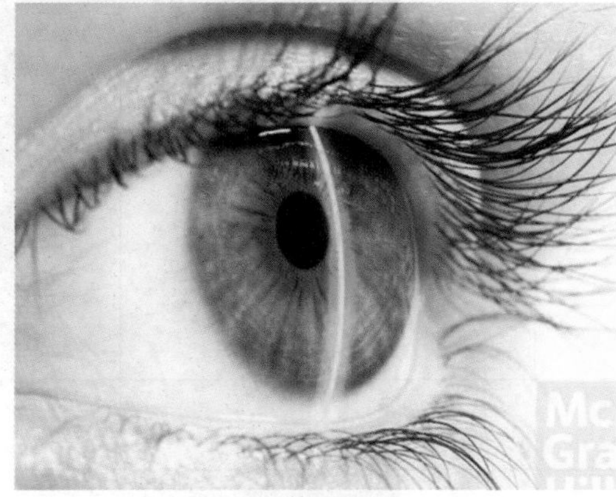

Figure 8

Extreme close-up view of a laser scanning a hazel eye. Photograph courtesy Anthony Lee/caia image/Alamy.

laser beams extremely important devices have been created for the industry and also defense. Figure 9 shows a focused laser beam drilling through concrete. Figure 10 shows a focused laser beam cutting through 4″ thick steel; the laser wavelength is in the infrared region, the light coming out is due to burning of steel. Pulsed lasers are extensively used in welding in the auto industry. As said by the famous author Al Ries

> *A laser is a weak source of energy. A laser takes* [only] *a few watts of energy ..... But with a laser, you can drill a hole in a diamond or wipe out cancer.*

Powerful laser beams can create temperatures which will result in generation of fusion power. Figure 11 shows the setup at the Lawrence Livermore Laboratory in the US; the

Figure 9

A focused laser beam drilling through concrete; photograph courtesy Dr. Brahma Nand Upadhyay @ RRCAT, Indore.

Figure 10

A focused laser beam cutting through thick steel. The laser wavelength is in the infrared region, the light coming out is due to burning of steel. Photo courtesy Professor David Payne, University of Southampton.

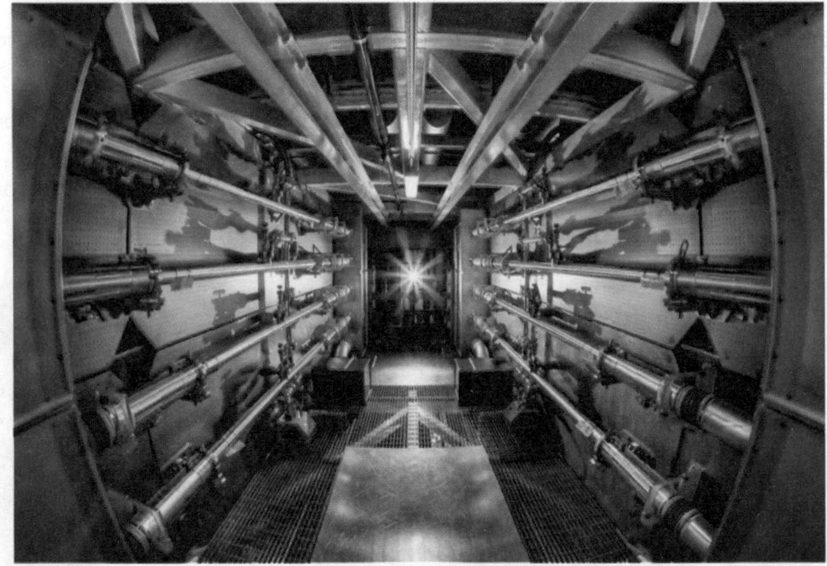

Figure 11

Laser Induced Fusion: Powerful laser beams can create temperatures which will result in generation of fusion power. The above photograph shows the setup at the Lawrence Livermore Laboratory in the US. It can deliver more than 500 trillion watts of peak power to the target. Photograph courtesy: Damien Jemison/LLNL

lasers can deliver more than 500 trillion watts of peak power to the target. Currently many research laboratories are working in building laser induced fusion reactors where the power generated from fusion reactions will far exceed the power required to produce the laser beams. When that happens, there will be no shortage of power anywhere!!!

One of the most important applications of lasers with its direct impact on our lives has been in communication. Use of electromagnetic waves in communication is quite old and the development of the laser gave communication engineers with a source of electromagnetic waves with extremely high frequency compared to microwaves and millimeter waves. The development of low loss optical fibers and also EDFAs (Erbium Doped Fiber Amplifiers) led to phenomenal growth in fiber optic communication systems (see Chapter 29). Laser pulses propagating through millions of kilometers of optical fibers connect us across the oceans and has revolutionized communications (see Figure 12). The fact that today we can

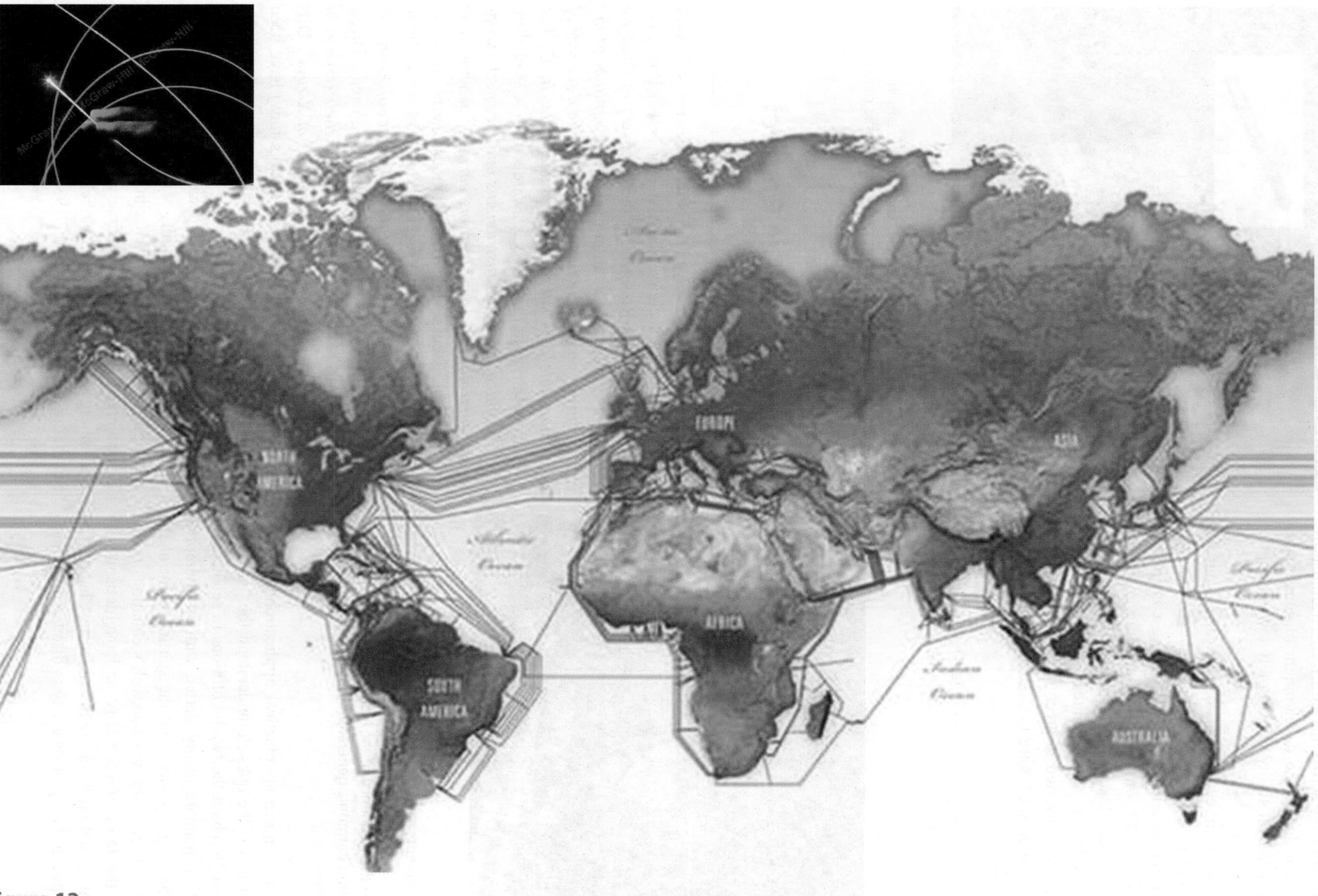

Figure 12
Laser pulses propagating through millions of km of optical fibers connect us across the oceans and has revolutionized communications . The above illustration is by Trevor Johnston; adapted from http://www.osa-opn.org/home/articles/volume_25/march _2014/features/sea_change_the_challenges_facing_submarine_optical/

do video conferencing across the continents (almost free of cost) has been due to the development of semiconductor lasers and also availability of extremely low loss optical fibers.

Also, very beautiful experiments can be carried out with a laser. In Figure 13 we have shown red light (from a laser) falling on a suitably oriented crystal getting converted to blue light!!! This is known as second harmonic generation. There are many such fascinating experiments that can be done with lasers. In many laser pointers, we actually have a red laser which is converted to green light through second harmonic generation (see Figure 14). Indeed Nobel Laureate Eric Cornell said

> *There are relatively few experiments in atomic physics these days that don't involve the use of a laser.*

Figure 13
Beautiful experiments can be carried out with a laser .. Here red laser beam enters a crystal and comes out as a blue beam having double the frequency of the incident beam. This is known as second harmonic generation [Photograph courtesy Dr. R W Terhune].

In addition to numerous practical applications of light, it is said that it was the quest to understand the "nature of light" that brought about the two revolutions in science: the development of quantum theory started with an attempt to understand the "light quanta", and the starting point of the special theory of relativity was Maxwell's equations which synthesized the laws of electricity and magnetism with those of light. Quantum theory is discussed in Chapters 24 and 26 and special theory of relativity is discussed in Chapters 31-33.

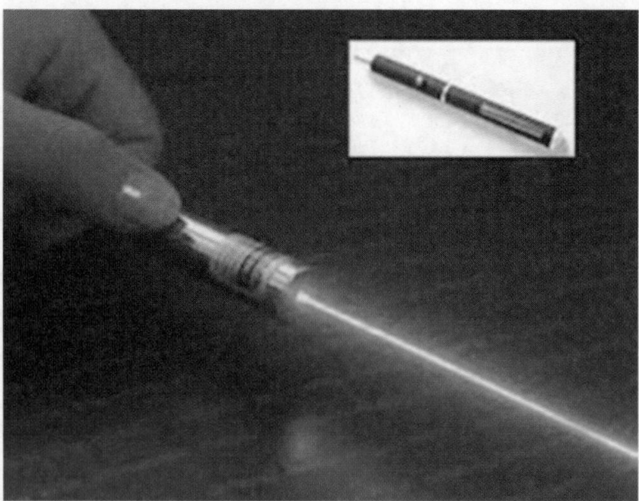

Figure 14
In many laser pointers, we actually have a red laser which is converted to green light through second harmonic generation.

Nobel Prizes In the General Area of Optics

Many scientists have received the Nobel Prize for their work related to optics. Of course the first ever Nobel Prize was awarded to Wilhelm Rontgen for the discovery of what we now call as X-rays; the citation read "***in recognition of the extraordinary services he has rendered by the discovery of the remarkable rays subsequently named after him***". The 1907 Nobel Prize in Physics was awarded to A A Michelson "***for his optical precision instruments and the spectroscopic and metrological investigations carried out with their aid***"; we will discuss Michelson's famous interferometer in Chapter 14. Max Von Laue received the 2014 Nobel Prize in Physics "***for his discovery of the diffraction of X-rays by crystals***". William Henry Bragg and William Lawrence Bragg shared the 2015 Nobel Prize in Physics "***for their services in the analysis of crystal structure by means of X-rays***". Diffraction of X-rays by crystals (and Braggs Law) have been discussed in Chapter 17. Then Albert Einstein received the 1921 Nobel Prize in Physics for his "***discovery of the law of the photoelectric effect***"; we discuss this in Chapter 24. This led to wave particle duality which eventually led to quantum theory (which we discuss in Chapter 26) for which Heisenberg, Schrodinger and Dirac received Nobel Prizes; Heisenberg received the 1932 Nobel Prize in Physics and Schrodinger and Dirac shared the 1933 Nobel Prize in Physics.

> The 1964 Nobel Prize in Physics were awarded to Townes, Basov and Prochorov for their *fundamental work in the field of Quantum Electronics, which has led to the construction of oscillators and amplifiers based on the laser-maser principle*

More recently, half of the 2009 Nobel Prize in Physics was awarded to Charles Kuen Kao ***"for groundbreaking achievements concerning the transmission of light in fibers for optical communication"***. Announcing the Prize, Professor Joseph Nordgren said how fiber optic communication has revolutionized the way in which information can be transmitted globally. Because of the tremendous applications of fiber optics, we have devoted Chapters 28, 29 and 30 covering this important area.

Dennis Gabor received the 1971 Nobel Prize in Physics for discovering the principle of holography. Chapter 20 discusses the underlying principle of holography and some of its applications.

Then, the 2014 Nobel Prize in Physics was awarded to Isamu Akasaki, Hiroshi Amano and Shuji Nakamura ***"for the invention of efficient blue light-emitting diodes which has enabled bright and energy-saving white light sources"***.

The 2017 Nobel Prize in Physics was awarded to Rainer Weiss, Barry Barish and Kip Thorne "***for decisive contributions to the LIGO detector and the observation of gravitational waves***". LIGO stands for Laser Interferometer Gravitational-Wave Observatory. It is a gigantic interferometer similar (in principle) to the Michelson interferometer that we will discuss in Chapter 14. In a gravitational-wave interferometer, laser light is split in 2 beams by a beam splitter; the two beams (at right angles to each other) after travelling for about 4 km get reflected by a mirror and they retrace their paths to recombine to form an interference pattern (see Figs. 15 and 16); this interference pattern is very sensitive to the vibration of the 2 mirrors. To quote from an article entitled LIGO* "*The world's first captured gravitational waves were created in a violent collision between two black holes, 1.3 billion light-years away. When these waves passed the Earth, 1.3 billion years later, they had weakened considerably: the disturbance in spacetime that LIGO measured was thousands of times smaller than an atomic nucleus.*" Incidentally, there are right now 4 operational Gravitational Wave Observatories in the world and one is under construction in Japan and one that is planned to be built in India!

The 2018 Nobel Prize in Physics was awarded ***"for groundbreaking inventions in the field of laser physics"***.

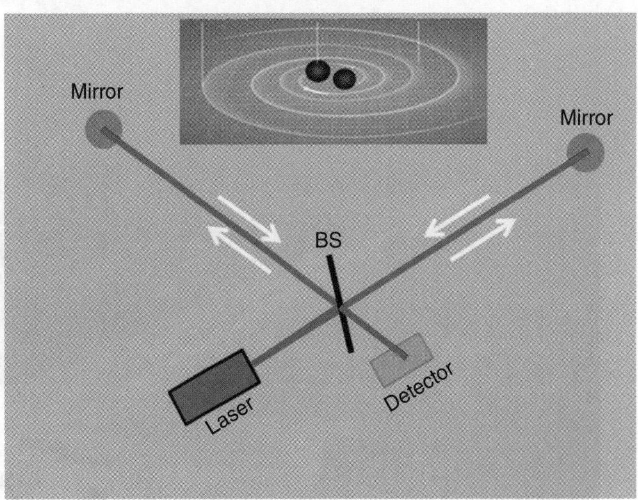

Figure 15

The LIGO set up. A beam splitter BS splits the light from the laser which get reflected by 2 mirrors at a distance of about 4 km from the beam splitter. Gravitational waves (created by a violent collision of 2 black holes about 1.3 billion light-years away, affect the 2 arms differently and the interference pattern is detected by the detector. Diagram partially adapted from https://phys.org/news/2019-05-ligo-virgo-neutron-star-smash-ups.html

There were 3 recipients of the 2018 Physics Nobel Prize:

> Arthur Ashkin ***"for the optical tweezers and their application to biological systems"*** (briefly discussed in Chapter 24 of this book);
>
> Gérard Mourou and Donna Strickland ***"for their method of generating high-intensity, ultra-short optical pulses"*** (briefly discussed in Chapter 11 of this book).

From above one can see the large number of Nobel Prizes awarded for research carried out in the general area of light. Therefore, because of the tremendous importance of applications of light, an undergraduate course in optics has become a "must" not only for students of physics but also for students of engineering. Although it is impossible to cover all areas in a single book, this book attempts to give a comprehensive account of a large number of important topics in this exciting field and should meet the requirements of a course on optics meant for undergraduate students of science and engineering. This book attempts to give a balanced account of traditional optics as well as some of the recent developments in this field. The plan of the book is given below.

* See https://directory.eoportal.org/web/eoportal/satellite-missions/content/-/article/gravitational-waves

Figure 16
LIGO Observatory at Livingston Lousiana in USA; photograph Courtesy Caltech/MIT/LIGO Laboratory.

Plan of the Book

- Chapter 1 gives a brief historical evolution of different models describing the nature of light. It starts with the corpuscular model of light and then discusses the evolution of the wave model and the electromagnetic character of light waves. This is followed by a discussion of the early twentieth-century experiments, which could only be explained by assuming a particle nature of light, and we end with a discussion on "wave-particle duality."
- Chapters 2 to 5 cover geometrical optics. Chapter 2 starts with Fermat's principle and discusses ray tracing through graded index media, explaining in detail the phenomena of mirage and looming, ray propagation through graded index optical waveguides, and reflection from the ionosphere. Chapter 3 covers ray tracing in lens systems, and Chapter 4 discusses the matrix method in paraxial optics, which is used in the industry. Chapter 5 gives a brief account of aberrations.
- Chapters 6 to 11 discuss the origin of refractive index and the basic physics of wave propagation including Huygens' principle. Many interesting experiments (such as the redness of the setting Sun, water waves, etc.) are discussed. In Chapter 11, the concept of group velocity and the dispersion of an optical pulse as it propagates through a dispersive medium are discussed in detail. Self phase modulation, which is one of the phenomena leading to the super continuum generation is also explained.
- Chapters 12 to 15 cover the very important and fascinating area of interference and many beautiful experiments associated with it—the underlying principle is the superposition principle, which is discussed in Chapter 12. Chapter 13 discusses interference by division of the wave front including the famous Young double-hole interference experiment. In Chapter 14, interference by division of amplitude is discussed which allows us to understand the colors of thin films and applications such as antireflection films. The basic working principle

of the Fiber Bragg Gratings (usually abbreviated as FBG) is discussed along with some of their important applications in the industry. In the same chapter, the Michelson interferometer is discussed for which Michelson received the 1907 Nobel Prize in Physics. Chapter 15 discusses the Fabry–Perot interferometer which is based on multiple-beam interference and is characterized by a high resolving power and hence finds applications in high-resolution spectroscopy.

- Chapter 16 discusses the basic concept of temporal and spatial coherence. The ingenious experiment of Michelson, which used the concept of spatial coherence to determine the angular diameter of stars, is discussed in detail. Topics such as optical beats and Fourier transform spectroscopy are also discussed.
- Chapters 17, 18, and 19 cover the very important area of diffraction and discuss the principle behind topics such as the diffraction divergence of laser beams, resolving power of telescopes, laser focusing, X-ray diffraction, Fourier optics and spatial frequency filtering.
- Chapter 20 discusses the underlying principle of holography and some of its applications. Dennis Gabor received the 1971 Nobel Prize in Physics for discovering the principle of holography.
- Chapters 21, 22 and 23 cover are on the electromagnetic character of light waves. Chapter 21 discusses the polarization phenomenon and propagation of electromagnetic waves in anisotropic media including first-principle derivations of wave and ray velocities. Phenomena such as optical activity and Faraday rotation (and its applications to measuring large currents) are explained from first principles. In Chapter 22, starting with Maxwell's equations, the wave equation is derived which led Maxwell to predict the existence of electromagnetic waves and to propound that light is an electromagnetic wave. Reflection and refraction of electromagnetic waves by a dielectric interface are discussed in Chapter 23. Results derived in this chapter directly explain phenomena such as polarization by reflection, total internal reflection, evanescent waves, and Fabry–Perot transmission resonances.
- Chapter 24 discusses photo-electric effect and Einstein's light quantum; the light quantum later came to be known as photon. The chapter also discusses the Compton effect (for which Compton received the 1927 Nobel Prize in Physics), which established that the photon has a momentum equal to $h\nu/c$.
- Chapter 25 is a new chapter and discusses the Bohr model of the hydrogen like atom and line spectra.
- Chapter 26 discusses the basic concepts of quantum theory, solutions of the Schrödinger equation, Entanglement and Bell's inequality.
- Chapter 27 is on lasers—a subject of tremendous technological importance. The basic physics of optical amplifiers and of lasers along with their special characteristics is also discussed.
- Chapters 28 to 30 discuss waveguide theory and fiber optics, an area that has revolutionized communications and has found important applications in sensor technology. Chapter 28 discusses the light guidance property of the optical fiber (using ray optics) with applications in fiber-optic communication systems; the chapter also gives a very brief account of fiber-optic sensors. Chapter 29 discusses basic waveguide theory and concept of modes with Maxwell's equations as the starting point. Chapter 30 discusses the propagation characteristics of single-mode optical fibers, which are now extensively used in optical communication systems.
- In 1905 Einstein put forward the special theory of relativity which is considered one of the revolutions of the 20th century. The starting point of the special theory of relativity was Maxwell's equations, which synthesized the laws of electricity and magnetism with those of light. Chapters 31, 32 and 33 describe briefly the important consequences of the special theory of relativity, i.e., the mass-energy relation, time dilation, length contraction and Lorentz transformations.

In summary, the book discusses quite a few important topics that have had a tremendous impact in the growth of science and technology.

A Brief History

Because of the tremendous importance of optics, in the online learning centre of the book at https://connect.mheducation.com we have given very briefly a few of the stalwarts who have contributed immensely to development of optics. Optics is such a vast field that it is extremely difficult to give a historical perspective of all the areas. My own interests lie in fiber optics, and hence there is a bias toward the evolution of fiber optics and related areas. In the process, I must have omitted the names of many individuals who have made important contributions to the growth of optics. Fortunately, there is now a wealth of information available through the Internet. In the website, I have included a number of references to various books and websites.

CHAPTER

What is Light: A Brief History

For the rest of my life, I will reflect on what light is

—Albert Einstein, CA 1917

All the fifty years of conscious brooding have brought me no close to the answer to the question, 'What are light quanta?' Of course today every rascal thinks he knows the answer, but he is deluding himself.

—Albert Einstein, 1951

LEARNING OBJECTIVES

After reading this chapter, the reader should be able to:

LO 1: *explain the laws of refraction using corpuscular model*

LO 2: *describe the characteristics of a wave*

LO 3: *describe electromagnetic waves*

LO 4: *explain particle nature of light and wave particle duality*

LO 5: *explain single slit diffraction pattern and the uncertainty principle*

LO 6: *explain double slit interference pattern and concepts in quantum theory*

Important Milestones

1637: Rene Descartes put forward the corpuscular model of light and he derived an equation describing the law of refraction (which we now know as Snell's law) in his book *"La dioptrique"*.

1672: Isaac Newton developed the corpuscular model of light. Later he elaborated the corpuscular model of light in his book on *OPTICKS* (Ref. 1.1) which was first published in 1704.

1678: Christiaan Huygens, a Dutch physicist and a contemporary of Isaac Newton, was the first scientist who in 1678, in a communication to the Academie des Science in Paris, proposed that light is a wave phenomenon. In 1690, Huygens published his famous book* *Traité de la Lumière* (Ref. 1.2) in which he put forward that light waves could propagate through space because of the presence of ether.

Above image: The rising sun. Photograph courtesy McGraw Hill Digital Access Library

* See https://en.wikipedia.org/wiki/Dioptrique. In this website some of the pages from Descartes book have also been shown.

1801: Thomas Young performed the very famous 2 hole interference experiment which could be explained by assuming a wave model for light; on November 24, 1803, he presented the details of the experiment in his *Bakerian Lecture* (see Ref. 1.3) at the Royal Society of London. Andrew Robinson has written a biography on Thomas Young with the title *The Last Man Who Knew Everything;* see Ref. 1.4

1865: James Clerk Maxwell propounded that *light is an electromagnetic wave*; associated with a light wave are oscillating electric and magnetic fields. He gave a detailed account in his book with the title *A Treatise on Electricity and Magnetism* (see Ref. 1.5).

1888: Heinrich Hertz carried out beautiful experiments which could produce and detect electromagnetic waves of frequencies much smaller than those of light.

1900: Max Planck derived a formula for the observed spectrum by a black body by assuming that the oscillators of the cavity could change its energy in discrete amounts which he called the "quantum of energy".

1905: Albert Einstein, in his Year of Miracles (1905), suggested that light can be emitted or absorbed only in discrete amounts (see Ref. 1.6); he called them *light quanta* whose energy is given by $E = h\nu$.

1923: Arthur Compton carried out beautiful scattering experiments which could be explained by assuming that the energy and momentum of Einstein's light quanta were given by $E = h\nu$ and $p = \frac{h\nu}{c}$; both expressions were put forward by Einstein.

1924: Louis de Broglie proposed that just as light exhibited wave-like and corpuscular behavior; electrons, protons must also show wavelike behavior with its wavelength given by $\lambda = h/p$. The 1929 Nobel Prize in Physics was awarded to de Broglie *for his discovery of the wave nature of electrons*

1926: Gilbert Lewis (at University of Berkeley) coined the word photon to describe Einstein's *light quantum*.

1926: Heisenberg and Schrödinger put forward quantum theory. The 1932 Nobel Prize in Physics was awarded to Heisenberg *"for the creation of quantum mechanics ..."* and the 1933 Nobel Prize in Physics was awarded jointly to Schrödinger and Dirac *"for the discovery of new productive forms of atomic theory."*

1927: Clinton Davisson and Lester Germer (in New York) and George Thomson (in Aberdeen, Scotland) carry out experiments demonstrating diffraction of an electron beam. The 1937 Nobel Prize in Physics was awarded jointly to CJ Davisson and GP Thomson *"for their experimental discovery of the diffraction of electrons by crystals"*; Germer missed out on the Prize!

1.1 Introduction

Ever since man could see, he has been wanting to know as to what light is. In this chapter we will briefly discuss the evolution of various theories of light. We will start with the corpuscular model of light which is usually attributed to Isaac Newton. This will be followed by a discussion on the wave model of light which was first put forward by Christiaan Huygens around 1678. Initially no one believed in the wave theory of Huygens; it got established only in 1801 when Thomas Young performed the very famous 2 hole interference experiment. Because of this experiment, scientists started believing in the wave theory of light; however, they wondered about the nature of these waves and as to how it could propagate through vacuum. Then came Maxwell's equations which described the laws of electricity and magnetism. Maxwell showed that wave like equations are solutions of these equations. This resulted in the prediction of electromagnetic waves. From his theory, Maxwell calculated the velocity of electromagnetic waves and found that this value was very close to the experimentally determined value of the speed of light. This led him to say (around 1864) that

light was an electromagnetic wave.

Maxwell's electromagnetic theory explained numerous experimental results and therefore towards the end of the nineteenth century, physicists thought that one had finally understood what light really is; namely, that light is an electromagnetic wave.

Then in 1905 Albert Einstein, in his year of miracles (1905), suggested that light can be emitted or absorbed only in discrete amounts (= $h\nu$), he called them "quanta of energy" which were later called 'photons'; here

$h(\approx 6.626 \times 10^{-34}$ Js) is the Planck's constant and ν is the frequency (Ref. 1.6). Using his 'quanta of energy', Einstein wrote down his famous 'photoelectric equation' which was verified to a tremendous degree of accuracy by Robert Millikan. Later Arthur Compton (in 1923) explained his scattering experiments by assuming that Einstein's light quanta carried energy $h\nu$ and momentum $h\nu/c$ where $c(\approx 3 \times 10^8$ m/s) is the speed of light in free space.

In 1924, de Broglie proposed that just as light exhibited wave-like and corpuscular behavior; electrons, protons, (which have very well defined mass and charge and therefore were thought of as particles) must also show wavelike behavior which was later confirmed by very beautiful diffraction experiments by Clinton Davisson and Lester Germer around 1927 and also independently around the same time by G.P. Thomson. This 'wave-particle duality' led to the development of quantum theory.

1.2 The Corpuscular Model of Light

LO1

In 1637 Rene Descartes put forward the corpuscular model of light in his book* "La dioptrique" (in English "Dioptrique", "Optics", or "Dioptrics") and wrote down a mathematical equation describing the law of refraction, which in today's notation is the Snell's law (see Ref. 1.7). In 1672 Isaac Newton put forward the corpuscular model of light according to which a luminous body emits a stream of particles in all directions. In his famous book entitled *OPTICKS* which was published in 1704 (Ref. 1.1), Newton wrote

> *Are not the ray of light very small bodies emitted from shining substance?*

The particles were assumed to be very tiny so that when two light beams overlap, a collision between the two particles rarely occurs. Using the corpuscular model, he explained the laws of reflection by considering the elastic reflection of a particle by a plane surface. In order to understand refraction we consider the incidence of a particle at a plane surface ($y = 0$) as shown in Fig. 1.1; we are assuming that the motion is confined to the x-y plane. The trajectory of the particle is determined by the conservation of the x-component of the momentum ($p \sin \theta$) where θ is the angle that the direction of propagation makes with the y-axis. The conservation condition leads to the following equation:

$$p_1 \sin \theta_1 = p_2 \sin \theta_2 \tag{1.1}$$

where the angles θ_1 and θ_2 are defined in Fig. 1.1. The above equation directly gives Snell's law

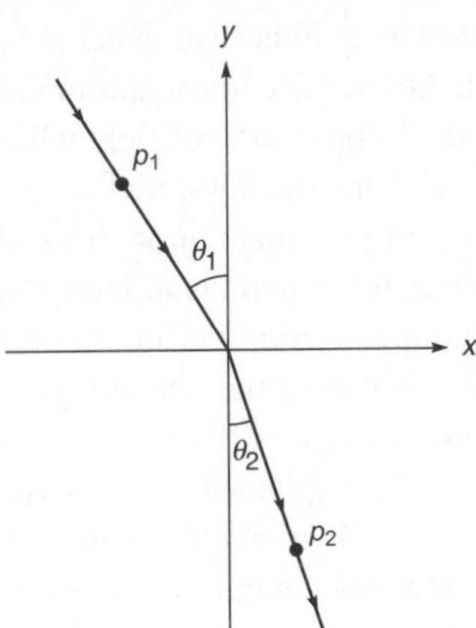

Figure 1.1
Refraction of a corpuscle.

$$\frac{\sin \theta_1}{\sin \theta_2} = \frac{p_2}{p_1} = \frac{v_2}{v_1} \tag{1.2}$$

According to Newton, corpuscles of different sizes give rise to the sensation of different colors at the retina of the eye. He explained the prismatic spectrum by assuming that particles of different sizes refract at different angles. He showed that light is composed of different spectral colors and white light is formed by mixing light of different colors.

As mentioned earlier, the corpuscular model of light was known much before Newton. According to Joyce & Joyce (Ref. 1.7), Rene Descartes, in 1637, derived the law of refraction (which in today's notation is the Snell's law) using a model very similar to the corpuscular model of light; an English translation of Descartes' original paper appears in Ref. 1.7. Newton was only about eight years old when Descartes (1596–1650) died and therefore Descartes did not get the corpuscular model from Newton! Also, according to Wikipedia†,

> *the corpuscular theory of light, arguably set forward by Pierre Gassendi and Thomas Hobbes states that light is made up of small discrete particles called "corpuscles" (little particles) which travel in a straight line with a finite velocity... About a half-century after Gassendi, Isaac Newton used existing corpuscularian theories to develop his particle theory of the physics of light.*

Pierre Gassendi (French astronomer, and mathematician) was born in 1592 and died in 1655 when Newton was just 13. In 1672 Newton put forward the corpuscular model of light and gave a detailed account in his book (Ref. 1.1) which was first published in 1704; this book became very famous and was extensively used because of which the corpuscular theory of light is usually attributed to Newton.

* See https://en.wikipedia.org/wiki/Dioptrique. In this website some of the pages from Descartes book have also been given.

† See http://en.wikipedia.org/wiki/Corpuscular_theory_of_light

Perhaps the two most important experimental facts which led to the early belief in the corpuscular model of light were:

(a) the rectilinear propagation of light which results in the formation of sharp shadows, and
(b) that light could propagate through vacuum.

However, as careful experiments later showed, shadows are not perfectly dark; some light does enter the geometrical shadow which is due to the phenomenon of diffraction. This phenomenon is essentially due to the wave character of light and cannot be explained on the basis of the simple corpuscular model. Diffraction effects are usually difficult to observe because the wavelength associated with light waves is extremely small.

We may mention here that if we are below the shade of a building then under the shade we can always read a book – the light that enters the shadow is *not* due to diffraction but due to scattering of light by air molecules. This phenomenon of scattering is also responsible for the blue color of the sky and the red color of the setting sun (see Sec. 6.6). If the earth did not have an atmosphere, then the shadows would have been extremely dark; this is indeed the case on the surface of the moon (see Fig. 1.2). Since the moon has almost no atmosphere, there is no air there which can scatter light and therefore the shadows would be extremely dark and we would never be able to read a book in our own shadow! And also, on the surface of the moon, the sky appears perfectly dark (see Fig. 1.2; see also Fig. 6.18). Once again, even on the surface of the moon, a very small amount of light does enter the geometrical shadow because of diffraction.

Figure 1.2
A photograph of the man on the moon. Notice the dark sky. [*Photograph courtesy: McGraw Hill Digital Access Library*]; see also Fig. 6.18.

1.3 The Wave Model

LO2

Christiaan Huygens, a Dutch physicist and a contemporary of Isaac Newton, was the first scientist who in 1678, proposed that light is a wave phenomenon. In 1690 Huygens published his famous book* ***Traité de la Lumière*** (Ref. 1.2) in which he put forward that light waves could propagate through space because of the presence of ether.

What is a wave? A wave is propagation of disturbance. When we make a sharp needle vibrate in a calm pool of water, a circular pattern spreads out from the point of impact (see Fig. 1.3). The vibrating needle creates a disturbance that propagates outwards. In this propagation, the water molecules do not move outward with the wave; instead they move in nearly circular orbits about an equilibrium position. Once the disturbance has passed a certain region, every drop of water is left at its original position. This fact can easily be verified by placing a small piece of wood on the surface of water. As the wave passes, the piece of wood comes back to its original position. Further, with time the circular ripples spread out, i.e., the disturbance (which is confined to particular region at a given time) produces a similar disturbance at a neighboring point at a slightly later time with the pattern of disturbance roughly remaining the same. Thus

> *Propagation of disturbances (without any translation of the medium in the direction of propagation) is termed as a wave.*

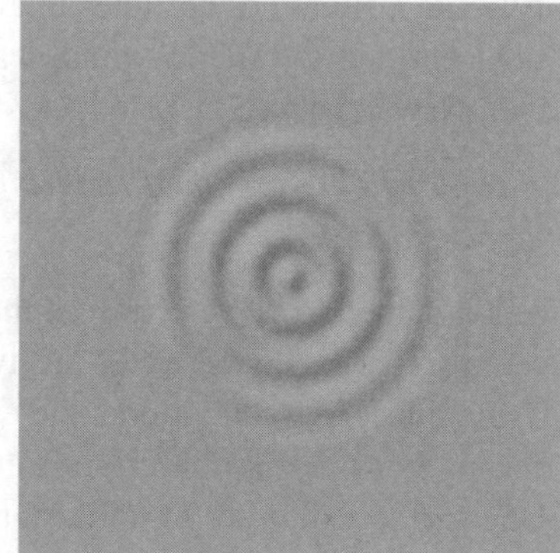

Figure 1.3
Water waves spreading out from a vibrating point source. [Adapted from the website http://www.colorado.edu/physics/2000/waves_particles/waves.html]

Also, waves carry energy; in this case the energy is in the form of kinetic energy of water molecules. All waves are characterized by certain properties such as wavelength and frequency. In order to understand wavelength and frequency, we consider the simplest form of wave, namely the propagation of a transverse wave on a string.

* See https://en.wikipedia.org/wiki/Treatise_on_Light

In order to understand this, consider yourself holding one end of a string, the other end being held tightly by another person so that the string does not sag. If we make the end of the string oscillate up and down motion ν times per second, then we will observe the propagation of a periodic disturbance towards the other end of the string [see Fig. 1.4(a)]; the wave is said to be transverse because the propagation of the wave is in the z-direction and the displacement (of each point on the string) is in the x-direction which is transverse to the z-direction. The displacement of the string [as shown in Fig. 1.4(a)] can be described by the following equation:

$$\left.\begin{aligned} x(z,t) &= a\cos\left[2\pi\left(\frac{z}{\lambda}-\nu t\right)\right] = a\cos\left[\frac{2\pi}{\lambda}(z-vt)\right] \\ y(z,t) &= 0 \end{aligned}\right\} \quad (1.3)$$

where a represents the maximum displacement of the particle (from its equilibrium position) and is known as the ***amplitude of the wave***; ν is the frequency and λ the wavelength of the wave and

$$v = \nu\lambda = \frac{\omega}{k} \quad (1.4)$$

which will be shown to represent the velocity of the wave. In the above equation

$$k \equiv \frac{2\pi}{\lambda} \quad \text{and} \quad \omega \equiv 2\pi\nu \quad (1.5)$$

represent what are known as the wave vector and angular frequency of the wave. We may say that **Equation (1.3) defines a wave.**

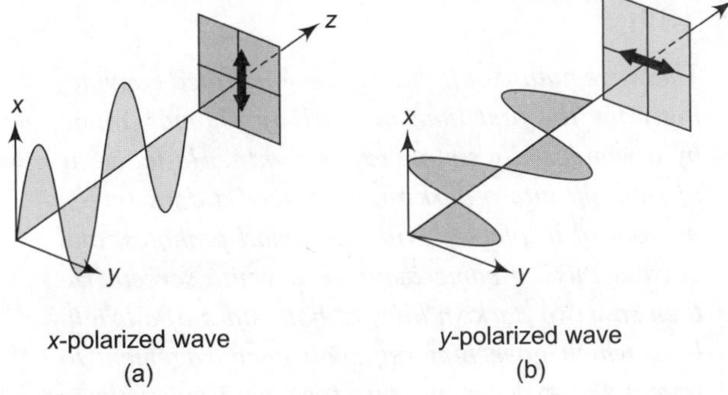

Figure 1.4

(a) If make one end of the string execute oscillatory motion in the x-direction, we will generate a x-polarized wave; (b) on the other hand, if make the end of the string execute oscillatory motion in the y-direction, we will generate a y-polarized wave).

Actually Eq. (1.3) defines an x-polarized wave because the displacement is in the x-direction. In Fig. 1.5, we have plotted the dependence of the displacement x on z at $t = 0$, and at $t = \Delta t$, which are given by

$$x(z, t = 0) = a\cos\left(\frac{2\pi}{\lambda}z\right) = a\cos(kz) \quad (1.6)$$

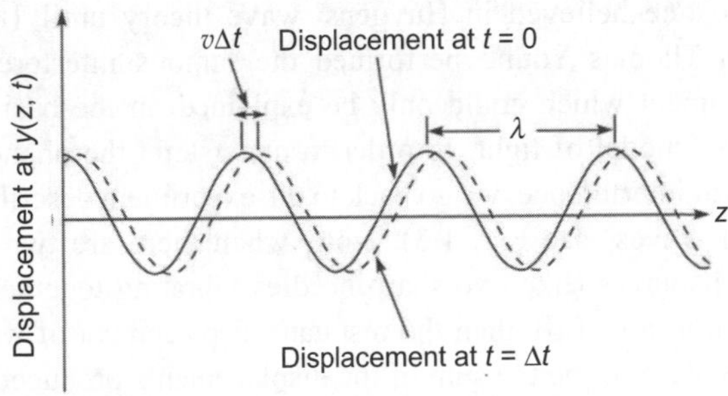

Figure 1.5

A transverse wave is propagating along the +z-axis on a string; the solid and dashed curves show the displacements at $t = 0$ and at a later time $t = \Delta t$ respectively. Since the displacement is in the x-direction, we call this an x-polarized wave.

and

$$x(z, t = \Delta t) = a\cos\left[\frac{2\pi}{\lambda}(z - v\Delta t)\right] = a\cos\left[k(z - v\Delta t)\right] \quad (1.7)$$

The two curves are the snapshots of the string at the two instants. It can be seen from the figure that, at a particular instant, any two points separated by a distance λ have identical displacements (at all times). This distance is known as the wavelength. Further, the displaced curve (which corresponds to the instant $t = \Delta t$) can be obtained by displacing the curve corresponding to $t = 0$ by a distance $v\Delta t$; this shows that the wave is propagating in the $+z$ direction with speed given by Eq. (1.4). The displacement of the string is often written in the form

$$\left.\begin{aligned} x(z,t) &= a\cos(kz - \omega t) \\ y(z,t) &= 0 \end{aligned}\right\} \quad (1.8)$$

The vibration of any point of the string can be written as

$$x(z = z_0, t) = a\cos(\omega t - \phi_0) \quad (1.9)$$

where $\phi_0 = kz_0$ (1.10)

is a constant. Thus each point on the string vibrates (in the x-direction) with the same frequency. The displacement of the string corresponding to a y-polarized wave will be given by [see Fig. 1.4(b)]:

$$\left.\begin{aligned} x(z,t) &= 0 \\ y(z,t) &= a\cos(kz - \omega t) \end{aligned}\right\} \quad (1.11)$$

If you would go to the link https://phet.colorado.edu/sims/html/wave-on-a-string/latest/wave-on-a-string_en.html, you will find very nice simulations which would allow you to understand wave propagation on a string.

Using the wave model, Huygens could explain the laws of reflection and refraction (see Chapter 10). However, so compelling was Newton's authority that it is said that

> *people around Newton had more faith in his corpuscular theory than Newton himself*

No one believed in Huygens' wave theory until 1801, when Thomas Young performed the famous interference experiment which could only be explained on the basis of a wave model of light. In order to understand the phenomenon of interference, we go back to the experiment describing water waves (see Fig. 1.3). Now, when there are two (or more) sources (like two sharp needles vibrating together as shown in Fig. 1.6), then the resultant displacement of water molecules will be the sum of the displacements produced by each of the wave – this is known as the principle of superposition. Thus, if one wave produces a displacement of 1 mm in the upward direction (from its equilibrium position) and the other wave produces a displacement of 1 mm in the downward direction, then the resultant displacement will be zero. We say that at that point, waves arrive "out of phase" and interfere destructively. Similarly, if one wave produces a displacement of 1 mm in the upward direction and the other wave also produces a displacement of 1 mm in the downward direction, then the resultant displacement will be 2 mm (in the downward direction). We say that at that point waves arrive 'in phase' and interfere constructively. Figure 1.6 shows the interference of two waves emanating from two point sources (vibrating in phase) in a water tank. We will discuss this in more detail in Chapter 13.

Figure 1.6

The actual interference pattern produced from two point sources vibrating in phase in a ripple tank (After Ref. 1.8; used with permission).

In 1801, Thomas Young carried out a beautiful experiment (see Fig. 1.7) demonstrating the interference phenomenon establishing without any doubt the wave nature of light. There are regions where the two waves (emanating from the holes) interfere destructively (to produce a dark fringe) and similarly, there are regions where the two waves interfere constructively to produce a bright fringe. The formation of these fringes is characteristic of wave phenomena and the superposition principle; we will discuss this in detail in

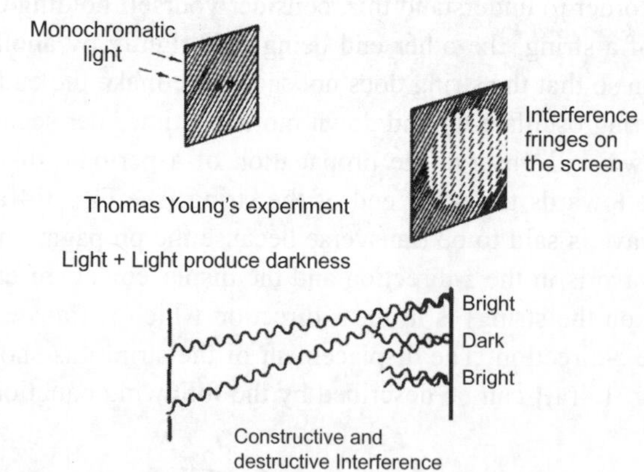

Figure 1.7

Thomas Young's set up of the interference experiment that he carried out in 1801. The waves emanating from the two holes interfere to form the interference fringes on the screen. Diagram adapted from the Dennis Gabor's Nobel Lecture: http://nobelprize.org/nobel_prizes/physics/laureates/1971/gabor-lecture.pdf

Chapter 13. Thomas Young's description of this experiment is described in Ref. 1.3 in which he (Thomas Young) wrote

> *I have found so simple and so demonstrative a proof of the general law of the interference of two portions of light.*

Thomas Young's interference experiment is considered as one of the 10 most beautiful experiments in Physics (see Ref. 1.9). To quote from Dennis Gabor's Nobel Lecture (see Ref. 1.10)

> *The wave nature of light was demonstrated convincingly for the first time in 1801 by Thomas Young by a wonderfully simple experiment... He let a ray of sunlight into a dark room, placed a dark screen in front of it, pierced with two small pinholes, and beyond this, at some distance a white screen. He then saw two darkish lines at both sides of a bright line, which gave him sufficient encouragement to repeat the experiment, this time with spirit flame as light source, with a little salt in it, to produce the bright yellow sodium light. This time he saw a number of dark lines, regularly spaced; the first clear proof that light added to light can produce darkness. This phenomenon is called interference. Thomas Young had expected it because he believed in the wave theory of light.*

The formation of interference fringes on the screen can never be explained on the basis of a simple corpuscular model of light. Figure 1.8 shows a gun emitting tiny particles (like bullets) which reach the backstop either through hole # 1 or

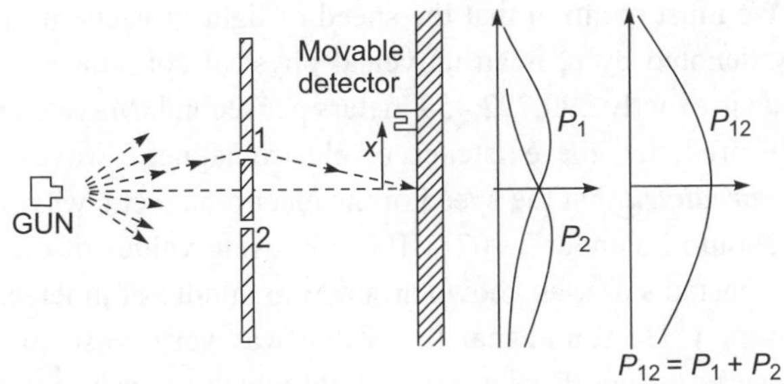

Figure 1.8
If there are bullets passing through a double slit apparatus, then the bullets will pass through either slit No. 1 or slit No. 2 and no interference pattern will be observed; diagram adapted from The Feynman Lectures on Physics Vol. III (Ref. 1.11).

through hole # 2. Thus the particles can pass though only one of the holes and therefore the intensity pattern when both holes are open will be

$$I = I_1 + I_2 \tag{1.12}$$

where I_1 represents the intensity when hole # 1 is open (and hole # 2 is closed), and I_2 represents the intensity when hole # 2 is open (and hole # 1 is closed). Thus the fact that

light added to light can produce darkness

(see Dennis Gabor's quotation above) can never be explained on the basis of a simple particle model of light. By measuring the fringe width, Young could calculate the wavelength of light waves which was about 0.6 μm. Because of the smallness of the wavelength, it was difficult to carry out interference experiments using visible light.

In the first half of the nineteenth century, there were many experiments which demonstrated interference and diffraction phenomena which could only be explained by using the wave theory of light. Thus the wave theory got well established; however, it was argued that a wave (like sound waves or water waves) would always require a medium and therefore scientists could not understand how light could propagate through vacuum; light from the sun passes through vacuum before reaching the earth. Physicists could calculate the interference and diffraction patterns but they could not figure out what the "displacement associated with the wave propagation" would be. Subsequently an "all pervading" elastic ether theory was developed – the ether would be present even in vacuum. Poisson, Navier, Cauchy and many other physicists contributed to the development of the ether theory which also necessitated the development of the theory of elasticity. There were considerable difficulties in the explanation of the models and since we now know that ether does not exist, we will not go into the details of the "ether" theory.

EXAMPLE 1.1 The displacement associated with a transverse wave on a string is given by

$$y(x, t) = 0.005 \cos (4\pi x - 200\pi t)$$

where the distances are measured in meters and time in seconds. Thus the amplitude of the wave is 0.005 m (= 0.5 cm). The corresponding wavelength and frequency would be given by

$$\frac{2\pi}{\lambda} = 4\pi \;\Rightarrow\; \lambda = 0.5 \text{ m}$$

and

$$2\pi\nu = 200\pi \;\Rightarrow\; \nu = 100 \text{ Hz}$$

We can write the displacement as

$$y(x, t) = 0.005 \cos[4\pi(z - 50t]$$

Thus the velocity of the wave would be 50 m/s which is the same as the value of $\lambda\nu$.

1.4 Maxwell's Electromagnetic Waves

LO3

The nineteenth century also saw the development of electricity and magnetism. In 1820, Oersted (often written as Ørsted) discovered that electric currents create magnetic fields and in 1826 Ampere discovered the law relating the magnetic field to the current; this law (usually referred to as Ampere's law) was later written in the form of a vector equation by Maxwell. Then, around 1830, Faraday carried out experiments which showed that

a time varying magnetic field induces an electromotive force

which is now referred to as Faraday's law; this law was also later written in the form of a vector equation by Maxwell. Around 1860, Maxwell generalized Ampere's law by stating that not only electric currents create magnetic fields, but

a time varying electric field can also create a magnetic field

– like between the plates of a capacitor when it gets charged or discharged. In 1865, Maxwell summed up all the laws of electricity and magnetism in the form of equations – which are now known as Maxwell's equations; these equations are based on experimental laws. Feynman writes (Ref. 1.12):

All of electromagnetism is contained in Maxwell's equations ... Untold number of experiments have confirmed Maxwell's equations. If we take away the scaffolding he used to build it, we find that Maxwell's edifice stands on its own.

In Chapter 22, we will discuss Maxwell's equations (and their solutions); if we write them in free space, then a wave like expression of the electric field

$$\mathbf{E}(z, t) = \hat{\mathbf{x}}\, E_0 \cos (kz - \omega t) \tag{1.13}$$

satisfies Maxwell's equations and the corresponding magnetic field is given by

$$\mathbf{H}(z, t) = \hat{\mathbf{y}}\, H_0 \cos (kz - \omega t) \tag{1.14}$$

where $$H_0 = \sqrt{\frac{\varepsilon_0}{\mu_0}}\, E_0 \tag{1.15}$$

with $\varepsilon_0 (= 8.8542 \times 10^{-12}\ \mathrm{C^2\ N^{-1}\ m^{-2}})$

and $\mu_0 (= 4\pi \times 10^{-7}\ \mathrm{Ns^2\ C^{-2}})$

represent respectively the dielectric permittivity and the magnetic permeability of free space. Equations (1.13) and (1.14) describe propagating electromagnetic waves (see Fig. 1.9). One can see that if $E_0 = 0$ then $H_0 = 0$ implying that the magnetic field cannot exist without the electric field and similarly, the electric field cannot exist without the magnetic field. Thus from the laws of electricity and magnetism, Maxwell ***predicted*** the existence of electromagnetic waves, and by substituting the above solutions in Maxwell's equations, we obtain the following expression for the velocity (in free space)

$$v = c = \frac{\omega}{k} = \frac{1}{\sqrt{\varepsilon_0 \mu_0}} = \frac{1}{\sqrt{8.8542... \times 10^{-12} \times 4\pi \times 10^{-7}}} \approx 3 \times 10^8 \text{ m/s} \tag{1.16}$$

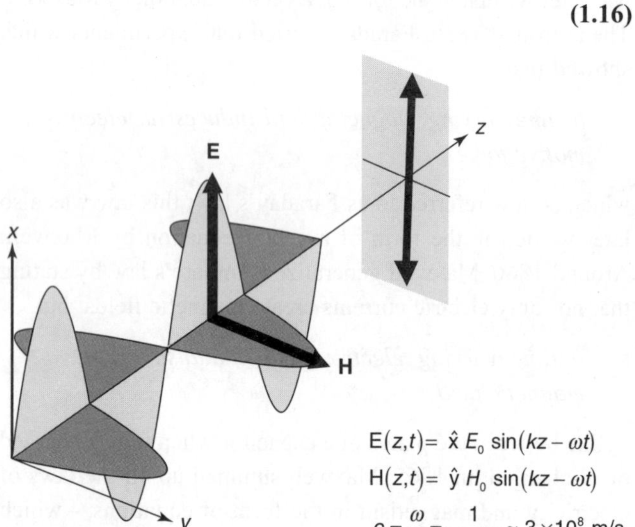

Figure 1.9
Around 1864 Maxwell predicted the existence of electromagnetic waves and said "*light itself is an electromagnetic wave*". This was one of the greatest unifications in physics. Associated with a light wave are changing electric and magnetic fields; the changing magnetic field produces a time and space varying electric field and the changing electric field produces a time and space varying magnetic field, and this results in the propagation of the electromagnetic wave even in vacuum. In the above diagram we have shown an *x*-polarized wave in which the electric field oscillates in the *x*-direction; the corresponding magnetic field oscillates in the *y*-direction.

We must mention that the speed of light in vacuum, usually denoted by *c*, is an universal physical constant and its value is exactly 299,792,458 meters per second. Maxwell not only predicted the existence of electromagnetic waves, he also ***predicted*** that the speed of the electromagnetic waves in air should be about 3.107×10^8 m/s (using values of different constants as was known around the middle of nineteenth century!). He found that this value was very close to the measured value of the speed of light which according to the measurement of Fizeau in 1849 was 3.14858×10^8 m/s. The sole fact that the two values were very close to each other led Maxwell to propound (around 1865) his famous electromagnetic theory of light according to which,

light waves are electromagnetic waves

This was one of the greatest unifications in physics. Associated with a light wave are changing electric and magnetic fields; the changing magnetic field produces a time and space varying electric field and the changing electric field produces a time and space varying magnetic field, and this results in the propagation of the electromagnetic wave even in vacuum.

The changing electric (or magnetic fields) can be assumed to represent the displacement associated with the light wave.

In 1888, Heinrich Hertz carried out beautiful experiments which could produce and detect electromagnetic waves of frequencies smaller than those of light. These waves were produced by discharging electrically charged plates through a spark gap. The frequency of the emitted electromagnetic waves could be calculated by knowing the inductance and capacitance of the circuit. Hertz also produced standing electromagnetic waves by getting them reflected by a metal sheet (see Fig. 1.10). He could calculate the wavelength of the waves and knowing the frequency, he showed that the speed of the electromagnetic waves (in air) was the same as that of light:

$$\text{velocity of electromagnetic waves} = \lambda\nu \approx 3 \times 10^8 \text{ m/s} \tag{1.17}$$

Using a collimated electromagnetic wave, and getting it reflected by a metal sheet, he could demonstrate the laws of reflection. Hertz's experimental results provided dramatic confirmation of Maxwell's electromagnetic theory. In addition, there were so many other experimental results, which were quantitatively explained by using Maxwell's theory that towards the end of the nineteenth century, physicists thought that one had finally understood what light really was: i.e., ***light was an electromagnetic wave.***

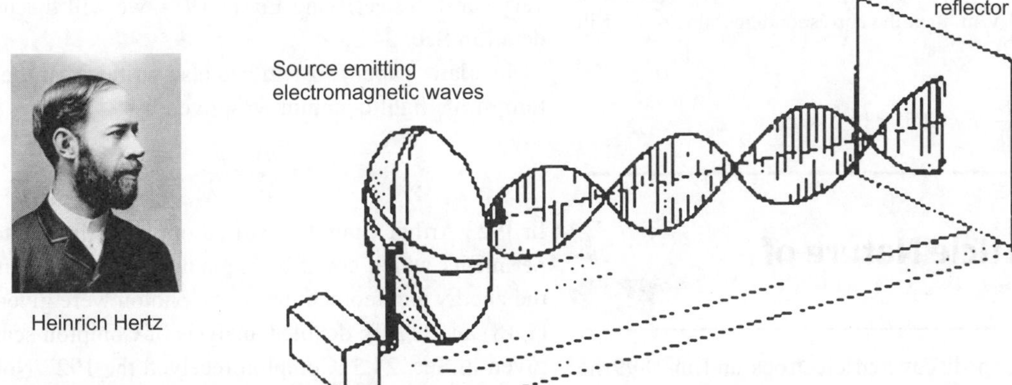

Figure 1.10
Hertz's arrangement for studying standing electromagnetic waves; diagram adapted from http://www.physics.usyd.edu.au/teach_res/hsp/u7/t7_hertz.pdf.

1.5 What is the Displacement Associated with the Light Wave?

Sound waves require a medium to propagate from one point to the other – in fact, when sound waves propagate in air, air molecules execute vibrations which transport energy from one point to the other and the displacement associated with a sound wave is the actual displacement of the air molecules. Thus sound waves cannot propagate in vacuum. Similarly, the displacement associated with a propagating water wave is the actual displacement of the water molecules and the displacement associated with a transverse wave propagating on a string is the actual displacement of each point on the string. Since light waves could propagate through vacuum, one of the main difficulties associated with the wave theory of light was the question that what is the displacement associated with the light wave? Because of this, as mentioned earlier, an '*all pervading ether*' theory was developed – i.e., ether exists even in vacuum – this led to great difficulties; we will not go into details of this because we now know that ether does not exist.

According to Maxwell's electromagnetic theory, there are oscillating electric and magnetic fields associated with the propagating electromagnetic wave [see, e.g., Eqs. (1.13) and (1.14)]. These fields are present even in vacuum. Thus

> ***the displacement associated with the propagating light wave is the electric field which oscillates in time with a certain frequency***

We could have equally well chosen the magnetic field as the displacement associated with the propagating electromagnetic wave because associated with a time varying electric field there is always a time varying magnetic field. We may mention that the concept of the field was first introduced by Michael Faraday; what Faraday said was that if there is an electric charge in vacuum, it creates an electric field in the space that surrounds it, and this field will exert a force on any other charge placed in the field.

EXAMPLE 1.2 For an electromagnetic wave propagating in vacuum, the electric field is given by

$$E_x(z, t) = 10 \cos [(4 \times 10^6 \pi)z - (1.2 \times 10^{15} \pi)t]$$

where the electric field is measured in V/m and, as before, distances are measured in meters and time in seconds. Thus the amplitude of the wave is 10 V/m. The corresponding wavelength and frequency would be given by

$$\frac{2\pi}{\lambda} = 4 \times 10^6 \pi \Rightarrow \lambda = 0.5 \text{ µm}$$

and $$2\pi\nu = 1.2 \times 10^{15} \pi \Rightarrow \nu = 0.6 \times 10^{15} \text{ Hz}$$

We can write the displacement as

$$E_x(z, t) = 10 \cos [4 \times 10^6 \pi(z - 3 \times 10^8 t)]$$

Thus the velocity of the electromagnetic wave would be 3×10^8 m/s which is the same as the value of $\lambda\nu$.

EXAMPLE 1.3 The wavelength of the visible region of the electromagnetic spectrum goes from 0.4 µm for the violet color to about 0.7 µm for the red color. The corresponding frequencies will be given by $\nu = \frac{c}{\lambda}$ to obtain 7.5×10^{14} Hz for the violet color to about 4.3×10^{14} Hz for the red color respectively.

EXAMPLE 1.4 The frequency associated with microwave ovens is about 2.45 GHz (= 2.45×10^9 Hz); the corresponding wavelength will be about 12 cm.

EXAMPLE 1.5 For an electromagnetic wave propagating in free space, if $E_0 = 10$ V/m, then the corresponding value of H_0 will be given by

$$H_0 = \sqrt{\frac{\varepsilon_0}{\mu_0}}\, E_0 = 2.65 \times 10^{-2}\ \text{A/m}$$

1.6 The Particle Nature of Radiation

LO4

In 1897 J J Thomson discovered electrons and in 1899 he showed that electrons are emitted when light falls on a metal surface. In 1902 Philip Lenard observed that

(i) the kinetic energy of the emitted electrons was independent of the intensity of the incident light and
(ii) that the energy of the emitted electron increased when the frequency of the incident light was increased.

which cannot be explained by a theory based on the wave model of light. Einstein, in his year of miracles (1905) published a paper (Ref. 1.6), in which he proposed that light can be emitted or absorbed only in discrete amounts, called *quanta*; the energy of each quanta is given by

$$E = h\nu \tag{1.18}$$

where ν is the frequency and $h(\approx 6.626 \times 10^{-34}$ Js) is the Planck's constant. (It was only in 1926 that Gilbert Lewis, an American chemist, coined the word 'photon' to describe Einstein's 'localized energy quanta'). At that point of time, Maxwell's electromagnetic theory was very well established and Einstein's concept of the light quantum was not readily accepted; however, it was this paper of Einstein which started the "wave particle duality" which eventually led to the development of quantum theory. In his *Autobiographical Notes* (Ref. 1.13, page 51), Einstein later wrote

> *... radiation energy consists of indivisible quanta of energy hν which are reflected undivided ... that radiation must, therefore, possess a kind of molecular structure in energy, which of course contradicts Maxwell's theory.*

In his 1905 paper, using the concept of his 'localized energy quanta', Einstein explained the photoelectric effect experiment by stating that the emission of a photoelectron was the result of the interaction of a single quantum (i.e., of the photon) with an electron and that the maximum kinetic energy of the emitted electron is linearly related to the frequency of the incident radiation and one may write

$$T_{\max} = h(\nu - \nu_c) \quad \text{Einstein's photoelectric equation} \tag{1.19}$$

where the frequency ν_c represents the cutoff frequency and is a characteristic of the metal. Einstein's theory gave a very satisfactory explanation of the photoelectric effect. Around 1914, Robert Millikan carried out a series of experiments very carefully verifying Eq. (1.19) – we will discuss this in detail in Sec. 24.2.

In a later paper Einstein had also written that the momentum of his light quantum was given by

$$p = \frac{h\nu}{c} = \frac{h}{\lambda} \tag{1.20}$$

In 1923 Arthur Compton carried out beautiful scattering experiments which could be explained only by assuming that the energy and momentum of the photon were given by Eqs. (1.18) and (1.20); detailed analysis of Compton scattering is given in Sec. 24.3. Compton received the 1927 Nobel Prize in Physics for this experiment. It was only after Compton's experiment that everyone started believing in Einstein's 'localized energy quanta'.

Although Newton had described light as a stream of particles, this view had been completely superseded by the wave picture of light, a picture that culminated in the electromagnetic theory of Maxwell. The revival of the particle picture now posed a severe conceptual problem, one of reconciling wave and particle like behavior of radiation. To quote from Ref. 1.14:

> *Owing to Einstein's paper of 1905, it was primarily the photoelectric effect to which physicists referred as an irrefutable demonstration of the existence of photons and which thus played an important part in the conceptual development of quantum mechanics.*

1.7 Wave Particle Duality

The electron was discovered in 1897 by J.J. Thomson; the mass and charge of the electron is known to a considerable degree of accuracy, and, it can be deflected by an electric (or a magnetic) field. Thus, on the back of our mind, we picture the electron (and similarly the proton or the alpha particle, ...) as a tiny particle with definite mass and charge. Also, cloud chamber experiments were carried out by C.T.R. Wilson (during the early years of the twentieth century), which had clearly shown the particle-like behavior of alpha and beta particles. These particles are emitted by radioactive elements and when they pass through supersaturated vapor, they form tracks of condensed droplets; tracks of fast moving protons are shown in Fig. 1.11. C.T.R. Wilson was awarded the 1927 Nobel Prize in Physics *for his method of making the paths of electrically charged particles visible by condensation of vapor*. The existence of continuous tracks suggests that electrons, protons, alpha particles, can be regarded as tiny particles moving with high speed. Further, the fact that electrons, protons, could be deflected by electric and magnetic fields and also the fact that one could accurately determine

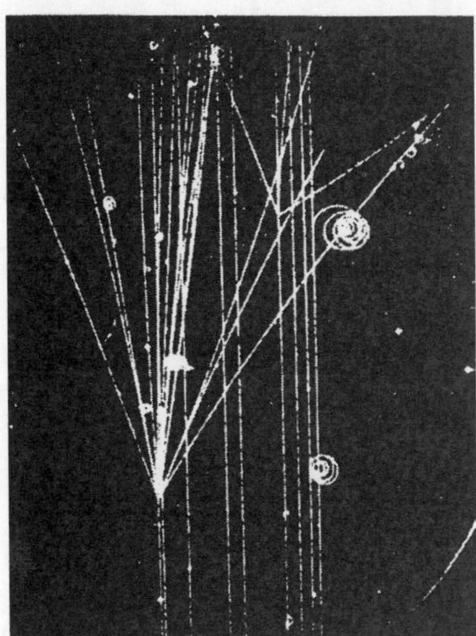

Figure 1.11
A bubble-chamber picture of a 25-GeV proton beam impinging on a hydrogen atom and producing new particles; photograph adapted from Ref. 1.15; see also Ref. 1.16.

the ratio of their charge to mass suggest very strongly that they are tiny particles. This view remained unchallenged for a number of years.

In 1924, de Broglie wrote his PhD thesis in which he proposed that just as light exhibited wave-like and corpuscular-like behavior, matter (like electrons, protons, ...) must show wavelike behavior also. He argued that the relation

$$\lambda = \frac{h}{p} \tag{1.21}$$

[see Eq.(1.20)] should be applied for electrons, protons, alpha particles ... as well. Using the above relation, de Broglie showed that the circumference of a Bohr orbit contains integral number of wavelengths (see Sec. 26.5). In 1927 (*after* de Broglie's work), Davisson and Germer studied the diffraction of electrons from single crystals of nickel and showed that the diffraction patterns could be explained if the electrons were assumed to have a wavelength given by the de Broglie relation [see Eq.(1.21)]. Shortly afterwards, in 1928, G.P. Thomson carried out electron diffraction experiments by passing electrons through thin polycrystalline metal targets (see Sec. 17.10 for more details). The diffraction pattern consisted of concentric rings similar to the Debye-Scherrer rings obtained in the X-ray diffraction pattern. By measuring the diameters of the rings and from the known structure of the crystals, Thomson calculated the wavelength associated with the electron beam which was in agreement with the de Broglie relation [Eq.(1.21)]. In 1937, Davisson and Thomson shared the Nobel Prize *for their experimental discovery of the diffraction of electrons by crystals*. We may note that the wave nature of electrons (or protons,...) were *predicted* by Louis de Broglie in 1924 and the experiments which demonstrated wave nature of matter were performed much later. In Fig. 1.12 we have shown the diffraction patterns (known as Debye Scherrer rings) produced by scattering of X-rays [see Fig. 1.12(a)], and by scattering of electrons [see Fig. 1.12(b)] by an aluminum foil. The two figures clearly show the similarity in the wave-like properties of X-rays and of electrons.

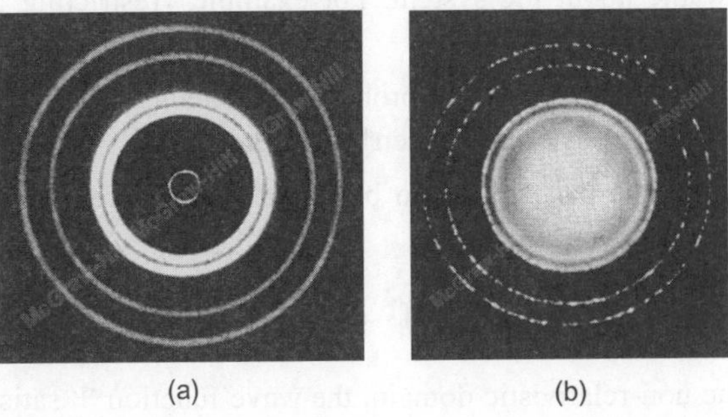

Figure 1.12
The diffraction pattern of aluminum foil produced (a) by X-rays and (b) by electrons; notice the similarity in the diffraction patterns. *Photographs courtesy: McGraw Hill Digital Access Library.*

EXAMPLE 1.6 In this example, we will calculate the number of photons emitted per second by a 1 mW laser beam with wavelength of 0.6 μm (= 6 × 10⁻⁷ m). The corresponding frequency would be 5 × 10¹⁴ Hz. Thus the number of photons emitted per second will be

$$N = \frac{1\,\text{mW}}{h\nu} = \frac{1\times10^{-3}\,\text{W}}{(6.626\times10^{-34}\,\text{Js})\times(5\times10^{14}\,\text{s}^{-1})} \approx 3\times10^{15}\ \text{photons/s}$$

EXAMPLE 1.7 For the $2P \rightarrow 1S$ transition in the hydrogen atom we get light of wavelength 0.1217 μm which is in the ultraviolet region; the corresponding frequency will be about 2.47×10^{15} Hz. Thus the energy of the photon will be given by

$E = h\nu \approx 6.626 \times 10^{-34} \times 2.47 \times 10^{15}\ \text{J} \approx 1.64 \times 10^{-18}\ \text{J} \approx 10.2\ \text{eV}$

where we have used the fact that $1\ \text{eV} \approx 1.602 \times 10^{-19}$ J

EXAMPLE 1.8 For a 20 keV X-ray photon, $E = 2 \times 10^4\ \text{eV} \approx 3.204 \times 10^{-15}$ J. Thus

$$\nu = \frac{E}{h} = \frac{3.204\times10^{-15}\,\text{J}}{6.626\times10^{-34}\,\text{Js}} \approx 4.84\times10^{18}\,\text{Hz}$$

Thus the wavelength is given by

$$\lambda = \frac{c}{\nu} = \frac{3\times10^{8}\,\text{m/s}}{4.84\times10^{18}\,\text{Hz}} \approx 6.2\times10^{-11}\,\text{m} = 0.62\ \text{Å}$$

Indeed the Molybdenum K-alpha line has a wavelength of 0.7107 Å and the corresponding energy of the photon is 17.45 keV.

This 'wave-particle duality' led to the development of quantum theory. The obvious question arises: Is the electron (or a proton or an alpha particle) a wave or a particle??? The answer is [to quote Feynman (Ref. 1.11)]:

It is neither a wave nor a particle.

According to quantum theory, it is described by the symbol Ψ (which is known as the wave function); the wave function depends on the position and contains all information that is knowable about the system. For example, (restricting to 1 dimension):

$|\Psi(x, t)|^2\, dx$ represents the probability of finding the electron's position between* x and $x + dx$ **(1.22)**

Since the particle has to be found somewhere, we must have

$$\int_{-\infty}^{+\infty} |\Psi(x,t)|^2\, dx = 1 \tag{1.23}$$

In the non-relativistic domain, the wave function Ψ satisfies what is known as the Schrödinger equation. If we know the wave function at $t = 0$; i.e., if we know $\Psi(x, t = 0)$, then by solving the Schrödinger equation, we can determine the time evolution of Ψ; i.e., we can determine $\Psi(x, t)$, and hence of probability of finding the particle in a small volume element at a later time. The Schrödinger equation is a bit complicated … see Sec. 26.6.

1.8 Diffraction by a Single Slit LO5

We consider an electron beam (propagating in the y-direction) incident on a single slit of width b [see Fig. 1.13]. For such a situation, if we solve the Schrödinger equation we would obtain (see Sec. 26.8)

$$P(p_x)\, dp_x = \frac{2b}{h} \frac{\sin^2 \beta}{\beta^2}\, dp_x \tag{1.24}$$

where $P(p_x)dp_x$ is the probability that (after interacting with the slit) the electron's x-component of the momentum lies between p_x and $p_x + dp_x$. The above equation implies that the electron acquires this x-component of the momentum from the slit. In the above equation

$$\beta = \frac{\pi b\, p_x}{h} = \frac{\pi b\, p \sin\theta}{h} = \frac{\pi b \sin\theta}{\lambda} \tag{1.25}$$

The function $\frac{\sin^2 \beta}{\beta^2}$ has the first zero at $\beta \approx \pi$; thus, if we plot the function $\frac{\sin^2 \beta}{\beta^2}$ as a function of β, the FWHM (Full Width at Half Maximum) will be approximately given by

$$\Delta\beta \approx \pi \tag{1.26}$$

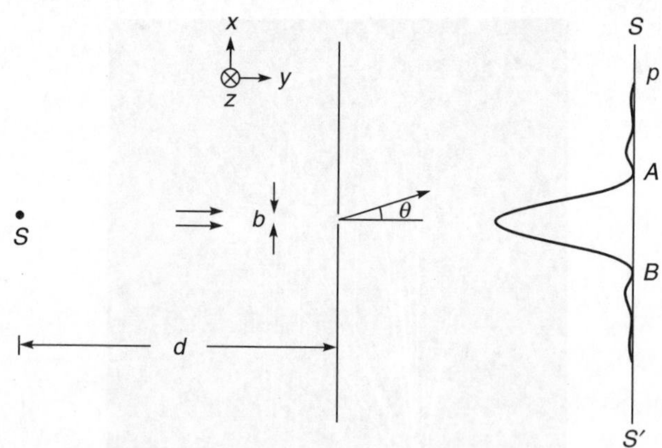

Figure 1.13
Diffraction of an electron by a narrow slit of width b.

Thus the spread in $\beta \approx \pi$; since $p_x = \frac{h\beta}{\pi b}$ the corresponding spread in p_x would be

$$\Delta p_x \approx \frac{h\Delta\beta}{\pi b} \approx \frac{h}{b} \tag{1.27}$$

Now, one can always choose the electron source to be so far away that (before entering the slit), p_x can be assumed to have an arbitrarily small value. Thus the electrons approaching the slit can be assumed to have momentum only in the y-direction. The expression for $P(p_x)dp_x$ tells us that by making the electron pass through a slit of width b, the slit imparts a momentum in the x-direction which is $\approx \frac{h}{b}$. It may be pointed out that *before* the photon entered the slit, p_x (and hence Δp_x, which represents the spread in p_x) can be made arbitrarily small by putting the source sufficiently far away. Thus we may write $\Delta p_x \approx 0$ before the electron passes through the slit. The slit imparts a momentum (in the x-direction) to the electron given by

$$|p_x| \approx \Delta p_x \approx \frac{h}{b} \tag{1.28}$$

Now, by making the electron pass through a slit (of width b), it is localized within a distance b (in the x-direction); thus

$$\Delta x \approx b \;\Rightarrow\; \Delta x \Delta p_x \approx h \tag{1.29}$$

This is the **Heisenberg's uncertainty principle**. According to the uncertainty principle, if we localize a particle within a distance of about Δx (in the x-direction), then the process of localization makes the (x-component) of the momentum uncertain by

$$\Delta p_x \approx \frac{h}{\Delta x} \tag{1.30}$$

Thus the uncertainty principle is contained in the solution of the Schrödinger equation. Also, since $p_x = p \sin\theta$, where

* Actually the wave function must depend on x, y, z and $|\Psi(x, y, z, t)|^2\, dxdydz$ would represent the probability of finding the particle's position in the volume element $dxdydz$.

θ is the angle that the electron coming out of the slit makes with the y-axis, we have

$$p\sin\theta \approx \frac{h}{b} \quad \Rightarrow \quad \sin\theta \approx \frac{h}{pb} = \frac{\lambda}{b} \qquad \textbf{(1.31)}$$

which is what we obtain when we consider the diffraction spreading of a wave passing through a long narrow slit of width b. Equation (1.31) predicts that smaller the value of b, greater is the value of θ and greater is the possibility of the electron to reach deep inside the geometrical shadow. This is indeed the diffraction phenomenon; thus everything is contained in the solution of the Schrödinger equation! Further, the intensity distribution as predicted by classical wave theory is given by (see Sec. 17.2)

$$I = I_0 \frac{\sin^2\beta}{\beta^2} \qquad \textbf{(1.32)}$$

where $\beta = \frac{\pi b \sin\theta}{\lambda}$ which is similar to Eq. (1.24). Thus the solution of the Schrödinger equation does not predict where exactly the electron will land up, it only predicts a probability distribution – but this probability distribution is the same as the intensity distribution given by the classical wave theory. Thus according to quantum theory, we cannot predict where exactly the electron will be detected on the screen but if we carry out the experiment with millions of electrons, the intensity distribution (as predicted by the wave theory) will slowly build up. Richard Feynman says (in his famous 1966 Messenger Lecture) that "electrons arrive in lumps – just like tiny bullets; however, the probability of arrival of the electrons is the same as predicted by the wave theory".

Indeed, the de Broglie relation has been verified by studying the diffraction patterns produced when electrons, neutrons, etc., pass through a single crystal; the patterns can be analyzed in a manner similar to X-ray diffractions (see Sec. 17.10). In Fig. 1.14, we show the experimental data of Shull (Ref. 1.17) who studied the Fraunhofer diffraction of neutrons by a single slit and his experimental results agree with the intensity distribution as predicted by the wave theory with $\lambda = h/p$.

Now, $\frac{\sin^2\beta}{\beta^2} = \frac{1}{2}$ when $\beta \approx 1.39$

Since $\beta = \frac{\pi b \sin\theta}{\lambda}$ we have $\Delta\theta \approx 2\sin^{-1}\left(\frac{1.39\lambda}{\pi b}\right)$

where $\Delta\theta$ is the FWHM [Full (angular) Width at Half Maximum].

For the top curve in Fig. 1.14, $b = 5.6$ µm

$\Rightarrow \Delta\theta \approx 0.00401 \approx 14.4''$

For the bottom curve in Fig. 1.14, $b = 4.1$ µm

$\Rightarrow \Delta\theta \approx 0.00548 \approx 19.7''$

which agrees with what is shown in Fig. 1.14.

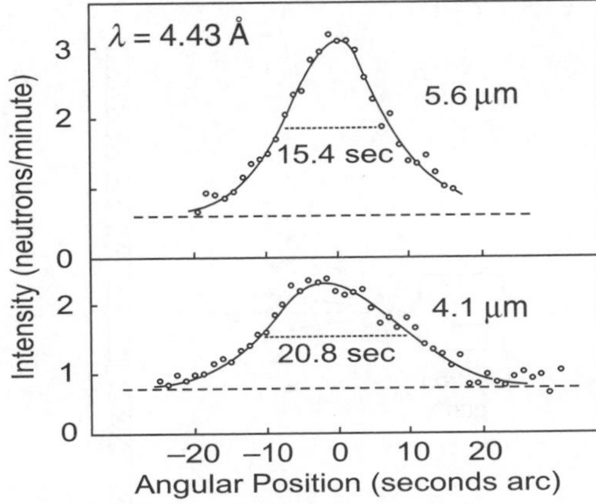

Figure 1.14

Angular broadening of a neutron beam by narrow slits; adapted from Ref. 1.17.

1.9 The Double Slit Interference Pattern

LO6

We next consider the incidence of an electron beam by two slits each of width b and separated by a distance d [see Fig. 1.15]. For such a situation, if we solve the Schrödinger equation we would obtain (see Sec. 26.9)

$$P(p_x)dp_x = \left[\frac{2b}{\pi h}\frac{\sin^2\beta}{\beta^2}\right]\left[4\cos^2\gamma\right]dp_x \qquad \textbf{(1.33)}$$

where, as before,

$P(p_x)dp_x$ is the probability that (after interacting with the slit) the electron's x-component of the momentum lies between p_x and $p_x + dp_x$,

$$\beta = \frac{\pi b \sin\theta}{\lambda} \quad \text{and} \quad \gamma = \frac{\pi d \sin\theta}{\lambda}$$

On the other hand, classical wave theory predicts (see Sec. 17.6)

$$I = \underbrace{\left[I_0 \frac{\sin^2\beta}{\beta^2}\right]}_{\text{Single Slit Diffraction Pattern}} \underbrace{\left[4\cos^2\gamma\right]}_{\text{2 point interference pattern}} \qquad (1.34)$$

Once again, the probability distribution is the same as the intensity distribution given by the wave theory. The corpuscular nature of the electron is evident from its detection in the form of a single electron and never a fraction of an electron. Quantum theory tells us that an electron passes through both the slits (S_1 and S_2) simultaneously. This is not the splitting of the electron into two halves but only implies that if we wish to find out through which slit the electron has passed, then half the time it will be found to have passed through the slit S_1 and half the time through S_2. We cannot say that the electron passes through either S_1 or through S_2 which is what we would expect classically. The electron is in a state which is a superposition of two states, one corresponding

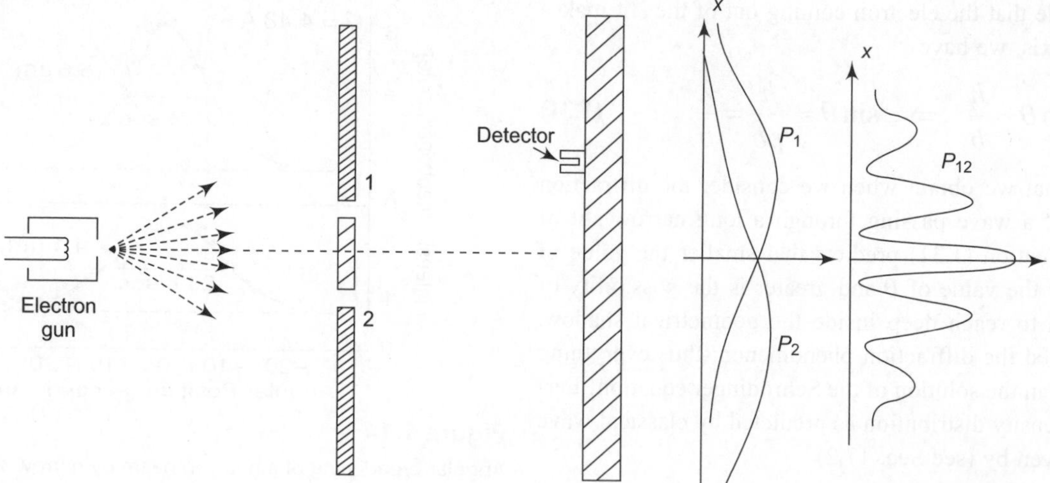

Figure 1.15

Interference experiment with electrons 2 narrow slits each of width *b* and separated by a distance *d*. [Adapted from Ref. 1.11].

to the disturbance emanating from the slit S_1 and the other emanating from hole S_2. The superposed state will give rise to a probability distribution of arrival of the electrons which is similar to the intensity distribution obtained by considering the superposition of two waves. Thus according to quantum theory, we cannot predict where exactly the electron will be detected on the screen but if we carry out the experiment with millions of electrons, the intensity distribution (as predicted by the wave theory) will slowly build up.

In the discussion above we said that according to quantum theory, an electron passes through both the slits (S_1 and S_2) simultaneously. The obvious question is: how can a single electron (or, a proton) which have very accurately determined mass and charge pass through both slits simultaneously? How can we physically understand that? In 1966, Richard Feynman delivered 6 wonderful Messenger Lectures at Cornell University on ***The Character of Physical Law***; in the 6th and final lecture, he spoke on ***Probability and Uncertainty*** in which he said:

> *Electrons do not behave just like particles, they do not behave just like waves. Electrons in orbits are not somewhat like a cloud or fog of some sort surrounding the nucleus. It behaves like nothing that you have seen before. Well there is one simplification at least electrons behave exactly the same way as photons.*

In the same lecture he had also said

> *I think I can safely say that nobody understands quantum mechanics*

I would urge all students to listen to the Messenger Lectures, particularly the one on ***Probability and Uncertainty*** which can be seen on the following website

https://www.youtube.com/watch?v=Ja0HSFj8Imc&t=387s

While discussing the double slit interference experiment with electrons, Feynman wrote in Ref. 1.11:

> *We choose to examine a phenomenon which is impossible,* ***absolutely*** *impossible, to explain in any classical way, and which has in it the heart of quantum mechanics. In reality, it contains the only mystery.*

In a recent paper, Tonomura and his co-workers (Ref. 1.18) have demonstrated the single electron build up of an interference pattern. Their results are shown in Fig. 1.16. It may be seen that when there are very few electrons they arrive randomly; however, when a large number of electrons are involved, one obtains an intensity distribution similar to the one predicted by wave theory. The corpuscular nature of the electron is evident from its detection in the form of a single electron and never fraction of an electron. Thus according to quantum theory, we cannot predict where exactly the electron will be detected on the screen but if we carry out the experiment with millions of electrons, the intensity distribution (as predicted by the wave theory) will slowly build up – see Fig. 1.16.

Sometime back, Professor Robert Crease, (currently at the State University of New York at Stony Brook and the historian at Brookhaven National Laboratory), asked physicists to nominate the most beautiful experiment of all time. Based on the nominations, **'Young's light-interference experiment'**

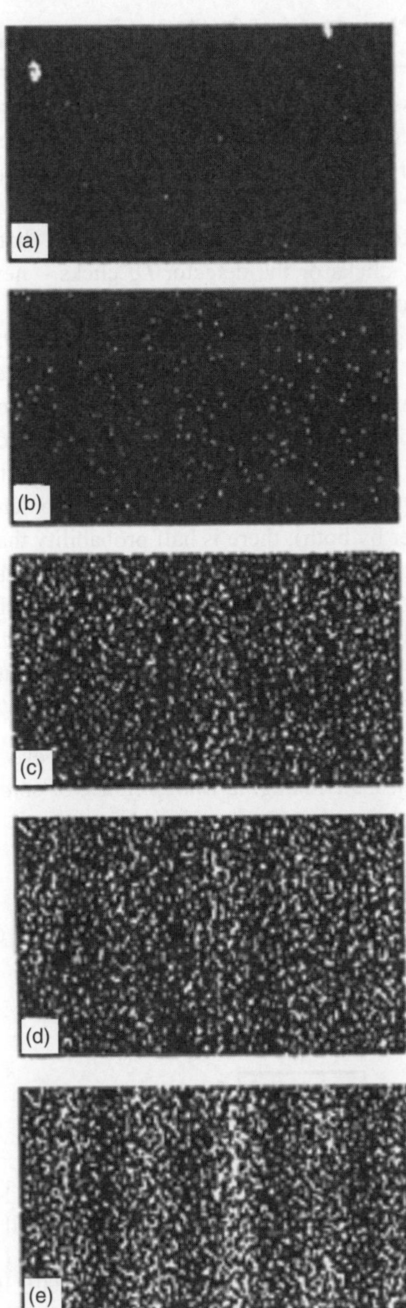

Figure 1.16
Buildup of the electron interference pattern. Number of electrons in (a), (b), (c), (d) and (e) are 10, 100, 3000, 20000 and 70000 respectively. [Adapted from Ref. 1.18; used with permission].

was chosen as one of the 10 most beautiful experiments of all time*. The list of 10 experiments was ranked according to popularity, and the first on the list was the **'Double-slit electron diffraction'**, which demonstrated the quantum nature of the physical world.

1.10 The Probabilistic Interpretation of Matter Waves

In the previous section, we have seen that if a photon passes through a slit of width b, then the momentum imparted in the x-direction (which is along the width of the slit) is $\approx h/b$. The question arises whether we can predict the trajectory of an individual photon. The answer is *no*. We cannot say where an individual photon will land up on the screen; we can only predict the probabilities of arrival of the photon in a certain region of the screen. We may, for example, say that the probability for the arrival of the photon in the region lying between the points A and B (see Fig. 1.13) is 0.65. This would imply that if the experiment was carried out with a large number of photons, about 65% of them would land up in the region AB; but the fate of an individual photon can never be predicted. This is in contrast to Newtonian mechanics where the trajectories are always predetermined. Also, if we place a light detector on the screen, then it will always record one photon or none and never half a photon. This essentially implies the corpuscular nature of the radiation. However, the probability distribution is the same as predicted by wave theory and therefore if one performs an experiment with a large number of photons (as is indeed the case in most experiments) the intensity distribution recorded on the screen is the same as predicted by the wave theory; we explicitly show this in Sec. 26.6.

The corpuscular nature of radiation and the fact that one cannot predict the trajectory of an individual photon can be seen from Fig. 1.17, which consists of series of photographs showing the quality of pictures obtainable from various number of photons (Ref. 1.19). The photograph clearly shows that the picture is built up by the arrival of concentrated packets of energy and the point at which a particular photon will arrive is entirely a matter of chance. The figure also shows that the photograph is featureless when a small number of photons are involved and as the number of photons reaching the photographic plate increases, the intensity distribution becomes the same as would be predicted by the wave theory. To quote Feynman:

> ... *it would be impossible to predict what would happen. We can only predict the odds! This would mean, if it were true, that physics has given up on the problem of trying to predict exactly what will happen in a definite circumstance. Yes! physics has given up. We do not know how to predict what would happen in a given circumstance, and we believe now that it is impossible—that the only thing that can*

* see https://www.nytimes.com/2002/09/24/science/here-they-are-science-s-10-most-beautiful-experiments.html

be predicted is the probability of different events. It must be recognized that this is a retrenchment in our earlier idea of understanding nature. It may be a backward step, but no one has seen a way to avoid it.

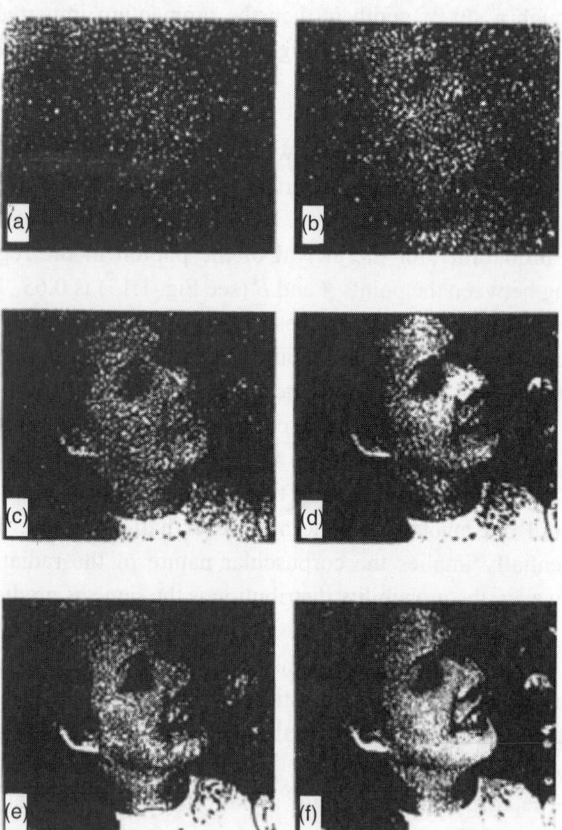

Figure 1.17
Photographs showing the quality of a picture obtainable from various numbers of photons
(a) 3×10^3 photons, (b) 1.2×10^4 photons,
(c) 9.3×10^4 photons (d) 7.6×10^5 photons
(e) 3.6×10^6 photons and (f) 2.8×10^7 photons.
[After Ref. 1.19; used with permission].

A somewhat similar situation arises in radioactivity. Consider a radioactive nucleus having a half-life of say 1 hour. If we start with 1000 such nuclei, then on an average 500 of them would undergo radioactive decay in 1 hour and about 250 of them in the next 1 hour and so on. Thus, although to start with, all nuclei are identical, some nuclei would decay in the very first minute and some nuclei can survive for hours without undergoing radioactive decay. Thus, one can never predict as to which nucleus will undergo decay in a specified period; one can only predict the probability of its undergoing decay in a certain interval of time and this probability can be calculated using quantum theory.

1.11 The Beam Splitter Experiment

We next assume light from a single photon source incident on a beam splitter [see Fig. 1.18(a)]. An ideal beam splitter is a partially silvered glass plate such that 50% of the light is reflected and 50% of the light is transmitted. We have two single photon detectors D_1 and D_2; we find that either the detector D_1 clicks or the detector D_2 clicks – never both at the same instant of time. Quantum theory tells us that before the photon gets detected (either by the detector D_1 or by D_2), the photon is in both the beams. The photon does not split into two halves – but when the photon gets detected, it collapses (from being in both the beams) to being detected by one of the detectors. This "collapsing" is unique to quantum theory. The photon gets detected either by the detector D_1 or by D_2 (never by both); there is half probability that it will be detected by the detector D_1 and half probability that it will be detected by the detector D_2. No one can predict beforehand as to which detector will detect the photon. According to Zeilinger (Ref. 1.20), who is one of the great authorities in quantum optics, this indeterminateness

is one of the most important discoveries ever made in physics. Just imagine what physics, or science in

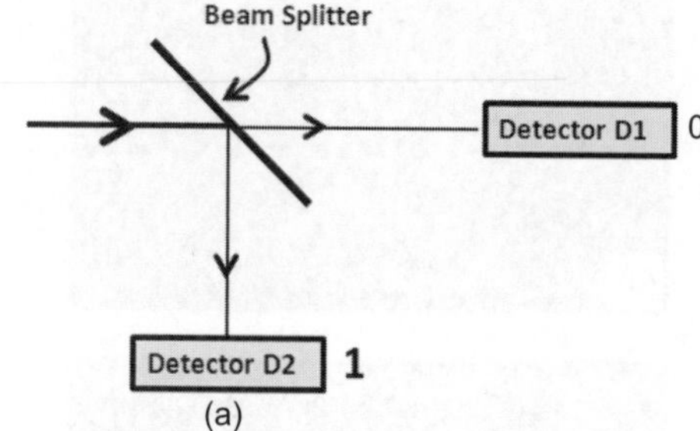

11110110101001010110111100110011101011111110010110
11001010110001000010010001100001110100101011101001
10010011001101101010101000100110001011010111101101
00011001011100001100101001100001010110001110010100
11011011101101000011001101011010011111100010010101
10100010000100001001010101000001100000010100110110
10111100110011001101010001001111000000000100110001
00011001111011100000000010001100110101010101011111
0101100100010110001010010001010

(b)

Figure 1.18
(a) A light beam splits into 2 beams by a beam splitter. D1 and D2 are single photon detectors. (b) Whenever the detector D1 clicks, we generate the number 0 and whenever the detector D2 clicks, we generate the number 1. The set of random numbers generated in (b) has been adapted from Ref. 1.21.

general, does. We have tried for centuries to look deeper and deeper into finding causes and explanations, and suddenly, when we go to the very depths, to the behavior of individual quanta, we find that this search for a cause comes to an end. There is no cause. In my eyes, this fundamental indeterminateness of the universe has not really been integrated into our world view yet.

This indeterminateness greatly bothered Einstein. He always felt that science should be deterministic. Although he was very impressed by the tremendous success of the quantum theory, he wrote to his friend Max Born

Quantum Mechanics is certainly imposing. But an inner voice tells me that it is not yet the real thing. ... I am, at any rate, convinced that ***God does not play dice ...***

This is one of the rare occasions when Einstein was not quite right. As Zeilinger writes (Ref. 1.20, p. 82)

Well, I believe that the Lord actually loves to play dice.

In fact we can use this indeterminateness to generate random numbers. If we assume that whenever the detector D_1 clicks, we create the number 0 and whenever the detector D_2 clicks, we create the number 1, then as the photons get detected we create a set of random numbers as shown in Fig. 1.18(b). Computer scientists use complex algorithms to generate random numbers. However, since they are based on calculations, after a large number, they would repeat itself; this repetition may be after 2^{100} numbers, therefore they are referred to as pseudo random number generators. But this is not the case with the quantum random number generator discussed above. Hence quantum random number generators find very important applications in computer science. To quote from Ref. 1.21:

we present the realization of a physical quantum random number generator based on the process of splitting a beam of photons on a beam splitter, a quantum mechanical source of true randomness. By utilizing either a beam splitter or a polarizing beam splitter, single photon detectors and high speed electronics the presented devices are capable of generating ... a continuous stream of random numbers at a rate of 1 Mbit/s.

For example, a company is selling a product by the name of QUANTIS which they claim to be *True Random Number Generator Exploiting Quantum Physics*; see Fig. 1.19. For more details see Reference 1.21.

QUANTIS

PRODUCTS
•True Random Number Generators (TRNG)

QUANTIS is a random number generator exploiting an elementary quantum optics process. Photons are sent one by one onto a semi-transparent mirror and detected. The exclusive events (reflection - transmission) are associated to "0" - "1" bit values.

Figure 1.19
A commercial product generating random numbers exploiting quantum physics; adapted from http://www.idquantique.com/component/content/article.html?id=9

EXAMPLE 1.9 Let a source (with $\lambda = 5 \times 10^{-5}$ cm) of power 1 W be used in the experimental arrangement shown in Fig. 1.20.

(a) Calculate the number of photons emitted by the source per second.

(b) Assume the radii of the holes S, S_1 and S_2 to be 0.02 cm and $S_0S = SS_1 = SS_2 = 100$ cm and the distance between the planes AB and PP' to be also 100 cm. Show that in the region between the planes AB and PP' one can almost never find two photons.

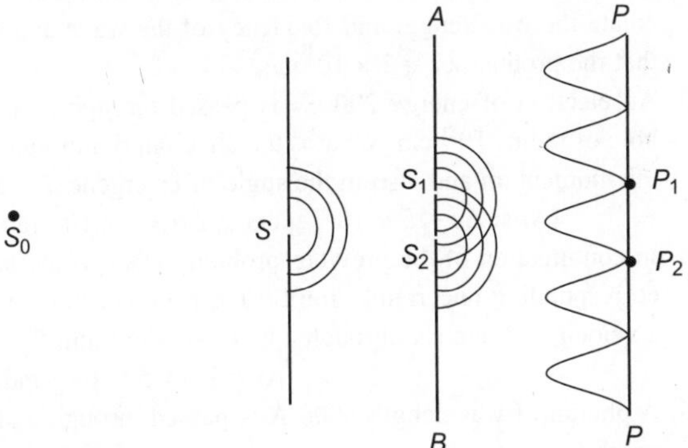

Figure 1.20
Young's double hole experimental arrangement for obtaining the interference pattern. S_0 represents a point source.

Solution:

(a) The energy of each photon will be

$$h\nu = \frac{hc}{\lambda} = \frac{6.6\times10^{-34}(\text{J.s})\times3\times10^{8}(\text{m/s})}{5\times10^{-7}(\text{m})}$$
$$\approx 4\times10^{-19}\ \text{J}$$

Thus, the number of photons emitted per second will be

$$\frac{1\text{ W}}{4\times10^{-19}\text{ J}} = 2.5\times10^{18}$$

(b) The number of photons passing through the hole S will approximately be

$$\frac{2.5\times10^{18}\times\pi\times(0.02)^2}{4\times\pi\times(100)^2} = 2.5\times10^{10} \text{ per second}$$

similarly, the number of photons passing through either S_1 or S_2 will approximately be

$$\frac{2.5\times10^{10}\times2\times\pi\times(0.02)^2}{2\pi\times(100)^2} = 1000 \text{ per second}$$

where we have assumed that after passing through S, the photons are evenly distributed in the hemisphere; this is strictly not correct because the diffraction pattern is actually an Airy pattern (see Chapter 17) – nevertheless, the above calculations are qualitatively correct. The distance between the planes AB and PP' is 100 cm which will be traversed by a photon in time $\approx 3\times10^{-9}$ s. Thus, approximately every thousandth of a second a photon enters the region and the space is traversed much before the second photon enters. Therefore, in the region between AB and PP' one will (almost) never find two photons. This is somewhat similar to the case when, on an average, 100 persons pass through a room in one year and the time that each person takes to cross the room is ≈ 1 s, thus it will be highly improbable to have two persons simultaneously in the room.

PROBLEMS

1.1 The displacement associated with a transverse wave on a string is given by

$y(x, t) = 0.001 \cos [100(x - 300t)]$

where the distances are measured in meters and time in seconds. Calculate the wavelength and frequency of the wave and show that the product $\lambda\nu = 300$ m/s.

1.2 For an electromagnetic wave propagating in vacuum, the electric field is given by

$E_x(z, t) = 20 \cos[1\times10^7(z - 2\times10^8\, t)]$

where the electric field is measured in V/m and, as before, distances are measured in meters and time in seconds. Calculate the wavelength and frequency of the wave and show that the product $\lambda\nu = 2\times10^8$ m/s.

1.3 An electron of energy 200 eV is passed through a circular hole of radius 10^{-4} cm. What is the uncertainty introduced in the momentum and also in the angle of emergence?

[**Ans:** $\Delta p \sim 5\times10^{-24}$ g cm/s; $\Delta\theta \approx 6\times10^{-6}$ radians]

1.4 In continuation of the previous problem, what would be the corresponding uncertainty for a 0.1 g lead ball thrown with a velocity 10^3 cm/sec through a hole 1 cm in radius?

[**Ans:** $\Delta\theta \approx 5\times10^{-30}$ radians]

1.5 A photon of wavelength 6000 Å is passed through a slit of width 0.2 mm

(a) Calculate the uncertainty introduced in the angle of emergence.

(b) The first minimum in the single slit diffraction pattern occurs at $\sin^{-1}(\lambda/b)$ where b is the width of the slit. Calculate this angle and compare with the angle obtained in part (a).

1.6 A 50 W bulb radiates light of wavelength 0.6 mm. Calculate the number of photons emitted per second.

[**Ans:** $\approx 3\times10^{20}$ photons/s]

1.7 Calculate the uncertainty in the momentum of a proton which is confined to a nucleus of radius equal to 10^{-13} cm. From this result, estimate the kinetic energy of the proton inside the nucleus and the strength of the nuclear interaction. What would be the kinetic energy for an electron if it had to be confined within a similar nucleus?

Solutions

1.7 This solution is based on the analysis given by Feynman (Ref. 1.11). The proton is confined within a sphere of radius $r_0 \approx 10^{-13}$ cm. Thus the uncertainty in the momentum must be at least of the order of $\hbar/r_0$, or

$$p \sim \frac{\hbar}{r_0}$$

Therefore, the kinetic energy of the proton will be given by

$$E = \frac{p^2}{2m_p} \sim \frac{\hbar^2}{2m_p r_0^2}$$

where m_p is the mass of the proton. On substitution, we get

$$E \sim \frac{(1.05\times10^{-27}\text{ erg-sec})^2}{2\times1.67\times10^{-24}\text{ g}\times(10^{-13}\text{ cm})^2}$$

$$\approx 3\times10^{-5}\text{ ergs} \approx 20\text{ MeV}$$

Since the proton is bound inside the nucleus, the average of the potential energy, $\langle V\rangle$, must be negative and greater in magnitude than the kinetic energy. Therefore

$$-\langle V\rangle \geq 20\text{ MeV}$$

which indeed gives the correct order of the potential energy. The uncertainty in momentum for the electron is again $\hbar/r_0$; however, since the rest mass of the electron is very much smaller than that of the proton, the velocity of the electron is very close to c and we have to use the extreme relativistic formula for the energy,

$$E = cp = \frac{c\hbar}{r_0} \simeq \frac{(3\times10^{10})(1.05\times10^{-27})}{10^{-13}\times1.6\times10^{-6}}\text{ MeV} \sim 200\text{ MeV}$$

Although electrons do emerge from nuclei in β-decay, they seldom have energies exceeding a few million electron volts. Thus one does not expect the electron to be a basic constituent of the nucleus; the rare occasions when β-decay occurs may be attributed to the transformation of a neutron into a proton and an electron (and the neutrino) so that the electron is in fact created at the instant the decay occurs.

PART 1

GEOMETRICAL OPTICS

Part 1 (consisting of four chapters, i.e., chapters 2 to 5) is entirely based on geometrical optics and includes

- Ray tracing through graded-index media explaining the phenomena of mirage and looming and also reflection from the ionosphere.
- Ray tracing through a system of lenses leading to various concepts used in the design of optical instruments.
- A detailed description of the matrix method in paraxial optics, which is extensively used in industry.
- A study of aberrations of optical systems.

CHAPTER

2

Now in the further development of science, we want more than just a formula. First we have an observation, then we have numbers that we measure, then we have a law which summarizes all the numbers. But the real ***glory*** *of science is that* ***we can find a way of thinking such that the law is evident****. The first way of thinking that made the law about the behavior of light evident was discovered by Fermat in about 1650, and it is called* ***the principle of least time****, or* ***Fermat's principle****.*

—Richard Feynman in *Feynman Lectures on Physics*, Vol. I

Fermat's Principle and its Applications

LEARNING OBJECTIVES

After reading this chapter, the reader should be able to:

LO 1: *state Fermat's principle and its modified version.*

LO 2: *derive laws of reflection and refraction from Fermat's principle.*

LO 3: *describe various phenomena by solving the ray equation.*

LO 4: *obtain ray paths in inhomogeneous media.*

LO 5: *calculate the time taken by the rays in propagating through a parabolic index medium.*

Important Milestones

140 AD: Greek physicist Claudius Ptolemy measured the angle of refraction in water for different angles of incidence in air and tabulated it.

1621: Although the above-mentioned numerical table was made in 140 AD, it was only in 1621 that Willebrord Snell, a Dutch mathematician, discovered the law of refraction which is now known as Snell's law.

1637: Descartes derived Snell's law; his derivation assumed corpuscular model of light.

1657: Pierre de Fermat enunciated his principle of 'least time' and derived Snell's law of refraction and showed that if the velocity of light in the second medium is less, the ray would bend towards the normal, contrary to what is predicted by the 'corpuscular theory'.

Above Image: A laser spirit level reflecting a beam off a mirror; Photograph courtesy McGraw Hill Digital Asset Library

2.1 Introduction

LO1

The study of the propagation of light in the realm of geometrical optics employs the concept of rays. To understand what a ray is, consider a circular aperture in front of a point source *P* as shown in Fig. 2.1. When the diameter of the aperture is quite large (~ 1 cm), then on the screen *SS*′, one can see a patch of light with well-defined boundaries. When we start decreasing the size of the aperture, then at first the size of the patch starts decreasing, but when the size of the aperture becomes very small ($\lesssim$ 0.1 mm) then the pattern obtained on *SS*′ ceases to have well-defined boundaries. This phenomenon is known as diffraction and is a direct consequence of the finiteness of the wavelength (which is denoted by λ). In Chapters 17, 18 and 19 we will discuss the phenomenon of diffraction in great detail and will show that the diffraction effects become smaller with decrease in wavelength and indeed in the limit of $\lambda \to 0$, the diffraction effects will be absent, and even for extremely small diameters of the aperture, we will obtain a well-defined shadow on the screen *SS*′. Therefore, in the zero wavelength limit one can obtain an infinitesimally thin pencil of light; this is called a *ray*. Thus,

> ***a ray defines the path of propagation of the energy in the limit of the wavelength going to zero***

Since light has a wavelength of the order of 10^{-5} cm, which is small compared to the dimensions of normal optical instruments like lenses, mirrors, etc., one can, in many applications, neglect the finiteness of the wavelength. The field of optics under such an approximation (i.e., the neglect of the finiteness of the wavelength) is called geometrical optics.

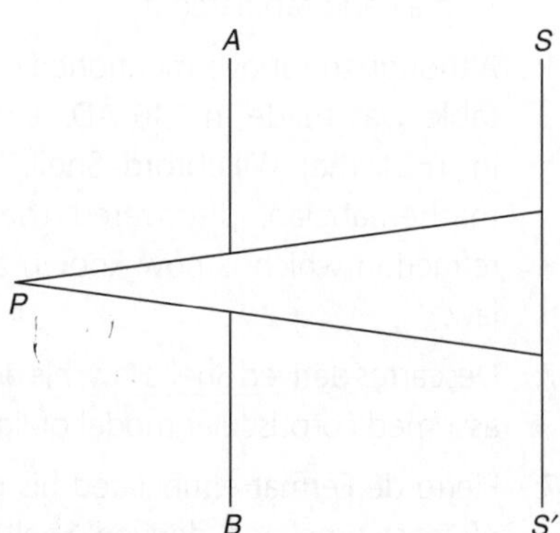

Figure 2.1
The light emitted by the point source *P* is allowed to pass through a circular hole and if the diameter of the hole is very large compared to the wavelength of light, then the light patch on the screen *SS*′ has well-defined boundaries.

The field of geometrical optics can be studied by using Fermat's principle which determines the path of the rays. According to this principle,

> ***the ray will correspond to that path for which the time taken is an extremum in comparison to nearby paths*, i.e., it is either a minimum or a maximum or stationary****

Let $n(x, y, z)$ represent the position-dependent refractive index. Then

$$\frac{ds}{c/n} = \frac{n\,ds}{c}$$

will represent the time taken to traverse the geometric path *ds* in a medium of refractive index *n*. Here, *c* represents the speed of light in free space. Thus, if τ represents the total time taken by the ray to traverse the path *AB* along the curve *C* (see Fig. 2.2) then

$$\tau = \frac{1}{c}\sum_i n_i\, ds_i = \frac{1}{c}\int_{A \xrightarrow[C]{} B} n\, ds \tag{2.1}$$

where ds_i represents the ith arc length and n_i the corresponding refractive index; the symbol $A \xrightarrow[C]{} B$ below the integral represents the fact that the integration is from the point *A* to *B* through the curve *C*. Let τ' be the time taken along the nearby path *AC*′*B* (shown as the dashed curve in Fig. 2.2), and if *ACB* indeed represents the path of a ray, then τ will be either less than, greater than or equal to τ' for *all* nearby paths like *AC*′*B*. Thus according to Fermat's principle, out of the many paths connecting the two points, the light ray would follow that path for which the time taken is an extremum. Since *c* is a constant, one can alternatively define a ray as the path for which

$$\int_{A \xrightarrow[C]{} B} n\, ds \tag{2.2}$$

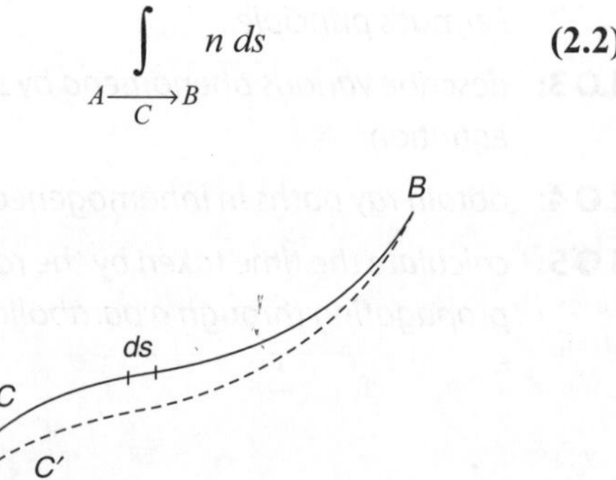

Figure 2.2
If the path *ACB* represents the actual ray path then the time taken in traversing the path *ACB* will be an extremum in comparison to any nearby path *AC*′*B*.

* The entire field of classical optics (both geometrical and physical) can be understood from Maxwell's equations, and of course, Fermat's principle can be derived from Maxwell's equations (see Refs. 2.1 and 2.2).

is an extremum*; the above integral represents the optical path from A to B along C; i.e., the ray would follow the path for which

$$\delta \int_{A\to B} n\, ds = 0 \qquad \textbf{(2.3)}$$

where the left-hand side represents the change in the value of the integral due to an infinitesimal variation of the ray path. We may mention here that according to the original statement of Fermat:

> *The actual path between two points taken by a beam of light is the one which is traversed in the least time.*

The above statement is incomplete and slightly incorrect. The correct form is:

> *The actual ray path between two points is the one for which the optical path length is stationary with respect to variations of the path.*

This is expressed by Eq. (2.3) and in this formulation, the ray paths may correspond to maxima, minima or stationary.

From the above principle one can immediately see that in a homogenous medium (i.e., in a medium whose refractive index is constant at each point), the rays will be straight lines because a straight line will correspond to a minimum value of the optical path connecting two points in the medium. Thus referring to Fig. 2.3, if A and B are two points in a homogenous medium, then the ray path will be along the straight line ACB because any nearby path like ADB or AEB will correspond to a longer optical path.

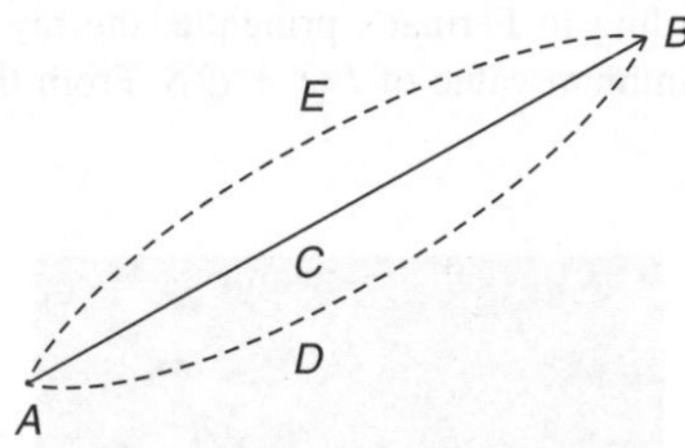

Figure 2.3
Since the shortest distance between two points is along a straight line, light rays in a homogenous medium are straight lines; all nearby paths like *AEB* or *ADB* will take longer times.

2.2 Laws of Reflection and Refraction from Fermat's Principle

LO2

To obtain the laws of reflection and refraction from Fermat's principle, consider a plane mirror MN as shown in Fig. 2.4. We have to determine the path from A to B (via the mirror) which has the minimum optical path length. Since the path would lie completely in a homogenous medium, we need to minimize only the path length. Thus we have to find that path APB for which $AP + PB$ is a minimum. To find the position of P on the mirror, we drop a perpendicular from A on the mirror and let A' be a point on the perpendicular such that $AR = RA'$; thus $AP = PA'$ and $AQ = A'Q$ where AQB is another path adjacent to APB. Thus we have to minimize the length $A'PB$. Clearly, for $A'PB$ to be a minimum, P must be on the straight line $A'B$. Thus, the points A, A', P and B will be in the same plane and if we draw a normal PS at P then this normal will also lie in the same plane. Simple geometric considerations show that

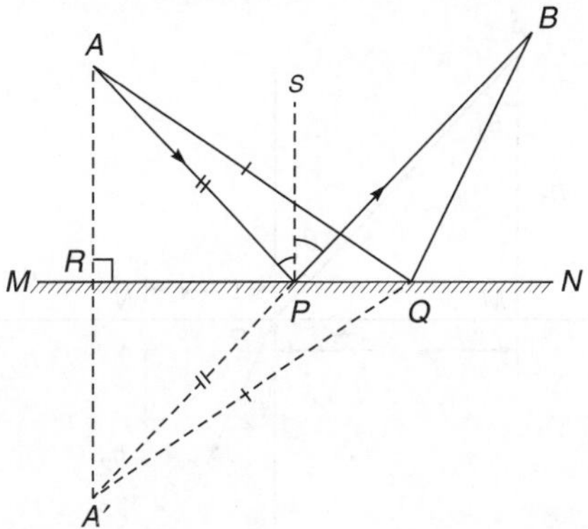

Figure 2.4
The shortest path connecting the two points *A* and *B* via the mirror is along the path *APB* where the point *P* is such that *AP*, *PS* and *PB* are in the same plane and $\angle APS = \angle SPB$; *PS* being the normal to the plane of the mirror. The straight line path *AB* is *also* a ray.

$$\angle APS = \angle SPB$$

Thus for minimum optical path length, the angle of incidence $i(=\angle APS)$ and the angle of reflection r $(=\angle SPB)$ must be equal and the incident ray, the reflected ray and the normal to the surface at the point of incidence on the mirror must be in the same plane. These form the laws of reflection. It should be pointed out that, in the presence of the mirror there will be two ray paths which will connect the points A and B; the two paths will be AB and APB. Fermat's principle tells us that whenever the optical path length is an extremum, we will have a ray, and thus, in general, there may be more than one ray path connecting two points.

To obtain the laws of refraction, let PQ be a surface separating two media of refractive indices n_1 and n_2 as shown in Fig. 2.5. Let a ray starting from the point A, intersect the interface at R and proceed to B along RB. Clearly, for minimum optical path length, the incident ray, the refracted ray and the normal to the interface must all lie in the same plane. To determine that point R for which the optical path length from A to B is a minimum, we drop perpendiculars AM and BN from A and B respectively on the interface PQ.

* A nice discussion on the extremum principle has been given in Chapter 26 of Ref. 2.3.

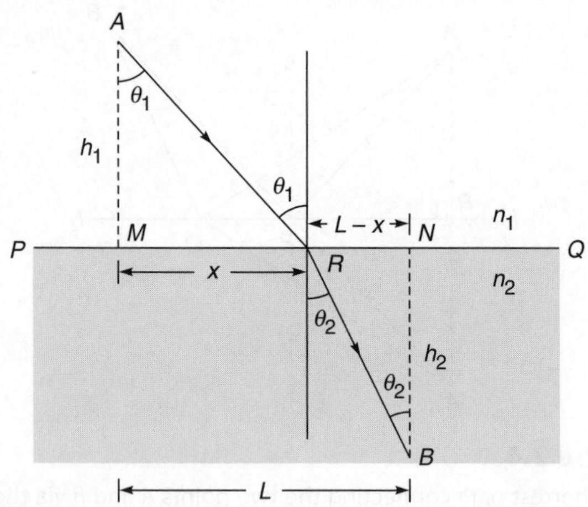

Figure 2.5
A and *B* are two points in media of refractive indices n_1 and n_2. The ray path connecting *A* and *B* will be such that $n_1 \sin \theta_1 = n_2 \sin \theta_2$.

Let $AM = h_1$, $BN = h_2$ and $MR = x$. Then since *A* and *B* are fixed, $RN = L - x$, where $MN = L$ is a fixed quantity. The optical path length from *A* to *B*, by definition, is

$$L_{\text{op}} = n_1 AR + n_2 RB$$

$$= n_1\sqrt{x^2 + h_1^2} + n_2\sqrt{(L - x)^2 + h_2^2} \tag{2.4}$$

To minimize this, we must have

$$\frac{dL_{\text{op}}}{dx} = 0$$

i.e., $$\frac{n_1 x}{\sqrt{x^2 + h_1^2}} - \frac{n_2(L - x)}{\sqrt{(L - x)^2 + h_2^2}} = 0 \tag{2.5}$$

Further, as can be seen from Fig. 2.5

$$\sin \theta_1 = \frac{x}{\sqrt{x^2 + h_1^2}}$$

and $$\sin \theta_2 = \frac{(L - x)}{\sqrt{(L - x)^2 + h_2^2}}$$

Thus, Eq. (2.5) becomes

$$n_1 \sin \theta_1 = n_2 \sin \theta_2 \tag{2.6}$$

which is the Snell's law of refraction.

The laws of reflection and refraction form the basic laws for tracing light rays through simple optical systems, like a system of lenses and mirrors, etc.

EXAMPLE 2.1 Consider a set of rays, parallel to the axis, incident on a paraboloidal reflector (see Fig. 2.6). Show by using Fermat's principle, that all the rays will pass through the focus of the paraboloid; a paraboloid is obtained by rotating a parabola about its axis. This is the reason why a paraboloidal reflector is used to focus parallel rays from a distant source, like in radio astronomy (see Figs. 2.7 and 2.8).

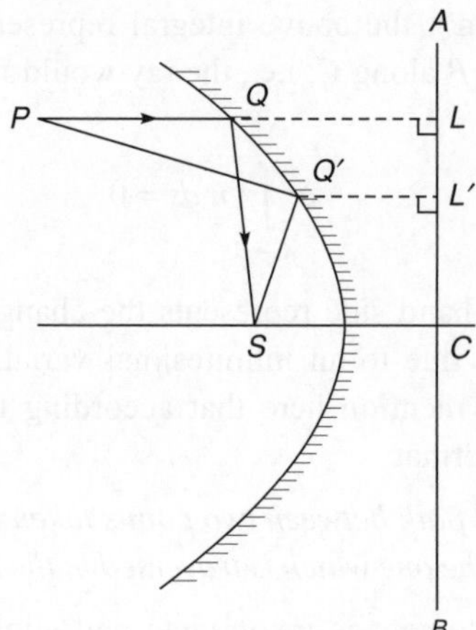

Figure 2.6
All rays parallel to the axis of a paraboloidal reflector pass through the focus after reflection (the line *ACB* is the directrix). It is for this reason that antennas (for collecting electromagnetic waves) or solar collectors are often paraboloidal in shape.

Solution: Consider a ray *PQ*, parallel to the axis of the parabola, incident at the point *Q* (see Fig. 2.6). In order to find the reflected ray, one has to draw a normal at the point *Q* and then draw the reflected ray. It can be shown from geometrical considerations that the reflected ray *QS* will always pass through the focus *S*. However, this procedure will be quite cumbersome and as we will show, the use of Fermat's principle leads us to the desired results immediately.

To use Fermat's principle, we try to find out the ray connecting the focus *S* and an arbitrary point *P* (see Fig. 2.6). Let the ray path be *PQ′S*. According to Fermat's principle, the ray path will correspond to a minimum value of *PQ′* + *Q′S*. From the point *Q′* we

Figure 2.7
A paraboloidal satellite dish. [*Photograph courtesy: McGraw-Hill Digital Access Library*].

Figure 2.8

Fully steerable 45 m paraboloidal dishes of the Giant Metrewave Radio Telescope (GMRT) in Pune, India. The GMRT consists of 30 dishes of 45 m diameter with 14 antennas in the Central Array. [*Photograph courtesy: Professor Govind Swarup, GMRT, Pune*].

drop a perpendicular $Q'L'$, on the directrix AB. From the definition of the parabola it follows that $Q'L' = Q'S$. Thus,

$$PQ' + Q'S = PQ' + Q'L'$$

Let L be the foot of the perpendicular drawn from the point P on AB. Then, for $PQ' + Q'L'$ to be a minimum, the point Q should lie on the straight line PQL, and thus the actual ray which connects the points P and S will be $PQ + QS$ where PQ is parallel to the axis. Therefore, all rays parallel to the axis will pass through S and conversely, all rays emanating from the point S will become parallel to the axis after suffering a reflection.

EXAMPLE 2.2 Consider an elliptical reflector whose foci are the points S_1 and S_2 (see Fig. 2.9). Show that all rays emanating from the point S_1 will pass through the point S_2 after undergoing a reflection.

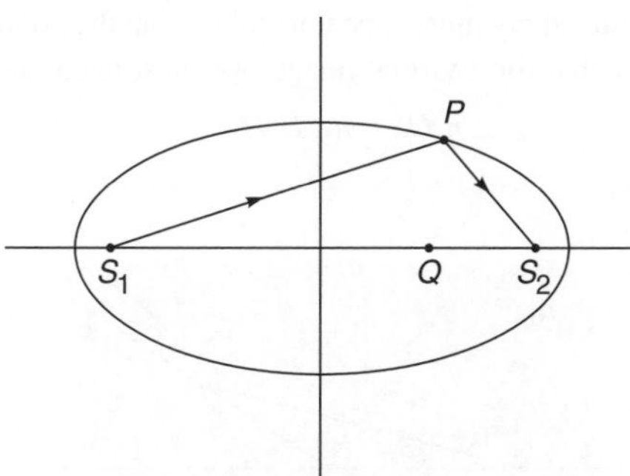

Figure 2.9

All rays emanating from one of the foci of an ellipsoidal reflector will pass through the other focus.

Solution: Consider an arbitrary point P on the ellipse (see Fig. 2.9). It is well known that $S_1P + S_2P$ is a constant and therefore, all rays emanating from the point S_1 will pass through S_2. (Notice that here we have an example where the time taken by the ray is stationary, i.e., it is neither a maximum nor a minimum but has a constant value for all points lying on the mirror.) As a corollary, we may note the following two points:

(a) Excepting the rays along the axis, no other ray (emanating from either of the foci) will pass through an arbitrary point Q which lies on the axis.

(b) The above considerations will remain valid even for an ellipsoid of revolution obtained by rotating the ellipse about its major axis.

Because of the above-mentioned property of elliptical reflectors, they are often used in laser systems. For example, in a ruby laser (see Sec. 27.3) one may have a configuration in which the laser rod and the flash lamp coincide with the focal lines of a cylindrical reflector of elliptical cross section; such a configuration leads to an efficient transfer of energy from the lamp to the ruby rod.

EXAMPLE 2.3 Consider a spherical refracting surface SPM separating two media of refractive indices n_1 and n_2 (see Fig. 2.10). The point C represents the center of the spherical surface SPM. Consider two points O and Q such that the points O, C and Q are in a straight line. Calculate the optical path length OSQ in terms of the distances x, y, r and the angle θ (see Fig. 2.10). Use Fermat's principle to find the ray connecting the two points O and Q. Also, assuming the angle θ to be small, determine the paraxial image of the point O.

[*Note*: We reserve the symbol R to represent the radius of curvature of a spherical surface which will be positive (or negative) depending upon whether the center of curvature lies on the right (or left) of the point P. The quantity r represents the magnitude of the radius of curvature which, for Fig. 2.10, happens to be R. Similarly, the quantities x and y are the magnitudes of the distances; the sign convention is discussed later on in this problem.]

Solution: From the triangle SOC, we have

$$OS = [(x + r)^2 + r^2 - 2(x + r)r \cos \theta]^{1/2}$$

$$\approx \left[x^2 + 2rx + 2r^2 - 2(xr + r^2)\left(1 - \frac{\theta^2}{2}\right)\right]^{1/2}$$

$$\approx x\left[1 + \frac{rx + r^2}{x^2}\theta^2\right]^{1/2} \approx x + \frac{1}{2}r^2\left(\frac{1}{r} + \frac{1}{x}\right)\theta^2$$

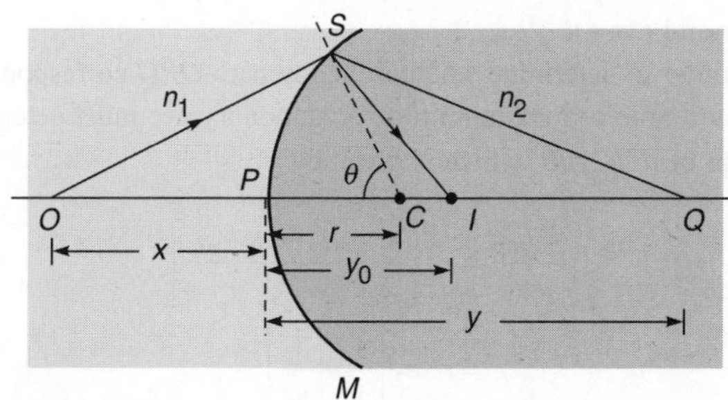

Figure 2.10

SPM is a spherical refracting surface separating two media of refractive indices n_1 and n_2. *C* represents the center of the spherical surface.

where we have assumed θ (measured in radians) to be small so that we may use the expression

$$\cos\,\theta \approx 1 - \frac{\theta^2}{2}$$

and also make a binomial expansion. Similarly, by considering the triangle SCQ, we would have

$$SQ \approx y - \frac{1}{2} r^2 \left(\frac{1}{r} - \frac{1}{y} \right) \theta^2$$

Thus the optical path length OSQ is given by

$$\begin{aligned} L_{\text{op}} &= n_1 OS + n_2 SQ \\ &\approx (n_1\,x + n_2\,y) + \frac{1}{2} r^2 \left[\frac{n_1}{x} + \frac{n_2}{y} - \frac{n_2 - n_1}{r} \right] \theta^2 \end{aligned} \quad \textbf{(2.7)}$$

For the optical path to be an extremum we must have

$$\frac{dL_{\text{op}}}{d\theta} = 0 = r^2 \left[\frac{n_1}{x} + \frac{n_2}{y} - \frac{n_2 - n_1}{r} \right] \theta \quad \textbf{(2.8)}$$

Thus, unless the quantity inside the square brackets is zero we must have $\theta = 0$ implying that the *only* ray connecting the points O and Q will be the straight line path OPQ which also follows from Snell's law because the ray OP hits the spherical surface normally and should proceed undeviated.

On the other hand, if the value of y was such that the quantity inside the square brackets was zero, i.e., if y was equal to y_0 such that

$$\frac{n_2}{y_0} + \frac{n_1}{x} = \frac{n_2 - n_1}{r} \quad \textbf{(2.9)}$$

then $dL_{\text{op}}/d\theta$ would vanish for *all* values of θ; of course, θ is assumed to be small—which is the paraxial approximation. Now, if the point I corresponds to $PI = y_0$ (see Fig. 2.10) then *all* paths like OSI are allowed ray paths implying that *all* (paraxial) rays emanating from O will pass through I and I will, therefore represent the paraxial image point. Obviously, all rays like OSI (which start from O and pass through I) take the *same* amount of time in reaching the point I.

We should mention that Eq. (2.9) is a particular form of the equation determining the paraxial image point

$$\frac{n_2}{v} - \frac{n_1}{u} = \frac{n_2 - n_1}{R} \quad \textbf{(2.10)}$$

with the sign convention that all distances measured to the right of the point P are positive and those to its left negative. Thus $u = -x$, $v = +y$ and $r = +R$.

In order to determine whether the ray path OPQ corresponds to minimum time or maximum time or stationary, we must determine the sign of $d^2L_{\text{op}}/d\theta^2$ which is given by

$$\begin{aligned} \frac{d^2 L_{\text{op}}}{d\theta^2} &= r^2 \left[\frac{n_1}{x} + \frac{n_2}{y} - \frac{n_2 - n_1}{r} \right] \\ &= r^2\, n_2 \left[\frac{1}{y} - \frac{1}{y_0} \right] \end{aligned}$$

Obviously, if $y > y_0$ (i.e., the point Q is on the right of the paraxial image point I) $d^2L_{\text{op}}/d\theta^2$ is negative and the ray path OPQ corresponds to *maximum* time in comparison with nearby paths and conversely. On the other hand, if $y = y_0$, $d^2L_{\text{op}}/d\theta^2$ will vanish implying that the extremum corresponds to a stationary value of the optical path length. Thus, in the paraxial approximation, all rays emanating from the point O will take the same amount of time in reaching the point I.

Alternatively, one can argue that if I is the paraxial image point of P then

$$n_1 OP + n_2 PI = n_1 OS + n_2 SI$$

Thus, when Q lies on the right of the point I, we have

$$\begin{aligned} n_1 OP + n_2 PQ &= n_1 OS + n_2 (SI - PI + PQ) \\ &= n_1 OS + n_2 (SI + IQ) \\ &> n_1 OS + n_2 SQ \end{aligned}$$

implying that the ray path OPQ corresponds to a maximum. Similarly, when Q lies on the left of the point I then the ray path OPQ corresponds to a minimum and when Q coincides with I, we have the stationarity condition.

EXAMPLE 2.4 We again consider refraction at a spherical surface; however, the refracted ray is assumed to diverge away from the principal axis (see Fig. 2.11). Let us consider paraxial rays and let I be a point (on the axis) such that $n_1\,OS - n_2\,SI$ is independent of the point S. Thus, for paraxial rays, the quantity

$$n_1\,OS - n_2\,SI \qquad \text{is independent of } \theta \quad \textbf{(2.11)}$$

and is an extremum. Let P be an arbitrary point in the second medium and we wish to find the ray path connecting the points O and P. For OSP to be an allowed ray path

$$L_{\text{op}} = n_1\,OS + n_2\,SP \text{ should be an extremum}$$

or

$$L_{\text{op}} = (n_1\,OS - n_2\,SI) + n_2\,(IS + SP) \text{ should be an extremum}$$

where we have added and subtracted $n_2\,SI$. Now, the point I is such that the first quantity is already an extremum thus, the quantity $SP + SI$ should be an extremum and therefore it should be a straight line. Thus the refracted ray must appear to come from the point I. We may therefore say that for a virtual image, we must make the quantity

$$n_1 OS - n_2 SI \quad \textbf{(2.12)}$$

an extremum.

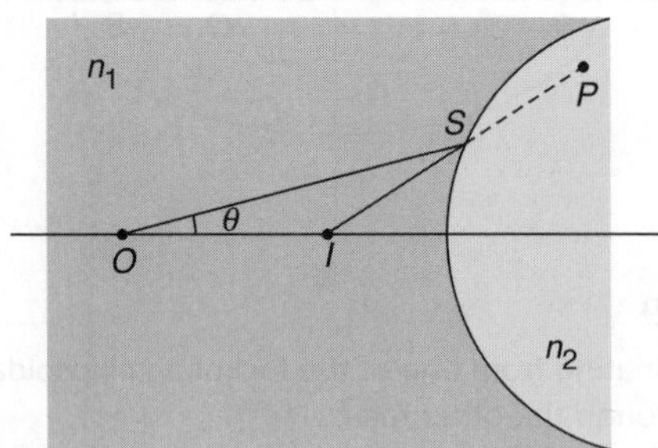

Figure 2.11
The refracted ray is assumed to diverge away from the principal axis.

2.3 Ray Paths in an Inhomogeneous Medium

LO3

In an inhomogeneous medium, the refractive index varies in a continuous manner and, in general, the ray paths are curved. For example, on a hot day, the air near the ground has a higher temperature than the air which is much above the surface. Since the density of air decreases with increase in temperature, the refractive index increases continuously as we go above the ground. This leads to the phenomenon known as *mirage*. We will use Snell's law (or Fermat's principle) to determine the ray paths in an inhomogeneous medium. We will restrict ourselves to the special case when the refractive index changes continuously along one direction only; we assume this direction to be along the x-axis.

The inhomogeneous medium can be thought of as a limiting case of a medium consisting of a continuous set of thin slices of media of different refractive indices—see Fig. 2.12(a). At each interface, the light ray satisfies Snell's law and one obtains [see Fig. 2.12(a)]

$$n_1 \sin\phi_1 = n_2 \sin\phi_2 = n_3 \sin\phi_3 = \ldots \tag{2.13}$$

Thus, we may state that the product

$$n(x)\cos\theta(x) = n(x)\sin\phi(x) \tag{2.14}$$

is an invariant of the ray path; we will denote this invariant by $\tilde{\beta}$. The value of this invariant may be determined from the fact that if the ray initially makes an angle θ_1 (with the z-axis) at a point where the refractive index is n_1, then the value of $\tilde{\beta}$ is $n_1 \cos\theta_1$. Thus, in the limiting case of a continuous variation of refractive index, the piecewise straight lines shown in Fig. 2.12(a) form a continuous curve which is determined from the equation

$$n(x)\cos\theta(x) = n_1\cos\theta_1 = \tilde{\beta} \tag{2.15}$$

implying that as the refractive index changes, the ray path bends in such a way that the product $n(x)\cos\theta(x)$ remains constant [see Fig. 2.12(b)]. Equation (2.15) can be used to derive the ray equation (see Sec. 2.4).

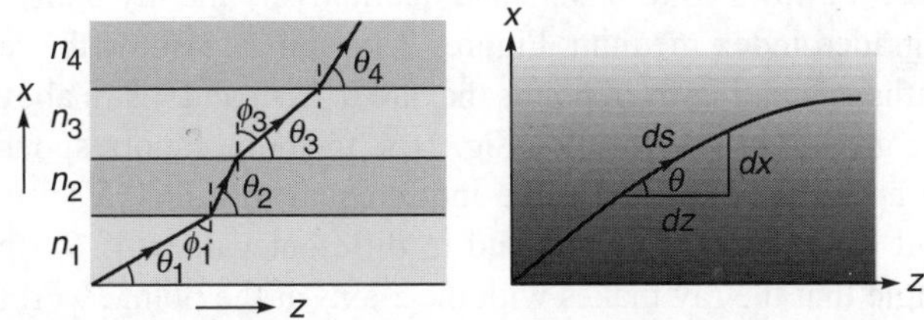

Figure 2.12
(a) In a layered structure, the ray bends in such a way that the product $n_i \cos\theta_i$ remains constant. (b) For a medium with continuously varying refractive index, the ray path bends in such a way that the product $n(x)\cos\theta(x)$ remains constant.

2.3.1 The Phenomenon of Mirage*

We are now in a position to qualitatively discuss the formation of a mirage. As mentioned earlier, on a hot day the refractive index continuously decreases as we go near the ground. Indeed, the refractive index variation can be approximately assumed to be of the form

$$n(x) \approx n_0 + kx \qquad 0 < x < \text{few meters} \tag{2.16}$$

where n_0 is the refractive index of air at $x = 0$ (i.e., just above the ground) and k is a constant. The exact ray paths (see Example 2.8) are shown in Fig. 2.13.

We consider a ray which becomes horizontal at $x = 0$. At the eye position E ($x = x_e$), if the refractive index is n_e, and if at that point the ray makes an angle θ_e with the horizontal then

$$\tilde{\beta} = n_0 = n_e \cos\theta_e \tag{2.17}$$

Usually $\theta_e << 1$ so that

$$\frac{n_0}{n_e} = \cos\theta_e \approx 1 - \frac{1}{2}\theta_e^2$$

$$\Rightarrow \qquad \theta_e \approx \sqrt{2\left(1 - \frac{n_0}{n_e}\right)} \tag{2.18}$$

At constant air pressure

$$(n_0 - 1)T_0 \approx (n_e - 1)T_e \tag{2.19}$$

From Eq. (2.19), we get

$$1 - \frac{n_0 - 1}{n_e - 1} = 1 - \frac{T_e}{T_0}$$

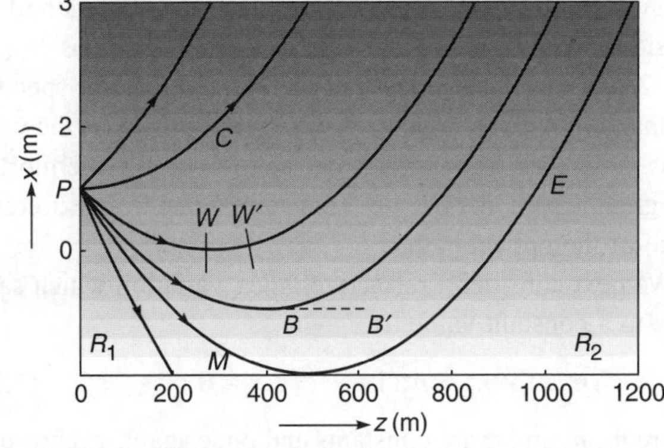

Figure 2.13
Ray paths in a medium characterized by a linear variation of refractive index [see Eq. (2.16)] with $k \approx 1.234 \times 10^{-5}\ \text{m}^{-1}$. The object point is at a height of 1.5 m and the curves correspond to +0.2°, 0°, –0.2°, –0.28°, –0.3486° and –0.5° The shading shows that the refractive index increases with x.

* For more details, see Refs. 2.4–2.8.

or
$$\frac{n_e - n_0}{n_e} = \frac{n_e - 1}{n_e}\left(1 - \frac{T_e}{T_0}\right)$$

so that
$$\theta_e \approx \sqrt{2\left(1 - \frac{1}{n_e}\right)\left(1 - \frac{T_e}{T_0}\right)} \tag{2.20}$$

On a typical hot day, the temperature near road surface $T_0 \approx 323\,\text{K}$ (= 50 °C) and, about 1.5 m above the ground, $T_e \approx 303\,\text{K}$ (= 30 °C). Now, at 30 °C, $n_e \approx 1.00026$ giving $\theta_e \approx 5.67 \times 10^{-3}$ radians $\approx 0.325°$. In Fig. 2.13, we have shown rays emanating (at different angles) from a point *P* which is 1.5 m above the ground; thus each ray has a specified value of the invariant $\tilde{\beta}$ (= $n_1 \cos \theta_1$). The figure shows that when the object point *P* and the observation point *E* are close to the ground, the only ray path connecting points *P* and *E* will be along the curve *PME* and that a ray emanating horizontally from the point *P* will propagate in the upward direction as *PC* as shown in the figure. Thus, in such a condition, the eye at *E* will see the mirage and *not see* the object directly at *P*. We also find that there is a region R_2 where none of the rays (emanating from the point *P*) reaches; thus, an eye in this region can neither see the object nor its image. This is therefore called the *shadow region*. Furthermore, there is also a region R_1 where only the object is directly visible and the virtual image is not seen.

We should mention here that the *bending up* of the ray after it becomes parallel to the *z*-axis cannot be directly inferred from Eq. (2.15) because at such a point, $\theta = 0$ and one may expect the ray to proceed horizontally beyond the turning point as shown by a dotted line in Fig. 2.13; the point at which $\theta = 0$ is known as the *turning point*. However, from considerations of symmetry and from the reversibility of ray paths, it immediately follows that the ray path should be symmetrical about the turning point and hence bend up. Physically, the bending of the ray can be understood by considering a small portion of a wave front such as *W* (see Fig. 2.13); the upper edge will travel with a lesser speed in comparison with the lower edge, and this will cause the wave front to tilt (see *W′*) making the ray to bend. Furthermore, a straight line path like *BB′* does not correspond to an extremum value of the optical path.

We next consider a refractive index variation which saturates to a constant value as $x \to \infty$:

$$n^2(x) = n_0^2 + n_2^2(1 - e^{-\alpha x});\ x > 0 \tag{2.21}$$

where n_0, n_2 and α are constants and once again, *x* represents the height above the ground. The refractive index at $x = 0$ is n_0 and for large values of *x*, it approaches $(n_0^2 + n_2^2)^{1/2}$. The exact ray paths are obtained by solving the ray equation (see Example 2.10) and are shown in Figs. 2.14 and 2.15; they correspond to the following values of various parameters:

$$n_0 = 1.000233,\quad n_2 = 0.45836$$
and
$$\alpha = 2.303\ \text{m}^{-1} \tag{2.22}$$

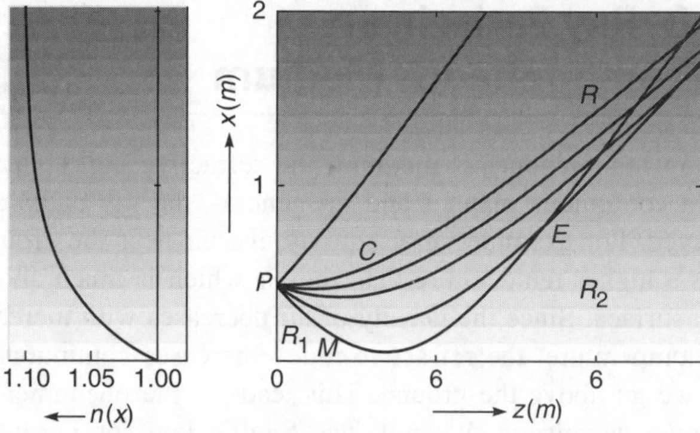

Figure 2.14

Ray paths in a medium characterized by Eqs. (2.21) and (2.22). The object point is at a height of $1/\alpha$ (≈0.43 m) and the curves correspond to θ_1 (the initial launch angle) = $+\pi/10$, 0, $-\pi/60$, $-\pi/30$, $-\pi/15$ and $-\pi/10$. The shading shows that the refractive index increases with *x*.

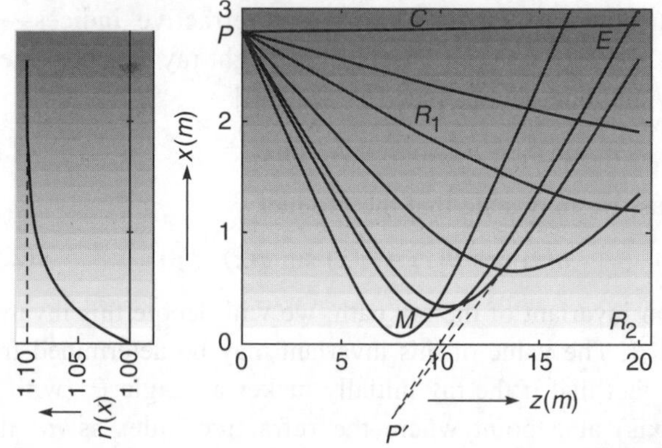

Figure 2.15

Ray paths in a medium characterized by Eqs. (2.21) and (2.22). The object point is at a height of 2.8 m and the curves correspond to θ_1 (the initial launch angle) = 0, $-\pi/60$, $-\pi/30$, $-\pi/16$, $-\pi/11$, $-\pi/10$ and $-\pi/8$. The shading shows that the refractive index increases with *x*.

The actual values of the refractive index for parameters given by the above equation are not very realistic—nevertheless, it allows us to understand qualitatively the ray paths in a graded index medium. Figures 2.14 and 2.15 show the ray paths emanating from points that are 0.43 m and 2.8 m above the ground respectively. In Fig. 2.14, the point *P* corresponds to a value of the refractive index equal to 1.06455 (= n_1) and different rays correspond to different values of θ_1, the angle that the ray makes with the *z*-axis at the point *P*. From Fig. 2.14 we again see that when the object point *P* and the observation point *E* are close to the ground, the only ray path connecting points *P* and *E* will be along the curve *PME* and that a ray emanating horizontally from the point *P* will propagate in the upward direction, shown as *PC* in Fig. 2.14. Thus, in such a condition, the eye at *E* will see the mirage and *not see* the object directly at *P*. However, if points *P* and *E* are much above the ground (see Fig. 2.15), the eye will see the object almost directly (because of rays like *PCE*) and will also receive rays appearing to emanate from points like *P*′. It may be readily seen that different rays do not appear to come from the same point and hence the reflected image seen will have considerable aberrations. Once again, there is a *shadow region* R_2 where none of the rays (emanating from the point *P*) reaches there; thus, an eye in this region can neither see the object nor its image. The actual formation of mirage is shown in Figs. 2.16 and 2.17.

Figure 2.16
A typical mirage as seen on a hot road on a warm day. *Photograph adapted from http://fizyka. phys.put.poznan. pl/~pieransk/Physics%20Around% 20Us/Air%20%mirror.jpg. [The Photograph was taken by Professor Pioter Pieranski of Ponz University of Technology in Poland; used with permission from Professor Pieranski].*

Figure 2.17
This is actually *not* a reflection in the ocean, but the miraged (inverted) image of the Sun's lower edge. A few seconds later [notice the motion of the bird to the left of the Sun! (the bird is inside the circle)], the reflection fuses with the erect image. The photographs were taken by Dr. George Kaplan of the U. S. Naval Observatory and are on the Naval Observatory website: *http://mintake.sdsu.edu/GF/explain/simulations/infmir/ Kaplan_photos.html. created by Dr. A Young. [Photograph used with kind permissions from Dr. Kaplan and Dr. Young].*

EXAMPLE 2.5 As an example, for an object shown in Fig. 2.14, let us calculate the angle at which the ray should be launched from the point *P* (which is at a height of 0.43 m) so that it becomes horizontal at $x = 0.2$ m. Now, using Eqs (2.21) and (2.22)

$$\text{at } x = 0.2 \text{ m}, \quad n(x) = 1.03827$$

Thus, if θ_1 represents the angle that the ray makes with the *z*-axis at the point *P* (see Fig. 2.14) then

$$n_1 \cos \theta_1 = 1.03827 \times \cos 0$$

implying $\theta_1 \approx 13°$. Further, for the ray which becomes horizontal at $x = 0.2$ m the value of the invariant is given by

$$\tilde{\beta} \approx 1.03827$$

EXAMPLE 2.6 In Fig. 2.15, the object point corresponds to $x = 2.8$ m where $n(x) \approx 1.1$. Thus for a ray launched with $\theta_1 = -\pi/8$,

$$\tilde{\beta} = 1.1 \cos \theta_1 = 1.01627$$

Thus if the ray becomes horizontal at $x = x_2$ then

$$n(x_2) = \tilde{\beta} = 1.01627$$

and

$$x_2 = -\frac{1}{\alpha} \ln\left[1 - \frac{n^2(x_2) - n_0^2}{n_2^2}\right] \approx 0.073 \text{ m}$$

2.3.2 The Phenomenon of Looming

The formation of mirage discussed above occurs due to increase in the refractive index of air above the hot surface. On the other hand, above cold sea water, the air near the water surface is colder than the air above it and hence there is an opposite temperature gradient. A suitable refractive index variation for such a case can be written as

$$n^2(x) = n_0^2 + n_2^2 e^{-\alpha x} \tag{2.23}$$

The equation describing the ray path is discussed in Problem 2.13. We assume the values of n_0, n_2 and α to be given by Eq. (2.22). For an object point *P* at a height of 0.5 m, the ray paths are shown in Fig. 2.18. If the eye is at *E*, then it will receive rays appearing to emanate from *P*′. Such a phenomenon in which the object appears to be above its

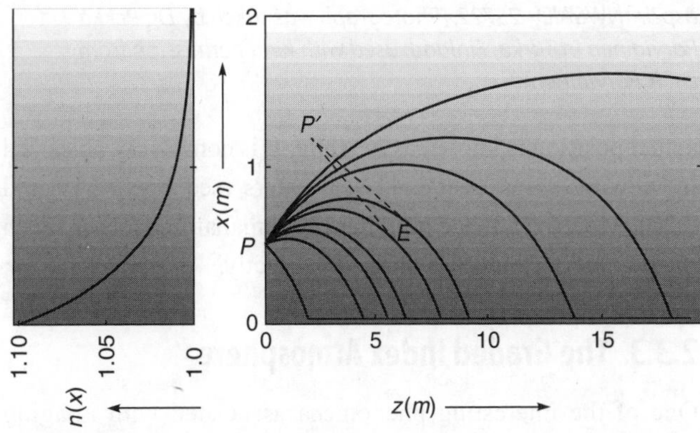

Figure 2.18
Ray paths corresponding to the refractive index distribution given by Eq. (2.23) for an object at a height of 0.5 m; the values of n_0, n_2 and α are given by Eq. (2.22).

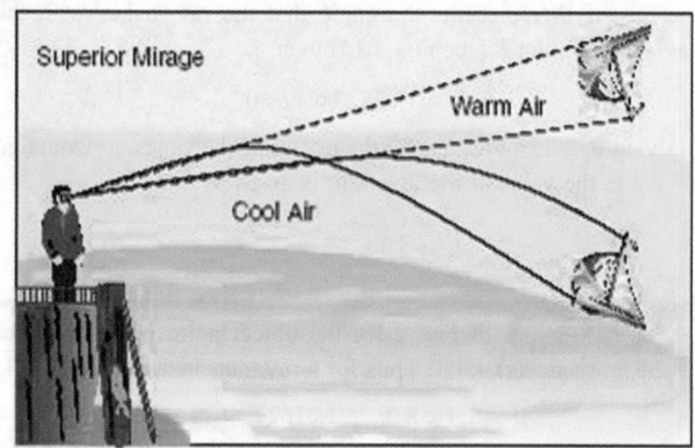

Figure 2.19
If we are looking at the ocean on a cold day, we find that the air near the surface of the water is cold and it gets warmer as we go up. Thus, as we go up, the refractive index decreases continuously and because of curved ray paths, one will observe an inverted image of the ship (at a greater height) as shown in the figure above; this is known as the *superior mirage.*

Fig. 2.20
A house in the archipelago with a superior mirage. *Figure adapted from http://virtual.finland.fi/netcomm/news/showarticle.asp?intNWSAID=25722. [Photograph was taken by Dr. Pekkà Parviainen in Turku, Finland; used with kind permission from Dr. P. Parviainen].*

actual position is known as *looming*. It is commonly observed in viewing ships over cold sea waters (see Figs. 2.19 and 2.20). Moreover, since no other rays emanating from P reach A, the object cannot be observed directly.

2.3.3 The Graded Index Atmosphere

One of the interesting phenomena associated with imaging in a graded index medium is the non-circular shape of the setting or the rising sun (see Fig. 2.21). This can easily be understood in the following manner: The refractive index of the air gradually decreases as we move outwards. If we approximate the continuous refractive index gradient by a

Figure 2.21
The non-circular shape of the setting sun. *[Photograph courtesy McGraw Hill Digital Access Library]*

finite number of layers (each layer having a specific refractive index) then the ray will bend in a way similar to that shown in Fig. 2.22. Thus the sun (which is actually at S) appears to be in the direction of S'. It is for this reason that the setting sun appears flattened and also leads to the fact that the days are usually about 5 minutes longer than they would have been in the absence of the atmosphere. Obviously, if we were on the surface of the moon, the rising or the setting sun would not only look white but also circular in shape!

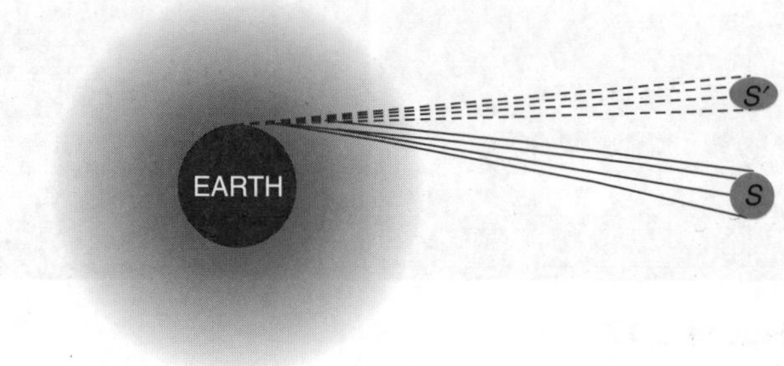

Figure 2.22
The atmosphere is a graded index medium and because of refraction, light from S appears to come from S'.

2.4 The Ray Equation and its Solutions

LO4

In this section, we will derive the ray equation, the solution of which will give the precise ray paths in an inhomogeneous medium. We will restrict ourselves to the special case when the refractive index changes continuously along only one direction, which we assume to be along the x-axis. This medium can be thought of as the limiting case of a medium comprising a continuous set of thin slices of media of different refractive indices. As discussed earlier, for a continuously varying refractive index, the product $n(x)\cos\theta(x)$ is an invariant of the ray path which we denote by $\tilde{\beta}$:

$$n(x)\cos\theta(x) = \tilde{\beta} \tag{2.24}$$

Furthermore, for a continuous variation of refractive index, the piecewise straight lines shown in Fig. 2.12(a) forms a continuous curve as in Fig. 2.12(b). If ds represents the infinitesimal arc length along the curve, then

$$(ds)^2 = (dx)^2 + (dz)^2$$

or

$$\left(\frac{ds}{dz}\right)^2 = \left(\frac{dx}{dz}\right)^2 + 1 \tag{2.25}$$

Now, if we refer to Fig. 2.12(b), we find that

$$\frac{dz}{ds} = \cos\theta = \frac{\tilde{\beta}}{n(x)} \tag{2.26}$$

Thus Eq. (2.25) becomes

$$\left(\frac{dx}{dz}\right)^2 = \frac{n^2(x)}{\tilde{\beta}^2} - 1 \tag{2.27}$$

For a given $n(x)$ variation, Eq. (2.27) can be integrated to give the ray path $x(z)$; however, it is often more convenient to put Eq. (2.27) in a slightly different form by differentiating it with respect to z:

$$2\frac{dx}{dz}\frac{d^2x}{dz^2} = \frac{1}{\tilde{\beta}^2}\frac{dn^2}{dx}\frac{dx}{dz}$$

or

$$\frac{d^2x}{dz^2} = \frac{1}{2\tilde{\beta}^2}\frac{dn^2}{dx} \tag{2.28}$$

Both, Eqs. (2.27) and (2.28), represent rigorously correct ray equations when the refractive index depends only on the x-coordinate.

EXAMPLE 2.7 As a simple application of Eq. (2.28), let us consider a homogeneous medium for which $n(x)$ is a constant. In such a case, the RHS of Eq. (2.28) is zero and one obtains

$$\frac{d^2x}{dz^2} = 0$$

Integrating the above equation twice with respect to z, we obtain

$$x = Az + B$$

which is the equation of a straight line, as it ought to be in a homogeneous medium.

EXAMPLE 2.8 We next consider the ray paths in a medium characterized by the following refractive index variation

$$n(x) = n_0 + kx \tag{2.29}$$

For the above profile, the ray equation [Eq. (2.28)] takes the form

$$\frac{d^2x}{dz^2} = \frac{1}{2\tilde{\beta}^2}\frac{dn^2}{dx} = \frac{k}{\tilde{\beta}^2}[n_0 + kx]$$

or

$$\frac{d^2X}{dz^2} = \kappa^2 X(z) \tag{2.30}$$

where

$$X \equiv x + \frac{n_0}{k} \quad \text{and} \quad \kappa = \frac{k}{\tilde{\beta}} \tag{2.31}$$

Thus the ray path is given by

$$x(z) = -\frac{n_0}{k} + C_1 e^{\kappa z} + C_2 e^{-\kappa z} \tag{2.32}$$

where the constants C_1 and C_2 are to be determined from initial conditions. We assume that at $z = 0$, the ray is launched at $x = x_1$ making an angle θ_1 with the z-axis; thus

$$x(z = 0) = x_1$$

and

$$\left.\frac{dx}{dz}\right|_{z=0} = \tan\theta_1$$

Elementary manipulations would give us

$$C_1 = \frac{1}{2}\left[x_1 + \frac{1}{k}(n_0 + n_1\sin\theta_1)\right] \tag{2.33}$$

and

$$C_2 = \frac{1}{2}\left[x_1 + \frac{1}{k}(n_0 - n_1\sin\theta_1)\right] \tag{2.34}$$

where $n_1 = n_0 + kx_1$ represents the refractive index at $x = x_1$ and we have used the fact that

$$\tilde{\beta} = n_1\cos\theta_1 \tag{2.35}$$

Figure 2.13 shows the ray paths as given by Eq. (2.32) with $x_1 = 1.5$ m, $n_1 = 1.00026$ and $k \approx 1.234 \times 10^{-5}\ \text{m}^{-1}$.

2.4.1 Ray Paths in Parabolic Index Media

We consider a parabolic index medium characterized by the following refractive index distribution:

$$n^2(x) = n_1^2 - \gamma^2 x^2 \tag{2.36}$$

We will use Eq. (2.27) to determine the ray paths. Equation (2.27) can be written as

$$\int \frac{dx}{\sqrt{n^2(x) - \tilde{\beta}^2}} = \pm\frac{1}{\tilde{\beta}}\int dz \tag{2.37}$$

Substituting for $n^2(x)$, we get

$$\int \frac{dx}{\sqrt{x_0^2 - x^2}} = \pm\Gamma\int dz \tag{2.38}$$

where

$$x_0 = \frac{1}{\gamma}\sqrt{n_1^2 - \tilde{\beta}^2} \tag{2.39}$$

and

$$\Gamma = \frac{\gamma}{\tilde{\beta}} \tag{2.40}$$

Writing $x = x_0 \sin\theta$ and carrying out the straightforward integration, we get

$$x = \pm x_0 \sin[\Gamma(z - z_0)] \quad (2.41)$$

We can always choose the origin such that $z_0 = 0$ so that the general ray path would be given by

$$x = \pm x_0 \sin\Gamma z \quad (2.42)$$

We could have also used Eq. (2.28) to obtain the ray path. Now, in an optical waveguide the refractive index distribution is usually written in the form*:

$$\left.\begin{aligned} n^2(x) &= n_1^2\left[1 - 2\Delta\left(\frac{x}{a}\right)^2\right], \quad |x| < a \text{ core} \\ &= n_2^2 = n_1^2(1-2\Delta), \quad |x| < a \text{ cladding} \end{aligned}\right\} \quad (2.43)$$

The region $|x| < a$ is known as the core of the wave guide and the region $|x| > a$ is usually referred to as the cladding. Thus,

$$\gamma = \frac{n_1\sqrt{2\Delta}}{a} \quad (2.44)$$

In a typical parabolic index fiber,

$$n_1 = 1.5, \quad \Delta = 0.01, \quad a = 20\ \mu\text{m} \quad (2.45)$$

giving $n_2 \approx 1.485$ and $\gamma \approx 1.0607 \times 10^4\ \text{m}^{-1}$.

Typical ray paths for different values of θ_1 are shown in Fig. 2.23. Obviously, the rays will be guided in the core if $n_2 < \tilde{\beta} < n_1$. When $\tilde{\beta} = n_2$, the ray path will become horizontal at the core-cladding interface. For $\tilde{\beta} < n_2$, the ray will be incident at the core-cladding interface at an angle and the ray will be refracted away. Thus, we may write

$$\begin{aligned} n_2 < \tilde{\beta} < n_1 \quad &\Rightarrow \quad \text{Guided rays} \\ \tilde{\beta} < n_2 \quad &\Rightarrow \quad \text{Refracting rays} \end{aligned} \quad (2.46)$$

In Fig. 2.23, the ray paths shown correspond to

$$z_0 = 0 \quad \text{and} \quad \theta_1 = 4°, 8.13° \text{ and } 20°;$$

the corresponding values of $\tilde{\beta}$ are approximately 1.496 ($> n_2$), 1.485 ($= n_2$) and 1.410 ($< n_2$)—the last ray undergoes refraction at the core–cladding interface. It may be readily seen that the periodical length z_p of the sinusoidal path is given by

$$z_p = \frac{2\pi}{\Gamma} = \frac{2\pi\, a\cos\theta_1}{\sqrt{2\Delta}} \quad (2.47)$$

Thus, for the two rays shown in Fig. 2.23 (with $\theta_1 = 4°$ and 8.13°), the values of z_p would be 0.8864 mm and 0.8796 mm, respectively. Indeed, in the paraxial approximation, $\cos\theta_1 \approx 1$ and all rays have the same periodic length. In Fig. 2.25, we have plotted typical paraxial ray paths for rays launched along the z-axis. Different rays (shown in the figure) correspond to different values of $\tilde{\beta}$.

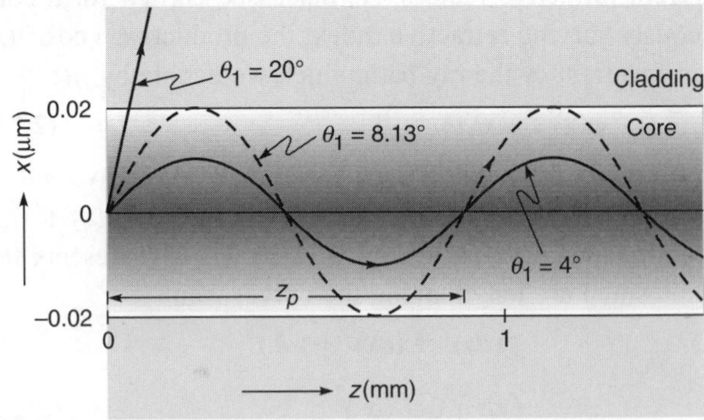

Figure 2.23

Typical ray paths in a parabolic index medium for parameters given by Eq. (2.45) for $\theta_1 = 4°$, 8.13° and 20°.

Four interesting features may be noted:

(i) In the paraxial approximation ($\tilde{\beta} \approx n_1$) all rays launched horizontally come to a focus at a particular point. Thus the medium acts as a converging lens of focal length given by

$$f \approx \frac{\pi}{2}\frac{a}{\sqrt{2\Delta}} \quad (2.48)$$

(ii) Rays launched at different angles with the axis (see, for instance, the rays emerging from point P) get trapped in the medium and hence the medium acts like a 'guide'. Indeed such media are referred to as optical waveguides and their study forms a subject of great contemporary interest.

(iii) Ray paths would be allowed only in the region where $\tilde{\beta}$ is less than or equal to $n(x)$ [see Eq. (2.26)]. Further, dx/dz would be zero (i.e., the ray would become parallel to the z-axis) when $n(x)$ equals $\tilde{\beta}$; this immediately follows from Eq. (2.27).

(iv) The rays periodically focus and defocus as shown in Fig. 2.25. In the paraxial approximation, all rays emanating from P will focus at Q and if we refer to our discussion in Example 2.3, all rays must take the same time to go from P to Q. Physically, although the ray PLQ traverses a larger path in comparison to PMQ, it does so in a medium of 'lower' average refractive index—thus the greater path length is compensated for by a greater 'average speed' and hence *all* rays take the same time to propagate through a certain distance of the waveguide (see Sec. 2.4.2 for exact calculation). Therefore, parabolic index waveguides are extensively used in fiber-optic communication systems (see Sec. 28.10.2).

* Ray paths in such media are of tremendous importance as they readily lead to very important results for parabolic index fibers which are extensively used in fiber-optic communication systems (see Sections 2.4.2 and 28.10.2).

We may mention here that Gradient-Index GRIN) lenses, characterized by parabolic variation of refractive index in the transverse direction, are now commercially available and find many applications (see Fig. 2.24). For example a GRIN lens can be used to couple the output of a laser diode to an optical fiber; the length of such a GRIN lens would be $z_P/4$ (see Fig. 2.25); typically $z_P \approx$ few cm and the diameter of the lens would be few millimeters. Such small-size lenses find many applications. Similarly, a GRIN lens of length $z_P/2$ can be used to transfer collimated light from one end of the lens to the other.

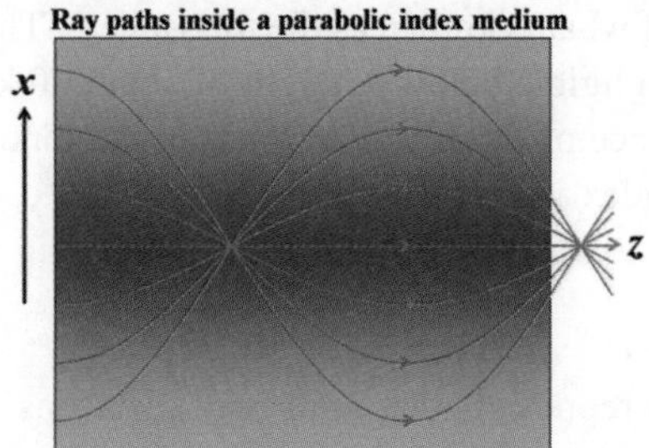

Figure 2.24
Paraxial ray paths in a graded index medium characterized by a refractive index variation which decreases parabolically in the transverse direction. Because of focusing properties, it has many important applications.

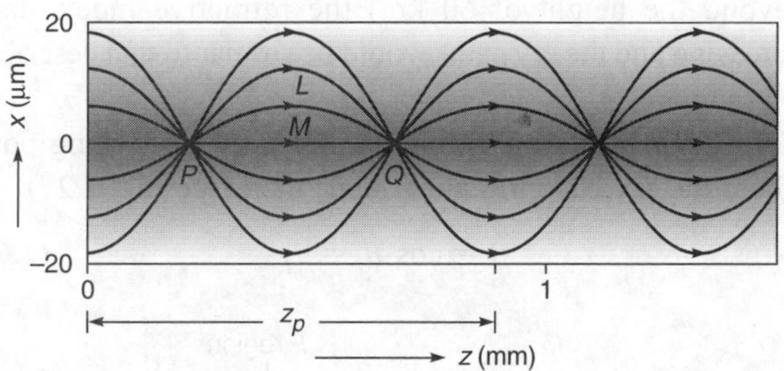

Figure 2.25
Paraxial ray paths in a parabolic index medium. Notice the periodic focussing and defocussing of the beam.

2.4.2 Transit Time Calculations in a Parabolic Index Waveguide

In this section, we will calculate the time taken by a ray to traverse a certain length through a parabolic index waveguide as described by Eq. (2.36). Such a calculation is of considerable importance in fiber-optic communication systems (see Sec. 28.7). As shown in Sec. 2.4.1, the ray path (inside the core) is given by

$$x = x_0 \sin \Gamma z \tag{2.49}$$

where x_0 and Γ have been defined through Eqs. (2.39) and (2.40). Let $d\tau$ represent the time taken by a ray to traverse the arc length ds [see Fig. 2.12(b)]:

$$d\tau = \frac{ds}{c/n(x)} \tag{2.50}$$

where c is the speed of light in free space. Since

$$n(x)\frac{dz}{ds} = \tilde{\beta}$$

[see Eq. (2.26)] we may write Eq. (2.50) as

$$d\tau = \frac{1}{c\tilde{\beta}} n^2(x)\, dz = \frac{1}{c\tilde{\beta}}[n_1^2 - \gamma^2 x^2]\, dz$$

or

$$d\tau = \frac{1}{c\tilde{\beta}}[n_1^2 - \gamma^2 x_0^2 \sin^2 \Gamma z]\, dz \tag{2.51}$$

where in the last step we have used Eq. (2.49). Thus if $\tau(z)$ represents the time taken by the ray to traverse a distance z along the waveguide, then

$$\tau(z) = \frac{n_1^2}{c\tilde{\beta}}\int_0^z dz - \frac{\gamma^2 x_0^2}{c\tilde{\beta}}\int_0^z \frac{1-\cos(2\Gamma z)}{2}\, dz$$

$$= \frac{1}{c\tilde{\beta}}\left[n_1^2 - \frac{1}{2}\gamma^2 x_0^2\right] z + \frac{\gamma^2 x_0^2}{2c\tilde{\beta}}\frac{1}{2\Gamma}\sin 2\Gamma z$$

or

$$\tau(z) = \frac{1}{2c\tilde{\beta}}[n_1^2 + \tilde{\beta}^2]z + \frac{(n_1^2 - \tilde{\beta}^2)}{4c\gamma}\sin 2\Gamma z \tag{2.52}$$

where we have used Eq. (2.39). When $\tilde{\beta} = n_1$ (which corresponds to the ray along the z-axis)

$$\tau(z) = \frac{z}{c/n_1} \tag{2.53}$$

This is what we should have expected as the ray will *always* travel with speed c/n_1. For large values of z, the second term on the RHS of Eq. (2.52) would make a negligible contribution to $\tau(z)$ and we may write

$$\tau(z) \approx \frac{1}{2c}\left[\tilde{\beta} + \frac{n_1^2}{\tilde{\beta}}\right] z \tag{2.54}$$

Now, if a pulse of light is incident on one end of the waveguide, it would, in general, excite all rays and since different rays take different amounts of time, the pulse will get temporally broadened. Thus, for a parabolic index waveguide, this broadening will be given by

$$\Delta\tau = \tau(\tilde{\beta} = n_2) - \tau(\tilde{\beta} = n_1)$$

or

$$\Delta\tau = \frac{z}{2c}\frac{(n_1 - n_2)^2}{n_2} \approx \frac{z n_2}{2c}\Delta^2 \tag{2.55}$$

where in the last step we have assumed

$$\Delta \equiv \frac{n_1^2 - n_2^2}{2n_1^2} \approx \frac{n_1 - n_2}{n_2} \tag{2.56}$$

For the fiber parameters given by Eq. (2.45), we get

$$\Delta\tau \approx 0.25 \text{ ns/km} \quad (2.57)$$

We will use this result in Chapter 28.

EXAMPLE 2.9 We next consider the ray paths in a medium characterized by the following refractive index variation:

$$\begin{aligned} n^2(x) &= n_1^2 & x < 0 \\ &= n_1^2 - gx & x > 0 \end{aligned} \quad (2.58)$$

Thus, in the region $x > 0$, $n^2(x)$ decreases linearly with x and Eq. (2.28) takes the form

$$\frac{d^2x}{dz^2} = -\frac{g}{2\tilde{\beta}^2}$$

The general solution of which is given by

$$x(z) = -\frac{g}{4\tilde{\beta}^2} z^2 + K_1 z + K_2 \quad (2.59)$$

Consider a ray incident on the origin ($x = 0$, $z = 0$) as shown in Fig. 2.26. Thus,

$$K_2 = 0 \quad \text{and} \quad \tilde{\beta} = n_1 \cos\theta_1 \quad (2.60)$$

Further, $$\left.\frac{dx}{dz}\right|_{z=0} = K_1 = \tan\theta_1 \quad (2.61)$$

Thus the ray path will be given by

$$x(z) = \begin{cases} (\tan\theta_1) z & z < 0 \\ -\dfrac{gz}{4\tilde{\beta}^2}(z - z_0) & 0 < z < z_0 \\ -\dfrac{gz_0}{4\tilde{\beta}^2}(z - z_0) & z > z_0 \end{cases} \quad (2.62)$$

where $$z_0 = \frac{2n_1^2}{g} \sin 2\theta_1$$

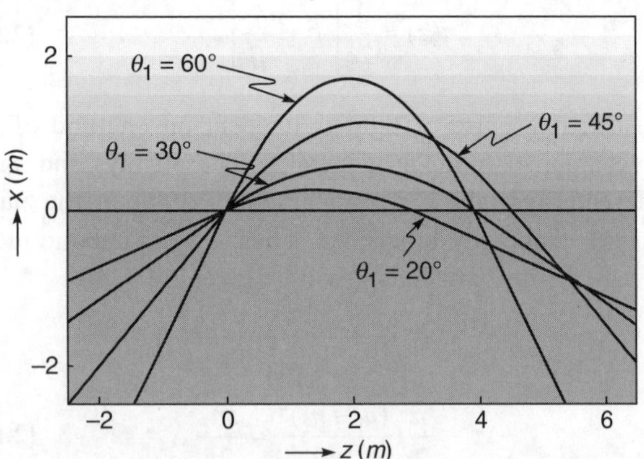

Figure 2.26
Parabolic ray paths (corresponding to $\theta_1 = 20°$, 30°, 45° and 60°) in a medium characterized by refractive index variation given by Eq. (2.58). The ray paths in the region $x < 0$ are straight lines.

Thus, in the region $0 < z < z_0$, the ray path is a parabola. Typical ray paths are shown in Fig. 2.26, the calculations correspond to

$$n_1 = 1.5, \quad g = 0.1 \text{ m}^{-1}$$

and different rays correspond to

$$\theta_1 = \frac{\pi}{9}, \frac{\pi}{6}, \frac{\pi}{4} \text{ and } \frac{\pi}{3}$$

2.4.3 Reflections from the Ionosphere

The ultraviolet rays in the solar radiation result in the ionization of the constituent gases in the atmosphere resulting in the formation of what is known as the ionosphere. The ionization is almost negligible below a height of about 60 km. Because of the presence of the free electrons (in the ionosphere), the refractive index is given by [see Eq. (6.76)]:

$$n^2(x) = 1 - \frac{N_e(x)\, q^2}{m\varepsilon_0\, \omega^2} \quad (2.63)$$

where $N_e(x)$ represents the number of electrons/unit volume in m^{-3}, x represents the height above the ground in meters, ω represents the angular frequency of the electromagnetic wave, $q \approx 1.60 \times 10^{-19}$ C represents the charge of the electron, $m \approx 9.11 \times 10^{-31}$ kg represents the mass of the electron, and $\varepsilon_0 \approx 8.854 \times 10^{-12} \times 10^{-12}$ $\text{C}^2/\text{N–m}^2$ represents the dielectric permittivity of vacuum

Thus, as the electron density starts increasing from 0 (beyond the height of 60 km) the refractive index starts decreasing and the ray paths would be similar to that described in Example 2.9.

If n_T represents the refractive index at the turning point (where the ray becomes horizontal) then (see Fig. 2.27)

$$\tilde{\beta} = \cos\theta_1 = n_T \quad (2.64)$$

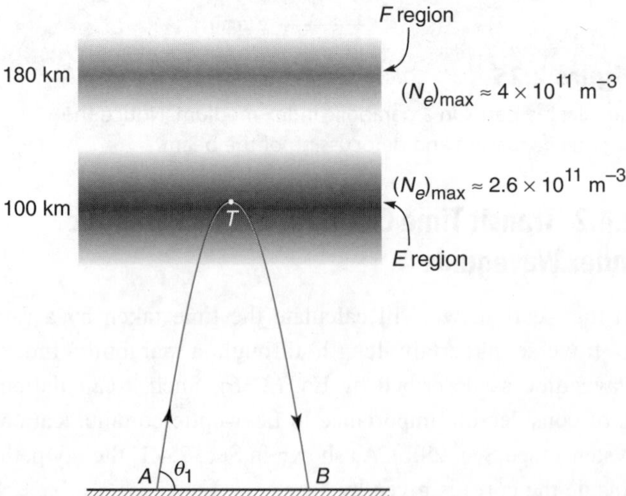

Figure 2.27
Reflection from the E region of the ionosphere. The point T represents the turning point. The shading shows the variation of electron density.

Thus if an electromagnetic signal is sent from the point A (at an angle θ_1) is received at the point B, one can determine the refractive index (and hence the electron density) of the ionospheric layer where the beam has undergone the reflection. This is how the short-wave radio broadcasts ($\lambda \approx 20\,\text{m}$) sent at a particular angle from a particular city (say London) would reach another city (say New Delhi) after undergoing reflection from the ionosphere. Further, for normal incidence, $\theta = \pi/2$ and $n_T = 0$ implying

$$N_e(x_T) = \frac{m\,\varepsilon_0\,\omega^2}{q^2} \tag{2.65}$$

In a typical experiment, an electromagnetic pulse (of frequency between 0.5 and 20 MHz) is sent vertically upwards and if the echo is received after a delay of Δt seconds, then

$$\Delta t \approx \frac{2h}{c} \tag{2.66}$$

where h represents the height at which it undergoes reflection. Thus, if electromagnetic pulse is reflected from the E layer of ionosphere (which is at a height of about 100 km), the echo will be received after about 670 μs. Alternatively, by measuring the delay Δt, one can determine the height (at which the pulse gets reflected) from the following relation

$$h \approx \frac{c}{2}\Delta t \tag{2.67}$$

In Fig. 2.28, we have plotted the frequency dependence of the equivalent height of reflection (as obtained from the delay time of echo) from the E and F regions of the ionosphere. From the figure we find that at $\nu = 4.6 \times 10^6$ Hz, echoes suddenly disappear from the 100 km height. Thus,

$$N_e(100\text{ km}) \approx \frac{m\,\varepsilon_0\,(2\,\pi\,\nu)^2}{q^2}$$

$$\approx \frac{9.11\times10^{-31}\times8.854\times10^{-12}\times(2\,\pi\times4.6\times10^6)^2}{(1.6\times10^{-19})^2}$$

$$\approx 2.6 \times 10^{11}\text{ electrons/m}^3$$

If we further increase the frequency, the echoes appear from the F region of the ionosphere. For more details of the studies on the ionosphere, the reader is referred to one of the most outstanding texts on the subject by Professor S. K. Mitra [Ref. 2.9].

EXAMPLE 2.10 In this example, we will obtain the solution of the ray equation for the refractive index variation given by

$$n^2(x) = n_0^2 + n_2^2(1 - e^{-\alpha x}) \tag{2.68}$$

Substituting in Eq. (2.27), we would obtain

$$\pm dz = \frac{\tilde{\beta}dx}{\left[(n_0^2 + n_2^2 - \tilde{\beta}^2) - n_2^2\,e^{-\alpha x}\right]^{1/2}}$$

$$= \frac{\tilde{\beta}\,e^{\alpha x/2}\,dx}{n_2[K^2 e^{\alpha x} - 1]^{1/2}}$$

or

$$\pm dz = \frac{2\tilde{\beta}}{K\,\alpha n_2}\frac{d\Phi}{(\Phi^2 - 1)^{1/2}} \tag{2.69}$$

where

$$K = \frac{1}{n_2}(n_0^2 + n_2^2 - \tilde{\beta}^2)^{1/2} \tag{2.70}$$

and

$$\Phi(x) = K e^{\alpha x/2} \tag{2.71}$$

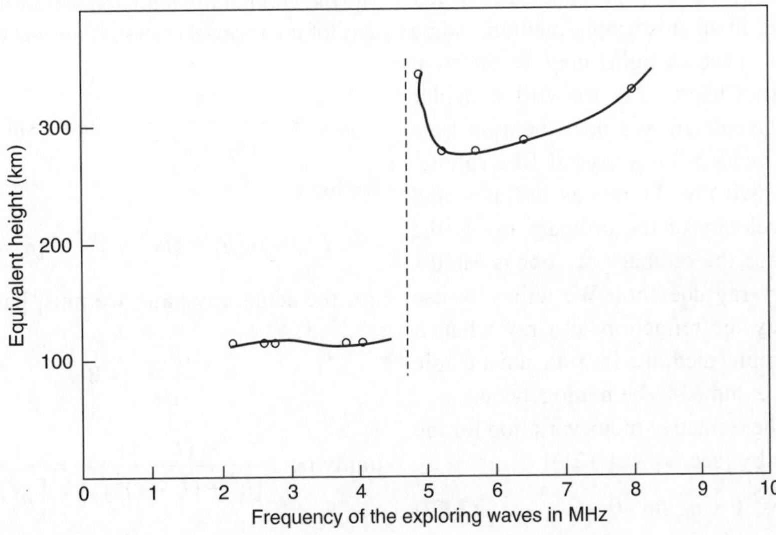

Figure 2.28
Frequency dependence of the equivalent height of reflection from the E and F regions of the ionosphere. [*Adapted from Ref. 2.9*].

The + and – sign in Eq. (2.69) correspond to a ray going up and a ray going down respectively. Further,

$$\tilde{\beta} = n_1 \cos\theta_1 \tag{2.72}$$

where θ_1 is the angle that the ray initially makes with the z-axis at $x = x_1$, $z = 0$ and $n_1 = n(x_1)$. Carrying out the elementary integration, we get

$$x(z) = \frac{2}{\alpha}\ln\left[\frac{1}{K}\cosh\gamma(C \pm z)\right] \tag{2.73}$$

where $$\gamma = \frac{\alpha K n_2}{2\tilde{\beta}} \tag{2.74}$$

which gives us the ray path. Since $x = x_1$ at $z = 0$ (the initial point)

$$C = \frac{1}{\gamma}\cosh^{-1}(K e^{\alpha x_1/2}) \tag{2.75}$$

Further, $$K e^{\alpha x1/2} = \left[\frac{n_0^2 + n_p^2 - \tilde{\beta}^2}{n_0^2 + n_p^2 - n_1^2}\right]^{1/2} \tag{2.76}$$

Thus for a ray launched horizontally at $x = x_1$, $C = 0$. Typically ray paths (for different values of θ_1) are shown in Figs. 2.14 and 2.15.

2.5 Refraction of Rays at the Interface Between an Isotropic Medium and an Anisotropic Medium

LO5

In this section, we will use Fermat's principle to determine the direction of the refracted ray for a ray incident at the interface of an isotropic and an anisotropic medium*. We may point out that in an isotropic medium the properties remain the same in all directions; typical examples are glass, water and air. On the other hand, in an anisotropic medium, some of the properties (such as speed of light) may be different in different directions. In Chapter 21, we will consider anisotropic media in greater detail; we may mention here that when a light ray is incident on a crystal like calcite, it (in general) splits into two rays known as ordinary and extraordinary rays. The velocity of the ordinary ray is the same in all directions. Thus the ordinary ray obeys Snell's laws but the extraordinary ray does not. We will now use Fermat's principle to study the refraction of a ray when it is incident from an isotropic medium into an anisotropic medium—both media are assumed to be homogeneous.

In a uniaxial medium, the refractive index variation for the extraordinary ray is given by [see Eq. (21.121)]

$$n^2(\theta) = n_o^2\cos^2\theta + n_e^2\sin^2\theta \tag{2.77}$$

where n_o and n_e are constants of the crystal and θ represents the angle that the ray makes with the optic axis. Obviously, when the extraordinary ray propagates parallel to the optic axis (i.e., when $\theta = 0$), its speed is c/n_o and when it propagates perpendicular to the optic axis ($\theta = \pi/2$) its speed is c/n_e.

2.5.1 Optic Axis Normal to the Surface

We first consider the particularly simple case of the optic axis being normal to the surface. Referring to Fig. 2.29, the optical path length from A and B is given by

$$L_{op} = n_1[h_1^2 + (L - x)^2]^{1/2} + n(\theta)[h_2^{\,2} + x^2]^{1/2} \tag{2.78}$$

where n_1 is the refractive index of medium I and we have assumed the incident ray, the refracted ray and the optic axis to lie in the same plane. Since

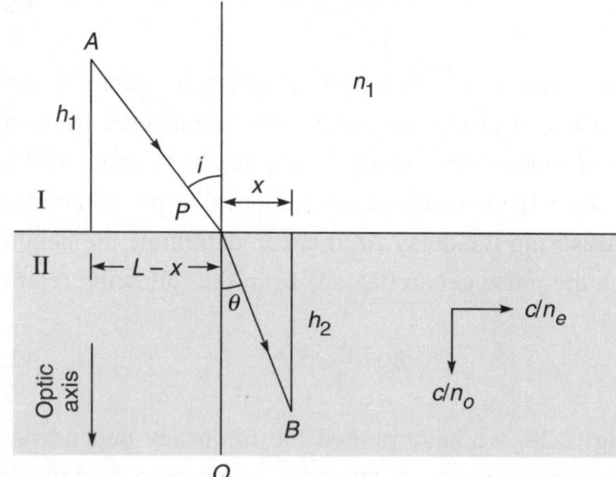

Figure 2.29
The direction of the refracted extraordinary ray when the optic axis (of the uniaxial crystal) is normal to the surface.

$$\cos\theta = \frac{h_2}{(h_2^2 + x^2)^{1/2}} \quad \text{and} \quad \sin\theta = \frac{x}{(h_2^2 + x^2)^{1/2}}$$

we have

$$L_{op} = n_1[h_1^2 + (L - x)]^{1/2} + [n_o^2 h_2^2 + n_e^2 x^2]^{1/2} \tag{2.79}$$

For the actual ray path, we must have

$$\frac{dL_{op}}{dx} = 0$$

implying $$\frac{n_1(L - x)}{[h_1^2 + (L - x)^2]^{1/2}} = \frac{n_e^2 x}{\left[n_o^2 h_2^2 + n_e^2 x^2\right]^{1/2}}$$

* A proof for the applicability of Fermat's principle in anisotropic media has been given by Newcomb (Ref. 2.10); the proof, however, is quite complicated. Ray paths in biaxial media are discussed in Ref. 2.11.

or
$$n_1 \sin i = \frac{n_e^2 \tan r}{\left[n_o^2 + n_e^2 \tan^2 r\right]^{1/2}} \tag{2.80}$$

where we have used the fact that the

$$\text{angle of refraction } r = \theta \quad \text{and} \quad \tan r = \frac{x}{h_2}.$$

Simple manipulations give us

$$\tan r = \frac{n_o n_1 \sin i}{n_e \sqrt{n_e^2 - n_1^2 \sin^2 i}} \tag{2.81}$$

using which we can calculate the angle of refraction for a given angle of incidence (when the optic axis is normal to the surface). As a simple example, we assume the first medium to be air so that $n_1 = 1$. Then

$$\tan r = \frac{n_o \sin i}{n_e \sqrt{n_e^2 - \sin^2 i}} \quad (\text{when } n_1 = 1) \tag{2.82}$$

If we assume the second medium to be calcite, then

$$n_o = 1.65836, \quad \text{and} \quad n_e = 1.48641$$

Thus for $i = 45°$, we get $r \approx 31.1°$. It may be seen that if $n_o = n_e = n_2$ (say) then Eq. (2.80) simplifies to

$$n_1 \sin i = n_2 \sin r \tag{2.83}$$

which is nothing but Snell's law.

2.5.2 Optic Axis in the Plane of Incidence*

We next consider a more general case of the optic axis making an angle ϕ with the normal; however, the optic axis is assumed to lie in the plane of incidence as shown in Fig. 2.30. We may mention here that in general, in an anisotropic medium, the refracted ray does not lie in the plane of incidence. However, it can be shown that if the optic axis lies in the plane of incidence then the refracted ray also lies in the plane of incidence. In the present calculation, we are assuming this and finding the direction of the refracted ray for a given angle of incidence. Now, the optical path length from A to B (see Fig. 2.30) is given by

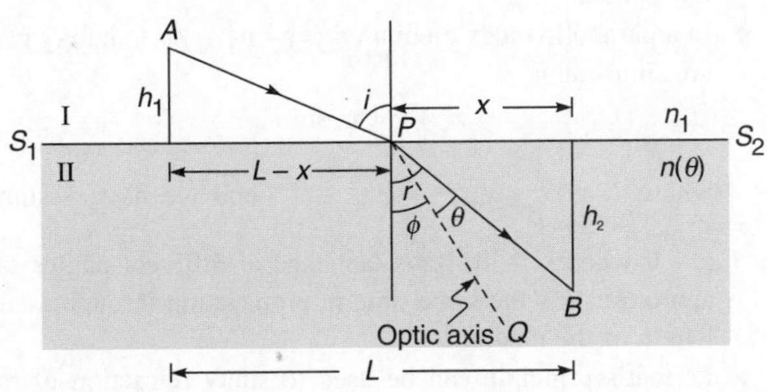

Figure 2.30
The direction of the refracted extraordinary ray when the optic axis (of the uniaxial crystal) lies in the plane of incidence making an angle ϕ with the normal to the interface.

$$L_{op} = n_1[h_1^2 + (L-x)^2]^{1/2} + n(\theta)[h_2^2 + x^2]^{1/2} \tag{2.84}$$

Since $\theta = r - \phi$, we have

$$n^2(\theta) = n_o^2 \cos^2(r-\phi) + n_e^2 \sin^2(r-\phi)$$
$$= n_o^2(\cos r \cos\phi + \sin r \sin\phi)^2 + n_e^2(\sin r \cos\phi - \cos r \sin\phi)^2$$
$$= n_o^2\left[\frac{h_2}{\sqrt{h_2^2+x^2}}\cos\phi + \frac{x}{\sqrt{h_2^2+x^2}}\sin\phi\right]^2 + n_e^2\left[\frac{x}{\sqrt{h_2^2+x^2}}\cos\phi - \frac{h_2}{\sqrt{h_2^2+x^2}}\sin\phi\right]^2$$

Thus,

$$n(\theta) = \frac{1}{\sqrt{h_2^2+x^2}}\left[n_o^2(h_2\cos\phi + x\sin\phi)^2 + n_e^2(x\cos\phi - h_2\sin\phi)^2\right]^{1/2} \tag{2.85}$$

and

$$L_{op} = n_1[h_1^2 + (L-x)^2]^{1/2} + [n_o^2(h_2\cos\phi + x\sin\phi)^2 + n_e^2(x\cos\phi - h_2\sin\phi)^2]^{1/2} \tag{2.86}$$

For the actual ray path, we must have

$$\frac{dL_{op}}{dx} = 0$$

implying

$$\frac{n_1(L-x)}{[h_1^2 + (L-x)^2]^{1/2}} = \frac{n_o^2(h_2\cos\phi + x\sin\phi)\sin\phi + n_e^2(x\cos\phi - h_2\sin\phi)\cos\phi}{[n_o^2(h_2\cos\phi + x\sin\phi)^2 + n_e^2(x\cos\phi - h_2\sin\phi)^2]^{1/2}}$$

or
$$n_1 \sin i = \frac{n_o^2 \cos\theta \sin\phi + n_e^2 \sin\theta\cos\phi}{[n_o^2\cos^2\theta + n_e^2\sin^2\theta]^{1/2}} \tag{2.87}$$

For given values of the angles i and ϕ, the above equation can be solved to give the values of θ and hence the angle of refraction r $(= \theta + \phi)$.

Some interesting particular cases may be noted.

(i) When $n_o = n_e = n_2$, the anisotropic medium becomes isotropic and Eq. (2.87) simplifies to

$$n_1 \sin i = n_2 \sin(\theta + \phi) = n_2 \sin r$$

which is nothing but Snell's law.

* May be skipped in the first reading.

(ii) When $\phi = 0$, i.e., the optic axis is normal to the surface, Eq. (2.87) becomes

$$n_1 \sin i = \frac{n_e^2 \sin\theta}{[n_o^2 \cos^2\theta + n_e^2 \sin^2\theta]^{1/2}}$$

$$= \frac{n_e^2 \sin r}{[n_o^2 \cos^2 r + n_e^2 \sin^2 r]^{1/2}} \quad \textbf{(2.88)}$$

where we have used the fact that $r = \theta$. The above equation is identical to Eq. (2.80).

(iii) Finally, we consider normal incidence, i.e., $i = 0$. Thus, Eq. (2.87) gives us

$$n_o^2 \cos\theta \sin\phi + n_e^2 \sin\theta \cos\phi = 0$$

or

$$n_o^2 \cos(r - \phi) \sin\phi + n_e^2 \sin(r - \phi) \cos\phi = 0$$

or

$$\cos r\,[n_o^2 \cos\phi \sin\phi - n_e^2 \sin\phi \cos\phi] + \sin r\,[n_o^2 \sin^2\phi + n_e^2 \cos^2\phi] = 0$$

or

$$\tan r = \frac{(n_e^2 - n_o^2)\sin\phi\cos\phi}{n_o^2 \sin^2\phi + n_e^2 \cos^2\phi} \quad \textbf{(2.89)}$$

Equation (2.89) shows that in general $r \neq 0$ (see Fig. 2.31). We may mention here that, for normal incidence, the above analysis is valid for an arbitrary orientation of the optic axis; the refracted (extraordinary) ray lies in the plane containing the normal and the optic axis. Furthermore, for normal incidence, when the crystal is rotated about the normal, the refracted ray also rotates on the surface of a cone [see Fig. 21.20(b)].

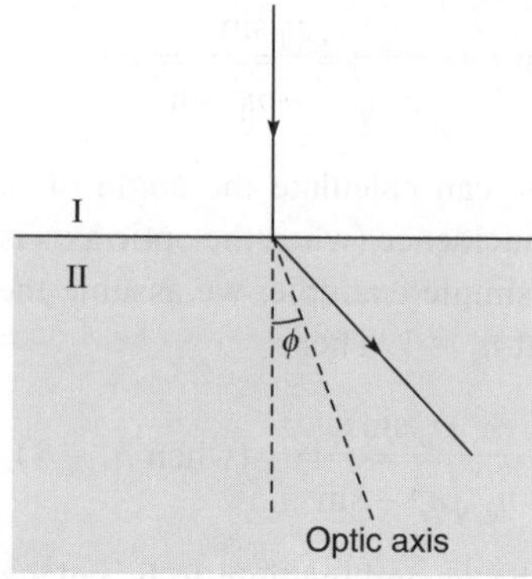

Figure 2.31
For normal incidence, in general, the refracted extraordinary ray undergoes finite deviation. However, the ray proceeds undeviated when the optic axis is parallel or normal to the surface.

Reverting to Eq. (2.89) we note that when the optic axis is normal to the surface ($\phi = 0$) or when the optic axis is parallel to the surface but lying in the plane of incidence ($\phi = \pi/2$), $r = 0$ and the ray goes undeviated.

SUMMARY

- The slightly modified version of Fermat's principle is, *the actual ray path between two points is the one for which the optical path length is stationary with respect to variations of the path.*
- Laws of reflections and Snell's law of refraction ($n_1 \sin \phi_1 = n_2 \sin \phi_2$, where ϕ_1 and ϕ_2 represent the angles of incidence and refraction) can be derived from Fermat's principle.
- For an inhomogeneous medium characterized by the refractive index variation $n(x)$, the ray paths [$x(z)$] are determined by solving the equations:

$$\frac{d^2x}{dz^2} = \frac{1}{2\tilde{\beta}^2}\frac{dn^2(x)}{dx}$$

where the invariant $\tilde{\beta}$ is determined from the initial launching condition of the ray.
- Ray paths obtained by solving the ray equation can be used to study mirage, looming and also reflections from the ionosphere.
- In a parabolic index medium $n^2(x) = n_1^2 - \gamma^2 x^2$, the ray paths are sinusoidal:

$$x(z) = \pm x_0 \sin \Gamma z$$

where $\Gamma = \frac{\gamma}{\tilde{\beta}}$, $x_0 = \frac{1}{\gamma}\sqrt{n_1^2 - \tilde{\beta}^2}$ and we have assumed $z = 0$ where $x = 0$. Rays launched at different angles take approximately the same time in propagating through a large length of the medium.
- Fermat's principle can be used to study refraction of rays at the interface of an isotropic medium and an anisotropic medium.

PROBLEMS

In the first three problems, we will use Fermat's principle to derive laws governing paraxial image formation by spherical mirrors.

2.1 Consider an object point O in front of a concave mirror whose center of curvature is at the point C. Consider an arbitrary point Q on the axis of the system and using a method similar to that used in Example 2.3, show that the optical path length L_{op} (= $OS + SQ$) is approximately given by

$$L_{op} \approx x + y + \frac{1}{2}r^2\left[\frac{1}{x} + \frac{1}{y} - \frac{2}{r}\right]\theta^2 \quad \textbf{(2.90)}$$

where the distances x, y and r and the angle θ are defined in Fig. 2.32; θ is assumed to be small. Determine the paraxial image point and show that the result is consistent with the mirror equation

$$\frac{1}{u} + \frac{1}{v} = \frac{2}{R} \quad \textbf{(2.91)}$$

where u and v are the object and image distance and R is the radius of curvature with the sign convention that all distances to the right of P are positive and to its left negative.

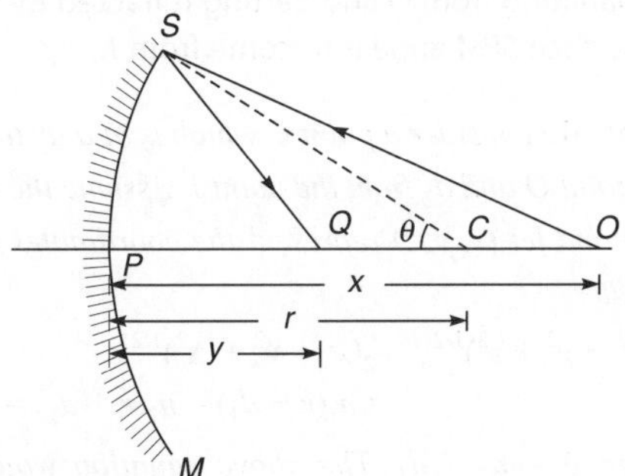

Figure 2.32
Paraxial image formation by a concave mirror.

2.2 Fermat's principle can also be used to determine the paraxial image points when the object forms a virtual image. Consider an object point O in front of the convex mirror SPM (see Fig. 2.33). Assume the optical path length L_{op} to be $OS - SQ$; the minus sign occurs because the rays at S point away from Q (see Example 2.4). Show that

$$L_{op} \approx OS - SQ \approx x - y + \frac{1}{2}r^2\left[\frac{1}{x} - \frac{1}{y} + \frac{2}{r}\right]\theta^2 \quad \textbf{(2.92)}$$

where the distances x, y and r and the angle θ are defined in Fig. 2.33. Show that the paraxial image is formed at $y = y_0$ which is given by

$$\frac{1}{x} - \frac{1}{y_0} = -\frac{2}{r} \quad \textbf{(2.93)}$$

and is consistent with Eq. (2.91). [Which the object distance u is positive, the image distance v and the radius of curvature R are negative since the image point and the center of curvature lie on the left of the point P.]

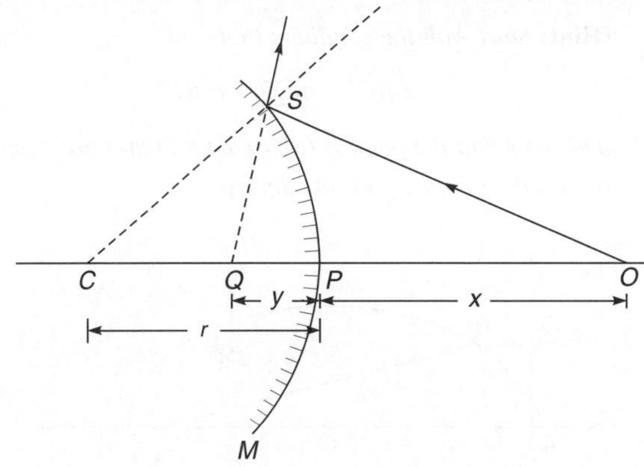

Figure 2.33
Paraxial image formation by a convex mirror.

2.3 Use Fermat's principle to determine the mirror equation for an object point at a distance less than $R/2$ from a concave mirror of radius of curvature R.

2.4 Consider a point object O in front of a concave refracting surface SPM separating two media of refracting indices n_1 and n_2 (see Fig. 2.34); C represents the center of curvature. In this case also one obtains a virtual image. Let Q represent an arbitrary point on the axis. We now have to consider the optical path length $L_{op} = n_1OS - n_2SQ$; show that it is given by

$$L_{op} = n_1OS - n_2SQ$$
$$\approx n_1x - n_2y - \frac{1}{2}r^2\left[\frac{n_2}{y} - \frac{n_1}{x} - \frac{n_2 - n_1}{r}\right]\theta^2 \quad \textbf{(2.94)}$$

Also show that the above expression leads to the paraxial image point which is consistent with Eq. (2.10); we may note that u, v and R are all negative quantities because they are on the left of the refracting surface.

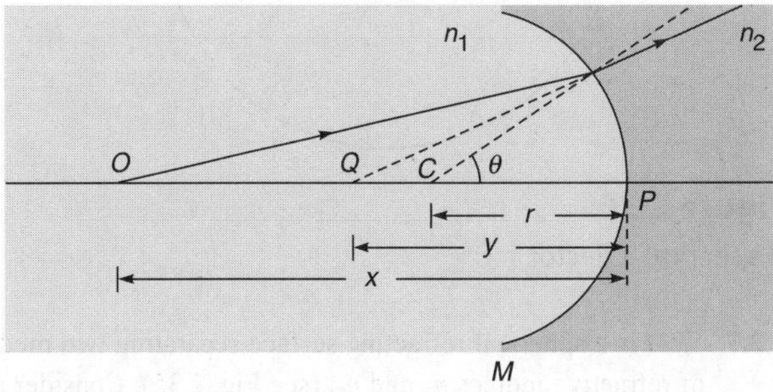

Figure 2.34
Paraxial image formation by a concave refracting surface *SPM*.

2.5 If we rotate an ellipse about its major axis we obtain what is known as an ellipsoid of revolution. Show by using Fermat's principle that all rays parallel to the major axis of the ellipse will focus to one of the focal points of the ellipse (see Fig. 2.35), provided the eccentricity of the ellipse equals n_1/n_2.

[**Hint:** *Start with the condition that*

$$n_2AC' = n_1QB + n_2BC'$$

and show that the point B (whose coordinates are x and y) lies on the periphery of an ellipse].

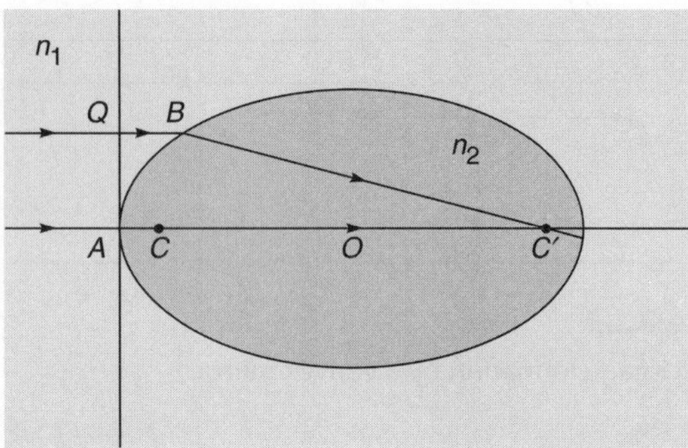

Figure 2.35
All rays parallel to the major axis of the ellipsoid of revolution will focus to one of the focal points of the ellipse provided the eccentricity = n_1/n_2.

2.6 C is the center of the reflecting sphere of radius R (see Fig. 2.36). P_1 and P_2 are two points on a diameter equidistant from the center. **(a)** Obtain the optical path length $P_1O + OP_2$ as a function of θ, and **(b)** find the values of θ for which P_1OP_2 is a ray path from reflection at the sphere.

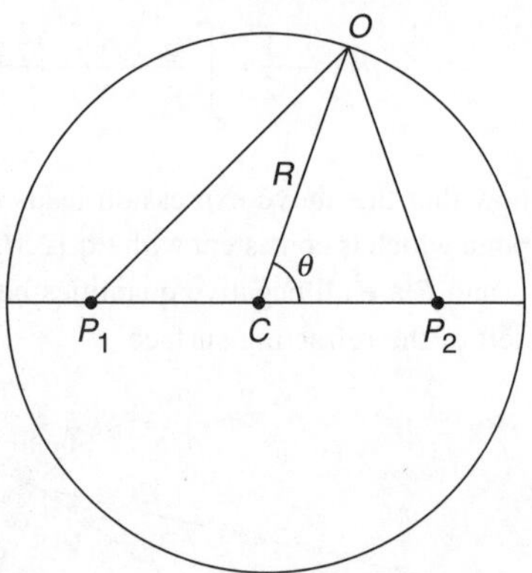

Figure 2.36
A spherical reflector.

2.7 *SPM* is a spherical refracting surface separating two media of refractive indices n_1 and n_2. (see Fig. 2.35). Consider an object point O forming a virtual image at the point I. We assume that *all* rays emanating from O appear to emanate from I so as to form a perfect image. Thus, according to Fermat's principle, we must have

$$n_1OS - n_2SI = n_1OP - n_2PI$$

where S is an arbitrary point on the refracting surface. Assuming the right-hand side to be zero, show that the refracting surface is spherical, with the radius given by

$$r = \frac{n_1}{n_1 + n_2}OP \qquad \textbf{(2.95)}$$

Thus show that

$$n_1^2 d_1 = n_2^2 d_2 = n_1 n_2 r \qquad \textbf{(2.96)}$$

where d_1 and d_2 are defined in Fig. 2.37. (see also Fig. 3.12 and Sec. 3.10).

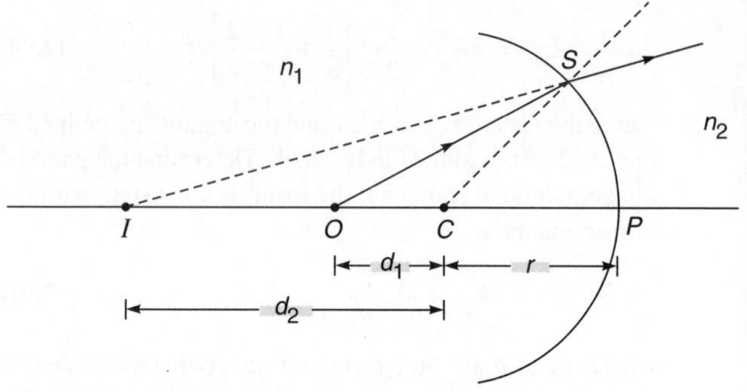

Figure 2.37
All rays emanating from O and getting refracted by the spherical surface *SPM* appear to come from I.

[**Hint:** *We consider a point C which is at a distance d_1 from the point O and d_2 from the point I. Assume the origin to be at O and let (x, y, z) represent the coordinates of the point S. Thus,*

$$n_1(x^2 + y^2 + z^2)^{1/2} - n_2(x^2 + y^2 + \Delta^2)^{1/2} = n_1(r + d_1) - n_2(r + d_2) = 0$$

where $\Delta = d_2 - d_1$. The above equation would give the equation of a sphere whose center is at a distance of n_2r/n_1 (= d_1) from O.]

2.8 Referring to Fig. 2.38, if I represents a perfect image of the point O, show that the equation of the refracting surface (separating two media of refractive indices n_1 and n_2) is given by

$$n_1[x^2 + y^2 + z^2]^{1/2} + n_2[x^2 + y^2 + (z_2 - z)^2]^{1/2} = n_1z_1 - n_2(z_2 - z_1) \qquad \textbf{(2.97)}$$

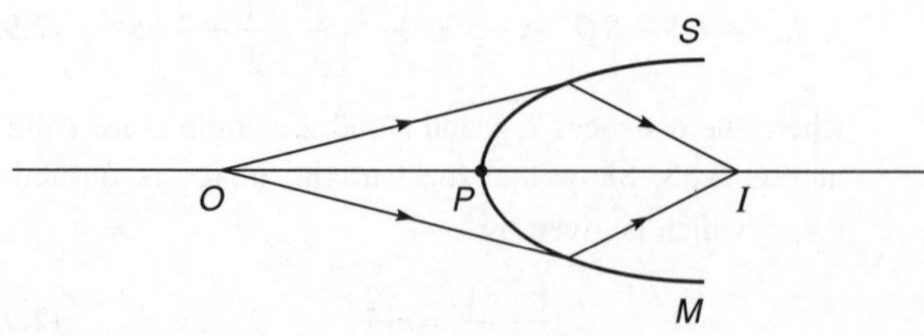

Figure 2.38
The Cartesian oval. All rays emanating from O and getting refracted by *SPM* pass through I.

where the origin is assumed to be at the point O and the coordinates of P and I are assumed to be $(0,0, z_1)$ and $(0,0,z_2)$ respectively. The surface corresponding to Eq. (2.97) is known as a Cartesian oval.

2.9 For the refractive index variation given by Eqs. (2.21) and (2.22), a ray is launched at x = 0.43 m making an angle $-\pi/60$ with the z-axis (see Fig. 2.14). Calculate the value of x at which it will become horizontal. [**Ans:** $x \approx 0.41$ m]

2.10 For the refractive index variation given by Eqs. (2.21) and (2.22), a ray is launched at x=2.8 m such that it becomes horizontal at x=0.2 m (see Fig. 2.15). Calculate the angle that the ray will make with the z-axis at the launching point. [**Ans:** $\theta_1 \approx 19°$]

2.11 Consider a parabolic index medium characterized the following refractive index variation:

$$n^2(x) = n_1^2\left[1-2\Delta\left(\frac{x}{a}\right)^2\right] \qquad |x| < a$$

$$= n_1^2(1 - 2\Delta) = n_2^2 \; |x| > a$$

Assume $n_1 = 1.50$, $n_2 = 1.48$, $a = 50$ μm. Calculate the value of Δ.

(a) Assume rays launched on the axis at z = 0 (i.e., x = 0 when z = 0) with
$\tilde{\beta}$ = 1.495, 1.490, 1.485, 1.480, 1.475 and 1.470
In each case, calculate the angle that the ray initially makes with the z-axis (θ_1) and plot the ray paths. In each case, find the height at which the ray becomes horizontal.

(b) Assume-rays incident normally on the plane z = 0 at x = 0, ±10 μm, ±20 mm, ±30 μm, and ±40 μm. Find the corresponding values of $\tilde{\beta}$, calculate the focal length for each ray and qualitatively plot the ray paths.

2.12 In an inhomogeneous medium the refractive index is given by

$$n^2(x) = 1 + \frac{x}{L} \qquad \text{for } x > 0$$

$$= 1 \qquad \text{for } x < 0$$

Write down the equation of a ray (in the x–z plane) passing through the point (0, 0, 0) where its orientation with respect to x-axis is 45°.

$$\left[\textbf{Ans: } x(z) = \frac{z^2}{4L\tilde{\beta}^2} + z\right]$$

2.13 For the refractive index profile given by Eq. (2.23), show that Eq. (2.27) can be written in the form

$$\pm\frac{\alpha K_1 n_2}{2\tilde{\beta}}\,dz = \frac{dG}{\sqrt{1-G^2}} \tag{2.98}$$

where

$$K_1 = \frac{\sqrt{\tilde{\beta}^2 - n_0^2}}{n_2} \quad \text{and} \quad G(x) = K_1 e^{\alpha x/2} \tag{2.99}$$

Integrate Eq. (2.98) to determine the ray paths.

2.14 Consider a graded index medium characterized by the following refractive index distribution:

$$n^2(x) = n_1^2 \operatorname{sech}^2 gx \tag{2.100}$$

Substitute in Eq. (2.27) and integrate to obtain

$$x(z) = \frac{1}{g}\sinh^{-1}\left[\frac{\sqrt{n_1^2 - \tilde{\beta}^2}}{\tilde{\beta}}\sin gz\right] \tag{2.101}$$

Note that the periodic length

$$z_p = \frac{2\pi}{g}$$

is independent of the launching angle (see Fig. 2.39) and *all* rays rigorously take the same amount of time in propagating through a distance z_p in the z-direction.

[**Hint:** *While carrying out the integration, make the substitution:* $\zeta = \dfrac{\tilde{\beta}}{\sqrt{n_1^2 - \tilde{\beta}^2}}\sinh gx$]

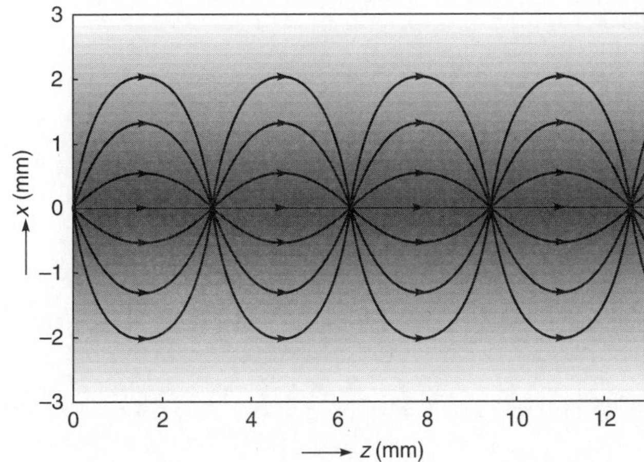

Figure 2.39
Ray paths in a graded index medium characterized by Eq. (2.100).

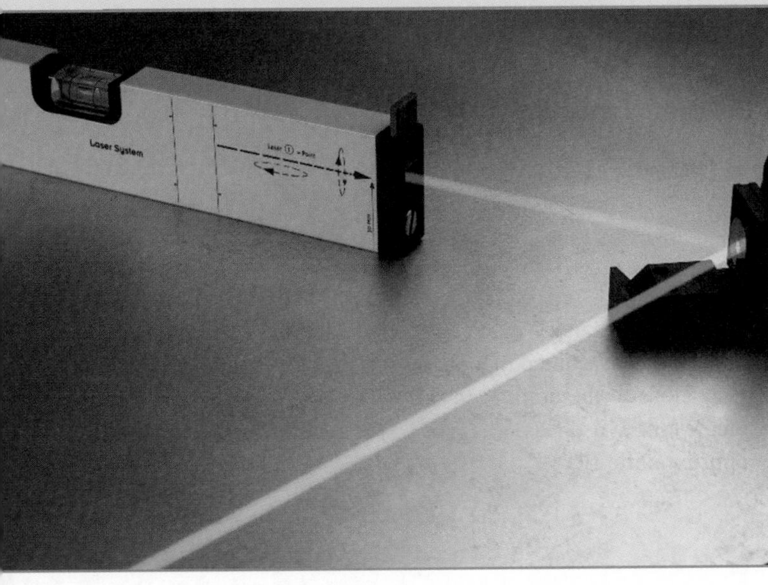

CHAPTER

3

The use of plane and curved mirrors and of convex and concave lenses were discovered independently in China and in Greece. References to burning mirrors go back almost to the start of history, and it is possible that Chinese and Greek knowledge were both derived from a common source in Mesopotamia, India or Egypt...

—The New Encyclopedia Britannica, Vol. 23

Refraction and Reflection by Spherical Surfaces

LEARNING OBJECTIVES

After reading this chapter, the reader should be able to:

LO 1: *describe the image formation at spherical surface.*

LO 2: *learn the formation of paraxial image by thin lens.*

LO 3: *derive the Newtonian lens formula in image formation.*

LO 4: *apply the principles of aplanatism in optical devices.*

LO 5: *define the sine condition.*

Important Milestones

Around 300 BC: Euclid, in his *Optica*, noted that light travels in straight lines and described the law of reflection.

Around 150 AD: Claudius Ptolemaus (also known as Ptolemy) measured the angle of refraction in water for different angles of incidence and made a table of it.

Around 1000 AD: Ibn al-Haytham, also known as Alhazen (965-1039 AD), wrote the first book on Optics; the original title of the book was *Kitab al Manazir* which was in 7 volumes. It is believed that Alhazen was the first person who gave a correct account of how light is refracted by a lens. He had also used spherical and parabolic mirrors .. he also investigated the magnification produced by lenses.

1621 Willebrord Snel van Royen discovered the law of refraction which is referred to as Snell's law.

Above Image: A laser spirit level reflecting a beam off a mirror; Photograph courtesy McGraw Hill Digital Asset Library

3.1 Introduction

In this chapter, we will study the formation of an image by simple optical systems, assuming the optical system to be made up of a number of refracting surfaces like a combination of lenses.* In order to trace a ray through such an optical system, it is necessary only to apply Snell's laws at each refracting surface which are as follows:

(a) the incident ray, the refracted ray and the normal (to the surface) lie in the same plane; and

(b) if ϕ_1 and ϕ_2 represent the angles of incidence and refraction, respectively, then

$$\frac{\sin \phi_1}{\sin \phi_2} = \frac{n_2}{n_1} \tag{3.1}$$

where n_1 and n_2 are the refractive indices of the two media (see Fig. 3.1). Although there is no additional physics involved (other than the Snell's laws) in the tracing of rays, the design of even a simple optical system involves tracing many rays and therefore considerable numerical computations. Nowadays, such numerical computations are usually done on a high-speed computer. It may be of interest to note that optical designers were among the first to make use of electronic computers when they were introduced in the early 1950s.

3.2 Refraction at a Single Spherical Surface

LO1

We will first consider refraction at a spherical surface *SPM* separating two media of refractive indices n_1 and n_2 (see Fig. 3.1(a)). Let C represent the center of curvature of the spherical surface. We will consider a point object O emitting rays in all directions. We will use Snell's laws of refraction to determine the image of the point O. We may mention that not all rays emanating from O converge to a single point; however, if we consider only those rays which make small angles with the line joining the points O and C then all rays do converge to a single point I [see Fig. 3.1(a)]. This is known as the *paraxial approximation* and according to Fermat's principle, all paraxial rays take the *same* amount of time to travel from O to I (see Example 2.3).

Now, in terms of the angles defined in Fig. 3.1(a) we have

$$\phi_1 = \beta + \alpha_1 \quad \text{and} \quad \phi_2 = \beta - \alpha_2$$

We next make use of the paraxial approximation, viz., all angles ϕ_1, ϕ_2, α_1, α_2 and β are small, so that we may write

$$\sin \phi_1 \approx \tan \phi_1 \approx \phi_1 \text{ etc.}$$

where the angles are obviously measured in radians. Thus, we have

$$\sin \phi_1 \approx \phi_1 = \beta + \alpha_1 \approx \tan \beta + \tan \alpha_1 \approx \frac{h}{r} + \frac{h}{x} \tag{3.2}$$

and

$$\sin \phi_2 \approx \phi_2 = \beta - \alpha_2 \approx \tan \beta - \tan \alpha_2 \approx \frac{h}{r} - \frac{h}{y} \tag{3.3}$$

where the distances h, x, y and r are defined in Fig. 3.1(a) and we have assumed that the foot of the perpendicular (D) is very close to the point P so that $OD \approx OP = x$, $ID \approx IP = y$, etc. We now use Eqs. (3.1) – (3.3) to obtain (in the paraxial approximation):

$$n_1\left(\frac{h}{r} + \frac{h}{x}\right) = n_2\left(\frac{h}{r} - \frac{h}{y}\right)$$

or

$$\frac{n_2}{y} + \frac{n_1}{x} = \frac{n_2 - n_1}{r} \tag{3.4}$$

$u < 0, v > 0, R > 0$
$n_1 \sin \phi_1 = n_2 \sin \phi_2$

(a)

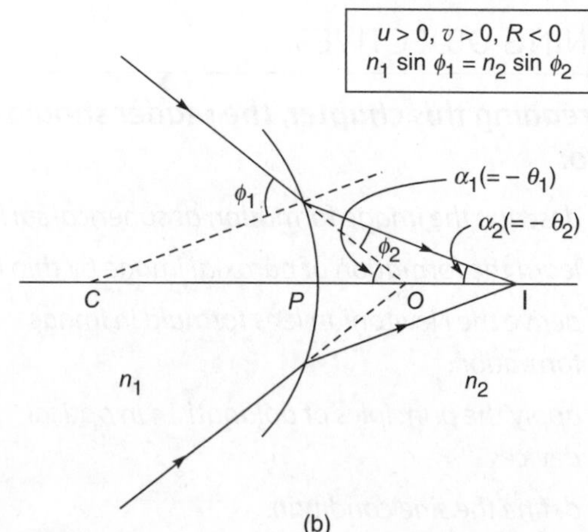

Figure 3.1
(a) Paraxial image formation by a spherical refracting surface separating media of refractive indices n_1 and n_2. O represents the object point and I the paraxial image point. (b) corresponds to positive u.

* The optical system may also consist of mirrors, in which case, the reflection of rays should also be taken into account (see Sec. 3.3).

3.2.1 The Sign Convention

Before we proceed further, we should state the sign convention which we will be using throughout in the book. We refer to Fig. 3.1(a) and consider the point P as the origin of the co-ordinate system. The sign convention is as follows:

1. The rays are always incident from the left on the refracting (or reflecting) surface.
2. All distances to the right of the point P are positive and distances to the left of the point P are negative. Thus in Fig. 3.1(a), the object distance u is a negative quantity and the image distance v and the radius of curvature R are positive quantities. For u to be positive, we must have a situation like the one shown in Fig. 3.1(b); in the absence of a refracting surface, the rays converge to a point to the *right* of P.
3. The angle that the ray makes with the axis is positive if the axis has to be rotated in the anticlockwise direction (through the acute angle) to coincide with the ray. Conversely, if the axis has to be rotated in the clockwise direction (through the acute angle) to coincide with the ray, then the slope angle is negative. Thus in Fig. 3.1(a), if θ_1 and θ_2 are the angles that the rays OS and SI make with the axis, then $\theta_1 = \alpha_1$ and $\theta_2 = -\alpha_2$; α_1, α_2 and β represent the magnitudes of the angles. (If the final result does not depend on the angles, then it is more convenient to use the magnitude of the angles as has indeed been done in Sec. 3.2). In Fig. 3.1(b), both θ_1 and θ_2 are negative quantities.
4. The angle that a ray makes with the normal to the surface is positive if the normal has to be rotated in the anticlockwise direction (through the acute angle) to coincide with the ray, and conversely. Thus, in Fig. 3.1(a), ϕ_1 and ϕ_2 are positive quantities.
5. All distances measured upward from the axis (along a perpendicular to the axis) are positive, and all distances measured in the downward direction are negative.

3.2.2 The Gaussian Formula for a Single Spherical Surface

If we now use the sign convention discussed above, then for the ray diagram shown in Fig. 3.1(a), $u = -x$, $v = y$ and $R = r$. Thus Eq. (3.4) becomes

$$\frac{n_2}{v} - \frac{n_1}{u} = \frac{n_2 - n_1}{R} \tag{3.5}$$

which gives the image point due to refraction at a spherical surface (see also Eq. 2.10 of the previous chapter). Equation (3.5) is known as the **Gaussian formula for a single spherical surface.** It should be noted that, corresponding to Fig. 3.1(a), u is negative and v positive, whereas for Fig. 3.1(b), u and v are both positive.

EXAMPLE 3.1 Consider a medium of refractive index 1.5 bounded by two spherical surfaces $S_1P_1M_1$ and $S_2P_2M_2$ as shown in Fig. 3.2. The radii of curvature of the two surfaces are 15 and 25 cm with their centers at C_1 and C_2, respectively. There is an object at a distance of 40 cm (from P_1) on the line joining C_1 and C_2. Determine the position of the paraxial image.

Solution: We first consider refraction by $S_1P_1M_1$. Obviously $u = -40$ cm, $R = +15$ cm, $n_1 = 1.0$ and $n_2 = 1.5$. Thus,

$$\frac{1.5}{v} + \frac{1}{40} = \frac{0.5}{15} \Rightarrow v = +180 \text{ cm}$$

In the absence of the second surface, the image is formed at O' at a distance of 150 cm from P_2. O' now acts as a virtual object and since it is to the right of $S_2P_2M_2$ we have, while considering refraction by the second surface, $u = +150$ cm, $R = -25$ cm, $n_1 = 1.5$ and $n_2 = 1.0$. Thus,

$$\frac{1.0}{v} - \frac{1.5}{150} = +\frac{0.5}{25}$$

giving

$$v = +33\tfrac{1}{3} \text{ cm}$$

and a real image is formed on the right of P_2 at a distance of $33\frac{1}{3}$ cm.

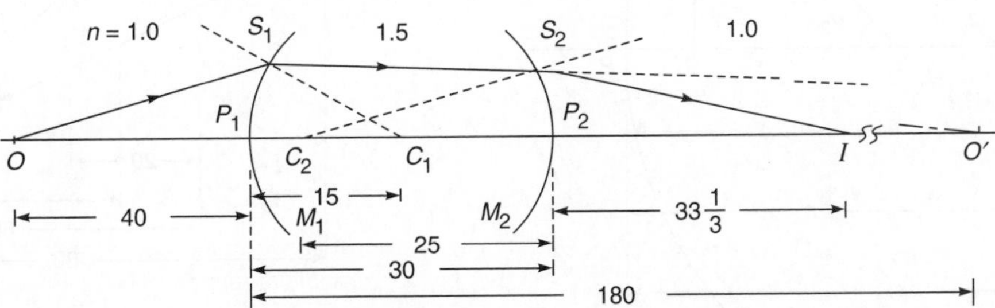

Figure 3.2
Paraxial image formation by a medium of refractive index 1.5 bounded by two spherical surfaces $S_1P_1M_1$ and $S_2P_2M_2$. All distances are measured in centimeters.

We should point out that while considering refraction by a single surface (as in Fig. 3.1), the axis of the system is defined by the line joining the object point O and the center of curvature C; thus *any* ray from the point O (like OS) will be in the plane containing the axis and the normal at the point S and consequently, the refracted ray will *always* intersect the axis. On the other hand, if there is second refracting surface (like in Fig. 3.2 or as in a lens) then the line joining the two centers of curvature is defined as the axis. In the latter case, as can be readily seen, not all rays from an off-axis point will intersect the axis and after refraction at the second surface will, in general, not remain confined to a single plane; these rays are known as *skew rays*. Rays which remain confined to a plane (containing the axis) are known as *meridional rays*; obviously, all rays emanating from a point on the axis are *meridional rays*.

3.3 Reflection by a Single Spherical Surface

We next consider the imaging of a point object O by a spherical mirror SPM (see Fig. 3.3) in the paraxial approximation; the point C represents the center of curvature. We proceed in a manner exactly similar to that in Sec. 3.2 and we refer to Fig. 3.3 to obtain

$$\phi_1 = \beta - \alpha_1 \approx \frac{h}{r} - \frac{h}{x}$$

and

$$\phi_2 = \alpha_2 - \beta \approx \frac{h}{y} - \frac{h}{r}$$

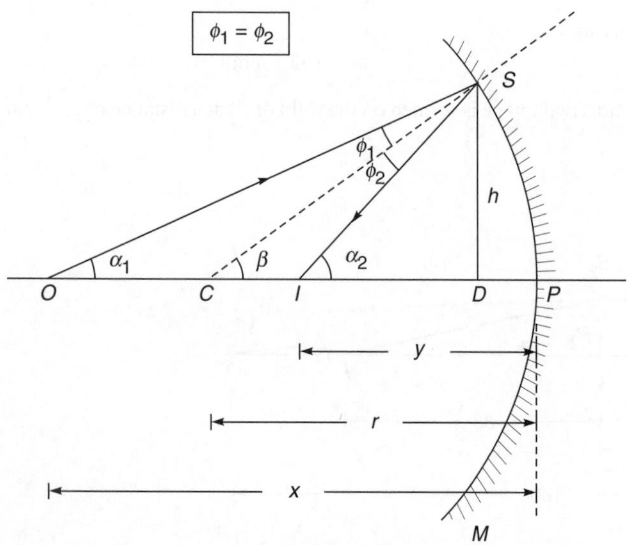

Figure 3.3
Paraxial image formation by a spherical reflecting surface *SPM*.

where the distances x, y, h and r are defined in Fig. 3.3. Since $\phi_1 = \phi_2$ (the law of reflection), we get

$$\frac{1}{x} + \frac{1}{y} = \frac{2}{r} \tag{3.6}$$

If we again use the sign convention that all the distances to the right of P are positive and those to its left negative, then $u = -x$, $v = -y$ and $R = -r$; thus we obtain the mirror equation

$$\frac{1}{u} + \frac{1}{v} = \frac{2}{R} \tag{3.7}$$

which is the same as was derived by using Fermat's principle (see Problem 2.1). It is interesting to note that if we set $n_2 = -n_1$ in Eq. (3.5), we get Eq. (3.7). This follows from the fact that Snell's law of refraction Eq. (3.1) becomes the law of reflection if we have $n_2 = -n_1$.

We illustrate the use of Eq. (3.7) through an example.

EXAMPLE 3.2 Consider an optical system consisting of a concave mirror $S_1P_1M_1$ and convex mirror $S_2P_2M_2$ of radii of curvatures 60 cm and 20 cm, respectively (see Fig. 3.4). We would like to determine the final image position of the object point O which is at a distance of 80 cm from the point P_1, the two mirrors being separated by a distance of 40 cm.

We first consider the imaging by $S_1P_1M_1$; since $u = -80$ cm and $R = -60$ cm (because both O and C are on the left of P_1), we have

$$-\frac{1}{80} + \frac{1}{v} = -\frac{2}{60} \quad \Rightarrow \quad v = -48 \text{ cm}$$

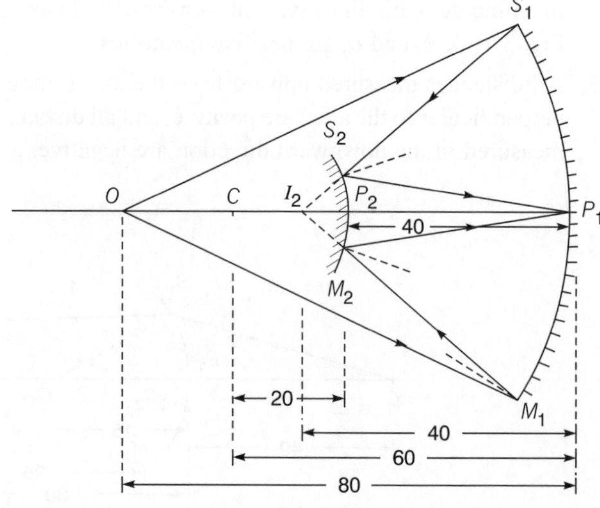

Figure 3.4
Paraxial image formation by an optical system comprising a concave mirror $S_1P_1M_1$ and a convex mirror $S_2P_2M_2$.

In the absence of the mirror $S_2P_2M_2$, a real image will be formed at I_1 which now acts as a virtual object for $S_2P_2M_2$. Since I_1 is to the left of P_2, we have (considering imaging by $S_2P_2M_2$), $u = -8$ cm and $R = -20$ cm, giving

$$\frac{1}{v} - \frac{1}{8} = -\frac{2}{20} \Rightarrow v = +40 \text{ cm}$$

Thus, the final image is formed on the right of $S_2P_2M_2$ at a distance of 40 cm, which happens to be the point P_1.

3.4 The Thin Lens

LO2

A medium bounded by two spherical refracting surfaces is referred to as a spherical lens. If the thickness of such a lens (shown as t in Fig. 3.5) is very small compared to object and image distances, and to the radii of curvature of the refracting surfaces then the lens is referred to as a thin spherical lens. In general, a lens may have non-spherical refracting surfaces (e.g., it may have cylindrical surfaces). However, most lenses employed in optical systems have spherical refracting surfaces. Therefore, we will simply use the term 'lens' to imply a spherical lens. Different types of lenses are shown in Fig. 3.6. The line joining the centers of curvature of the spherical refracting surfaces is referred to as the *axis* of the lens.

In this section, we will consider the paraxial image formation by a thin lens. The corresponding considerations for a thick lens will be discussed in Problem 3.6.

We consider a point object O on the axis of a (thin) lens as shown in Fig. 3.5. The lens is placed in a medium of refractive index n_1 and the refractive index of the material of the lens is n_2. Let R_1 and R_2 be the radii of curvature of the left and right surfaces of the lens; for the lens shown in Fig. 3.5, R_1 is positive and R_2 is negative. In order to determine the position of the image, we will consider successive refractions at the two surfaces; the image formed by the first surface is considered as the object (which may be real or virtual) for the second surface. Thus, if the second refracting surface had not been there, the image of the point O would have been formed at Q whose position (given by v') is determined from Eq. (3.8) (see also Eq. (3.5))

$$\frac{n_2}{v'} - \frac{n_1}{u} = \frac{n_2 - n_1}{R_1} \tag{3.8}$$

where u is the object distance which is negative for the object point O shown in the figure. Obviously if v' is positive, then the point Q lies to the right of the surface and if v' is negative then Q lies to the left of the surface. The point Q now acts as the (virtual) object for the second refracting surface and the final image is formed at I whose position is determined from the equation

$$\frac{n_1}{v} - \frac{n_2}{v'} = \frac{n_1 - n_2}{R_2} \tag{3.9}$$

In Eqs. (3.8) and (3.9) the distances are measured from the center of the lens P; this is justified because the lens has been assumed to be thin. Adding Eqs. (3.8) and (3.9), we get

$$\frac{1}{v} - \frac{1}{u} = (n-1)\left(\frac{1}{R_1} - \frac{1}{R_2}\right) \tag{3.10}$$

where $$n \equiv \frac{n_2}{n_1}$$

Equation (3.10) is known as the *thin lens formula* and is usually written in the form

$$\frac{1}{v} - \frac{1}{u} = \frac{1}{f} \tag{3.11}$$

where f, known as the focal length of the lens, is given by

$$\frac{1}{f} = (n-1)\left(\frac{1}{R_1} - \frac{1}{R_2}\right) \tag{3.12}$$

For a lens placed in air (which is usually the case), $n > 1$ and if $[(1/R_1) - (1/R_2)]$ is a positive quantity then the

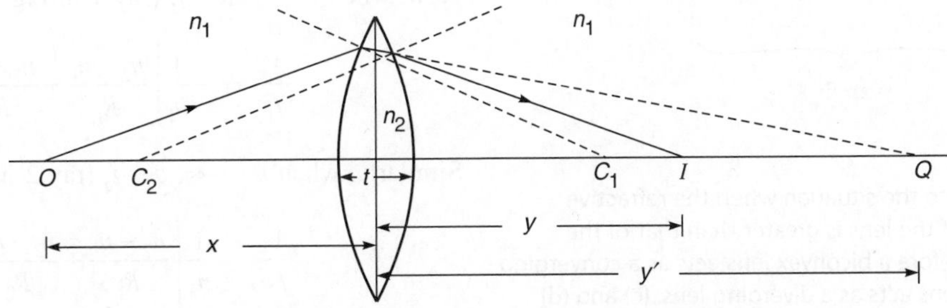

Figure 3.5
Image formation by a thin lens. The line joining the two centers of curvature is known as the axis of the lens [$u = -x$, $v' = y'$ $v = y$].

focal length is positive and the lens acts as a converging lens [see Fig. 3.7(a)]. Similarly, if $(1/R_1) - (1/R_2)$ is a negative quantity then the lens acts as a diverging lens (see Fig. 3.7(b)). However, if the double convex lens is placed in a medium whose refractive index is greater than that of the material of the lens, then the focal length becomes negative and the lens acts as a diverging lens [see Fig. 3.7(c)]; similarly for the double concave lens [see Fig. 3.7(d)].

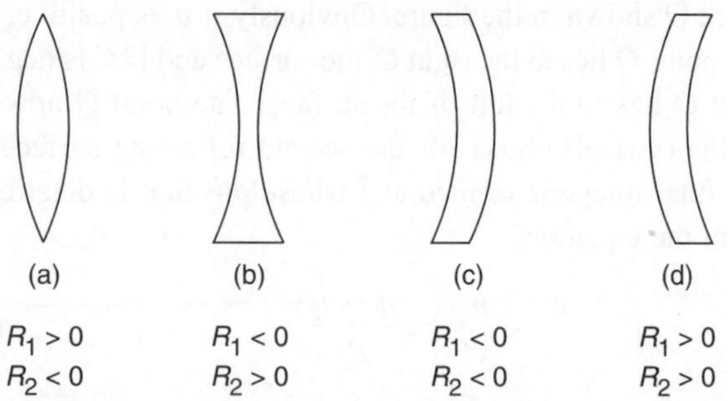

Figure 3.6
Signs of R_1 and R_2 for different lens types.

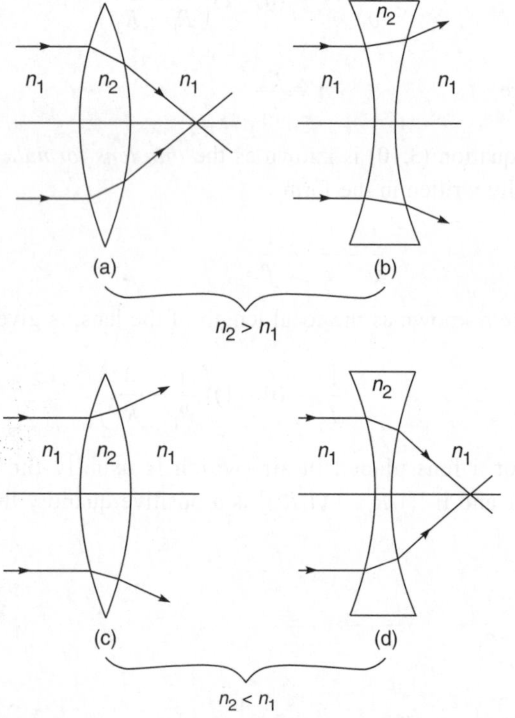

Figure 3.7
(a) and (b) correspond to the situation when the refractive index of the material of the lens is greater than that of the surroundings and therefore a biconvex lens acts as a converging lens and a biconcave lens acts as a diverging lens. (c) and (d) correspond to the situation when the refractive index of the material of the lens is smaller than that of the surrounding medium and therefore a biconvex lens acts as a diverging lens and a biconcave lens as a converging lens.

3.5 The Principal Foci and Focal Lengths of a Lens

For a converging lens, the *first principal focus* is defined as the point (on the axis) such that a ray passing through that point will, after refraction through the lens, emerge parallel to the axis—see ray 1 in Fig. 3.8(a); the point F_1 is the first principal focus. For a diverging lens, the ray which (in the absence of the lens) would have passed through the first principal focus emerges, after refraction by the lens, as a ray parallel to the axis—see ray 1 in Fig. 3.8(b). The point F_1 is the **first principal focus** and its distance from the lens (denoted by f_1) is known as the **first focal length** of the lens. Obviously, f_1 is negative for a converging lens and positive for a diverging lens.

We next consider a ray which travels parallel to the axis [see ray 2 in Figs. 3.8(a) and (b)]. For a converging lens, the point at which the ray will intersect the axis [shown as F_2 in Fig. 3.8(a)] is known as the **second principal focus** of the lens. Similarly, for a diverging lens, the point at which the ray would have intersected the axis (if produced backwards) is the second principal focus [see the point F_2 in Fig. 3.8(b)]. The distance of the second principal focus from the lens is known as the **second focal length** and is denoted by f_2. As can be seen from Fig. 3.8, f_2 is positive for a converging lens and negative for a diverging lens.

For a thin lens placed in a medium such that the refractive indices on both sides of the lens are the same ($n_3 = n_1$ in Fig. 3.8), the values of f_1 and f_2 can be readily obtained by considering the thin lens formula [see Eq. (3.10)] and one gets

$$\frac{1}{f_2} = -\frac{1}{f_1} = \left[(n-1)\left(\frac{1}{R_1} - \frac{1}{R_2}\right)\right] = \frac{1}{f} \quad \textbf{(3.13)}$$

However, if $n_3 \neq n_1$ then the thin lens formula assumes the form as given in Eq. (3.14) (see also Problem 3.2):

$$\frac{n_3}{v} - \frac{n_1}{u} = \frac{n_2 - n_1}{R_1} + \frac{n_3 - n_2}{R_2} \quad \textbf{(3.14)}$$

Now, when $v = \infty$, $u = f_1$ (ray 1 in Fig. 3.8), we have

$$\frac{1}{f_1} = -\frac{1}{n_1}\left[\frac{n_2 - n_1}{R_1} + \frac{n_3 - n_2}{R_2}\right] \quad \textbf{(3.15)}$$

Similarly, when $u = -\infty$, $v = f_2$ (ray 2 in Fig. 3.8) we have

$$\frac{1}{f_2} = \frac{1}{n_3}\left[\frac{n_2 - n_1}{R_1} + \frac{n_3 - n_2}{R_2}\right] \quad \textbf{(3.16)}$$

Once we know f_1 and f_2 (and therefore the positions of the first and second principal foci) the (paraxial) image can be graphically constructed from the following rules:

(i) A ray passing through the first principal focus will, after refraction, emerge parallel to the axis [see ray 1 in Figs. 3.8(a) and (b)]

(ii) A ray parallel to the axis will, after refraction, either pass through or appear to come from (depending on the sign of f_2) the second principal focus [see ray 2 in Figs. 3.8(a) and (b)]

(iii) A ray passing through the center of the lens *P* will pass through undeviated* [see ray 3 in Figs. 3.8(a) and (b)]

3.6 The Newton Formula

LO3

Let x_1 be the distance of the object from the first principal focus F_1 (x_1 will be positive if the object point is on the right of F_1 and conversely) and let x_2 be the distance of the image from the second principal focus F_2 as shown in Figs. 3.8(a) and (b). Considering similar triangles in Fig. 3.8(a), we have

$$\frac{-y'}{y} = \frac{-f_1}{-x_1} \tag{3.17}$$

and

$$\frac{-y'}{y} = \frac{x_2}{f_2} \tag{3.18}$$

where the vertical distances are positive if measured above the line and negative if measured below the line (see Sec. 3.2.1). Equations (3.17) and (3.18) give

$$f_1 f_2 = x_1 x_2 \tag{3.19}$$

which is known as the *Newtonian lens formula*. It may be noted that for a diverging lens [see Fig. 3.8(b)], Eqs. (3.17) and (3.18) would be

$$\frac{y'}{y} = \frac{f_1}{-x_1} = \frac{x_2}{-f_2}$$

which are identical to Eqs. (3.17) and (3.18).

When the thin lens has the same medium on the two sides, then using Eq. (3.13) we have

$$x_1 x_2 = -f^2 \tag{3.20}$$

showing that x_1 and x_2 must be of opposite signs. Thus, if the object lies on the left of the first principal focus, then the image will lie on the right of the second principal focus, and vice versa.

3.7 Lateral Magnification

The lateral magnification *m* is the ratio of the height of the image to that of the object. Considering either Fig. 3.8(a) or (b) we readily get

$$m = \frac{y'}{y} = \frac{v}{u} = \frac{f_2 + x_2}{f_1 + x_1} = -\frac{f_1}{x_1} = -\frac{x_2}{f_2} \tag{3.21}$$

where we have made use of Eqs. (3.17) and (3.18). Obviously, if *m* is positive, the image is erect [as in Fig. 3.8(b) and conversely if *m* is negative, the image is inverted as in Fig. 3.8(a)].

The magnification can also be calculated as the product of the individual magnifications produced by each of the

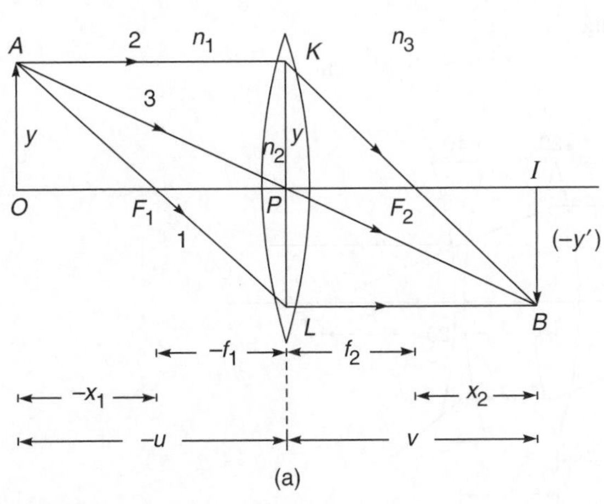

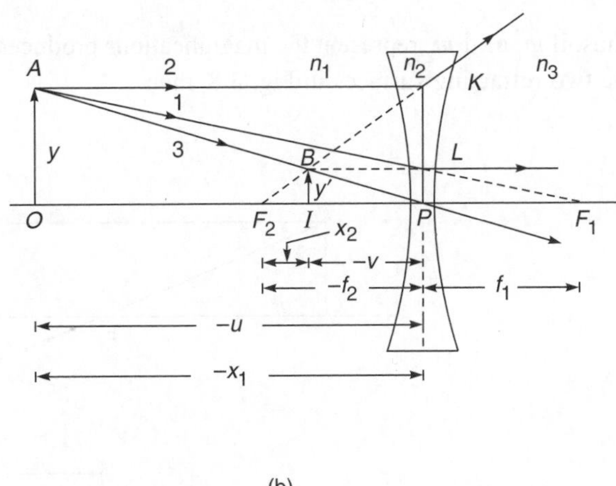

Figure 3.8

(a) Paraxial imaging by a converging lens; x_1, f_1 and u are negative quantities and x_2, f_2, and v are positive quantities.
(b) Paraxial imaging by a diverging lens; here x_1, f_2, u and v are negative quantities and x_2 and f_1 are positive quantities.

* This follows from the fact that, for a thin lens, when $u = 0$, v is also equal to zero [see Eqs. (3.10) and (3.14)].

refracting surfaces; referring to Fig. 3.9, the magnification produced by a single refracting surface is given by

$$m = \frac{y'}{y}$$

and considering triangles AOC and ICB, we get

$$\frac{-y'}{y} = \frac{v - R}{-u + R} = \frac{\frac{v}{R} - 1}{-\frac{u}{R} + 1} \tag{3.22}$$

Now, Eq. (3.5) gives us

$$\frac{n_2}{n_1}\frac{v}{u} - \frac{v}{u} = \frac{n_2 - n_1}{n_1}\frac{v}{R}$$

and

$$\frac{u}{v} - \frac{n_1}{n_2} = \frac{n_2 - n_1}{n_2}\frac{u}{R}$$

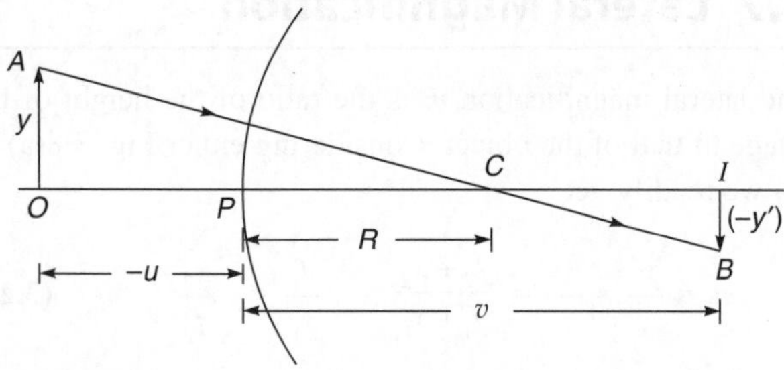

Figure 3.9
Imaging of an object of height y by a spherical refracting surface.

Substituting for v/R and u/R in Eq. (3.22), we get

$$m = \frac{y'}{y} = \frac{n_1 v}{n_2 u} \tag{3.23}$$

Thus, if m_1 and m_2 represent the magnifications produced by the two refracting surfaces in Fig. 3.8, then

$$m = \frac{n_1}{n_2}\frac{v'}{u}$$

and

$$m_2 = \frac{n_2}{n_1}\frac{v}{v'}$$

where v' represents the distance of the image formed by the first refracting surface. Thus,

$$m = m_1 m_2 = \frac{v}{u} \tag{3.24}$$

consistent with Eq. (3.21).

EXAMPLE 3.3 Consider a system of two thin lenses as shown in Fig. 3.10. The convex lens has a focal length of +20 cm and the concave lens has a focal length of –10 cm. The two lenses are separated by 8 cm. For an object of height 1 cm (at a distance of 40 cm from the convex lens), calculate the position and size of the image. (The same problem will be solved again in Chapter 4 by using the matrix method.)

Solution: Let us first calculate the position and size of the image formed by the first lens:

$$u = -40 \text{ cm}, f = +20 \text{ cm}$$

Therefore, using Eq. (3.11), we get

$$\frac{1}{v} = \frac{1}{u} + \frac{1}{f} = -\frac{1}{40} + \frac{1}{20} = +\frac{1}{40}$$

Thus, $v = +40$ cm and $m_1 = -1$; the image is of the same size but inverted. This image acts as a virtual object for the concave lens with $u = +32$ cm and $f = -10$ cm. Thus,

$$\frac{1}{v} = \frac{1}{32} - \frac{1}{10} = -\frac{22}{320}$$

giving

$$v \simeq -14.5 \text{ cm}$$

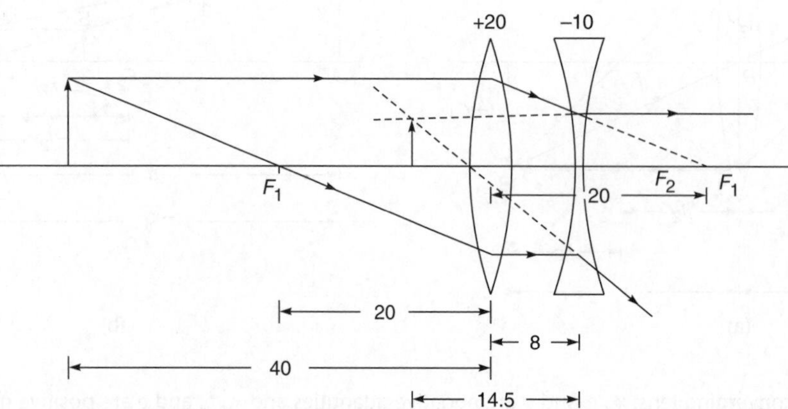

Figure 3.10
Paraxial imaging by an optical system consisting of a converging lens of focal length 20 cm and a diverging lens of focal length −10 cm separated by 8 cm. All distances in the figure are in centimeters.

Further,

$$m_2 = -\frac{320/22}{32} = -\frac{1}{2.2}$$

Thus,

$$m = m_1 m_2 = +\frac{1}{2.2}$$

The final image is formed at a distance of 14.5 cm on the left of the concave lens. The image is virtual, erect and smaller in size by a factor of 2.2.

3.8 Aplanatic Points of a Sphere

LO4

In Sec. 3.2, while discussing image formation by a single refracting surface we had made use of the paraxial approximation, i.e., we had considered rays which made small angles with the axis. In this approximation, it was found that the images of point objects are perfect, i.e., *all* rays emanating from a given object point were found to intersect at *one* point which is the image point. If we had considered rays which make large angles with the axis, then we would have observed that, in general, (after refraction) they do not pass through the same point on the axis (see Fig. 3.11) and a perfect image is not formed. The image is said to be afflicted with aberrations. However, for a given spherical surface, there exist two points for which *all* rays emanating from one point intersect each other at the other point. This point is at a distance equal to $n_2 |R|/n_1$ from the center of the spherical surface and a virtual image is formed at a distance of $n_1|R|/n_2$ from the center [see Figs. 3.12(a) and (b)]. This can be easily proved by using Fermat's principle (see Problem 2.7) or by using geometrical methods (see Sec. 3.10). The two points are said to be the *aplanatic points* of the sphere and are utilized in the construction of aplanatic lenses (see Fig. 3.13) which are

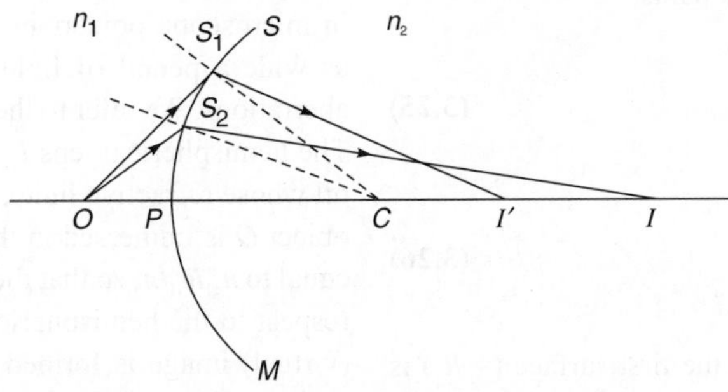

Figure 3.11
The point I represents the paraxial image point of the object point O formed by a spherical refracting surface *SPM*. However, if we consider non-paraxial rays like OS_1 (which make large angles with the axis) then the refracted ray, in general, will not pass through the point I—this leads to aberrations in the image.

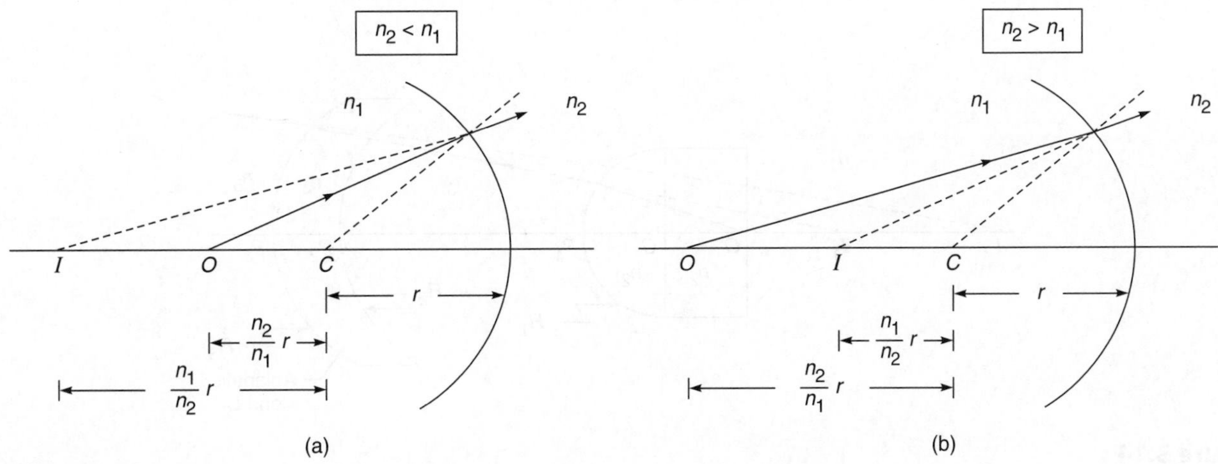

Figure 3.12
O and I represent the aplanatic points of a spherical surface, i.e., *all* rays emanating from O appear to come from I; (a) and (b) correspond to $n_2 < n_1$ and $n_2 > n_1$, respectively.

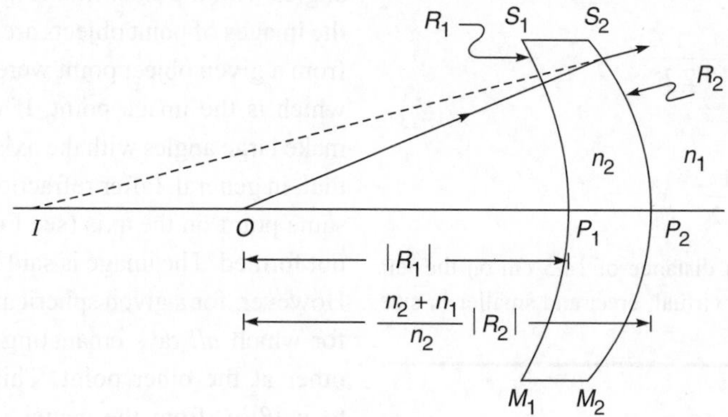

Figure 3.13
The aplanatic lens. The object point O is at the center of curvature of the first surface $S_1P_1M_1$. The points O and I are the aplanatic points of the spherical surface $S_2P_2M_2$—thus a perfect (virtual) image is formed at I.

used in wide aperture oil immersion microscope objectives. The points O and I are the aplanatic points of the spherical surface of radius R_2 (see Fig. 3.13). Thus,

$$OP_2 = |R_2| \left[1 + \frac{n_1}{n_2}\right] \tag{3.25}$$

and

$$IP_2 = |R_2| \left[1 + \frac{n_2}{n_1}\right] \tag{3.26}$$

Now, the radius of curvature of the first surface (= R_1) is such that the point O coincides with its center of curvature. Hence, *all* rays emanating from O hit the first surface normally and move on undeviated. Therefore, for all practical purposes, we may assume O to be embedded in a medium of refractive index n_2. A perfect (virtual) image of O is formed at I.

3.8.1 The Oil Immersion Objective

The principle of aplanatism has a very important application in microscope objectives where one is interested in having as wide a pencil of light as possible without causing any aberrations. We refer to the optical system shown in Fig. 3.14. The hemispherical lens L_1 is placed in contact with a drop of oil whose refractive index is the same as that of the lens. The object O is immersed in the oil and the distance OC is made equal to $n_3|R_1|/n_2$ so that the point O is the aplanatic point with respect to the hemispherical surface, which is why a perfect (virtual) image is formed at I_1. Now L_2 is an aplanatic lens with respect to the object point at I_1 and therefore, a perfect image of I_1 is formed at I. The lateral magnifications caused by the refracting surface R_1 and lens L_2 are

$$m_1 = \frac{n_2(I_1P_1)}{n_3(OP_1)} \tag{3.27}$$

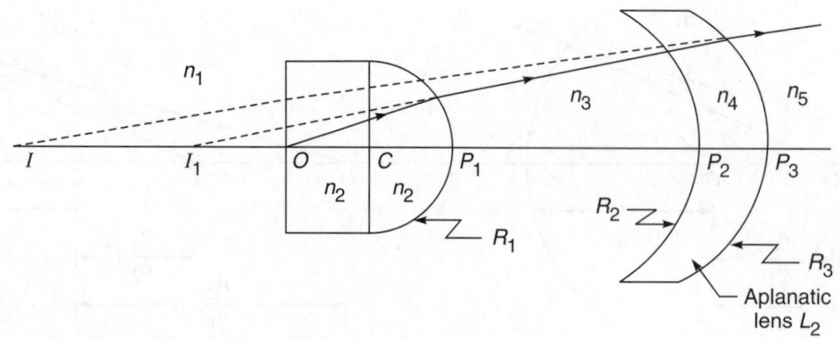

Figure 3.14
The oil immersion objective. The points O and I_1 are the aplanatic points corresponding to the hemispherical surface of radius R_1; the lens L_2 acts as an aplanatic lens for the (virtual) object at I_1.

and $$m_2 = \frac{n_4(IP_3)}{n_5(I_1P_3)} \tag{3.28}$$

Thus, the oil immersion objective reduces considerably the angular divergence of the rays and results in an increase in lateral magnification without introducing spherical aberration. We should, however, mention that a perfect image is formed only of one point and, therefore, nearby points have some aberrations. Moreover, oil immersion objectives have a certain degree of chromatic aberration.

3.9 The Cartesian Oval

In general, for two points to form perfect images of each other, the refracting surface is not, in general, spherical. Figure 3.15 shows the two points O and I such that all rays emanating from O (and allowed by the system) intersect each other at the other point I. Thus the curve SPM shown in Fig. 3.15 is the locus of the point S such that

$$n_1 OS + n_2 SI = \text{constant} \tag{3.29}$$

The refracting surface is obtained by revolving the curve shown in the figure (Fig. 2.38) about the z-axis (see also Problem 2.8). The refracting surface is known as a Cartesian oval.

When the object point is at infinity, the surface becomes an ellipsoid of revolution (see Problem 2.5) and under certain circumstances the surface is spherical; however, the image is then virtual [see Figs. 3.12(a) and (b)].

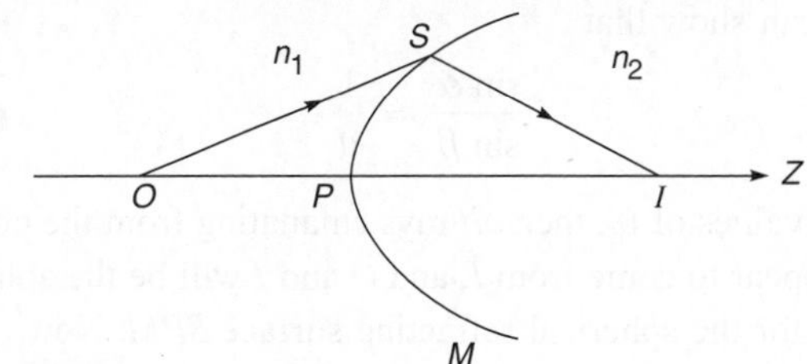

Figure 3.15

The refracting surface (known as the Cartesian oval) is such that all rays emanating from the point O intersect at I.

3.10 Geometrical Proof for the Existence of Aplanatic Points

In this section, we will show the existence of aplanatic points using geometrical considerations. We consider a spherical refracting surface SPM of radius r separating two media of refractive indices n_1 and n_2 (see Fig. 3.16). We will assume $n_2 < n_1$ and define

$$\mu = \frac{n_1}{n_2} \tag{3.30}$$

where $\mu > 1$. The point C represents the centre of the spherical surface SPM. With C as center, we draw two spheres of radii μr and r/μ as shown in Fig. 3.16. Let $IOCP$ represent *any* common diameter of the three spheres intersecting the outer and inner spheres at I and O, respectively. From the point O, we draw an arbitrary line hitting the refracting surface at the point S. We join I and S and extend the line further as SQ.

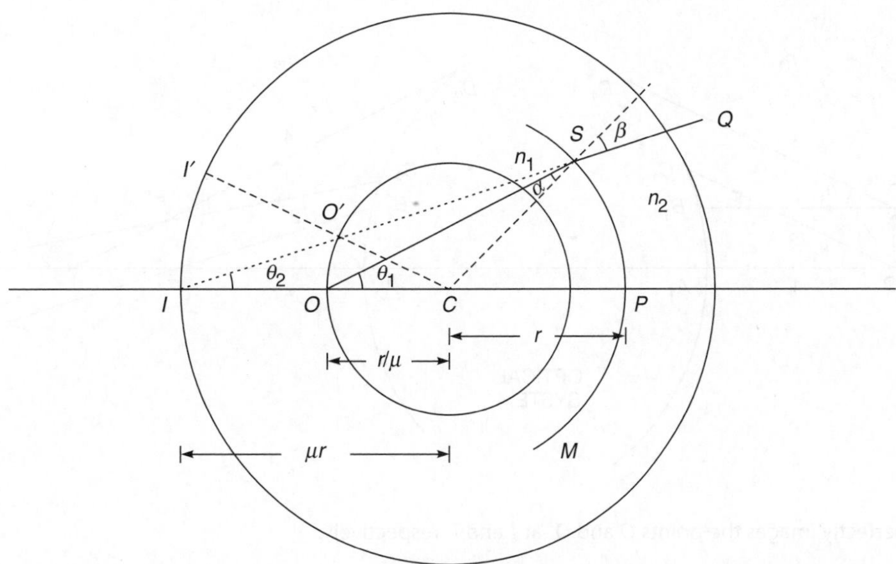

Figure 3.16

Geometrical construction for the derivation of aplanatic points. *SPM* is the refracting the surface of radius *r*. The inner and outer spheres are of radii r/μ and μr, respectively. *O* and *I* are the aplanatic points.

If we can show that

$$\frac{\sin\alpha}{\sin\beta} = \frac{1}{\mu} \tag{3.31}$$

for *all* values of θ_1, then *all* rays emanating from the point O will appear to come from I, and O and I will be the aplanatic points for the spherical refracting surface *SPM*. Now,

$$\frac{IC}{CS} = \frac{\mu r}{r} = \mu \tag{3.32}$$

and

$$\frac{CS}{OC} = \frac{r}{r/\mu} = \mu = \frac{IC}{CS} \tag{3.33}$$

Thus, the two triangles *SOC* and *SIC* are similar, and therefore,

$$\alpha = \theta_2 \quad \text{and} \quad \beta = \angle ISC = \theta_1 \tag{3.34}$$

Now, considering the triangle *SOC*, we have

$$\frac{\sin\alpha}{\sin\theta_1} = \frac{r/\mu}{r} = \frac{1}{\mu} \tag{3.35}$$

and using Eq. (3.34), we get

$$\frac{\sin\alpha}{\sin\beta} = \frac{1}{\mu} = \frac{n_2}{n_1} \tag{3.36}$$

proving that O and I are aplanatic points. We also have

$$\frac{\sin\theta_1}{\sin\theta_2} = \frac{\sin\beta}{\sin\alpha} = \frac{n_1}{n_2} \tag{3.37}$$

It is obvious that the points O' and I' will also be aplanatic and therefore, the image formed by a *small* planar object at O will be sharp even for the off-axis points. The system is said to be free not only from spherical aberration but also from coma. Furthermore, the linear magnification is given by

$$m \approx \frac{I'I}{O'O} \approx \frac{\mu r}{r/\mu} = \mu^2 = \left(\frac{n_1}{n_2}\right)^2 \tag{3.38}$$

3.11 The Sine Condition

LO5

We consider a general optical system as shown in Fig. 3.17. We *assume* that the point O (on the axis of the system) is perfectly imaged at I, i.e., all rays emanating from O intersect each other at I. This implies that the optical system has no spherical aberration corresponding to O. We next consider a slightly off-axis point O' (directly above O) and, according to the *sine-condition*, for O' to be sharply imaged at I we must have*

$$\frac{n_1 \sin\theta_1}{n_2 \sin\theta_2} = \frac{y_2}{y_1} = \text{linear magnification} \tag{3.39}$$

where θ_1 and θ_2 are defined in Fig. 3.17. Thus, the linear magnification will be constant if the ratio $\sin\theta_1/\sin\theta_2$ is constant for all points on the refracting surface and the image will be free from the aberration known as **coma**. It is of interest to note that according to Eq. (3.39) perfect imaging of (nearby) *off-axis points* requires a condition to be satisfied by rays from an *on-axis point*. Also, when the condition given by Eq. (3.39) is satisfied, sharp imaging of a nearby point on the axis (like O_1) is *not* obtained; indeed the condition for sharp imaging of O and O_1 is quite different.

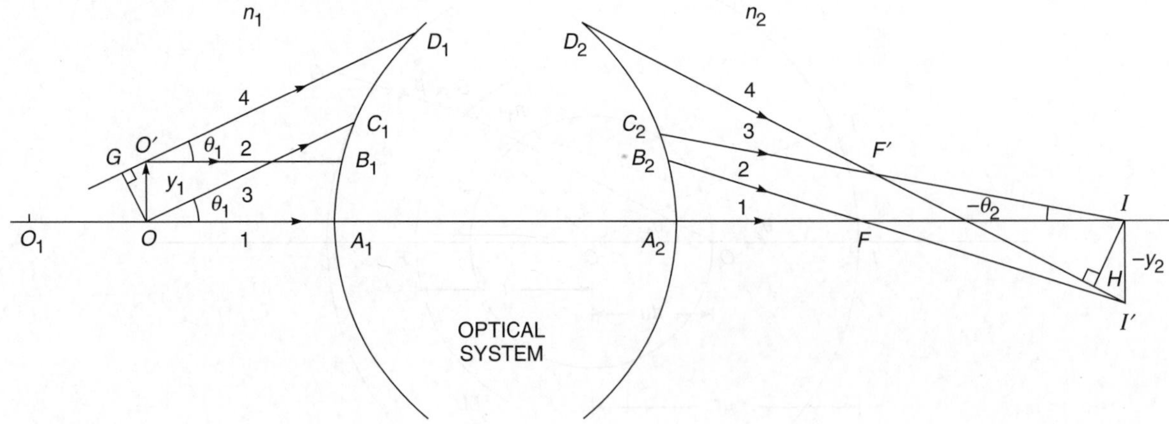

Figure 3.17
The optical system perfectly images the points O and O' at I and I, respectively.

* It may be noted that if we use Eqs. (3.37) and (3.38), we get

$$m = \frac{y_2}{y_1} = \left(\frac{n_1}{n_2}\right)^2 = \frac{n_1 \sin\theta_1}{n_2 \sin\theta_2}$$

consistent with Eq. (3.39).

3.11.1 Proof of the Sine Condition*

We refer to Fig. 3.17. We will assume that the axial point O is perfectly imaged at I and will use Fermat's principle to determine the condition for perfect imaging of the nearby off-axis point O'. The ray $O'B_1$ is parallel to the ray OA_1 and the ray $O'D_1$ is parallel to OC_1. Now, since I is the image of the point O, we have

$$OPL[OA_1A_2I] = OPL[OC_1C_2I] \tag{3.40}$$

where OPL stands for the *optical path length*. Further

$$OPL[O'B_1B_2I'] = OPL[O'D_1D_2I'] \tag{3.41}$$

Now, the rays $O'B_1$ and OA_1 meet at infinity and therefore

$$OPL[O'B_1B_2F] = OPL[OA_1A_2F] \tag{3.42}$$

We next consider the triangle FII'

$$FI' = [FI^2 + |y_2|^2]^{1/2} = FI\left[1 + \frac{1}{2}\frac{|y_2|^2}{FI^2}\right]$$

Thus,

$$FI' \approx FI \tag{3.43}$$

where we are assuming that $|y_2|$ is small enough so that terms proportional to $|y_2|^2$ can be neglected. If we add Eqs. (3.42) and (3.43), we get

$$\begin{aligned} OPL[O'B_1B_2I'] &= OPL[OA_1A_2I] \\ &= OPL[OC_1C_2I] \end{aligned} \tag{3.44}$$

Since the left-hand side of the above equation is $OPL[O'D_1D_2I']$, we get

$$OPL[O'D_1D_2I'] = OPL[OC_1C_2I] \tag{3.45}$$

Now, the rays 3 and 4 meet at infinity and intersect at F', so that

$$OPL[GD_1D_2F'] = OPL\ [OC_1CF'] \tag{3.46}$$

where the point G is the foot of the perpendicular drawn from the point O on ray 4. We subtract Eq. (3.45) from Eq. (3.46) to obtain

$$OPL[F'I'] - OPL[GO'] = OPL[F'I] \tag{3.47}$$

or

$$n_2(F'I') - n_1(GO') = n_2(F'I)$$

or

$$n_1(GO') = n_2(F'I' - F'I) \tag{3.48}$$

But

$$GO' = y_1 \sin\theta_1 \tag{3.49}$$

and

$$F'I' - F'I \approx HI' \approx (-y_2)\sin(-\theta_2) \tag{3.50}$$

where H is the foot of the perpendicular from the point I on ray 4. Substituting the above two equations in Eq. (3.48), we get

$$\frac{n_1\sin\theta_1}{n_2\sin\theta_2} = \frac{y_2}{y_1} = \text{linear magnification} \tag{3.51}$$

showing that the linear magnification is constant if the ratio $\sin\theta_1/\sin\theta_2$ is constant for all points on the refracting surface. The sine condition is of extensive use in the design of optical systems.

SUMMARY

- Consider refraction at a spherical surface separating two media of refractive indices n_1 and n_2. For a point object at a distance $|u|$ on the left, the paraxial image is formed at a distance v where

$$\frac{n_2}{v} - \frac{n_1}{u} = \frac{n_2 - n_1}{R}$$

The sign convention is as follows:

1. The rays are always incident from the left on the refracting surface.
2. All distances to the right of the refracting surface are positive and distances to the left of the refracting surface are negative.

- For a thin lens of refractive index n (placed in air), let R_1 and R_2 be the radii of curvature of the left and right surfaces of the lens; then the image distance is given by

$$\frac{1}{v} - \frac{1}{u} = (n-1)\left(\frac{1}{R_1} - \frac{1}{R_2}\right)$$

which is usually referred to as the 'thin-lens formula'; the quantity f is known as the focal length of the lens.

- If refractive index of the medium is more than the refractive index of double concave or convex lens, then the focal length of the lens becomes negative.
- For a given spherical surface, there are two points for which *all* rays emanating from one point intersect each other at the other point. This point is at a distance equal to $n_2|R|/n_1$ from the center of the spherical surface and a virtual image is formed at a distance of $n_1|R|/n_2$ from the center. The two points are said to be the *aplanatic points* of the sphere and are utilized in the construction of aplanatic lenses.
- For two points to form perfect images of each other, the refracting surface is a Cartesian oval.

* For a rigorous proof of the sine condition, See Ref. 3.3.

PROBLEMS

3.1 **(a)** Consider a thin biconvex lens (as shown in Fig. 3.18) made of a material whose refractive index is 1.5. The radii of curvature of the first and second surfaces (R_1 and R_2) are +100 and –60 cm, respectively. The lens is placed in air (i.e., $n_1 = n_3 = 1$). For an object at a distance of 100 cm from the lens, determine the position and linear magnification of the (paraxial) image. Also calculate x_1 and x_2 and verify Newton's formula [Eq. (3.20)].

[**Ans:** $x_1 = -25$ cm and $x_2 = +225$ cm]

(b) Repeat the calculations of the above problem when the object is at a distance of 50 cm.

3.2 Consider a thin lens (made of a material of refractive index n_2) having different media on the two sides; let n_1 and n_3 be the refractive indices of the media on the left and on the right of the lens, respectively. Using Eq. (3.5) and considering successive refractions at the two surfaces, derive Eq. (3.14).

3.3 Referring again to Fig. 3.18, assume a biconvex lens with $|R_1| = 100$ cm, $|R_2| = 60$ cm with $n_1 = 1.0$ but $n_3 = 1.6$. For $u = -50$ cm determine the position of the (paraxial) image. Also determine the first and second principal foci and verify Newton's formula. Draw the ray diagram.

[**Ans:** $x_1 = 250$ cm, $x_2 = 576$ cm]

3.4 **(a)** In Fig. 3.18, assume the convex lens to be replaced by a (thin) biconcave lens with $|R_1| = 100$ cm and $|R_2| = 60$ cm. Assume $n_1 = n_3 = 1$ and $n_2 = 1.5$. Determine the position of the image and draw an approximate ray diagram for $u = -100$ cm.

(b) In (a), assume $n_1 = n_3 = 1.5$ and $n_2 = 1.3$. Repeat the calculations and draw the ray diagram. What is the qualitative difference between the systems in (a) and (b)?

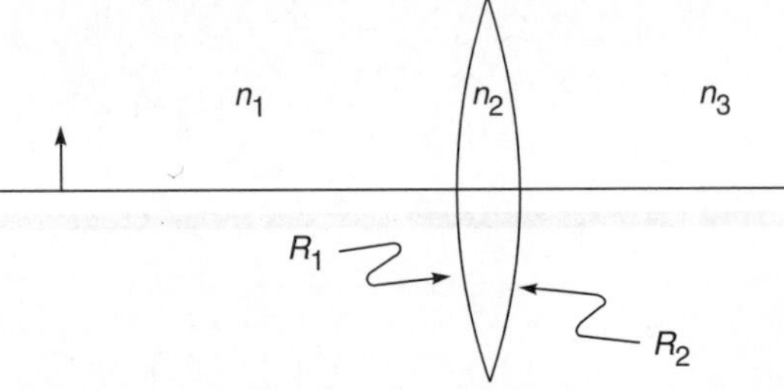

Figure 3.18

3.5 Consider an object of height 1 cm placed at a distance of 24 cm from a convex lens of focal length 15 cm (see Fig. 3.19). A concave lens of focal length –20 cm is placed beyond the convex lens at a distance of 25 cm. Draw the ray diagram and determine the position and size of the final image.

[**Ans:** Real image at a distance of 60 cm from the concave lens.]

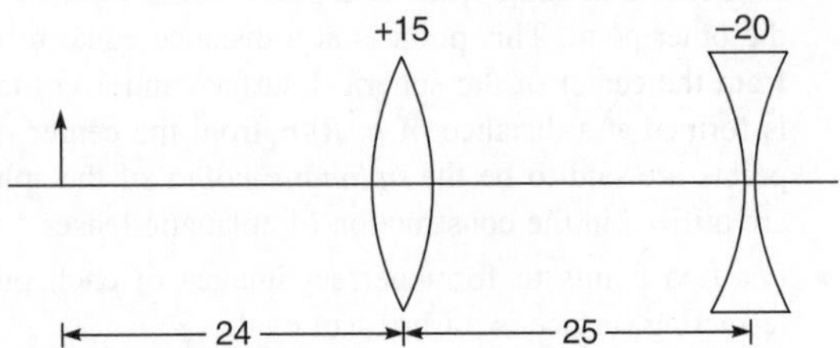

Figure 3.19

An optical system consisting of a thin convex and a thin concave lens. All distances are measured in centimeters.

3.6 Consider a thick biconvex lens whose magnitude of the radii of curvature of the first and second surfaces are 45 and 30 cm, respectively. The thickness of the lens is 5 cm and the refractive index of the material, it is made of, is 1.5. For an object of height 1 cm at distance of 90 cm from the first surface, determine the position and size of the image. Draw the ray diagram for the axial point of the object.

[**Ans:** Real image at a distance of 60 cm from the second surface.]

3.7 In Problem 3.6, assume that the second surface is silvered so that it acts like a concave mirror. For an object of height 1 cm at a distance of 90 cm from the first surface, determine the position and size of the image and draw the ray diagram.

[**Ans:** Real image at a distance of about 6.2 cm from the first surface. (Remember the sign convention.)]

3.8 Consider a sphere of radius 20 cm of refractive index 1.6 (see Fig. 3.20). Show that the paraxial focal point is at a distance of 6.7 cm from the point P_2.

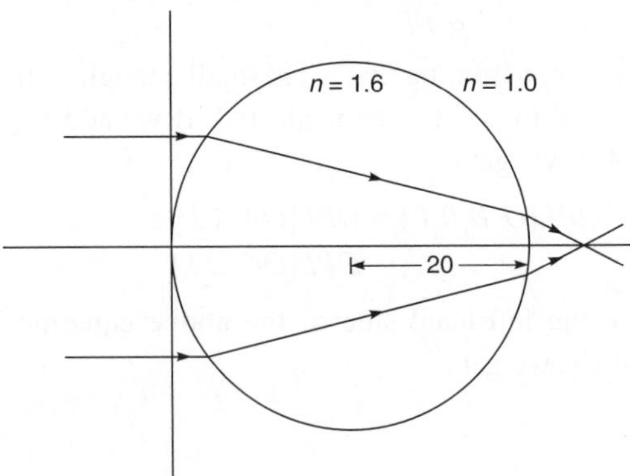

Figure 3.20

3.9 Consider a hemisphere of radius 20 cm and refractive index 1.5. Show that parallel rays will focus at a point 40 cm from P_2 (see Fig. 3.21).

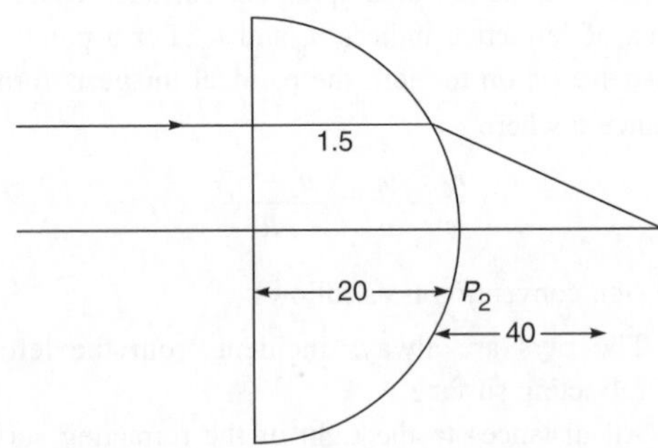

Figure 3.21

3.10 Consider a lens of thickness 1 cm, made of a material of refractive index 1.5, placed in air. The radii of curvature of the first and second surfaces are +4 cm and –4 cm, respectively. Determine the point at which parallel rays will focus.

[**Ans:** At a distance of about 3.55 cm from the second surface.]

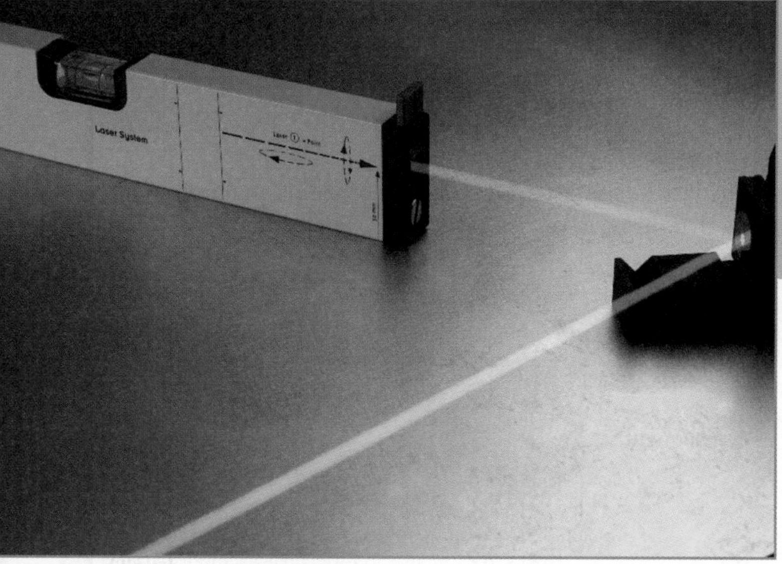

CHAPTER

4

In dealing with a system of lenses we simply chase the ray through the succession of lenses. That is all there is to it.

—Richard Feynman in *Feynman Lectures on Physics*

The Matrix Method in Paraxial Optics

LEARNING OBJECTIVES

After reading this chapter, the reader should be able to:

LO 1: *calculate the effect of translation and refraction on paraxial rays.*

LO 2: *define unit planes using elements of system matrix.*

LO 3: *obtain the position of nodal points in an optical system.*

LO 4: *analyze the combination of lenses using matrix formulation.*

4.1 Introduction*

Let us consider a ray *PQ* incident on a refracting surface *SQS′* separating two media of refractive indices n_1 and n_2 (see Fig. 4.1). Let *NQN′* denote the normal to the surface. The direction of the refracted ray is completely determined from the following conditions:

(a) the incident ray, the refracted ray and the normal lie in the same plane; and

(b) if θ_1 and θ_2 represent the angles of incidence and refraction respectively, then

$$\frac{\sin\theta_1}{\sin\theta_2} = \frac{n_2}{n_1} \qquad (4.1)$$

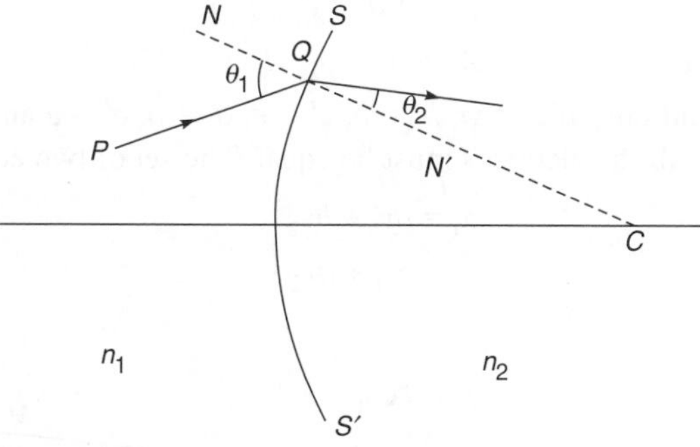

Figure 4.1

Refraction of a ray by a surface *SQS′* which separates two media of refractive indices n_1 and n_2; *NQN′* denotes the normal at the point *Q*. If the refracting surface is spherical then the normal *NQN′* will pass through the centre of curvature *C*.

Above Image: A laser spirit level reflecting a beam off a mirror; Photograph courtesy McGraw Hill Digital Asset Library

* The author thanks Professor K. Thyagarajan for his help in writing this chapter.

Optical systems, in general, are made up of a large number of refracting surfaces (like in a combination of lenses) and any ray can be traced through the system by using the above conditions. In order to obtain the position of the final image due to such a system, one has to calculate step-by-step the position of the image due to each surface and this image will act as an object for the next surface. Such a step-by-step analysis becomes complicated as the number of elements of an optical system increases. We shall, in this chapter, develop the matrix method which can be applied with ease under such situations. This method indeed lends itself to direct use in computers for tracing rays through complicated optical systems.

Before we describe the matrix formulation of geometric optics, it is necessary to mention the rule of matrix multiplication and the use of matrices for solving linear equations. A $(m \times n)$ matrix has m rows and n columns and has $(m \times n)$ elements; thus the matrix

$$A = \begin{pmatrix} a & b & c \\ d & e & f \end{pmatrix} \tag{4.2}$$

has 2 rows and 3 columns and has $2 \times 3 = 6$ elements. A $(m \times n)$ matrix can be multiplied only to a $(n \times p)$ matrix to obtain a $m \times p$ matrix. Let

$$B = \begin{pmatrix} g \\ h \\ i \end{pmatrix} \tag{4.3}$$

represent a (3×1) matrix. Then the product

$$AB = \begin{pmatrix} a & b & c \\ d & e & f \end{pmatrix}\begin{pmatrix} g \\ h \\ i \end{pmatrix} = \begin{pmatrix} (ag + bh + ci) \\ (dg + eh + fi) \end{pmatrix} \tag{4.4}$$

will be a (2×1) matrix, and the product BA has no meaning. If we define a (2×3) matrix

$$A' = \begin{pmatrix} a' & b' & c' \\ d' & e' & f' \end{pmatrix}$$

then $\qquad A' = A$

if and only if $a' = a$, $b' = b$, $c' = c$, $d' = d$, $e' = e$ and $f' = f$, i.e., all the elements must be equal. The set of two equations

$$\left.\begin{aligned} x_1 &= ay_1 + by_2 \\ x_2 &= cy_1 + dy_2 \end{aligned}\right\} \tag{4.5}$$

can be written in the following form:

$$\begin{pmatrix} x_1 \\ x_2 \end{pmatrix} = \begin{pmatrix} (ay_1 + by_2) \\ (cy_1 + dy_2) \end{pmatrix} = \begin{pmatrix} a & b \\ c & d \end{pmatrix}\begin{pmatrix} y_1 \\ y_2 \end{pmatrix} \tag{4.6}$$

The last step follows from the rule of matrix multiplication. Further, if we have

$$\text{and} \quad \left.\begin{aligned} y_1 &= ez_1 + fz_2 \\ y_2 &= gz_1 + hz_2 \end{aligned}\right\} \tag{4.7}$$

then

$$\begin{pmatrix} y_1 \\ y_2 \end{pmatrix} = \begin{pmatrix} e & f \\ g & h \end{pmatrix}\begin{pmatrix} z_1 \\ z_2 \end{pmatrix} \tag{4.8}$$

Consequently,

$$\begin{pmatrix} x_1 \\ x_2 \end{pmatrix} = \begin{pmatrix} a & b \\ c & d \end{pmatrix}\begin{pmatrix} e & f \\ g & h \end{pmatrix}\begin{pmatrix} z_1 \\ z_2 \end{pmatrix} \tag{4.9}$$

or

$$X = BZ, \tag{4.10}$$

where X and Z represent (2×1) matrices:

$$X \equiv \begin{pmatrix} x_1 \\ x_2 \end{pmatrix}, \; Z \equiv \begin{pmatrix} z_1 \\ z_2 \end{pmatrix}, \tag{4.11}$$

and B represents a (2×2) square matrix

$$\begin{aligned} B &= \begin{pmatrix} a & b \\ c & d \end{pmatrix}\begin{pmatrix} e & f \\ g & h \end{pmatrix} \\ &= \begin{pmatrix} [ae + bg] & [af + bh] \\ [ce + dg] & [cf + dh] \end{pmatrix} \end{aligned} \tag{4.12}$$

Equations (4.9) and (4.12) tell us that

$$\text{and} \quad \left.\begin{aligned} x_1 &= (ae + bg)z_1 + (af + bh)z_2 \\ x_2 &= (ce + dg)z_1 + (df + dh)z_2 \end{aligned}\right\} \tag{4.13}$$

which can be verified by direct substitution. We will now use the matrix method to trace paraxial rays through a cylindrically symmetric optical system.

4.2 The Matrix Method

LO1

We will consider a cylindrically symmetric optical system similar to the one shown in Fig. 4.2. The axis of symmetry is chosen as the z-axis. We will be considering only paraxial rays in this chapter; non-paraxial rays lead to what are known as aberrations which will be discussed in Chapter 5.

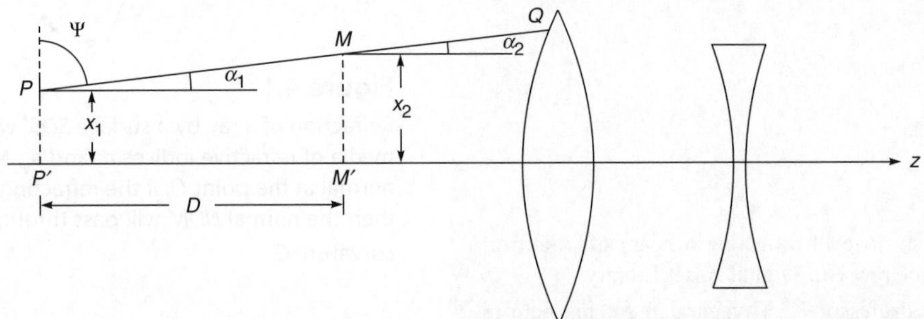

Figure 4.2

In a homogeneous medium the ray travels in a straight line.

In the paraxial approximation, we may confine ourselves to rays which pass through the axis of the system; these rays remain confined to a single plane. Such a ray can be specified by its distance from the axis of the system and the angle made by the ray with the axis; for example, in Fig. 4.2, the point P on the ray is at a distance x_1 from the axis and makes an angle α_1 with the axis. The quantities (x_1, α_1) represent the coordinates of the ray. However, instead of specifying the angle made by the ray with the z-axis, we will specify the quantity.

$$\lambda = n \cos \psi \; (= n \sin \alpha)$$

which represents the product of the refractive index with the sine of the angle that the ray makes with the z-axis this quantity is known as the optical direction cosine.

Now, when a ray propagates through an optical system, it undergoes only two operations: *(a)* translation and *(b)* refraction. The rays undergo translation when they propagate through a homogeneous medium as in the region PQ (see Fig. 4.2). However, when it strikes an interface of two media, it undergoes refraction. We will now study the effect of translation and of refraction on the coordinates of the ray.

(a) Effect of Translation Consider a ray traveling in a homogeneous medium of refractive index n_1 which is initially at a distance x_1 from the z-axis and makes an angle α_1 with the axis (see point P in Fig. 4.2). Let (x_2, α_2) represent the coordinates of the ray at the point M (see Fig. 4.2). Since the medium is homogeneous, the ray travels in a straight line and, therefore,

$$\alpha_2 = \alpha_1 \tag{4.14}$$

Further, if PP' and MM' are perpendiculars on the axis and if $P'M' = D$, then

$$x_2 = x_1 + D \tan \alpha_1 \tag{4.15}$$

Since we are interested only in paraxial rays, α_1 is very small and hence we can make use of the approximation $\tan \alpha_1 \simeq \alpha_1$, where α_1 is measured in radians. Thus, Eq. (4.15) reduces to

$$x_2 \simeq x_1 + \alpha_1 D \tag{4.16}$$

If
$$\lambda_1 = n_1 \alpha_1 \tag{4.17}$$

and
$$\lambda_2 = n_2 \alpha_2 \tag{4.18}$$

then, using Eqs. (4.14) and (4.17), we get

$$\left.\begin{aligned} \lambda_2 &= \lambda_1 \\ x_2 &= x_1 + \frac{D}{n_1}\lambda_1, \end{aligned}\right\} \tag{4.19}$$

which may be combined into the following matrix equation:

$$\begin{pmatrix} \lambda_2 \\ x_2 \end{pmatrix} = \begin{pmatrix} 1 & 0 \\ D/n_1 & 1 \end{pmatrix} \begin{pmatrix} \lambda_1 \\ x_1 \end{pmatrix} \tag{4.20}$$

Thus, if a ray is initially specified by a (2×1) matrix with elements λ_1 and x_1, then the effect of translation through a distance D in a homogeneous medium of refractive index n_1, is completely given by the 2×2 matrix

$$T = \begin{pmatrix} 1 & 0 \\ D/n_1 & 1 \end{pmatrix} \tag{4.21}$$

and the final ray is given by Eq. (4.20). The matrix T is known as the translation matrix. Notice that

$$\det T = \begin{vmatrix} 1 & 0 \\ D/n_1 & 1 \end{vmatrix} = 1 \tag{4.22}$$

(b) Effect of Refraction We will now determine the matrix which would represent the effect of refraction through a spherical surface of radius of curvature R. Consider the ray AP intersecting a spherical surface (separating two media of refractive indices n_1 and n_2 respectively) at the point P and getting refracted along PB (see Fig. 4.3). If θ_1 and θ_2 are the angles made by the incident and the refracted ray with the normal to the surface at P (i.e., with the line joining P to the centre of curvature C), then according to Snell's law

$$n_1 \sin \theta_1 = n_2 \sin \theta_2 \tag{4.23}$$

Since we are dealing with paraxial rays, one can make use of the approximation $\sin \theta \simeq \theta$. Thus, Eq. (4.23) reduces to

$$n_1 \theta_1 \simeq n_2 \theta_2 \tag{4.24}$$

From Fig. 4.3 it follows that

$$\theta_1 = \phi_1 + \alpha_1 \quad \text{and} \quad \theta_2 = \phi_1 + \alpha_2 \tag{4.25}$$

where α_1, α_2 and ϕ_1 are respectively the angles that the incident ray, the refracted ray and the normal to the surface make with the z-axis. Also, since ϕ_1 is small, we may write

$$\phi_1 = \frac{x}{R} \tag{4.26}$$

Now, from Eqs. (4.24) and (4.25), we get

$$n_1(\phi_1 + \alpha_1) \simeq n_2(\phi_1 + \alpha_2)$$

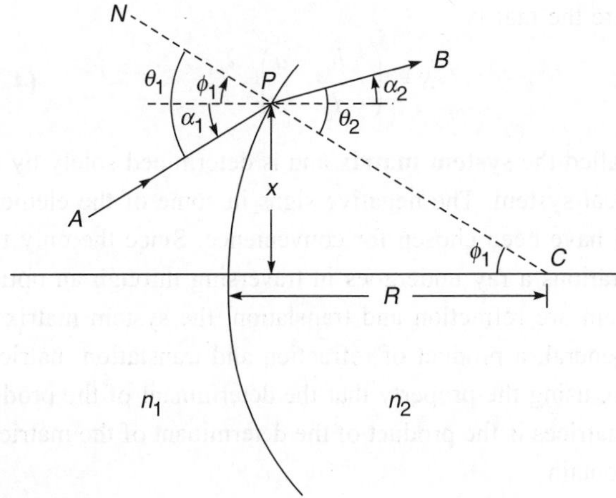

Figure 4.3
The refraction of a ray at a spherical surface.

or

$$n_2\alpha_2 \simeq n_1\alpha_1 - \frac{n_2 - n_1}{R}x \tag{4.27}$$

where we have used Eq. (4.26). Thus,

$$\lambda_2 = \lambda_1 - Px \tag{4.28}$$

where
$$P = \frac{n_2 - n_1}{R} \tag{4.29}$$

is known as the **power of the refracting surface**. Also, since the height of the ray at P, before and after refraction, is the same (i.e., $x_2 = x_1$) we obtain, for the refracted ray,

$$\begin{pmatrix}\lambda_2\\ x_2\end{pmatrix} = \begin{pmatrix}1 & -P\\ 0 & 1\end{pmatrix}\begin{pmatrix}\lambda_1\\ x_1\end{pmatrix} \tag{4.30}$$

Thus, refraction through a spherical surface can be characterized by a 2 × 2 matrix:

$$\mathscr{R} = \begin{pmatrix}1 & -P\\ 0 & 1\end{pmatrix} \tag{4.31}$$

It may be noted here that

$$\det \mathscr{R} = \begin{vmatrix}1 & -P\\ 0 & 1\end{vmatrix} = 1 \tag{4.32}$$

In general, an optical system made up of a series of lenses, can be characterized by the refraction and translation matrices.

If a ray is specified by $\begin{pmatrix}\lambda_1\\ x_1\end{pmatrix}$ when it enters an optical system and is specified by $\begin{pmatrix}\lambda_2\\ x_2\end{pmatrix}$ when it leaves the system, then one can, in general, write

$$\begin{pmatrix}\lambda_2\\ x_2\end{pmatrix} = \begin{pmatrix}b & -a\\ -d & c\end{pmatrix}\begin{pmatrix}\lambda_1\\ x_1\end{pmatrix} \tag{4.33}$$

where the matrix

$$S = \begin{pmatrix}b & -a\\ -d & c\end{pmatrix} \tag{4.34}$$

is called the **system matrix** and is determined solely by the optical system. The negative signs in some of the elements of S have been chosen for convenience. Since the only two operations a ray undergoes in traversing through an optical system are refraction and translation, the system matrix is, in general, a product of refraction and translation matrices. Also, using the property that the determinant of the product of matrices is the product of the determinant of the matrices, we obtain

$$\det S = 1 \tag{4.35}$$

i.e.,
$$bc - ad = 1 \tag{4.36}$$

We should mention here that the quantities b and c are dimensionless. The quantities a and P have the dimension of inverse length and the quantity d has the dimension of length. In general, the units will not be given; however, it will be implied that a and P are in cm^{-1} and d is in cm.

4.2.1 Imaging by a Spherical Refracting Surface

As a simple illustration of the use of the matrix method, we consider imaging by a spherical surface separating two media of refractive indices n_1 and n_2 (see Fig. 4.4); the same problem was discussed in the previous chapter using the standard geometrical method. Let (λ_1, x_1), (λ', x'), (λ'', x'') and (λ_2, x_2) represent the coordinates of the ray at O, A' (just before refraction), A'' (just after refraction) and at I respectively.

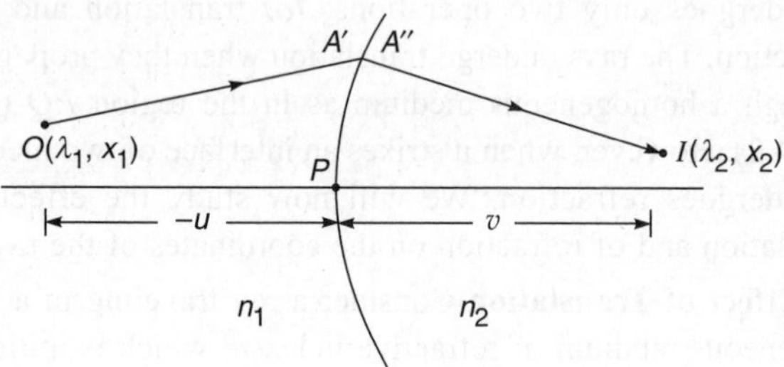

Figure 4.4
Imaging by a spherical refracting surface separating two media of refractive indices n_1 and n_2.

We will be using the analytical geometry sign convention so that the coordinates on the left of the point P are negative and coordinates on the right of P are positive (see Sec. 3.2.1). Thus,

$$\begin{pmatrix}\lambda'\\ x'\end{pmatrix} = \begin{pmatrix}1 & 0\\ -u/n_1 & 1\end{pmatrix}\begin{pmatrix}\lambda_1\\ x_1\end{pmatrix}$$

$$\begin{pmatrix}\lambda''\\ x''\end{pmatrix} = \begin{pmatrix}1 & -P\\ 0 & 1\end{pmatrix}\begin{pmatrix}\lambda'\\ x'\end{pmatrix}$$

$$\begin{pmatrix}\lambda_2\\ x_2\end{pmatrix} = \begin{pmatrix}1 & 0\\ v/n_2 & 1\end{pmatrix}\begin{pmatrix}\lambda''\\ x''\end{pmatrix}$$

or

$$\begin{pmatrix}\lambda_2\\ x_2\end{pmatrix} = \begin{pmatrix}1 & 0\\ v/n_2 & 1\end{pmatrix}\begin{pmatrix}1 & -P\\ 0 & 1\end{pmatrix}\begin{pmatrix}1 & 0\\ -u/n_1 & 1\end{pmatrix}\begin{pmatrix}\lambda_1\\ x_1\end{pmatrix}$$

Simple manipulations give

$$\begin{pmatrix}\lambda_2\\ x_2\end{pmatrix} = \begin{pmatrix}1+\dfrac{Pu}{n_1} & -P\\ \dfrac{v}{n_2}\left(1+\dfrac{Pu}{n_1}\right)-\dfrac{u}{n_1} & \left(1-\dfrac{vP}{n_2}\right)\end{pmatrix}\begin{pmatrix}\lambda_1\\ x_1\end{pmatrix} \tag{4.37}$$

from which we obtain

$$x_2 = \left[\frac{v}{n_2}\left(1+\frac{Pu}{n_1}\right)-\frac{u}{n_1}\right]\lambda_1 + \left[1-\frac{vP}{n_2}\right]x_1 \quad \textbf{(4.38)}$$

For a ray emanating from an axial object point (i.e., for $x_1 = 0$) the image plane is determined by the condition $x_2 = 0$. Thus Eq. (4.38) the coefficient of λ_1 should vanish and, therefore,

$$\frac{u}{n_1} = \frac{v}{n_2}\left(1+\frac{Pu}{n_1}\right)$$

or

$$\frac{n_2}{v} - \frac{n_1}{u} = P = \frac{n_2 - n_1}{R} \quad \textbf{(4.39)}$$

which is the same as derived in the previous chapter. Hence, on the image plane

$$\begin{pmatrix}\lambda_2\\ x_2\end{pmatrix} = \begin{pmatrix} 1+\dfrac{Pu}{n_1} & -P \\ 0 & 1-\dfrac{vP}{n_2}\end{pmatrix}\begin{pmatrix}\lambda_1\\ x_1\end{pmatrix} \quad \textbf{(4.40)}$$

giving $\quad x_2 = \left(1-\dfrac{vP}{n_2}\right)x_1$

Thus, the magnification is given by

$$m = \frac{x_2}{x_1} = 1 - \frac{vP}{n_2}$$

which on using Eq. (4.39) gives

$$m = \frac{n_1 v}{n_2 u}$$

which is consistent with Eq. (3.23).

4.2.2 Imaging by a Coaxial Optical System

We will next derive the position of the image plane for an object plane, which is at distance $-D_1$ from the first refracting surface of the optical system (see Fig. 4.5). Let the image be formed at a distance D_2 from the last refracting surface. Now, according to our sign convention, for points on the left of a refracting surface, the distances will be negative and for points on the right of the refracting surface the distances will be positive, thus D_1 is an intrinsically negative quantity. Further, if D_2 is found to be positive the image is real and is formed on the right of the refracting surface; on the other hand, if D_2 is found to be negative, the image will be virtual and will be formed on the left of the last refracting surface.

Let us consider a ray $O'P$ starting from the point O' which lies in the object plane. Let QI' be the ray emerging from the last surface; the point I' is assumed to lie on the image plane—see Fig. 4.5 (the point I is the paraxial image of the point O and the image plane is defined to be the plane which contains the point I and is normal to the axis). Let (λ_1, x_1), (λ', x'), (λ'', x'') and (λ_2, x_2) represent the coordinates of the ray at O', P, Q and I', respectively. Then

$$\left.\begin{aligned}
\begin{pmatrix}\lambda'\\ x'\end{pmatrix} &= \begin{pmatrix}1 & 0\\ -D_1 & 1\end{pmatrix}\begin{pmatrix}\lambda_1\\ x_1\end{pmatrix}\\
\begin{pmatrix}\lambda''\\ x''\end{pmatrix} &= \begin{pmatrix}b & -a\\ -d & c\end{pmatrix}\begin{pmatrix}\lambda'\\ x'\end{pmatrix}\\
\begin{pmatrix}\lambda_2\\ x_2\end{pmatrix} &= \begin{pmatrix}1 & 0\\ D_2 & 1\end{pmatrix}\begin{pmatrix}\lambda''\\ x''\end{pmatrix}
\end{aligned}\right\}$$

Thus,

$$\begin{pmatrix}\lambda_2\\ x_2\end{pmatrix} = \begin{pmatrix}1 & 0\\ D_2 & 1\end{pmatrix}\begin{pmatrix}b & -a\\ -d & c\end{pmatrix}\begin{pmatrix}1 & 0\\ -D_1 & 1\end{pmatrix}\begin{pmatrix}\lambda_1\\ x_1\end{pmatrix} \quad \textbf{(4.41)}$$

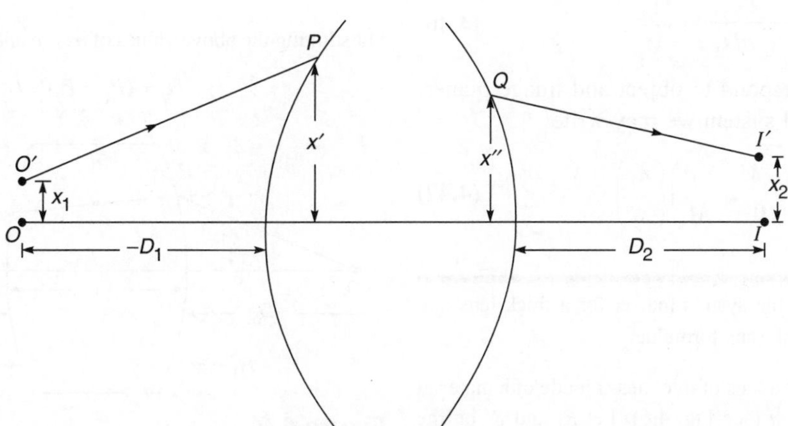

Figure 4.5
The object point O is at a distance $(-D_1)$ from the first refracting surface. The paraxial image is assumed to be formed at a distance D_2 from the last refracting surface.

where the first and the third matrices on the RHS correspond to translations by distances D_2 and $(-D_1)$, respectively (in a medium of refractive index unity); the second matrix correspond to the system matrix of the optical system. Carrying out the matrix multiplications, we obtain

$$\begin{pmatrix} \lambda_2 \\ x_2 \end{pmatrix} = \begin{pmatrix} b + aD_1 & -a \\ bD_2 + aD_1D_2 - cD_1 - d & c - aD_2 \end{pmatrix} \begin{pmatrix} \lambda_1 \\ x_1 \end{pmatrix} \tag{4.42}$$

Thus,

$$x_2 = (bD_2 + aD_1D_2 - cD_1 - d)\lambda_1 + (c - aD_2)x_1$$

For a ray emanating from the axial object point (i.e., for $x_1 = 0$) the image plane is determined by the condition $x_2 = 0$. Thus, for the image plane we must have

$$bD_2 + aD_1D_2 - cD_1 - d = 0 \tag{4.43}$$

which would give us the relationship between the distances D_1 and D_2. Thus, corresponding to the image plane, we have

$$\begin{pmatrix} \lambda_2 \\ x_2 \end{pmatrix} = \begin{pmatrix} b + aD_1 & -a \\ 0 & c - aD_2 \end{pmatrix} \begin{pmatrix} \lambda_1 \\ x_1 \end{pmatrix} \tag{4.44}$$

For $x_2 \neq 0$, we obtain

$$x_2 = (c - aD_2)x_1$$

Consequently, the magnification of the system, $M \left(= \dfrac{x_2}{x_1}\right)$ would be given by

$$M = \frac{x_2}{x_1} = c - aD_2 \tag{4.45}$$

Further, since

$$\begin{vmatrix} b + aD_1 & -a \\ 0 & c - aD_2 \end{vmatrix} = 1$$

we obtain

$$b + aD_1 = \frac{1}{c - aD_2} = \frac{1}{M} \tag{4.46}$$

Hence, if x_1 and x_2 correspond to object and image planes, then for a general optical system we may write

$$\begin{pmatrix} \lambda_2 \\ x_2 \end{pmatrix} = \begin{pmatrix} 1/M & -a \\ 0 & M \end{pmatrix} \begin{pmatrix} \lambda_1 \\ x_1 \end{pmatrix} \tag{4.47}$$

EXAMPLE 4.1 Obtain the system matrix for a thick lens and derive the thin lens and thick lens formulae.

Solution: Let us consider a lens of thickness t made of a material of relative refractive index n (see Fig. 4.6). Let R_1 and R_2 be the radii of curvatures of the two surfaces. The ray is assumed to strike the first surface of the lens at P and emerge from the point Q; let the coordinates of the ray at P and Q be

$$\begin{pmatrix} \lambda_1 \\ x_1 \end{pmatrix} \quad \text{and} \quad \begin{pmatrix} \lambda_2 \\ x_2 \end{pmatrix} \tag{4.48}$$

where λ_1 and λ_2 are the optical direction cosines of the ray at P and Q, x_1 and x_2 are the distances of the points P and Q from the axis (see Fig. 4.6). The ray, in propagating from P to Q, undergoes two refractions [one at the first surface (whose radius of curvature is R_1) and the other at the second surface (whose radius of curvature is R_2)] and a translation through a distance* t in a medium of refractive index n. Thus,

$$\begin{pmatrix} \lambda_2 \\ x_2 \end{pmatrix} = \begin{pmatrix} 1 & -P_2 \\ 0 & 1 \end{pmatrix} \begin{pmatrix} 1 & 0 \\ t/n & 1 \end{pmatrix} \begin{pmatrix} 1 & -P_1 \\ 0 & 1 \end{pmatrix} \begin{pmatrix} \lambda_1 \\ x_1 \end{pmatrix} \tag{4.49}$$

where

$$P_1 = \frac{n-1}{R_1} \quad \text{and} \quad P_2 = \frac{1-n}{R_2} = -\frac{n-1}{R_2} \tag{4.50}$$

represent the powers of the two refracting surfaces. Thus, our system matrix is given by

$$S = \begin{pmatrix} b & -a \\ -d & c \end{pmatrix} = \begin{pmatrix} 1 & -P_2 \\ 0 & 1 \end{pmatrix} \begin{pmatrix} 1 & 0 \\ t/n & 1 \end{pmatrix} \begin{pmatrix} 1 & -P_1 \\ 0 & 1 \end{pmatrix}$$

$$= \begin{pmatrix} 1 - \dfrac{P_2 t}{n} & -P_1 - P_2\left(1 - \dfrac{t}{n}P_1\right) \\ \dfrac{t}{n} & 1 - \dfrac{t}{n}P_1 \end{pmatrix} \tag{4.51}$$

For a thin lens, $t \to 0$ and the system matrix takes the following form:

$$S = \begin{pmatrix} 1 & -P_1 - P_2 \\ 0 & 1 \end{pmatrix} \tag{4.52}$$

Thus for a thin lens,

$$a = P_1 + P_2,\ b = 1,\ c = 1 \quad \text{and} \quad d = 0 \tag{4.53}$$

Substituting the above values of a, b, c and d in Eq. (4.43), we obtain

$$D_2 + (P_1 + P_2)D_1D_2 - D_1 = 0,$$

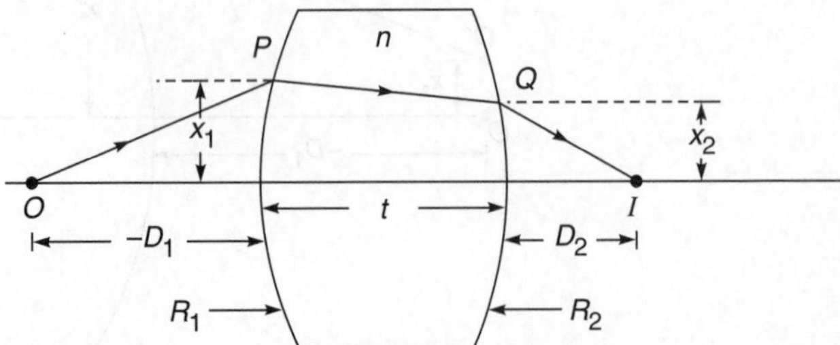

Figure 4.6
A paraxial ray passing through a thick lens of thickness t.

* Note that since we are dealing with paraxial rays, the distance between P and Q is approximately t.

or

$$\frac{1}{D_2} - \frac{1}{D_1} = (P_1 + P_2)$$

$$= (n-1)\left(\frac{1}{R_1} - \frac{1}{R_2}\right) \quad (4.54)$$

or

$$\frac{1}{D_2} - \frac{1}{D_1} = \frac{1}{f} \quad (4.55)$$

where

$$f = \frac{1}{P_1 + P_2} = \left[(n-1)\left(\frac{1}{R_1} - \frac{1}{R_2}\right)\right]^{-1} \quad (4.56)$$

represents the focal length of the lens. Equation (4.55) is the well-known thin lens formula. (The signs of R_1 and R_2 for different kinds of lenses are shown in Fig. 4.7). Thus the system matrix for a thin lens is given by

$$S = \begin{pmatrix} 1 & -\frac{1}{f} \\ 0 & 1 \end{pmatrix} \quad (4.57)$$

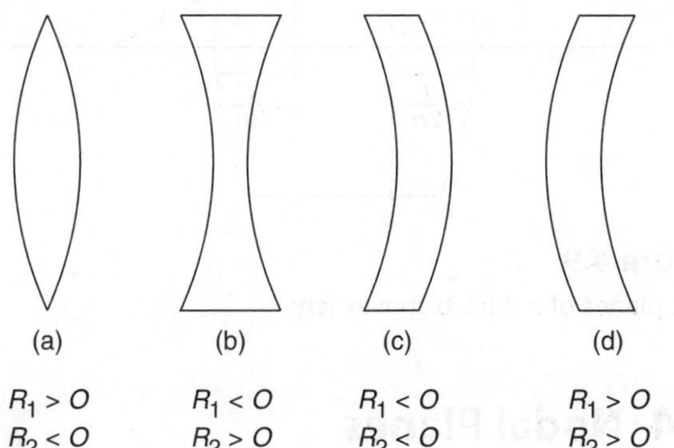

Figure 4.7
Signs of R_1 and R_2 for different lens types.

For a thick lens, we have from Eq. (4.51)

$$\left.\begin{aligned} a &= P_1 + P_2\left(1 - \frac{t}{n}P_1\right), \quad b = 1 - \frac{P_2 t}{n} \\ c &= 1 - \frac{t}{n}P_1, \quad d = -\frac{t}{n} \end{aligned}\right\} \quad (4.58)$$

If we substitute the above values for a, b, c and d in Eq. (4.43), we get the required relation between D_1 and D_2; however, for thick lenses, it is more convenient to define the unit and the nodal planes which we shall do in the following sections.

4.3 Unit Planes

LO2

Unit planes are two planes, one each in the object and the image space, between which the magnification M is unity, i.e., any paraxial ray emanating from the unit plane in the object space will emerge at the same height from the unit plane in the image space. Thus, if d_{u1} and d_{u2} represent the distances of the unit planes from the refracting surfaces (see Fig. 4.8)* we obtain from Eq. (4.46):

$$b + ad_{u1} = \frac{1}{c - ad_{u2}} = 1 \quad (4.59)$$

or

$$d_{u1} = \frac{1-b}{a} \quad (4.60)$$

$$d_{u2} = \frac{c-1}{a} \quad (4.61)$$

Hence, the unit planes are determined completely by the elements of the system matrix S.

It will be convenient to measure distances from the unit planes. Thus, if u is the distance of the object plane from the first unit plane and v is the distance of the corresponding

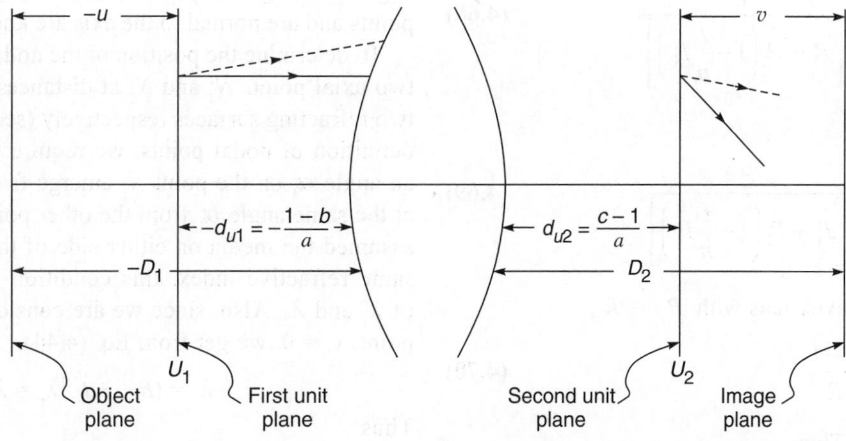

Figure 4.8
U_1 and U_2 are the two unit planes. A ray emanating at any height from the first unit plane will cross the second unit plane at the same height.

* Obviously, if we consider U_1 as an object plane, then U_2 is the corresponding image plane.

image plane from the second unit plane (see Fig. 4.8), we would obtain

$$D_1 = u + d_{u1} = u + \frac{1-b}{a} \tag{4.62}$$

and

$$D_2 = v + d_{u2} = v + \frac{c-1}{a} \tag{4.63}$$

Now, from Eq. (4.43), we have

$$D_2 = \frac{d + cD_1}{b + aD_1} \tag{4.64}$$

Substituting for D_1 and D_2 from Eqs. (4.62) and (4.63), we get

$$v + \frac{c-1}{a} = \frac{d + cu + \frac{c(1-b)}{a}}{b + au + (1-b)}$$

or

$$v = \frac{ad - bc + c(au+1) - (c-1)(1+au)}{a(1+au)}$$

$$= \frac{au}{a(1+au)} \tag{4.65}$$

where we have used the condition that

$$\det S = bc - ad = 1 \tag{4.66}$$

On simplification, we obtain

$$\frac{1}{v} - \frac{1}{u} = a \tag{4.67}$$

Thus $1/a$ represents the focal length of the system if the distances are measured from the two unit planes. For example, for a thick lens one obtains [using Eqs. (4.58), (4.60) and (4.61)]:

$$d_{u1} = \frac{P_2 t}{n} \frac{1}{\left[P_1 + P_2\left(1 - \frac{t}{n}P_1\right)\right]} \tag{4.68}$$

and

$$d_{u2} = -\frac{t}{n} \frac{P_1}{\left[P_1 + P_2\left(1 - \frac{t}{n}P_1\right)\right]} \tag{4.69}$$

For a thick double convex lens with $|R_1| = |R_2|$

$$P_1 = P_2 = \frac{n-1}{R} \tag{4.70}$$

where $R = |R_1| = |R_2|$. Thus,

$$d_{u1} = \frac{t}{n} \frac{1}{\left[2 - \frac{t}{n}\frac{n-1}{R}\right]} \simeq \frac{t}{2n} \tag{4.71}$$

and

$$d_{u2} = -\frac{t}{n} \frac{1}{\left[2 - \frac{t}{n}\frac{n-1}{R}\right]} \simeq -\frac{t}{2n} \tag{4.72}$$

where we have assumed $t << R$ which is indeed the case for most thick lenses. The positions of the unit planes are shown in Fig. 4.9. In order to calculate the focal length we note from Eq. (4.67) that

$$\frac{1}{f} = a = P_1 + P_2\left(1 - \frac{t}{n}P_1\right) \tag{4.73}$$

where we have used Eq. (4.58). Thus,

$$\frac{1}{f} = (n-1)\left(\frac{1}{R_1} - \frac{1}{R_2}\right) + \frac{(n-1)^2 t}{nR_1R_2} \tag{4.74}$$

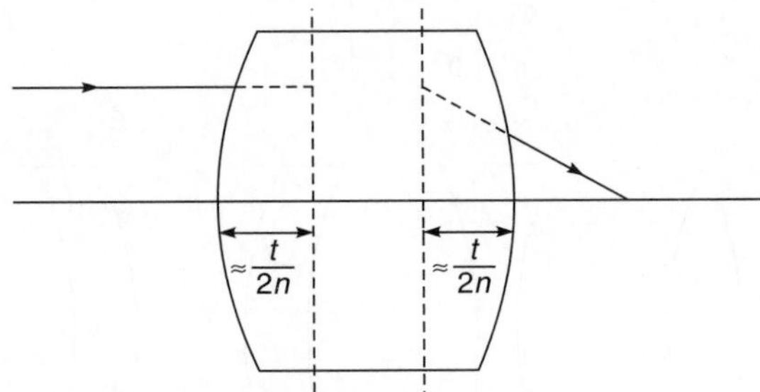

Figure 4.9
Unit planes of a thick biconvex lens.

4.4 Nodal Planes

LO3

Nodal points are two points on the axis which have a relative angular magnification of unity, i.e., a ray striking the first point at an angle α emerges from the second point at the same angle (see Fig. 4.10). The planes which pass through these points and are normal to the axis are known as **nodal planes**.

To determine the position of the nodal points, we consider two axial points N_1 and N_2 at distances d_{n1} and d_{n2} from the two refracting surfaces respectively (see Fig. 4.10). From the definition of nodal points, we require that a ray incident at an angle α_1 on the point N_1 emerge from the optical system at the same angle α_1 from the other point N_2. Since we have assumed the media on either side of the system to have the same refractive index, this condition requires the equality of λ_1 and λ_2. Also, since we are considering an axial object point, $x_1 = 0$, we get from Eq. (4.44)

$$\lambda_2 = (b + ad_{n1})\lambda_1 = \lambda_1 \tag{4.75}$$

Thus,

$$b + ad_{n1} = 1 \tag{4.76}$$

or

$$d_{n1} = \frac{1-b}{a} \tag{4.77}$$

Comparing this with Eq. (4.60) we find that $d_{n1} = d_{u1}$. This has arisen because of the equality of the indices of refraction on either side of the optical system. Similarly, we can get

$$d_{n2} = \frac{c-1}{a} \tag{4.78}$$

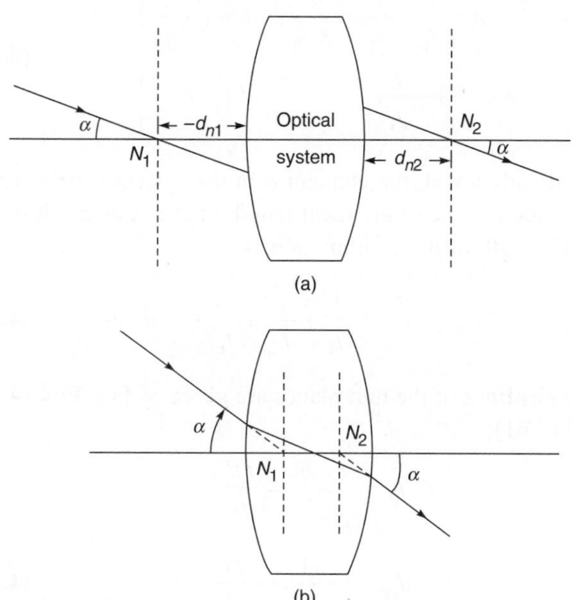

Figure 4.10

N_1 and N_2 denote the two nodal points of an optical system. The nodal points can also lie inside the optical system as shown in (b).

Thus, when the media on either side of an optical system have the same refractive index (which is indeed the case for most optical systems), the nodal planes coincide with the unit planes. In general, if we know the elements of the system matrix *S* (i.e., if we know *a*, *b*, *c* and *d* which are also called the Gaussian constants of the system), one can obtain all the properties of the system.

EXAMPLE 4.2 Consider a thick equiconvex lens (made of a material of refractive index 1.5) of the type shown in Fig. 4.9. The magnitudes of the radii of curvature of the two surfaces is 4 cm. The thickness of the lens is 1 cm and the lens is placed in air. Obtain the system matrix and determine the focal length and the positions of unit planes.

Solution:

$$R_1 = +4 \text{ cm} \qquad R_2 = -4 \text{ cm} \qquad t = 1 \text{ cm}$$

Both surfaces have equal power

$$P_1 = P_2 = \frac{n-1}{R_1} = \frac{0.5}{4} = 0.125 \text{ cm}^{-1}$$

Thus, the system matrix is from Eq. (4.51)

$$\begin{pmatrix} 1-\dfrac{0.125\times 1}{1.5} & -0.125-0.125\left(1-\dfrac{1}{1.5}\times 0.125\right) \\ \dfrac{1}{1.5} & 1-\dfrac{0.125}{1.5} \end{pmatrix}$$

$$= \begin{pmatrix} 0.9167 & -0.240 \\ 0.6667 & 0.9167 \end{pmatrix}$$

Thus,

$$a = \frac{1}{f} = 0.24 \Rightarrow f \simeq 4.17 \text{ cm}$$

$$b = 0.9167 = c, \qquad d = -0.6667$$

Using Eqs. (4.60) and (4.61), we get the positions of the unit planes

$$d_{u1} = \frac{1-b}{a} \simeq 0.348 \text{ cm}$$

$$d_{u2} = \frac{c-1}{a} \simeq -0.348 \text{ cm}$$

Thus the unit planes are as shown in Fig. 4.9. The nodal planes coincide with the unit planes because the lens is immersed in air.

EXAMPLE 4.3 Consider a sphere of radius 20 cm of refractive index 1.6 (see Fig. 4.11). Find the positions of the paraxial focal point and the unit planes.

Solution: The matrices from the first refracting surface to the image plane are given by

Second surface to image	Refraction at second surface	Transmission through glass	Refraction at the first surface
$\begin{pmatrix} 1 & 0 \\ v & 1 \end{pmatrix}$	$\begin{pmatrix} 1 & (1-1.6)/20 \\ 0 & 1 \end{pmatrix}$	$\begin{pmatrix} 1 & 0 \\ 40/1.6 & 1 \end{pmatrix}$	$\begin{pmatrix} 1 & -(1.6-1)/20 \\ 0 & 1 \end{pmatrix}$

$$= \begin{pmatrix} 1 & 0 \\ v & 1 \end{pmatrix}\begin{pmatrix} 0.25 & -0.0375 \\ 25 & 0.25 \end{pmatrix}$$

$$= \begin{pmatrix} 0.25 & -0.0375 \\ 25+0.25\,v & 0.25-0.0375\,v \end{pmatrix}$$

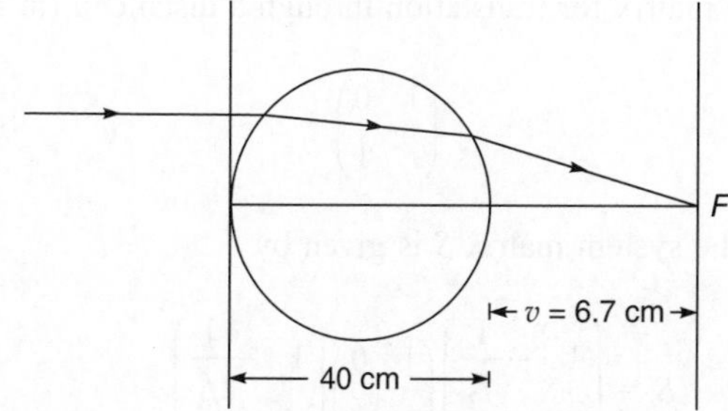

Figure 4.11

Imaging by a sphere of radius 20 cm and refractive index 1.6.

Thus at the image plane, the ray coordinates are

$$\begin{pmatrix}\lambda_2\\ x_2\end{pmatrix}=\begin{pmatrix}0.25 & -0.0375\\ 25+0.25\,v & 0.25-0.0375\,v\end{pmatrix}\begin{pmatrix}\lambda_1\\ x_1\end{pmatrix}$$

This gives us

$$x_2 = (25 + 0.25\,v)\lambda_1 + (0.25 - 0.0375\,v)x_1$$

To determine the focal distance v, consider a ray incident parallel to the axis for which $\lambda_1 = 0$. The focal plane would be that plane for which x_2 is also zero. This gives us

$$0.0375v = 0.25 \quad \text{or} \quad v = 6.7 \text{ cm}$$

The system matrix elements are

$$a = \frac{1}{f} = 0.0375 \text{ cm}^{-1} \quad \Rightarrow \quad f \simeq 26.7 \text{ cm}$$

$$b = 0.25, \qquad c = 0.25, \qquad d = -25 \text{ cm}$$

The unit planes are given by

$$d_{u1} = \frac{1-b}{a} = 20 \text{ cm}$$

and $$d_{u2} = \frac{c-1}{a} = -20 \text{ cm}$$

Thus, both the unit planes pass through the center of the sphere.

4.5 A System of Two Thin Lenses

LO4

We finally use the matrix formulation for the analysis of a combination of two thin lenses of focal lengths f_1 and f_2 separated by a distance t. The system matrix for the combination of the two lenses can be obtained by noting that the matrix of the two lenses are [see Eq. (4.57)]

$$\begin{pmatrix}1 & -\dfrac{1}{f_1}\\ 0 & 1\end{pmatrix} \quad \text{and} \quad \begin{pmatrix}1 & -\dfrac{1}{f_2}\\ 0 & 1\end{pmatrix} \tag{4.79}$$

and the matrix for translation through a distance t (in air) is

$$\begin{pmatrix}1 & 0\\ t & 1\end{pmatrix} \tag{4.80}$$

Thus, the system matrix S is given by

$$S = \begin{pmatrix}1 & -\dfrac{1}{f_2}\\ 0 & 1\end{pmatrix}\begin{pmatrix}1 & 0\\ t & 1\end{pmatrix}\begin{pmatrix}1 & -\dfrac{1}{f_1}\\ 0 & 1\end{pmatrix}$$

$$= \begin{pmatrix}\left(1-\dfrac{t}{f_2}\right) & -\left(\dfrac{1}{f_1}+\dfrac{1}{f_2}-\dfrac{t}{f_1 f_2}\right)\\ t & \left(1-\dfrac{t}{f_1}\right)\end{pmatrix} \tag{4.81}$$

Thus,

$$\left.\begin{aligned} a &= \frac{1}{f_1}+\frac{1}{f_2}-\frac{t}{f_1 f_2}, & b &= 1-\frac{t}{f_2}\\ c &= 1-\frac{t}{f_1}, & d &= -t \end{aligned}\right\} \tag{4.82}$$

As already noted, the element a in the system matrix represents the inverse of the focal length of the system. Thus, the focal length of the combination is

$$\frac{1}{f} = \frac{1}{f_1}+\frac{1}{f_2}-\frac{t}{f_1 f_2} = a \tag{4.83}$$

The positions of the unit planes are given by [see Eqs. (4.60) and (4.61)]

$$d_{u1} = \frac{1-b}{a} = \frac{tf}{f_2}$$

$$d_{u2} = \frac{c-1}{a} = -\frac{tf}{f_1} \tag{4.84}$$

It is easy to see that if we have a system of four thin lenses, we simply have to multiply seven matrices [four of them being of the type given by Eq. (4.79) and three of them of the type given by Eq. (4.80)].

EXAMPLE 4.4 Consider a lens combination consisting of a convex lens (of focal length +15 cm) and a concave lens (of focal length –20 cm) separated by 25 cm (see Fig. 4.12 and Problem 3.5). Determine the system matrix elements and the positions of the unit planes. For an object (of height 1 cm) placed at a distance of 27.5 cm from the convex lens, determine the size and position of the image.

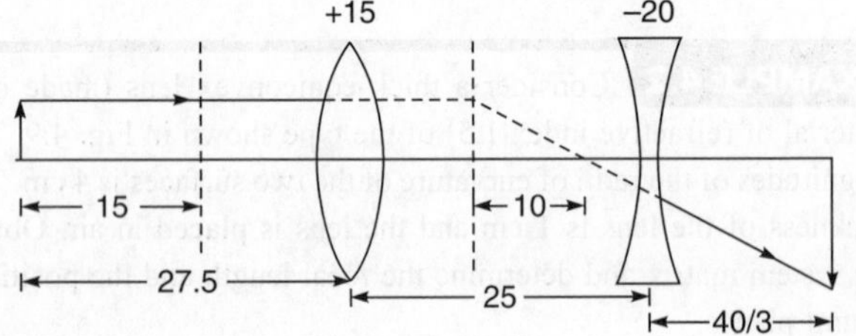

Figure 4.12

Solution:

$$f_1 = +15 \text{ cm} \qquad f_2 = -20 \text{ cm} \qquad t = 25 \text{ cm}$$

Thus, using Eq. (4.82), we readily get

$$a = \frac{1}{10} = \frac{1}{f}, \quad b = \frac{45}{20}, \quad c = -\frac{2}{3}, \quad d = -25$$

and

$$d_{u1} = \frac{1-b}{a} = -12.5 \text{ cm}, \quad d_{u2} = \frac{c-1}{a} = -\frac{50}{3} \text{ cm}$$

Thus, the distance of the object from the first unit plane is given by

$$u = -27.5 - (-12.5) = -15 \text{ cm}$$

Since $f = +10$ cm, we get [using Eq. (4.67)]

$$v = 30 \text{ cm}$$

which represents the distance of the image plane from the second unit plane. Thus the image is at a distance of 30 – (50/3) = 40/3 cm from the concave lens. The magnification is given by

$$M = \frac{v}{u} = -2$$

EXAMPLE 4.5 Consider a system of two thin lenses as shown in Fig. 3.10. For a 1-cm tall object at a distance of 40 cm from the convex lens, calculate the position and size of the image.

Solution: Let v be the distance of the image plane from the concave lens. Thus the matrix, which when operated on the object column matrix gives the image column matrix, is given by

Concave lens to image	Concave lens	Convex lens to cocave lens	Convex lens	Object to convex lens
$\begin{pmatrix} 1 & 0 \\ v & 1 \end{pmatrix}$	$\begin{pmatrix} 1 & +1/10 \\ 0 & 1 \end{pmatrix}$	$\begin{pmatrix} 1 & 0 \\ 8 & 1 \end{pmatrix}$	$\begin{pmatrix} 1 & -1/20 \\ 0 & 1 \end{pmatrix}$	$\begin{pmatrix} 1 & 0 \\ 40 & 1 \end{pmatrix}$

$$= \begin{pmatrix} 1 & 0 \\ v & 1 \end{pmatrix}\begin{pmatrix} 2.2 & 0.01 \\ +32 & 0.6 \end{pmatrix}$$

$$= \begin{pmatrix} 2.2 & 0.01 \\ 2.2\,v + 32 & 0.6 + 0.01\,v \end{pmatrix}$$

The image plane would correspond to

$$32 + 2.2v = 0$$

or

$$v \simeq -14.5 \text{ cm}$$

i.e., it is at a distance of 14.5 cm to the left of the concave lens. If we compare this with Eq. (4.45), we obtain

$$M = 0.6 + 0.01v = 0.6 - 0.01\frac{32}{2.2} = +\frac{1}{2.2}$$

EXAMPLE 4.6 In the above example, determine the system matrix and hence the positions of the unit planes. Finally, use Eq. (4.67) to determine the position of the image.

Solution: The system matrix is given by

$$S = \begin{pmatrix} 1 & 1/10 \\ 0 & 1 \end{pmatrix}\begin{pmatrix} 1 & 0 \\ 8 & 1 \end{pmatrix}\begin{pmatrix} 1 & -1/20 \\ 0 & 1 \end{pmatrix}$$

$$= \begin{pmatrix} 9/5 & 1/100 \\ 8 & 3/5 \end{pmatrix}$$

Thus,

$$a = -\frac{1}{100} \Rightarrow f = -100 \text{ cm}$$

$$b = \frac{9}{5}, \quad c = \frac{3}{5}, \quad d = -8$$

If we now use Eqs. (4.60) and (4.61), we have

$$d_{u1} = \frac{1-b}{a} = 80 \text{ cm}$$

and

$$d_{u2} = \frac{c-1}{a} = 40 \text{ cm}$$

Thus the first unit plane is at a distance of 80 cm to the right of the convex lens and the second unit plane is at 40 cm to the right of the concave lens. The object distance from the first unit plane is therefore given by

$$u = -(80 + 40) = -120 \text{ cm}$$

We now use Eq. (4.67) to obtain

$$\frac{1}{v} = a + \frac{1}{u} = -\frac{1}{100} - \frac{1}{120} = -\frac{22}{1200}$$

$$\Rightarrow \quad v = -\frac{600}{11} \text{ cm}$$

Thus, the image is at 54.5 cm to the left of the second unit plane or at 14.5 cm to the left of the concave lens as shown in Fig. 4.10. The magnification is

$$M = \frac{v}{u} = +\frac{1}{2.2}$$

SUMMARY

- In the paraxial approximation, we may confine ourselves to rays which pass through the axis of the system; these rays remain confined to a single plane. Such a ray can be specified by its distance from the axis of the system x, and the quantity $\lambda = n \sin \alpha$ which represents the product of the refractive index with the sine of the angle that the ray makes with z-axis.
- If a ray is initially specified by a (2 × 1) matrix with elements λ_1 and x_1, then the effect of translation through a distance D in a homogenous medium of refractive index n_1, is given by

$$\begin{pmatrix} \lambda_2 \\ x_2 \end{pmatrix} = T\begin{pmatrix} \lambda_1 \\ x_1 \end{pmatrix}$$

where the translation matrix T is given by

$$T = \begin{pmatrix} 1 & 0 \\ D/n_1 & 1 \end{pmatrix}$$

- The effect of refraction through a spherical refracting surface (separating media of refractive indices n_1 and n_2) is given by

$$\begin{pmatrix} \lambda_2 \\ x_2 \end{pmatrix} = \mathcal{R} \begin{pmatrix} \lambda_1 \\ x_1 \end{pmatrix}$$

where the refraction matrix is given by

$$\mathcal{R} = \begin{pmatrix} 1 & -P \\ 0 & 1 \end{pmatrix}$$

with

$$P = \frac{n_2 - n_1}{R}$$

- By successive application of the above matrices, one can study paraxial imaging by a coaxial optical system.
- In an optical system, unit planes are two planes, one each in the object and the image space, between which the magnification M is unity, i.e., any paraxial ray emanating from the unit plane in the object space will emerge at the same height from the unit plane in the image space.
- Nodal points are two points on the axis, which have a relative angular magnification of unity, i.e., a ray striking the first point at an angle α emerges from the second point at the same angle. The planes that pass through these points and are normal to the axis are known as nodal planes.
- To determine the focal length of multiple lenses, for instance 4, we simply have to multiply 7 matrices, of which 4 are system matrices and 3 are matrices for translation.

PROBLEMS

4.1 Consider a system of two thin convex lenses of focal lengths 10 and 30 cm separated by a distance of 20 cm in air.

(a) Determine the system matrix elements and the positions of the unit planes.

(b) Assume a parallel beam of light incident from the left. Use Eq. (4.67) and the positions of the unit planes to determine the image point. Using the unit planes draw the ray diagram.

[**Ans:** (a) $a = 1/15$, $b = 1/3$, $c = -1$, $d = -20$; the first convex lens is in the middle of the two unit planes. (b) The final image is virtual and is 15 cm away (on the left) from the second lens.]

4.2 Consider a thick biconvex lens whose magnitudes of the radii of curvature of the first and second surfaces are 45 cm and 30 cm, respectively. The thickness of the lens is 5 cm and the refractive index of the material of the lens is 1.5. Determine the elements of the system matrix and positions of the unit planes and use Eq. (4.67) to determine the image point of an object at a distance of 90 cm from the first surface.

[**Ans:** $a = 0.02716$, $b = 0.9444$, $c = 0.9630$, $d = -3.3333$, $d_{u1} = 2.0455$, $d_{u2} = -1.3636$. Final image at a distance of 60 cm from the second surface.]

4.3 Consider a hemisphere of radius 20 cm and refractive index 1.5. If H_1 and H_2 denote the positions of the first and second principal points, then show that $AH_1 = 13.3$ cm and that H_2 lies on the second surface as shown in Fig. 4.13. Further, show that the focal length is 40 cm.

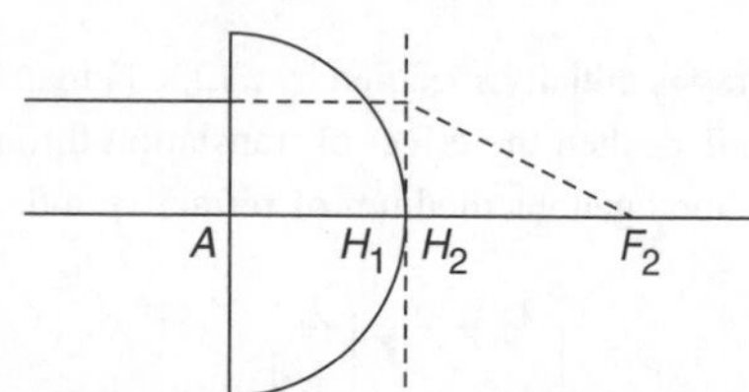

Figure 4.13

4.4 Consider a thick lens of the form shown in Fig. 4.14. The radii of curvature of the first and second surfaces are −10 cm and +20 cm, respectively and the thickness of the lens is 1.0 cm. The refractive index of the material of the lens is 1.5. Determine the positions of the principal planes.

[**Ans:** $d_{u1} = 20/91$ cm, $d_{u2} = 40/91$ cm]

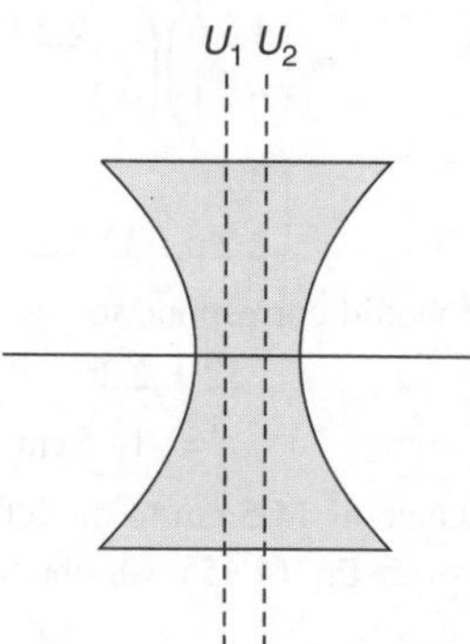

Figure 4.14

4.5 Consider a combination of two thin lenses of focal lengths f_1 and f_2 separated by a distance $(f_1 + f_2)$. Show that the angular magnification of the lens combinations (which is just $\frac{\lambda_2}{\lambda_1} = \frac{\alpha_2}{\alpha_1}$) is given by $-f_1/f_2$. Interpret the negative sign in the expression for magnification.

4.6 Consider a spherical refracting surface as shown in Fig. 3.12. Using matrix method show that for an object at a distance of $\left(1+\frac{n_2}{n_1}\right)r$ from the surface, the image is virtual and at a distance of $\left(1+\frac{n_1}{n_2}\right)r$ from the surface.

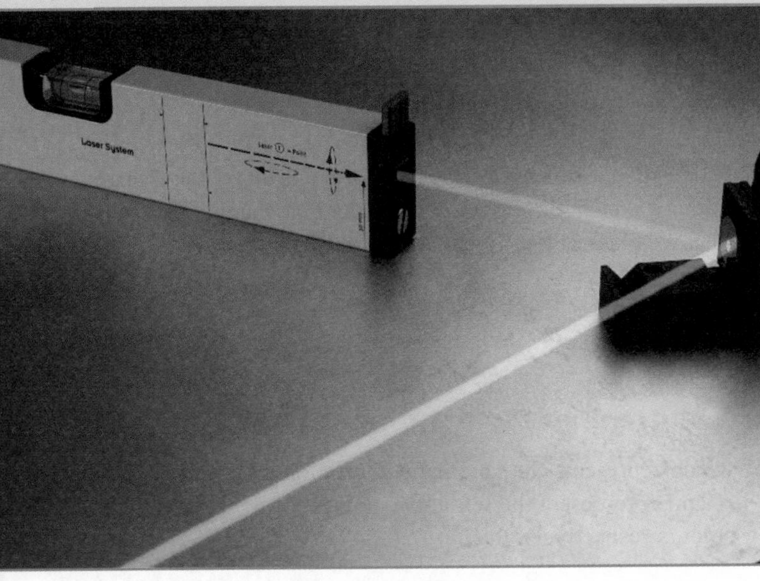

CHAPTER

5

Aberrations

Geometrical optics is either very simple or else it is very complicated...... If one has an actual, detailed problem in lens design, including analysis of aberrations, then he has to simply trace the rays through the various surfaces using the law of refraction and find out where they come out and see if they form a satisfactory image. People have said that this is too tedious, but today, with computing machines, it is the right way to do it. One can set up the problem and make the calculation one ray after another very easily. So the subject is really ultimately quite simple, and involves no new principles.

—Richard Feynman in *Feynman Lectures on Physics*, Vol. I

LEARNING OBJECTIVES

After reading this chapter, the reader should be able to:

LO 1: *explain the phenomenon of chromatic aberration.*

LO 2: *describe the effect of spherical aberration.*

LO 3: *illustrate the coma aberration suffered during image formation.*

LO 4: *understand the origin of astigmatism for object point lying away from the axis.*

LO 5: *understand the aberration due to non-uniform magnification of image.*

Above Image: A laser spirit level reflecting a beam off a mirror; Photograph courtesy McGraw Hill Digital Asset Library

5.1 Introduction

In Chapter 3, while studying the formation of images by refracting surfaces and thin lenses, we had made the assumption that the object point does not lie far away from the axis of the optical system and that the rays taking part in image formation are essentially those which make small angles with the axis of the system. In practice, neither of the above assumptions is true; one in fact has to deal with rays making large angles with the axis. The domain of optics dealing with rays lying close to the optical axis and making small angles with it is called paraxial optics. We had found that in the realm of paraxial optics, the images of objects were perfect, i.e., all rays emanating from a single object point converged to a single image point and the magnification of the system was a constant of the optical system, independent of the particular ray under consideration. Since in real optical systems, non-paraxial rays also take part in image formation, the actual images depart from the ideal images. This departure leads to what are known as **aberrations**.

It can be shown that the primary aberrations of any rotationally symmetric system can be specified by five coefficients. The five coefficients represent the spherical aberration, coma, astigmatism, curvature of field and distortion. These are called the **Seidal aberrations**. Since these aberrations are present even for light of a single wavelength, they are also called **monochromatic aberrations**. In this chapter, we will consider the five kinds of aberrations separately and discuss the effect on the image when each one of them is present separately.

It should be mentioned that if a polychromatic source (like white light) is used for image formation (which is indeed the case for many optical instruments) then, in general, the images will be colored; this is known as **chromatic aberration.** Physically, chromatic aberration is due to the dependence of the refractive index of the material of the lens on wavelength of the radiation under consideration. Since image formation is accompanied by refraction at refractive index discontinuities, the wavelength dependence of the refractive index results in the colored image. For a polychromatic source, different wavelength components (after refraction) proceed along different directions and form images at different points; this leads to colored images. Since chromatic aberration is the easiest to understand, we would discuss this first. This will be followed by a discussion of monochromatic aberrations.

5.2 Chromatic Aberration

LO1

Let us consider a parallel beam of white light incident on a thin convex lens as shown in Fig. 5.1. Since blue light gets refracted more than red light, the point at which the blue light would focus is nearer the lens than the point at which the red light would focus. Thus, the image will appear to be colored; it may be mentioned that this aberration is independent of the five Seidel aberrations to be discussed in later sections.

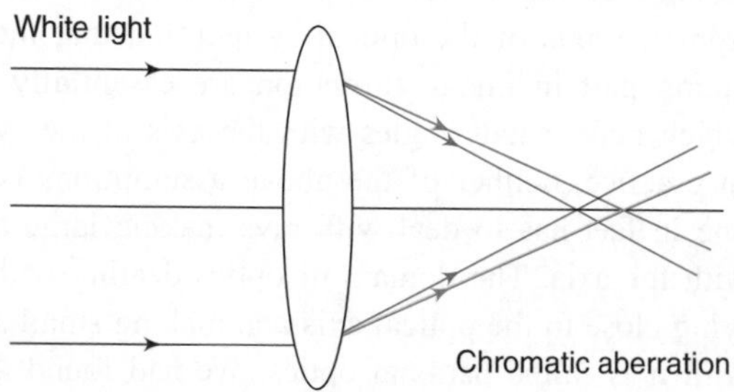

Figure 5.1

A parallel beam of white light is incident on a lens. Different wavelengths of light have slightly differing focal lengths leading to chromatic aberration.

For the case of a thin lens, the expression for chromatic aberration can easily be derived. The focal length of a thin lens is given by

$$\frac{1}{f} = (n-1)\left(\frac{1}{R_1} - \frac{1}{R_2}\right) \tag{5.1}$$

If a change of n by δn (the change of n is due to the change in the wavelength of the light) results in a change of f by δf then we obtain by differentiating Eq. (5.1)

$$-\frac{\delta f}{f^2} = \delta n\left(\frac{1}{R_1} - \frac{1}{R_2}\right) = \frac{\delta n}{n-1}\frac{1}{f}$$

i.e.,

$$\delta f = -f\frac{\delta n}{n-1} \tag{5.2}$$

which represents the chromatic aberration of a thin lens. If n_b and n_r represent the refractive indices for the blue and red colours respectively, then

$$f_r - f_b = f\left(\frac{n_b - n_r}{n-1}\right) \tag{5.3}$$

would represent the chromatic aberration.

5.2.1 The Achromatic Doublet

We will first consider an optical system of two thin lenses made of different materials placed in contact with each other. For example, one of the lenses may be made of crown glass and the other of flint glass. We will find the condition for this lens combination to have the same focal length for the blue and red colors. Let n_b, n_y and n_r represent the refractive indices for the material of the first lens corresponding to the blue, yellow and red colors, respectively. Similarly, n_b', n_y' and n_r' represent the corresponding refractive indices for the second lens. If f_b and f_b' represent the focal lengths for the first and the second lens corresponding to the blue color, and if F_b represents the focal length of the combination of the two lenses (placed in contact), then

$$\frac{1}{F_b} = \frac{1}{f_b} + \frac{1}{f_b'} = (n_b - 1)\left(\frac{1}{R_1} - \frac{1}{R_2}\right) + (n_b' - 1)\left(\frac{1}{R_1'} - \frac{1}{R_2'}\right) \tag{5.4}$$

where R_1 and R_2 represent the radii of curvatures of the first and second surface for the first lens and, as before, the primed quantities refer to the second lens. Thus, we may write

$$\frac{1}{F_b} = \frac{n_b - 1}{n-1}\frac{1}{f} + \frac{n_b' - 1}{n' - 1}\frac{1}{f'} \tag{5.5}$$

where

$$\frac{1}{f} \equiv (n-1)\left(\frac{1}{R_1} - \frac{1}{R_2}\right),$$

$$\frac{1}{f'} \equiv (n'-1)\left(\frac{1}{R_1'} - \frac{1}{R_2'}\right) \tag{5.6}$$

$$n \equiv \frac{n_b + n_r}{2} \approx n_y,\; n' \equiv \frac{n'_b + n'_r}{2} \approx n'_y \quad \textbf{(5.7)}$$

f and f' represent the focal lengths of the first and second lens corresponding to a mean color which is around the yellow region. Similarly, the focal length of the combination corresponding to the red color would be given by

$$\frac{1}{F_r} = \frac{n_r - 1}{n - 1}\frac{1}{f} + \frac{n'_r - 1}{n' - 1}\frac{1}{f'} \quad \textbf{(5.8)}$$

For the focal length of the combination to be equal for blue and red colours, we must have

$$\frac{n_b - 1}{n - 1}\frac{1}{f} + \frac{n'_b - 1}{n' - 1}\frac{1}{f'} = \frac{n_r - 1}{n - 1}\frac{1}{f} + \frac{n'_r - 1}{n' - 1}\frac{1}{f'}$$

or

$$\frac{\omega}{f} + \frac{\omega'}{f'} = 0 \quad \textbf{(5.9)}$$

where

$$\omega = \frac{n_b - n_r}{n - 1} \quad \text{and} \quad \omega' = \frac{n'_b - n'_r}{n' - 1} \quad \textbf{(5.10)}$$

are known as the **dispersive powers**. Since ω and ω' are both positive, f and f' must be of opposite signs for the validity of Eq. (5.9). A lens combination which satisfies Eq. (5.9) is known as an **achromatic doublet** (see Fig. 5.2). It may be mentioned that if the two lenses are made of the same material, then $\omega = \omega'$ and Eq. (5.9) would imply $f = -f'$; such a combination will have an infinite focal length. Thus, for an achromatic doublet the two lenses must be of different materials.

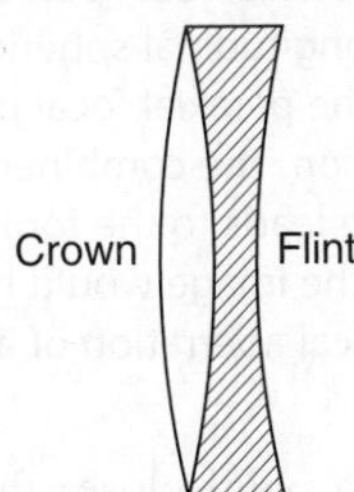

Figure 5.2
An achromatic doublet.

EXAMPLE 5.1 An achromatic doublet of focal length 20 cm is to be made by placing a convex lens of borosilicate crown glass in contact with a diverging lens of dense flint glass. Assuming $n_r = 1.51462$, $n_b = 1.52264$, $n'_r = 1.61216$ and $n'_b = 1.62901$, calculate the focal length of each lens; here the unprimed and the primed quantities refer to the borosilicate crown glass and dense flint glass respectively.

Solution:

$$n \approx \frac{n_b + n_r}{2} = \frac{1.52264 + 1.51462}{2} = 1.51863$$

$$n' \approx \frac{n'_b + n'_r}{2} = \frac{1.62901 + 1.61216}{2} = 1.62058$$

Thus,

$$\omega = \frac{1.52264 - 1.51462}{1.51863 - 1} = 0.01546$$

and

$$\omega' = \frac{1.62901 - 1.61216}{1.62058 - 1} = 0.02715$$

Substituting in Eq. (5.9), we obtain

$$\frac{0.01546}{f} + \frac{0.02715}{f'} = 0$$

or

$$\frac{f}{f'} = -0.56942$$

Now, for the lens combination to be of focal length 20 cm, we must have

$$\frac{1}{f} + \frac{1}{f'} = \frac{1}{20}$$

or

$$\frac{1}{f}[1 - 0.56942] = \frac{1}{20}$$

or

$$f = 20 \times 0.43058 = 8.61 \text{ cm}$$

and

$$f' = -\frac{f}{0.56942} \simeq -15.1 \text{ cm}$$

5.2.2 Removal of Chromatic Aberration of a Separated Doublet

Let us consider two thin lenses of focal lengths f and f' and separated by a distance t (see Fig. 5.3). The focal length of the combination F, would be

$$\frac{1}{F} = \frac{1}{f} + \frac{1}{f'} - \frac{t}{ff'} \quad \textbf{(5.11)}$$

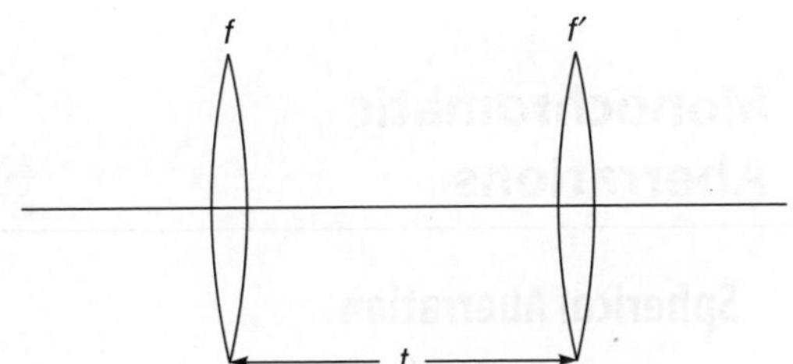

Figure 5.3
The separated doublet.

The focal length of the first lens would be given by

$$\frac{1}{f} = (n - 1)\left(\frac{1}{R_1} - \frac{1}{R_2}\right) \quad \textbf{(5.12)}$$

with a similar expression for $1/f'$. If Δf and Δn represent the changes in the focal length and in the refractive index due to a change $\Delta\lambda$ in the wavelength, then by differentiating Eq. (5.12), we obtain

$$-\frac{\Delta f}{f^2} = \Delta n\left(\frac{1}{R_1} - \frac{1}{R_2}\right) = \frac{\Delta n}{(n-1)f}$$

Thus, differentiating Eq. (5.11), we obtain

$$-\frac{\Delta F}{F^2} = -\frac{\Delta f}{f^2} - \frac{\Delta f'}{f'^2} + \frac{t}{f}\frac{\Delta f'}{f'^2} + \frac{t}{f'}\frac{\Delta f}{f^2}$$

$$= \frac{\Delta n}{(n-1)f} + \frac{\Delta n'}{(n'-1)f'} - \frac{t}{f}\frac{\Delta n'}{(n'-1)f'} - \frac{t}{f'}\frac{\Delta n}{(n-1)f}$$

$$= \frac{\omega}{f} + \frac{\omega'}{f'} - \frac{t}{ff'}(\omega + \omega') \quad (5.13)$$

where, as before, ω and ω' represent the dispersive powers. Consequently, for the combination to have the same focal length for blue and red colors, we should have

$$\frac{t(\omega + \omega')}{ff'} = \frac{\omega}{f} + \frac{\omega'}{f'}$$

or

$$t = \frac{\omega f' + \omega' f}{\omega + \omega'} \quad (5.14)$$

If both the lenses are made of the same material, then $\omega = \omega'$ and the above equation simplifies to

$$t = \frac{f + f'}{2} \quad (5.15)$$

implying that the chromatic aberration is very small if the distance between the two lenses is equal to the mean of the focal lengths. This is indeed the case for the Huygens' eyepiece.

5.3 Monochromatic Aberrations

LO2

5.3.1 Spherical Aberration

Let a beam of light parallel to the axis be incident on a thin lens (see Fig. 5.4). The light rays after passing the lens bend towards the axis and cross the axis at some point. If we restrict ourselves to the paraxial region, then we can see that all rays cross the z-axis at the same point which is at a distance f_P from the lens; f_P represents the paraxial focal length of the lens. If one does not restrict to the paraxial region, then in general, rays which are incident at different heights on the lens, hit the axis at different points. For example, for a convex lens, the marginal rays (which are incident near the periphery

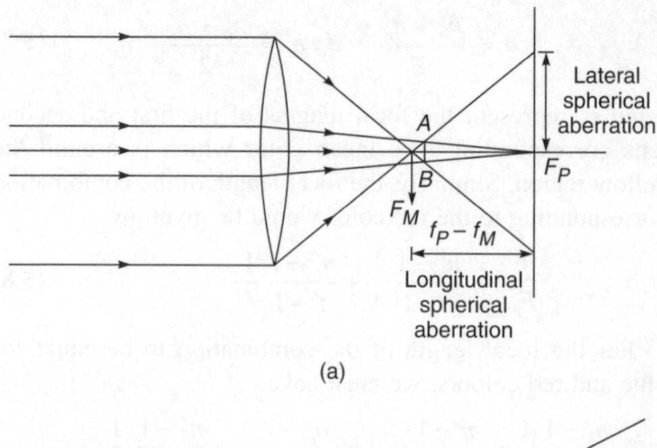

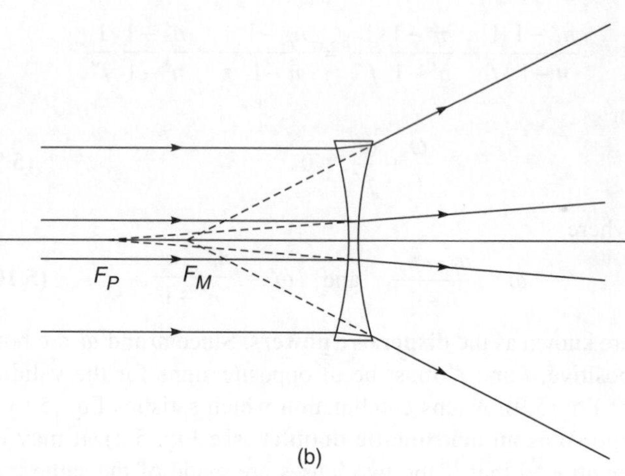

Figure 5.4
(a) For a converging lens the focal point for marginal rays lies closer to the lens than the focal point for paraxial rays. The distance between the paraxial focal point and the marginal focal point is known as the longitudinal spherical aberration and the radius of the image at the paraxial focal plane is known as the lateral spherical aberration. The combined effect of defocusing and spherical aberration leads to the formation of a circle of least confusion, where the image would have the minimum diameter. (b) The spherical aberration of a diverging lens.

of the lens) focus at a point closer than the focal point of paraxial rays [see Fig. 5.4(a)]. Similarly, for a concave lens, rays which are incident farther from the axis appear to be emerging from a point which is nearer to the lens [see Fig. 5.4(b)]. The point at which the paraxial rays strike the axis (F_P) is called the **paraxial focus** and the point at which the rays near the periphery strike is called the **marginal focus** (F_M). The distance between the two foci is the measure of spherical aberration in the lens. Thus if O represents an axial object, then different rays emerging from the object converge to different points; consequently, the image of a point object will not be a point. The distance along the axis between the paraxial image point and the image corresponding to marginal rays (i.e., rays striking the edge of the lens) is termed **longitudinal spherical aberration**. Similarly, the distance between the paraxial image point and the point at which the marginal ray strikes the paraxial image plane is called the lateral **spherical aberration** [see Fig. 5.4(a)]. The image on any plane (normal to the z-axis) is a circular patch of light; however, as can be seen from Fig. 5.4(a), on a plane AB the circular patch has the least diameter. This is called the **circle of least confusion** (see Fig. 5.5). It may be mentioned that for an object lying on the axis of a cylindrically symmetric system (like a system of coaxial lenses), the image will suffer only from spherical aberration. All other off-axis aberrations like coma, astigmatism, etc., will be absent.

Figure 5.5
The spherical aberration of a convex lens. [*Photograph courtesy: Dr. K.K. Gupta*].

To see how the rays hitting the refracting surface at different heights could focus to different points on the axis, let us consider the simple case of a plane refracting surface as shown in Fig. 5.6. Let the plane of the refracting surface be chosen as the plane $z = 0$. Let P be the object point. The z-axis is chosen to be along the normal (PO) from the point P to the surface. The plane $z = 0$ separates two media of refractive indices n_1 and n_2 (see Fig. 5.6); in the figure we have assumed $n_2 > n_1$. Consider a ray PM incident on the refracting surface (from the object) at a height h as shown in Fig. 5.6.

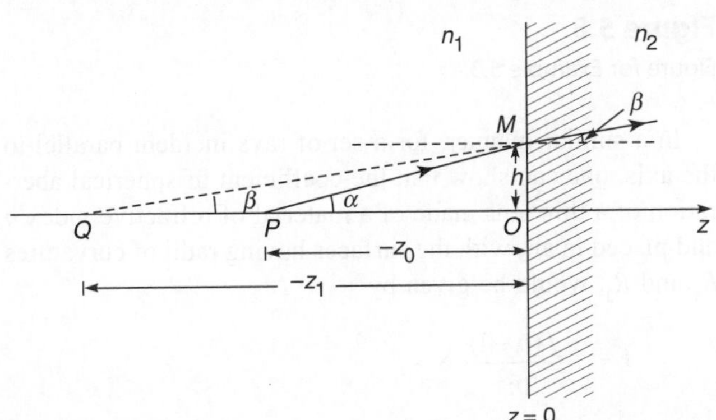

Figure 5.6
Refraction at a plane surface.

The refracted ray appears to emerge from the point Q. We assume the origin to be at the point O. Let the z-coordinates of the points P and Q be z_0 and z_1, respectively. Obviously, both z_0 and z_1 would be negative quantities and the distances OP and OQ would be $-z_0$ and $-z_1$, respectively (see Fig. 5.6). We have to determine z_1 in terms of z_0. From Snell's law we know that

$$\sin \alpha = n \sin \beta \quad \textbf{(5.16)}$$

where α and β are the angles that the incident and refracted rays make with the z-axis and

$$n = \frac{n_2}{n_1} \quad \textbf{(5.17)}$$

Now, from Fig. 5.6 we have

$$(-z_1) = h \cot \beta = \frac{h}{\sin \beta}\sqrt{1 - \sin^2 \beta}$$

or

$$z_1 = -\frac{nh}{\sin \alpha}\left(1 - \frac{1}{n^2}\sin^2 \alpha\right)^{1/2} \quad \textbf{(5.18)}$$

where we have used Eq. (5.16). Since

$$\sin \alpha = \frac{h}{\sqrt{h^2 + z_0^2}} \quad \textbf{(5.19)}$$

we obtain

$$z_1 = -\frac{nh}{h}(h^2 + z_0^2)^{1/2}\left[1 - \frac{1}{n^2}\frac{h^2}{(h^2 + z_0^2)}\right]^{1/2} \quad \textbf{(5.20)}$$

or $$z_1 = -n|z_0|\left[1 + \frac{h^2}{z_0^2}\right]^{1/2}\left[1 - \frac{h^2}{n^2 z_0^2}\left(1 + \frac{h^2}{z_0^2}\right)^{-1}\right]^{1/2} \quad \textbf{(5.21)}$$

The value of z_1 given in Eq. (5.21) is an exact expression in terms of z_0. It can at once be seen that the image distance, z_1, is a complicated function of the height h, at which the ray strikes the refracting surface. In the limit of $h \to 0$, i.e., for paraxial rays, we get

$$z_1 = -n|z_0| \quad \textbf{(5.22)}$$

which is the expression for the image distance in the paraxial region. To the next order of approximation, assuming $|h/z_0| << 1$, we get

$$z \simeq -n|z_0|\left[1 + \frac{h^2}{2z_0^2}\right]\left[1 - \frac{h^2}{2n^2 z_0^2}\right]$$

$$\simeq -n|z_0|\left[1 + \frac{h^2}{2z_0^2 n^2}(n^2 - 1)\right] \quad \textbf{(5.23)}$$

Thus the aberration is given by

$$\Delta z = -\frac{h^2}{2n|z_0|}(n^2 - 1) \tag{5.24}$$

Equation (5.24) gives the longitudinal spherical aberration. The negative sign implies that the non-paraxial rays appear to emanate from a point which is farther away from the paraxial image point.

From the above example, it can be seen that even a single plane refracting surface suffers from spherical aberration. Thus, spherical refracting surfaces and thin lenses must also suffer from spherical aberration.

The calculation of the spherical aberration even for a single spherical refracting surface is quite cumbersome (see, e.g., Ref. 5.5); therefore, we just give the final results:

$$\Delta z = -\frac{(n_2 - n_1)}{2n_2\left(\frac{1}{z_0} + \frac{n_2 - n_1}{n_1 R}\right)^2}\left(\frac{1}{R} + \frac{1}{z_0}\right)^2 \times \left(-\frac{n_2 + n_1}{n_1 z_0} + \frac{1}{R}\right)h^2 \tag{5.25}$$

where R represents the radius of curvature of the surface, n_1 and n_2 represent the refractive indices of the media on the left and right of the spherical surface (see Fig. 5.7). For a plane surface $R = \infty$, Eq. (5.25) reduces to Eq. (5.24) with $n = n_2/n_1$.

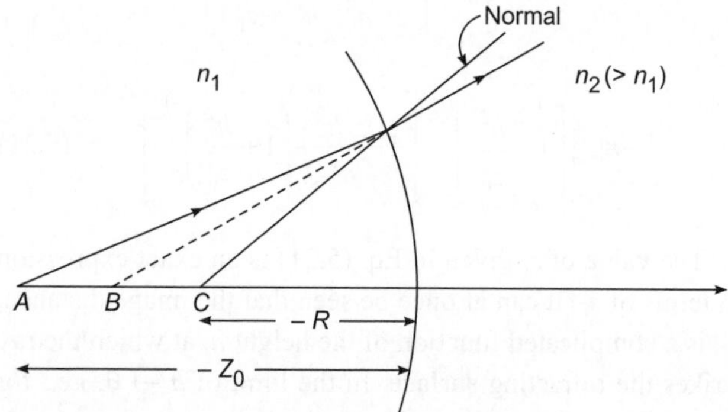

Figure 5.7
The aplanatic points of a spherical refracting surface.

EXAMPLE 5.2 Consider a spherical refracting surface of radius R. Show that for a point A (see Fig. 5.7) such that

$$z_0 = \frac{n_1 + n_2}{n_1} R \tag{5.26}$$

the spherical aberration is zero. Notice that both R and z_0 are negative quantities. The corresponding image point B is at a distance $\frac{n_2 - n_1}{n_2} z_0$. The points A and B are known as the aplanatic points and are utilized in microscope objectives.

Solution: For $z_0 = \frac{n_1 + n_2}{n_1} R$, one of the factors in Eq. (5.25) vanishes and the spherical aberration is zero. Indeed, it can be rigorously shown that all rays emanating from the point A appear to diverge from the point B (see also Sec. 3.8).

EXAMPLE 5.3 Consider a refracting surface obtained by revolving an ellipse about its major axis. Show that all the rays parallel to the major axis will focus at one of the foci if the eccentricity of the ellipse is equal to n_1/n_2.

[**Hint:** *The eccentricity of the ellipse is given by*

$$\varepsilon = \frac{OF}{a} = \left(1 - \frac{b^2}{a^2}\right)^{1/2}$$

where a and b are the semi-major and semi-minor axes, respectively (see Fig. 5.8). If we assume $n_1(QP) + n_2(PF) = n_2(BF)$, *then show that the coordinates of the point P(x, y) will satisfy the equation of the ellipse.*]

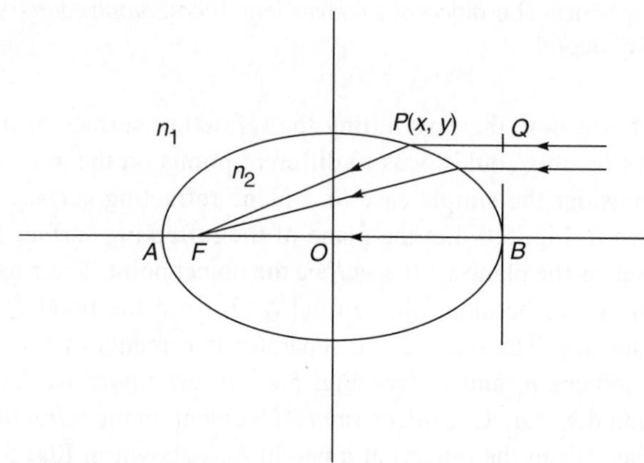

Figure 5.8
Figure for Example 5.3.

In a similar manner, for a set of rays incident parallel to the axis, one can show that the coefficient of spherical aberration of a thin lens made of a material of refractive index n and placed in air, with the surfaces having radii of curvatures R_1 and R_2, would be given by

$$A = -\frac{f(n-1)}{2n^2} \times \left[-\left(\frac{1}{R_2} - P\right)^2\left\{\frac{1}{R_2} - P(n+1)\right\} + \frac{1}{R_1^3}\right] \tag{5.27}$$

where

$$P = \frac{1}{f} = \left[(n-1)\left(\frac{1}{R_1} - \frac{1}{R_2}\right)\right] \quad \textbf{(5.28)}$$

represents the power of the lens. The coefficient A is such that when it is multiplied by the cube of the height of the ray at the lens, one obtains the lateral spherical aberration. Thus, the lateral spherical aberration for rays hitting the lens at a height h would be

$$S_{\text{lat}} = Ah^3 = -\frac{f(n-1)h^3}{2n^2} \times$$

$$\left[-\left(\frac{1}{R_2} - P\right)^2 \left\{\frac{1}{R_2} - P(n+1)\right\} + \frac{1}{R_1^3}\right] \quad \textbf{(5.29)}$$

The longitudinal spherical aberration which corresponds to the difference between the marginal focal length and the paraxial focal length would be given by

$$S_{\text{long}} = Ah^2 f$$

$$= -\frac{(n-1)f^2h^2}{2n^2} \times$$

$$\left[\frac{1}{R_1^3} - \left(\frac{1}{R_2} - \frac{n+1}{f}\right)\left(\frac{1}{R_2} - \frac{1}{f}\right)^2\right] \quad \textbf{(5.30)}$$

For a converging lens, S_{long} will always be negative implying that the marginal rays focus closer to the lens.

For a thin lens of given power (i.e., of a given focal length), one can define a quantity q, called the shape factor, by the following relation:

$$q = \frac{R_2 + R_1}{R_2 - R_1} \quad \textbf{(5.31)}$$

where R_1 and R_2 are the radii of curvatures of the two surfaces. For a given focal length of the lens, one can control the spherical aberration by changing the value of q. This procedure is called bending of the lens. Figure 5.9 shows the variation of spherical aberration with q for $n = 1.5$, $f = 40$ cm (i.e., $P = 0.025$ cm^{-1}) and $h = 1$ cm. It can be seen that for values of q lying near $q \simeq +0.7$, the (magnitude of the) spherical aberration is minimum (but not zero). Thus, by choosing proper values of the radii, the spherical aberration can be minimized. It may be mentioned that the value $q = +1$ implies $R_2 = \infty$ and hence it corresponds to a plano-convex lens with the convex side facing the incident light. On the other hand, for a plano-convex lens with the plane side facing the incident light $R_1 = \infty$ and $q = -1$. Thus the spherical

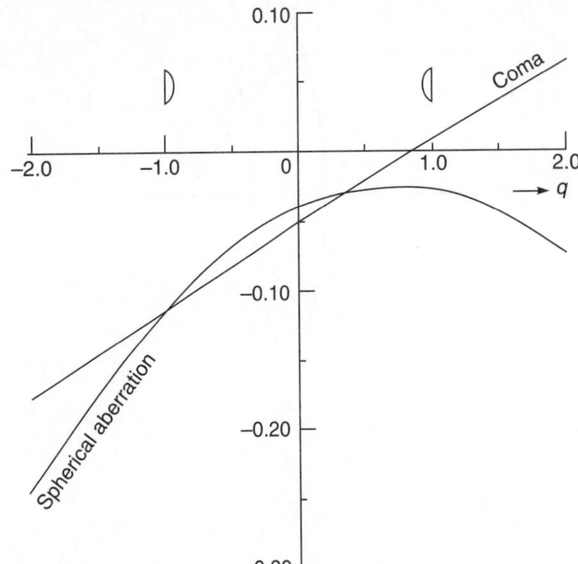

Figure 5.9
Variation of spherical aberration and coma with the shape factor of a thin lens with $n = 1.5$, $f = 40$ cm and $h = 1$ cm. For calculating the coma we have assumed $\tan\theta = 1$, i.e., rays make an angle of 45° with the axis.

aberration is dependent on how the deviation is divided between the surfaces.

The physical reason for the minimum of $|S_{\text{long}}|$ to occur at $q \simeq 0.7$ is as follows: It has already been mentioned before that (for a converging lens) the marginal rays undergo a large deviation which results in the spherical aberration [see Fig. 5.4(a)]. As such we should expect the spherical aberration to be minimum when the angle of deviation δ [see Fig. 5.10(a)] is minimum. As in the case of the prism [see Fig. 5.10(b)], this would occur when the deviations suffered at each of the refracting surfaces are exactly equal, i.e.,

$$\delta_1 = \delta_2;\ (\delta = \delta_1 + \delta_2) \quad \textbf{(5.32)}$$

Indeed for $q = 0.7$, the deviations suffered at each of the surface are equal and one obtains minimum spherical aberration.

Using the criterion of equal deviation discussed above, we will determine the separation between two thin lenses which would lead to minimum spherical aberration. Let L_1 and L_2 be two lenses of focal lengths f_1 and f_2 respectively separated by a distance x (see Fig. 5.11). If θ_1 and θ_2 represent the deviations of the ray at the two lenses, then for minimum spherical aberration, we get

$$\theta_1 = \theta_2 \quad \textbf{(5.33)}$$

To obtain an expression for the deviation suffered by a ray when it encounters a lens, we refer to Fig. 5.12 where a

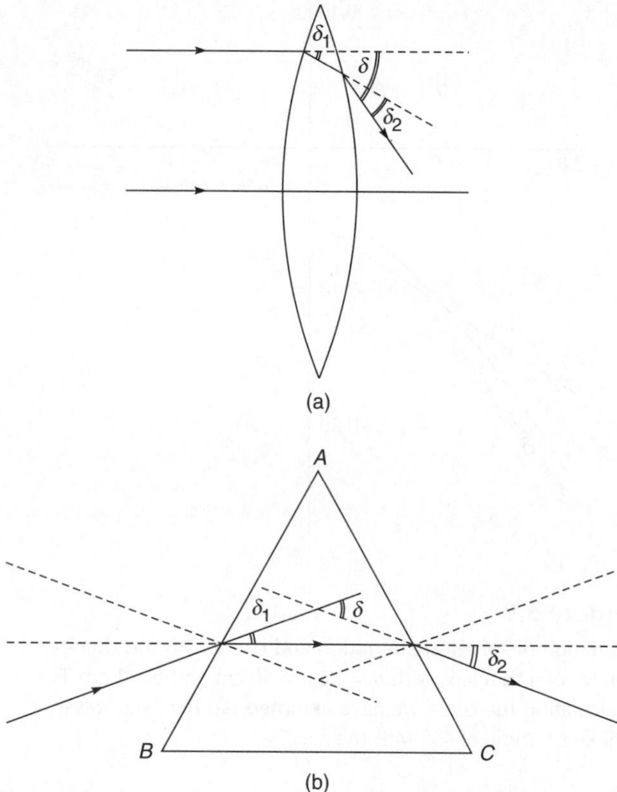

Figure 5.10

(a) Refraction at the two refracting surfaces of a thin lens; the diagram is exaggerated to show clearly the angles.
(b) For a prism, the minimum deviation position corresponds to $\delta_1 = \delta_2$.

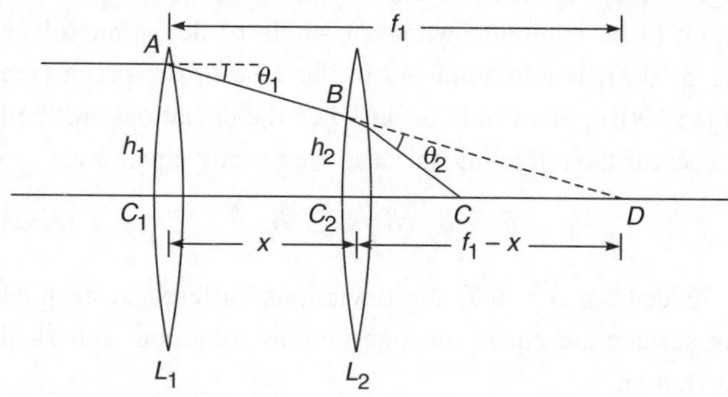

Figure 5.11

Condition for minimum spherical aberration for a combination of two thin lenses.

ray PA gets refracted along AQ after suffering a deviation through an angle θ. From triangle PAQ, we can see that

$$\theta = \theta_1 + \theta_2 \simeq \frac{h}{v} + \frac{h}{(-u)}$$

$$= h\left(\frac{1}{v} - \frac{1}{u}\right) = \frac{h}{f} \tag{5.34}$$

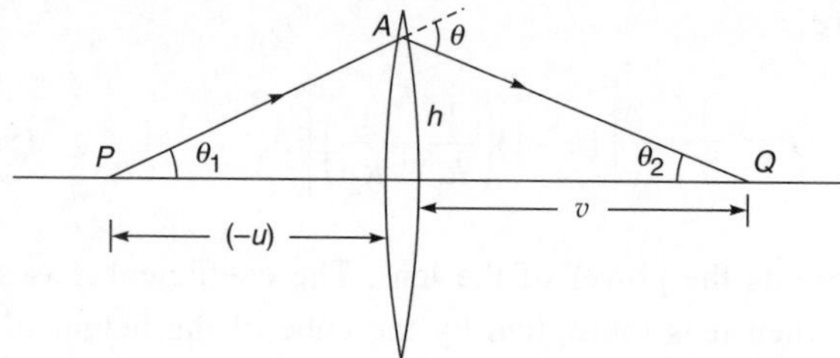

Figure 5.12

Calculation of the angle of deviation.

where we have used the paraxial relation

$$\frac{1}{v} - \frac{1}{u} = \frac{1}{f} \tag{5.35}$$

The quantity u is an intrinsically negative quantity. Thus Eq. (5.33) becomes

$$\frac{h_1}{f_1} = \frac{h_2}{f_2} \tag{5.36}$$

From similar triangles AC_1D and BC_2D (see Fig. 5.11), we can write

$$\frac{h_1}{f_1} = \frac{h_2}{f_1 - x} \tag{5.37}$$

If we use Eqs. (5.6) and (5.7), we obtain

$$x = f_1 - f_2 \tag{5.38}$$

Thus, the spherical aberration of a combination of two thin lenses is minimum when their separation is equal to the difference in their focal lengths. Indeed, in the Huygens eyepiece (see Fig. 5.13), the focal length of the field lens is $3f$ where f represents the focal length of the eye lens. The distance between the two lenses is $2f$. We can immediately see that the conditions for achromatism [see Eq. (5.15)] and minimum spherical aberration [see Eq. (5.38)] are simultaneously satisfied. Since the eyepiece as a whole is corrected and the individual lenses are not, the image of the cross wires (which are placed in the plane PQ) will show aberrations. A discussion of the procedure for reducing the aberrations in various optical instruments requires a very detailed analysis involving the tracing of the rays, which is beyond the scope of this book.

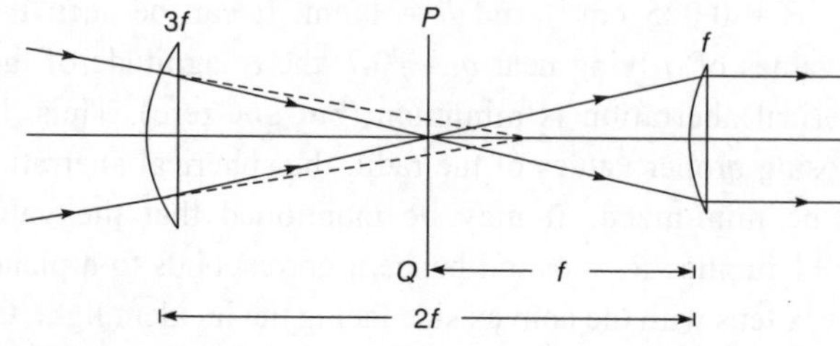

Figure 5.13

The Huygens eyepiece.

It should be mentioned that even when the system is free from all aberrations the image of a point object will still not be a point because of diffraction effects (see Sec. 17.3). For example, if a perfectly spherical wave is emanating from a lens, the ray theory predicts a point image whereas the diffraction theory (which takes into account the finiteness of the wavelength) predicts that the image formed in the image plane will be an Airy pattern [see Sec. 17.3], and the first dark ring will occur at a distance of $\frac{1.22\lambda f}{D}$ from the paraxial image point (see Fig. 5.14) where D is the diameter of the exit pupil. The Airy pattern shown in Fig. 5.14 is highly magnified. For example, for $\lambda = 5000$ Å, $D = 5$ cm, $f = 10$ cm, the radii of the first and second dark rings in the Airy pattern will be about 0.00012 mm and 0.00022 mm, respectively (see Sec. 17.3). The spatial extent of the Airy pattern will become larger with decrease in the value of D. Often one uses a 'stop' to restrict to the paraxial region; however, if the diameter of the 'stop' is made very small then the diffraction effects would dominate. Indeed, a camera gives best image when $f/D \approx 5.6$; at high apertures aberrations degrade the image and at low apertures diffraction degrades the image.

5.3.2 Coma

LO3

As mentioned earlier for a point object lying on the axis the image will suffer only from spherical aberration. For off-axis points, the image will also suffer from coma, astigmatism, curvature of field and distortion. The first off-axis aberration is coma, i.e., for points lying very close to the axis, the image will suffer from spherical aberration and coma only. In this section, we will briefly discuss the effect of coma, assuming that all other aberrations are absent.

The effect of coma is schematically shown in Fig. 5.15(a). The rays which proceed near the axis of the lens focus at a point different from that of the marginal rays. Thus, it appears that the magnification is different for different parts of the lens. It may be mentioned that if we consider the image formation by different zones of a lens, then the spherical aberration arises due to the fact that different zones have different powers and coma arises due to the fact that different zones have different magnifications. In Fig. 5.15(a), we have shown only those rays which lie in the meridional plane, i.e., that plane containing the optical axis and the object point. To see the shape of the image one has to consider the complete set of rays.* In Fig. 5.15(b), we have shown a three-dimensional perspective in which we have considered a set of rays which hit the lens at the same distance from the center. Rays which intersect the lens at diametrically opposite points focus to a single point on the paraxial image plane. These different pairs of rays focus to different points in the image plane such that these foci lie on a circle. The radius of the circle and the distance at which the center lies from the ideal image point measures the coma. As the radius of the zone [shown as h in Fig. 5.15(b)] increases, the center of the circle also shifts away from the ideal image. Thus the composite image will have a form as shown in Fig. 5.15(c). The image of a point object thus has a comet-like appearance and hence the name coma (see Fig. 5.16).

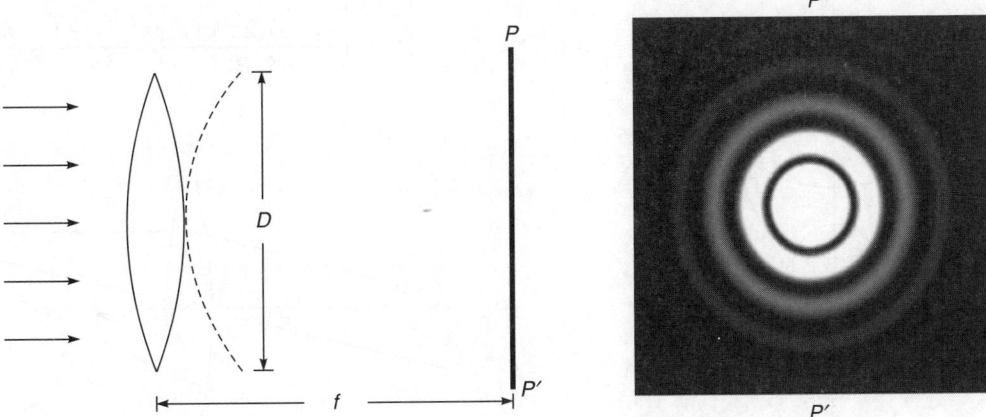

Figure 5.14
A perfectly spherical wave (converging on the plane PP') will produce an Airy pattern in the image plane.

* It must be mentioned that a proper understanding of the aberrations can only be obtained by a careful and thorough mathematical analysis. This, however, is beyond the scope of this book. Interested readers may look up Refs. 5.1 and 5.3.

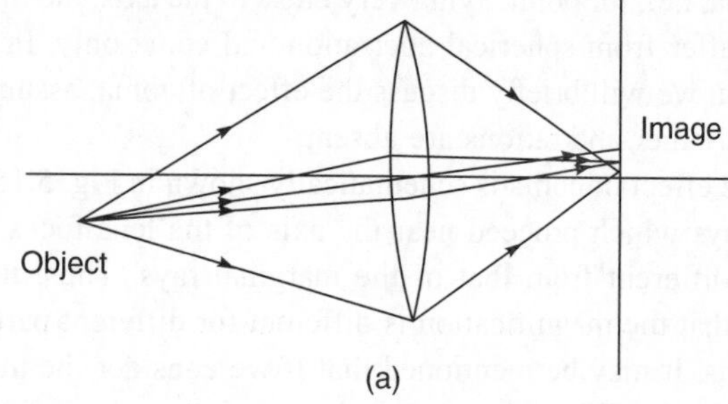

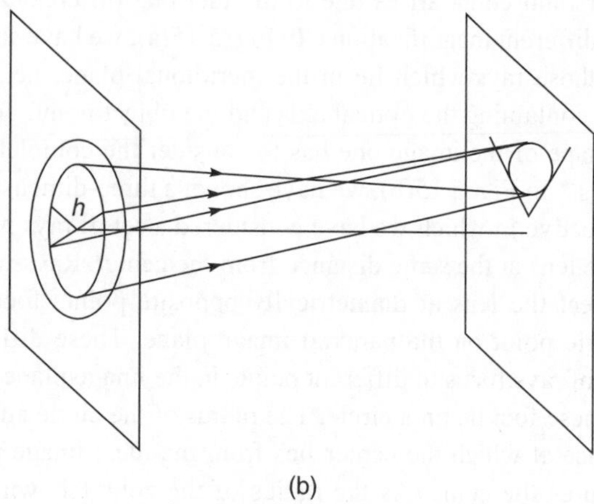

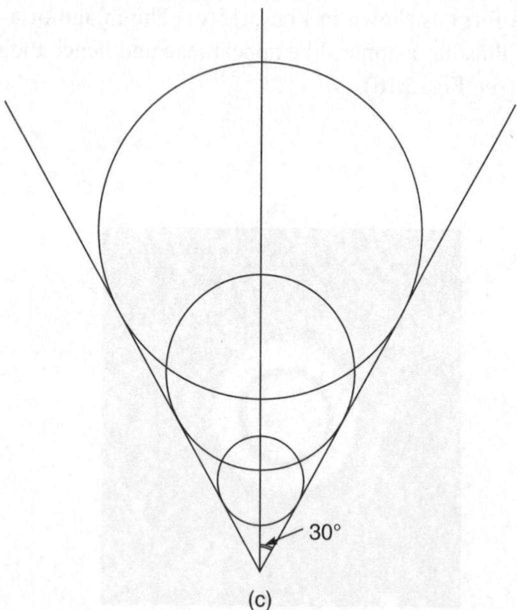

Figure 5.15

The image formation in the presence of coma. In (a), we have shown only those rays which lie in the meridional plane, (b) a three-dimensional perspective is shown. In (c), we have shown the composite image.

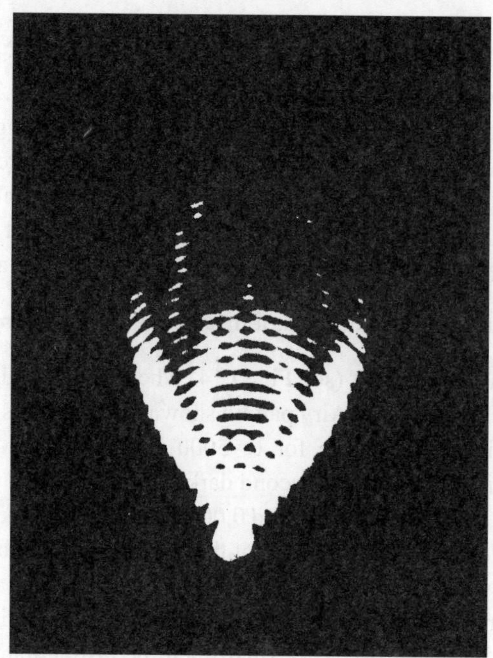

Figure 5.16

Image of a point source showing coma. [*After H.F. Meiners, Physics Demonstration Experiments, Vol. II, The Ronald Press Co., New York, 1970; used with permission*].

For a parallel bundle of rays incident on a lens and inclined at an angle θ with the z-axis (see Fig. 5.17), one can show that the coma in the image is given by (see, e.g., Ref. 5.1):

$$\text{coma} = \frac{3(n-1)}{2} fh^2 \tan\theta \times \left[\frac{(n-1)(2n+1)}{nR_1 R_2} - \frac{n^2-n-1}{n^2 R_1^2} - \frac{n}{R_2^2}\right] \quad \textbf{(5.39)}$$

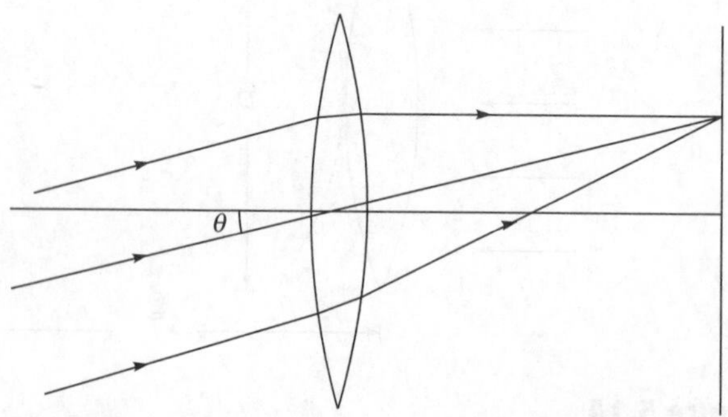

Figure 5.17

Parallel rays (inclined at an angle θ with the axis) incident on a thin lens.

In Fig. 5.9, we have plotted the variation of coma with the shape factor q. It can immediately be seen that for a lens with $q = +0.8$, coma is zero. It can also be seen that both spherical aberration and coma are close to a minimum for a plano-convex lens (with the convex side facing the incident light) for which $q = 1.0$ and as such plano-convex lenses are extensively used in eyepieces.

We may mention here that in Sec. 3.11 we had derived the Abbe sine condition which when satisfied, the optical system is free from spherical aberration and coma.

5.3.3 Astigmatism and Curvature of Field

LO4

When an optical system is free from spherical aberration and coma then the system will image sharply those object points lying on or near the axis. But for points far away from the axis, the image of a point will not be a point and then the optical system is said to be afflicted with astigmatism.

Consider an object point P far away from the axis. The plane containing the axis and the object point is called the **meridional plane** and the plane perpendicular to the meridional plane (containing the axis) is called the **sagittal plane**. Figure 5.18 shows the image formation when the optical system suffers from astigmatism only. The rays in the meridional plane converge at a different point as compared to those in the sagittal plane. For example, rays PA and PB focus at the point T and rays PC and PD focus at a point S which is different from T. Since at the point T, the rays in the sagittal plane have not still focused, one in fact has a focal line which is normal to the meridional plane. This focal line T is called the **tangential focus**. Similarly since at S, the rays in the meridional plane have defocussed, one obtains a focal line lying in the tangential plane; this is called the **sagittal focal line.** The distance between S and T is a measure of astigmatism.

To see the origin of astigmatism one observes that for a point on the axis (when the lens is free from other aberrations) the wavefront emerging from the lens is spherical and thus as the wavefront progresses, it converges to a single point. But when the object point is non-axial, then the emerging wavefront is not spherical and thus as the wavefront converges, it does not focus to a point but to two lines, which are normal to each other and called the tangential and the sagittal focal lines. Somewhere between the two focal lines, the image is circular in shape and is called the circle of least confusion.

The distance between the tangential and the sagittal foci increases as the object point moves away from the axis. Thus, the tangential foci and the sagittal foci of points at different distances from the axis lie on two surfaces as shown in Fig. 5.19. The optical system will be said to be free from astigmatism when the two surfaces coincide. But even when they coincide it can be shown that the resultant image surface will be curved. This defect of the image is termed **curvature of the field**.

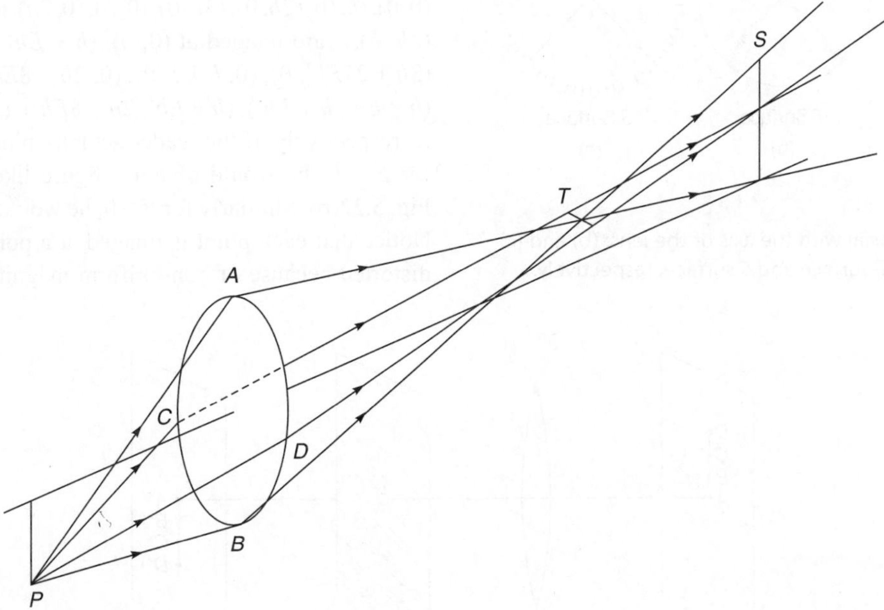

Figure 5.18
Image formation in the presence of astigmatism.

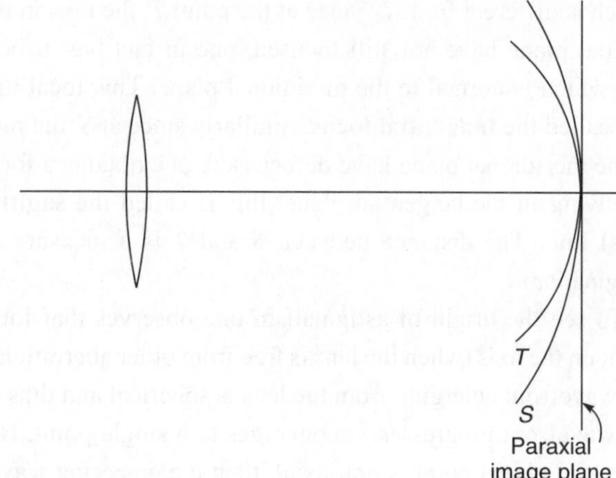

Figure 5.19
Tangential and sagittal foci.

As an example of image formation in the presence of astigmatism, consider a spoked wheel coaxial with the lens axis as shown in Fig. 5.20(a). Since on the *T*-surface the image of a point source is a line perpendicular to the meridional plane, on the *T*-surface, the complete rim of the wheel will be in focus while the spokes will be out of focus as shown in Fig. 5.20(b). Similarly, since on the *S*-surface the image of a point is a line in the meridional plane, the spokes will be in focus and the rim will not be in focus as shown in Fig. 5.20(c).

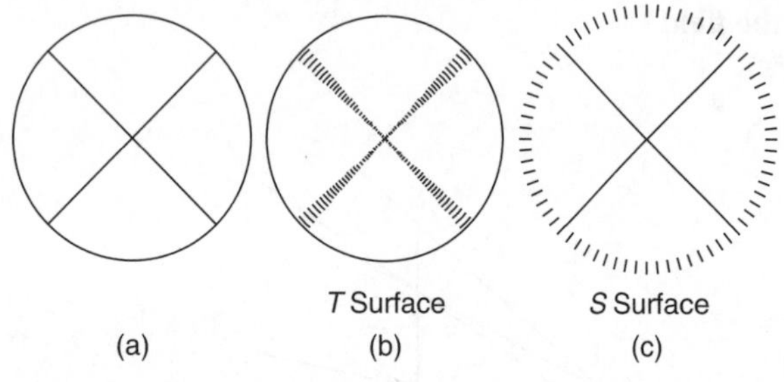

Figure 5.20
(a) Spoked object coaxial with the axis of the lens; (b) and (c) show images on the *T*-surface and *S*-surface, respectively.

5.4 Distortion

LO5

The last of the Seidel aberrations is called **distortion** and is caused by non-uniform magnification of the system. When we discussed spherical aberration we had mentioned that for a point object on the axis of the optical system, the images will suffer only form spherical aberration. Similarly, if we have a pinhole on the axis at any plane of the optical system (see Fig. 5.21), then the image will suffer only from distortion. This is because of the fact that corresponding to any point in the object plane, only one of the rays emanating from this point will pass through the pinhole; consequently, all other aberrations will be absent. Obviously, for such a configuration, each point will be imaged as a point but if the system suffers from non-uniform magnification, the image will be distorted. This can be illustrated if we consider the imaging of four equally spaced points *A*, *B*, *C* and *D* which are imaged as *A′*, *B′*, *C′* and *D′*, respectively. Mathematical analysis shows that

$$X_d = Mx_0 + E(x_0^2 + y_0^2)x_0 \tag{5.40}$$

and

$$Y_d = My_0 + E(x_0^2 + y_0^2)y_0 \tag{5.41}$$

where (x_0, y_0) and (X_d, Y_d) represent the coordinates of the object and the image point, respectively, *M* represents the magnification of the system and *E* represents the coefficient of distortion. Figure 5.22(b) corresponds to a negative value of *E* and is known as **barrel distortion.** The distortion of the image can be easily understood if we consider the imaging of a square grid as shown in Fig. 5.22. Assuming unit magnification (i.e., $M = 1$), the points having coordinates $(0, 0), (h, 0), (2h, 0), (3h, 0), (0, h), (0, 2h), (0, 3h), (h, h), (h, 2h), (2h, h), \ldots$ are imaged at $(0, 0)$, $(h + Eh^3, 0)$, $(2h + 8Eh^3, 0)$, $(3h + 27Eh^3, 0)$, $(0, h + Eh^3)$, $(0, 2h + 8Eh^3)$, $(0, 3h + 27Eh^3)$, $(h + Eh^3, h + Eh^3)$, $(h + Eh^3, 2h + 8Eh^3)$, $(2h + 8Eh^3, h + Eh^3)$, … respectively. If the reader actually plots these points, then for $E < 0$, he would obtain a figure like the one shown in Fig. 5.22(b). Similarly for $E > 0$, he would obtain Fig. 5.22(c). Notice that each point is imaged at a point, but the image is distorted because of non-uniform magnification.

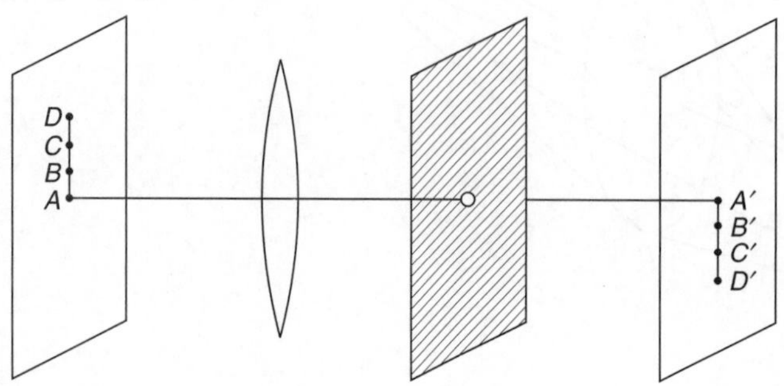

Figure 5.21
In the presence of a pinhole on the axis, the image suffers only from distortion.

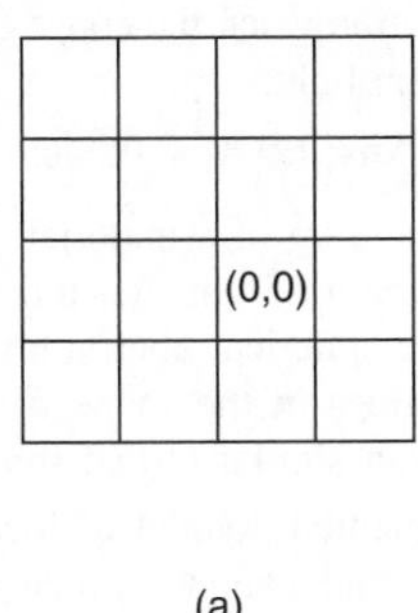

(a)

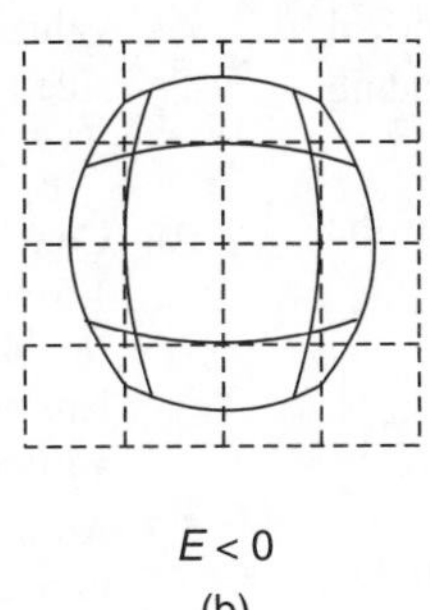

(b)

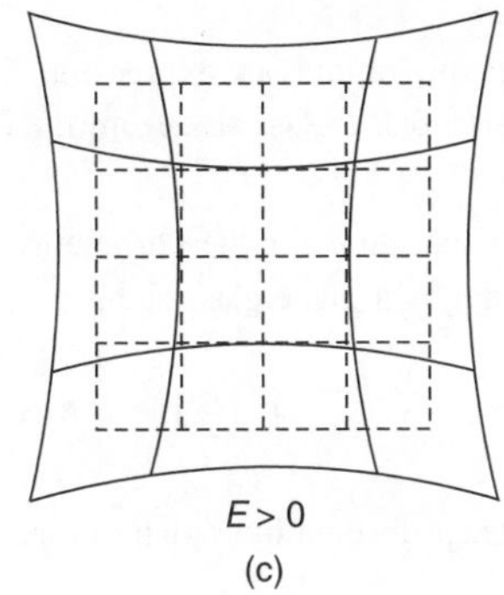

(c)

Figure 5.22
(a) Shows the object, (b) represents the image when $E < 0$ and (c) when $E > 0$.

SUMMARY

- For a polychromatic source, different wavelength components (after refraction) proceed along different directions and form images at different points; this leads to chromatic aberrations. If we consider two thin lenses made of different materials placed in contact with each other, the focal length of the combination will be the same for blue and red colors if

$$\frac{\omega}{f} + \frac{\omega'}{f'} = 0$$

where

$$\omega = \frac{n_b - n_r}{n - 1} \quad \text{and} \quad \omega' = \frac{n'_b - n'_r}{n' - 1}$$

are known as the dispersive powers. Further,

$$n \equiv \frac{n_b + n_r}{2} \approx n_y, \; n' \equiv \frac{n'_b + n'_r}{2} \approx n'_y$$

where n_b, n_y and n_r represent the refractive indices for the material of the first lens corresponding to the blue, yellow and red colors, respectively. Similarly, n_b', n_y' and n_r' represent the refractive indices for the second lens. Since ω and ω' are both positive, f and f' must be of opposite signs.

- For an achromatic doublet to be functional, the two lenses must be of different materials.
In a separated doublet, chromatic aberration is greatly reduced if $w = w'$ and the distance between the two lenses is equal to the mean of the focal length.
- For a lens, the marginal rays (which are incident near the periphery of the lens) focus at a point which is different than the focal point of paraxial rays. The distance along the axis between the paraxial image point and the image corresponding to marginal rays (i.e., rays striking the edge of the lens) is termed longitudinal spherical aberration.
- The spherical aberration of a combination of two thin lenses is a minimum when their separation is equal to the difference in their focal lengths.
- Coma is the first off axis aberrations suffered by the image formed due to point object lying very close to the axis.
- For a non-axial object point, the emerging wave front is not spherical and doesn't focus.
- Distortion is caused due to presence of pinhole on the axis.

PROBLEMS

5.1 Consider a plane glass slab of thickness d made of a material of refractive index n, placed in air. By simple application of Snell's law obtain an expression for the spherical aberration of the slab. What are other kinds of aberrations that the image will suffer from?

[**Ans:** Spherical aberration $= -\dfrac{(n^2 - 1)dh^2}{2n^3u^2}$, where h is the height at which the ray strikes the slab, and u is the distance of the object point from the front surface of the slab.]

5.2 Why can't you obtain an expression for the spherical aberration of a plane glass slab from Eq. (5.27) by tending R_1, R_2 to ∞?

5.3 Obtain an expression for the chromatic aberration in the image formed by a plane glass slab.

$$\left[\textbf{Ans: } \approx d\left(\frac{1}{n_r} - \frac{1}{n_b}\right)\right]$$

5.4 Does the image formed by a plane mirror suffer from any aberration?

5.5 Calculate the longitudinal spherical aberration of a thin plano-convex lens made of a material of refractive index 1.5 and whose curved surface has a radius of curvature of 10 cm, for rays incident at a height of 1 cm. Compare the values of the aberration when the convex side and the plane side face the incident light.

[**Ans: (a)** ≈ -0.058 cm; **(b)** ≈ -0.225 cm]

5.6 Consider a lens made up of a material of refractive index 1.5 with a focal length 25 cm. Assuming $h = 0.5$ cm and $\theta = 45°$, obtain the spherical aberration and coma for the lens for various values of the shape factor q and plot the variation in a manner similar to that shown in Fig. 5.9.

5.7 An achromatic cemented doublet of focal length 25 cm is to be made from a combination of an equiconvex flint glass lens (n_b = 1.50529, n_r = 1.49776) and a crown glass lens (n_b = 1.66270, n_r = 1.64357). Calculate the radii of curvatures of the different surfaces and the focal lengths of each of the two lenses.

[**Ans:** R_1 = 14.2 cm = $-R_2 = -R'_1$; $R'_2 \approx -42$ cm]

PART 2

WAVE OPTICS

This part (consisting of 18 chapters) discusses many extremely interesting aspects of wave optics. Chapter 6 starts with simple harmonic motion which is the most fundamental vibration associated with wave motion. The chapter also gives first principle derivations of the refractive index variation with frequency and also of the Rayleigh scattering formula which explains the redness of the setting sun and the blue color of the sky. Chapters 7 and 8 discuss Fourier Series and Fourier Transforms. Chapter 9 discusses the wave equation which represents the basic physics of wave propagation. Chapter 10 discusses Huygens' principle which is used to derive the laws of reflection and refraction. In Chapter 11 we have used Fourier transforms to discuss dispersion of optical pulses and also the physics of Chirped Pulse Amplification for which 2 scientists were awarded (half of) the 2017 Nobel Prize in Physics.

Chapter 12 discusses the superposition principle which is the basic physics behind all interference experiments discussed in Chapters 13-15. Chapter 14 discusses the Michelson Interferometer which is perhaps one of the most ingenious and sensational optical instrument for which Michelson received the Nobel Prize in Physics in 1907. Chapter 16 discusses the basic concept of temporal and spatial coherence and also Michelson's ingenious experiment to determine the angular diameter of stars. Chapters 17, 18 and 19 cover the very important area of diffraction and discuss the principle behind diffraction grating, divergence of laser beams, X-ray diffraction, Fourier Optics, etc. Chapter 20 is on Holography for which Dennis Gabor received the 1971 Nobel Prize in Physics. In Chapter 21, the generation and analysis of various forms of polarized light is discussed followed by a detailed analysis of propagation of electromagnetic waves in anisotropic media. In Chapter 22 starting with Maxwell's equations, the wave equation has been derived which had led Maxwell to predict the existence of electromagnetic waves. Reflection and refraction of electromagnetic waves have been discussed in Chapter 23.

CHAPTER

6

Simple Harmonic Motion, Forced Vibrations and Origin of Refractive Index

The correct picture of an atom, which is given by the theory of wave mechanics, says that, **so far as problems involving light are concerned**, *the electrons behave as though they were held by springs. So we shall suppose that the electrons have a linear restoring force which, together with their mass m, makes them behave like little oscillators, with a resonant frequency ω_0. .... The electric field of the light wave polarizes the molecules of the gas, producing oscillating dipole moments. The acceleration of the oscillating charges radiates new waves of the field. This new field, interfering with the old field, produces a changed field which is equivalent to a phase shift of the original wave. Because this phase shift is proportional to the thickness of the material, the effect is equivalent to having a different phase velocity in the material.*

—Richard Feynman in *Feynman Lectures on Physics*, Vol. I

LEARNING OBJECTIVES

After reading this chapter, the reader should be able to:

LO 1: *explain simple harmonic motion.*

LO 2: *interpret the effect of damping on simple harmonic motion.*

LO 3: *understand the relationship between damping and resonance.*

LO 4: *understand the origin of refractive index.*

LO 5: *describe the phenomenon of Rayleigh scattering.*

Important Milestones

1807 It seems Thomas Young was the first person who had used the name "index of refraction".

1859 John Tyndall had discovered what is now known as "Rayleigh scattering"; the blue component gets scattered more than the red component because of which the sky is blue.

1871 Lord Rayleigh published two papers in which he showed that the scattering of light by small particles (whose size would be about one-tenth of the wavelength of light) is inversely proportional to the fourth

Above Image: View of a rainbow against a background of clouds. Photograph courtesy McGraw Hill Digital Access Library.

power of the wavelength. Thus the blue color is scattered 10 times more than the red color (because the red color has a wavelength which is about 1.75 times the wavelength of blue). This is the reason why the sky appears blue. Although the wavelength of violet is less than that of blue, the sky does not appear violet because there is very little violet in the sunlight. Lord Rayleigh received the 1904 Nobel Prize in Physics. On the other hand, Mie scattering (named after the German physicist Gustav Mie) is caused by particles that are of much bigger size and is roughly independent of the wavelength. The grey/white colour of the clouds (see Fig. 6.16) is caused by Mie scattering.

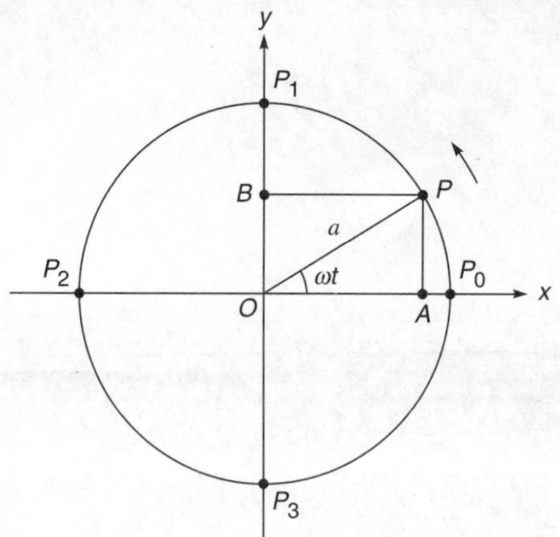

Figure 6.1
The point P is rotating in the anticlockwise direction on the circumference of a circle of radius a, with uniform angular velocity ω. The foot of the perpendicular on any one of the diameters executes simple harmonic motion. P_0 is the position of the point at $t = 0$.

6.1 Introduction

The most fundamental vibration associated with wave motion is the simple harmonic motion; in Sec. 6.2 we will discuss simple harmonic motion and in Sec. 6.3 we will discuss the effects (on the vibratory motion) due to damping. If a periodic force acts on a vibrating system, the system undergoes what are known as **forced vibrations**; in Sec. 6.4, we will study such vibrations which will allow us to understand the origin of refractive index (see Sec. 6.5) and even Rayleigh scattering (see Sec. 6.6), which is responsible for the red color of the setting (or rising) sun and blue color of the sky.

6.2 Simple Harmonic Motion LO1

A periodic motion is a motion which repeats itself after regular intervals of time and the simplest kind of periodic motion is a simple harmonic motion in which the displacement varies sinusoidally with time. In order to understand simple harmonic motion, we consider a point P rotating on the circumference of a circle of radius a with an angular velocity ω (see Fig. 6.1). We choose the center of the circle as our origin and we assume that at $t = 0$ the point P lies on the x-axis (i.e., at the point P_0). At an arbitrary time t the point will be at the position P where $\angle POP_0 = \omega t$.

Let A be the foot of the perpendicular from the point P on the x-axis. Clearly, the distance

$$OA = a \cos \omega t \tag{6.1}$$

and as the point P rotates on the circumference of the circle, the point A moves to and fro about the origin on the diameter. When the point P is at P_1, then the foot of the perpendicular is at O. This can also be seen from Eq. (6.1) because when P coincides with P_1, $\omega t = \pi/2$ and hence $a \cos \omega t = a \cos \pi/2 = 0$. As the point still moves further, the foot of the perpendicular would lie on the other side of the origin and thus OA would be negative as is also evident from Eq. (6.1) because ωt would then be greater than $\pi/2$. When P coincides with P_2, then $OA = OP_2 = -a$. When the point P moves from P_2 to P_3, OA starts decreasing and it finally becomes zero when P coincides with P_3. After P crosses P_3, OA starts increasing again and finally acquires the value a when P coincides with P_0. After crossing the point P_0, the motion repeats itself.

A motion in which the displacement varies sinusoidally with time [as in Eq. (6.1)] is known as a **simple harmonic motion**. *Thus, when a point rotates on the circumference of a circle with a uniform angular velocity, the foot of the perpendicular on any one of its diameters will execute simple harmonic motion.* The quantity a is called the **amplitude of the motion**, and the period of the motion, T, will be the time required to complete one revolution. Since the angular velocity is ω, the time taken for one complete revolution will be $2\pi/\omega$. Thus,

$$T = \frac{2\pi}{\omega} \tag{6.2}$$

The inverse of the time period is known as the frequency:

$$\nu = \frac{1}{T} = \frac{\omega}{2\pi}$$

or

$$\omega = 2\pi\nu \tag{6.3}$$

It should be pointed out that we could as well have studied the motion of the point B, which is the foot of the perpendicular from the point P on the y-axis. The distance OB is given by (see Fig. 6.1)

$$OB = y = a \sin \omega t \tag{6.4}$$

We had conveniently chosen $t = 0$ as the time when P was on the x-axis. The choice of the time $t = 0$ is arbitrary and we could have chosen time $t = 0$ to be the instant when P was at P' (see Fig. 6.2). If the angle $P'OX = \theta$ then the projection on the x-axis at any time t would be given by

$$OA = x = a \cos (\omega t + \theta) \tag{6.5}$$

The quantity $(\omega t + \theta)$ is known as the **phase of the motion** and θ represents the initial phase. It is obvious from the above discussion that the value of θ is quite arbitrary and depends on the instant from which we start measuring time.

We next consider two points P and Q rotating on the circle with the same angular velocity and P' and Q' be their respective positions at $t = 0$. Let the angles $\angle P'OX$ and $\angle Q'OX$ be θ and ϕ, respectively (see Fig. 6.3). Clearly, at an arbitrary time t, the distance of the foot of the perpendiculars from the origin would be

$$x_P = a \cos (\omega t + \theta) \tag{6.6a}$$

$$x_Q = a \cos (\omega t + \phi) \tag{6.6b}$$

The quantity

$$(\omega t + \theta) - (\omega t + \phi) = \theta - \phi \tag{6.7}$$

represents the phase difference between the two simple harmonic motions and if $\theta - \phi = 0$ (or an even multiple of π) the motions are said to be in phase, and if $\theta - \phi = \pi$ (or an odd multiple of π) the motions are said to be out of phase. If we choose a different origin of time, the quantities θ and ϕ would change by the same additive constant; consequently, the phase difference $(\theta - \phi)$ is independent of the choice of the instant $t = 0$.

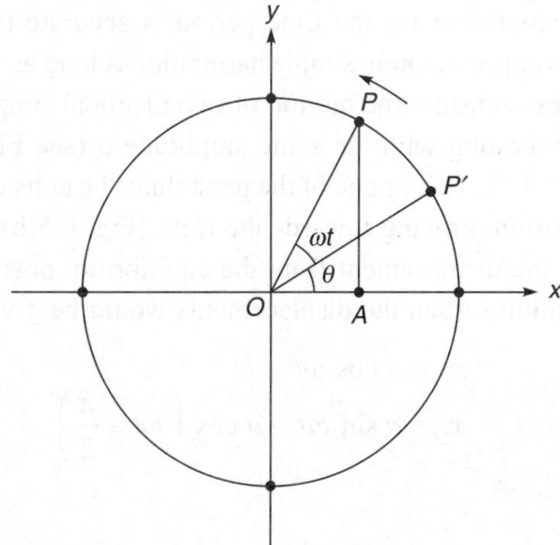

Figure 6.2

At $t = 0$, the point P is at P' and therefore, the initial phase is θ.

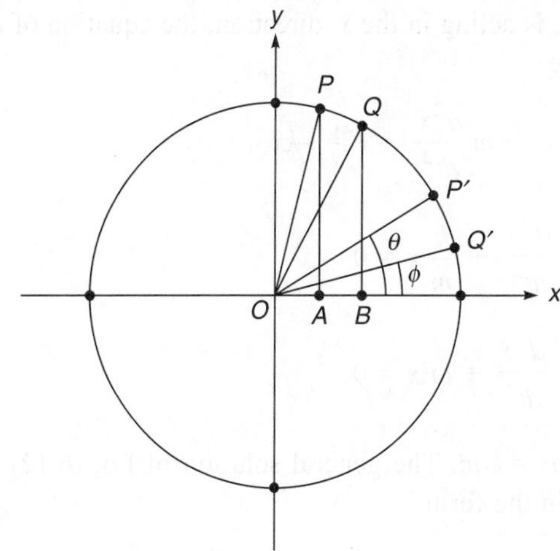

Figure 6.3

The points A and B execute simple harmonic motions with the same frequency ω. The initial phases of A and B are θ and ϕ, respectively.

Thus, the displacement of a particle, which executes simple harmonic motion, can be written as

$$x = a \sin (\omega t + \theta) \tag{6.8}$$

Therefore, the velocity and the acceleration of the particle would be given by the following equations:

$$v = \frac{dx}{dt} = a\omega \cos(\omega t + \theta) \tag{6.9}$$

and $$f = \frac{d^2x}{dt^2} = -a\omega^2 \sin(\omega t + \theta)$$

or $$f = \frac{d^2x}{dt^2} = -\omega^2 x \tag{6.10}$$

Equation (6.10) shows that the acceleration of the particle is proportional to the displacement and the negative sign indicates that the acceleration is always directed towards the origin. Equation (6.10) can be used to define the simple harmonic motion as the motion of a particle in a straight line in which the acceleration is proportional to the displacement from a fixed point (on the straight line) and always directed towards the fixed point. (Here the point $x = 0$ is the fixed point and is usually referred to as the equilibrium position.) If we multiply Eq. (6.10) by the mass of the particle, then we obtain the following expression for the force acting on the particle:

$$F = mf = -m\omega^2 x$$

or $$F = -kx \tag{6.11}$$

where k (= $m\omega^2$) is known as the **force constant**. We could have equally well started from Eq. (6.11) and obtained simple harmonic motion. This can easily be seen by noting that since the force is acting in the x–direction, the equation of motion would be

$$m\frac{d^2x}{dt^2} = F = -kx$$

or $$\frac{d^2x}{dt^2} + \frac{k}{m}x = 0$$

or $$\frac{d^2x}{dt^2} + \omega^2 x = 0 \quad \textbf{(6.12)}$$

where $\omega^2 = k/m$. The general solution of Eq. (6.12) can be written in the form

$$x = A \sin \omega t + B \cos \omega t \quad \textbf{(6.13)}$$

which can be rewritten in either of the following forms:

$$x = a \sin (\omega t + \theta) \quad \textbf{(6.14)}$$

or $$x = a \cos (\omega t + \theta) \quad \textbf{(6.15)}$$

which describes a simple harmonic motion.

6.2.1 Examples of Simple Harmonic Motion

In this section we will discuss three simple examples of simple harmonic motion.

(a) The simple pendulum The simplest example of simple harmonic motion is the motion of the bob of a simple pendulum in the gravitational field. If the bob of the pendulum is displaced slightly from the equilibrium position (see Fig. 6.4) then the forces acting on the bob are the gravitational force *mg* acting vertically downwards and the tension *T*, in the direction *B′A*. In the equilibrium position (*AB*) the tension is equal and opposite to the gravitational force. However, in the displaced position the tension *T* is not in the direction of the gravitational force and if we resolve the gravitational force along the direction of the string and perpendicular to it, we see that the component $mg \cos \theta$ balances the tension in the string and the component $mg \sin \theta$ is the restoring force. The motion of the bob is along the arc of a circle but if the length of the pendulum is large and the angle θ is small, the motion can be assumed to be approximately in a straight line [see Fig. 6.4(b)]. Under such an approximation, we may assume that this force is always directed towards the point *B* and the magnitude of this force will be*

$$mg \sin \theta \approx mg\frac{x}{l} \quad \textbf{(6.16)}$$

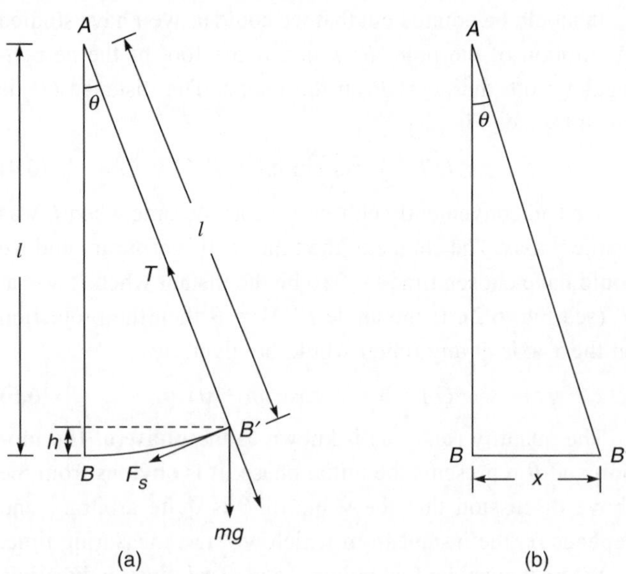

Figure 6.4

(a) The forces on the bob of the pendulum when it is displaced from its equilibrium position. The restoring force is F_s which is equal to $mg \sin \theta$. (b) If the angle θ is small, the motion of the bob can be approximately assumed to be in a straight line.

Thus the equation of motion will be

$$F = m\frac{d^2x}{dt^2} = -mg\frac{x}{l} \quad \textbf{(6.17)}$$

or $$\frac{d^2x}{dt^2} + \omega^2 x = 0 \quad \textbf{(6.18)}$$

where $\omega^2 = g/l$. Equation (6.18) is of the same form as Eq. (6.12); thus the motion of the bob is simple harmonic with its time period given by the following equation:

$$T = \frac{2\pi}{\omega} = 2\pi\sqrt{\frac{l}{g}} \quad \textbf{(6.19)}$$

The expression for the time period is accurate (i.e., the motion is approximately simple harmonic) as long as $\theta \lesssim 4°$.

We next consider the motion of two identical simple pendulums vibrating with the same amplitude *a* (see Fig. 6.5). Let, at $t = 0$, the bob of one of the pendulums be at its extreme right position, moving towards the right [Fig. 6.5(b)]. If we measure the displacement from the equilibrium positions of the pendulums, then the displacements would be given by

$$x_1 = a \cos \omega t$$
$$x_2 = a \sin \omega t = a \cos\left(\omega t - \frac{\pi}{2}\right) \quad \textbf{(6.20)}$$

* We will be assuming that θ is small so that $\sin \theta \approx \theta$, where θ is in radians. The above approximation is valid for $\theta \lesssim 0.07$ radians ($\approx 4°$).

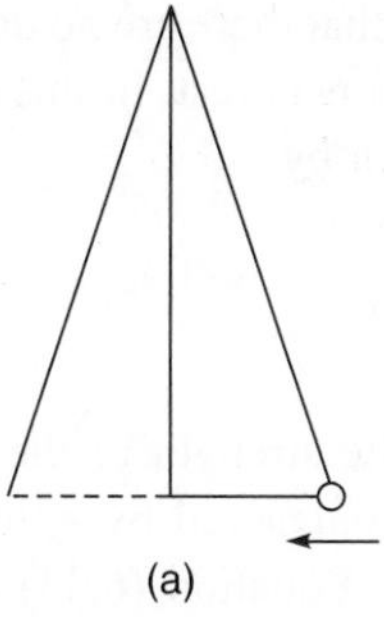

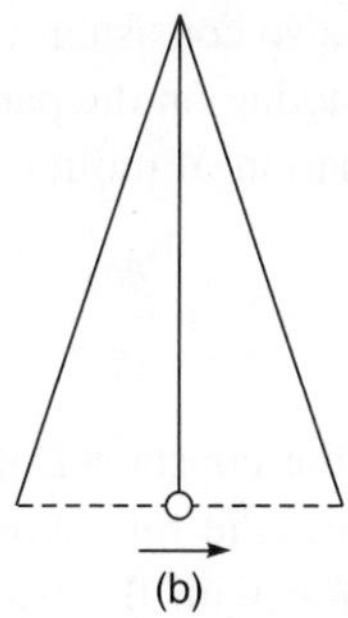

Figure 6.5

(a) and (b) show the motion of two identical pendulums which are vibrating with the same amplitude but having a phase difference of $\pi/2$. The small circles denote the position of the bobs at $t = 0$.

Thus, the two bobs execute simple harmonic motion with a phase difference of $\pi/2$ and in fact the first pendulum is ahead in phase by $\pi/2$. In Fig. 6.5(b), if the bob was moving towards the left, then the equation of motion would have been

$$x_2 = -a \sin \omega t = a \cos \left(\omega t + \frac{\pi}{2} \right)$$

and then the second pendulum would have been ahead of phase by $\pi/2$. Since, in general, the displacement of the bob of the pendulum can be written as

$$x = a \cos (\omega t + \phi) \tag{6.21}$$

the velocity of the particle would be given by

$$\frac{dx}{dt} = -a\omega \sin (\omega t + \phi) \tag{6.22}$$

Thus, the kinetic energy of the mass would be

$$T = \frac{1}{2} m \left(\frac{dx}{dt} \right)^2$$

$$= \frac{1}{2} ma^2\omega^2 \sin^2 (\omega t + \phi) \tag{6.23}$$

Comparing Eqs. (6.21) and (6.23), we see that when the particle is at its extreme positions, the kinetic energy is zero and when the particle passes through equilibrium position, the kinetic energy is maximum. At the extreme positions, the kinetic energy gets transformed into potential energy. From Fig. 6.4(a) it can immediately be seen that

$$\text{Potential energy,} \quad V = mgh = mgl(1 - \cos \theta)$$

$$= mgl\, 2 \sin^2 \frac{\theta}{2} \approx 2\, mgl \left(\frac{\theta}{2} \right)^2$$

[θ measured in radians]

$$\approx \frac{1}{2} mgl \left(\frac{x}{l} \right)^2 = \frac{1}{2}\, m\, \omega^2 x^2 \tag{6.24}$$

or

$$V = \frac{1}{2} m\, \omega^2 a^2 \cos^2(\omega t + \phi) \tag{6.25}$$

where we have used the fact that $\omega^2 = g/l$. We may mention that the expression for potential energy could have been directly written down by noting the fact that if the potential energies at x and at $x + dx$ are V and $V + dV$, then

$$dV = -F\, dx = +kx\, dx \tag{6.26}$$

Thus,

$$V = \int_0^x kx\, dx = \frac{1}{2} kx^2 \tag{6.27}$$

where we have assumed the zero of the potential energy to be at $x = 0$. Thus, the total energy E would be given by

$$E = T + V = \frac{1}{2} m\, \omega^2 a^2 \tag{6.28}$$

which, as expected, is independent of time. We can also see from Eq. (6.26) that the energy associated with the simple harmonic motion is proportional to the square of the amplitude and the square of the frequency.

(b) Vibrations of a mass held by two stretched springs Another simple example is the motion of a mass m, held by two stretched springs on a smooth table as shown in Fig. 6.6. The two springs are of natural length l_0 [Fig. 6.6(a)] and corresponding to the equilibrium position of the mass, the lengths of the stretched springs are l. If the mass is displaced slightly from the equilibrium position, then the resultant force acting on the mass will be

$$F = k[(l - x) - l_0] - k[(l + x) - l_0]$$

$$= -2kx \tag{6.29}$$

where k represents the force constant of the spring. Once again we get a force which is proportional to the displacement and directed towards the equilibrium position and consequently, the motion of the mass on the frictionless table will be simple harmonic in nature.

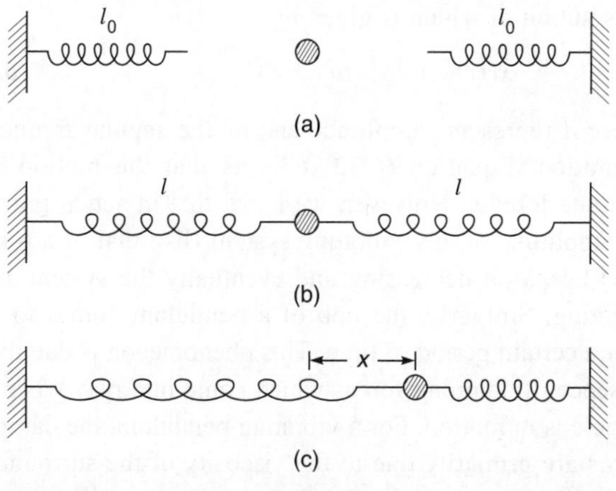

Figure 6.6

Two springs of natural length l_0 [see (a)] are stretched to a length l [see (b)] to hold the mass. If the mass is displaced by a small distance x from its equilibrium position [see (c)], the mass will execute simple harmonic motion.

(c) Vibrations of a stretched string When a stretched string (as in a sonometer) is made to vibrate in its fundamental mode (see Fig. 6.7), then each point on the string executes simple harmonic motion with different amplitudes but having the same initial phase. The displacement can be written in the form

$$y = a \sin\left(\frac{\pi}{L}x\right) \cos \omega t \quad \textbf{(6.30)}$$

The amplitude is therefore zero at $x = 0$ and at $x = L$ and is maximum at $x = L/2$. On the other hand, if the string is vibrating in its first harmonic, then each point on the first half of the string vibrates out of phase with each point on the other half.

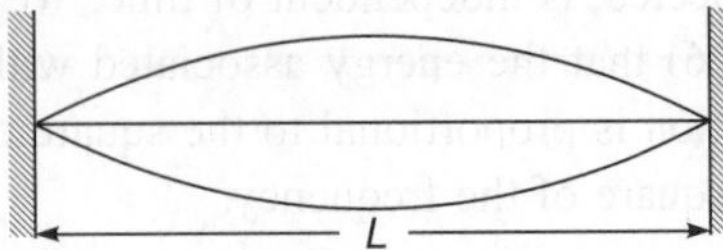

Figure 6.7
When a string clamped at both the ends is made to vibrate in its fundamental mode, all particles execute simple harmonic motions with same frequency and same initial phase but having different amplitudes.

6.3 Damped Simple Harmonic Motion

LO2

In Sec. 6.2, we had shown that for a particle executing SHM, the equation of motion will be of the form

$$\frac{d^2x}{dt^2} + \omega_0^2 x(t) = 0 \quad \textbf{(6.31)}$$

the solution of which is given by

$$x(t) = A \cos(\omega_0 t + \theta) \quad \textbf{(6.32)}$$

where A represents amplitude and ω_0 the angular frequency of motion. Equation (6.32) tells us that the motion will continue forever. However, we know that in actual practice the amplitude of any vibrating system (like that of a tuning fork) keeps on decreasing and eventually the system stops vibrating. Similarly, the bob of a pendulum comes to rest after a certain period of time. This phenomenon is due to the presence of damping forces which come into play when the particle is in motion. For a vibrating pendulum, the damping forces are primarily due to the viscosity of the surrounding medium. Consequently, the damping forces will be much larger in liquids than in gases. In general, the exact dependence of the damping force on the velocity of the particle is quite complicated; however, as a first approximation we may assume it to be proportional to the velocity of the particle. This is also consistent with the fact that there are no damping forces acting on the particle when it is at rest. In this model, the equation of motion will be given by

$$m\frac{d^2x}{dt^2} = -\Gamma\frac{dx}{dt} - k_0 x \quad \textbf{(6.33)}$$

where the constant Γ determines the strength of the damping force; the force constant is now denoted by k_0 to avoid confusion with the wave vector k. Equation (6.33) can be rewritten in the form

$$\frac{d^2x}{dt^2} + 2K\frac{dx}{dt} + \omega_0^2 x(t) = 0 \quad \textbf{(6.34)}$$

where $$2K = \frac{\Gamma}{m} \quad \text{and} \quad \omega_0 = \sqrt{\frac{k_0}{m}} \quad \textbf{(6.35)}$$

In order to solve Eq. (6.34) we introduce a new variable $\xi(t)$ which is defined by the following equation:

$$x(t) = \xi(t)e^{-Kt} \quad \textbf{(6.36)}$$

Thus, $$\frac{dx}{dt} = \left[\frac{d\xi}{dt} - K\,\xi(t)\right]e^{-Kt}$$

and $$\frac{d^2x}{dt^2} = \left[\frac{d^2\xi}{dt^2} - 2K\frac{d\xi}{dt} + K^2\,\xi(t)\right]e^{-Kt}$$

On substitution in Eq. (6.34) we get

$$\frac{d^2\xi}{dt^2} + (\omega_0^2 - K^2)\,\xi(t) = 0 \quad \textbf{(6.37)}$$

Equation (6.37) is similar to Eq. (6.31); however, depending on the strength of the damping force, the quantity $(\omega_0^2 - K^2)$ can be positive, negative or zero. Consequently, we must consider three cases.

Case I $(\omega_0^2 > K^2)$

If the damping is small, ω_0^2 is greater than K^2, and the solution of Eq. (6.37) would be of the form

$$\xi(t) = A\cos\left[\sqrt{\omega_0^2 - K^2}\,t + \theta\right] \quad \textbf{(6.38)}$$

or $$x(t) = Ae^{-Kt}\cos\left[\sqrt{\omega_0^2 - K^2}\,t + \theta\right] \quad \textbf{(6.39)}$$

where A and θ are constants which are determined from the amplitude and phase of the motion at $t = 0$. Equation (6.39) represents a damped simple harmonic motion (see Fig. 6.8). Notice that the amplitude decreases exponentially with time and the time period of vibration $\left(= 2\pi/\sqrt{\omega_0^2 - K^2}\right)$ is greater than in the absence of damping.

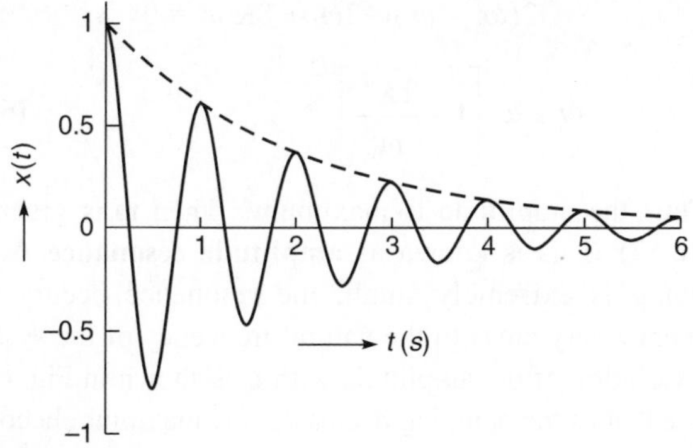

Figure 6.8
The exponential decrease of amplitude in a damped simple harmonic motion. The figure corresponds to $\frac{2\pi}{\sqrt{\omega_0^2 - K^2}} = 1$ s and $K = 0.5$ s^{-1}.

Case II $(K^2 > \omega_0^2)$

If the damping is too large, K^2 is greater than ω_0^2, and Eq. (6.37) should be written in the form

$$\frac{d^2\xi}{dt^2} - (K^2 - \omega_0^2)\,\xi(t) = 0 \qquad \textbf{(6.40)}$$

the solution of which is given by

$$\xi(t) = A \exp\left[\sqrt{K^2 - \omega_0^2}\; t\right] + B \exp\left[-\sqrt{K^2 - \omega_0^2}\; t\right] \qquad \textbf{(6.41)}$$

Thus,

$$x(t) = A \exp\left[\left(-K + \sqrt{K^2 - \omega_0^2}\right)t\right] + B \exp\left[\left(-K - \sqrt{K^2 - \omega_0^2}\right)t\right] \qquad \textbf{(6.42)}$$

and we can have two kinds of motion; one in which the displacement decreases uniformly to zero, or the other, in which the displacement first increases, reaches a maximum and then decreases to zero (see Fig. 6.9). In either case, there are no oscillations and the motion is said to be **overdamped** or **dead beat.** A typical example is the motion of a simple pendulum in a highly viscous liquid (like glycerine) where the pendulum can hardly complete a fraction of the vibration before coming to rest.

Case III $(K^2 = \omega_0^2)$

When $K^2 = \omega_0^2$, Eq. (6.37) becomes

$$\frac{d^2\xi}{dt^2} = 0 \qquad \textbf{(6.43)}$$

the solution of which is given by

$$\xi = At + B \qquad \textbf{(6.44)}$$

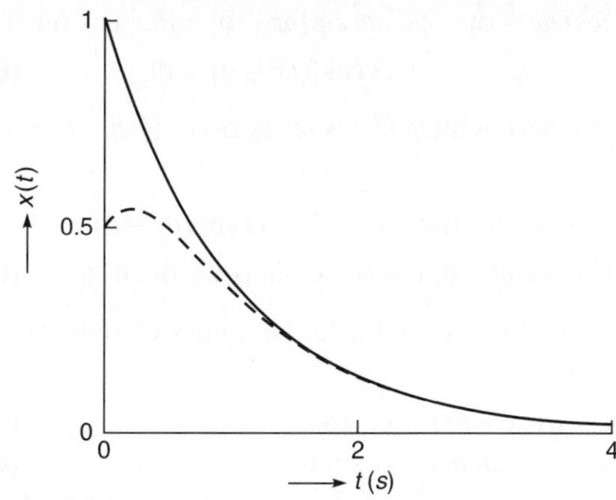

Figure 6.9
The variation of displacement with time in an overdamped motion. The solid and the dashed curves correspond to $B = 0$ and $B = -A/2$, respectively [see Eq. (6.42)]. In carrying out the calculations we have assumed $K = 2$ s^{-1} and $\sqrt{K^2 - \omega_0^2} = 1$ s^{-1}.

Thus,

$$x(t) = (At + B)e^{-Kt} \qquad \textbf{(6.45)}$$

The motion is again non–oscillatory and is said to correspond to **critical damping**.

6.4 Forced Vibrations

We consider the effect of a periodic sinusoidal force (see also Sec. 7.3) on the motion of a vibrating system. If the frequency of the external force is ω then the equation of motion would be [see Eq. (6.33)]:

$$m\frac{d^2x}{dt^2} = F\cos\omega t - \Gamma\frac{dx}{dt} - k_0 x \qquad \textbf{(6.46)}$$

where the first term on the RHS represents the external force; the other terms are the same as in Eq. (6.33). Equation (6.46) is rewritten in the form*

$$\frac{d^2x}{dt^2} + 2K\frac{dx}{dt} + \omega_0^2\, x(t) = G\cos\omega t \qquad \textbf{(6.47)}$$

where $G = F/m$ and other symbols have been defined in Sec. 6.3. For the particular solution of Eq. (6.47) we try

$$x(t) = a\cos(\omega t - \phi) \qquad \textbf{(6.48)}$$

Thus,

$$\frac{dx}{dt} = -a\omega\sin(\omega t - \phi)$$

and

$$\frac{d^2x}{dt^2} = -a\omega^2\cos(\omega t - \phi)$$

Substituting the above forms for $x(t)$, dx/dt and d^2x/dt^2 in Eq. (6.47), we obtain

* Notice that the RHS of Eq. (6.47) is independent of x; such an equation is said to be an inhomogeneous equation. An equation of the type given by Eq. (6.34) is said to be homogeneous.

$$-a\omega^2 \cos(\omega t - \phi) - 2K\,a\omega \sin(\omega t - \phi) + a\omega_0^2 \cos(\omega t - \phi) = G\cos[(\omega t - \phi) + \phi] \qquad (6.49)$$

where we have written $G \cos \omega t$ as $G \cos[(\omega t - \phi) + \phi]$. Thus,

$$a(\omega_0^2 - \omega^2)\cos(\omega t - \phi) - 2K\,a\omega \sin(\omega t - \phi) = G\cos(\omega t - \phi)\cos\phi - G\sin(\omega t - \phi)\sin\phi \qquad (6.50)$$

For Eq. (6.50) to be valid for all values of time we must have

$$a(\omega_0^2 - \omega^2) = G\cos\phi \qquad (6.51)$$

$$2Ka\omega = G\sin\phi \qquad (6.52)$$

If we square and add, we get

$$a = \frac{G}{\left[(\omega_0^2 - \omega^2)^2 + 4K^2\omega^2\right]^{1/2}} \qquad (6.53)$$

Further

$$\tan\phi = \frac{2K\omega}{(\omega_0^2 - \omega^2)} \qquad (6.54)$$

Since K, ω and a are positive, ϕ is uniquely determined by noting that $\sin\phi$ should be positive, i.e., ϕ must be either in the first or in the second quadrant.

To the solution given by Eq. (6.48), we must add the solution of the homogeneous equation, Eq. (6.34). Thus, assuming ω_0^2 to be greater than K^2 (i.e., weak damping), the general solution of Eq. (6.47) will be of the form

$$x(t) = Ae^{-Kt}\cos\left[\sqrt{\omega_0^2 - K^2}\; t - \theta\right] + a\cos(\omega t - \phi) \qquad (6.55)$$

The first term on the RHS represents the transient solution (corresponding to the natural vibrations of the system) which eventually dies out. The second term represents the steady state solution which corresponds to the forced vibrations imposed by the external force. Notice that the frequency of the forced vibrations is the same as that of the external force.

6.4.1 Resonance

LO3

The amplitude of the forced vibration,

$$a = \frac{G}{\left[(\omega_0^2 - \omega^2)^2 + 4K^2\omega^2\right]^{1/2}} \qquad (6.56)$$

depends on the frequency of the driving force and is a maximum when $(\omega_0^2 - \omega^2)^2 + 4K^2\omega^2$ is a minimum, i.e., when

$$\frac{d}{d\omega}[(\omega_0^2 - \omega^2)^2 + 4K^2\omega^2] = 0$$

or

$$2(\omega_0^2 - \omega^2)(-2\omega) + 8K^2\omega = 0$$

or

$$\omega = \omega_0\left[1 - \frac{2K^2}{\omega_0^2}\right]^{1/2} \qquad (6.57)$$

Thus the amplitude is maximum* when ω is given by Eq. (6.57). This is known as **amplitude resonance**. When damping is extremely small, the resonance occurs at a frequency very close to the natural frequency of the system. The variation of the amplitude with ω is shown in Fig. 6.10. Notice that as the damping decreases, the maximum becomes very sharp and the amplitude falls off rapidly as we go away from the resonance. The maximum value of a is given by

$$a_{max} = \frac{G}{\left[(2K^2)^2 + 4K^2\omega_0^2\left(1 - \frac{2K^2}{\omega_0^2}\right)\right]^{1/2}}$$

$$= \frac{G}{2K\left[\omega_0^2 - K^2\right]^{1/2}} = \frac{G}{2K\left[\omega^2 + K^2\right]^{1/2}} \qquad (6.58)$$

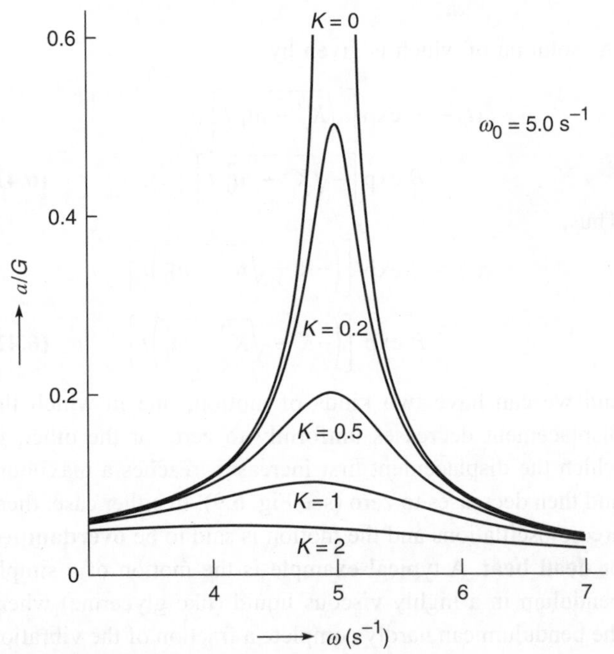

Figure 6.10

The variation of amplitude with the frequency of the external driving force for various values of K. The calculations correspond to ω_0 = 5 s^{-1} and the values of K are in sec^{-1}. Notice that with increase in damping, the resonance occurs at a smaller value of ω.

Thus, with increase in damping, the maximum occurs at lower values of ω and the resonance becomes less sharper.

In order to discuss the phase of the forced vibrations, we refer to Eq. (6.54) from where we find that for small damping

* There is no resonance condition when $K^2 \geq \frac{1}{2}\omega_0^2$.

the phase angle is small unless it is near resonance. For $\omega = \omega_0$, $\tan\phi = \infty$ and ϕ is $\pi/2$; i.e., the phase of forced vibrations is $\pi/2$ ahead of the phase of the driving force. As the frequency of the driving force is increased beyond ω_0, the phase also increases and approaches π (see Fig. 6.11).

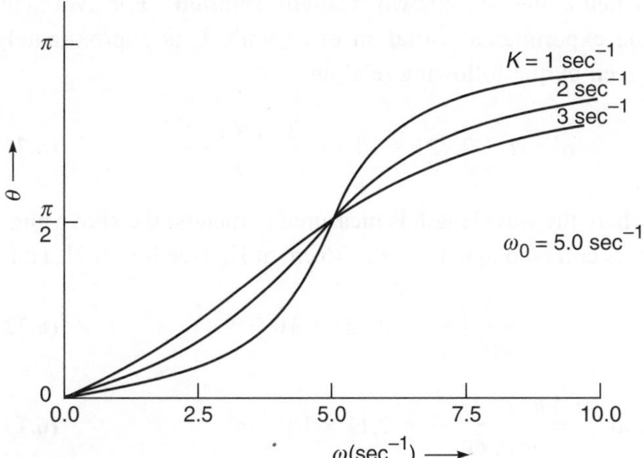

Figure 6.11
The dependence of the phase of the forced vibration on the frequency of the driving force.

All the salient features of forced vibrations can be easily demonstrated by means of an arrangement shown in Fig. 6.12. In the figure, *AC* is a metal rod with a movable bob *B* and *LM* is a simple pendulum with a bob at *M*. The metal rod and the simple pendulum are suspended from a string *PQ* as shown in Fig. 6.12. With *B* at the bottom, when the rod *AC* is set in motion, the pendulum *LM* also vibrates. As the bob *B* is moved upwards, the time period decreases and the frequency of the rod becomes closer to the natural frequency of the simple pendulum and eventually the resonance condition is satisfied. At resonance, the amplitude of vibration of the simple pendulum is maximum and the phase difference between the vibrations is nearly $\pi/2$, i.e., when the metal rod is at its lowest position and moving towards right, the simple pendulum is at the extreme left position. If the bob *B* is further moved upward, the frequency increases and the amplitude of the forced vibrations decreases.

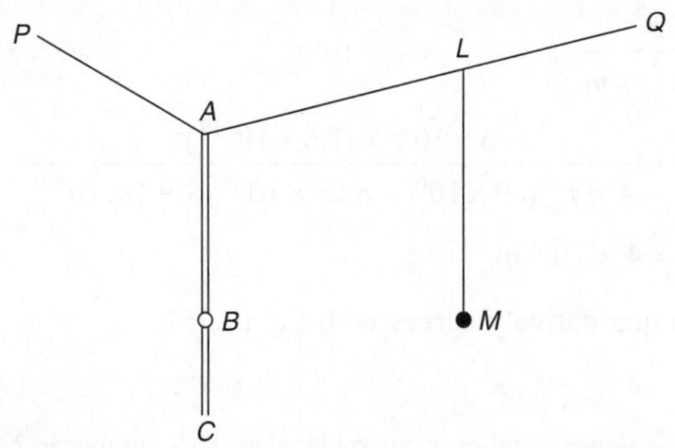

Figure 6.12
An arrangement for demonstration of forced vibrations.

We may mention here that study of the resonance phenomenon is of extreme importance in the design of bridges and civil structures. Indeed, when the frequency of external disturbance is close to its natural frequency of vibration, the amplitude of vibration will increase which may result in the collapse of a bridge. For more details you may like to Google the words *How can resonance collapse bridges?* And you will find many sites discussing about this phenomenon.

6.5 Origin of Refractive Index LO4

In this section, we will study the origin of refractive index. We know that an atom consists of a heavy positively charged nucleus surrounded by electrons. In the simplest model of the atom, the electrons are assumed to be bound elastically to their rest positions (see the Feynman quote at the beginning of the chapter). Thus, when these electrons are displaced by an electric field, a restoring force (proportional to the displacement) will act on the electrons which will tend to return the electrons to their rest positions. In this model, the equation of motion for the electron, in the presence of an external electric field **E**, would be

$$m\frac{d^2\mathbf{x}}{dt^2} + k_0\mathbf{x} = -q\mathbf{E} \tag{6.59}$$

or

$$\frac{d^2\mathbf{x}}{dt^2} + \omega_0^2\mathbf{x} = -\frac{q}{m}\mathbf{E} \tag{6.60}$$

where **x** represents the position of the electron, m and $-q$ represent the mass and charge of the electron ($q \approx +1.6 \times 10^{-19}$ C), k_0 the force constant and $\omega_0 \left(= \sqrt{k_0/m}\right)$ represents the frequency of the oscillator. We assume

$$\mathbf{E} = \hat{\mathbf{x}}\, E_0 \cos(kz - \omega t) \tag{6.61}$$

i.e., the field is in the x-direction having an amplitude E_0 and propagating in the $+z$ direction; $\hat{\mathbf{x}}$ represents the unit vector in the x-direction and $k = 2\pi/\lambda$, λ representing the wavelength. Thus

$$\frac{d^2x}{dt^2} + \omega_0^2 x = -\frac{qE_0}{m}\cos(kz - \omega t) \tag{6.62}$$

where we have replaced the vectors by the corresponding scalar quantities because the displacement and the electric field are in the same direction. Except for the damping term, Eq. (6.62) is similar to Eq. (6.46) and therefore, the solution corresponding to the forced vibrations will be given by*

$$x = -\frac{qE_0}{m(\omega_0^2 - \omega^2)}\cos(kz - \omega t) \tag{6.63}$$

* Notice that in the absence of damping (i.e., when $\Gamma = 0$), $\phi = 0$; see Eq. (6.54).

In the simplest model of the atom, the center of the negative charge (due to the electrons) is assumed to be at the center of the nucleus. In the presence of an electric field, the center of the negative charge gets displaced from the nucleus which results in a finite value of the dipole moment of the atom. In particular, if we have a positive charge $+q$ at the origin and a negative charge $-q$ at a distance x, then the dipole moment would be $-qx$; thus, if there are N dispersion-electrons* per unit volume then the polarization (i.e., dipole moment per unit volume) would be given by

$$\mathbf{P} = -Nq\mathbf{x} = \frac{Nq^2}{m(\omega_0^2 - \omega^2)}\mathbf{E} = \chi\,\mathbf{E} \tag{6.64}$$

where $$\chi = \frac{Nq^2}{m(\omega_0^2 - \omega^2)} \tag{6.65}$$

is known as the **electric susceptibility** of the material. The dielectric permittivity is therefore given by (see Chapter 22)

$$\varepsilon = \varepsilon_0 + \chi \tag{6.66}$$

or $$\frac{\varepsilon}{\varepsilon_0} = 1 + \frac{Nq^2}{m\varepsilon_0(\omega_0^2 - \omega^2)} \tag{6.67}$$

Now, $\varepsilon/\varepsilon_0$ is the dielectric constant, which is equal to the square of the refractive index (see Chapter 22). Thus,

$$n^2 = 1 + \frac{Nq^2}{m\varepsilon_0\,\omega_0^2}\left[1 - \frac{\omega^2}{\omega_0^2}\right]^{-1} \tag{6.68}$$

showing that the refractive index depends on the frequency; this is known as **dispersion.** Assuming that the characteristic frequency ω_0 lies in the far ultraviolet [see Eq. (6.74)]**, the quantity $\left[1 - \frac{\omega^2}{\omega_0^2}\right]^{-1}$ is positive in the entire visible region. Further, as ω increases, n^2 also increases, i.e., the refractive index increases with frequency; this is known as **normal dispersion**. If we further assume $\omega/\omega_0 << 1$, then

$$\left[1 - \frac{\omega^2}{\omega_0^2}\right]^{-1} \approx 1 + \frac{\omega^2}{\omega_0^2}$$

and $$n^2 \approx 1 + \frac{Nq^2}{m\varepsilon_0\,\omega_0^2}\left[1 + \frac{\omega^2}{\omega_0^2}\right] \approx 1 + \frac{Nq^2}{m\,\varepsilon_0\,\omega_0^2} + \frac{4\pi^2c^2Nq^2}{m\,\varepsilon_0\,\omega_0^4}\frac{1}{\lambda_0^2} \tag{6.69}$$

where $\lambda_0 = 2\pi c/\omega$ is the free space wavelength. Equation (6.69) can be written in the form

$$n^2 = A + \frac{B}{\lambda_0^2} \tag{6.70}$$

which is the well-known '**Cauchy relation**'. For hydrogen, the experimental variation of n^2 with λ_0 is approximately given by the following relation:

$$n^2 = 1 + 2.721 \times 10^{-4} + \frac{2.11\times10^{-18}}{\lambda_0^2} \tag{6.71}$$

where the wavelength is measured in meters; the above numbers correspond to 0° C and 76 cm of Hg [see Ref. 6.9]. Thus,

$$\frac{Nq^2}{m\varepsilon_0\,\omega_0^2} = 2.721 \times 10^{-4} \tag{6.72}$$

and $$\frac{4\pi^2c^2Nq^2}{m\,\varepsilon_0\,\omega_0^4} = 2.11 \times 10^{-18}\ \text{m}^2 \tag{6.73}$$

If we divide the second equation by the first, we would get

$$\frac{4\pi^2c^2}{\omega_0^2} = \frac{2.11\times10^{-18}}{2.721\times10^{-4}}$$

or $$\nu_0 = \frac{\omega_0}{2\pi} \approx 3 \times 10^{15}\ \text{s}^{-1} \tag{6.74}$$

which is indeed in the ultraviolet region. One can eliminate ω_0 from Eqs. (6.72) and (6.73) to obtain

$$\frac{Nq^2}{4\pi^2c^2\,\varepsilon_0\,m} \approx \frac{(2.721\times10^{-4})^2}{2.11\times10^{-18}} \approx 3.5 \times 10^{10}\ \text{m}^{-2} \tag{6.75}$$

Now at NTP, 22400 cc of H_2 contains 6×10^{23} molecules; thus,

$$N = 2 \times \frac{6\times10^{23}}{22400\times10^{-6}}\ \text{m}^{-3} \approx 5 \times 10^{25}\ \text{m}^{-3}$$

where the factor 2 arises from the fact that a hydrogen molecule consists of two electrons. Hence,

$$\frac{Nq^2}{4\pi^2c^2\,\varepsilon_0\,m} \approx \frac{5\times10^{25}\times(1.6\times10^{-19})^2}{4\times\pi^2\times9\times10^{16}\times8.85\times10^{-12}\times9.1\times10^{-31}} \approx 4 \times 10^{10}\ \text{m}^{-2}$$

which qualitatively agrees with Eq. (6.75).

---

* The number of 'dispersion-electrons' in a molecule of an ideal gas is the valence number of the molecules. This number is 2 for H_2, 6 for N_2, etc.

** This also follows from the fact that according to classical electrodynamics, an oscillating dipole vibrating with frequency ω_0 will radiate electromagnetic waves with frequency ω_0; and as an example if we consider hydrogen, then $\hbar\,\omega_0 \approx 13.6$ eV from which one obtains $\omega_0 \approx 2 \times 10^{16}\ \text{s}^{-1}$. This frequency corresponds to the far ultraviolet.

For a gas of free electrons (as we have in the upper atmosphere) there is no restoring force and we must set $\omega_0 = 0$. Thus, the expression for the refractive index becomes [see Eq. (6.67)]

$$n^2 = 1 - \frac{N q^2}{m \varepsilon_0 \omega^2} \tag{6.76}$$

where N represents the density of free electrons. Equation (6.76) shows that the refractive index is less than unity; however, this does not imply that one can send signals faster than the speed of light in free space (see Chapter 11). To quote Feynman (Ref. 6.4):

> *For free electrons, $\omega_0 = 0$ (there is no elastic restoring force). Setting $\omega_0 = 0$ in our dispersion equation yields the correct formula for the index of refraction for radiowaves in the stratosphere, where N is now to represent the density of free electrons (number per unit volume) in the stratosphere. But let us look again at the equation, if we beam X-rays on the matter, or radiowaves (or any electric waves) on free electrons, the term $(\omega_0^2 - \omega^2)$ becomes negative, and we obtain the result that n is less that one. That means that the effective speed of the waves in the substance is faster than c! Can that be correct? It is correct. In spite of the fact that it is said that you cannot send signals any faster than the speed of light, it is nevertheless true that the index of refraction of materials at a particular frequency can be either greater or less than* 1.

Equation (6.76) is usually written in the form

$$n^2 = 1 - \left(\frac{\omega_p}{\omega}\right)^2 \tag{6.77}$$

where

$$\omega_p = \left(\frac{N q^2}{m \varepsilon_0}\right)^{1/2} \tag{6.78}$$

is known as the **plasma frequency**. Notice that for $\omega < \omega_p$, the refractive index is purely imaginary which gives rise to attenuation and for $\omega > \omega_p$, the refractive index is real. Indeed in 1933, Wood discovered that alkali metals are transparent to ultraviolet light. For example, for sodium if we assume that the refractive index is primarily due to the free electrons and that there is one free electron per atom then

$$N = \frac{6 \times 10^{23} \times 0.9712}{22.99} \approx 2.535 \times 10^{22} \text{ cm}^{-3}$$

where we have assumed that the atomic weight of Na is 22.99 and its density is 0.9712 g/cm^3. Substituting the values of $m \approx 9.109 \times 10^{-31}$ kg, $q \approx 1.602 \times 10^{-19}$ C and $\varepsilon_0 \approx 8.854 \times 10^{-12}$ C/N-m^2 we would get

$$\lambda_p \left(= \frac{2\pi c}{\omega_p}\right) \approx 2098 \text{ Å}$$

Thus for $\lambda < 2098$ Å, the refractive index of Na becomes real and the metal would become transparent; the corresponding experimental value is 2100 Å. The theoretical and experimental values of λ_p for Li, K and Rb are discussed in Problem 6.6.

As mentioned above, Eq. (6.76) gives the correct dependence of the refractive index of the stratosphere for radiowaves; in Sec. 2.4.3 we had used Eq. (6.76) to study reflection of electromagnetic waves by the ionosphere.

Returning to Eq. (6.68), we note that as $\omega \to \omega_0$, the refractive index tends to ∞. This is due to the fact that we have neglected the presence of damping forces in our treatment. If we do take into account the damping forces, Eq. (6.62) would modify to [see Eq. (6.46)]

$$m\frac{d^2x}{dt^2} + \Gamma\frac{dx}{dt} + k_0 x = qE_0 \cos(kz - \omega t) \tag{6.79}$$

In order to derive an expression for the refractive index, it is more convenient to rewrite the above equation in the form

$$\frac{d^2x}{dt^2} + 2K\frac{dx}{dt} + \omega_0^2 x = \frac{qE_0}{m} e^{i(kz - \omega t)} \tag{6.80}$$

where the solution of Eq. (6.79) will be the real part of the solution of Eq. (6.80). The solution of the homogeneous equation will give the transient behavior which will die out as $t \to \infty$ (see Sec. 6.4); the steady state solution will correspond to frequency ω. Thus, if we substitute a solution of the type

$$x(t) = A e^{i(kz - \omega t)} \tag{6.81}$$

in Eq. (6.80), we would obtain

$$(-\omega^2 - 2iK\omega + \omega_0^2) A = \frac{qE_0}{m}$$

or

$$A = \frac{qE_0}{m[\omega_0^2 - \omega^2 - 2iK\omega]} \tag{6.82}$$

Notice that A is complex; however, if we substitute the expression for A from Eq. (6.82) in Eq. (6.81) and take the real part we would get the same expression for $x(t)$ as we had obtained in Sec. 6.4. Thus, we get

$$\mathbf{P} = \frac{Nq^2}{m[\omega_0^2 - \omega^2 - 2iK\omega]}\mathbf{E} \tag{6.83}$$

The electric susceptibility would therefore be given by

$$\chi = \frac{Nq^2}{m[\omega_0^2 - \omega^2 - 2iK\omega]}$$

Thus, $$n^2 = \frac{\varepsilon}{\varepsilon_0} = 1 + \frac{\chi}{\varepsilon_0}$$

$$= 1 + \frac{N q^2}{m \varepsilon_0 [\omega_0^2 - \omega^2 - 2 i K \omega]} \tag{6.84}$$

Notice that the refractive index is complex, which implies absorption of the propagating electromagnetic wave. Indeed, if we write

$$n = \eta + i \kappa \tag{6.85}$$

where η and κ are real numbers, then the wave number k, which equals $n\omega/c$, would be given by

$$k = (\eta + i \kappa) \frac{\omega}{c} \tag{6.86}$$

If we consider a plane electromagnetic wave propagating in the $+z$ direction, then its z and t dependence would be of the form $\exp [i(kz - \omega t)]$; consequently

$$\mathbf{E} = \mathbf{E}_0 \, e^{i(kz - \omega t)}$$

$$= \mathbf{E}_0 \exp \left[i \left\{ (\eta + i \kappa) \frac{\omega}{c} z - \omega t \right\} \right]$$

$$= \mathbf{E}_0 \exp \left[-i \omega \left(t - \frac{\eta z}{c} \right) - \frac{\kappa \omega}{c} z \right] \tag{6.87}$$

which shows an exponential attenuation of the amplitude. This should not be unexpected because damping causes a loss of energy.

In order to obtain expressions for η and κ, we substitute the expression for n from Eq. (6.85) in Eq. (6.84) to obtain

$(\eta + i \kappa)^2$

$$= 1 + \frac{N q^2 (\omega_0^2 - \omega^2 + 2 i K \omega)}{m \varepsilon_0 (\omega_0^2 - \omega^2 - 2 i K \omega)(\omega_0^2 - \omega^2 + 2 i K \omega)}$$

or $$\eta^2 - \kappa^2 = 1 + \frac{N q^2 (\omega_0^2 - \omega^2)}{m \varepsilon_0 [(\omega_0^2 - \omega^2)^2 + 4 K^2 \omega^2]} \tag{6.88}$$

and $$2 \eta \kappa = \frac{N q^2}{m \varepsilon_0} \frac{2 K \omega}{[(\omega_0^2 - \omega^2)^2 + 4 K^2 \omega^2]} \tag{6.89}$$

The above equations can be rewritten in the form

$$\eta^2 - \kappa^2 = 1 - \frac{\alpha \Omega}{[\Omega^2 + \beta^2 (\Omega + 1)]} \tag{6.90}$$

and $$2 \eta \kappa = \frac{\alpha \beta \sqrt{1 + \Omega}}{[\Omega^2 + \beta^2 (\Omega + 1)]} \tag{6.91}$$

where we have introduced the following dimensionless parameters:

$$\alpha = \frac{N q^2}{m \varepsilon_0 \omega_0^2}; \quad \Omega = \frac{\omega^2 - \omega_0^2}{\omega_0^2} \quad \text{and} \quad \beta = \frac{2K}{\omega_0}$$

The qualitative variations of $\eta^2 - \kappa^2$ and $2\eta\kappa$ with Ω are shown in Fig. 6.13. It can be easily shown that at $\Omega = -\beta$ and at $\Omega = +\beta$, the function $(\eta^2 - \kappa^2)$ attains its maximum and minimum values respectively.

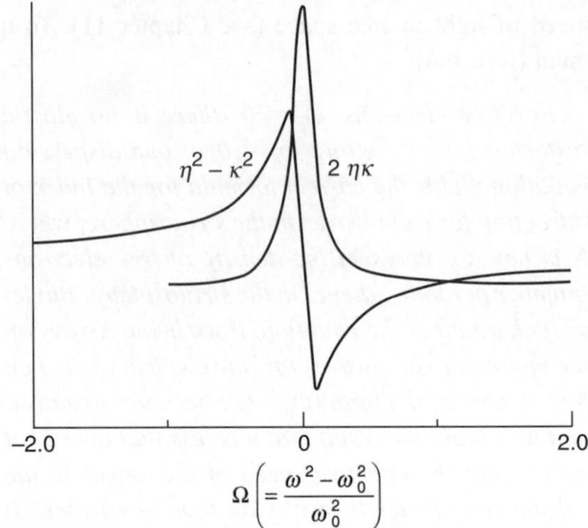

Figure 6.13
Qualitative variation of $(\eta^2 - \kappa^2)$ and $2\eta\kappa$ with Ω.

It should be pointed out that, in general, an atom can execute oscillations corresponding to different resonant frequencies and we have to take into account the various contributions. If ω_0, ω_1, … represent the resonant frequencies and if f_j represents the fractional number of electrons per unit volume whose resonant frequency is ω_j, Eq. (6.84) would get modified to the following expression:*

$$n^2 = 1 + \frac{N q^2}{m \varepsilon_0} \sum_j \frac{f_j}{[\omega_j^2 - \omega^2 - 2 i K_j \omega]} \tag{6.92}$$

where K_j represents the damping constant corresponding to the resonant frequency ω_j. Indeed, Eq. (6.92) describes correctly the variation of refractive index for most gases. Figure 6.14 shows the dependence of the refractive index of sodium vapor around $\lambda_0 = 5800$ Å. Since D_1 and D_2 lines occur at 5890 Å and 5896 Å, one should expect resonant oscillations around these frequencies. This is indeed borne out by the data shown in Fig. 6.14. The variation of the refractive index can be accurately fitted with the formula,

$$n^2 = 1 + \frac{A}{\nu^2 - \nu_1^2} + \frac{B}{\nu^2 - \nu_2^2} \tag{6.93}$$

where we have neglected the presence of damping forces which is justified except when one is very close to the resonance.

* Quantum mechanics also gives a similar result (see, for example, Ref. 6.6).

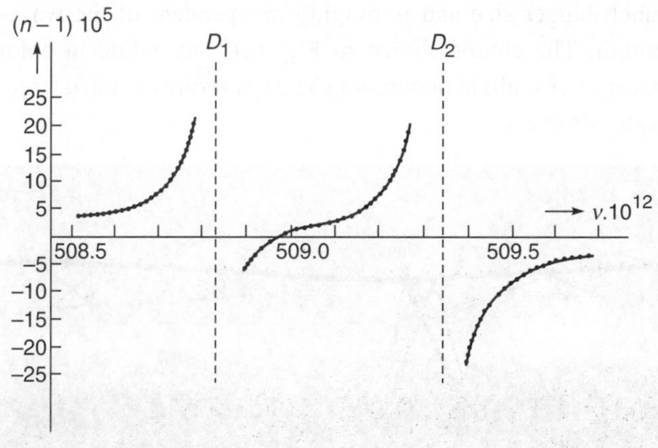

Figure 6.14
The measured variation of refractive index of sodium with frequency around the D_1 and D_2 lines. The measurements are of Roschdestwensky. [*The figure has been adapted from Ref. 6.1*].

Figure 6.15
The glass on the right contains distilled water and the glass on the left contains distilled water with few drops of milk. Because of scattering, the laser beam can be easily seen as it traverses through the liquid. Figure adapted from http://silver-lightning.com/tyndall/. The photograph was taken by Mr. Marshall Dudley; used with kind permission from Mr. Marshall Dudley.

In a liquid, the molecules are very close to one another and the dipoles interact between themselves. If we take this interaction into account, we would get*

$$\frac{n^2-1}{n^2+2} = \frac{Nq^2}{3m\varepsilon_0}\sum_j \frac{f_j}{\omega_j^2-\omega^2} \tag{6.94}$$

where we have neglected the presence of damping. For liquids, whose molecules do not have a permanent dipole moment (e.g., H_2, O_2, etc.) Eq. (6.94) gives a fairly accurate description. However, liquids whose molecules posses permanent dipole moments (e.g., H_2O) one has to carry out a different analysis.

6.6 Rayleigh Scattering

LO5

We end this chapter by giving a brief account of Rayleigh scattering. The phenomenon of scattering is demonstrated in Fig. 6.15; the glass on the right contains distilled water and the glass on the left contains distilled water with few drops of milk. Because of scattering, the laser beam can be easily seen as it traverses through the liquid.

In our analysis, we will assume that each scattering center behaves independently—an assumption which will be valid for a gas. As discussed in Sec. 6.5, the incident electric field **E** produces a dipole moment given by [see Eqs. (6.64) and (6.65)]

$$\mathbf{p} = \frac{q^2}{m(\omega_0^2-\omega^2)}\mathbf{E} \tag{6.95}$$

where ω_0 represents the natural frequency of the atom. To keep the analysis simple, we are neglecting the effect of damping although it can be taken into account without much difficulty. Now, an oscillating dipole given by

$$\mathbf{p} = \mathbf{p}_0\, e^{-i\omega t} \tag{6.96}$$

radiates energy at a rate (see Sec. 22.5.1)

$$\overline{P} = \frac{\omega^4 p_0^2}{12\pi\varepsilon_0 c^3} \tag{6.97}$$

or

$$\overline{P} = \frac{\omega^4}{12\pi\varepsilon_0 c^3}\frac{q^4}{m^2(\omega_0^2-\omega^2)^2}E_0^2 \tag{6.98}$$

Thus if N represents the number of atoms per unit volume, then the total energy radiated away (per unit volume) would be $N\overline{P}$.

We assume the electromagnetic wave to be propagating along the x-direction. The intensity of the wave is given by [see Sec. 22.6]

$$I = \frac{1}{2}\varepsilon_0 c E_0^{\,2} \tag{6.99}$$

Thus, the change in the intensity of the electromagnetic wave as it propagates through a distance dx is given by

$$dI = -N\overline{P}\, dx$$

* See, for example, Ref. 6.1. Notice that when n is very close to unity (i.e., for a dilute fluid), Eq. (6.94) reduces to Eq. (6.92).

or
$$\frac{dI}{I} = -\gamma dx \tag{6.100}$$

where
$$\gamma = \frac{N\,\omega^4}{6\pi\varepsilon_0^2 c^4}\,\frac{q^4}{m^2(\omega_0^2 - \omega^2)^2} \tag{6.101}$$

The integration of Eq. (6.100) is simple:

$$I = I_0 e^{-\gamma x} \tag{6.102}$$

implying that γ represents the attenuation coefficient. For most atoms ω_0 lies in the ultraviolet region, for example, for the hydrogen atom $\hbar\,\omega_0 \approx$ few electron volts. Thus, if we assume $\omega << \omega_0$, then γ becomes proportional to ω^4 or

$$\gamma \propto \frac{1}{\lambda^4} \tag{6.103}$$

which represents the famous $1/\lambda^4$ ***Rayleigh scattering law***. Now, the red color has a wavelength of about 0.7 μm which is about 1.75 times the wavelength of blue (which is about 0.4 μm), thus, the blue color is scattered 10 times more than the red color. This is the reason why the color of sky is blue (see Fig. 6.16). Similarly, the blue component of the light coming from the setting sun is predominantly scattered out resulting in the red color of the setting sun – see Fig. 6.17. Indeed, if the color of the setting (or rising) sun is deep red, one can infer that the pollution level is high. On the other hand, Mie scattering [named after the German physicist Gustav Mie (1868 – 1957)] is caused by particles that are of much bigger size and is roughly independent of the wavelength. The clouds shown in Fig. 6.17 are white in color because of sunlight undergoing Mie scattering by much larger water droplets.

Figure 6.16
White clouds with blue sky. The blue sky is due to Rayleigh scattering in which smaller wavelengths get predominantly scattered by air molecules; indeed the blue color is scattered 10 times more than the red color). The clouds are white in colour because of Mie scattering in which all wavelengths are scattered (by water droplets) almost equally.

Figure 6.17
The setting sun is red in colour because small wavelengths (like the blue components) get predominantly scattered by air molecules. Photograph courtesy McGraw Hill Digital Access Library.

Now, for a gas,

$$n^2 - 1 = \frac{N q^2}{m\,\varepsilon_0(\omega_0^2 - \omega^2)} \tag{6.104}$$

[See Eq. (6.68)]. For air, since the refractive index is very close to unity, we may write

$$n - 1 \approx \frac{N q^2}{2m\,\varepsilon_0(\omega_0^2 - \omega^2)} \tag{6.105}$$

using which, Eq. (6.101) can be written in the following convenient form:

$$\gamma = \frac{2}{3\pi N}\left(\frac{\omega}{c}\right)^4 (n-1)^2$$

$$= \frac{2k^4}{3\pi N}(n-1)^2; \quad k = \frac{\omega}{c} \tag{6.106}$$

For air at NTP, the quantity $n - 1 \approx 2.78 \times 10^{-4}$ in the entire region of the visible spectrum. With $N \approx 2.7 \times 10^{19}$ molecules/cm^3 we obtain

$$L = \frac{1}{\gamma} = 27 \text{ km, } 128 \text{ km and } 188 \text{ km}$$

for $\lambda = 4000$ Å (violet), 5900 Å (yellow) and 6500 Å (red), respectively. The quantity L represents the distance in which the intensity decreases by a factor of e.

We may conclude this chapter by mentioning that in the 1929 edition of Encylopaedia Britannica, Lord Rayliegh wrote an article on SKY:

***SKY:** The apparent covering of the atmosphere, the overarching heaven... It is a matter of common observation that the blue of the sky is highly variable, even on days that are free from clouds. The color usually deepens toward the zenith and also with the elevation of the observer... Closely associated with the color is the polarization of light from the sky. This takes place in a plane passing through the sun, and attains a maximum about 90° therefrom.*

In Fig. 6.18 we have shown a view of the Earth from the Moon. Notice that the sky looks black (see also Fig. 1.2) because there is very little atmosphere on the moon and hence no Rayleigh scattering.

Figure 6.18
View of the Earth rising over Moon. Image credit: NASA/Apollo 8

SUMMARY

- The most fundamental vibration associated with wave motion is the simple harmonic motion.
- When an external sinusoidal force is applied to a vibrating system, we have what is known as forced vibrations. In steady state, the frequency of the forced vibrations is the same as that of the external force.
- When a lightwave interacts with an atom, we may assume the electrons to behave like oscillators with resonant frequency ω_0. The electric field of the lightwave polarizes the molecules of the gas, producing oscillating dipole moments from which one can make a first principle calculation of the refractive index to obtain

$$n^2(\omega) \approx 1 + \frac{Nq^2}{m\varepsilon_0(\omega_0^2 - \omega^2 - 2iK\omega)}$$

where m is the mass of the electron, q the magnitude of the charge of the electron, N is the number of electrons per unit volume and K is the damping constant.
- Because of the fact that an oscillating dipole radiates energy, the lightwave gets attenuated; this leads to the famous $\frac{1}{\lambda^4}$ Rayleigh scattering law which is responsible for the red color of the rising sun and blue color of the sky.

PROBLEMS

6.1 The displacement associated with a standing wave on a sonometer is given by the following equation:

$$y(x, t) = 2a \sin\left(\frac{2\pi}{\lambda}x\right) \cos(2\pi\nu t)$$

If the length of the string is L then the allowed values of λ are $2L$, $2L/2$, $2L/3$, ... (see Sec. 12.2). Consider the case when $\lambda = 2L/5$; study the time variation of displacement in each loop and show that alternate loops vibrate in phase (with different points in a loop having different amplitudes) and adjacent loops vibrate out of phase.

6.2 A tunnel is dug through the earth as shown in Fig. 6.19. A mass is dropped at the point A along the tunnel. Show that it will execute simple harmonic motion. What will the time period be?

[**Ans:** The time period will be $T = 2\pi\sqrt{\frac{R}{g}}$.]

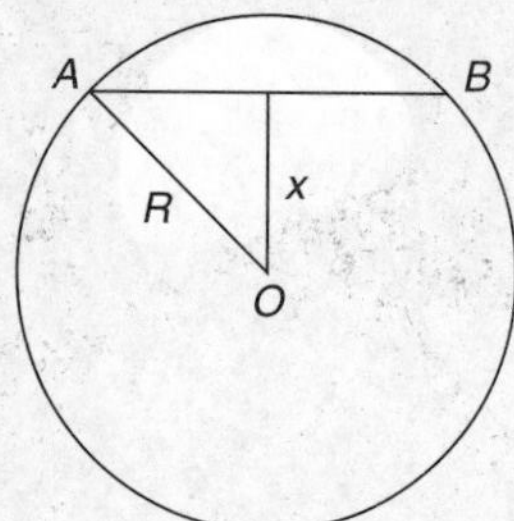

Figure 6.19
Figure for Problem 6.3.

6.3 A 1 g mass is suspended from a vertical spring. It executes simple harmonic motion with period 0.1 sec. By how much distance had the spring stretched when the mass was attached? You may assume $g = 9.8$ m/s^2.

[**Ans:** $\Delta x \approx 0.25$ cm]

6.4 A stretched string is given simultaneous displacement in the x- and y-directions such that

$$x(z, t) = a \cos\left(\frac{2\pi}{\lambda} z - 2\pi \nu t\right)$$

and
$$y(z, t) = a \cos\left(\frac{2\pi}{\lambda} z - 2\pi \nu t\right)$$

Show that the string will vibrate along a direction making an angle $\pi/4$ with the x and y axes.

6.5 In Problem 6.4, if

$$x(z, t) = a \cos\left(\frac{2\pi}{\lambda} z - 2\pi \nu t\right)$$

and
$$y(z, t) = a \sin\left(\frac{2\pi}{\lambda} z - 2\pi \nu t\right)$$

what will be the resultant displacement?

6.6 As mentioned in Sec. 6.5, alkali metals are transparent to ultraviolet light. Assuming that the refractive index is primarily due to the free electrons and that there is one free electron per atom, calculate $\lambda_p \left(= \frac{2\pi c}{\omega_p}\right)$ for Li, K and Rb. You may assume that the atomic weights of Li, K and Rb are 6.94, 39.10 and 85.48, respectively and that the corresponding densities are 0.534, 0.870 and 1.532 g/cm^3. Also, the values of various physical constants are: $m = 9.109 \times 10^{-31}$ kg, $q = 1.602 \times 10^{-19}$ C and $\varepsilon_0 = 8.854 \times 10^{-12}$ C/N-m^2.

[**Ans:** 1550 Å, 2890 Å and 3220 Å; the corresponding experimental values are 1551 Å, 3150 Å and 3400 Å, respectively].

6.7 **(a)** In a metal, the electrons can be assumed to be essentially free. The drift velocity of the electron satisfies the following equation

$$m \frac{d\mathbf{v}}{dt} + m\nu\mathbf{v} = \mathbf{F} = -q\,\mathbf{E}_0\, e^{-i\omega t}$$

where ν represents the collision frequency. Calculate the steady state current density ($\mathbf{J} = -Nq\mathbf{v}$) and show that the conductivity is given by

$$\sigma(\omega) = \frac{Nq^2}{m} \frac{1}{\nu - i\omega}$$

(b) If $\mathbf{r}$ represents the displacement of the electron, show that

$$\mathbf{P} = -Nq\mathbf{r} = -\frac{Nq^2}{m(\omega^2 + i\omega\nu)}\mathbf{E}$$

which represents the polarization. Using the above equation show that

$$\kappa(\omega) = 1 - \frac{Nq^2}{m\varepsilon_0(\omega^2 + i\omega\nu)}$$

which represents the dielectric constant variation for a free electron gas.

6.8 Assuming that each atom of copper contributes one free electron and that the low frequency conductivity σ is about 6×10^7 mhos/metre, show that the collision frequency (see Problem 6.7) is given by $\nu \approx 4 \times 10^{13}$ s^{-1}. Using this value of ν, show that the conductivity is almost real for $\omega < 10^{11}$ s^{-1}. For $\omega = 10^8$ s^{-1} calculate the complex dielectric constant and compare its value with the one obtained for infrared frequencies.

It may be noted that for small frequencies, only one of the electrons of a copper atom can be considered to be free. On the other hand, for X-ray frequencies all the electrons may be assumed to be free (see Problems 6.9, 6.10 and 6.11).

6.9 Show that for high frequencies ($\omega >> \nu$) the dielectric constant (as derived in Problem 6.7) is essentially real with frequency dependence of the form

$$\kappa = 1 - \frac{\omega_p^2}{\omega^2}$$

where $\omega_p = \left(\frac{Nq^2}{m\varepsilon_0}\right)^{1/2}$ is known as the plasma frequency.

The above dielectric constant variation is indeed valid for X-ray wavelengths in many metals. Assuming that at such frequencies all the electrons can be assumed to be free, calculate ω_p for copper for which the atomic number is 29, mass number is 63, and density is 9 g/cm^3.

[**Ans:** ~9×10^{16} sec^{-1}]

6.10 For sodium, at $\lambda = 1$ Å, all the electrons can be assumed to be free; under this assumption show that $\omega_p \approx 3 \times 10^{16}$ s^{-1} and $n^2 \approx 1$ and the metal will be completely transparent.

6.11 In an ionic crystal (like NaCl, CaF$_2$, etc.), one has to take into account infrared resonance oscillations of the ions and Eq. (6.68) modifies to

$$n^2 = 1 + \frac{Nq^2}{m\varepsilon_0(\omega_1^2 - \omega^2)} + \frac{pNq^2}{M\varepsilon_0(\omega_2^2 - \omega^2)}$$

where M represents the reduced mass of the two ions and p represents the valency of the ion ($p = 1$ for Na$^+$, Cl$^-$;

$p = 2$ for Ca^{++}, F_2^{--}). Show that the above equation can be written in the form*

$$n^2 = n_\infty^2 + \frac{A_1}{\lambda^2 - \lambda_1^2} + \frac{A_2}{\lambda^2 - \lambda_2^2}$$

where $n_\infty^2 = 1 + \frac{A_1}{\lambda_1^2} + \frac{A_2}{\lambda_2^2}$

$$\lambda_1 = \frac{2\pi c}{\omega_1}, \quad \lambda_2 = \frac{2\pi c}{\omega_2}$$

$$A_1 = \frac{N q^2}{4\pi^2 c^2 \varepsilon_0 m} \lambda_1^4, \quad A_2 = \frac{p N q^2}{4\pi^2 c^2 \varepsilon_0 M} \lambda_2^4$$

6.12 The refractive index variation for CaF_2 (in the visible region of the spectrum) can be written in the form*

$$n^2 = 6.09 + \frac{6.12 \times 10^{-15}}{\lambda^2 - 8.88 \times 10^{-15}} + \frac{5.10 \times 10^{-9}}{\lambda^2 - 1.26 \times 10^{-9}}$$

where λ is in meters

(a) Plot the variation of n^2 with λ in the visible region.

(b) From the values of A_1 and A_2 show that $m/M \approx 2.07 \times 10^{-5}$ and compare this with the exact value.

(c) Show that using the constants A_1, A_2, λ_1 and λ_2 we obtain $n_\infty^2 \approx 5.73$ which agrees reasonably well with the experimental value given above.

6.13 **(a)** The refractive index of a plasma (neglecting collisions) is approximately given by (see Sec. 6.5)

$$n^2 = 1 - \frac{\omega_p^2}{\omega^2}$$

where $\omega_p = \left(\frac{N q^2}{m \varepsilon_0}\right)^{1/2} = 56.414 \sqrt{N}\ \text{s}^{-1}$

is known as the plasma frequency. In the ionosphere, the maximum value of N_0 is $\approx 10^{10}$–10^{12} electrons/m^3. Calculate the plasma frequency. Notice that at high frequencies $n^2 \approx 1$; thus high frequency waves (like the one used in TV) are not reflected by the ionosphere. On the other hand, for low frequencies, the refractive index is imaginary (like in a conductor—see Sec. 23.3) and the beam gets reflected. This fact is used in long distance radio communications (see Fig. 2.20).

(b) Assume that for $x \approx 200$ km, $N = 10^{12}$ electrons/m^3 and that the electron density increases to 2×10^{12} electrons/m^3 at $x \approx 300$ km. For $x < 300$ km, the electron density decreases. Assuming a parabolic variation of N, plot the corresponding refractive index variation.

[**Ans:** For 2×10^5 m $< x < 4 \times 10^5$ m,

$$n^2(x) \approx 1 - \frac{6.4 \times 10^{15}}{\omega^2}[1 - 5 \times 10^{-11} (x - 3 \times 10^5)^2$$

where ω is measured in s^{-1} and x in m.]

* Quoted from Ref. 6.9; measurements are of Paschen.

CHAPTER

7

Fourier Series and Applications

LEARNING OBJECTIVES

After reading this chapter, the reader should be able to:

LO 1: *express a periodic function as a Fourier series.*

LO 2: *use Fourier series in analyzing transverse vibrations of a plucked string.*

LO 3: *use Fourier series in forced vibrations of a damped oscillator.*

... Reimann (in one of his publications in 1867) asserts that when Fourier, in his first paper to the Paris Academy in 1807, stated that a completely arbitrary function could be expressed in such a series, his statement so surprised Lagrange that he denied possibility in the most definite terms. It should also be noted that he (Fourier) was the first to allow that the arbitrary function might be given by different analytical expressions in different parts of the interval.

—H.A. Carslaw (1930)

7.1 Introduction

LO1

Fourier series and Fourier integrals are extensively used in the theory of vibrations and waves. As such, we devote this and the following chapter to the study of Fourier series and Fourier integrals. The results obtained will be used in subsequent chapters. Now, according to Fourier's theorem, any periodic vibration can be expressed as a sum of the sine and cosine functions whose frequencies increase in the ratio of natural numbers. Thus, a periodic function with period T, i.e.,

$$f(t + nT) = f(t); \quad n = 0, \ \pm 1, \ \pm 2, \ \ldots; \tag{7.1}$$

can be expanded in the form,

$$\begin{aligned} f(t) &= \frac{1}{2}a_0 + \sum_{n=1}^{\infty} a_n \cos\left(\frac{2n\pi}{T}t\right) + \sum_{n=1}^{\infty} b_n \sin\left(\frac{2n\pi}{T}t\right) \\ &= \frac{1}{2}a_0 + \sum_{n=1}^{\infty} a_n \cos(n\omega t) + \sum_{n=1}^{\infty} b_n \sin(n\omega t) \end{aligned} \tag{7.2}$$

where

$$\omega = \frac{2\pi}{T} \tag{7.3}$$

represents the fundamental frequency. Actually, for the expansion to be possible, the function $f(t)$ must satisfy certain conditions. The conditions are that the function

Above Image: View of a rainbow against a background of clouds. Photograph courtesy McGraw Hill Digital Access Library.

$f(t)$ in one period (i.e., in the interval $t_0 < t < t_0 + T$) must be **(a)** single valued, **(b)** piecewise continuous (i.e., it can have at most a finite number of finite discontinuities) and **(c)** can have only a finite number of maxima and minima. These conditions are known as **Dirichlet's conditions** and are almost always satisfied in all problems that one encounters in physics.

The coefficients a_n and b_n can easily be determined by using the following properties of the trigonometric functions:

$$\int_{t_0}^{t_0+T} \cos n\omega t \cos m\omega t \, dt = \begin{cases} 0 & \text{if} \quad m \neq n \\ T/2 & \text{if} \quad m = n \end{cases} \tag{7.4}$$

$$\int_{t_0}^{t_0+T} \sin n\omega t \sin m\omega t \, dt = \begin{cases} 0 & \text{if} \quad m \neq n \\ T/2 & \text{if} \quad m = n \end{cases} \tag{7.5}$$

$$\int_{t_0}^{t_0+T} \sin n\omega t \cos m\omega t \, dt = 0 \tag{7.6}$$

The above equations can easily be derived. For example, for $m = n$,

$$\int_{t_0}^{t_0+T} \cos n\omega t \cos m\omega t \, dt = \int_{t_0}^{t_0+T} \cos^2 n\omega t \, dt$$

$$= \frac{1}{2}\int_{t_0}^{t_0+T} [1 + \cos 2n\omega t] \, dt = \frac{T}{2}$$

Similarly, for $m \neq n$

$$\int_{t_0}^{t_0+T} \cos n\omega t \cos m\omega t \, dt$$

$$= \frac{1}{2}\int_{t_0}^{t_0+T} [\cos (n-m)\,\omega t + \cos (n+m)\,\omega t] \, dt$$

$$= \frac{1}{2}\left[\frac{1}{(n-m)\,\omega}\sin (n-m)\,\omega t + \frac{1}{(n+m)\,\omega}\sin (n+m)\,\omega t\right]_{t_0}^{t_0+T} = 0$$

In order to determine the coefficients a_n and b_n we first multiply Eq. (7.2) by dt and integrate from t_0 to $t_0 + T$:

$$\int_{t_0}^{t_0+T} f(t)\, dt = \frac{1}{2} a_0 \int_{t_0}^{t_0+T} dt + \sum_{n=1}^{\infty} a_n \int_{t_0}^{t_0+T} \cos n\omega t \, dt + \sum_{n=1}^{\infty} b_n \int_{t_0}^{t_0+T} \sin n\omega t \, dt = \frac{T}{2} a_0$$

where we have used Eqs. (7.4) and (7.6) for $m = 0$. Thus,

$$a_0 = \frac{2}{T}\int_{t_0}^{t_0+T} f(t)\, dt \tag{7.7}$$

Next, if we multiply Eq. (7.2) by $\cos (m\omega t)\, dt$ and integrate from t_0 to $t_0 + T$ we would obtain

$$\int_{t_0}^{t_0+T} f(t) \cos (m\omega t)\, dt = \frac{1}{2} a_0 \int_{t_0}^{t_0+T} \cos (m\omega t)\, dt + \sum_{n=1}^{\infty} a_n \int_{t_0}^{t_0+T} \cos (m\omega t) \cos (n\omega t)\, dt + \sum_{n=1}^{\infty} b_n \int_{t_0}^{t_0+T} \cos (m\omega t) \sin (n\omega t)\, dt$$

$$= \frac{T}{2} a_m$$

where we have used Eqs. (7.4) and (7.6). We may combine the above equation with Eq. (7.7) to write

$$a_n = \frac{2}{T}\int_{t_0}^{t_0+T} f(t) \cos n\omega t \, dt\,; \quad n = 0, 1, 2, 3, \ldots \tag{7.8}$$

Similarly,

$$b_n = \frac{2}{T}\int_{t_0}^{t_0+T} f(t) \sin n\omega t \, dt\,; \quad n = 1, 2, 3, \ldots \tag{7.9}$$

It should be pointed out that the value of t_0 is quite arbitrary. In some problems, it is convenient to choose

$$t_0 = -T/2$$

then $a_n = \dfrac{2}{T}\displaystyle\int_{-T/2}^{+T/2} f(t) \cos n\omega t \, dt; \quad n = 0, 1, 2, \ldots$

and $b_n = \dfrac{2}{T}\displaystyle\int_{-T/2}^{+T/2} f(t) \sin n\omega t \, dt; \; n = 0, 1, 2, \ldots$

Such a choice is particularly convenient when the function is even (i.e., $f(t) = f(-t)$) or odd (i.e., $f(t) = -f(-t)$). In the former case, $b_n = 0$ whereas in the latter case, $a_n = 0$. In some problems, it is convenient to choose $t_0 = 0$.

If we substitute the above expressions for a_n and b_n in Eq. (7.2) and let $T \to 0$, we can arrive at the Fourier integral theorem.* A more straightforward way of deriving the Fourier integral theorem is discussed in Sec. 8.4.

* To know more on Fourier Integral Theorem, visit the student resources available at www.mheducation.co.in. See inside back cover for more details.

EXAMPLE 7.1 Consider a periodic function of the form

$$\left.\begin{aligned} f(t) &= t \quad \text{for} \quad -\tau < t < +\tau \\ f(t+2n\tau) &= f(t) \end{aligned}\right\} \tag{7.10}$$

(see Fig. 7.1). Such a function is referred to as a saw tooth function. In this example, we will expand the above function in a Fourier series. Now, since *f*(*t*) is an odd function of *t*, $a_n = 0$ and

$$b_n = \frac{2}{T}\int_{-\tau}^{+\tau} f(t)\sin(n\omega t)\,dt$$

$$= \frac{1}{\tau}2\int_0^{\tau} t\sin(n\omega t)\,dt$$

Notice that the periodicity is 2τ and, therefore, $\omega = \pi/\tau$. Carrying out the integration we obtain

$$b_n = \frac{2}{\tau}\left[-\frac{t}{n\omega}\cos n\omega t + \frac{1}{n\omega}\left\{\frac{1}{n\omega}\sin n\omega t\right\}\right]_0^{\tau}$$

$$= -\frac{2\tau}{n\pi}\cos n\pi = (-1)^{n+1}\frac{2\tau}{n\pi} \tag{7.11}$$

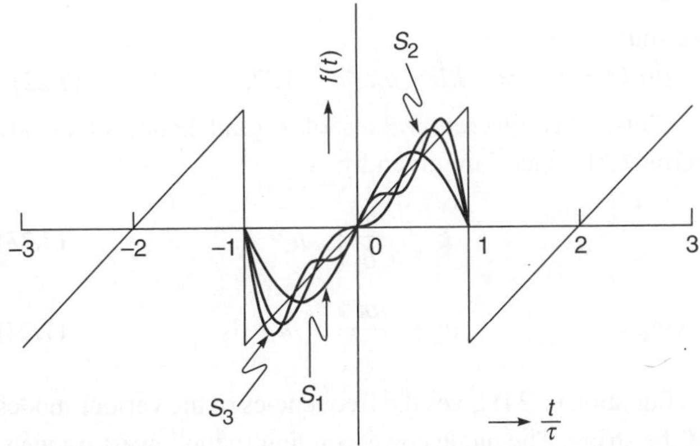

Figure 7.1
The saw tooth function; S_1, S_2 and S_3 represent the partial sums corresponding to the saw tooth function.

Thus,

$$f(t) = \frac{2\tau}{\pi}\sum_{n=1,2,\ldots}\frac{(-1)^{n+1}}{n}\sin n\omega t$$

$$= \frac{2\tau}{\pi}\left[\sin\omega t - \frac{1}{2}\sin 2\omega t + \frac{1}{3}\sin 3\omega t - \ldots\right] \tag{7.12}$$

In Fig. 7.1, we have also plotted the partial sums which are given by

$$S_1 = \frac{2\tau}{\pi}\sin\omega t;\quad S_2 = \frac{2\tau}{\pi}\left[\sin\omega t - \frac{1}{2}\sin 2\omega t\right]$$

$$S_3 = \frac{2\tau}{\pi}\left[\sin\omega t - \frac{1}{2}\sin 2\omega t + \frac{1}{3}\sin 3\omega t\right]$$

It can be seen from the figure that as *n* increases, the sum S_n approaches the function *f*(*t*).

EXAMPLE 7.2 In this example, we will Fourier expand the function defined by the following equations:

$$\begin{aligned} f(t) &= -A \quad \text{for} \quad -\frac{T}{2} < t < 0 \\ &= +A \quad \text{for} \quad 0 < t < +\frac{T}{2} \end{aligned} \tag{7.13}$$

and $\quad f(t+T) = f(t)$

The function is plotted in Fig. 7.2. Once again the function is an odd function; consequently $a_n = 0$ and

$$b_n = \frac{2}{T}2\int_0^{T/2} A\sin(n\omega t)\,dt = \frac{4A}{T}\frac{1}{n\omega}\left[-\cos n\omega t\right]_0^{T/2}$$

$$= \frac{2A}{n\pi}[1-\cos n\pi] = \frac{2A}{n\pi}[1-(-1)^n]$$

Thus, $\quad f(t) = \dfrac{2A}{\pi}\displaystyle\sum_{n=1,2,3,\ldots}\frac{1}{n}\left[1-(-1)^n\right]\sin n\omega t$

$$= \frac{4A}{\pi}\left[\sin\omega t + \frac{1}{3}\sin 3\omega t + \frac{1}{5}\sin 5\omega t + \ldots\right]$$

The partial sums

$$S_1 = \frac{4A}{\pi}\sin\omega t;\quad S_2 = \frac{4A}{\pi}\left(\sin\omega t + \frac{1}{3}\sin 3\omega t\right)$$

$$S_3 = \frac{4A}{\pi}\left[\sin\omega t + \frac{1}{3}\sin 3\omega t + \frac{1}{5}\sin 5\omega t\right]$$

are also plotted in Fig. 7.2.

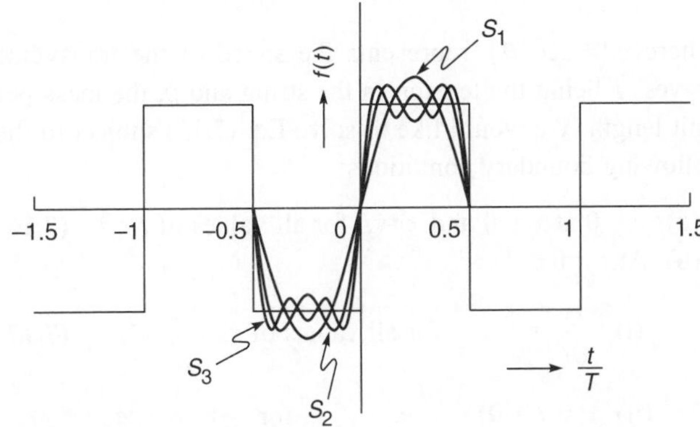

Figure 7.2
A plot of the periodic step function defined by Eq. (7.13). S_1, S_2 and S_3 represent the corresponding partial sums.

7.2 Transverse Vibrations of a Plucked String

LO2

An interesting application of the Fourier series lies in studying the transverse vibrations of a plucked string.

Let us consider a stretched string, fixed at the two ends A and B. One of the ends (A) is chosen as the origin. In the equilibrium position of the string, it is assumed to lie along the x-axis (see Fig. 7.3). A point of the string is moved upwards by a distance d; the corresponding shape of the string is shown as dashed line in Fig. 7.3. If the displacement occurs at a distance a from the origin, the equation of the string (in its displaced position) would be given by the following equation:

$$y = \frac{d}{a}x \quad \text{for} \quad 0 < x < a$$

$$= \frac{d}{L-a}(L-x) \quad \text{for} \quad a < x < L \tag{7.14}$$

where L represents the length of the string. Now, if the string is released from this position at $t = 0$, we would like to determine the shape of the string at any subsequent time.

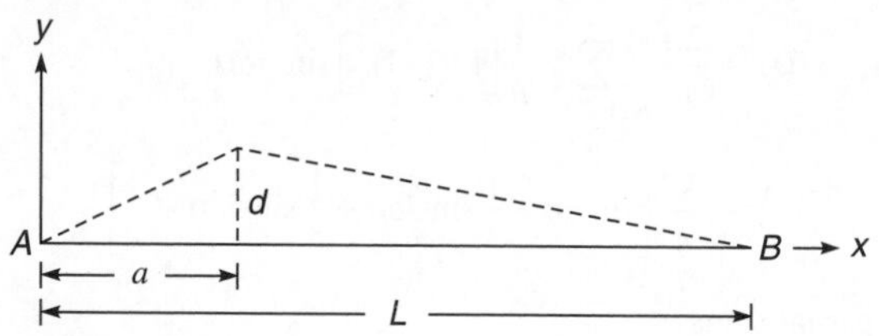

Figure 7.3
The plucked string; AB represents the equilibrium position. The dashed lines show the displaced position at $t = 0$.

We will show in Sec. 9.6 that the displacement $y(x, t)$ satisfies the following wave equation:

$$\frac{\partial^2 y}{\partial x^2} = \frac{1}{v^2}\frac{\partial^2 y}{\partial t^2} \tag{7.15}$$

where $v \left(= \sqrt{T/\rho}\right)$ represents the speed of the transverse waves, T being the tension in the string and ρ, the mass per unit length. We would like to solve Eq. (7.15) subject to the following boundary conditions:

(a) $y = 0$ at $x = 0$ and $x = L$ for all values of t **(7.16)**

(b) At $t = 0$

(i) $\frac{\partial y}{\partial t} = 0$ for all values of x. **(7.17)**

(ii) $y(x, t = 0) = \frac{d}{a}x$ for $0 < x < a$

$= \frac{d}{L-a}(L-x)$ for $a < x < L$ **(7.18)**

Assuming a time dependence of the form $\cos \omega t$ (or $\sin \omega t$),

$$y(x, t) = X(x) \cos \omega t$$

we obtain

$$\frac{d^2 X}{dx^2} = -\frac{\omega^2}{v^2} X(x)$$

or

$$\frac{d^2 X}{dx^2} + k^2 X(x) = 0 \tag{7.19}$$

where

$$k = \frac{\omega}{v} \tag{7.20}$$

The solution of Eq. (7.19) is simple*:

$$X(x) = A \sin kx + B \cos kx \tag{7.21}$$

Thus,

$$y(x, t) = (A \sin kx + B \cos kx)(C \cos \omega t + D \sin \omega t)$$

Now, $\quad y(x,t)\big|_{x=0} = 0 \quad$ for all values of t

Thus, $B = 0$ and we obtain

$$y(x, t) = \sin kx\, [C \cos \omega t + D \sin \omega t]$$

where we have absorbed A in C and D. Since

$$y(x,t)\big|_{x=L} = 0 \text{ (for all values of } t)$$

we must have

$$\sin kL = 0 \;\Rightarrow\; kL = n\pi;\; n = 1, 2, \ldots \tag{7.22}$$

Thus, only discrete values of k (and hence of ω) are permissible; these are given by

$$k_n = \frac{n\pi}{L}; \quad n = 1, 2, \ldots \tag{7.23}$$

giving

$$\omega_n = \frac{n\pi v}{L}; \quad n = 1, 2, \ldots \tag{7.24}$$

Equation (7.24) gives the frequencies of the various modes of the string. The mode corresponding to the lowest frequency ($n = 1$) is known as the **fundamental mode**.

Thus the solution of Eq. (7.15) satisfying the boundary condition given by Eq. (7.16) would be given by

$$y(x, t) = \sum_{n=1,2,3,\ldots} \sin k_n x\, [C_n \cos \omega_n t + D_n \sin \omega_n t] \tag{7.25}$$

Differentiating partially with respect to t, we get

$$\left.\frac{\partial y}{\partial t}\right|_{t=0} = \sum_n \sin k_n x\, [-\omega_n C_n \sin \omega_n t + \omega_n D_n \cos \omega_n t]\Big|_{t=0}$$

$$= \sum_n \omega_n D_n \sin k_n x \tag{7.26}$$

* Rigorously, we should proceed by using the method of separation of variables; see Example 9.5.

Since $\left.\dfrac{\partial y}{\partial t}\right|_{t=0} = 0$ for all values of x

we must have $D_n = 0$ for all n. Thus,

$$y(x, t) = \sum_{n=1,2,3,\ldots} C_n \sin k_n x \cos \omega_n t \tag{7.27}$$

or
$$y(x, 0) = \sum_n C_n \sin\left(\frac{n\pi}{L} x\right) \tag{7.28}$$

The above equation is essentially a Fourier series and in order to determine C_n, we multiply both sides of Eq. (7.28) by $\sin\left(\dfrac{m\pi}{L} x\right) dx$ and integrate from 0 to L to obtain:

$$C_m = \frac{2}{L}\int_0^L y(x, 0) \sin\left(\frac{m\pi}{L} x\right) dx \tag{7.29}$$

where we have used the relation

$$\int_0^L \sin\frac{n\pi x}{L} \sin\frac{m\pi x}{L} dx = \begin{cases} 0 & \text{if } m \neq n \\ L/2 & \text{if } m = n \end{cases} \tag{7.30}$$

[see Eq. (7.5)]. Substituting the expression for $y(x, 0)$ from Eq. (7.18) in Eq. (7.29), we obtain

$$C_n = \frac{2dL^2}{a(L-a)\pi^2 n^2} \sin\left(\frac{n\pi}{L} a\right)$$

On substituting in Eq. (7.27), we finally obtain

$$y(x, t) = \frac{2dL^2}{a(L-a)\pi^2} \sum_{n=1,2,3,\ldots} \frac{1}{n^2} \sin\left(\frac{n\pi}{L} a\right) \times \sin\left(\frac{n\pi}{L} x\right) \cos\left(\frac{n\pi v}{L} t\right) \tag{7.31}$$

Equation (7.31) can be used to determine the shape of the string at an arbitrary time t. If the string is plucked at the centre (i.e., $a = L/2$), terms corresponding to $n = 2, 4, 6, \ldots$ are absent (i.e., the even harmonics are absent) and Eq. (7.31) simplifies to

$$y(x, t) = \frac{8d}{\pi^2} \sum_m (-1)^{m+1} \frac{1}{(2m-1)^2} \sin\frac{(2m-1)\pi x}{L} \times \cos\frac{(2m-1)(\pi v t)}{L} \tag{7.32}$$

7.3 Application of Fourier Series in Forced Vibrations

LO3

Let us consider the forced vibrations of a damped oscillator. The equation of motion would be

$$m\frac{d^2 y}{dt^2} + \Gamma\frac{dy}{dt} + k_0 y = F(t) \tag{7.33}$$

where Γ represents the damping constant (see Sec. 7.3) and F represents the external force. It has been shown in Sec. 6.4 that if $\Gamma > 0$ and

$$F(t) = F_0 \cos(pt + \theta) \tag{7.34}$$

then the steady state solution of Eq. (7.33) is a simple harmonic motion with the frequency of the external force. If $F(t)$ is not a sine or cosine function, a general solution of Eq. (7.33) is difficult to obtain; however, if $F(t)$ is periodic then we can apply Fourier's theorem to obtain a solution of Eq. (7.33). For example, let

$$F(t) = \alpha t \quad \text{for} \quad -\tau < t < \tau \tag{7.35}$$

and
$$F(t + 2n\tau) = F(t);\ n = 1, 2, \ldots$$

The Fourier expansion of such a function was discussed in Example 7.1 and is of the form,

$$F(t) = \sum_n F_n \sin n\omega t$$

$$= \frac{2\alpha\tau}{\pi}\left[\sum_{n=1,2,\ldots} \frac{(-1)^{n+1}}{n} \sin n\omega t\right] \tag{7.36}$$

We next consider the solution of the differential equation

$$m\frac{d^2 y_n}{dt^2} + \Gamma\frac{dy_n}{dt} + k_0 y_n = F_n \sin n\omega t$$

or
$$\frac{d^2 y_n}{dt^2} + K\frac{dy_n}{dt} + \omega_0^2 y_n = A_n \sin n\omega t \tag{7.37}$$

where
$$K \equiv \frac{\Gamma}{m};\quad \omega_0^2 \equiv \frac{k_0}{m}$$

and
$$A_n = \frac{F_n}{m} = \frac{(-1)^{n+1}}{n}\frac{2\alpha\tau}{\pi m} \tag{7.38}$$

The steady state solution of Eq. (7.37) will be of the form

$$y_n = C_n \sin n\omega t + D_n \cos n\omega t$$

and the solution of Eq. (7.33) will be of the form

$$y = \sum_n y_n \tag{7.39}$$

In order to determine C_n and D_n we substitute the above solution in Eq. (7.37) to obtain

$$-n^2\omega^2[C_n \sin n\omega t + D_n \cos n\omega t] + n\omega K[C_n \cos n\omega t - D_n \sin n\omega t] + \omega_0^2[C_n \sin n\omega t + D_n \cos n\omega t] = A_n \sin n\omega t$$

Thus,

$$\left.\begin{aligned} (\omega_0^2 - n^2\omega^2) C_n - n\omega K D_n &= A_n \\ (\omega_0^2 - n^2\omega^2) D_n - n\omega K C_n &= 0 \end{aligned}\right\} \tag{7.40}$$

Solving the above equations, we get

$$D_n = -\frac{n\omega K}{(\omega_0^2 - n^2\omega^2)^2 + n^2\omega^2 K^2} A_n$$

and

$$C_n = \frac{\omega_0^2 - n^2\omega^2}{(\omega_0^2 - n^2\omega^2)^2 + n^2\omega^2 K^2} A_n$$

Thus, the steady state solution can be written in the form

$$y = \sum_n G_n \sin(n\omega t + \theta_n) \tag{7.41}$$

where the amplitude G_n is given by

$$G_n = (C_n^2 + D_n^2)^{1/2}$$

$$= \frac{A_n}{[(\omega_0^2 - n^2\omega^2)^2 + n^2\omega^2 K^2]^{1/2}} \tag{7.42}$$

SUMMARY

- A periodic function with period T, i.e.,

$$f(t + nT) = f(t); \quad n = 0, \pm1, \pm2, \ldots$$

can be expanded in the form

$$f(t) = \frac{1}{2}a_0 + \sum_{n=1}^{\infty} a_n \cos\left(\frac{2\pi n}{T}t\right) + \sum_{n=1}^{\infty} b_n \sin\left(\frac{2\pi n}{T}t\right)$$

$$= \frac{1}{2}a_0 + \sum_{n=1}^{\infty} a_n \cos(n\omega t) + \sum_{n=1}^{\infty} b_n \sin(n\omega t)$$

where $\omega = \dfrac{2\pi}{T}$ represents the fundamental frequency. The above infinite series is known as the Fourier series and the coefficients a_n and b_n are given by

$$a_n = \frac{2}{T}\int_{t_0}^{t_0+T} f(t)\cos n\omega t; \qquad n = 0, 1, 2, 3, \ldots$$

and

$$b_n = \frac{2}{T}\int_{t_0}^{t_0+T} f(t)\sin n\omega t; \qquad n = 1, 2, 3, \ldots$$

- Transverse vibrations of a plucked string and forced vibrations in damped oscillator can be studied by using Fourier series.

PROBLEMS

7.1 Consider a periodic force of the form,

$$F(t) = F_0 \sin \omega t \quad \text{for} \quad 0 < t < T/2$$
$$= 0 \quad \text{for} \quad T/2 < t < T$$

and

$$F(t + T) = F(t)$$

where

$$\omega = \frac{2\pi}{T}$$

Show that

$$F(t) = \frac{1}{\pi}F_0 + \frac{1}{2}F_0 \sin\omega t$$
$$- \frac{2}{\pi}F_0\left(\frac{1}{3}\cos 2\omega t + \frac{1}{15}\cos 4\omega t + \ldots\right)$$

One obtains a periodic voltage of the above form in a half-wave rectifier. What will be the Fourier expansion corresponding to full wave rectification?

7.2 Consider the periodic function

$$f(x) = \sin x \qquad 0 < x < \pi$$

with $f(x + \pi) = f(x)$

Evaluate the coefficients a_n and b_n and show that

$$\sin x = \frac{2}{\pi} - \frac{4}{\pi}\left[\frac{1}{3}\cos 2x + \frac{1}{3}\cos 4x + \ldots\right]; \qquad 0 < x < \pi$$

[Hint: In Eq. (7.3) $T = \pi \Rightarrow \omega = 2$].

7.3 Consider the periodic function

$$f(t) = \begin{cases} 0 & -T/2 < t < 0 \\ t & 0 < t < T/2 \end{cases}$$

with $f(t + T) = f(t)$

Evaluate the coefficients a_n and b_n and show that

$$f(t) = \frac{T}{2\pi}\left[\frac{\pi}{4} + \sum_{n=1}^{\infty}\left(\frac{(-1)^n - 1}{\pi n^2}\cos n\omega t + \frac{(-1)^n}{\pi n^2}\sin n\omega t\right)\right];$$

$$-T/2 < x < +T/2$$

CHAPTER

8

The Dirac Delta Function and Fourier Transforms

Strictly of course, δ(x) is not a proper function of x, but can be regarded only as a limit of a certain sequence of functions. All the same one can use δ(x) as though it were a proper function for practically all the purposes of quantum mechanics without getting incorrect results. One can also use the differential coefficients of δ(x), namely, δ′(x), δ″(x),… which are even more discontinuous and less 'proper' than δ(x) itself.

—P.A.M. Dirac in The *Physical Interpretation of Quantum Dynamics*, Proceedings of the Royal Society of London (A), 113, 621–641 (1926)

LEARNING OBJECTIVES

After reading this chapter, the reader should be able to:

LO 1: *describe different representations of the Dirac delta function.*

LO 2: *prove Fourier integral theorem and obtain Fourier transform pair.*

LO 3: *describe delta function as a distribution.*

LO 4: *analyze multi-dimensional form of Fourier transformation.*

Above Image: View of a rainbow against a background of clouds. Photograph courtesy McGraw Hill Digital Access Library.

8.1 Introduction

The Dirac delta function is defined through the equations

$$\delta(x-a) = 0 \qquad x \neq a \tag{8.1}$$

$$\int_{a-\alpha}^{a+\beta} \delta(x-a)dx = 1 \tag{8.2}$$

where $\alpha, \beta > 0$. Thus, the delta function has an infinite value at $x = a$ such that the area under the curve is unity. For an arbitrary function that is continuous at $x = a$, we have

$$\int_{a-\alpha}^{a+\beta} f(x)\,\delta(x-a)dx = f(a)\int_{a-\alpha}^{a+\beta} \delta(x-a)dx \qquad \text{[using Eq. (8.1)]}$$

$$= f(a) \tag{8.3}$$

It is readily seen that if x has the dimension of length, $\delta(x-a)$ would have the dimension of inverse length. Similarly, if x has the dimension of time then $\delta(x-a)$ would have the dimension of $(\text{time})^{-1}$.

8.2 Representations of the Dirac Delta Function

LO1

There are many representations of the Dirac delta function. Perhaps the simplest representation is the limiting form of the rectangle function $R_\sigma(x)$ defined through the following equation:

$$R_\sigma(x) = \frac{1}{2\sigma} \quad \text{for} \quad a - \sigma < x < a + \sigma$$
$$= 0 \quad \text{for} \quad |x - a| > \sigma \tag{8.4}$$

The function $R_\sigma(x)$ is plotted in Fig. 8.1 for various values of σ. Now,

$$\int_{-\infty}^{+\infty} R_\sigma(x)dx = \frac{1}{2\sigma}\int_{a-\sigma}^{a+\sigma} dx = 1 \text{ (irrespective of the value of } \sigma)$$

For $\sigma \to 0$, the function $R_\sigma(x)$ becomes more and more sharply peaked but the area under the curve remains unity. In the limit of $\sigma \to 0$, the function $R_\sigma(x)$ has all the properties of the delta function and we may write

$$\delta(x - a) = \lim_{\sigma\to 0} R_\sigma(x)$$

Now,

$$\int_{-\infty}^{+\infty} f(x)\, R_\sigma(x)dx = \frac{1}{2\sigma}\int_{a-\sigma}^{a+\sigma} f(x)dx \tag{8.5}$$

We assume the function $f(x)$ to be continuous at $x = a$. Thus when $\sigma \to 0$, in the infinitesimal interval $a - \sigma < x < a + \sigma$, $f(x)$ may be assumed to be a constant $[= f(a)]$ and taken out of the integral. Thus,

$$\int_{-\infty}^{+\infty} f(x)\delta(x - a)dx = \lim_{\sigma\to 0}\int_{-\infty}^{+\infty} f(x)\, R_\sigma(x)dx$$

$$= \lim_{\sigma\to 0}\frac{1}{2\sigma} f(a)\int_{a\to\sigma}^{a+\sigma} dx$$

$$= f(a)$$

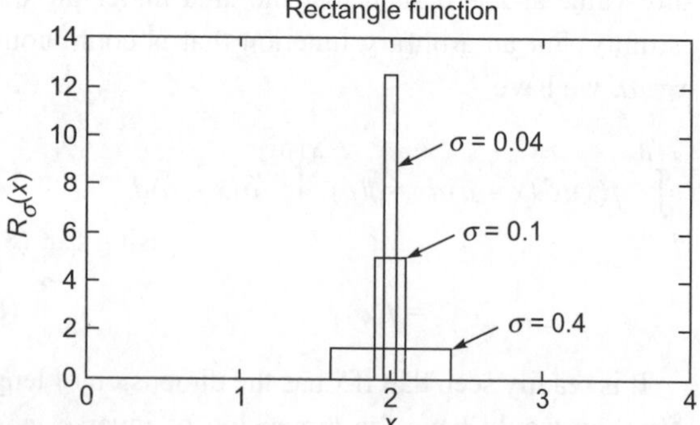

Figure 8.1
Plots of $R_\sigma(x)$ for $a = 2$ and $\sigma = 0.4$, 0.1 and 0.04. In each case, the area under the curve is unity. For $\sigma \to 0$, the function $R_\sigma(x)$ has all the properties of the Dirac delta function.

8.3 Integral Representation of the Delta Function

An extremely important representation of the Dirac delta function is through the following integral:

$$\delta(x - a) = \frac{1}{2\pi}\int_{-\infty}^{+\infty} e^{\pm ik(x-a)}dk \tag{8.6}$$

In order to prove Eq. (8.6) we first note that

$$\frac{1}{2\pi}\int_{-g}^{+g} e^{\pm ik(x-a)}dk = \frac{\sin g\,(x - a)}{\pi\,(x - a)} \tag{8.7}$$

In Appendix *A*, we have shown that

$$\int_{-\infty}^{+\infty} \frac{\sin gx}{\pi x}dx = 1;\ g > 0 \tag{8.8}$$

irrespective of the value of g which is assumed to be greater than zero. Further,

$$\lim_{x\to 0}\frac{\sin gx}{x} = g$$

Thus for a large value of g, the function

$$\frac{\sin g\,(x - a)}{\pi\,(x - a)}$$

is very sharply peaked around $x = a$ (see Fig. 8.2; see also Fig. 16.16(b)) and has a unit area under the curve irrespective of the value of g; thus in the limit of $g \to \infty$, it has all the properties of the delta function and we may write

$$\delta(x - a) = \lim_{g\to\infty}\frac{\sin g\,(x - a)}{\pi\,(x - a)} = \lim_{g\to\infty}\frac{1}{2\pi}\int_{-g}^{+g} e^{\pm ik(x-a)}\,dk \tag{8.9}$$

from which Eq. (8.6) readily follows.

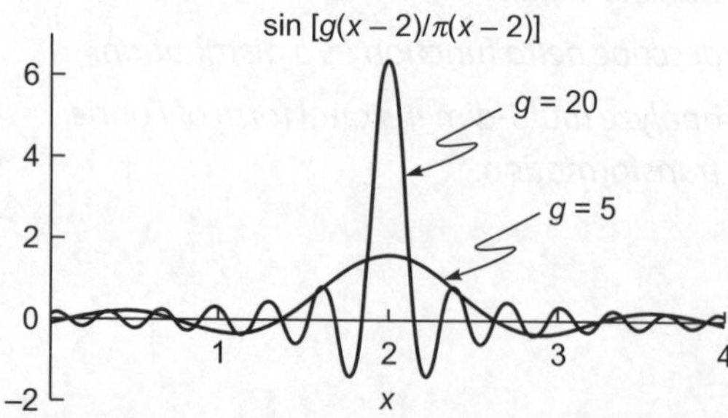

Figure 8.2
Plots of the function $\left[\frac{\sin g(x - a)}{\pi(x - a)}\right]$ for $a = 2$ and $g = 5, 20$.
In each case, the area under the curve is unity. For $g \to \infty$, the function is very sharply peaked at $x = a$ and has all the properties of Dirac delta function.

8.4 Fourier Integral Theorem and Fourier Transforms

LO2

In the previous section we derived the following integral representation of the Dirac delta function

$$\delta(x-x') = \frac{1}{2\pi}\int_{-\infty}^{+\infty} e^{\pm ik(x-x')}\,dk \tag{8.10}$$

Since $$f(x) = \int_{-\infty}^{+\infty} \delta(x-x')\,f(x')\,dx' \tag{8.11}$$

we may write

$$f(x) = \frac{1}{2\pi}\int_{-\infty}^{+\infty}\int_{-\infty}^{+\infty} e^{\pm ik(x-x')}\,f(x')\,dx'\,dk \tag{8.12}$$

Thus if we define

$$F(k) = \frac{1}{2\pi}\int_{-\infty}^{+\infty} f(x)e^{-ikx}\,dx \tag{8.13}$$

then $$f(x) = \int_{-\infty}^{+\infty} F(k)\,e^{+ikx}\,dk \tag{8.14}$$

The function $F(k)$ is known as the ***Fourier transform*** of the function $f(x)$ and Eq. (8.14) enables us to calculate the original function from the Fourier transform. Equation (8.12) represents what is known as the ***Fourier Integral Theorem*** that is valid when the following conditions are satisfied (see, e.g. References 7.4 and 7.5):

(i) The function $f(x)$ must be a single valued function of the real variable x throughout the range $-\infty < x < \infty$. It may however have a finite number of finite discontinuities.

(ii) The integral $\int_{-\infty}^{+\infty} |f(x)|\,dx$ must exist.

The Fourier transform of a function is often written in the form

$$\mathbf{F}[f(x)] = F(k) = \frac{1}{2\pi}\int_{-\infty}^{+\infty} f(x)\,e^{-ikx}\,dx \tag{8.15}$$

To have a symmetric Fourier transform pair, one often defines the Fourier transform with a $\frac{1}{\sqrt{2\pi}}$ factor:

$$G(k) \equiv \frac{1}{\sqrt{2\pi}}\int_{-\infty}^{+\infty} f(x)\,e^{-ikx}\,dx \tag{8.16}$$

then $$f(x) = \frac{1}{\sqrt{2\pi}}\int_{-\infty}^{+\infty} G(k)\,e^{+ikx}\,dx \tag{8.17}$$

From Eq. (8.12) it is obvious that in Eqs. (8.13) and (8.14) there is no reason why the factors e^{+ikx} and e^{+ikx} cannot be interchanged, i.e., we could have defined

$$F(k) \equiv \frac{1}{2\pi}\int_{-\infty}^{+\infty} f(x)\,e^{+ikx}\,dx \tag{8.18}$$

then $$f(x) = \int_{-\infty}^{+\infty} F(k)\,e^{-ikx}\,dk \tag{8.19}$$

However, in all of what follows we will use the definitions given by Eqs. (8.13) and (8.14). See Fig. 8.3.

EXAMPLE 8.1 As an example, we consider a Gaussian function given by

$$f(x) = A\exp\left[-\frac{x^2}{\sigma^2}\right] \tag{8.20}$$

Solution: The FWHM (Full Width at Half Maximum) of $f(x)$ is denoted by Δx; thus at

$$x = \pm\frac{1}{2}\Delta x$$

$f(x)$ attains half of its maximum value; therefore the value of Δx is obtained from the following equation

$$\frac{1}{2} = \exp\left[-\left(\frac{\Delta x}{2}\right)^2\frac{1}{\sigma^2}\right] \Rightarrow \left(\frac{\Delta x}{2\sigma}\right)^2 = \ln 2$$

Thus $$\text{FWHM} = \Delta x = 2\sqrt{\ln 2}\,\sigma \approx 1.67\,\sigma \tag{8.21}$$

which represents the spatial extent of the pulse. Now, if we substitute the expression for $f(x)$ from Eq. (8.20) in Eq. (8.13) we would obtain

$$F(k) = \frac{1}{2\pi}\int_{-\infty}^{+\infty} f(x)\,e^{-ikx}\,dx$$

$$= \frac{A}{2\pi}\int_{-\infty}^{+\infty} \exp\left[-\frac{x^2}{\sigma^2}\right]e^{-ikx}\,dx$$

or, $$F(k) = \frac{A\sigma}{2\sqrt{\pi}}\exp\left[-\frac{k^2\sigma^2}{4}\right] \tag{8.22}$$

where we have used

$$\int_{-\infty}^{+\infty} \exp[-\alpha x^2 + \beta x]dx = \sqrt{\frac{\pi}{\alpha}}\,\exp\left[\frac{\beta^2}{4\alpha}\right] \tag{8.23}$$

(derived in Appendix A). As can be seen from Eqs. (8.20) and (8.22), the Fourier transform of a Gaussian function is also a Gaussian. The FWHM of $F(k)$ is denoted by Δk and will be given by

$$\text{FWHM} = \Delta k = \frac{4\sqrt{\ln 2}}{\sigma} \approx \frac{3.33}{\sigma} \tag{8.24}$$

Thus we have the "uncertainty product":

$$\Delta x\,\Delta k \approx 5 \tag{8.25}$$

implying that smaller the value of the spatial spread Δx, greater will be Δk which represents the spread in the value of k. Since the spreads are order of magnitude, we may write

$$\Delta x\,\Delta k \sim 1 \tag{8.26}$$

The above equation represents a general characteristic of the Fourier transform pair. In Sec. 27.5 we will use similar equations to discuss the "uncertainty principle" in quantum mechanics and obtain the famous "Heisenberg's uncertainty principle":

$$\Delta x \, \Delta p_x \sim \hbar \tag{8.27}$$

where $\hbar \approx 1.055 \times 10^{-34}$ J.s. For a time dependent function $E(t)$, we can write its Fourier transform as:

$$\mathbf{F}[E(t)] = A(\omega) = \frac{1}{2\pi}\int_{-\infty}^{+\infty} E(t)\, e^{\pm i\omega t}\, dt \tag{8.28}$$

The inverse Fourier transform will then be given by

$$E(t) = \int_{-\infty}^{+\infty} A(\omega)\, e^{\mp i\omega t}\, dt \tag{8.29}$$

The above equations are nothing but Eqs. (8.15) and (8.16) with x and k replaced by t and ω respectively. The function $A(\omega)$ is usually referred to as the frequency spectrum of the time dependent function $E(t)$.

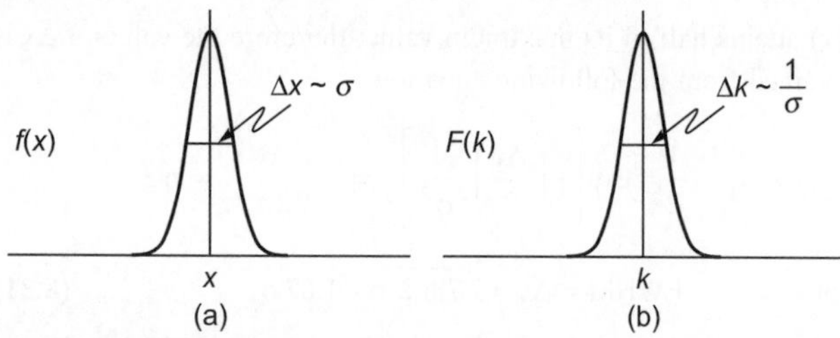

Figure 8.3
(a) The Gaussian function $f(x)$ as given by Eq. (8.19).
(b) The Fourier transform of the Gaussian function is also a Gaussian in the k-space [see Eq. (8.20)].

EXAMPLE 8.2 We will calculate the Fourier transform of a time dependent Gaussian pulse for which the electric field is given by

$$E(t) = E_0 \exp\left[-\frac{t^2}{\tau_0^2}\right] e^{+i\omega_0 t} \tag{8.30}$$

The real part of the electric field is shown in Fig. 11.4(a). If we substitute the above expression in Eq. (8.27) we would obtain

$$A(\omega) = \frac{1}{2\pi}\int_{-\infty}^{+\infty} E(t)\, e^{-i\omega t}\, dt$$

$$= \frac{E_0}{2\pi}\int_{-\infty}^{+\infty} \exp\left[-\frac{t^2}{\tau_0^2}\right] e^{-i(\omega-\omega_0)t}\, dt$$

$$= \frac{E_0}{2\pi}\sqrt{\pi\tau_0^2}\, \exp\left[-\frac{(\omega-\omega_0)^2\,\tau_0^2}{4}\right]$$

where we have again used Eq. (8.23). Thus

$$A(\omega) = \frac{E_0\tau_0}{2\sqrt{\pi}} \exp\left[-\frac{(\omega-\omega_0)^2\,\tau_0^2}{4}\right] \tag{8.31}$$

Once again, we see that the Fourier transform of a Gaussian function (in the time domain) is a Gaussian function in the frequency domain. We will have a physical interpretation of the above equations in Sec. 11.3 (see, in particular, Example 11.4 and Fig. 11.4). However, we would like to mention here that the temporal duration of the pulse is given by

$$\Delta t \sim \tau_0 \tag{8.32}$$

and the spectral width of the pulse is given by

$$\Delta\omega \sim \frac{1}{\tau_0} \tag{8.33}$$

implying the "uncertainty product":

$$\Delta\omega \, \Delta t \sim 1 \tag{8.34}$$

EXAMPLE 8.3 As another example, we calculate the Fourier transform of the rectangle function

$$E(t) = E_0\, e^{+i\omega_0 t} \quad \text{for} \quad -\frac{1}{2}\tau_c < t < \frac{1}{2}\tau_c$$
$$= 0 \quad \text{for} \quad |t| > \frac{1}{2}\tau_c \tag{8.35}$$

Thus

$$A(\omega) = \frac{1}{2\pi}\int_{-\infty}^{+\infty} E(t)\, e^{-i\omega t}\, dt$$

$$= \frac{E_0}{2\pi}\int_{-\tau_c/2}^{+\tau_c/2} e^{-i(\omega-\omega_0)t}\, dt$$

Evaluating the integral we get

$$A(\omega) = \frac{E_0}{\pi}\, \frac{\sin\left\{\frac{1}{2}(\omega-\omega_0)\tau_c\right\}}{(\omega-\omega_0)} \tag{8.36}$$

We will have a physical interpretation of the above equations in Sec. 16.6 (see, in particular, Fig. 16.16). Once again we will have the "uncertainty product" given by Eq. (8.34).

8.5 Delta Function as a Distribution

LO3

The delta function is actually a distribution. In order to understand this, let us consider the Maxwellian distribution

$$N(E)\, dE = N_0 \frac{2}{\sqrt{\pi}} \frac{1}{(kT)^{3/2}} E^{1/2} e^{-\frac{E}{kT}}\, dE \tag{8.37}$$

where k represents the Boltzmann's constant, T the absolute temperature and m the mass of each molecule. In Eq. (8.37), $N(E)\, dE$ represents the number of molecules whose energies lie between E and $E + dE$. The total number of molecules is given by N_0

$$\int_0^\infty N(E)dE = N_0 \frac{2}{\sqrt{\pi}} \frac{1}{(kT)^{3/2}} \int_0^\infty E^{1/2} e^{-E/kT}\, dE$$

$$= N_0 \frac{2}{\sqrt{\pi}} \int_0^\infty x^{\frac{1}{2}} e^{-x} dx$$

where $x = E/kT$. The integral is $\Gamma\left(\frac{3}{2}\right) = \frac{1}{2}\sqrt{\pi}$. Thus,

$$\int_0^\infty N(E)dE = N_0$$

It may be noted that whereas N_0 is just a number, the quantity $N(E)$ has dimensions of (energy)$^{-1}$. Obviously, if we ask ourselves how many molecules have the precise energy E_1 the answer would be zero. This is a characteristic of a distribution. On the other hand, in addition to the distribution given by Eq. (8.37), if we do have N_1 molecules, all of them having the same energy E_1, the corresponding distribution function would be given by

$$N(E) = N_0 \frac{2}{\sqrt{\pi}} \frac{1}{(kT)^{3/2}} E^{1/2} e^{-\frac{E}{kT}} + N_1 \delta(E - E_1) \qquad \textbf{(8.38)}$$

where $\delta(E - E_1)$ represents the Dirac delta function and has the dimensions of inverse energy.

8.6 The Two- and Three-Dimensional Fourier Transform LO4

One can generalize the analysis of Sec. 8.4 to two or three dimensions. For example, the two-dimensional Fourier transform of a function $f(x, y)$ is defined through the equation

$$F(u, v) = \frac{1}{2\pi} \int_{-\infty}^{+\infty}\int_{-\infty}^{+\infty} f(x, y) e^{\pm i(ux+vy)}\, dxdy \qquad \textbf{(8.39)}$$

where u and v are referred to as **spatial frequencies**. The inverse transform would be given by

$$f(x, y) = \frac{1}{2\pi} \int_{-\infty}^{+\infty}\int_{-\infty}^{+\infty} F(u, v) e^{\mp i(ux+vy)}\, dudv \qquad \textbf{(8.40)}$$

We will use Eqs. (8.39) and (8.40) in Sec. 18.9. Similarly, we can define the three-dimensional Fourier transform

$$F(u, v, w) = \frac{1}{(2\pi)^{3/2}} \int_{-\infty}^{+\infty}\int_{-\infty}^{+\infty}\int_{-\infty}^{+\infty} f(x, y, z) e^{\pm i(ux+vy+wz)}\, dxdydz \qquad \textbf{(8.41)}$$

with its inverse Fourier transform given by

$$f(x, y, z) = \frac{1}{(2\pi)^{3/2}} \int_{-\infty}^{+\infty}\int_{-\infty}^{+\infty}\int_{-\infty}^{+\infty} F(u, v, w) e^{\mp i(ux+vy+wz)}\, dudvdw \qquad \textbf{(8.42)}$$

8.6.1 The Convolution Theorem

The convolution of two functions $f(x)$ and $g(x)$ is defined by the relation,

$$f(x) * g(x) = \int_{-\infty}^{+\infty} f(x') g(x - x') dx' = g(x) * f(x) \qquad \textbf{(8.43)}$$

The convolution has this important property:

The Fourier transform of the convolution of two functions is $\sqrt{2\pi}$ times the product of their Fourier transforms.

The proof is as follows:

$$\mathbf{F}(f(x) * g(x)) = \frac{1}{\sqrt{2\pi}} \int_{-\infty}^{+\infty} dx e^{-ikx} \left[\int_{-\infty}^{+\infty} dx' f(x') g(x - x')\right]$$

$$= \sqrt{2\pi} \left[\frac{1}{\sqrt{2\pi}} \int_{-\infty}^{+\infty} dx' f(x') e^{-ikx'}\right]$$

$$\times \left[\frac{1}{\sqrt{2\pi}} \int_{-\infty}^{+\infty} dx\, g(x - x') e^{-ik(x-x')}\right]$$

In the second equation, we substitute $(x - x')$ by ξ to obtain

$$\mathbf{F}(f(x) * g(x)) = \sqrt{2\pi}\, F(k)\, G(k)$$

where $F(k)$ and $G(k)$ are Fourier transforms of $f(x)$ and $g(x)$, respectively. The convolution can be used to obtain the Fourier transforms of the product of two functions:

$$\mathbf{F}(f(x)g(x)] = \frac{1}{\sqrt{2\pi}} \int_{-\infty}^{+\infty} f(x)\, g(x) e^{-ikx}\, dx$$

$$= \frac{1}{\sqrt{2\pi}} \int_{-\infty}^{+\infty} dx\, g(x)\, e^{-ikx} \left[\frac{1}{\sqrt{2\pi}} \int_{-\infty}^{+\infty} F(k') e^{ik'x} dk'\right]$$

$$= \frac{1}{\sqrt{2\pi}} \int_{-\infty}^{+\infty} dk' F(k') \left[\frac{1}{\sqrt{2\pi}} \int_{-\infty}^{+\infty} dx\, g(x) e^{-i(k-k')x}\right]$$

$$= \frac{1}{\sqrt{2\pi}} \int_{-\infty}^{+\infty} F(k') G(k - k') dk'$$

Thus, $$\mathbf{F}(f(x)\, g(x)) = \frac{1}{\sqrt{2\pi}} F(k) * G(k)$$

The above result tells us that the Fourier transform of the product of two functions is $\frac{1}{\sqrt{2\pi}}$ times the convolution of their Fourier transforms.

SUMMARY

- The Dirac delta function is defined through the equations
$$\delta(x-a) = 0 \qquad x \neq a$$
and for a well-behaved function $f(x)$, which is continuous at $x = a$
$$\int_{-\infty}^{+\infty} f(x)\delta(x-a)\,dx = f(a)$$
- For a time dependent function $f(t)$, its Fourier transform is defined by the equation
$$A(\omega) = \frac{1}{2\pi}\int_{-\infty}^{+\infty} f(t)\, e^{\pm i\omega t}\, dt$$
Then,
$$f(t) = \int_{-\infty}^{+\infty} A(\omega)\, e^{\mp i\omega t}\, dt$$
- The Fourier transform of the Gaussian function
$$f(t) = A\exp\left(-\frac{t^2}{t_0^2}\right)$$
is given by
$$A(\omega) = \frac{At_0}{2\sqrt{\pi}} e^{-\frac{\omega^2 t_0^2}{4}}$$
- In general, if a function has a temporal spread of Δt, then its Fourier transform $A(\omega)$ will have a spectral spread $\Delta\omega \approx 1/\Delta t$.
- The two-dimensional Fourier transform of a function $f(x, y)$ is defined through the equation,
$$F(u, v) = \frac{1}{2\pi}\int_{-\infty}^{+\infty}\int_{-\infty}^{+\infty} f(x, y)\, e^{\pm i(ux+vy)}\, dxdy$$
where u and v are referred to as *spatial frequencies*. The inverse transform would be given by
$$f(x, y) = \frac{1}{2\pi}\int_{-\infty}^{+\infty}\int_{-\infty}^{+\infty} F(u, v)\, e^{\mp i(ux+vy)}\, dudv$$
- The convolution of two functions $f(x)$ and $g(x)$ is defined by the relation
$$f(x)^* g(x) = \int_{-\infty}^{+\infty} f(x')\, g(x-x')dx' = g(x)^* f(x)$$
The Fourier transform of the convolution of two functions is $\sqrt{2\pi}$ times the product of their Fourier transforms.

PROBLEMS

8.1 Consider the Gaussian function
$$G_\sigma(x) \equiv \frac{1}{\sigma\sqrt{2\pi}}\exp\left[-\frac{(x-a)^2}{2\sigma^2}\right]; \ \sigma > 0$$
Using Eq. (8.21) show that $\int_{-\infty}^{+\infty} G_\sigma(x)dx = 1$. Plot $G_\sigma(x)$ for $a = 2$ and $\sigma = 1.0$, 5.0 and 10.0. Hence show that
$$\delta(x-a) = \lim_{\sigma\to 0}\frac{1}{\sigma\sqrt{2\pi}}\exp\left[-\frac{(x-a)^2}{2\sigma^2}\right] \qquad \textbf{(8.44)}$$
which is the Gaussian representation of the delta function.

8.2 Consider the ramp function defined by the following equation:
$$F_\sigma(x) = \begin{cases} 0 & \text{for } x < a-\sigma \\ \dfrac{1}{2\sigma}(x-a+\sigma) & \text{for } |x-a| < \sigma \\ 1 & \text{for } x > a+\sigma \end{cases} \qquad \textbf{(8.45)}$$
Show that $\frac{dF_\sigma}{dx} = R_\sigma(x)$, where $R_\sigma(x)$ is the rectangle function defined by Eq. (8.4). Taking the limit $\sigma \to 0$, show that $\delta(x-a) = \frac{d}{dx}H(x-a)$ where $H(x-a)$ is the unit step function. Thus we get the following important result:
If a function has a discontinuity of α at $x = a$ then its derivative (at $x = a$) is $\alpha\delta(x-a)$.

8.3 Consider the symmetric function
$$\psi(x) = A\exp(-K|x|)$$
Show that
$$\psi''(x) = K^2\psi(x) - 2AK\delta(x)$$

8.4 Consider the function $f(t) = A\exp\left(-\frac{t^2}{2\tau^2}\right)\exp(i\omega_0 t)$

Calculate its Fourier spectrum $F(\omega) = \frac{1}{\sqrt{2\pi}}\int_{-\infty}^{+\infty} f(t)\exp(-i\omega t)dt$ and evaluate approximately $\Delta\omega\Delta t$. Evaluate $f(t)$ using the expression for $F(\omega)$.

8.5 Calculate the Fourier transform of the following functions

(a) $f(x) = Ae^{ik_0 x} \quad |x| < L/2$

$= 0 \quad |x| > L/2$

(b) $f(x) = A\exp\left[-\frac{|x|}{L}\right]$

In each case, make an estimate of Δx and Δk interpret physically.

8.6 Show that the convolution of two Gaussian functions is another Gaussian function:
$$\left[\exp\left(-\frac{x^2}{a^2}\right)\right] * \left[\exp\left(-\frac{x^2}{b^2}\right)\right]$$
$$= ab\left[\frac{\pi}{a^2+b^2}\right]^{1/2}\exp\left(-\frac{x^2}{a^2+b^2}\right)$$

CHAPTER 9

Wave Propagation and the Wave Equation

'If you are dropping pebbles into a pond and do not watch the spreading rings, your occupation should be considered as useless', said the fictional Russian philosopher, Kuzma Prutkoff. And, indeed we can learn much by observing these graceful circles spreading out from the punctured surface of calm water.

—Gamow and Cleveland

Important Milestones

1746 Jean-Baptiste le Rond d'Alembert (a French mathematician) discovered the one dimensional wave equation.

1755 Leonhard Euler (a Swiss mathematician) discovered the three dimensional wave equation.

LEARNING OBJECTIVES

After reading this chapter, the reader should be able to:

LO 1: *understand the concept of frequency and wavelength for sinusoidal waves.*

LO 2: *discuss different types of waves.*

LO 3: *calculate the energy transported for a propagating wave.*

LO 4: *derive the one dimensional wave equation for different types of waves.*

LO 5: *construct the general solution of the one-dimensional wave equation.*

Above Image: View of a rainbow against a background of clouds. Photograph courtesy McGraw Hill Digital Access Library.

9.1 Introduction

Christiaan Huygens, a Dutch physicist and a contemporary of Isaac Newton, was the first scientist who in 1678, proposed that light is a wave phenomenon. What is a wave? A wave is propagation of disturbance. When we make a sharp needle vibrate in a calm pool of water, a circular pattern spreads out from the point of impact (see Fig. 9.1). The vibrating needle creates a disturbance that propagates outwards. In this propagation, the water molecules do not move outward with the wave; instead they move in nearly circular orbits about an equilibrium position. Once the disturbance has passed a certain region, every drop of water is left at its original position. This fact can easily be verified by placing a small piece of wood on the surface of water. As the wave passes, the piece of wood comes back to its original position. Further, with time the circular ripples spread out, i.e., the disturbance (which is confined to particular region at a given time) produces a similar disturbance at a neighboring point at a slightly later time with the pattern of disturbance roughly remaining the same. Thus

Propagation of disturbances (without any translation of the medium in the direction of propagation) is termed as a wave.

Also, waves carry energy; in this case the energy is in the form of kinetic energy of water molecules. All waves are characterized by certain properties such as wavelength and frequency.

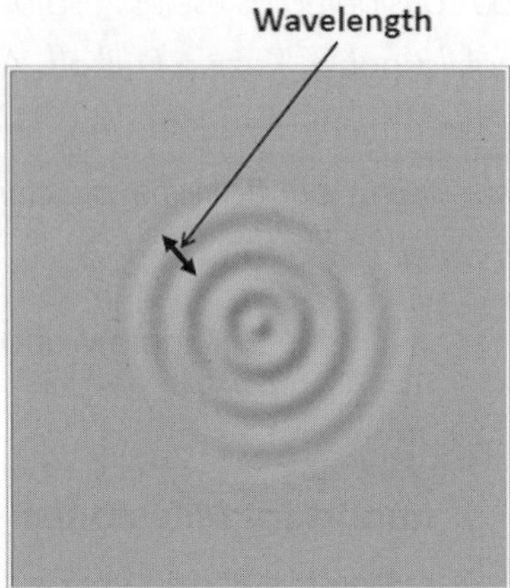

Figure 9.1

Water waves spreading out from a vibrating point source. [Adapted from the University of Colorado website http://www.colorado.edu/physics/2000/waves_particles/waves.html]

9.2 Simple Sinusoidal Waves: Concept of Frequency and Wavelength

LO1

In order to understand wavelength and frequency, we consider the simplest form of wave, namely the propagation of a transverse wave on a string. Consider yourself holding one end of a string, the other end being held tightly by another person so that the string does not sag. If we make the end of the string oscillate up and down motion ν times per second, then we will observe the propagation of a periodic disturbance towards the other end of the string (see Fig. 9.2); the wave is said to be transverse because the propagation of the wave is in the x-direction and the displacement (of each point on the string) is in the y-direction which is transverse to the x-direction. The displacement of the string can be described by the following equation:

$$\left.\begin{aligned} y(x,t) &= a\cos\left[2\pi\left(\frac{x}{\lambda}-\nu t\right)\right] = a\cos\left[\frac{2\pi}{\lambda}(x-vt)\right] \\ z(x,t) &= 0 \end{aligned}\right\} \tag{9.1}$$

where a represents the maximum displacement of the particle (from its equilibrium position) and is known as the ***amplitude of the wave***; ν is the frequency and λ the wavelength of the wave and

$$v = \nu\lambda = \frac{\omega}{k} \tag{9.2}$$

which will be shown to represent the velocity of the wave. In the above equation

$$k \equiv \frac{2\pi}{\lambda} \quad \text{and} \quad \omega \equiv 2\pi\nu \tag{9.3}$$

represent what are known as the wave vector and angular frequency of the wave. We may say that

Equation (9.1) defines a wave propagating in the +x direction.

[We are assuming here that as the disturbance propagates through the string, there is negligible attenuation.] Actually Eq. (9.1) defines a y-polarized wave. In Fig. 9.3(a), we have plotted the dependence of the displacement y on x at $t = 0$, and at $t = \Delta t$, which are given by

$$y(x, t = 0) = a\cos\left(\frac{2\pi}{\lambda}x\right) = a\cos(kx) \tag{9.4}$$

and

$$\begin{aligned} y(x, t = \Delta t) &= a\cos\left[\frac{2\pi}{\lambda}(x - v\Delta t)\right] \\ &= a\cos\left[k(x - v\Delta t)\right] \end{aligned} \tag{9.5}$$

The two curves are the snapshots of the string at the two instants. The displaced curve (which corresponds to the instant $t = \Delta t$) can be obtained by displacing the curve corresponding to $t = 0$ by a distance $v\Delta t$; this shows that the wave is propagating in the $+z$ direction with speed v given by Eq. (9.2). Also, at a particular instant, any two points separated by a distance λ have identical displacements (at all times). This distance is known as the wavelength.

The displacement of the string is often written in the form

$$\left.\begin{aligned} y(x,t) &= a\cos(kx - \omega t) \\ z(x,t) &= 0 \end{aligned}\right\} \tag{9.6}$$

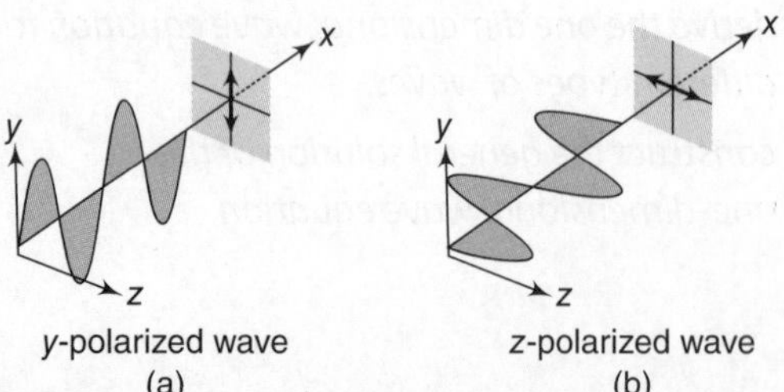

Figure 9.2

(a) If we make one end of the string execute oscillatory motion in the y-direction, we will generate a y-polarized wave; (b) on the other hand, if we make the end of the string execute oscillatory motion in the z-direction, we will generate a z-polarized wave).

The vibration of any point of the string can be written as

$$y(x = x_0, t) = a \cos(\omega t - \phi_0) \quad \textbf{(9.7)}$$

where $\phi_0 = kx_0$ **(9.8)**

is a constant and is known as the phase (see Sec. 6.2). Thus each point on the string vibrates (in the y-direction) with the same frequency. The displacement of the string corresponding to a z-polarized wave will be given by [see Fig. 9.2(b)]:

$$\left.\begin{array}{l} y(x,t) = 0 \\ z(x,t) = a\cos(kx - \omega t) \end{array}\right\} \quad \textbf{(9.9)}$$

If you would go to the link https://phet.colorado.edu/sims/html/wave-on-a-string/latest/wave-on-a-string_en.html, you will find very nice simulations which would allow you to understand wave propagation on a string (see Fig. 9.4).

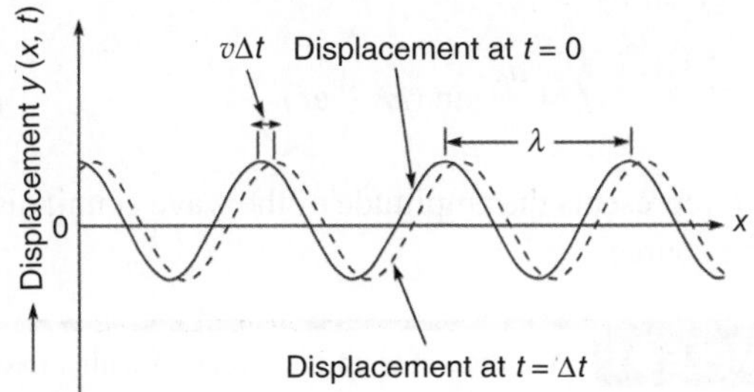

Figure 9.3
A transverse wave is propagating along the +x-axis on a string; the solid and dashed curves show the displacements at $t = 0$ and at a later time $t = \Delta t$, respectively. Since the displacement is in the x-direction, we call this a y-polarized wave.

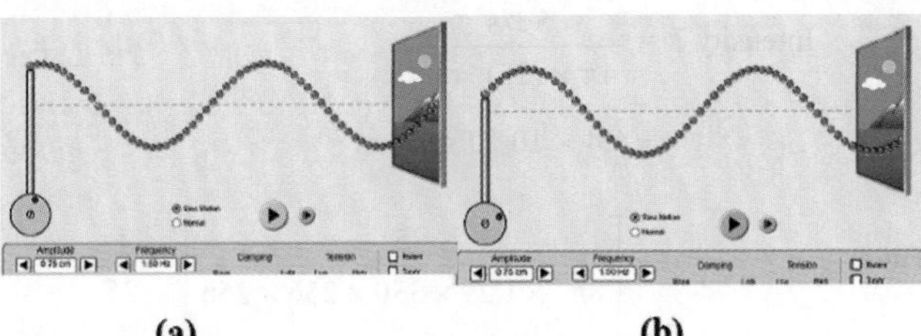

Figure 9.4
(a) and (b) are snapshots of the simulation (at slightly different times) showing the propagation of waves on a string; adapted from https://phet.colorado.edu/sims/html/wave-on-a-string/latest/wave-on-a-string_en.html

Now, if we rotate one end of the string (with uniform angular velocity) on the circumference of a circle, we will generate a circularly polarized wave [see Fig. 9.5(a)]. If the rotation is in the clockwise direction (as shown in the diagram), we will have what is known as a RCP (Right Circularly Polarized) wave; on the other hand, if the rotation is in the anti-clockwise direction, we will have what is known as a LCP (Left Circularly Polarized) wave. All points on the string rotate on the circumference of a circle as shown in Fig. 9.5(b). A detailed description of RCP and LCP electromagnetic waves will be given in Chapter 21.

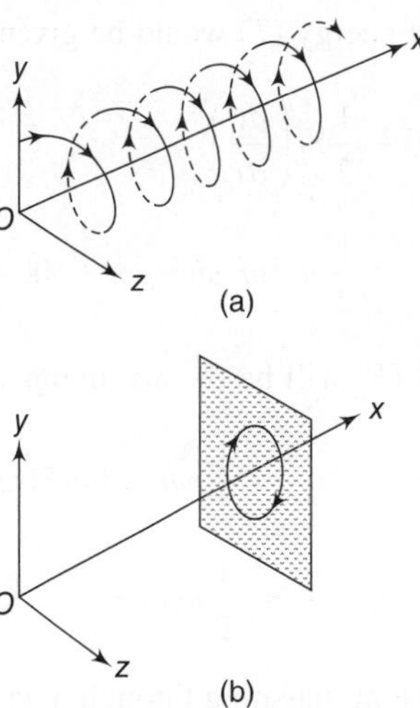

Figure 9.5
When we generate an RCP (Right Circularly Polarized) wave, each point of the string rotates on the circumference of a circle.

9.3 Types of Waves

LO2

As mentioned earlier, when a wave is propagating through a string, the displacement is at right angles to the direction of propagation. Such a wave is known as a transverse wave; electromagnetic waves are also transverse in nature (the electric and magnetic fields are at right angles to the direction of propagation; see Fig. 1.9). Similarly, when a sound wave propagates through air, the displacement of the air molecules is along the direction of propagation of the wave; such waves are known as longitudinal waves. However, there are waves which are neither longitudinal nor transverse in character; for example, when a wave propagates through the surface of water, the water molecules move approximately in circular orbits.

9.4 Energy Transport in Wave Motion

LO2

A wave carries energy; for example, when a transverse wave propagates through a string, the particles execute simple harmonic motions about their equilibrium positions and associated with this motion is a certain amount of energy. As the wave propagates through, the energy gets transported from one end of the string to the other. We consider the time variation of the displacement of a particle, which can be written as

$$y = a\cos(\omega t + \phi) \quad \textbf{(9.10)}$$

The instantaneous velocity of the particle would be

$$v = \frac{dy}{dt} = -a\omega\sin(\omega t + \phi) \quad \textbf{(9.11)}$$

Thus, the kinetic energy (T) would be given by

$$T = \frac{1}{2} m \left(\frac{dy}{dt}\right)^2$$

$$= \frac{1}{2} ma^2\omega^2 \sin^2 (\omega t + \phi) \quad \textbf{(9.12)}$$

The total energy (E) will be the maximum value of T

$$E = (T)_{max} = \frac{1}{2} ma^2\omega^2 [\sin^2 (\omega t + \phi)]_{max}$$

$$= \frac{1}{2} ma^2\omega^2 \quad \textbf{(9.13)}$$

For a sound wave propagating through a gas, the energy per unit volume, ε, would be given by

$$\varepsilon = \frac{1}{2} mna^2\omega^2 = \frac{1}{2} \rho a^2\omega^2$$

$$= 2\pi^2 \rho a^2 \nu^2 \quad \textbf{(9.14)}$$

where m represents the mass of the gas molecule, n represents the number of molecules per unit volume and $\rho(= nm)$ the density of the gas. With such a wave, we can associate the intensity which is defined as the energy flow per unit time across a unit area perpendicular to the direction of propagation. Since the speed of propagation of the wave is v, the intensity (I) would be given by

$$I = 2\pi^2 \rho v a^2 \nu^2 \quad \textbf{(9.15)}$$

This can be easily understood from the fact that if we have N particles per unit volume, each moving with the same velocity v, then the number of particles crossing a unit area (normal to v) per unit time is Nv. Thus the intensity is proportional to the square of the amplitude.

Let us consider a wave emanating from a point source in a uniform isotropic medium. Now, when waves emanate from a point source in an isotropic medium, all the points on the surface of a sphere (whose center is at the point source) have the same amplitude and the same phase; in other words, the locus of points which have the same amplitude and the same phase is a sphere. Such waves are known as spherical waves. Far away from the source, over a small area, the spherical waves are essentially plane waves.

We will assume that there is no absorption and that the point source is emitting W Joules per second. We consider a sphere of radius r whose center is at the point source. Clearly, W (Joules per second) will cross the spherical surface whose area is $4\pi r^2$. Thus, the intensity I will be given by

$$I = \frac{W}{4\pi r^2} \quad \textbf{(9.16)}$$

which is nothing but the inverse square law. Using Eqs. (9.15) and (9.16), we obtain

$$\frac{W}{4\pi r^2} = 2\pi^2 \rho v a^2 \nu^2 \Rightarrow a = \left[\frac{W}{8\pi^3 \rho v \nu^2}\right]^{1/2} \frac{1}{r} \quad \textbf{(9.17)}$$

showing that the amplitude falls off as $1/r$. Indeed, for a spherical wave emanating from a point source, the displacement is given by

$$f = \frac{a_0}{r} \sin (kr - \omega t) \quad \textbf{(9.18)}$$

where a_0 represents the amplitude of the wave at unit distance from the source.

EXAMPLE 9.1 A source of sound is vibrating with a frequency of 256 vibrations per second in air and propagating energy uniformly in all directions at the rate of 5 Joules per second. Calculate the intensity and the amplitude of the wave at a distance of 25 m from the source. Assume that there is no absorption [speed of sound waves in air = 330 m/sec; density of air = 1.29 kg/m³].

Solution:

$$\text{Intensity } I = \frac{5 \text{ J/s}}{4\pi \times (25)^2 \text{ m}^2}$$

$$\approx 6.4 \times 10^{-4} \text{ J sec}^{-1} \text{ m}^{-2}$$

Thus,
$$a = \left[\frac{5}{8\pi^3 \times 1.29 \times 330 \times 256 \times 256}\right]^{1/2} \frac{1}{25}$$

$$\approx 1 \times 10^{-6} \text{ m.}$$

EXAMPLE 9.2 Show that when a transverse wave propagates through a string, the energy transmitted per unit time is $\frac{1}{2}\rho\omega^2 a^2 v$ where ρ is the mass per unit length, a the amplitude of the wave and v the speed of propagation of the wave.

Solution: The energy associated per unit length of the string is $\frac{1}{2}\rho\omega^2 a^2$; since the speed of the wave is v, the result follows.

9.5 The One-Dimensional Wave Equation

LO4

A general one–dimensional wave is described by the function $\psi(x - vt)$, where ψ represents the displacement associated with the wave. For a wave propagating on a string, the displacement ψ will be the actual displacement y of the string; on the other hand, for an electromagnetic wave, the displacement ψ will be the electric field E associated with wave (see Fig. 1.9). Thus if the shape of the string at $t = 0$ is given by $y(x)$ then the shape of the string at $t = \Delta t$ is given by $y(x - v\Delta t)$ implying that the whole disturbance has traveled through a distance $v\Delta t$ in time Δt. Thus, the function $y(x - vt)$ describes a disturbance propagating in the $+x$ direction with speed v. Similarly, the function $y(x + vt)$ describes a disturbance propagating in the $-x$ direction with speed v. One may now ask as to how we can predict the existence of waves and what would be the velocity of propagation of these waves. The answer is as follows: If we can derive an equation of the form

$$\frac{\partial^2 \psi}{\partial x^2} = \frac{1}{v^2}\frac{\partial^2 \psi}{\partial t^2} \tag{9.19}$$

from physical considerations, then we can be sure that waves will result and ψ will represent the displacement associated with the wave. This follows from the fact that the general solution of Eq. (9.19) is of the form

$$\psi(x, t) = f(x - vt) + g(x + vt) \tag{9.20}$$

where f and g are arbitrary functions of their argument (see Sec. 9.9). Consequently, if we ever obtain an equation of the form of Eq. (9.19) from physical considerations, we can predict the existence of waves, the speed of which would be v. Of course, the simplest particular solutions of the wave equation correspond to sinusoidal variations as discussed in Sec. 9.2.

EXAMPLE 9.3 Study the propagation of a semicircular pulse in the $+x$ direction whose displacement at $t = 0$ is given by the following equations:

$$\begin{aligned} y(x, t = 0) &= [R^2 - x^2]^{1/2} \qquad &|x| \le R \\ &= 0 &|x| \ge R \end{aligned} \tag{9.21}$$

Solution: For a wave propagating in the $+x$ direction the dependence of $y(x, t)$ on x and t should be through the function $(x - vt)$. Consequently,

$$\begin{aligned} y(x, t) &= [R^2 - (x - vt)^2]^{1/2} \qquad &|x - vt| \le R \\ &= 0 &|x - vt| \ge R \end{aligned} \tag{9.22}$$

The shape of the pulse at $t = 0$ and at a later time t_0 is shown in Fig. 9.6. Equation (9.22) immediately follows from the fact that $y(x, t)$ has to be of the form $y(x - vt)$ and at $t = 0$, $y(x, t)$ is given by Eq. (9.21).

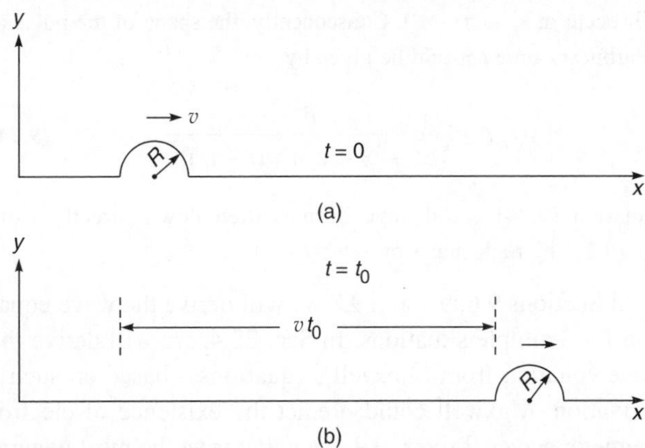

Figure 9.6

The propagation of a semicircular pulse along the $+x$-axis; (a) and (b) show the shape of the pulse at $t = 0$ and at a later time t_0, respectively.

EXAMPLE 9.4 Consider a pulse propagating in the minus x-direction with speed v. The shape of the pulse at $t = t_0$ is given by

$$y(x, t = t_0) = \frac{b^2}{a^2 + (x - x_0)^2} \tag{9.23}$$

(Such a pulse is known as a *Lorentzian pulse*.) Determine the shape of the pulse at an arbitrary time t.

Solution: The shape of the pulse at $t = t_0$ is shown in Fig. 9.7(a). The maximum displacement occurs at $x = x_0$. Since the pulse is propagating in the $-x$ direction, at a later time t, the maximum will

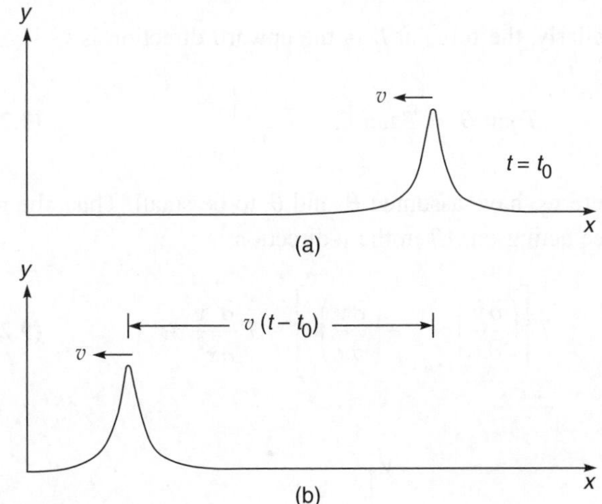

Figure 9.7

The propagation of a Lorentzian pulse along the minus x-axis; (a) and (b) show the shape of the pulse at $t = t_0$ and at a later instant t, respectively.

will occur at $x_0 - v(t - t_0)$. Consequently, the shape of the pulse at an arbitrary time t would be given by

$$y(x, t) = \frac{b^2}{a^2 + [x - x_0 + v(t - t_0)]^2} \tag{9.24}$$

Equation (9.24) could have been written down directly from Eq. (9.23) by replacing x by $x + v(t - t_0)$.

In Sections 9.6, 9.7 and 9.8 we will derive the wave equation for 3 simple situations. In Sec. 22.4, we will derive the wave equation from Maxwell's equations – based on such a derivation, Maxwell could predict the existence of electromagnetic waves. In Sec. 9.9, we will derive the most general solution of the wave equation.

9.6 Transverse Vibrations of a Stretched String

LO4

Let us consider a stretched string having a tension T. In its equilibrium position, the string is assumed to lie on the x-axis. If the string is pulled in the y-direction then forces will act on the string which will tend to bring it back to its equilibrium position. Let us consider a small length AB of the string and calculate the net force acting on it in the y-direction. Due to the tension T, the end points A and B experience force in the direction of the arrows shown in Fig. 9.8. The force at A in the downward direction is

$$-T \sin \theta_1 \approx -T \tan \theta_1 = -T \left.\frac{\partial y}{\partial x}\right|_x \tag{9.25}$$

Similarly, the force at B in the upward direction is

$$T \sin \theta_2 \approx T \tan \theta_2 = T \left.\frac{\partial y}{\partial x}\right|_{x+dx} \tag{9.26}$$

where we have assumed θ_1 and θ_2 to be small. Thus, the net force acting on AB in the y-direction is

$$T\left[\left(\frac{\partial y}{\partial x}\right)_{x+dx} - \left(\frac{\partial y}{\partial x}\right)_x\right] = T\frac{\partial^2 y}{\partial x^2}dx, \tag{9.27}$$

where we have used the Taylor series expansion of $\left(\frac{\partial y}{\partial x}\right)_{x+dx}$ about the point x:

$$\left(\frac{\partial y}{\partial x}\right)_{x+dx} = \left(\frac{\partial y}{\partial x}\right)_x + \left.\frac{\partial}{\partial x}\left(\frac{\partial y}{\partial x}\right)\right|_x dx$$

and have neglected higher order terms because dx is infinitesimal. The equation of motion is, therefore,

$$\Delta m \frac{\partial^2 y}{\partial t^2} = T\frac{\partial^2 y}{\partial x^2}dx$$

where Δm is the mass of the element AB. If ρ is the mass per unit length, then

$$\Delta m = \rho\, dx$$

and we get

$$\frac{\partial^2 y}{\partial x^2} = \frac{1}{T/\rho}\frac{\partial^2 y}{\partial t^2} \tag{9.28}$$

which is the one-dimensional wave equation. Thus we may conclude that transverse waves can propagate through a stretched string and if we compare the above equation with Eq. (9.19), we obtain the following expression for the speed of the transverse waves:

$$v = \sqrt{T/\rho} \tag{9.29}$$

The vibrations of a clamped string will be discussed in Sec. 12.2. It should be mentioned that in an actual string, the displacement is not rigorously of the form given by Eq. (9.1) [or Eq. (9.6)]; this is a consequence of the various approximations made in the derivation of the wave equation. There is, in general, an attenuation of the wave and also the shape does not remain unaltered.

9.7 Longitudinal Sound Waves in a Solid

LO4

In this section, we will derive an expression for the velocity of longitudinal sound waves propagating in an elastic solid. Let us consider a solid cylindrical rod of cross-sectional area A. Let

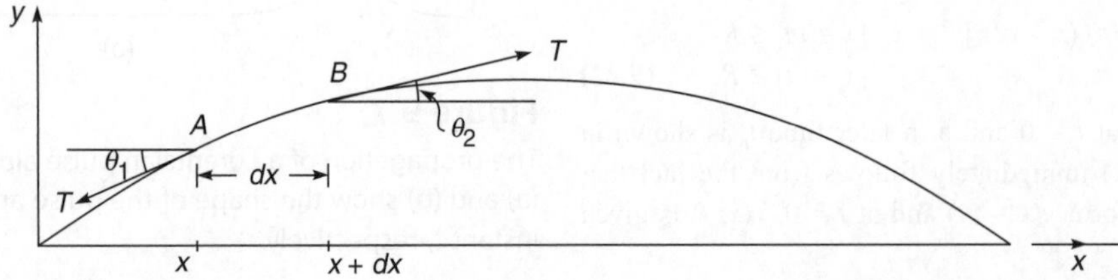

Figure 9.8
Transverse vibrations of a stretched string.

PQ and RS be two transverse sections of the rod at distances x and $x + \Delta x$ from a fixed point O, where we have chosen the x-axis to be along the length of the rod (see Fig. 9.9).

Let the longitudinal displacement of a plane be denoted by $\xi(x)$. Thus, the displacements of the planes PQ and RS would be $\xi(x)$ and $\xi(x + \Delta x)$, respectively. In the displaced position, the distance between the planes $P'Q'$ and $R'S'$ would be

$$\xi(x + \Delta x) - \xi(x) + \Delta x = \xi(x) + \frac{\partial \xi}{\partial x}\Delta x - \xi(x) + \Delta x$$

$$= \Delta x + \frac{\partial \xi}{\partial x}\Delta x$$

The elongation of the element would be $\frac{\partial \xi}{\partial x}\Delta x$ and, therefore, the longitudinal strain would be

$$\frac{\text{Increase in length}}{\text{Original length}} = \frac{\frac{\partial \xi}{\partial x}\Delta x}{\Delta x} = \frac{\partial \xi}{\partial x} \tag{9.30}$$

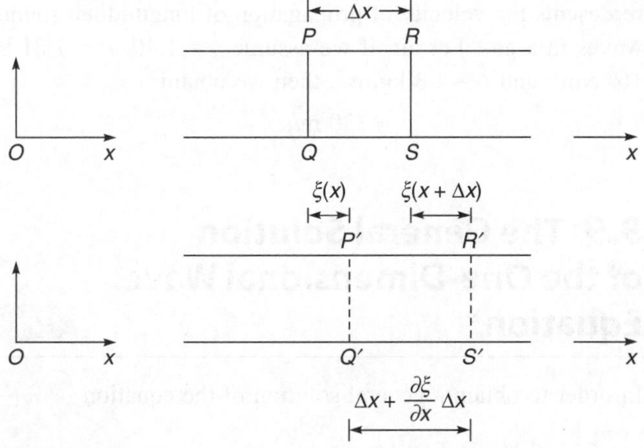

Figure 9.9
Propagation of longitudinal sound waves through a cylindrical rod.

Since the Young's modulus (Y) is defined as the ratio of the longitudinal stress to the longitudinal strain, we have

$$\text{Longitudinal stress} = \frac{F}{A} = Y \times \text{Strain}$$

$$= Y\frac{\partial \xi}{\partial x} \tag{9.31}$$

where F is the force acting on the element $P'Q'$. Thus,

$$F(x) = YA\frac{\partial \xi}{\partial x} \tag{9.32}$$

and, therefore,

$$\frac{\partial F}{\partial x} = YA\frac{\partial^2 \xi}{\partial x^2} \tag{9.33}$$

Now, if we consider the volume $P'Q'S'R'$ then a force F is acting on the element $P'Q'$ *in the negative* x-direction and a force $F(x + \Delta x)$ is acting on the plane $R'S'$ *along the positive* x-direction. Thus, the resultant force acting on the element $P'Q'S'R'$ will be

$$F(x + \Delta x) - F(x) = \frac{\partial F}{\partial x}\Delta x$$

$$= YA\frac{\partial^2 \xi}{\partial x^2}\Delta x \tag{9.34}$$

If ρ represents the density, then the mass of the element would be $\rho A\, \Delta x$. Thus, the equation of motion will be

$$\rho A \Delta x \frac{\partial^2 \xi}{\partial t^2} = YA\Delta x \frac{\partial^2 \xi}{\partial x^2} \tag{9.35}$$

or

$$\frac{\partial^2 \xi}{\partial x^2} = \frac{1}{v_l^2}\frac{\partial^2 \xi}{\partial t^2} \tag{9.36}$$

where

$$v_l = \left(\frac{Y}{\rho}\right)^{1/2} \tag{9.37}$$

represents the velocity of the waves and the subscript l refers to the fact that we are considering longitudinal waves. In a similar manner, one can consider transverse waves propagating through an elastic solid, the velocity of which would be given by [see, for example, Ref. 9.6]

$$v_t = \sqrt{\eta/\rho} \tag{9.38}$$

where η represents the modulus of rigidity.

The above derivation is valid when the transverse dimension of the rod is small compared with the wavelength of the disturbance so that one may assume that the longitudinal displacement at all points on any transverse section (like PQ) are the same. We must mention that the transverse wave [whose velocity is given by Eq. (9.38)] is due to the restoring forces arising because of the elastic properties of the material, whereas corresponding to the transverse waves discussed in Sec. 9.6, the string moved as a whole and the restoring force was due to the externally applied tension.

9.8 Longitudinal Sound Waves in a Gas

LO4

In order to determine the speed of propagation of longitudinal sound waves in a gas, we consider a column $PQSR$ as shown in Fig. 9.10(a). Once again, because of a longitudinal displacement, the plane PQ gets displaced by $\xi(x)$ and the plane RS gets displaced by a distance $\xi(x + \Delta x)$ (see Fig. 9.10). Let

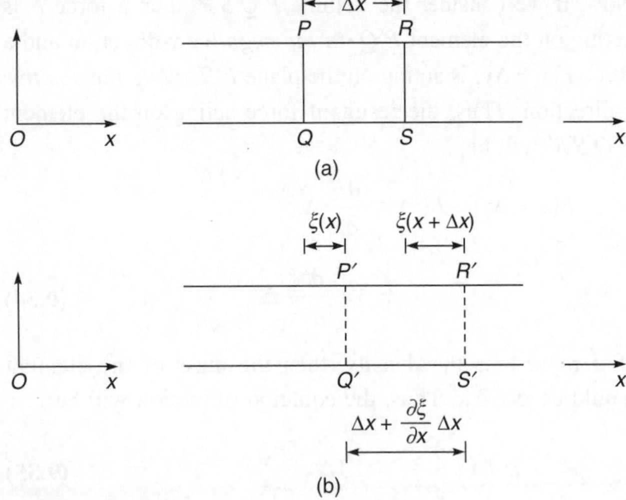

Figure 9.10
Propagation of longitudinal sound waves through air.

the pressure of the gas in the absence of any disturbance be P_0. Let $P_0 + \Delta P(x)$ and $P_0 + \Delta P(x + \Delta x)$ denote the pressures at the planes $P'Q'$ and $R'S'$, respectively. Now, if we consider the column $P'Q'S'R'$ then the pressure $P_0 + \Delta P(x)$ on the face $P'Q'$ acts in the $+x$ direction whereas the pressure $P_0 + \Delta P(x + \Delta x)$ on the face $R'S'$ acts in the $-x$ direction. Thus, the force acting on the column $P'Q'S'R'$ would be

$$[\Delta P(x) - \Delta P(x + \Delta x)]A = -\frac{\partial}{\partial x}(\Delta P)\Delta x A \qquad (9.39)$$

where A represents the cross-sectional area. Consequently, the equation of motion for the column $P'Q'S'R'$ would be

$$-\frac{\partial}{\partial x}(\Delta P)A\,\Delta x = \rho A\,\Delta x\frac{\partial^2 \xi}{\partial t^2} \qquad (9.40)$$

where ρ represents the density of the gas. Thus,

$$-\frac{\partial}{\partial x}(\Delta P) = \rho\frac{\partial^2 \xi}{\partial t^2} \qquad (9.41)$$

Now, a change in pressure gives rise to a change in volume, and if the frequency of the wave is large ($\gtrsim$ 20 Hz), the pressure fluctuations will be rapid and one may assume the process to be adiabatic. Thus, we may write

$$PV^{\gamma} = \text{constant} \qquad (9.42)$$

where $\gamma = C_p/C_v$ represents the ratio of the two specific heats. If we differentiate the above expression, we get

$$\Delta P\,V^{\gamma} + \gamma\,V^{\gamma-1}P\Delta V = 0$$

$$\Delta P = -\frac{\gamma P}{V}\Delta V \qquad (9.43)$$

The change in the length of the column $PQSR$ is

$$[\xi(x + \Delta x) - \xi(x) + \Delta x] - \Delta x = \frac{\partial \xi}{\partial x}\Delta x$$

Thus, the change in the volume

$$\Delta V = \frac{\partial \xi}{\partial x}A\,\Delta x \qquad (9.44)$$

The original volume V of the element is $A\,\Delta x$. Thus,

$$\Delta P = -\frac{\gamma P}{A\Delta x}\frac{\partial \xi}{\partial x}A\,\Delta x = -\gamma P\frac{\partial \xi}{\partial x} \qquad (9.45)$$

or

$$\frac{\partial}{\partial x}(\Delta P) = -\gamma P\frac{\partial^2 \xi}{\partial x^2} \qquad (9.46)$$

Using Eqs. (9.40) and (9.44), we obtain

$$\frac{\partial^2 \xi}{\partial x^2} = \frac{1}{v^2}\frac{\partial^2 \xi}{\partial t^2} \qquad (9.47)$$

where

$$v = \left(\frac{\gamma P}{\rho}\right)^{1/2} \qquad (9.48)$$

represents the velocity of propagation of longitudinal sound waves in a gas. For air, if we assume $\gamma = 1.40$, $P = 1.01 \times 10^6$ Nm^{-2} and $\rho = 1.3$ kg m^{-3}, then we obtain

$$v \approx 330 \text{ m/s}$$

9.9 The General Solution of the One-Dimensional Wave Equation*

LO5

In order to obtain a general solution of the equation

$$\frac{\partial^2 \psi}{\partial x^2} = \frac{1}{v^2}\frac{\partial^2 \psi}{\partial t^2} \qquad (9.49)$$

we introduce two new variables

$$\xi = x - vt \qquad (9.50)$$

$$\eta = x + vt \qquad (9.51)$$

and write Eq. (9.49) in terms of these variables. Now,

$$\frac{\partial \psi}{\partial x} = \frac{\partial \psi}{\partial \xi}\frac{\partial \xi}{\partial x} + \frac{\partial \psi}{\partial \eta}\frac{\partial \eta}{\partial x} \qquad (9.52)$$

or

$$\frac{\partial \psi}{\partial x} = \frac{\partial \psi}{\partial \xi} + \frac{\partial \psi}{\partial \eta} \qquad (9.53)$$

where we have used the fact that

$$\frac{\partial \xi}{\partial x} = 1 \quad \text{and} \quad \frac{\partial \eta}{\partial x} = 1$$

* This section may be skipped in the first reading.

Differentiating Eq. (9.53) with respect to x, we get

$$\frac{\partial^2 \psi}{\partial x^2} = \frac{\partial}{\partial x}\left(\frac{\partial \psi}{\partial \xi}\right) + \frac{\partial}{\partial x}\left(\frac{\partial \psi}{\partial \eta}\right)$$

$$= \frac{\partial}{\partial \xi}\left(\frac{\partial \psi}{\partial \xi}\right)\frac{\partial \xi}{\partial x} + \frac{\partial}{\partial \eta}\left(\frac{\partial \psi}{\partial \xi}\right)\frac{\partial \eta}{\partial x}$$

$$+ \frac{\partial}{\partial \xi}\left(\frac{\partial \psi}{\partial \eta}\right)\frac{\partial \xi}{\partial x} + \frac{\partial}{\partial \eta}\left(\frac{\partial \psi}{\partial \eta}\right)\frac{\partial \eta}{\partial x}$$

or $$\frac{\partial^2 \psi}{\partial x^2} = \frac{\partial^2 \psi}{\partial \xi^2} + 2\frac{\partial^2 \psi}{\partial \eta \partial \xi} + \frac{\partial^2 \psi}{\partial \eta^2} \qquad \textbf{(9.54)}$$

Similarly,

$$\frac{\partial \psi}{\partial t} = \frac{\partial \psi}{\partial \xi}\frac{\partial \xi}{\partial t} + \frac{\partial \psi}{\partial \eta}\frac{\partial \eta}{\partial t}$$

$$= -v\frac{\partial \psi}{\partial \xi} + v\frac{\partial \psi}{\partial \eta}$$

and $$\frac{\partial^2 \psi}{\partial t^2} = -v\left[\frac{\partial}{\partial \xi}\left(\frac{\partial \psi}{\partial \xi}\right)\frac{\partial \xi}{\partial t} + \frac{\partial}{\partial \eta}\left(\frac{\partial \psi}{\partial \xi}\right)\frac{\partial \eta}{\partial t}\right]$$

$$+ v\left[\frac{\partial}{\partial \xi}\left(\frac{\partial \psi}{\partial \eta}\right)\frac{\partial \xi}{\partial t} + \frac{\partial}{\partial \eta}\left(\frac{\partial \psi}{\partial \eta}\right)\frac{\partial \eta}{\partial t}\right]$$

or $$\frac{\partial^2 \psi}{\partial t^2} = v^2\left[\frac{\partial^2 \psi}{\partial \xi^2} - 2\frac{\partial^2 \psi}{\partial \eta \partial \xi} + \frac{\partial^2 \psi}{\partial \eta^2}\right] \qquad \textbf{(9.55)}$$

Substituting the expressions for $\partial^2\psi/\partial x^2$ and $\partial^2\psi/\partial t^2$ from Eqs. (9.54) and (9.55) in Eq. (9.49), we obtain

$$\frac{\partial^2 \psi}{\partial \xi^2} + 2\frac{\partial^2 \psi}{\partial \eta \partial \xi} + \frac{\partial^2 \psi}{\partial \eta^2} = \frac{\partial^2 \psi}{\partial \xi^2} - 2\frac{\partial^2 \psi}{\partial \eta \partial \xi} + \frac{\partial^2 \psi}{\partial \eta^2}$$

or

$$\frac{\partial}{\partial \eta}\left(\frac{\partial \psi}{\partial \xi}\right) = 0 \qquad \textbf{(9.56)}$$

Thus, $\partial\psi/\partial\xi$ has to be independent of η; however, it can be an arbitrary function of ξ:

$$\frac{\partial \psi}{\partial \xi} = F(\xi) \qquad \textbf{(9.57)}$$

or $$\psi = \int F(\xi)\, d\xi + \text{constant of integration.}$$

The constant of integration can be an arbitrary function of η and since the integral of an arbitrary function is again an arbitrary function, we obtain the following as the most general solution of the wave equation

$$\psi = f(\xi) + g(\eta) = f(x - vt) + g(x + vt) \qquad \textbf{(9.58)}$$

where f and g are arbitrary functions of their argument. The function $f(x - vt)$ represents a disturbance propagating in the $+x$ direction with speed v and the function $g(x + vt)$ represents a disturbance propagating in the $-x$ direction.

EXAMPLE 9.5 Solve the one-dimensional wave equation [Eq. (9.49)] by the method of separation of variables* and show that the solution can indeed be expressed in the form of sinusoidal waves given on the right hand side of Eq. (9.1).

Solution: In the method of separation of variables, we try a solution of the wave equation

$$\frac{\partial^2 \psi}{\partial x^2} = \frac{1}{v^2}\frac{\partial^2 \psi}{\partial t^2} \qquad \textbf{(9.59)}$$

of the form

$$\psi(x, t) = X(x)\,T(t) \qquad \textbf{(9.60)}$$

where $X(x)$ is a function of x alone and $T(t)$ is a function of t alone. Substituting in Eq. (9.59), we get

$$T(t)\frac{d^2X}{dx^2} = \frac{1}{v^2}X(x)\frac{d^2T}{dt^2}$$

or** $$\frac{1}{X(x)}\frac{d^2X}{dx^2} = \frac{1}{v^2 T(t)}\frac{d^2T}{dt^2} \qquad \textbf{(9.61)}$$

The LHS is a function of x alone and the RHS is a function of t alone. This implies that a function of one independent variable x is equal to a function of another independent variable t for all values of x and t. This is possible only when each side is equal to a constant; we set this constant equal to $-k^2$, thus,

$$\frac{1}{X(x)}\frac{d^2X}{dx^2} = \frac{1}{v^2}\frac{1}{T(t)}\frac{d^2T}{dt^2} = -k^2 \qquad \textbf{(9.62)}$$

or $$\frac{d^2X}{dx^2} + k^2X(x) = 0 \qquad \textbf{(9.63)}$$

and $$\frac{d^2T}{dt^2} + \omega^2T(t) = 0 \qquad \textbf{(9.64)}$$

where $$\omega = kv = \frac{2\pi v}{\lambda} \qquad \textbf{(9.65)}$$

represents the angular frequency of the wave. The solutions of Eqs. (9.63) and (9.64) can easily be written down:

* The method of separation of variables is a powerful method for solving certain kinds of partial differential equations. According to this method, the solution is assumed to be a product of functions, each function depending only on one independent variable [see Eq. (9.60)]. On substituting this solution, if the variables separate out, then the method is said to work and the general solution is a linear sum of all possible solutions. If the variables do not separate out one has to try some other method to solve the equation.

** Notice that partial derivatives have been replaced by total derivatives.

$$X(x) = (A \cos kx + B \sin kx)$$

and $$T(t) = (C \cos \omega t + D \sin \omega t)$$

Thus,

$$\psi(x, t) = (A \cos kx + B \sin kx) \times (C \cos \omega t + D \sin \omega t) \quad (9.66)$$

Suitable choice of the constants A, B, C and D would give

$$\psi(x, t) = a \cos(kx - \omega t + \phi)$$

or $$\psi(x, t) = a \cos(kx + \omega t + \phi)$$

representing waves propagating in the $+x$ and $-x$ directions respectively. One can also have

$$\psi(x, t) = a \exp[\pm i(kx \pm \omega t + \phi)]$$

as a solution.

In general, all values of the frequencies are possible, but the frequency and wavelength have to be related through Eq. (9.65). However, there are systems (like a string under tension and fixed at both ends) where only certain values of frequencies are possible (see Sec. 7.2).

EXAMPLE 9.6 Till now, we have confined our discussion to waves in one dimension. The three-dimensional wave equation is of the form,

$$\nabla^2 \psi = \frac{1}{v^2} \frac{\partial^2 \psi}{\partial t^2} \quad (9.67)$$

where $$\nabla^2 \psi \equiv \frac{\partial^2 \psi}{\partial x^2} + \frac{\partial^2 \psi}{\partial y^2} + \frac{\partial^2 \psi}{\partial z^2} \quad (9.68)$$

Solve the three-dimensional wave equation by the method of separation of variables and interpret the solution physically.

Solution: Using the method of separation of variables, we write

$$\psi(x, y, z, t) = X(x)\, Y(y)\, Z(z)\, T(t) \quad (9.69)$$

where $X(x)$ is a function of x alone, etc. Substituting in Eq. (9.67), we obtain

$$YZT\frac{d^2X}{dx^2} + XZT\frac{d^2Y}{dy^2} + XYT\frac{d^2Z}{dz^2} = \frac{1}{v^2} XYZ \frac{d^2T}{dt^2}$$

or dividing throughout by ψ

$$\left[\frac{1}{X}\frac{d^2X}{dx^2}\right] + \left[\frac{1}{Y}\frac{d^2Y}{dy^2}\right] + \left[\frac{1}{Z}\frac{d^2Z}{dz^2}\right] = \frac{1}{v^2}\left[\frac{1}{T}\frac{d^2T}{dt^2}\right] \quad (9.70)$$

Since the first term on the LHS is a function of x alone, the second term is a function of y alone, etc., each term must be set equal to a constant. We write

$$\frac{1}{X}\frac{d^2X}{dx^2} = -k_x^2; \quad \frac{1}{Y}\frac{d^2Y}{dy^2} = -k_y^2; \quad \frac{1}{Z}\frac{d^2Z}{dz^2} = -k_z^2 \quad (9.71)$$

where k_x^2, k_y^2 and k_z^2 are constants. Thus,

$$\frac{1}{v^2}\left[\frac{1}{T}\frac{d^2T}{dt^2}\right] = -(k_x^2 + k_y^2 + k_z^2)$$

or $$\frac{d^2T}{dt^2} + \omega^2 T(t) = 0 \quad (9.72)$$

where $$\omega^2 = k^2 v^2 \quad (9.73)$$

and $$k^2 = k_x^2 + k_y^2 + k_z^2$$

The solutions of Eqs. (9.71) and (9.72) could be written in terms of sine and cosine functions; it is more convenient to write these in terms of the exponentials:

$$\psi = A \exp[i(k_x x + k_y y + k_z z \pm \omega t + \phi)]$$
$$= A \exp[i(\mathbf{k} \cdot \mathbf{r} \pm \omega t + \phi)] \quad (9.74)$$

where the vector $\mathbf{k}$ is defined such that its x, y and z-components are k_x, k_y and k_z, respectively. One could have also written

$$\psi = A \cos(\mathbf{k} \cdot \mathbf{r} - \omega t + \phi) \quad (9.75)$$

Consider a vector $\mathbf{r}$ which is normal to $\mathbf{k}$; thus $\mathbf{k} \cdot \mathbf{r} = 0$; consequently at a given time the phase of the disturbance is constant on a plane normal to $\mathbf{k}$. The direction of propagation of the disturbance is along $\mathbf{k}$ and the phase fronts are planes normal to $\mathbf{k}$; such waves are known as *plane waves* (see Fig. 9.11). Notice that for a given value of the frequency, the value of k^2 is fixed [see Eq. (9.73)]; however, we can have waves propagating in different directions depending on the values of k_x, k_y and k_z. For example, if

$$k_x = k \quad \text{and} \quad k_y = k_z = 0 \quad (9.76a)$$

we have a wave propagating along the x-axis, the phase fronts are parallel to the y–z plane. Similarly, for

$$k_x = \frac{k}{\sqrt{2}}, \; k_y = \frac{k}{\sqrt{2}}, \; k_z = 0 \quad (9.76b)$$

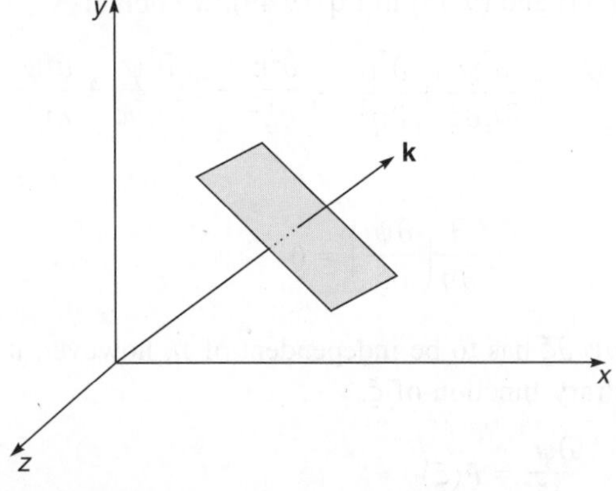

Figure 9.11

Propagation of a plane wave along the direction **k.** $\left(k_x = k_y = \frac{k}{\sqrt{2}}, k_z = 0\right)$

the waves are propagating in a direction which makes equal angles with x- and y-axes (see Fig. 9.9).

EXAMPLE 9.7 For a spherical wave, the displacement ψ depends only on r and t where r is the magnitude of the distance from a fixed point. Obtain a general solution of the wave equation for a spherical wave.

Solution: For a spherical wave

$$\nabla^2\psi = \frac{\partial^2\psi}{\partial r^2} + \frac{2}{r}\frac{\partial\psi}{\partial r} = \frac{1}{r^2}\frac{\partial}{\partial r}\left(r^2\frac{\partial\psi}{\partial r}\right) \quad \textbf{(9.77)}$$

Thus, the wave equation for a spherical wave simplifies to

$$\nabla^2\psi = \frac{1}{r^2}\frac{\partial}{\partial r}\left(r^2\frac{\partial\psi}{\partial r}\right) = \frac{1}{v^2}\frac{\partial^2\psi}{\partial t^2} \quad \textbf{(9.78)}$$

If we make the substitution

$$\psi = \frac{u(r,t)}{r}$$

then

$$\frac{1}{r^2}\frac{\partial}{\partial r}\left(r^2\frac{\partial\psi}{\partial r}\right) = \frac{1}{r^2}\frac{\partial}{\partial r}\left(r\frac{\partial u}{\partial r} - u\right) = \frac{1}{r}\frac{\partial^2 u}{\partial r^2}$$

Thus Eq. (9.78) becomes

$$\frac{\partial^2 u}{\partial r^2} = \frac{1}{v^2}\frac{\partial^2 u}{\partial t^2} \quad \textbf{(9.79)}$$

which is of the same form as the one-dimensional wave equation. The general solution of Eq. (9.78) is therefore given by

$$\psi = \frac{f(r - vt)}{r} + \frac{g(r + vt)}{r} \quad \textbf{(9.80)}$$

the first and the second terms (on the RHS) representing an outgoing spherical wave and an incoming spherical wave, respectively. For time dependence of the form exp $(\pm i\omega t)$ one obtains

$$\psi = \frac{A}{r}\exp[i(kr \pm \omega t)] \quad \textbf{(9.81)}$$

Notice that the factor $1/r$ term implies that the amplitude of a spherical wave decreases inversely with r, and, therefore, the intensity will fall off as $1/r^2$.

SUMMARY

- For a sinusoidal wave, the displacement is given by

$$\Psi = a\cos[kx \pm \omega t + \phi]$$

where a represents the amplitude of the wave, $\omega(= 2\pi\nu)$ the angular frequency of the wave, k $(= 2\pi/\lambda)$ the wave number and λ represents the wavelength associated with the wave. The upper and lower signs correspond to waves propagating in the $-x$ and $+x$ directions, respectively. Such a displacement is indeed produced in a long-stretched string at the end of which a continuously vibrating tuning fork is placed. The quantity ϕ is known as the phase of the wave.
- The intensity of the wave is proportional to the square of the amplitude and square of the frequency.
- The most general solution of the wave equation

$$\frac{\partial^2\psi}{\partial x^2} = \frac{1}{v^2}\frac{\partial^2\psi}{\partial t^2}$$

is of the form

$$\psi = f(x - vt) + g(x + vt)$$

where f and g are arbitrary functions of their argument. The first term on the RHS of the above equation represents a disturbance propagating in the $+x$ direction with speed v and similarly, the second term represents a disturbance propagating in the $-x$ direction with speed v. Thus, if we can derive the wave equation from physical considerations, then we can be sure that waves will result and ψ will represent the displacement associated with the wave.
- The speed of the transverse waves propagating through the string is $\sqrt{T/\rho}$, where T is the tension on the string and ρ is mass per unit length.
- For a spherical wave, the displacement is given by

$$\psi = \frac{A}{r}e^{i(kr \pm \omega t)}$$

where the + and – signs correspond to incoming and outgoing waves respectively. Notice that the factor $1/r$ term implies that the amplitude of a spherical wave decreases inversely with r, and therefore, the intensity will fall off as $1/r^2$.

PROBLEMS

9.1 The displacement associated with a wave is given by
(a) $y(x, t) = 0.1\cos(0.2x - 2t)$
(b) $y(x, t) = 0.2\sin(0.5x + 3t)$
(c) $y(x, t) = 0.5\sin 2\pi(0.1x - t)$
where in each case x and y are measured in centimeters and t in seconds. Calculate the wavelength, amplitude, frequency and the velocity in each case.

[**Ans:** (a) $\nu \approx 0.32$ s^{-1}; $v = 10$ cm/s; (b) $\nu \approx 0.48$ s^{-1}; $v = 6$ cm/s; (c) $\nu = 1$ s^{-1}; $v = 10$ cm/s]

9.2 A transverse wave ($\lambda = 15$ cm, $\nu = 200$ sec^{-1}) is propagating on a stretched string in the $+x$-direction with an amplitude of 0.5 cm. At $t = 0$, the point $x = 0$ is at its equilibrium position moving in the upward direction. Write the equation describing the wave and if $\rho = 0.1$ g/cm, calculate the energy associated with the wave per unit length of the wire.

[**Ans:** Energy associated with the wave $\approx 1.97 \times 10^4$ ergs/cm]

9.3 Assuming that the human ear can hear in the frequency range $20 < \nu < 20{,}000$ Hz, what will be the corresponding wavelength range?

[**Ans:** $16.5 \text{ m} > \lambda > 0.0165 \text{ m}$]

9.4 Calculate the speed of longitudinal waves at NTP in **(a)** argon ($\gamma = 1.67$), **(b)** Hydrogen ($\gamma = 1.41$).

[**Ans:** (a) 308 m/s, (b) 1.26×10^5 cm/s]

9.5 Consider a wave propagating in the $+x$-direction with speed 100 cm/s. The displacement at $x = 10$ cm is given by the following equation:

$$y(x = 10, t) = 0.5 \sin (0.4t)$$

where x and y are measured in centimeter and t in seconds. Calculate the wavelength and the frequency associated with the wave and obtain an expression for the time variation of the displacement at $x = 0$.

[**Ans:** $\lambda \approx 1571$ cm: $y(x, t) = 0.5 \sin 0.4t - 0.004(x - 10)$]

9.6 Consider a wave propagating in the $-x$-direction whose frequency is 100 sec^{-1}. At $t = 5$ sec the displacement associated with the wave is given by the following equation:

$$y(x, t = 5) = 0.5 \cos (0.1x)$$

where x and y are measured in centimeter and t in seconds. Obtain the displacement (as a function of x) at $t = 10$ s. What is the wavelength and the velocity associated with the wave?

[**Ans:** $y(x, t) = 0.5 \cos[0.1x + 200\pi(t - 5)]$]

9.7 Repeat the above problem corresponding to

$$y(x, t = 5) = 0.5 \cos (0.1x) + 0.4 \sin (0.1x + \pi/3)$$

9.8 A Gaussian pulse is propagating in the $+x$-direction and at $t = t_0$ the displacement is given by

$$y(x, t = t_0) = a \exp\left[-\frac{(x-b)^2}{\sigma^2}\right]$$

Find $y(x, t)$.

$$\textbf{Ans: } y(x, t) = a \exp\left[-\frac{(x - b - v(t - t_0))^2}{\sigma^2}\right]$$

9.9 A sonometer wire is stretched with a tension of 1 N. Calculate the velocity of transverse waves if $\rho = 0.2$ g/cm.

[**Ans:** $v \approx 707$ cm/s]

9.10 The displacement associated with a three-dimensional wave is given by

$$\psi(x, y, z, t) = a \cos\left[\frac{\sqrt{3}}{2}kx + \frac{1}{2}ky - \omega t\right]$$

Show that the wave propagates along a direction making an angle 30° with the x-axis.

9.11 Obtain the unit vector along the direction of propagation for a wave, the displacement of which is given by

$$\psi(x, y, z, t) = a \cos [2x + 3y + 4z - 5t]$$

where x, y and z are measured in centimeter and t in seconds. What will be the wavelength and the frequency of the wave?

$$\left[\textbf{Ans:} \frac{2}{\sqrt{29}}\hat{\mathbf{x}} + \frac{3}{\sqrt{29}}\hat{\mathbf{y}} + \frac{4}{\sqrt{29}}\hat{\mathbf{z}}\right]$$

9.12 Assume $\psi(x, t) = A\, e^{-(2x + 10t)^2}$ where x is measured in meters and t in seconds. Calculate $\frac{\partial^2 \psi}{\partial x^2}$ and $\frac{\partial^2 \psi}{\partial t^2}$ show that ψ satisfies Eq. (9.19). What will be the velocity of the wave?

CHAPTER 10

Huygens' Principle and its Applications

Christiaan Huygens, a Dutch physicist, in a communication to the Académie des Science in Paris, propounded his wave theory of light (published in his Traite de Lumiere in 1690). He considered that light is transmitted through an all-pervading ether that is made up of small elastic particles, each of which can act as a secondary source of wavelets. On this basis, Huygens explained many of the known propagation characteristics of light, including the double refraction in calcite discovered by Bartholinus.

—From the Internet

LEARNING OBJECTIVES

After reading this chapter, the reader should be able to:

LO 1: *describe Huygens' wave theory of light.*

LO 2: *apply Huygens' principle to study refraction and reflection.*

LO 3: *use Huygens' principle in studying propagation of wavefront in inhomogeneous media.*

Above Image: View of a rainbow against a background of clouds. Photograph courtesy McGraw Hill Digital Access Library.

10.1 Introduction

The wave theory of light was first put forward by Christiaan Huygens in 1678. During that period, everyone believed in Newton's corpuscular theory, which had satisfactorily explained the phenomena of reflection, refraction, the rectilinear propagation of light and the fact that light could propagate through vacuum. So empowering was Newton's authority that the scientists around Newton believed in the corpuscular theory much more than Newton himself; as such, when Huygens put forward his wave theory, no one really believed him. On the basis of his wave theory, Huygens explained satisfactorily the phenomena of reflection, refraction and total internal reflection and also provided a simple explanation of the then recently discovered birefringence (see Chapter 21). As we will see later, Huygens' theory predicted that the velocity of light in a medium (like water) shall be less than the velocity of light in free space, which is just the converse of the prediction made from Newton's corpuscular theory (see Sec. 1.2).

The wave character of light was not really accepted until the interference experiments of Young and Fresnel (in the early part of the nineteenth century) which could only be explained on the basis of a wave theory. At a later date, the data on the speed of light through transparent media were also available which was consistent with the results obtained by using the wave theory. It should be pointed out that Huygens did not know whether the light waves were longitudinal or transverse and also how they propagate through vacuum. It was only in the later part of the nineteenth century, when Maxwell propounded his famous electromagnetic theory, could the nature of light waves be understood properly.

10.2 Huygens' Theory

LO1

Huygens' theory is essentially based on a geometrical construction which allows us to determine the shape of the wavefront at any time, if the shape of the wavefront at an earlier time is known. A wavefront is the locus of the points which are in the same phase; for example, if we drop a small stone in a calm pool of water, circular ripples spread out from the point of impact, each point on the circumference of the circle (whose center is at the point of impact) oscillates with the same amplitude and same phase and thus we have a circular wavefront. On the other hand, if we have a point source emanating waves in a uniform isotropic medium, the locus of points which have the same amplitude and are in the same phase are spheres. In this case, we have spherical wavefronts as shown in Fig. 10.1(a). At large distances from the source, a small portion of the sphere can be considered as a plane and we have what is known as a **plane wave** [see Fig. 10.1(b)].

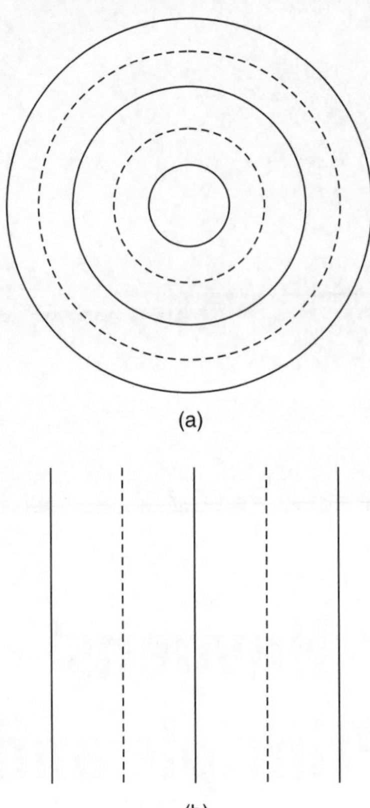

Figure 10.1
(a) A point source emitting spherical waves.
(b) At large distances, a small portion of the spherical wavefront can be approximated to a plane wavefront thus resulting in plane waves.

Now, according to Huygens' principle, each point of a wavefront is a source of secondary disturbance and the wavelets emanating from these points spread out in all directions with the speed of the wave. The envelope of these wavelets gives the shape of the new wavefront. In Fig. 10.2, S_1S_2 represents the shape of the wavefront (emanating from the point O) at a particular time which we denote as $t = 0$. The medium is assumed to be homogeneous and isotropic, i.e., the medium is characterized by the same property at all points and the speed of propagation of the wave is the same in all directions. Let us suppose we want to determine the shape of the wavefront after a time interval of Δt. Then, with each point on the wavefront as center, we draw spheres of radius $v\,\Delta t$, where v is the speed of the wave in that medium. If we draw a common tangent to all these spheres, then we obtain the envelope which is again a sphere centered at O. Thus, the shape of the wavefront at a later time Δt is the sphere $S_1'S_2'$.

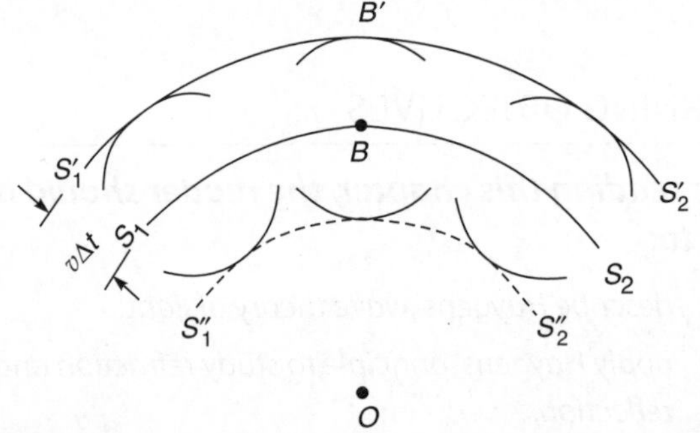

Figure 10.2
Huygens' construction for the determination of the shape of the wavefront, given the shape of the wavefront at an earlier time. S_1S_2 is a spherical wavefront centered at O at a time, say $t = 0$. $S_1'S_2'$ corresponds to the state of the wavefront at a time Δt, which is again spherical and centered at O. The dashed curve represents the backwave.

There is, however, one drawback with the above model, because we also obtain a backwave which is not present in practice. This backwave is shown as $S_1''S_2''$ in Fig. 10.2. In Huygens' theory, the presence of the backwave is avoided by assuming that the amplitude of the secondary wavelets is not uniform in all directions; it is maximum in the forward direction and zero in the backward direction*. The absence of the backwave is really justified through the more rigorous wave theory.

In the next section, we will discuss the original argument of Huygens to explain the rectilinear propagation of light. In Sec. 10.4, we will derive the laws of refraction and reflection by using Huygens' principle. Finally, in Sec. 10.5, we will show how Huygens' principle can be used in inhomogeneous media.

10.3 Rectilinear Propagation

Let us consider spherical waves emanating from the point source *O* and striking the obstacle *A* (see Fig. 10.3). According to the rectilinear propagation of light (which is also predicted by corpuscular theory) one should obtain a shadow in the region *PQ* of the screen. As we will see in a later chapter, this is not rigorously true and one does obtain a finite intensity in the region of the geometrical shadow. However, at the time of Huygens, light was known to travel in straight lines and Huygens explained this by assuming that the secondary wavelets do not have any amplitude at any point not enveloped by the wavefront. Thus, referring back to Fig. 10.2, the secondary wavelets emanating from a typical point *B* will give rise to a finite amplitude at *B′* only and not at any other point.

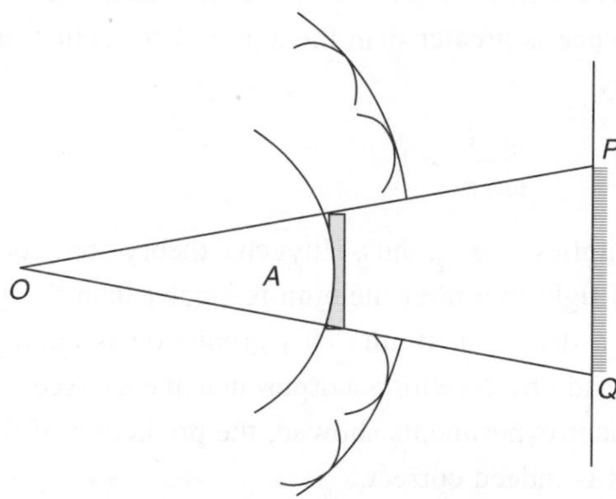

Figure 10.3

Rectilinear propagation of light. *O* is a point source emitting spherical waves and *A* is an obstacle which forms a shadow in the region *PQ* of the screen.

The above explanation of the rectilinear propagation of light is indeed unsatisfactory and is incorrect. Further, as pointed out earlier, one does observe a finite intensity of light in the geometrical shadow. A satisfactory explanation was put forward by Fresnel, who postulated that the secondary wavelets mutually interfere. The Huygens' principle along with the fact that the secondary wavelets mutually interfere, is known as the Huygens–Fresnel principle. It may be mentioned that if a plane wave is allowed to fall on a tiny hole, then the hole approximately acts as a point source and spherical waves emanate from it (see Figs. 10.4 and 13.1); by a tiny hole we imply that the diameter of the hole should be smaller than the wavelength. This fact is in direct contradiction to the original proposition of Huygens according to which the secondary wavelets do not have any amplitude at any point not enveloped by the wavefront. However, as we will see in the chapter on diffraction, it can be explained satisfactorily on the basis of Huygens–Fresnel principle. Use of the Huygens' principle in determining the shape of the wavefront in anisotropic media will be discussed in Chapter 21.

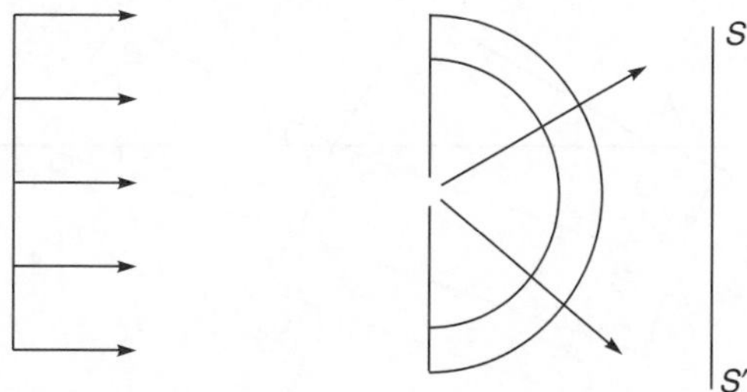

Figure 10.4

A plane wavefront is incident on a pin hole. If the diameter of the pinhole is small (compared to the wavelength) the entire screen *SS′* will be illuminated.

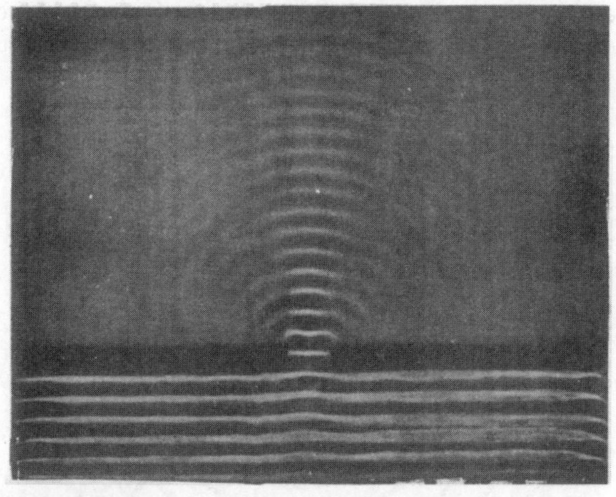

Figure 10.4

(b) Diffraction of straight water waves when it passes through an opening (adapted from Ref. 10.6 with permission).

---

* Indeed it can be shown from diffraction theory that one does obtain (under certain approximations) an obliquity factor, which is of the form $\frac{1}{2}(1 + \cos\theta)$ where θ is the angle between the normal to the wavefront and the direction under consideration. Clearly, when $\theta = 0$, the obliquity factor is 1 (thereby giving rise to maximum amplitude in the forward direction) and when $\theta = \pi$, the obliquity factor is zero (thereby giving rise to zero amplitude in the backward direction).

10.4 Application of Huygens' Principle to Study Refraction and Reflection

LO2

10.4.1 Refraction of a Plane Wave at a Plane Interface

We will first derive the laws of refraction. Let S_1S_2 be a surface separating two media with different speeds of propagation of light v_1 and v_2 as shown in Fig. 10.5. Let A_1B_1 be a plane wavefront incident on the surface at an angle i; A_1B_1 represents the position of the wavefront at an instant $t = 0$.

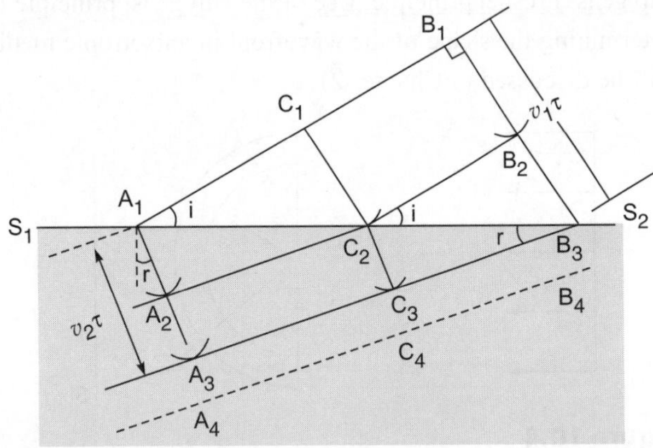

Figure 10.5
Refraction of a plane wavefront A_1B_1 by a plane interface S_1S_2 separating two media with different velocities of propagation of light v_1 and v_2 ($<v_1$); i and r are the angles of incidence and refraction respectively. $A_2C_2B_2$ corresponds to the shape of the wavefront at an intermediate time τ_1. Notice that $r < i$; *see also Fig. 10.6.*

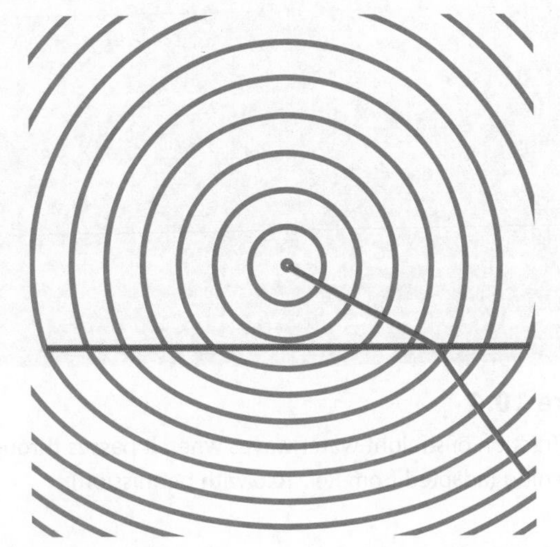

Figure 10.6
Refraction of a spherical wave at an interface. *The diagram is by Dr. Oleg Alexandrov and is in public domain.*

Let τ be the time taken for the wavefront to travel the distance B_1B_3. Then $B_1B_3 = v_1\tau$. In the same time, the light would have traveled a distance $A_1A_3 = v_2\tau$ in the second medium. (Note that the lines A_1A_3, B_1B_3, etc., are always normal to the wavefront; these represent rays in isotropic media). It can easily be seen that the incident and refracted rays make angles i and r with the normal. In order to determine the shape of the wavefront at the instant $t = \tau$ we consider an arbitrary point C_1 on the wavefront. Let the time taken for the disturbance to travel the distance C_1C_2 be τ_1. Thus $C_1C_2 = v_1\tau_1$. From the point C_2 we draw a secondary wavelet of radius $v_2(\tau - \tau_1)$. Similarly, from the point A_1, we draw a secondary wavelet of radius $v_2\tau$. The envelope of these secondary wavelets is shown as $A_3C_3B_3$. The shape of the wavefront at the intermediate time τ_1 is shown as $A_2C_2B_2$ and clearly $B_1B_2 = C_1C_2 = v_1\tau_1$ and $A_1A_2 = v_2\tau_1$. In the right-angled triangles $B_2C_2B_3$ and $C_3C_2B_3$, $\angle B_2C_2B_3 = i$ (the angle of incidence) and $\angle C_2B_3C_3 = r$ (the angle of refraction). Clearly,

$$\frac{\sin i}{\sin r} = \frac{B_2B_3/C_2B_3}{C_2C_3/C_2B_3} = \frac{B_2B_3}{C_2C_3}$$

$$= \frac{v_1(\tau - \tau_1)}{v_2(\tau - \tau_1)} = \frac{v_1}{v_2} \tag{10.1}$$

which is known as the **Snell's law**. It is observed that when light travels from a rarer to a denser medium, the angle of incidence is greater than the angle of refraction and consequently

$$\frac{\sin i}{\sin r} > 1$$

which implies $v_1 > v_2$; thus, Huygens' theory predicts that the speed of light in a rarer medium is greater than the speed of light in a denser medium. This prediction is contradictory to that made by Newton's corpuscular theory (see Sec. 1.2) and as later experiments showed, the prediction of the wave theory was indeed correct.

If c represents the speed of light in free space then the ratio $\frac{c}{v}$ (where v represents the speed of light in the particular medium) is called the refractive index n of the medium. Thus, if $n_1\left(=\frac{c}{v_1}\right)$ and $n_2\left(=\frac{c}{v_2}\right)$ are the refractive indices of the two media, then Snell's law can also be written as

$$n_1 \sin i = n_2 \sin r \tag{10.2}$$

Let $A_1C_1B_1$, $A_2C_2B_2$, $A_3C_3B_3$ and $A_4C_4B_4$ denote the successive positions of crests. If λ_1 and λ_2 denote the wavelength of light in medium 1 and medium 2, respectively then, the distance B_1B_2 ($= B_2B_3 = C_1C_2$) will be equal to λ_1 and the distance A_1A_2 (= A_2A_3 = C_2C_3) will be equal to λ_2. From Fig. 10.5 it is obvious that

$$\frac{\lambda_1}{\lambda_2} = \frac{\sin i}{\sin r} = \frac{v_1}{v_2} \tag{10.3}$$

or

$$v_1/\lambda_1 = v_2/\lambda_2 \tag{10.4}$$

Thus, when a wave gets refracted into a denser medium ($v_1 > v_2$) the wavelength and the speed of propagation decrease but the frequency (= v/λ) remains the same; when refracted into a rarer medium the wavelength and the speed of propagation will increase (see Fig. 10.6). In Table 10.1, we have given the indices of refraction of several materials with respect to vacuum. In Table 10.2, the wavelength dependence of the refractive index for crown glass and vitreous quartz are given. The three wavelengths correspond roughly to the red, yellow and blue colors. Notice the accuracy with which the wavelength and the refractive index can be measured.

TABLE 10.1 Refractive Indices of various Materials Relative to Vacuum. (*Adapted from Ref. 10.1*).

(For light of wavelength λ = 5.890 × 10^{-5} cm)[1]

Material	*n*	*Material*	*n*
Vacuum	1.0000	Quartz (fused)	1.46
Air	1.0003	Rock salt	1.54
Water	1.33	Glass (ordinary crown)	1.52
Quartz (crystalline)	1.54	Glass (dense flint)	1.66

TABLE 10.2 Refractive Indices of Telescope Crown Glass and Vitreous Quartz for Various Wavelengths. (*Adapted from Ref. 10.7*).

	Wavelength	*Telescope crown*	*Vitreous quartz*
1	6.562816 × 10^{-5} cm	1.52441	1.45640
2	5.889953 × 10^{-5} cm	1.52704	1.45845
3	4.861327 × 10^{-5} cm	1.53303	1.46318

Note: The wavelengths specified at serial numbers 1, 2 and 3 correspond roughly to the red, yellow and blue colors. The table shows the accuracy with which the wavelengths and refractive indices can be measured; see also Problem 11.5.

10.4.2 Total Internal Reflection

In Fig. 10.5, the angle of incidence has been shown to be greater than the angle of refraction. This corresponds to the case when $v_2 < v_1$, i.e., the light wave is incident on a denser medium. However, if the second medium is a rarer medium (i.e., $v_1 < v_2$) then the angle of refraction will be greater than the angle of incidence, and a typical refracted wavefront would be of the form as shown in Fig. 10.7, where $B_1B_2 = v_1\tau$ and $A_1A_2 = v_2\tau$. Clearly, if the angle of incidence is such that $v_2\tau$ is greater than A_1B_2, then the refracted wavefront will be absent and we will have, what is known as, **total internal reflection**. The critical angle will correspond to

$$A_1B_2 = v_2\tau$$

Thus,

$$\sin i_c = \frac{B_1B_2}{A_1B_2} = \frac{v_1}{v_2} = n_{12}, \tag{10.5}$$

where i_c denotes the critical angle and n_{12} represents the refractive index of the second medium with respect to the first. For all angles of incidence greater than i_c, we will have total internal reflection.

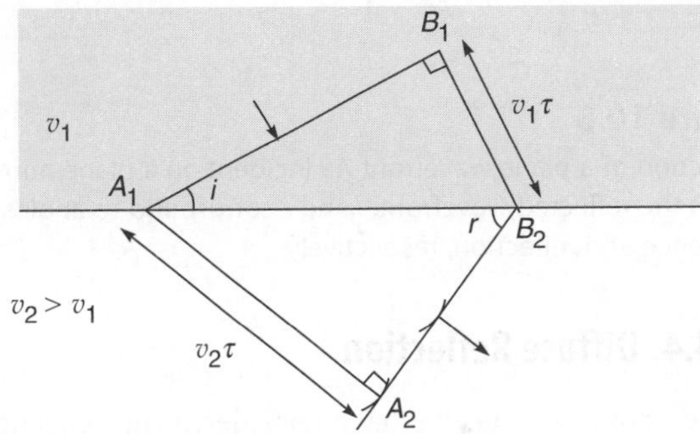

Figure 10.7
Refraction of a plane wavefront incident on a rarer medium (i.e., $v_2 > v_1$). Notice that the angle of refraction r is greater than the angle of incidence i. The value of i, when r is equal to $\pi/2$, gives the critical angle.

10.4.3 Reflection of a Plane Wave by a Plane Surface

Let us consider a plane wave AB incident at an angle i on a plane mirror as shown in Fig. 10.8. We consider the reflection of the plane wave and try to obtain the shape of the reflected wavefront. Let the position of the wavefront at $t = 0$ be AB. If the mirror was not present, then at a later time τ the position of the wavefront would have been CB', where $BB' = PP' = AC = v\tau$ and v is the speed of propagation of the wave. In order to determine the shape of the reflected wavefront at the instant $t = \tau$, we consider an arbitrary point P on the wavefront AB and let τ_1 be the time taken by a disturbance to reach the point P_1 from P. From the point P_1, we draw a sphere of radius $v(\tau - \tau_1)$. We draw a tangent plane on this sphere from the point B'. Since $BB_1 = PP_1 = v\tau_1$, the distance B_1B' will be equal to P_1P_2 [= $v(\tau - \tau_1)$]. If we consider triangles P_2P_1B' and B_1P_1B' then the side P_1B' is common to both and since $P_1P' = B'B_2$, and since both the triangles are right-angled triangles, $\angle P_2B'P_1 = \angle B_1P_1B'$. The former is the angle of reflection and the latter is the angle of incidence. Thus, we have the law of reflection; when a plane wavefront gets reflected from a plane surface, the angle of reflection is equal to the angle of incidence and the reflected wave is a plane wave.

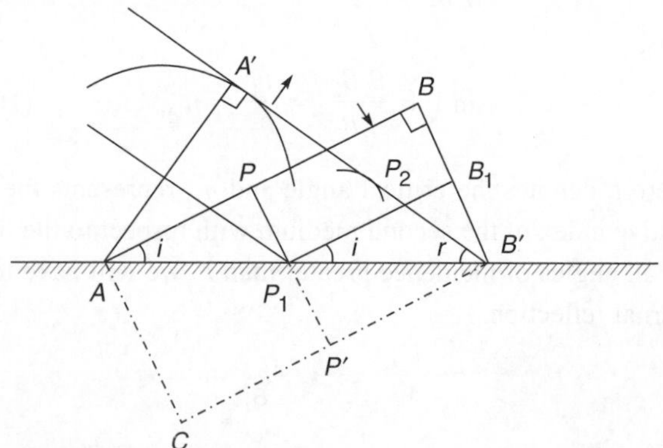

Figure 10.8
Reflection of a plane wavefront *AB* incident on a plane mirror. *A′B′* is the reflected wavefront; *i* and *r* correspond to angles of incidence and reflection, respectively.

10.4.4 Diffuse Reflection

In the above section, we have considered the reflection of light from a smooth surface. This is known as **specular reflection**. If the surface is irregular (as shown in Fig. 10.9) we have, what is known as **diffuse reflection**. The secondary wavelets emanating from the irregular surface travel in many directions and we do not have a well-defined reflected wave. Indeed, it can be shown that if the irregularity in the surface is considerably greater than the wavelength, we will have diffuse reflection.

Figure 10.9
Diffuse reflection of a plane wavefront from a rough surface. It is evident that one does not have a well-defined reflected beam.

10.4.5 Reflection of Light from a Point Source Near a Mirror

Let us consider spherical waves (emanating from a point source *P*) incident on a plane mirror *MM′* as shown in Fig. 10.10. Let *ABC* denote the shape of the wavefront at time $t = 0$. In the absence of the mirror, the shape of the wavefront at a later time τ would have been $A_1B_1C_1$ where $AA_1 = QQ_1 = BB_1 = CC_1 = v\tau$, Q being an arbitrary point on the wavefront. If the time taken for the disturbance to

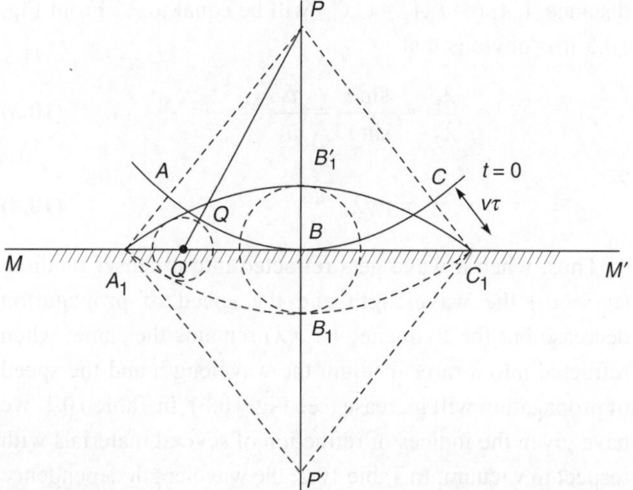

Figure 10.10
P is a point source placed in front of a plane mirror *MM′*. *ABC* is the incident wavefront (which is spherical and centered at *P*) and $A_1B_1'C_1$ is the corresponding reflected wavefront (which is spherical and centered at *P′*). *P′* is the virtual image of *P*.

traverse the distance QQ' be τ_1 then, in order to determine the shape of the reflected wavefront, we draw a sphere of radius $v(\tau - \tau_1)$ whose center is at the point Q'. In a similar manner, we can draw the secondary wavelets emanating from other points on the mirror and, in particular, from the point B we have to draw a sphere of radius $v\tau$. The shape of the reflected wavefront is obtained by drawing a common tangent plane to all these spheres, which is shown as $A_1B_1'C_1$ in the figure. It can immediately be seen that $A_1B_1'C_1$ will have an exactly similar shape as $A_1B_1C_1$ except that $A_1B_1'C_1$ will have its center of curvature at the point P' where $PB = BP'$. Thus, the reflected waves will appear to emanate from the point P' which will be the virtual image of the point P.

10.4.6 Refraction of a Spherical Wave by a Spherical Surface

Let us consider spherical waves (emanating from the point *P*) incident on the curved spherical surface *SBS′*. Let the shape of the wavefront at the time $t = 0$ be *ABC* [see Fig. 10.11(a)]. Let the refractive indices on the left and on the right of the spherical surface be n_1 and n_2, respectively. In the absence of the spherical surface, the shape of the wavefront at a later time τ would have been $A_1B_1C_1$ where $AA_1 = BB_1 = CC_1 = v_1\tau$. We consider an arbitrary point Q on the wavefront *ABC* and let τ_1 be the time taken for the disturbance to reach the point Q' (on the surface of the spherical wave); thus $QQ' = v_1\tau_1$. In order to determine the shape of the refracted wavefront at a later time τ, we draw a sphere of radius $v_2(\tau - \tau_1)$ from the point Q'. We may draw similar spheres from other points on

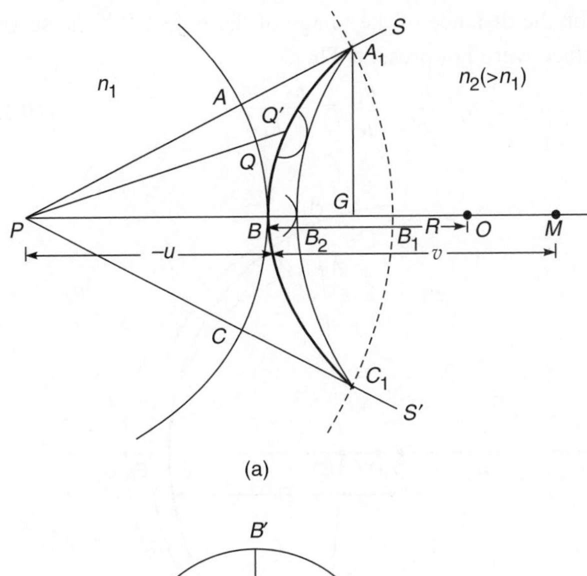

(a)

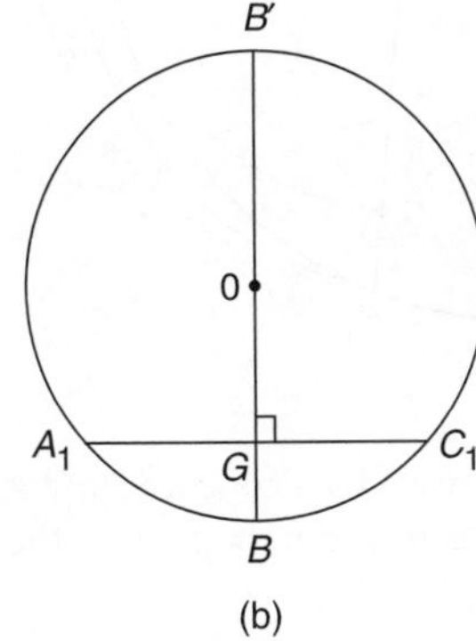

(b)

Figure 10.11

(a) Refraction of a spherical wave *ABC* (emanating from the point source *P*) by a convex spherical surface *SBS′* separating media of refractive indices n_1 and n_2 ($> n_1$). $A_1B_2C_1$ is the refracted wavefront, which is approximately spherical and whose center of curvature is at *M*. Thus, *M* is the real image of *P*. *O* is the center of curvature of *SS′*. (b) The diameter *B′OB* intersects the chord A_1GC_1 normally.

the spherical surface; in particular, the radius of the spherical wavefront from the point *B*, which is equal to BB_2 will be $v_2\tau$. The envelope of these spherical wavelets is shown as $A_1B_2C_1$ which, in general, will not be a sphere.* However, a small portion of any curved surface can be considered as a sphere and in this approximation we may consider $A_1B_2C_1$ to be a sphere whose center of curvature is at the point *M*. The spherical wavefront will, therefore, converge towards the point *M* and hence the point *M* represents the real image of the point *P*.

We adopt a sign convention in which all distances, measured to the left of the point *B*, are negative and all distances measured to the right of the point *B* are positive. Thus,

$$PB = -u$$

where *u* itself is a negative quantity. Further, since the point *M* lies on the right of *B*, we have

$$BM = v$$

and similarly,

$$BO = R$$

where *O* represents the center of curvature of the spherical surface.

In order to derive a relation between *u*, *v* and *R* we use a theorem in geometry, according to which,

$$(A_1G)^2 = GB \times (2R - GB) \tag{10.6}$$

where *G* is the foot of the perpendicular on the axis *PM* [see Fig. 10.11(b)]. In Fig. 10.11(b), the diameter *B′OB* intersects the chord A_1GC_1 normally. If $GB \ll R$, then

$$(A_1G)^2 \simeq 2R(GB)$$

Consider the spherical surface *SBS′* [see Fig. 10.11(a)] whose radius is *R*. Clearly,

$$(A_1G)^2 = (2R - GB)GB \simeq 2R(GB) \tag{10.7}$$

where we have assumed $GB \ll R$. Similarly by considering the spherical surface $A_1B_2C_1$ (whose center is at the point *M*) we obtain

$$(A_1G)^2 \simeq 2v(GB_2) \tag{10.8}$$

where $v = BM \simeq B_2M$. In a similar manner,

$$(A_1G)^2 \simeq 2(-u)GB_1 \tag{10.9}$$

Since *u* is a negative quantity, $(A_1G)^2$ is positive. Now,

$$BB_1 = v_1\tau \quad \text{and} \quad BB_2 = v_2\tau$$

Therefore,

$$\frac{BB_1}{BB_2} = \frac{v_1}{v_2} = \frac{n_2}{n_1}$$

or

$$n_1BB_1 = n_2BB_2$$

or

$$n_1(BG + GB_1) = n_2(BG - GB_2)$$

or

$$n_1\left[\frac{(A_1G)^2}{2R} - \frac{(A_1G)^2}{2u}\right] = n_2\left[\frac{(A_1G)^2}{2R} - \frac{(A_1G)^2}{2v}\right]$$

* The fact that the refracted wavefront is not, in general, a sphere leads to, what are known as *aberrations*.

where we have used Eqs. (10.7), (10.8) and (10.9). Thus,

$$\frac{n_2}{v} - \frac{n_1}{u} = \frac{n_2 - n_1}{R} \tag{10.10}$$

which may be rewritten in the form

$$\frac{n_2}{v} = \frac{n_1}{u} + \frac{n_2 - n_1}{R} \tag{10.11}$$

Thus, if

$$\frac{n_1}{|u|} > \frac{n_2 - n_1}{R}$$

or

$$|u| < \frac{Rn_1}{n_2 - n_1}$$

we will obtain a virtual image. (We are of course assuming that the second medium is a denser medium, i.e., $n_2 > n_1$; if $n_2 < n_1$, we will always have a virtual image).

A converging spherical wavefront will propagate in a manner shown in Fig. 10.12. Beyond the focal point, it will start diverging as shown in the figure.*

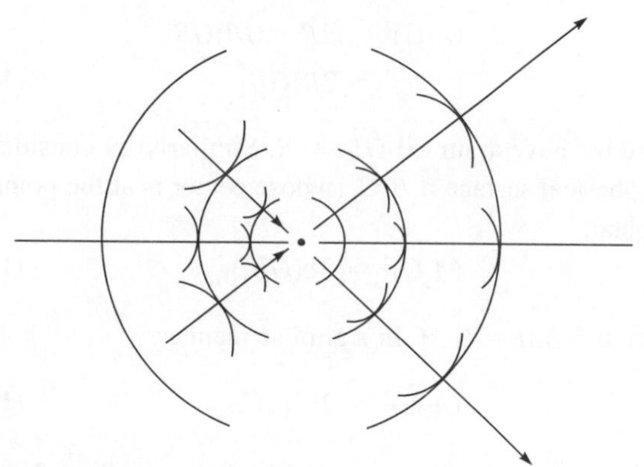

Figure 10.12

Propagation of a converging spherical wave using Huygens' principle.

In a similar manner, we can consider the refraction of a spherical wave from a surface *SBS′* shown in Fig. 10.13 ($n_2 > n_1$). Here the center of curvature will also lie on the left of the point *B* and both *u* and *R* will be negative quantities. Thus no matter what the values of *u* and *R* may be, *v* will be negative and we will obtain a virtual image.

Using Eq. (10.10) we can easily derive the thin lens formula. We assume a thin lens made of a material of refractive index n_2 to be placed in a medium of refractive index n_1 (see Fig. 10.14). Let the radii of curvatures of the first and the second surface be R_1 and R_2, respectively. Let v' be the distance of the image of the object *P* if the second surface were not present. Then,

$$\frac{n_2}{v'} - \frac{n_1}{u} = \frac{n_2 - n_1}{R_1} \tag{10.12}$$

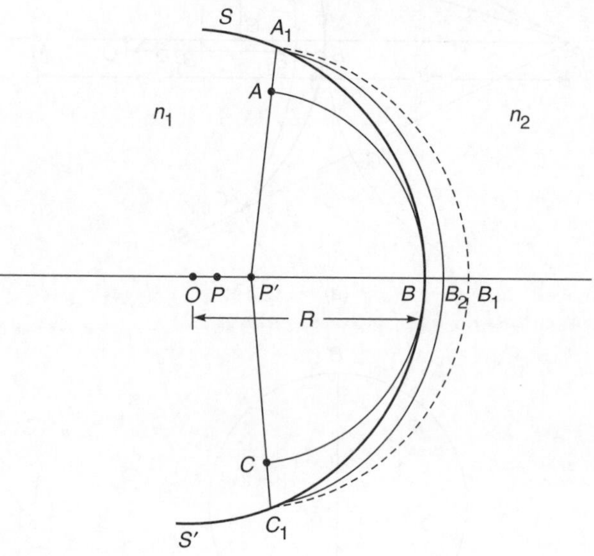

Figure 10.13

Refraction of a spherical wave by a concave surface separating media of refractive indices n_1 and n_2 ($> n_1$). *P′* is the virtual image of *P*.

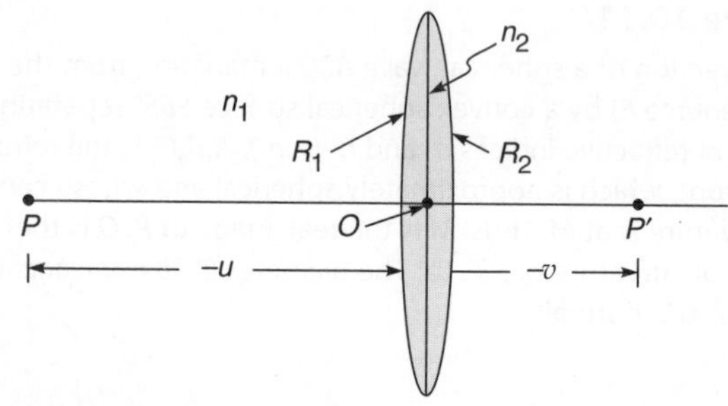

Figure 10.14

A thin lens made of a medium of refractive index n_2 placed in a medium of refractive index n_1. The radii of curvatures of the two surfaces are R_1 and R_2. *P* is the image (at a distance *v* from the point *O*) of the point object *P* (at a distance –*u* from the point *O*).

(Since the lens is assumed to be thin, all the distances are measured from the point *O*). This image now acts as an object to the spherical surface R_2 on the left of which is the medium of refractive index n_2 and on the right of which is the medium of refractive index n_1. Thus, if *v* is the distance of the final image point from *O*, then,

$$\frac{n_1}{v} - \frac{n_2}{v'} = \frac{n_1 - n_2}{R_2} \tag{10.13}$$

* Very close to the focal point, one has to use a more rigorous wave theory and the shape of the wavefront is very much different from spherical (see Ref. 10.8). However, much beyond the focal point the wavefronts again become spherical.

Adding Eqs. (10.12) and (10.13), we obtain

$$\frac{n_1}{v} - \frac{n_1}{u} = (n_2 - n_1)\left(\frac{1}{R_1} - \frac{1}{R_2}\right) \quad \textbf{(10.14)}$$

or

$$\frac{1}{v} - \frac{1}{u} = \frac{1}{f} \quad \textbf{(10.15)}$$

where

$$\frac{1}{f} = \frac{n_2 - n_1}{n_1}\left(\frac{1}{R_1} - \frac{1}{R_2}\right) \quad \textbf{(10.16)}$$

Notice that we do not have to worry whether v' is positive or negative; it is automatically taken care of through the sign convention. Further, the relation derived is valid for any lens; for example, for a double convex lens, R_1 is positive and R_2 is negative and for a double concave lens, R_1 is negative and R_2 is positive. Similarly, it follows for other types of lenses (see Fig. 4.6).

EXAMPLE 10.1 Consider a vibrating source moving through a medium with a speed V. Let the speed of propagation of the wave in the medium be v. Show that if $V > v$ then a conical wavefront is set up whose half-angle is given by

$$\theta = \sin^{-1}\left(\frac{v}{V}\right) \quad \textbf{(10.17)}$$

Solution: Let at $t = 0$, the source be at the point P_0 moving with a speed V in the x-direction (see Fig. 10.15). We wish to find out the wavefront at a later time τ. The disturbance emanating from the point P_0 traverses a distance $v\tau$ in time τ. Thus from the point P_0, we draw a sphere of radius $v\tau$. We next consider the waves emanating from the source at a time τ_1 ($<\tau$). At time τ_1 let the source be at the position P_1; consequently,

$$P_0P_1 = V\tau_1$$

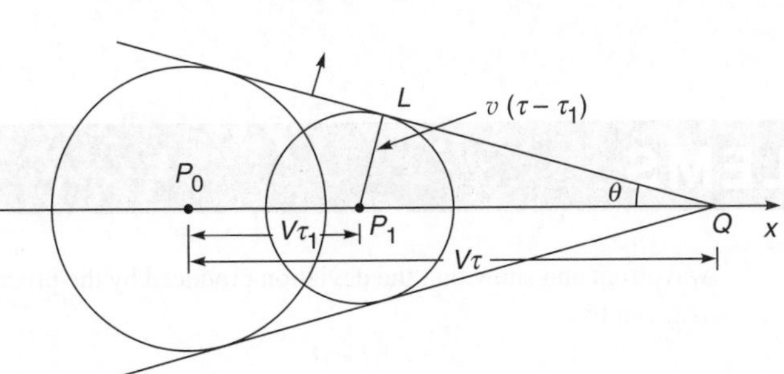

Figure 10.15
Generation of a shock wavefront by a vibrating particle P_0 moving with a speed V, in a medium in which the velocity of propagation of the wave is v ($< V$).

In order to determine the shape of the wavefront at τ, we draw a sphere of radius $v(\tau - \tau_1)$ centered at P_1. Let the source be at the position Q at the instant τ. Then,

$$P_0Q = V\tau$$

We draw a tangent plane from the point Q, on the sphere whose origin is the point P_1. Since

$$P_1L = v(\tau - \tau_1) \quad \text{and} \quad P_1Q = V(\tau - \tau_1)$$

$$\sin\theta = \frac{P_1L}{P_1Q} = \frac{v}{V} \quad \text{(independent of } \tau_1\text{)}$$

Since θ is independent of t_1, all the spheres drawn from any point on the line P_0Q will have a common tangent plane. This plane is known as the *shock wavefront* and propagates with a speed v.

It is interesting to point out that even when the source is **not vibrating,** if its speed is greater than the speed of sound waves, a shock wavefront is always set up. A similar phenomenon also occurs when a charged particle (like an electron) moves in a medium with a speed greater than the speed of light in that medium.* The emitted light is known as **Cerenkov radiation**. If you ever see a swimming pool-type reactor, you will find a blue glow coming out from it; this is because of the Cerenkov radiation emitted by the fast moving electrons.

10.5 Huygens' Principle in Inhomogeneous Media

LO4

Huygens' principle can also be used to study the propagation of a wavefront in an inhomogeneous medium. For definiteness, we consider a medium whose refractive index decreases continuously from a given axis, which we define as the z-axis; x and y-axis being the transverse axis. A simple example is a Selfoc fiber,** whose refractive index variation is of the form

$$n^2(x, y) = n_1^2 - \gamma^2(x^2 + y^2) \quad \textbf{(10.18)}$$

where n_1 is the refractive index on the z-axis. Let the plane wavefront be incident along the z-axis as shown in Fig. 10.16. Since the refractive index decreases as x and y increase, the speed of the secondary wavelets emanating from portions of the incident wavefront will increase as we move away from the axis. Let us try to determine the shape of the wavefront at a time Δt; given that the wavefront at $t = 0$ is a plane wavefront A_1B_1 (see Fig. 10.16). We will have to draw spheres of radius

* This does not contradict the theory of relativity according to which no particle can have a speed greater than the speed of light in free space ($= 3 \times 10^8$ m/sec). The speed of light in a medium will be equal to c/n, where n represents the refractive index. For example, in water, the speed of light will be about 2.25×10^8 m/sec and the speed of the electron could be greater than this value.

** See Sec. 2.4.1

$v(x, y)\,\Delta t$, centered at (x, y), where $v(x, y)$ is the velocity of the wave at the point (x, y), which increases as x and y increase. Thus, the radii of the spheres increase as we move away from the axis and if we draw a common tangent to all these spheres then the resulting wavefront is shown in Fig. 10.16 as A_2B_2. It is at once evident that the wavefront which was initially plane has now become curved. If we again use the same procedure, then the shape of the wavefront at time $2\Delta t$ (say) is shown as A_3B_3. Thus, it is evident that in the present case the wavefront is getting focused. It should be borne in mind that since we are considering an inhomogeneous medium, the refractive index varies continuously with position. For the above construction to be valid, Δt should be small so that during this short interval the secondary wavelets may be assumed to be spherical.

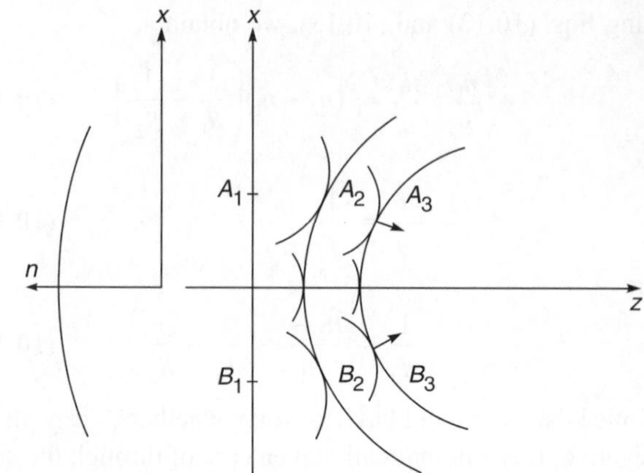

Figure 10.16
The focusing of an incident plane wavefront in an inhomogeneous medium characterized by a refractive index variation given by Eq. (10.18).

SUMMARY

- According to Huygens' principle, each point of a wavefront is a source of secondary disturbance and the wavelets emanating from these points spread out in all directions with the speed of the wave. The envelope of these wavelets gives the shape of the new wavefront.
- Huygens' principle along with the fact that the secondary wavelets mutually interfere is known as the Huygens–Fresnel principle.
- Diffuse reflection is seen when the irregularity in the surface is considerably greater than the wavelength.
- Laws of reflection and Snell's law of refraction can be derived using Huygens' principle.
- Using Huygens' principle one can derive the lens formula $\frac{1}{v} - \frac{1}{u} = \frac{1}{f}$.
- In an inhomogeneous medium where refractive index varies continuously, the initial wavefront is plane. It turns into curved wavefront with increase in time.

PROBLEMS

10.1 Use Huygens' principle to study the reflection of a spherical wave emanating from a point on the axis at a concave mirror of radius of curvature R and obtain the mirror equation

$$\frac{1}{u} + \frac{1}{v} = \frac{2}{R}$$

10.2 Consider a plane wave incident obliquely on the face of a prism. Using Huygens' principle, construct the transmitted wavefront and show that the deviation produced by the prism is given by

$$\delta = i + t - A$$

where A is the angle of the prism, i and t are the angles of incidence and transmittance.

CHAPTER

11

Group Velocity and Pulse Dispersion

In a perfect wave, you cannot say when it ***starts****, so you cannot use it for a timing signal. In order to send a* ***signal*** *you have to change the wave somehow, make a notch in it, make it a little bit fatter or thinner. That means that you have to have more than one frequency in the wave, and it can be shown that the speed at which* ***signals*** *travel is not dependent upon the index alone, but upon the way that the index changes with the frequency.*

—Richard Feynman in *Feynman Lectures on Physics*, Vol. I

LEARNING OBJECTIVES

After reading this chapter, the reader should be able to:

LO 1: *explain the concept of group velocity.*

LO 2: *illustrate group velocity of a wave packet using Guassian pulse.*

LO 3: *discuss the chirping of a dispersed pulse.*

LO 4: *interpret the effect of self phase modulation on frequency.*

Important Milestone

1672: Isaac Newton reported to the Royal Society his observations on the dispersion of sunlight as it passed through a prism. From this experiment, Newton concluded that sunlight is composed of light of different colours which are refracted by glass to different extents.

1973: Akira Hasegawa and Frederick Tappert (while working at Bell Telephone Laboratories, Murray Hill, NJ) were the first to predict solitons in optical fibers.

1985: Gérard Mourou and Donna Strickland (while working at University of Rochester) used chirped-pulse amplification to solve the problem of high peak powers in amplifier systems. They were awarded (half of the) 2018 Nobel Prize in Physics *"for their method of generating high-intensity, ultra-short optical pulses"*.

Above Image: View of a rainbow against a background of clouds. Photograph courtesy McGraw Hill Digital Access Library.

11.1 Introduction

When we switch on and switch off a light source, we produce a pulse. This pulse propagates through a medium with what is known as the group velocity which will be discussed in this chapter. In addition, as the pulse propagates, it undergoes distortion which will also be discussed. A study of this distortion of optical pulses is a subject of great importance in many areas. For example, this would help us to understand CPA (Chirped Pulse Amplification) which was used in 1985 to create ultrashort high-intensity laser pulses which find extremely important applications in industry; for this work in 1985, Gérard Mourou and Donna Strickland received (half of) the 2018 Nobel Prize in Physics. Also, a study of pulse dispersion is of very important significance in fiber-optic communication systems; this will be discussed in Chapters 28 and 30.

11.2 Group Velocity

LO1

Let us consider two plane waves (having the same amplitude A) with slightly different frequencies $\omega + \Delta\omega$ and $\omega - \Delta\omega$ propagating along the $+z$ direction:

$$E_1(z, t) = A\cos\left[(\omega + \Delta\omega)t - (k + \Delta k)z\right] \quad \textbf{(11.1)}$$

$$E_2(z, t) = A\cos\left[(\omega - \Delta\omega)t - (k - \Delta k)z\right] \quad \textbf{(11.2)}$$

where $k + \Delta k$ and $k - \Delta k$ are the wave numbers corresponding to the frequencies $\omega + \Delta\omega$ and $\omega - \Delta\omega$, respectively. The superposition of the two waves will be given by

$$E(z,t) = A\cos\left[(\omega + \Delta\omega)t - (k + \Delta k)z\right] + A\cos\left[(\omega - \Delta\omega)t - (k - \Delta k)z\right]$$

or

$$E(z,t) = 2A\cos(\omega t - kz)\cos\left[(\Delta\omega)t - (\Delta k)z\right] \quad \textbf{(11.3)}$$

In Fig. 11.1(a), we have shown the variation of the rapidly varying $\cos(\omega t - kz)$ term at $t = 0$; the distance between two consecutive peaks is $2\pi/k$. In Fig. 11.1(b), we have shown the variation of the slowly varying envelope term, represented by $\cos[(\Delta\omega)t - (\Delta k)z]$ at $t = 0$; the distance between two consecutive peaks is $2\pi/\Delta k$. In Fig. 11.2(a) and (b), we have plotted $E(z, t)$ at

$$t = 0 \quad \text{and} \quad t = \Delta t$$

Obviously, the rapidly varying first term moves with the velocity

$$v_p = \frac{\omega}{k} \quad \textbf{(11.4)}$$

and the slowly varying envelope [which is represented by the second term in Eq. (11.3)] moves with velocity

$$v_g = \frac{\Delta\omega}{\Delta k} \quad \textbf{(11.5)}$$

The quantities v_p and v_g are known as the **phase velocity** and the **group velocity**, respectively. The group velocity is a concept of great importance; indeed in the next section, we will rigorously show that a temporal pulse travels with the group velocity given by

$$v_g = \frac{1}{dk/d\omega} \quad \textbf{(11.6)}$$

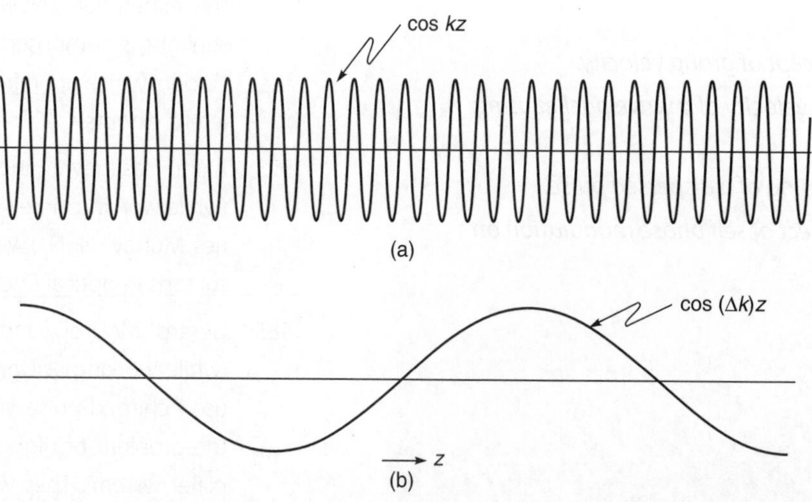

Figure 11.1
(a) Variation of the rapidly varying $\cos(\omega t - kz)$ term at $t = 0$; the distance between two consecutive peaks is $2\pi/k$. (b) Variation of the slowly varying envelope term, represented by $\cos[(\Delta\omega)t - (\Delta k)z]$, at $t = 0$. The distance between two consecutive peaks is $2\pi/\Delta k$.

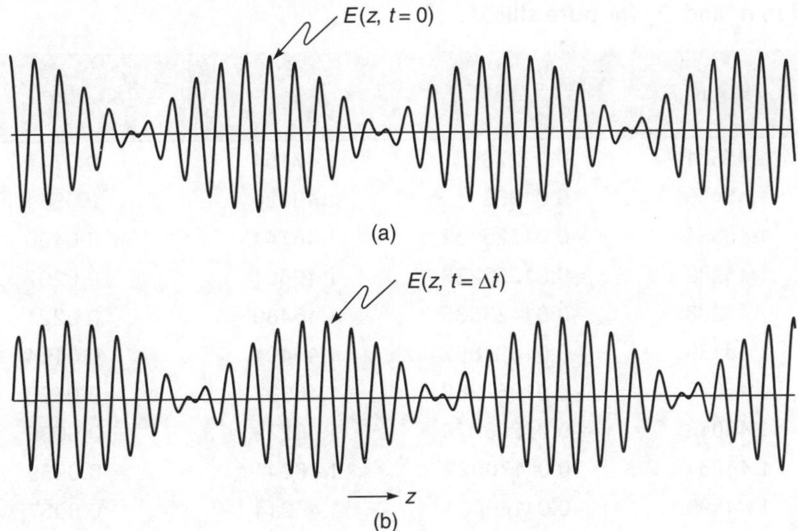

Figure 11.2
(a) and (b) show the variation of $E(z, t)$ at $t = 0$ and at $t = \Delta t$; the envelope moves with the group velocity $\Delta\omega/\Delta k$.

Now, in a medium characterized by the refractive index variation $n(\omega)$

$$k(\omega) = \frac{\omega}{c}\, n(\omega) \tag{11.7}$$

Thus,
$$\frac{1}{v_g} = \frac{dk}{d\omega} = \frac{1}{c}\left[n(\omega) + \omega \frac{dn}{d\omega}\right] \tag{11.8}$$

In free space $n(\omega) = 1$ at all frequencies; hence

$$v_g = v_p = c \tag{11.9}$$

Returning to Eq. (11.8), we may mention that it is customary to express in terms of the free space wavelength λ_0 which is related to ω through the following equation:

$$\omega = \frac{2\pi c}{\lambda_0} \tag{11.10}$$

Thus,
$$\frac{dn}{d\omega} = \frac{dn}{d\lambda_0}\frac{d\lambda_0}{d\omega} = -\frac{\lambda_0^2}{2\pi c}\frac{dn}{d\lambda_0} \tag{11.11}$$

or
$$\frac{1}{v_g} = \frac{1}{c}\left[n(\lambda_0) - \lambda_0 \frac{dn}{d\lambda_0}\right] \tag{11.12}$$

The group index n_g is defined as

$$n_g = \frac{c}{v_g} = n(\lambda_0) - \lambda_0 \frac{dn}{d\lambda_0} \tag{11.13}$$

In Table 11.1, we have tabulated $n(\lambda_0)$, $dn/d\lambda_0$ and $n_g(\lambda_0)$ for pure silica as a function of the free space wavelength λ_0. In Fig. 11.3, we have plotted (for pure silica) the wavelength variations of the group velocity v_g; we may notice that the group velocity attains a maximum value at $\lambda_0 \approx 1.27$ µm. As we will show later in this chapter (and also in Chapter 28), this wavelength is of great significance in optical communication systems.

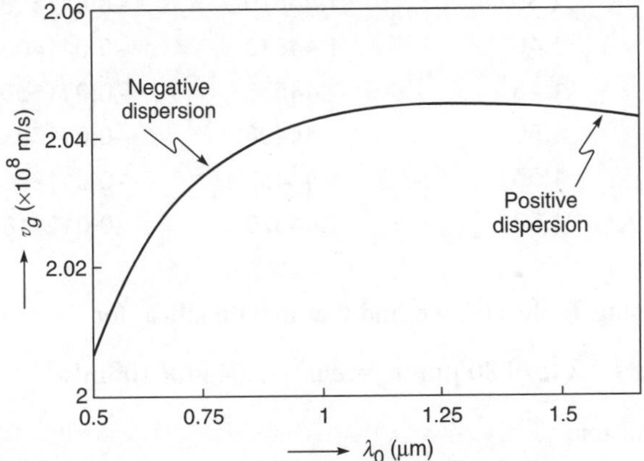

Figure 11.3
Variation of the group velocity v_g with wave-length for pure silica.

EXAMPLE 11.1 For pure silica the refractive index variation in the wavelength domain 0.5 µm < λ_0 < 1.6 µm can be assumed to be given by the following approximate empirical formula:

$$n(\lambda_0) \approx C_0 - a\lambda_0^2 + \frac{a}{\lambda_0^2} \tag{11.14}$$

where $C_0 \approx 1.451$, $a \approx 0.003$ and λ_0 is measured in µm. [A more accurate expression for $n(\lambda_0)$ is given in Problem 11.6]. Simple algebra shows

$$n_g(\lambda_0) = C_0 + a\lambda_0^2 + \frac{3a}{\lambda_0^2} \tag{11.15}$$

Thus at $\lambda_0 = 1$ µm,

$$n(\lambda_0) \approx 1.451$$

and
$$n_g(\lambda_0) \approx 1.463$$

indicating that the difference between group and phase velocities is about 0.8%. More accurate values of $n(\lambda_0)$ and $n_g(\lambda_0)$ (as obtained by using the expression given in Problem 11.6) are given in Table 11.1.

TABLE 11.1 **Values of n, n_g and D_m for pure silica***.

λ_0 (μm)	$n(\lambda_0)$	$\frac{dn}{d\lambda_0}$ (μm^{-1})	n_g (λ_0)	$\frac{d^2n}{d\lambda_0^2}$ (μm^{-2})	D_m (ps/nm.km)
0.70	1.45561	−0.02276	1.47154	0.0741	−172.9
0.75	1.45456	−0.01958	1.46924	0.0541	−135.3
0.80	1.45364	−0.01725159	1.46744	0.0400	−106.6
0.85	1.45282	−0.01552236	1.46601	0.0297	−84.2
0.90	1.45208	−0.01423535	1.46489	0.0221	−66.4
0.95	1.45139	−0.01327862	1.46401	0.0164	−51.9
1.00	1.45075	−0.01257282	1.46332	0.0120	−40.1
1.05	1.45013	−0.01206070	1.46279	0.0086	−30.1
1.10	1.44954	−0.01170022	1.46241	0.0059	−21.7
1.15	1.44896	−0.01146001	1.46214	0.0037	−14.5
1.20	1.44839	−0.01131637	1.46197	0.0020	−8.14
1.25	1.44783	−0.01125123	1.46189	0.00062	−2.58
1.30	1.44726	−0.01125037	1.46189	−0.00055	2.39
1.35	1.44670	−0.01130300	1.46196	−0.00153	6.87
1.40	1.44613	−0.01140040	1.46209	−0.00235	10.95
1.45	1.44556	−0.01153568	1.46229	−0.00305	14.72
1.50	1.44498	−0.01170333	1.46253	−0.00365	18.23
1.55	1.44439	−0.01189888	1.46283	−0.00416	21.52
1.60	1.44379	−0.01211873	1.46318	−0.00462	24.64

Using Table 11.1 we find that in pure silica, for

$$\lambda_0 = 0.80\ \mu\text{m},\ v_g = c/n_g = 2.0444 \times 10^8\ \text{m/s}$$

and for

$$\lambda_0 = 0.85\ \mu\text{m},\ v_g = c/n_g = 2.0464 \times 10^8\ \text{m/s}$$

implying that (for $\lambda_0 < 1.27$ μm) higher wavelength components travel faster; similarly for $\lambda_0 > 1.27$ μm lower wavelength components travel faster. Now, every source of light would have a certain wavelength spread, which is usually referred to as the spectral width of the source. Thus, a white light source (like coming from the sun) would have a spectral width of about 3000 Å; on the other hand, a light emitting diode (usually abbreviated as LED) would have a spectral width of about 25 nm and a typical laser diode (usually abbreviated as LD) operating around 1.3 μm would have a spectral width of about 2 nm; this spectral width is usually denoted by $\Delta\lambda_0$. Since each wavelength component (of a pulse) will travel with a slightly different group velocity it will, in general, result in the broadening of the pulse. In order to calculate this broadening, we note that the time taken by a pulse to traverse a length L of the dispersive medium is given by

$$\tau = \frac{L}{v_g} = \frac{L}{c}\left[n(\lambda_0) - \lambda_0 \frac{dn}{d\lambda_0}\right] \tag{11.16}$$

Since the RHS depends on λ_0, Eq. (11.16) implies that different wavelengths will travel with different group velocities in propagating through a certain length of the dispersive medium. Thus, the pulse broadening will be given by

$$\Delta\tau_m = \frac{d\tau}{d\lambda_0}\Delta\lambda_0 = -\frac{L\Delta\lambda_0}{\lambda_0 c}\left[\lambda_0^2 \frac{d^2n}{d\lambda_0^2}\right] \tag{11.17}$$

We may mention here that under certain conditions, a pulse may undergo compression; this is discussed in Sec. 11.3.3 (see also Fig. 11.8). The quantity $\Delta\tau_m$ is usually referred as *material dispersion* because it is due to the material properties of the medium—hence the subscript m. In Eq. (11.17), the quantity inside the square brackets is dimensionless. Indeed, after propagating through a length L of the dispersive medium, a pulse of temporal width τ_0 will get broadened to τ_f where

$$\tau_f^2 \approx \tau_0^2 + (\Delta\tau_m)^2 \tag{11.18}$$

* The numerical values in the Table have been calculated using the refractive index variation as given in Ref. 11.2 (see Problem 11.6).

In the next section, we will explicitly show this for a Gaussian pulse. From Eq. (11.17), we see that the broadening of the pulse is proportional to the length L traversed in the medium and also to spectral width of the source $\Delta\lambda_0$. We assume

$$\Delta\lambda_0 = 1 \text{ nm} = 10^{-9}\text{m} \quad \text{and} \quad L = 1 \text{ km} = 1000 \text{ m}$$

and define the dispersion coefficient as (see Sec. 28.10.3)

$$D_m = \frac{\Delta\tau_m}{L\Delta\lambda_0} \approx -\frac{1}{3\lambda_0}\left(\lambda_0^2 \frac{d^2n}{d\lambda_0^2}\right) \times 10^4 \text{ ps/km.nm} \quad \textbf{(11.19)}$$

where λ_0 is measured in μm and we have assumed $c \approx 3 \times 10^8$ m/s. The quantity D_m is usually referred as the *material dispersion coefficient* (because it is due to the material properties of the medium) and hence the subscript m on D. A medium is said to be characterized by positive dispersion when D_m is positive and it is said to be characterized by negative dispersion when D_m is negative.

We may note that the spectral width of a pulse is usually due to the intrinsic spectral width of the source—which for a typical LED is about 25 nm and for a commercially available laser diode is about 1–2 nm. On the other hand, for a nearly monochromatic source, the intrinsic spectral width could be extremely small and the actual spectral width of a pulse is determined from its finite duration (such a pulse is often referred to as a Fourier transformed pulse). Thus, a 20 ps (Fourier transformed) pulse will have a spectral width

$$\Delta\nu \approx \frac{1}{20 \times 10^{-12}} \approx 5 \times 10^{10} \text{ Hz}$$

implying

$$\Delta\lambda_0 \approx \frac{\lambda_0^2\,\Delta\nu}{c} \approx 0.3 \text{ nm}$$

where we have assumed $\lambda_0 \approx 1.3$ μm. We may see that

$$\frac{d^2n}{d\lambda_0^2} \approx 0$$

around $\lambda_0 \approx 1.27$ μm. Indeed the wavelength $\lambda_0 \approx 1270$ nm is usually referred to as the *zero material dispersion wavelength* and it is because of low material dispersion, the second and third generation optical communication systems operated around $\lambda_0 \approx 1300$ nm; more details will be given in Sections 28.10 and 28.11.

EXAMPLE 11.2 In the I-generation optical communication system, one used LED's with $\lambda_0 \approx 0.85$ μm and $\Delta\lambda_0 \approx 25$ nm. Now at $\lambda_0 \approx 0.85$ μm

$$\frac{d^2n}{d\lambda_0^2} \approx 0.030 \ (\mu\text{m})^{-2}$$

giving

$$D_m \approx -85 \text{ ps/km.nm}$$

the negative sign indicating that higher wavelengths travel faster than lower wavelengths. Thus for $\Delta\lambda_0 \approx 25$ nm, the actual broadening of the pulse will be

$$\Delta\tau_m \approx 2.1 \text{ ns/km}$$

implying that the pulse will broaden by 2.1 ns after traversing through 1 km of the silica fiber.

EXAMPLE 11.3 In the IV-generation optical communication systems, one uses laser diodes with $\lambda_0 = 1.55$ μm and $\Delta\lambda_0 \approx 2$ nm. Now at $\lambda_0 \approx 1.55$ μm

$$\frac{d^2n}{d\lambda_0^2} \approx 0.0042 \ (\mu\text{m})^{-2}$$

giving

$$D_m \approx +21.7 \text{ ps/km.nm}$$

the positive sign indicating that higher wavelengths travel slower than lower wavelengths. (Notice from Table 11.1 that for $\lambda_0 \geq 1.27$ μm, n_g increases with λ_0). Thus for $\Delta\lambda_0 \approx 2$ nm, the actual broadening of the pulse will be

$$\Delta\tau_m \approx 43 \text{ ps/km}$$

implying that the pulse will broaden by about 43 ps after traversing through 1 km of the silica fiber.

11.3 Group Velocity of a Wave Packet

LO2

The displacement corresponding to a one–dimensional plane wave propagating in the $+z$ direction can be written in the form

$$E(z, t) = Ae^{i(\omega t - kz)} \quad \textbf{(11.20)}$$

where A represents the amplitude of the wave and

$$k(\omega) = \frac{\omega}{c} n(\omega) \quad \textbf{(11.21)}$$

n being the refractive index of the medium. The wave described by Eq. (11.20) is said to describe a monochromatic wave which propagates with the phase velocity given by

$$v_p = \frac{\omega}{k} = \frac{c}{n} \quad \textbf{(11.22)}$$

We may mention here that, in general, A may be complex and if we write

$$A = |A|e^{i\phi}$$

then Eq. (11.20) becomes

$$E = |A|e^{i(\omega t - kz + \phi)}$$

The actual displacement is the real part of E and is, therefore, given by

$$\begin{aligned}\text{Actual electric field} &= \text{Re}(E)\\ &= |A| \cos(\omega t - kz + \phi) \quad \textbf{(11.23)}\end{aligned}$$

The plane wave represented by Eq. (11.20) is a practical impossibility because at an arbitrary value of z, the displacement is finite for *all* values of t; for example,

$$E(z = 0, t) = Ae^{+i\omega t}; \; -\infty < t < \infty \tag{11.24}$$

which corresponds to a sinusoidal variation for *all* values of time. In practice, the displacement is finite only over a certain domain of time and we have what is known as a **wave packet**. A wave packet can always be expressed as a superposition of plane waves of different frequencies:

$$E(z, t) = \int_{-\infty}^{+\infty} A(\omega)e^{i[\omega t - kz]}\, d\omega \tag{11.25}$$

Now, $$E(z = 0, t) = \int_{-\infty}^{+\infty} A(\omega)e^{+i\omega t}\, d\omega \tag{11.26}$$

Thus, $E(z = 0, t)$ is the Fourier transform of $A(\omega)$ and using the results of Sec. 8.4, we obtain

$$A(\omega) = \frac{1}{2\pi}\int_{-\infty}^{+\infty} E\,(z = 0, t)\, e^{-i\omega t}\, dt \tag{11.27}$$

Thus, if $E(z = 0, t)$ we know we can determine $E(z, t)$ using the following recipe:

We first determine $A(\omega)$ from Eq. (11.27), substitute it in Eq. (11.25) and carry out the resulting integration.

EXAMPLE 11.4 Gaussian Pulse: As an example, we consider a Gaussian pulse for which we may write

$$E(z = 0, t) = E_0 e^{-\frac{t^2}{\tau_0^2}}\, e^{+i\omega_0 t} \tag{11.28}$$

If we substitute Eq. (11.28) in Eq. (11.27), we would obtain (see Example 9.2)

$$A(\omega) = \frac{E_0\tau_0}{2\sqrt{\pi}}\exp\left[-\frac{1}{4}(\omega - \omega_0)^2\tau_0^2\right] \tag{11.29}$$

In general, $A(\omega)$ can be complex and as such one defines the power spectral density

$$S(\omega) = |A(\omega)|^2 \tag{11.30}$$

For the Gaussian pulse

$$S(\omega) = \frac{E_0^2\tau_0^2}{4\pi}\exp\left[-\frac{1}{2}(\omega - \omega_0)^2\tau_0^2\right] \tag{11.31}$$

In Fig. 11.4(a), we have plotted the function

$$E_0 e^{-\frac{t^2}{\tau_0^2}} \cos(\omega_0 t)$$

[which is the real part of Eq. (11.28)] for a 20 fs pulse ($\tau_0 = 20 \times 10^{-15}$s) corresponding to $\lambda_0 = 1$ μm ($\omega_0 \approx 6\pi \times 10^{14}$ Hz); the corresponding spectral density function $S(\omega)$ is plotted in Fig. 11.4(b). As can be seen, $S(\omega)$ is a very sharply peaked function of ω around $\omega = \omega_0$. The full width at half maximum of $S(\omega)$ (usually abbreviated as FWHM) is denoted by $\Delta\omega$; thus at

$$\omega = \omega_0 \pm \frac{1}{2}\Delta\omega \tag{11.32}$$

$S(\omega)$ attains half of its maximum value; the value of $\Delta\omega$ is obtained from the following equation:

$$\frac{1}{2} = \exp\left[-\frac{(\Delta\omega)^2\tau_0^2}{8}\right]$$

or $$\text{FWHM} = \Delta\omega = \frac{2\sqrt{2\ln 2}}{\tau_0} \approx \frac{2.35}{\tau_0} \tag{11.33}$$

Thus the Gaussian pulse with $\tau_0 = 20$ fs has a frequency spread $\Delta\omega$ given by

$$\Delta\omega \approx 1.18 \times 10^{14} \text{ Hz} \tag{11.34}$$

Thus, $$\frac{\Delta\omega}{\omega_0} \approx 0.06$$

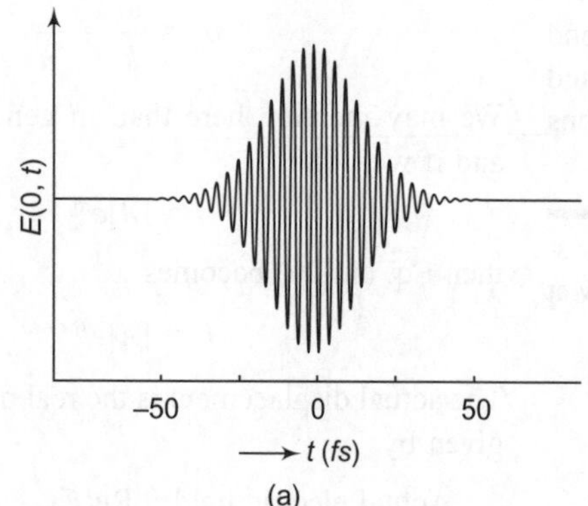

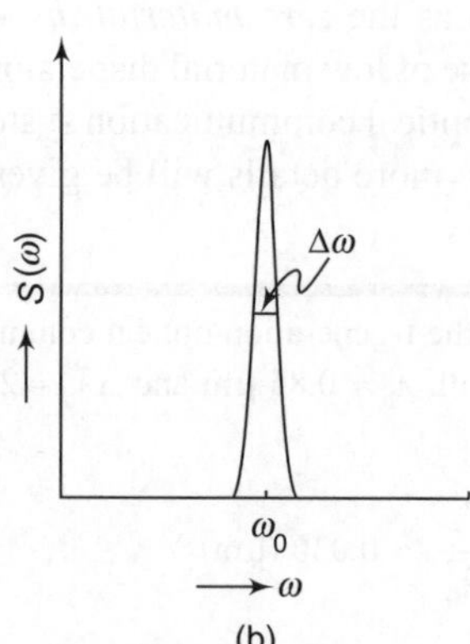

Figure 11.4

(a) A 20 fs (= 20 × 10^{-15} s) Gaussian pulse corresponding to $\lambda_0 = 1$ μm. (b) The corresponding frequency spectrum which is usually a very sharply peaked function around $\omega = \omega_0$.

We may mention here that in order to have clarity in the figure we have chosen a very small value of τ_0; usually τ_0 has a much larger value. A larger value of τ_0 will imply a much smaller value of $\Delta\omega$ (resulting in greater monochromaticity of the pulse) and obviously Fig. 11.4(b) will be much more sharply peaked. We will discuss this in greater detail in the chapter on coherence (See Sec. 16.6).

Returning to Eq. (11.25), we consider the following cases:

11.3.1 Propagation in a Non-Dispersive Medium

For electromagnetic waves, the free space is a non-dispersive medium in which all frequencies propagate with the same velocity c; thus,

$$k(\omega) = \frac{\omega}{c}$$

and Eq. (11.25) can be written in the form

$$E(z, t) = \int_{-\infty}^{+\infty} A(\omega) e^{-i\frac{\omega}{c}(z-ct)} d\omega \qquad \textbf{(11.35)}$$

The right-hand side is a function of $(z-ct)$ and thus any pulse would propagate with velocity c without undergoing any distortion. Thus, for the Gaussian pulse given by Eq. (11.28).

$$E(z,t) = E_0 \exp\left[-\frac{(z-ct)^2}{c^2\tau_0^2}\right] \exp\left[-i\frac{\omega_0}{c}(z-ct)\right] \qquad \textbf{(11.36)}$$

which represents a distortionless propagation of a Gaussian pulse in a non-dispersive medium*; in Fig. 11.5 we have shown the distortionless propagation of a 20 fs pulse.

11.3.2 Propagation in a Dispersive Medium

For a wave propagating in a medium characterized by the refractive index variation $n(\omega)$, we will have

$$k(\omega) = \frac{\omega}{c} n(\omega)$$

Now, in most problems, $A(\omega)$ is a very sharply peaked function [see, e.g., Fig. 11.4(b)] so that we may write

$$E(z, t) \approx \int_{\omega_0-\Delta\omega}^{\omega_0+\Delta\omega} A(\omega) e^{i[\omega t - k(\omega) z]} d\omega \qquad \textbf{(11.37)}$$

because for $\omega > \omega_0 + \Delta\omega$ and for $\omega < \omega_0 - \Delta\omega$, the function $A(\omega)$ is negligibly small. In this tiny domain of integration, we may make a Taylor series expansion of $k(\omega)$

$$k(\omega) = k(\omega_0) + (\omega - \omega_0) \left.\frac{dk}{d\omega}\right|_{\omega=\omega_0} + \frac{1}{2}(\omega-\omega_0)^2 \left.\frac{d^2k}{d\omega^2}\right|_{\omega=\omega_0} + \ldots \qquad \textbf{(11.38)}$$

or $$k(\omega) = k_0 + \frac{1}{v_g}(\omega - \omega_0) + \frac{1}{2}(\omega-\omega_0)^2 \gamma \qquad \textbf{(11.39)}$$

where

$$k_0 \equiv k(\omega_0) \qquad \textbf{(11.40)}$$

$$\frac{1}{v_g} \equiv \left.\frac{dk}{d\omega}\right|_{\omega=\omega_0} \qquad \textbf{(11.41)}$$

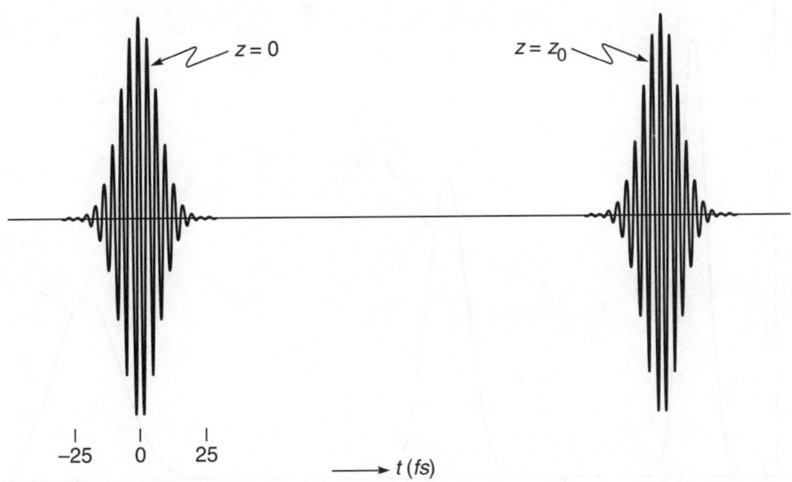

Figure 11.5
Distortionless propagation of a Gaussian pulse in a non-dispersive medium.

* While Eq. (11.36) follows directly from Eq. (11.35), it is left as an exercise to the reader to show that if we substitute for $A(\omega)$ from Eq. (11.29) in Eq. (11.35), we would readily get Eq. (11.36).

and $$\gamma \equiv \left.\frac{d^2k}{d\omega^2}\right|_{\omega=\omega_0} \qquad \textbf{(11.42)}$$

We may mention here that we have now *defined* v_g through Eq. (11.41)—we will show below that the envelope of the pulse moves with velocity v_g which is the group velocity. Now, if we retain only the first two terms on the RHS of Eq. (11.39), then Eq. (11.37) would give us

$$E(z, t) \approx \int_{-\infty}^{+\infty} A(\omega)\exp\left[-i\left(k_0 z+\frac{\omega-\omega_0}{v_g}z-\omega t\right)\right] d\omega \qquad \textbf{(11.43)}$$

where we have replaced the limits from $-\infty$ to $+\infty$ because, in any case, the contribution from the region $|\omega - \omega_0| > \Delta\omega$ is going to be extremely small. Writing

$$\omega t = (\omega - \omega_0)t + \omega_0 t \qquad \textbf{(11.44)}$$

Eq. (11.43) can be rewritten in the form

$$E(z, t) \approx \underbrace{e^{i(\omega_0 t-k_0 z)}}_{\text{Phase Term}} \underbrace{\int_{-\infty}^{+\infty} A(\Omega) e^{-\frac{i\Omega}{v_g}(z-v_g t)}\, d\Omega}_{\text{Envelope Term}} \qquad \textbf{(11.45)}$$

where $$\Omega \equiv \omega - \omega_0 \qquad \textbf{(11.46)}$$

We see that in the envelope term, z and t do not appear independently but only as $z - v_g t$; thus, the envelope of the pulse moves undistorted with the group velocity

$$v_g = \frac{1}{(dk/d\omega)_{\omega_0}} \qquad \textbf{(11.47)}$$

Thus, if we neglect γ [and other higher order terms in Eq. (11.39)], the pulse moves undistorted with group velocity v_g. Next, if we take into account all the three terms in Eq. (11.39), we would obtain

$$E(z,t) \approx \underbrace{e^{i(\omega_0 t-k_0 z)}}_{\text{Phase Term}} \underbrace{\int_{-\infty}^{+\infty} A(\Omega)\exp\left[i\Omega\left(t-\frac{z}{v_g}\right)-\frac{i}{2}\Omega^2\gamma z\right]d\Omega}_{\text{Envelope Term}} \qquad \textbf{(11.48)}$$

For the Gaussian pulse [see Eq. (11.28)], $A(\omega)$ is given by Eq. (11.29); if we now substitute $A(\omega)$ in the above equation and use Eq. (11.30) to carry out the integration, we would readily obtain

$$E(z,t) = \frac{E_0}{\sqrt{1+ip}} e^{i(\omega_0 t-k_0 z)} \exp\left[-\frac{\left(t-\frac{z}{v_g}\right)^2}{\tau_0^2(1+ip)}\right] \qquad \textbf{(11.49)}$$

where $$p \equiv \frac{2\gamma z}{\tau_0^2} \qquad \textbf{(11.50)}$$

The corresponding intensity distribution would be given by

$$I(z,t) = \frac{I_0}{\tau(z)/\tau_0} \exp\left[-\frac{2\left(t-\frac{z}{v_g}\right)^2}{\tau^2(z)}\right] \qquad \textbf{(11.51)}$$

where $$\tau^2(z) \equiv \tau_0^2(1 + p^2) \qquad \textbf{(11.52)}$$

In Figs. 11.6 and 11.7 we have shown the propagation of an unchirped Gaussian pulse [see Eq. (11.28)] through

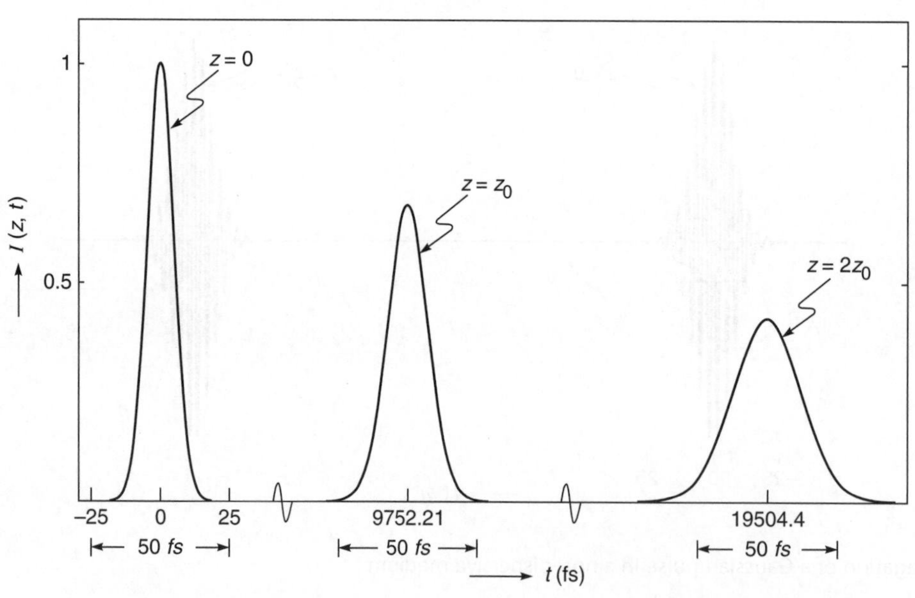

Figure 11.6
Temporal broadening of $I(z, t)$ [as given by Eq. (11.51) for $\lambda_0 = 1.55$ µm, $\tau_0 = 10$ fs, $z_0 = 2$ mm and $v_g \approx 2.050814 \times 10^8$ m/s [using Eq. (11.12) and Table 11.1].

pure silica. We have plotted the time evolution of $I(z,t)$ and of $\text{Re}[E(z,t)]$ at $z = z_0 = 2$ mm and at $z = 2z_0 = 4$ mm; we have assumed $\lambda_0 = 1.55$ μm for which (using Table 11.1) we have $v_g = \dfrac{c}{n(\lambda_0) - \lambda_0[dn/d\lambda_0]} \approx 2.050814 \times 10^8$ m/s. Thus, the pulse will propagate through 2 mm (= z_0) in $z_0/v_g \approx 9.752 \times 10^{-12}$ s = 9752 fs. From Eq. (11.52), we find that as the pulse propagates it undergoes temporal broadening. We define the pulse broadening $\Delta\tau$ as

$$\Delta\tau = \sqrt{\tau^2(z) - \tau_0^2}$$

$$= |p|\tau_0 = \frac{2|\gamma|z}{\tau_0} \tag{11.53}$$

Now
$$\gamma = \frac{d^2k}{d\omega^2} = \frac{1}{c}\frac{d}{d\lambda_0}\left[n(\lambda_0) - \lambda_0\frac{dn}{d\lambda_0}\right]\frac{d\lambda_0}{d\omega}$$

$$= \frac{\lambda_0}{2\pi c^2}\left[\lambda_0^2\frac{d^2n}{d\lambda_0^2}\right] \tag{11.54}$$

where the quantity inside the square brackets is dimensionless. Further, since the spectral width of the Gaussian pulse is given by [see Eq. (11.33)]

$$\Delta\omega \approx \frac{2}{\tau_0} \tag{11.55}$$

we may write
$$\frac{1}{\tau_0} \approx \frac{1}{2}\Delta\omega \approx \frac{1}{2}\frac{2\pi c}{\lambda_0^2}|\Delta\lambda_0| \tag{11.56}$$

Substituting for τ_0 from Eq. (11.56) and for γ from Eq. (11.54) in Eq. (11.53), we get

$$\Delta\tau = \frac{z}{\lambda_0 c}\left|\lambda_0^2\frac{d^2n}{d\lambda_0^2}\right|\Delta\lambda_0 \tag{11.57}$$

which is identical to the result obtained in the earlier section [see Eq. (11.17)].

EXAMPLE 11.5 As an example, we assume $\lambda_0 = 1.55$ μm. For pure silica, at this wavelength (see Table 11.1)

$$\frac{d^2n}{d\lambda_0^2} \approx -0.004165\ (\mu\text{m})^{-2}$$

Thus,
$$\gamma \approx -\frac{1.55\times10^{-6}}{2\pi\times9\times10^{16}}[1.55\times1.55\times0.004165]$$

$$\approx -2.743\times10^{-26}\ \text{m}^{-1}\text{s}^2$$

For a 100 ps pulse propagating through a 2 km long fiber

$$\Delta\tau \approx \frac{2\times2.743\times10^{-26}\times2\times10^3}{(10^{-10})} \approx 1.1\ \text{ps}$$

On the other hand, for a 10 fs pulse, at $z = 2z_0 = 4$ mm, we will have

$$\Delta\tau \approx 22\ \text{fs}$$

implying $\tau_f \approx [\tau_0^2 + (\Delta\tau)^2]^{1/2} \approx 24$ fs

showing that a 10 fs pulse doubles its temporal width after propagating through a very small distance (see Figs. 11.6 and 11.7).

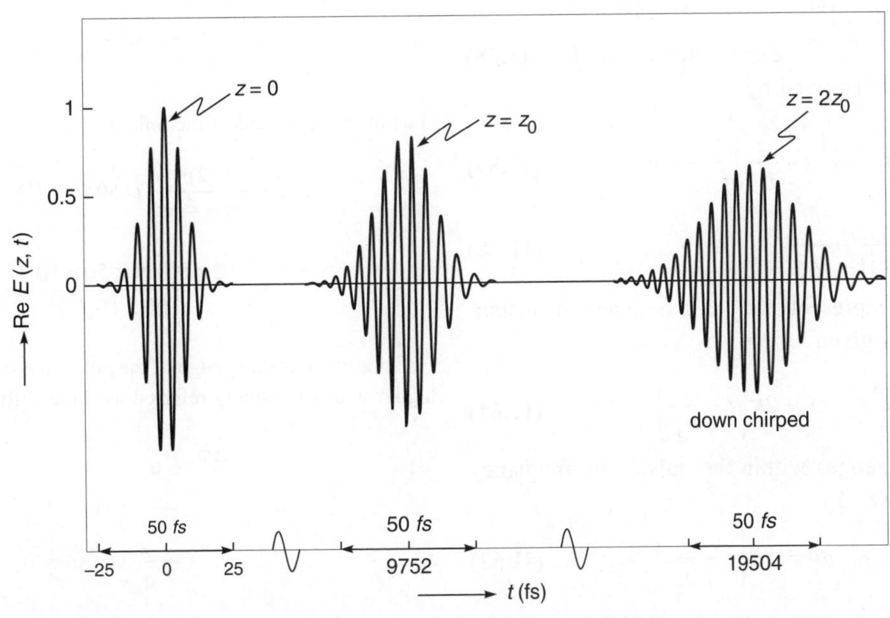

Figure 11.7
Temporal broadening of Re[E(z, t)] [as given by Eq. (11.49) for $\lambda_0 = 1.55$ μm, $\tau_0 = 10$ fs, $z_0 = 2$ mm and $v_g \approx 2.050814 \times 10^8$ m/s [using Eq. (11.12) and Table 11.1].

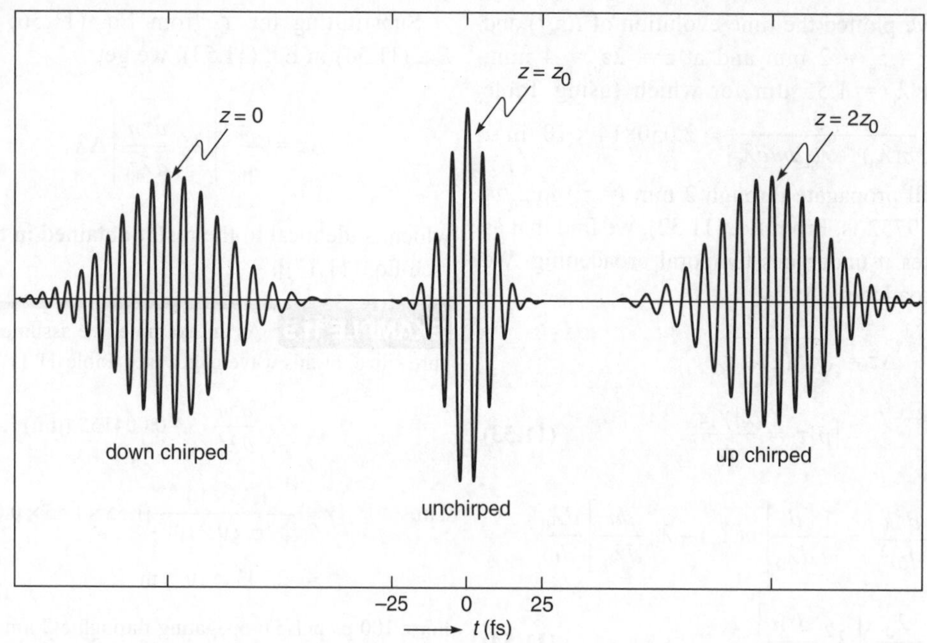

Figure 11.8
If a down-chirped pulse is passed through a medium characterized by negative dispersion, it will get compressed until it becomes unchirped and then it will broaden again with opposite chirp.

11.3.3 The Chirping of the Dispersed Pulse LO3

If we carry out simple manipulations, Eq. (11.49) can be written in the form,

$$E(z,t) = \frac{E_0}{[\tau(z)/\tau_0]^{1/2}} \exp\left[-\frac{\left(t-\dfrac{z}{v_g}\right)^2}{\tau^2(z)}\right] \times \exp\,[i(\Phi(z,t) - k_0 z] \quad (11.58)$$

where the phase term is given by

$$\Phi(z,t) = \omega_0 t + \kappa\left(t-\frac{z}{v_g}\right)^2 - \frac{1}{2}\tan^{-1} p \quad (11.59)$$

and $$\kappa(z) = \frac{p}{\tau_0^2(1+p^2)} \quad (11.60)$$

Equation (11.59) represents the phase term and the instantaneous frequency is given by

$$\omega(t) = \frac{\partial\Phi}{\partial t} = \omega_0 + 2\kappa\left(t-\frac{z}{v_g}\right) \quad (11.61)$$

showing that $\omega(t)$ changes within the pulse. The frequency chirp is therefore given by

$$\Delta\omega = \omega(t) - \omega_0 = 2\kappa\left(t-\frac{z}{v_g}\right) \quad (11.62)$$

The phenomenon of chirping is used in dispersion compensation (see Sec. 30.6 and Fig 30.10) and also in CPA (see Sec. 11.3.4).

EXAMPLE 11.6 In continuation of Example 11.5, we assume $\lambda_0 = 1.55$ μm and consider the chirping produced in a 100 ps pulse propagating in pure silica at $z = 2$ km. Now,

$$p = \frac{2\gamma z}{\tau_0^2} = -\frac{2\times 2.743\times 10^{-26}\times 2\times 10^3}{(100\times 10^{-12})^2} \approx -0.011$$

At $$t-\frac{z}{v_g} = -50 \text{ ps}$$

(i.e., at the front end of the pulse)

$$\Delta\omega \approx \frac{2p}{\tau_0^2(1+p^2)}(-50\times 10^{-12})$$

$$\approx +\frac{2\times 0.011\times 50\times 10^{-12}}{(100\times 10^{-12})^2} = +1.1\times 10^8 \text{ Hz}$$

Thus at the leading edge of the pulse, the frequencies are slightly higher which is usually referred as 'blue shifted'. Notice

$$\frac{\Delta\omega}{\omega_0} \approx 9\times 10^{-8}$$

at $$t = \frac{z}{v_g}, \quad \Delta\omega = 0$$

and at $$t-\frac{z}{v_g} = +50 \text{ ps}$$

(i.e., at the trailing edge of the pulse)

$$\Delta\omega \approx -1.1 \times 10^8 \text{ Hz}$$

Thus, at the trailing edge of the pulse, the frequencies are slightly lower which is usually referred as 'red-shifted'.

From Example 11.6, we can conclude the following:

For positive dispersion (i.e., negative value of γ), p and κ will also be negative implying that the instantaneous frequency (within the pulse) decreases with time (we are of course assuming $z > 0$); this is known as a **down-chirped pulse** in which the **leading edge** of the pulse ($t < z/v_g$) is **blue-shifted** (i.e., it has frequency higher than ω_0) and the **trailing edge** of the pulse ($t > z/v_g$) is **red-shifted** (i.e., it has frequency lower than ω_0).

This is shown in Fig. 11.7 where at $t = 0$, we have an unchirped pulse. As the pulse propagates further, it will get further broadened and also get further down chirped.

From Eq. (11.61), it can be readily seen that at negative values of z, p (and therefore κ) will be positive and the **leading edge** of the pulse ($t < z/v_g$) will be **red-shifted** (i.e., it will have frequency lower than ω_0) and the **trailing edge** of the pulse ($t > z/v_g$) will be **blue-shifted** (i.e., it will have frequency higher than ω_0) see also Fig. 30.10.

This implies that we will have an up-chirped pulse. Thus, if an up-chirped pulse is passed through a medium characterized by positive dispersion, it will get compressed until it becomes unchirped and then it will broaden again with opposite chirp.

Similarly, we can discuss the case of negative dispersion (implying a positive value of γ). If a down-chirped pulse is passed through a medium characterized by negative dispersion, it will get compressed until it becomes unchirped and then it will broaden again with opposite chirp (see Fig. 11.8).

Figure 11.9 shows computer calculations of a pulse propagating through a material characterized by negative group velocity.

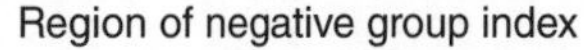

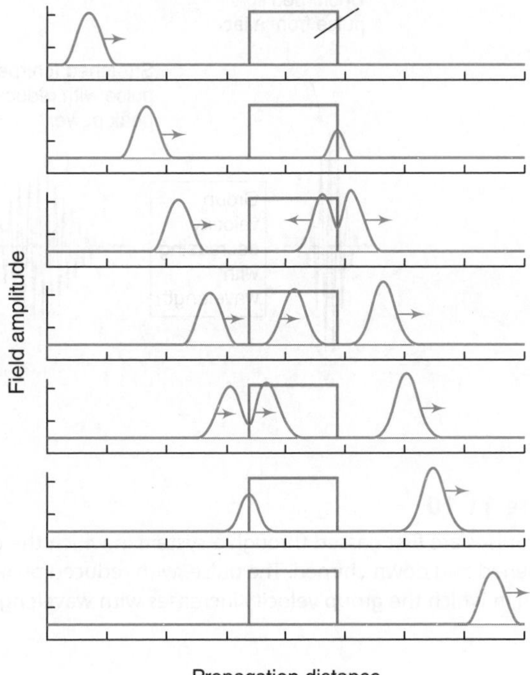

Figure 11.9

Propagation of a pulse through a material characterized by negative group velocity. The peak of the transmitted pulse appears to emerge from the material medium before the peak of the incident pulse enters the medium. It may be seen that the pulse appears to move backward in the medium. Such backward propagation has been observed in the laboratory. The plots are based on a simple model that assumes that all spectral components of the pulse propagate without loss at the same group velocity. [*Adapted from Ref. 11.9; used with permission from Professor Boyd and Professor Gauthier*].

11.3.4 Chirped Pulse Amplification

The 2018 Nobel Prize in Physics was awarded *"for groundbreaking inventions in the field of laser physics"* with one half to **Arthur Ashkin** *"for the optical tweezers and their application to biological systems"*; and the other half jointly to **Gérard Mourou** and **Donna Strickland**

> *"for their method of generating high-intensity, ultrashort optical pulses"*

Indeed, in 1985, Gérard Mourou and Donna Strickland used Chirped Pulse Amplification (usually abbreviated as CPA) to create ultrashort high-intensity laser pulses (Ref. 11.4). In 1985 Donna Strickland was doing her doctoral work under Gérard Mourou at University of Rochester. What is Chirped Pulse Amplification? To quote Strickland (Ref. 11.10),

> *the technique involves taking a short, low-energy laser pulse, stretching it to make a long, low-energy pulse, amplifying it to get a long, high-energy pulse, before finally compressing it to get a short, high-energy pulse.*

What is actually done is somewhat like this: First the laser pulses are passed through a system in which the group velocity decreases with wavelength so that the laser pulses are broadened and down chirped (see Fig. 11.10). The pulse, with reduced peak power, is amplified. Finally the amplified pulse is passed through a system in which the group velocity

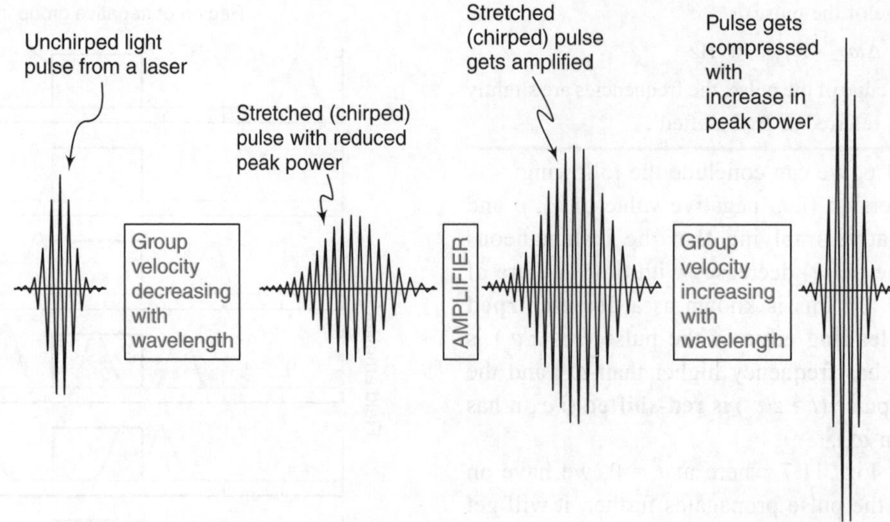

Figure 11.10

Laser pulses are first passed through a system in which the group velocity decreases with wavelength so that the laser pulses are broadened and down chirped. The pulse, with reduced peak power, is amplified. Finally the amplified pulse is passed through a system in which the group velocity increases with wavelength so that the laser pulses get compressed.

decreases with wavelength so that the laser pulses get compressed; we may mention here that grating pairs are often used to introduce negative (or positive) dispersion*. Such ultrashort high-intensity laser pulses (produced by CPA) find extremely important applications in industry**; for example, in cancer treatment, in many commercial products, in eye surgery, etc. Indeed, since 2011, to quote from Ref. 11.10, CPA has been used in 24 million eye operations.

11.4 Self-Phase Modulation LO4

It may be mentioned that as a pulse propagates through a dispersive medium, the frequency spectrum remains the same—i.e., no new frequencies are generated. Different frequencies superpose with different phases to distort the temporal shape of the pulse (see Problem 11.10). New frequencies are generated when the medium is non-linear—we will briefly discuss this here.

The refractive index of any material is a constant only for small intensities of the propagating laser beam. If the intensities are large, the refractive index variation is approximately given by

$$n \simeq n_0 + n_2 I \tag{11.63}$$

where n_2 is a constant and I represents the intensity of the beam. For example, for fused silica, $n_0 \simeq 1.47$ and $n_2 \simeq 3.2 \times 10^{-20}$ m²/W. Further, if the effective area of the light beam is A_{eff}, then the intensity is given by

$$I = \frac{P}{A_{eff}} \tag{11.64}$$

where P is the power associated with the light beam. Now in a single mode fiber, the spot size w of the beam is about 5 μm (see Sec. 30.4.2). Thus the effective*** cross-sectional area of the beam, $A_{eff} \approx \pi w^2 \approx 50\ \mu\text{m}^2$. For a 5 mW laser beam propagating through such a fiber, the resultant intensity is given by

$$I = \frac{P}{A_{eff}} \approx \frac{5\times10^{-3}\,W}{50\times10^{-12}\ \text{m}^2} = 10^8\ \text{W/m}^2 \tag{11.65}$$

Thus, the change in refractive index is given by

$$\Delta n = n_2 I \simeq 3.2 \times 10^{-12} \tag{11.66}$$

Although this is very small, but when the beam propagates over an optical fiber over long distances (a few hundred to a few thousand kilometers), the accumulated nonlinear effects can be significant. That is the great advantage of the optical

* See, for example, the article on *Pulse stretching and compressing using grating pairs* by Dr. Clara Saraceno in https://ibsen.com/wp-content/uploads/White-paper-Pulse-stretching-and-compressing-using-grating-pairs_v1.pdf

** See, for example, https://www.rochester.edu/newscenter/what-is-chirped-pulse-amplification-nobel-prize-341072/

*** Values adapted from Ref. 11.2.

fiber—the beam remains confined to a very small area for long distances!

We consider a laser pulse (of frequency ω_0) propagating through an optical fiber; the effective propagation constant is given by

$$k = \frac{\omega_0}{c}[n_0 + n_2 I] = \frac{\omega_0}{c}\left[n_0 + n_2\frac{P(t)}{A_{eff}}\right] \quad \textbf{(11.67)}$$

Thus, for such a propagating beam, the phase term is approximately given by

$$e^{+i(\omega_0 t - kz)} = \exp\left[+i\left\{\omega_0 t - \frac{\omega_0}{c}\left(n_0 + n_2\frac{P(t)}{A_{eff}}\right)z\right\}\right] = e^{+i\Phi}$$

where the phase Φ is defined as

$$\Phi(z,t) \equiv \omega_0 t - \frac{\omega_0}{c}\left(n_0 + n_2\frac{P(t)}{A_{eff}}\right)z \quad \textbf{(11.68)}$$

We can define an instantaneous frequency as [see Eq. (11.61)]:

$$\omega(t) \equiv \frac{\partial\Phi}{\partial t} = \omega_0 - g\frac{dP(t)}{dt}z$$

where

$$g = \frac{n_2\omega_0}{cA_{eff}} = \frac{2\pi n_2}{\lambda_0 A_{eff}} \quad \textbf{(11.69)}$$

For $A_{eff} \approx 50\ \mu m^2$, $\lambda_0 \approx 1.55\ \mu m$ and $n_2 \approx 3.2 \times 10^{-20}\ m^2/W$, $g \approx 2.6 \times 10^{-3}\ W^{-1}\ m^{-1}$. Now, for a Gaussian pulse propagating with group velocity v_g [see Eq. (11.51)]:

$$P(z,t) = P_0 \exp\left[-\frac{2\left(t - \frac{z}{v_g}\right)^2}{\tau_0^2}\right]$$

where we have neglected dispersion [i.e., $p = 0$ in Eqs. (11.49) and (11.52)]. Thus,

$$\omega(t) = \omega_0\left[1 + \frac{2gz}{\omega_0\tau_0^2}P_0\left(t - \frac{z}{v_g}\right)\exp\left[-\frac{2\left(t - \frac{z}{v_g}\right)^2}{\tau_0^2}\right]\right]$$

For $\lambda_0 = 1.55\ \mu m$

$$\omega_0 = \frac{2\pi c}{\lambda_0} = \frac{2\pi \times 3 \times 10^8}{1.55 \times 10^{-6}} \approx 1.22 \times 10^{15}\ s^{-1}$$

Further, for $P_0 = 15$ mW, $\tau_0 = 20$ fs and $z = 200$ km

$$\frac{2gzP_0}{\omega_0\tau_0^2}\left(t - \frac{z}{v_g}\right)$$

$$= \frac{2 \times 2.6 \times 10^{-3} \times 2 \times 10^5 \times 15 \times 10^{-3}}{1.22 \times 10^{15} \times (20 \times 10^{-15})^2}\left(t - \frac{z}{v_g}\right)$$

$$\approx 3.2 \times 10^{13}\left(t - \frac{z}{v_g}\right)$$

$$\approx +0.64 \quad \text{for } t - \frac{z}{v_g} \approx 20 \text{ fs (trailing edge of the pulse)}$$

$$\approx -0.64 \text{ for } t - \frac{z}{v_g} \approx -20 \text{ fs (front end of the pulse)}$$

Thus, the instantaneous frequency within the pulse changes with time leading to chirping of the pulse as shown in Fig. 11.10. This is known as **self-phase modulation** (usually abbreviated as SPM). Note that since the pulse width has not changed, but the pulse is chirped, the frequency content of the pulse has increased. Thus, if we take the Fourier transform of Eq. (11.58) no new frequencies will be generated. However, if the phase term is given by Eq. (11.68) and if we take the Fourier transform, new frequencies will be generated. Thus, SPM leads to generation of new frequencies. Indeed by passing a pulse through a fiber characterized by very small cross-sectional area (so that the value of g is large) it is possible to generate the entire visible spectrum (see Fig. 11.11 and 11.12).

If we compare the chirps shown in Figs. 11.7 and 11.11, we find that when a laser pulse propagates through a system in which the group velocity decreases with wavelength, the chirp introduced is opposite to that due to nonlinearity. Indeed we can have a situation where the chirp introduced by nonlinearity is compensated by the opposite chirp introduced by dispersion; when this happens, the pulse neither broadens in time nor in its spectrum and such a pulse is called a ***soliton***. Thus a soliton would propagate without any broadening as shown in Fig. 11.13; more details can be found in Ref. 11.5 and 11.6. Indeed, in 1973, Akira Hasegawa and Frederick Tappert (while working at Bell Telephone Laboratories in Murray Hill, NJ) were the first to predict solitons in optical fibers (Ref. 11.7). Such solitons are very important for fiber optic communication systems since by eliminating dispersion it is possible to achieve increased bit rates and hence increase the information capacity of the system. Typically for a pulse width of 10 picoseconds, the required power for the formation of a soliton is about 35 mW which is indeed not very large. Figure 11.13 shows the input and output soliton pulses as they emerge after propagating through 2000 km of an optical fiber. It can be seen that even after propagating through 2000 km, the pulse shows hardly any dispersion.

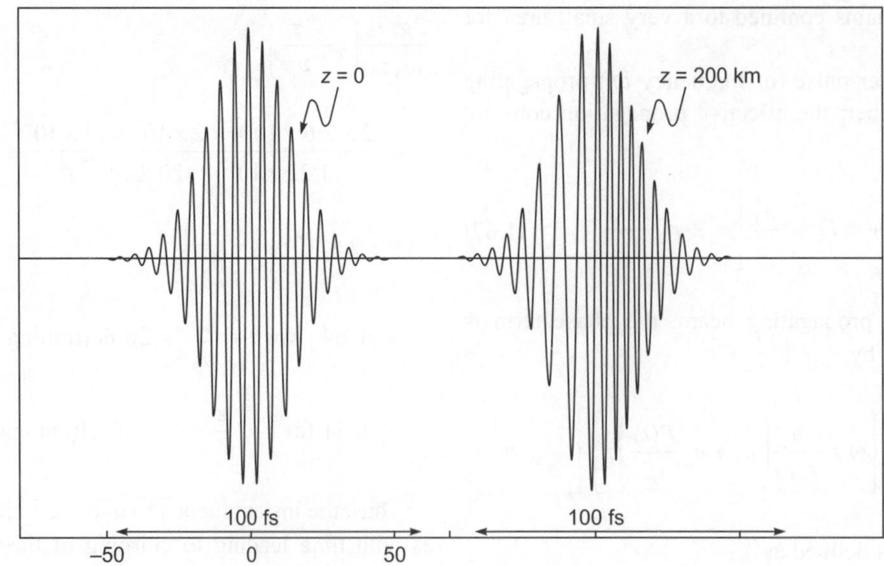

Figure 11.11
Due to self-phase modulation, the instantaneous frequency within the pulse changes with time leading to chirping of the pulse. Calculations correspond to $P_0 = 15$ mW, $\lambda_0 = 1550$ nm, $\tau_0 = 20$ fs, $A_{eff} = 5$ µm^2 and $v_g = 2 \times 10^8$ m/s.

Figure 11.12
Supercontinuum white light source. Laser pulses of 6 ps duration are incident on a special optical fiber characterized by a very small mode field diameter which leads to very high intensities. Because of the high intensities we have SPM (Self-Phase Modulation) and other non-linear effects; these non-linear effects result in the generation of new frequencies. In this experiment, the entire visible spectrum gets generated which can be observed by passing the light coming out of the optical fiber through a grating. The repetition rate of the laser pulses is 20 MHz. The wavelengths generated range from 460 nm to 2200 nm. [*Photograph courtesy: Fianium, UK.*].

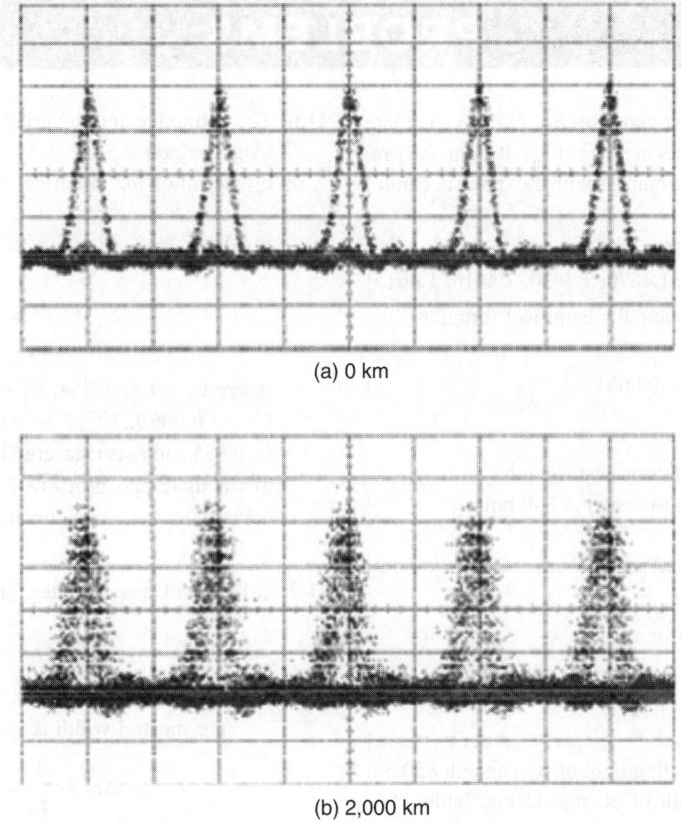

Figure 11.13
Soliton propagation over 2000 km of single mode fiber; adapted from Ref. 11.8.

SUMMARY

- When we switch a light source on and off, we produce a pulse. This pulse propagates through a medium with what is known as the group velocity, which is given by

$$v_g = \frac{1}{dk/d\omega}$$

For a medium characterized by the refractive index variation $n(\omega)$ the group velocity is given by

$$\frac{1}{v_g} = \frac{1}{c}\left[n(\lambda_0) - \lambda_0 \frac{dn}{d\lambda_0}\right]$$

where λ_0 is the wavelength in free space and $c \approx (3\times10^8 \text{ m/s})$ is the speed of light in free space.

- For a Gaussian pulse

$$E(z = 0, t) = E_0 \exp\left(-\frac{t^2}{\tau_0^2}\right) e^{+i\omega_0 t}$$

the temporal width after propagating through a distance z is given by $\tau(z) = \tau_0\sqrt{1+p^2}$; thus the temporal broadening is given by

$$\Delta\tau = \sqrt{\tau^2(z) - \tau_0^2} = |p|\,\tau_0$$

where

$$p = \frac{2}{\tau_0^2}\cdot\frac{\lambda_0}{2\pi c^2}\left[\lambda_0^2 \frac{d^2 n}{d\lambda_0^2}\right]\cdot z$$

Thus at $\lambda_0 \approx 1.55$ μm, for a $\tau_0 \approx 100$ ps pulse (propagating in pure silica), $\Delta\tau \approx 0.55$ ps/km.

- If an up-chirped pulse is passed through a medium characterized by positive dispersion, it will get compressed until it becomes unchirped and then it will broaden again with opposite chirp.
- When a pulse propagates through a dispersive medium, the frequency spectrum remains the same, no new frequencies are generated. The different frequencies superpose with different phases to distort the temporal shape of the pulse.

PROBLEMS

11.1 Using the empirical formula given by Eq. (11.14) calculate the phase and group velocities in silica at $\lambda_0 = 0.7\,\mu$m, $0.8\,\mu$m, $1.0\,\mu$m, $1.2\,\mu$m and $1.4\,\mu$m. Compare with the (more accurate) values given in Table 11.1.

[**Ans:** $n(\lambda_0) \approx 1.456, 1.454, 1.451, 1.449, 1.455$; $n_g(\lambda_0) \approx 1.4708, 1.4670, 1.4630, 1.4616, 1.4615$]

11.2 For pure silica, we may assume the empirical formula

$$n(\lambda_0) \approx 1.451 - 0.003\left(\lambda_0^2 - \frac{1}{\lambda_0^2}\right)$$

where λ_0 is measured in µm.

(a) Calculate the zero dispersion wavelength.

(b) Calculate the material dispersion at 800 nm in ps/km.nm.

[**Ans:** 1.32 µm; –101 ps/km.nm]

11.3 Let

$$n(\lambda_0) = n_0 + A\lambda_0$$

where λ_0 is the free space wavelength. Derive expressions for phase and group velocities.

[**Ans:** $v_g = c/n_0$]

11.4 Consider a LED source emitting light of wavelength 850 nm and having a spectral width of 50 nm. Using Table 11.1, calculate the broadening of a pulse propagating in pure silica.

[**Ans:** 4.2 ns/km]

11.5 In 1836, Cauchy gave the following approximate formula to describe the wavelength dependence of refractive index in glass in the visible region of the spectrum

$$n(\lambda) = A + \frac{B}{\lambda_0^2}$$

Now (see also Table 12.2)

$$\left.\begin{aligned} n(\lambda_1) &= 1.50883 \\ n(\lambda_2) &= 1.51690 \end{aligned}\right\} \text{ for borosilicate glass}$$

$$\left.\begin{aligned} n(\lambda_1) &= 1.45640 \\ n(\lambda_2) &= 1.46318 \end{aligned}\right\} \text{ for vitreous quartz}$$

where $\lambda_1 = 0.6563$ µm and $\lambda_2 = 0.4861$ µm.

(a) Calculate the values of A and B.

(b) Using the Cauchy formula calculate the refractive index at 0.5890 µm and 0.3988 µm and compare with the corresponding experimental values:

(i) (1.51124 and 1.52546) for borosilicate glass and

(ii) (1.45845 and 1.47030) for vitreous quartz.

[**Ans:** (a) For borosilicate glass $A = 1.499$, $B \approx 4.22 \times 10^{-15}$ m² giving $n = 1.51120$ at $\lambda = 0.5890$ µm, and $n = 1.52557$ at $\lambda = 0.3988$ µm; for vitreous quartz $A = 1.44817$, $B \approx 3.546 \times 10^{-15}$ m²]

11.6 The refractive index variation for pure silica in the wavelength region $0.5\,\mu\text{m} < \lambda_0 < 1.6\,\mu\text{m}$ is accurately described by the following empirical formula:

$$n(\lambda_0) = C_0 + C_1\lambda_0^2 + C_2\lambda_0^4 + \frac{C_3}{(\lambda_0^2 - l)} + \frac{C_4}{(\lambda_0^2 - l)^2} + \frac{C_5}{(\lambda_0^2 - l)^3}$$

where $C_0 = 1.4508554$, $C_1 = -0.0031268$, $C_2 = -0.0000381$, $C_3 = 0.0030270$, $C_4 = -0.0000779$, $C_5 = 0.0000018$, $l = 0.035$ and λ_0 is measured in µm. Develop a simple program to calculate and plot $n(\lambda_0)$ and $d^2n/d\lambda_0^2$ in the wavelength domain $0.5 < \lambda_0 < 1.6$ µm and compare with the results given in Table 11.1.

11.7 **(a)** For a Gaussian pulse given by

$$E = E_0\, e^{-\frac{t^2}{\tau_0^2}}\, e^{i\omega_0 t}$$

the spectral width is approximately given by

$$\Delta\omega \approx \frac{1}{\tau_0}$$

Assume $\lambda_0 = 8000$ Å.

Calculate $\dfrac{\Delta\omega}{\omega_0}$ for $\tau_0 = 1$ ns and for $\tau_0 = 1$ ps.

(b) For such a Gaussian pulse, the pulse broadening is given by $\Delta\tau = \dfrac{2z}{\tau_0}|\gamma|$ where $\gamma = \dfrac{d^2k}{d\omega^2}$. Using Table 11.1, calculate $\Delta\tau$ and interpret the result physically.

[**Ans:** (a) $\dfrac{\Delta\omega}{\omega_0} \approx 4 \times 10^{-7}$ and 4×10^{-4};
(b) $\gamma \approx 3.62 \times 10^{-26}$ m⁻¹ s²;
$\Delta\tau \approx 0.072$ and ≈ 72 ps/km for $\tau_0 = 1$ ns and 1 ps, respectively]

11.8 As a Gaussian pulse propagates the frequency chirp is given by

$$\Delta\omega = \frac{2p}{\tau_0^2(1+p^2)}\left(t - \frac{z}{v_g}\right)$$

where p is defined in Eq. (11.50). Assume a 100 ps ($= \tau_0$) pulse at $\lambda_0 = 1$ µm. Calculate the frequency chirp $\dfrac{\Delta\omega}{\omega_0}$ at $t - z/v_g = -100$ ps, –50 ps, +50 ps and +100 ps. Assume $z = 1$ km and other values from Table 11.1.

[**Ans:** $\dfrac{\Delta\omega}{\omega_0} \approx -4.5 \times 10^{-8}, -2.25 \times 10^{-8}, +2.25 \times 10^{-8}$ and $+4.5 \times 10^{-8}$ at $(t - z/v_g) = -100$ ps, –50 ps, +50 ps and +100 ps, respectively].

11.9 Repeat the previous problem for $\lambda_0 = 1.5\ \mu\text{m}$; the values of τ_0 and z remain the same. Show that the qualitative difference in the results obtained in the previous and in the present problem is the fact that at $\lambda = 1\ \mu\text{m}$ we have negative dispersion and the front end is red shifted ($\Delta\omega$ is negative) and the trailing end is blue shifted. The converse is true at $\lambda = 1.5\ \mu\text{m}$ where we have positive dispersion.

11.10 The frequency spectrum of $E(0, t)$ is given by the function $A(\omega)$. Show that the frequency spectrum of $E(z, t)$ is simply

$$A(\omega)e^{-ik(\omega)z}$$

implying that no new frequencies are generated—different frequencies superpose with different phases at different values of z.

11.11 The time evolution of a Gaussian pulse in a dispersive medium is given by

$$E(z, t) = \frac{E_0}{\sqrt{1+ip}}\, e^{i(\omega_0 t - k_0 z)} \exp\left[-\frac{\left(t - \dfrac{z}{v_g}\right)^2}{\tau_0^2(1+ip)}\right]$$

where $p \equiv \dfrac{2\gamma z}{\tau_0^2}$. Calculate explicitly the frequency spectrum of $E(0,t)$ and $E(z,t)$ and show that the results agree with that of Problem 11.10.

CHAPTER 12

Superposition of Waves

The experiments described appear to me, at any rate, eminently adapted to remove any doubt as to the identity of light, radiant heat, and electromagnetic wave motion. I believe that from now on we shall have greater confidence in making use of the advantages which this identity enables us to derive both in the study of optics and of electricity.

—Heinrich Hertz (1888)*

LEARNING OBJECTIVES

After reading this chapter, the reader should be able to:

LO 1: *understand superposition of waves.*

LO 2: *illustrate nodes and antinodes in stationary waves.*

LO 3: *describe stationary waves through Ives and Wiener's experiments.*

LO 4: *formulate the complex representation of superposition of waves.*

12.1 Introduction

LO1

In this chapter, we will discuss the applications of the principle of superposition of waves according to which the resultant displacement (at a particular point) produced by a number of waves is the vector sum of the displacements produced by each one of the disturbances. As a simple example, we consider a long stretched string *AB* (see Fig. 12.1). From the end *A*, a triangular pulse is generated which propagates to the right with a certain speed v. In the absence of any other disturbance, this pulse would have propagated in the $+x$-direction without any change in shape; we are, of course, neglecting any attenuation or distortion of the pulse. We next assume that from the end *B* an identical pulse is generated which starts moving to the left with the same speed v. (As has been shown in Sec. 9.6, the speed of the wave is determined by the ratio of the tension in the string to its mass per unit length.) At $t = 0$, the snapshot of the string is shown in Fig. 12.1(a). At a little later time each pulse moves close to the other as shown in Fig. 12.1(b), without any interference. Figure 12.1(c) represents a snapshot at an instant when the two pulses interfere; the dashed curves represent the profile of the string if each of the impulses was moving all by itself, whereas the solid curve shows the resultant displacement obtained

* The author found this quotation in the book by Smith and King (Ref. 12.1).

Above Image: View of a rainbow against a background of clouds. Photograph courtesy McGraw Hill Digital Access Library.

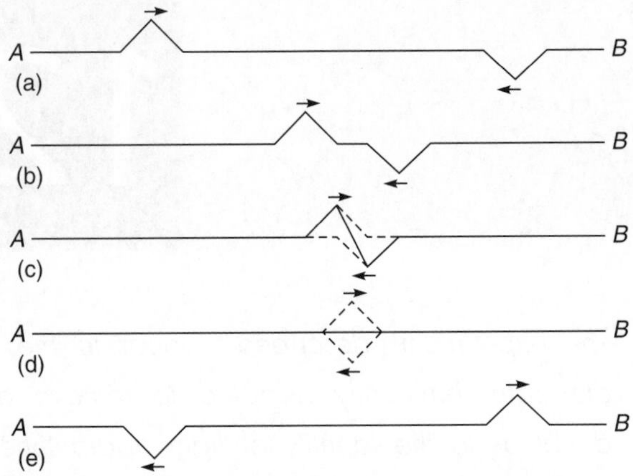

Figure 12.1
The propogation in opposite directions of two triangular pulses in a stretched string. The solid line gives the actual shape of the string; (a), (b), (c), (d) and (e) correspond to different instants of time.

by algebraic addition of each displacement. Shortly later [Fig. 12.1(d)] the two pulses exactly overlap each other and the resultant displacement is zero everywhere. Where has the energy gone? At a much later time, the impulses sort of cross each other [Fig. 12.1(e)] and move as if nothing had happened. This is a characteristic feature of superposition of waves.

The phenomenon of interference contains no more physics than embodied in the above example. In the following sections, we will consider some more examples.

12.2 Stationary Waves on a String

LO2

Consider a string which is fixed at the point A (see Fig. 12.2). A transverse sinusoidal wave is sent down the string along the $-x$ direction. The displacement at any point on the string due to this wave would be given by

$$y_i = a \sin\left[\frac{2\pi}{\lambda}(x + vt) + \phi\right] \quad (12.1)$$

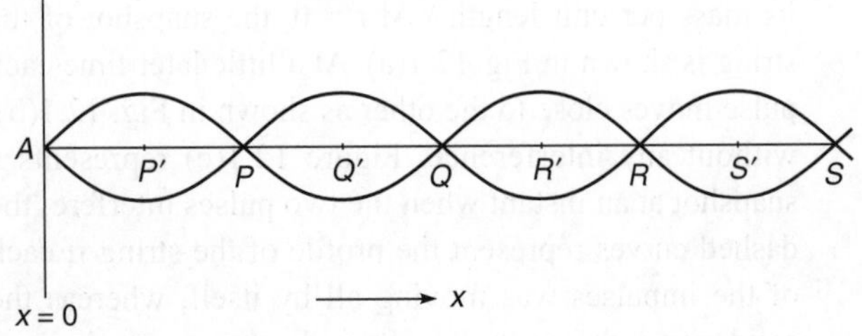

Figure 12.2
Reflection of a wave at $x = 0$.

where the subscript i refers to the fact that we are considering the incident wave. Without any loss of generality we can set $\phi = 0$; thus we may write

$$y_i = a \sin\left[\frac{2\pi}{\lambda}(x + vt)\right] = a \sin\left[2\pi\left(\frac{x}{\lambda} + \nu t\right)\right] \quad (12.2)$$

Thus, because of the incident wave, the displacement at the point A would have been

$$y_i\big|_{x=0} = a \sin(2\pi\nu t) \quad (12.3)$$

where $\nu = v/\lambda$ and we have assumed the point A to correspond to $x = 0$. Since the point A is fixed, there must be a reflected wave such that the displacement due to this reflected wave (at the point A) is equal and opposite to y_i:

$$y_r\big|_{x=0} = -a \sin(2\pi\nu t) \quad (12.4)$$

where the subscript r refers to the fact that we are considering the reflected wave. Since the reflected wave propagates in the $+x$-direction, we must have

$$y_r = +a \sin 2\pi\left(\frac{x}{\lambda} - \nu t\right) \quad (12.5)$$

The resultant displacement would be given by

$$y = y_i + y_r = a\left[\sin 2\pi\left(\frac{x}{\lambda} + \nu t\right) + \sin 2\pi\left(\frac{x}{\lambda} - \nu t\right)\right]$$

$$= 2a \sin\frac{2\pi}{\lambda}x \cos 2\pi\nu t \quad (12.6)$$

Thus, for values of x such that

$$\sin\frac{2\pi}{\lambda}x = 0 \quad (12.7)$$

the displacement y is zero *at all times*. Such points are known as **nodes**; the x-coordinates of the nodes are given by

$$x = 0, \frac{\lambda}{2}, \lambda, \frac{3\lambda}{2}, 2\lambda, \ldots \quad (12.8)$$

and are marked as points A, P, Q and R in Fig. 12.2. The nodes are separated by a distance $\lambda/2$ and at the midpoint between two consecutive nodes, i.e., at

$$x = \frac{\lambda}{4}, \frac{3\lambda}{4}, \frac{5\lambda}{4}, \ldots\ldots$$

the amplitude of the vibration is maximum. The displacements at these points (which are known as **antinodes**) are given by

$$y = \pm 2a \cos 2\pi\nu t \quad (12.9)$$

At the antinodes the kinetic energy density would be given by (see Sec. 6.2)

$$\text{Kinetic energy/unit length} = \frac{1}{2}\rho(2a)^2\omega^2\cos^2\omega t$$
$$= 2\rho a^2\omega^2\cos^2\omega t \qquad (12.10)$$

where $\omega = 2\pi\nu$ is the angular frequency and ρ is the mass per unit length of the string.

We can also carry out a similar experiment for electromagnetic waves; see Fig. 12.3. One may approximately assume plane waves to be incident on the reflector; the incident and reflected waves interfere and produce nodes and antinodes. The result of a typical experiment is shown in Fig. 12.4. One can see the periodic variation of intensity. Two consecutive maxima are separated by about 5.8 cm; thus $\lambda \approx 11.6$ cm. The corresponding frequency ($\approx 2.6 \times 10^9\ \text{s}^{-1}$) can easily be generated in the laboratory. If the frequency is changed, one can observe the change in the distance between the antinodes. One should notice that the minima do not really correspond to zero intensity and the intensities at the maxima are not constant. This is because of the fact that the incident wave is really not a plane wave and that the reflection is not really perfect. In fact, one can introduce a coefficient of reflection (r) which is defined as the ratio of the energy of the reflected beam to the energy of the incident beam. Thus, the ratio of the amplitudes would be $\sqrt{r}$ and if the incident wave is given by

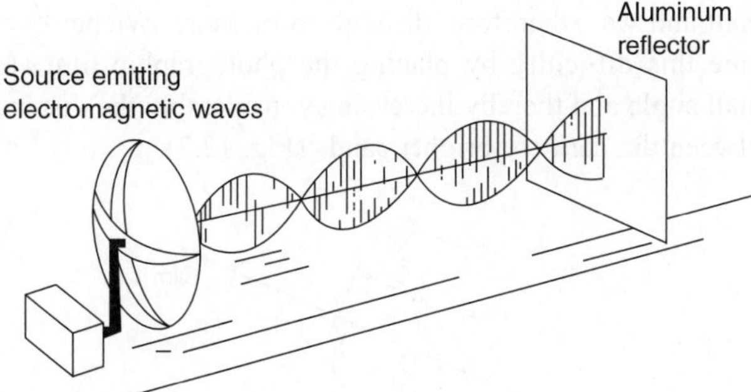

Figure 12.3
Hertz's arrangement for studying standing electromagnetic waves; diagram adapted from http://www.physics.usyd.edu.au/teach_res/hsp/u7/t7_hertz.pdf.

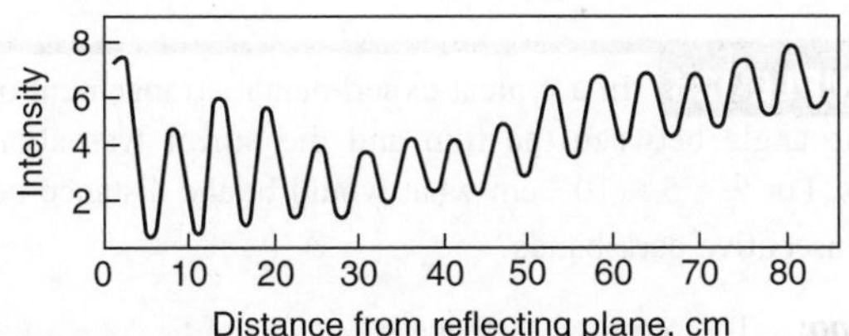

Figure 12.4
A typical variation of the intensity between the reflector and the transmitter [adapted from Ref. 12.2].

$$E_{\text{incident}} = a\sin\left[2\pi\left(\frac{x}{\lambda}+\nu t\right)\right] \qquad (12.11)$$

then the reflected wave would be given by

$$E_{\text{reflected}} = a\sqrt{r}\sin\left[2\pi\left(\frac{x}{\lambda}-\nu t\right)\right] \qquad (12.12)$$

where the plane $x = 0$ corresponds to the plane of the reflector. Here E represents the electric field associated with the electromagnetic wave. Thus, the resultant field would be given by

$$E_{\text{resultant}} = E_{\text{incident}} + E_{\text{reflected}}$$
$$= a\sin\left[2\pi\left(\frac{x}{\lambda}+\nu t\right)\right] + a\sqrt{r}\sin\left[2\pi\left(\frac{x}{\lambda}-\nu t\right)\right]$$
$$= a\sqrt{r}\left\{\sin\left[2\pi\left(\frac{x}{\lambda}+\nu t\right)\right] + \sin\left[2\pi\left(\frac{x}{\lambda}-\nu t\right)\right]\right\}$$
$$+a(1-\sqrt{r})\sin\left[2\pi\left(\frac{x}{\lambda}+\nu t\right)\right]$$
$$= 2a\sqrt{r}\sin\left(\frac{2\pi}{\lambda}x\right)\cos 2\pi\nu t$$
$$+a(1-\sqrt{r})\sin\left[2\pi\left(\frac{x}{\lambda}+\nu t\right)\right] \qquad (12.13)$$

The first term represents the stationary component of the wave and the second term (which is small if r is close to unity) represents the propagating part of the beam.

12.3 Stationary Waves on a String With Fixed Ends

In Sec. 12.2, while discussing the stationary waves on a string we had assumed only one end of the string ($x = 0$) to be fixed; and the resultant displacement was shown to be given by [see Eq. (12.6)]:

$$y = 2a\sin\left(\frac{2\pi}{\lambda}x\right)\cos(2\pi\nu t) \qquad (12.14)$$

If the other end of the string (say at $x = L$) is also fixed, then we must have

$$2a\sin\left(\frac{2\pi}{\lambda}L\right)\cos(2\pi\nu t) = 0 \qquad (12.15)$$

Equation (12.15) is to be valid at all times, therefore,

$$\sin\left(\frac{2\pi}{\lambda}L\right) = 0 = \sin n\pi \qquad (12.16)$$

or

$$\lambda = \lambda_n = \frac{2L}{n}, \quad n = 1, 2, 3, \ldots \qquad (12.17)$$

The corresponding frequencies are

$$\nu_n = \frac{v}{\lambda_n} = \frac{nv}{2L}, \quad n = 1, 2, 3, \ldots \qquad (12.18)$$

Thus, if a string of length L is clamped at both ends (as in a sonometer wire) then it can only vibrate with certain well-defined wavelengths. When $\lambda = 2L$ (i.e., $n = 1$) the string is said to vibrate in its fundamental mode [Fig. 12.5(a)]. Similarly, when $\lambda = 2L/2$ and $2L/3$ the string is said to vibrate in its first and second harmonic. In general, if the string is plucked and then made to vibrate then the displacement would be given by

$$y(x, t) = \sum_{n=1}^{\infty} a_n \sin\left(\frac{2\pi}{\lambda_n} x\right) \cos(2\pi\nu_n t + \phi_n) \qquad (12.19)$$

where the constants a_n and ϕ_n are determined by the values of $y(x, t = 0)$ and $\left.\frac{\partial y}{\partial t}\right|_{t=0}$; these are known as the **initial conditions**. A more detailed discussion on the vibration of stretched strings has been given in Sec. 7.2.

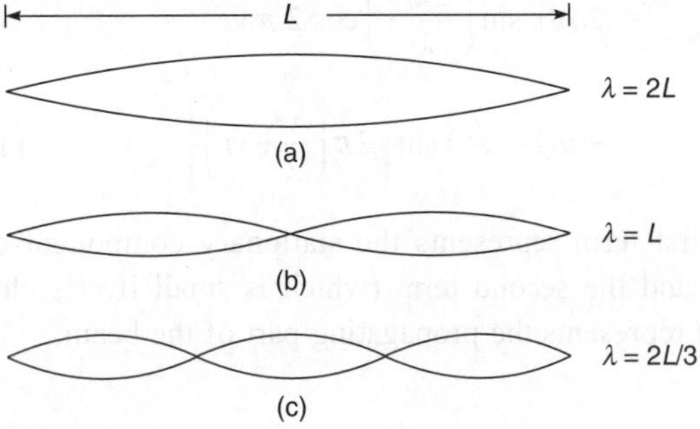

Figure 12.5
Standing waves on a stretched string clamped at both ends.

When a string is vibrating in a particular mode there is no net transfer of energy although each element of the string is associated with a certain energy density [see Eq. (12.10)]. The distances between two successive antinodes and successive nodes are $\lambda/2$.

12.4 Stationary Light Waves: Ives and Wiener's Experiments LO3

It is difficult to carry out experiments in which one obtains stationary light waves. This is because of the fact that light wavelengths are extremely small ($\approx 5 \times 10^{-5}$ cm). In the experimental arrangement of Ives, the emulsion side of a photographic plate was placed in contact with a film of mercury as shown in Fig. 12.6. A parallel beam of monochromatic light was allowed to fall normally on the glass plate. The beam was reflected on the mercury surface and the incident wave interfered with the reflected wave forming standing waves. A section of the photographic film was cut along a plane normal to the surface. The cut section was viewed under a microscope and bright and dark bands (separated by regular intervals) were observed. By measuring the distance between two consecutive dark bands (which is equal to $\lambda/2$) one can calculate the wavelength.

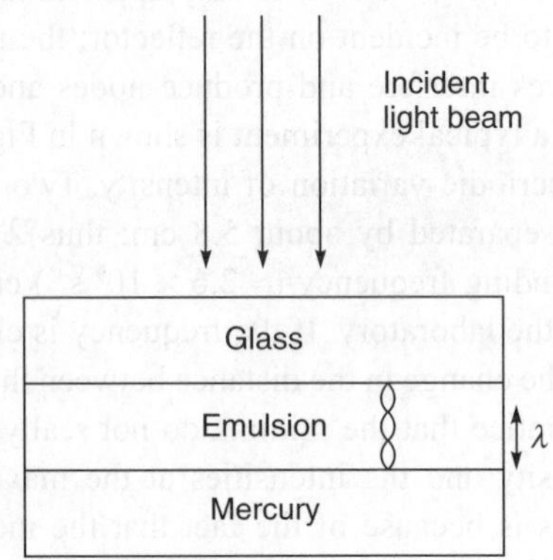

Figure 12.6
The experimental arrangement of Ives for studying stationary light waves.

Because of the small wavelength of light, the distance between two consecutive dark (or bright) bands was extremely small and was, therefore, difficult to measure. Wiener overcame this difficulty by placing the photographic film at a small angle and thereby increasing considerably the distance between the dark (or bright) bands (Fig. 12.7).

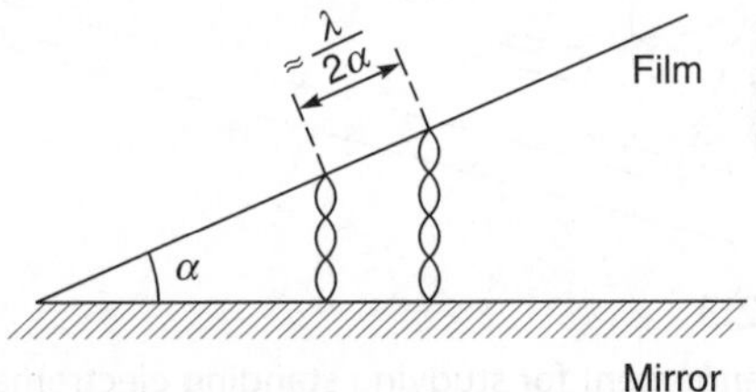

Figure 12.7
The experimental arrangement of Wiener for studying stationary light waves.

EXAMPLE 12.1 In a typical experimental arrangement of Wiener, the angle between the film and the mirror was about 10^{-3} radians. For $\lambda = 5 \times 10^{-5}$ cm what would be the distance between two consecutive dark bands?

Solution: The required distance is

$$\frac{\lambda}{2\alpha} = \frac{5 \times 10^{-5}}{2 \times 10^{-3}} \text{ cm} = 0.25 \text{ mm}$$

On the other hand, in the set up of Ives the distance would be 2.5×10^{-4} mm.

12.5 Superposition of Two Sinusoidal Waves

Let us consider the superposition of two sinusoidal waves (having the same frequency) at a particular point. Let

$$\left.\begin{aligned} x_1(t) &= a_1 \cos(\omega t + \theta_1) \\ \text{and} \quad x_2(t) &= a_2 \cos(\omega t + \theta_2) \end{aligned}\right\} \tag{12.20}$$

represent the displacements produced by each of the disturbances: we are assuming that the displacements are in the same direction*, however, they may have different amplitudes and different initial phases. In Sec. 16.5 now, according to the superposition principle the resultant displacement $x(t)$ would be given by

$$\begin{aligned} x(t) &= x_1(t) + x_2(t) \\ &= a_1 \cos(\omega t + \theta_1) + a_2 \cos(\omega t + \theta_2) \end{aligned} \tag{12.21}$$

which can be written in the form

$$x(t) = a \cos(\omega t + \theta) \tag{12.22}$$

where

$$a \cos\theta = a_1 \cos\theta_1 + a_2 \cos\theta_2 \tag{12.23}$$

and
$$a \sin\theta = a_1 \sin\theta_1 + a_2 \sin\theta_2 \tag{12.24}$$

Thus, the resultant disturbance is also simple harmonic in character having the same frequency but different amplitude and different initial phase. If we square and add Eqs. (12.23) and (12.24), we would obtain

$$a = [a_1^2 + a_2^2 + 2a_1a_2 \cos(\theta_1 - \theta_2)]^{1/2} \tag{12.25}$$

Further

$$\tan\theta = \frac{a_1 \sin\theta_1 + a_2 \sin\theta_2}{a_1 \cos\theta_1 + a_2 \cos\theta_2} \tag{12.26}$$

Though angle θ is not uniquely determined from Eq. (12.26); however, if we assume a to be always positive, then $\cos\theta$ and $\sin\theta$ can be determined from Eqs. (12.23) and (12.24) which will uniquely determine θ. From Eq. (12.25) we find that if

$$\theta_1 \sim \theta_2 = 0, 2\pi, 4\pi, \ldots \tag{12.27}$$

then
$$a = a_1 + a_2 \tag{12.28}$$

Thus, if the two displacements are in phase, then the resultant amplitude will be the sum of the two amplitudes; this is known as **constructive interference**. Similarly, if

$$\theta_1 \sim \theta_2 = \pi, 3\pi, 5\pi, \ldots \tag{12.29}$$

then
$$a = a_1 \sim a_2 \tag{12.30}$$

and the resultant amplitude is the difference of the two amplitudes. This is known as **destructive interference**. If we refer to Fig. 12.2, then we can see that constructive interference occurs at $x = \frac{\lambda}{4}, \frac{3\lambda}{4}, \frac{5\lambda}{4}, \ldots$ (i.e., at the points P', Q', R', ...) and destructive interference occurs at $x = 0, \lambda/2, \lambda, 3\lambda/2, \ldots$ (i.e., at points A, P, Q, R, ...). It may be mentioned that when constructive and destructive interferences occur, there is no violation of the principle of conservation of energy; the energy is just redistributed.

In general, if we have n displacements

$$\left.\begin{aligned} x_1 &= a_1 \cos(\omega t + \theta_1) \\ x_2 &= a_2 \cos(\omega t + \theta_2) \\ &\cdots\cdots\cdots \\ x_n &= a_n \cos(\omega t + \theta_n) \end{aligned}\right\} \tag{12.31}$$

then
$$x = x_1 + x_2 + \ldots + x_n = a \cos(\omega t + \theta) \tag{12.32}$$

where

$$a \cos\theta = a_1 \cos\theta_1 + \ldots + a_n \cos\theta_n \tag{12.33}$$

and
$$a \sin\theta = a_1 \sin\theta_1 + \ldots + a_n \sin\theta_n \tag{12.34}$$

12.6 The Graphical Method for Studying Superposition of Sinusoidal Waves

In this section, we will discuss the graphical method for adding displacements of the same frequency. This method is particularly useful when we have a large number of superposing waves as it indeed happens when we consider the phenomenon of diffraction.

Let us first try to obtain the resultant of the two displacements given by Eq. (12.20) using the graphical method. We draw a circle of radius a_1 and let the point P on the circle be such that OP makes an angle θ_1 with the x-axis** (see Fig. 12.8). We next draw a circle of radius a_2 and let the point Q on the circle be such that OQ makes an angle θ_2 with the x-axis. We use the law of parallelograms to find the resultant $\overrightarrow{OR}$ of the vectors $\overrightarrow{OP}$ and $\overrightarrow{OQ}$. The length of the vector $\overrightarrow{OR}$ will represent the amplitude of the resultant displacement

* In Sec. 16.5, we will consider the superposition of waves having nearly equal frequencies which leads to the phenomenon of beats. Indeed in Sec. 12.2, while discussing stationary waves on a string, we had, at a particular value of x, two sinusoidal waves of the same frequency (but having different initial phases) superposing on each other. However, in general, one could have superposition of displacements which are in different directions; for example, the superposition of two linearly polarized waves to produce a circularly polarized wave (see Sec. 21.4).

** Clearly, if we assume the vector $\overrightarrow{OP}$ to rotate (in the anticlockwise direction) with angular velocity ω then the x-coordinate of the vector $\overrightarrow{OP}$ will be $a_1 \cos(\omega t + \theta_1)$ where $t = 0$ corresponds to the instant when the rotating vector is at the point P.

and if θ is the angle that OR makes with the x-axis, then the initial phase of the resultant will be θ. This can be easily seen by noting that

$$\begin{aligned} OR\cos\theta &= OP\cos\theta_1 + PR\cos\theta_2 \\ &= a_1\cos\theta_1 + a_2\cos\theta_2 \end{aligned} \tag{12.35}$$

Similarly,

$$OR\sin\theta = a_1\sin\theta_1 + a_2\sin\theta_2 \tag{12.36}$$

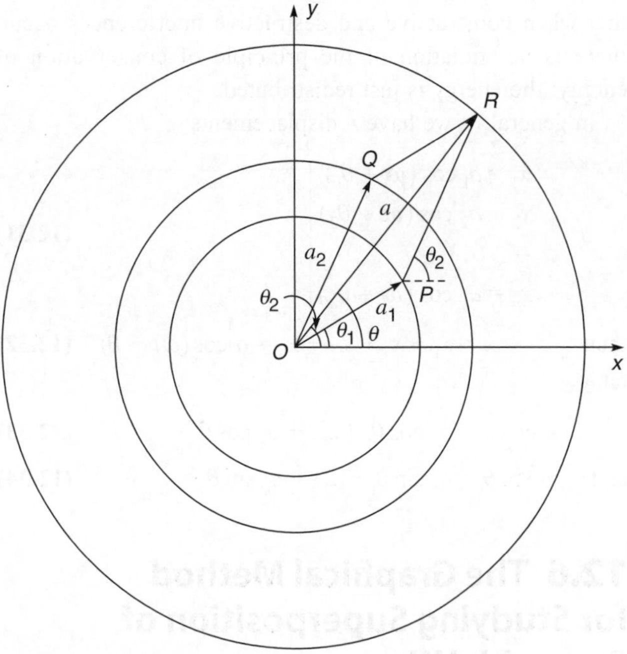

Figure 12.8
The graphical method for determining the resultant of two simple harmonic motions along the same direction and having the same frequency.

consistent with Eqs. (12.23) and (12.24). Further, as the vectors $\overrightarrow{OP}$ and $\overrightarrow{OQ}$ rotate on the circumference of the circles of radii a_1 and a_2, the vector $\overrightarrow{OR}$ rotates on the circumference of the circle of radius OR with the same frequency.

Thus, if we wish to find the resultant of the two displacements given by Eq. (12.20) then we must first draw a vector ($\overrightarrow{OP}$) of length a_1 making an angle θ_1 with the axis; from the tip of this vector we must draw another vector ($\overrightarrow{PR}$) of length a_2 making an angle θ_2 with the axis. The length of the vector $\overrightarrow{OR}$ will represent the resultant amplitude and the angle that it makes with the axis will represent the initial phase of the resultant displacement. It can be easily seen that if we have a third displacement

$$x_3 = a_3\cos(\omega t + \theta_3) \tag{12.37}$$

then from the point R we must draw a vector $\overrightarrow{RR'}$ of length a_3 which makes an angle θ_3 with the axis; the vector $\overrightarrow{OR'}$ will represent the resultant of x_1, x_2 and x_3.

As an illustration of the above procedure we consider the resultant of N simple harmonic motions all having the same amplitude and with their phases increasing in arithmetic progression. Thus,

$$\begin{aligned} x_1 &= a\cos\omega t \\ x_2 &= a\cos[\omega t + \theta_0] \\ &\dots\dots\dots\dots\dots\dots\dots\dots \\ x_N &= a\cos[\omega t + (N-1)\theta_0] \end{aligned} \tag{12.38}$$

In Fig. 12.9, the vectors $\overrightarrow{OP_1}$, $\overrightarrow{P_1P_2}$, $\overrightarrow{P_2P_3}$, … correspond to x_1, x_2, x_3, …, respectively. The resultant is denoted by the

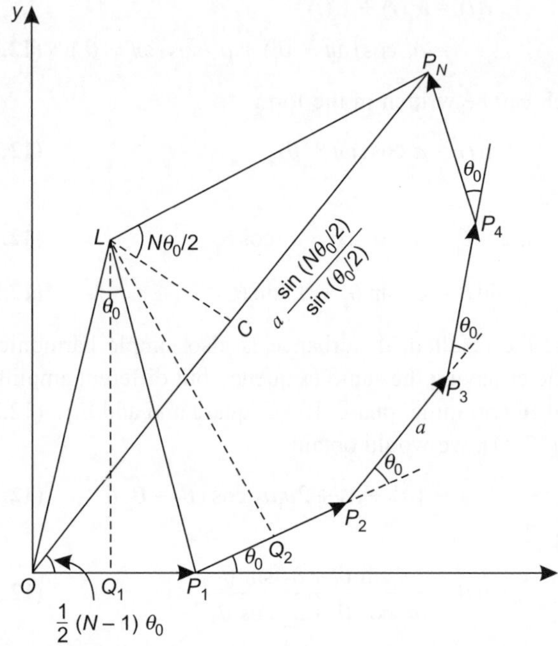

Figure 12.9
The graphical method for determining the resultant of N simple harmonic motions along the same direction and having the same frequency.

vector $\overrightarrow{OP_N}$. Let Q_1L and Q_2L be the perpendicular bisectors of OP_1 and P_1P_2. It is easy to prove that

$$\Delta LQ_1P_1 \equiv \Delta LQ_2P_1$$

Thus $LO = LP_1 = LP_2$. Therefore, the points $O, P_1, P_2, P_3, \dots, P_N$ will lie on the circumference of a circle whose center is L and radius is LO. Further, $\angle LP_1O = \dfrac{\pi - \theta_0}{2}$ and, therefore,

$\angle OLP_1 = \theta_0$. Thus,

$$LO = \frac{a/2}{\sin \theta_0/2}$$

and $$OP_N = 2OC = 2LO \sin \frac{N\theta_0}{2}$$

$$= a\frac{\sin \frac{N\theta_0}{2}}{\sin \frac{\theta_0}{2}} \tag{12.39}$$

Further, the phase of the resultant displacement would be

$$\angle P_N OX = \frac{1}{2}(N-1)\theta_0$$

Thus,

$$a \cos \omega t + a \cos (\omega t + \theta_0) + \ldots + a \cos [\omega t + (N-1)\theta_0]$$
$$= A \cos (\omega t + \theta) \tag{12.40}$$

where $$A = \frac{a \sin \frac{N\theta_0}{2}}{\sin \frac{\theta_0}{2}} \tag{12.41}$$

and $$\theta = \frac{1}{2}(N-1)\theta_0 \tag{12.42}$$

We will use this result in Chapter 17.

12.7 The Complex Representation

LO4

Often it is more convenient to use the complex representation in which the displacement

$$x_1 = a_1 \cos(\omega t + \theta_1) \tag{12.43}$$

is written as

$$x_1 = a_1 e^{i(\omega t+\theta_1)} \tag{12.44}$$

where it is implied that the actual displacement is the real part of x_1. Further, if

$$x_2 = a_2 e^{i(\omega t+\theta_2)}$$

then

$$x_1 + x_2 = (a_1 e^{i\theta_1} + a_2 e^{i\theta_2})e^{i\omega t} = ae^{i(\omega t + \theta)} \tag{12.45}$$

where

$$ae^{i\theta} = a_1 e^{i\theta_1} + a_2 e^{i\theta_2} \tag{12.46}$$

If we equate the real and imaginary parts of Eq. (12.46), we would obtain Eqs. (12.23) and (12.24).

An interesting illustration of the usefulness of this method is to consider the resultant of the N displacements described by Eq. (12.38). Thus, we write

$$x_1 = ae^{i\omega t},\ x_2 = ae^{i(\omega t + \theta_0)}, \ldots$$

Hence,

$$x = x_1 + x_2 + \ldots$$
$$= ae^{i\omega t}[1 + e^{i\theta_0} + e^{2i\theta_0} + \ldots + e^{i(N-1)\theta_0}]$$
$$= ae^{i\omega t}\frac{1-e^{Ni\theta_0}}{1-e^{i\theta_0}}$$
$$= ae^{i\omega t}\frac{e^{iN\theta_0/2}}{e^{i\theta_0/2}} \cdot \frac{e^{iN\theta_0/2} - e^{-iN\theta_0/2}}{e^{i\theta_0/2} - e^{-i\theta_0/2}}$$
$$= \frac{a \sin \frac{N\theta_0}{2}}{\sin \frac{\theta_0}{2}} \exp\left[i\left\{\omega t + (N-1)\frac{\theta_0}{2}\right\}\right] \tag{12.47}$$

which is consistent with Eq. (12.40). The complex representation is also very useful in considering the spreading of a wave packet (see Sec. 9.3).

It may be noted that whereas

$$\text{Re}(x_1) + \text{Re}(x_2) = \text{Re}(x_1 + x_2)$$

but $$(\text{Re}\,x_1)(\text{Re}\,x_2) \neq \text{Re}(x_1 x_2)$$

where Re (…) denotes the 'real part of' the quantity inside the brackets. Thus, one must be careful in calculating the intensity of a wave which is proportional to the square of the amplitude. While using the complex representation, one must calculate the amplitude first and then the intensity.

SUMMARY

- According to the principle of superposition of waves, the resultant displacement (at a particular point) produced by a number of waves is the vector sum of the displacements produced by each one of the disturbances.
- The stationary waves on a string and the formation of standing electromagnetic waves are formed by the superposition of waves traveling in opposite direction.
- If the two displacements (produced by two sinusoidal waves) are in phase, then the resultant amplitude will be the sum of the two amplitudes; this is known as constructive interference. On the other hand, if the two displacements are π out of phase, then the resultant amplitude will be the difference of the two amplitudes; this is known as destructive interference.
- The resultant disturbance of two sinusoidal waves is also simple harmonic in character having same frequency but different amplitude and different initial phase.

PROBLEMS

12.1 Standing waves are formed on a stretched string under tension of 1 Newton. The length of the string is 30 cm and it vibrates in 3 loops. If the mass per unit length of the wire is 10 mg/cm, calculate the frequency of the vibrations.

12.2 In Problem 12.1, if the string is made to vibrate in its fundamental mode, what will be the frequency of vibration?

12.3 In the experimental arrangement of Wiener, what should be the angle between the film and the mirror if the distance between two consecutive dark bands is 7×10^{-3} cm. Assume $\lambda = 6 \times 10^{-5}$ cm.

[**Ans:** ~1/4°]

12.4 Standing waves with five loops are produced on a stretched string under tension. The length of the string is 50 cm and the frequency of vibrations is 250 s^{-1}. Calculate the time variation of the displacement of the points which are at distances of 2 cm, 5 cm, 15 cm, 18 cm, 20 cm, 35 cm and 45 cm from one end of the string.

12.5 The displacements associated with two waves (propagating in the same direction) having same amplitude but slightly different frequencies can be written in the form

$$a \cos 2\pi\left(\nu t - \frac{x}{\lambda}\right)$$

and

$$a \cos 2\pi\left((\nu + \Delta\nu)t - \frac{x}{(\lambda - \Delta\lambda)}\right)$$

(Such displacements are indeed obtained when we have two tuning forks with slightly different frequencies.) Discuss the superposition of the displacements and show that at a particular value of x, the intensity will vary with time.

12.6 In Problem 12.5 assume $v = 330$ m/s, $\nu = 256\ \text{s}^{-1}$, $\Delta\nu = 2\ \text{s}^{-1}$ and $a = 0.1$ cm. Plot the time variation of the intensity at $x = 0$, $\dfrac{\lambda}{4}$ and $\dfrac{\lambda}{2}$.

12.7 Use the complex representation to study the time variation of the resultant displacement at $x = 0$ in Problems 12.5 and 12.6.

12.8 Discuss the superposition of two plane waves (of the same frequency and propagating in the same direction) as a function of the phase difference between them. (Such a situation indeed arises when a plane wave gets reflected at the upper and lower surfaces of a glass slab; see Sec. 14.2.)

12.9 In Example 9.3, we had discussed the propagation of a semi-circular pulse on a string. Consider two semi-circular pulses propagating in opposite directions. At $t = 0$, the displacement associated with the pulses propagating in the $+x$ and in the $-x$ directions are given by

$$[R^2 - x^2]^{1/2} \text{ and } -[R^2 - (x - 10R)^2]^{1/2}$$

respectively. Plot the resultant disturbance at $t = R/v$, $2.5R/v$, $5R/v$, $7.5R/v$ and $10R/v$; where v denotes the speed of propagation of the wave.

CHAPTER

13

Two Beam Interference by Division of Wavefront

The wave nature of light was demonstrated convincingly for the first time in 1801 by Thomas Young by a wonderfully simple experiment... He let a ray of sunlight into a dark room, placed a dark screen in front of it, pierced with two small pinholes, and beyond this, at some distance a white screen. He then saw two darkish lines at both sides of a bright line, which gave him sufficient encouragement to repeat the experiment, this time with spirit flame as light source, with a little salt in it, to produce the bright yellow sodium light. This time he saw a number of dark lines, regularly spaced; the first clear proof that light added to light can produce darkness. This phenomenon is called interference. Thomas Young had expected it because he believed in the wave theory of light.

—Dennis Gabor in his Nobel Lecture, December 11, 1971

Important Milestone

1801 Thomas Young, a medical doctor by profession, demonstrated interference of light waves by a wonderfully simple experiment. Helmoholtz described the mind of Thomas Young as *one of the most profound minds that the world has ever seen*. Andrew Robinson has written a book on Thomas Young; the title of the book is ***The Last Man Who Knew Everything***.

LEARNING OBJECTIVES

After reading this chapter, the reader should be able to:

LO 1: *explain the interference pattern produced on water surface.*

LO 2: *understand the coherence phenomenon.*

LO 3: *discuss interference patterns produced by light waves.*

LO 4: *understand Young's interference pattern and obtain expression for fringe width.*

LO 5: *discuss intensity distribution in the interference pattern.*

LO 6: *illustrate Fresnel's two-mirror arrangement and biprism to produce interference pattern.*

LO 7: *describe interference pattern when the slit is illuminated by white light.*

LO 8: *discuss displacement of fringes in the interference pattern when a thin sheet is introduced in one of the beams.*

LO 9: *illustrate Lloyd's mirror arrangement for producing interference patterns.*

LO 10: *understand the phase change that occurs when a light beam undergoes reflection.*

Above Image: View of a rainbow against a background of clouds. Photograph courtesy McGraw Hill Digital Access Library.

13.1 Introduction

In the previous chapter, we had considered the superposition of one-dimensional waves propagating on a string and had shown that there is a variation of energy density along the length of the string due to the interference of two waves (see Fig. 12.5). In general, whenever two waves superpose, one obtains an intensity distribution which is known as the interference pattern. In this chapter, we will consider the interference pattern produced by waves emanating from two point sources. It may be mentioned that with sound waves the interference pattern can be observed without much difficulty because the two interfering waves maintain a constant phase relationship; this is also the case for microwaves. However, for light waves, due to the very process of emission, one cannot observe interference between the waves from two independent sources, although the interference does take place (see Sec. 13.4); it is difficult to observe the interference pattern even with two laser beams unless they are phase locked. Thus, one tries to derive interfering waves from a single wave so that the phase relationship is maintained. The methods to achieve this can be classified under two broad categories. Under the first category, in a typical arrangement, a beam is allowed to fall on two closely spaced holes and the two beams emanating from the holes interfere. This method is known as **division of wavefront** and will be discussed in detail in this chapter. In the other method, known as **division of amplitude**, a beam is divided at two or more reflecting surfaces and the reflected beams interfere. This will be discussed in the next chapter. We must, however, emphasize that the present and the following chapters are based on one underlying principle, namely the superposition principle.

It is also possible to observe interference using multiple beams; this is known as **multiple beam interferometry** and will be discussed in Chapter 15. It will be shown that multiple beam interferometry offers some unique advantages over two beam interferometry.

13.2 Interference Pattern Produced on the Surface of Water

LO1

We consider surface waves emanating from two point sources in a water tank. We may have, for example, two sharp needles vibrating up and down at the points S_1 and S_2 (see Fig. 13.1). Although water waves are not strictly transverse, we will, for the sake of simplicity, assume water waves to produce displacements which are transverse to the direction of propagation.

If there was only one needle (say at S_1) vibrating with a certain frequency ν then circular ripples would have spread out from the point S_1. The wavelength would have been v/ν and the crests and troughs would have moved outwards. Similarly for the vibrating needle at S_2. However, if both needles are vibrating, then waves emanating from S_1 will interfere with the waves emanating from S_2. We assume that the needle at S_2 vibrates in phase with the needle at S_1, i.e., S_1 and S_2 go up simultaneously, they also reach the lowest position at the same time. Thus, if at a certain instant, the disturbance emanating from the source S_1 produced a crest at a distance ρ from S_1 then the disturbance from S_2 would also produce a crest at a distance ρ from S_2, etc. This is explicitly shown in Fig. 13.1, where the solid curves represent (at a particular instant) the positions of the crests due to disturbances emanating from S_1 and S_2. Similarly, the dashed curves represent (at the same instant) the positions of the troughs. Notice that at all points on the perpendicular bisector OZ the disturbances reaching from S_1 and from S_2 will always be in phase. Consequently, at an arbitrary point A (on the perpendicular bisector) we may write the resultant disturbance as

$$y = y_1 + y_2$$
$$= 2a \cos \omega t \tag{13.1}$$

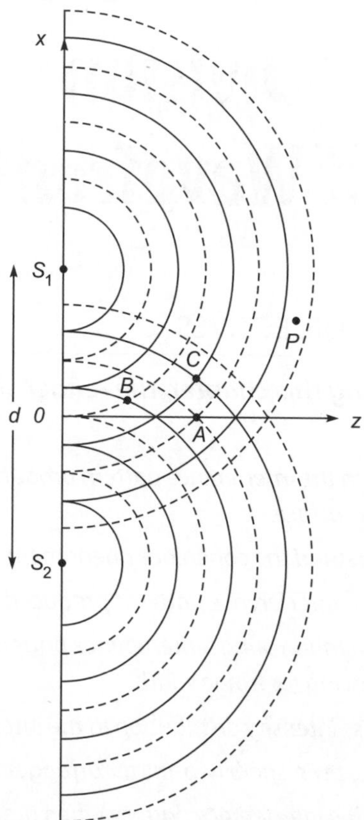

Figure 13.1
Waves emanating from two point sources S_1 and S_2 vibrating in phase. The solid and the dashed curves represent the positions of the crests and troughs, respectively.

where y_1 (= $a \cos \omega t$) and y_2 (= $a \cos \omega t$) represent the displacements at the point A due to S_1 and S_2, respectively. We see that the amplitude at A is twice the amplitude produced by each one of the source. It should be noted that at $t = \frac{T}{4}\left(=\frac{1}{4\nu}=\frac{\pi}{2\omega}\right)$ the displacements produced at the point A by each of the source would be zero and the resultant will also be zero. This is also obvious from Eq. (13.1).

Next, let us consider a point B such that

$$S_2B - S_1B = \lambda/2 \tag{13.2}$$

At such a point the disturbance reaching from the source S_1 will always be out of phase with the disturbance reaching from S_2. This follows from the fact that the disturbance reaching the point B from the source S_2 must have started half a period (= $T/2$) earlier than the disturbance reaching B from S_1. Consequently, if the displacement at B due to S_1 is given by

$$y_1 = a \cos \omega t$$

then the displacement at B due to S_2 would be given by

$$y_2 = a \cos(\omega t - \pi) = -a \cos \omega t$$

and the resultant $y = y_1 + y_2$ is zero at all times. Such a point corresponds to destructive interference and is known as a node and corresponds to minimum intensity. It may be pointed out that the amplitudes of the two vibrations reaching the point B will not really be equal as it is at different distances from S_1 and S_2. However, if the distances involved are large (in comparison to the wavelength), the two amplitudes will be very nearly equal and the resultant intensity will be very nearly zero.

In a similar manner, we may consider a point C such that

$$S_2C - S_1C = \lambda$$

where the phase of the vibrations (reaching from S_1 and S_2) are exactly the same as at the point A. Consequently, we will again have constructive interference. In general, if a point P is such that

$$S_2P \sim S_1P = n\lambda \text{ (maxima)} \tag{13.3}$$

$n = 0, 1, 2, \ldots$, then the disturbances reaching the point P from the two sources will be in phase, the interference will be constructive and the intensity will be maximum. On the other hand, if the point P is such that

$$S_2P \sim S_1P = \left(n+\frac{1}{2}\right)\lambda \text{ (minima)} \tag{13.4}$$

then the disturbances reaching the point P from the two sources will be out of phase, the interference will be destructive and the intensity will be minimum. The actual interference pattern produced from two point sources vibrating in phase in a ripple tank is shown in Fig. 13.2.

EXAMPLE 13.1 The intensity at the point which neither satisfies Eq. (13.3) nor Eq. (13.4) will neither be a maximum nor zero. Consider a point P such that $S_2P - S_1P = \lambda/3$. Find the ratio of the intensity at the point P to that at a maximum.

Solution: If the disturbance reaching the point P from S_1 is given by

$$y_1 = a \cos \omega t$$

then the disturbance from S_2 would be given by

$$y_2 = a \cos\left(\omega t - \frac{2\pi}{3}\right)$$

because a path difference of $\lambda/3$ corresponds to a phase difference of $\frac{2\pi}{3}$. Thus the resultant displacement would be

$$\begin{aligned} y &= y_1 + y_2 \\ &= a\left[\cos \omega t + \cos\left(\omega t - \frac{2\pi}{3}\right)\right] \\ &= 2a \cos\left(\omega t - \frac{\pi}{3}\right)\cos\frac{\pi}{3} \\ &= a \cos\left(\omega t - \frac{\pi}{3}\right) \end{aligned}$$

The intensity is therefore 1/4th of the intensity at the maxima. In a similar manner, one can calculate the intensity at any other point.

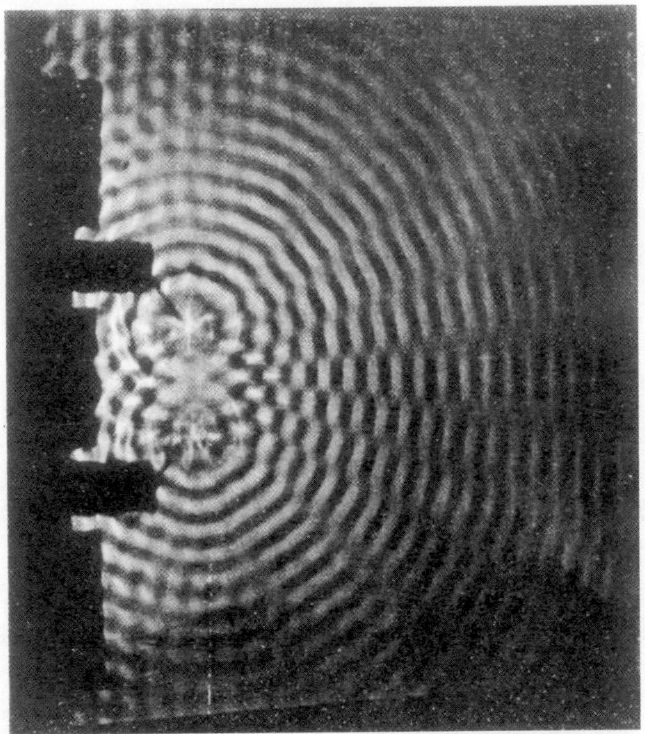

Figure 13.2

The actual interference pattern produced from two point sources vibrating in phase in a ripple tank (After Ref. 13.9, used with permission).

EXAMPLE 13.2 The locus of points which correspond to minima are known as nodal lines. Show that the equation of a nodal line is a hyperbola. Also obtain the locus of points which correspond to maxima.

Solution: For the sake of generality, we find the locus of the point P which satisfies the following equation:

$$S_2P - S_1P = \Delta \tag{13.5}$$

Thus, if $\Delta = n\lambda$, we have a maximum and if $\Delta = \left(n + \frac{1}{2}\right)\lambda$ we have a minimum. We choose the midpoint of S_1S_2 as the origin, with the x-axis along S_1S_2 and the z-axis perpendicular to it (see Figs. 13.1 and 13.3). We will find the locus of the point P on the x-z plane. If the distance between S_1 and S_2 is d, then the coordinates of the points S_1 and S_2 are $\left(+\frac{d}{2}, 0\right)$ and $\left(-\frac{d}{2}, 0\right)$, respectively. Let the coordinates of the point P [see Fig. 13.3] be (x, z). Then,

$$S_1P = \left[\left(x - \frac{d}{2}\right)^2 + z^2\right]^{1/2}$$

and

$$S_2P = \left[\left(x + \frac{d}{2}\right)^2 + z^2\right]^{1/2}$$

Therefore,

$$S_2P - S_1P = \left[\left(x + \frac{d}{2}\right)^2 + z^2\right]^{1/2} - \left[\left(x - \frac{d}{2}\right)^2 + z^2\right]^{1/2} = \Delta$$

or

$$\left(x + \frac{d}{2}\right)^2 + z^2 = \left(x - \frac{d}{2}\right)^2 + z^2 + \Delta^2 + 2\Delta\left[\left(x - \frac{d}{2}\right)^2 + z^2\right]^{1/2}$$

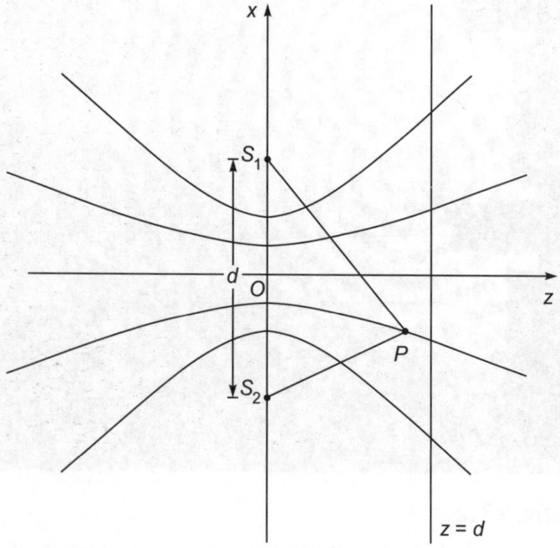

Figure 13.3
The nodal curves.

or

$$2xd - \Delta^2 = 2\Delta\left[\left(x - \frac{d}{2}\right)^2 + z^2\right]^{1/2}$$

On squaring, and simplifying we obtain

$$\frac{x^2}{\frac{1}{4}\Delta^2} - \frac{z^2}{\frac{1}{4}(d^2 - \Delta^2)} = 1 \tag{13.6}$$

which is the equation of a hyperbola. When $\Delta = \left(n + \frac{1}{2}\right)\lambda$ the curve corresponds to minima and when $\Delta = n\lambda$ the curve corresponds to maxima. For large value of x and z the curves asymptotically tend to the straight lines

$$z = \pm\left(\frac{d^2 - \Delta^2}{\Delta^2}\right)^{1/2} x \tag{13.7}$$

It may be pointed out that $S_2P \sim S_1P$ equals d only on the x-axis and that there is no point P for which $S_2P \sim S_1P > d$. Now, it appears from Eq. (13.6) that when $\Delta > d$, the resulting equation is an ellipse which we know is impossible. The fallacy is a result of the fact that because of a few squaring operations, Eq. (13.6) also represents the locus of all those points for which $S_2P + S_1P = \Delta$ and obviously in this case Δ can exceed d.

EXAMPLE 13.3 Consider a line parallel to the x-axis at a distance D from the origin (see Fig. 13.3). Show that for path differences small compared to d, the points on the line where minimum intensity occurs are equally spaced.

Solution: The equation of the line would be

$$z = D \tag{13.8}$$

Further at large distances from the origin the equation of the nodal lines would be

$$z = \pm\left(\frac{d^2 - \Delta_n^2}{\Delta_n^2}\right)^{1/2} x \tag{13.9}$$

where $\Delta_n = \left(n + \frac{1}{2}\right)\lambda$; $n = 0, 1, 2, \ldots$ Clearly the points at which minima will occur (on the line $z = D$) would be given by

$$x_n = \pm\left(\frac{\Delta_n^2}{d^2 - \Delta_n^2}\right)^{1/2} D$$

$$= \pm\frac{\Delta_n}{d}\left(1 - \frac{\Delta_n^2}{d^2}\right)^{-1/2} D$$

$$\approx \pm\left(n + \frac{1}{2}\right)\frac{\lambda D}{d} \tag{13.10}$$

where we have assumed $\Delta_n \ll d$. Thus, the points corresponding to minima will be (approximately) equally spaced with a spacing of $\lambda D/d$.

EXAMPLE 13.4 Till now we have assumed the needles at S_1 and S_2 (see Fig. 13.1) to vibrate in phase. Assume now that the needles vibrate with a phase difference of π and obtain the nodal lines.

Generalize the result for an arbitrary phase difference between the vibrations of the two needles.

Solution: The two needles S_1 and S_2 vibrate out of phase. Thus if, at any instant, the needle at S_1 produces a crest at a distance R from it then the needle at S_2 would produce a trough at a distance R from S_2. Therefore, at all points on the perpendicular bisector OZ (see Fig. 13.4) the two vibrations will always be out of phase and we will have minimum. On the other hand, at the point B which satisfies the equation

$$S_2B - S_1B = \lambda/2$$

the two vibrations will be in phase and we will have maximum. Thus, because of the initial phase difference of π, the conditions for maxima and minima are reversed, i.e., when

$$S_2P \sim S_1P = \left(n + \frac{1}{2}\right)\lambda \text{ (maxima)}$$

the interference will be constructive and we will have maxima, and when

$$S_2P \sim S_1P = n\lambda \text{ (minima)}$$

the interference will be destructive and we will have minima. Notice that one again obtains a stationary interference pattern with nodal lines as hyperbolae.

The above analysis can easily be generalized for arbitrary phase difference between the two needles. Assume, for example, that there is a phase difference of $\pi/3$, i.e., if there is a crest at a distance R from S_1 then there is a crest at a distance $R - \lambda/6$ from S_2. Consequently, the condition

$$S_1P - S_2P = n\lambda + \frac{\lambda}{6};\ n = 0, \pm 1, \pm 2, \ldots$$

will correspond to maxima.

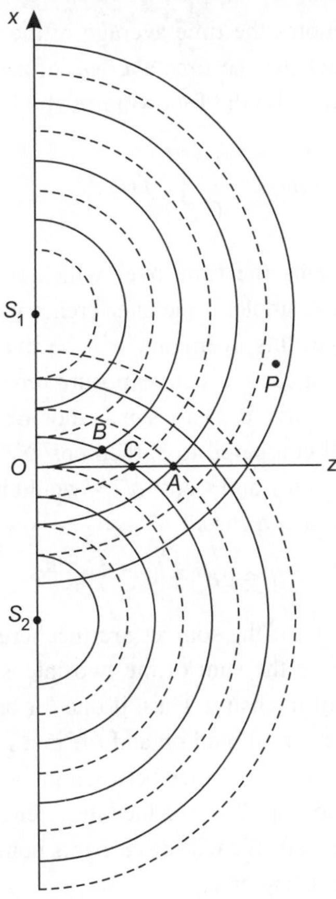

Figure 13.4
Waves emanating from two point sources S_1 and S_2 vibrating out of phase.

13.3 Coherence

LO2

From the above examples, we find that whenever the two needles vibrate with a constant phase difference, a stationary interference pattern is produced. The positions of the maxima and minima will, however, depend on the phase difference in the vibration of the two needles. Two sources which vibrate with a fixed phase difference between them are said to be coherent.

We next assume that the two needles are sometimes vibrating in phase, sometimes vibrating out of phase, sometimes vibrating with a phase difference of $\pi/3$, etc., then the interference pattern will keep on changing. If the phase difference changes with such great rapidity that a stationary interference cannot be observed then the sources are said to be *incoherent*.

Let the displacement produced by the sources at S_1 and S_2 be given by

$$\left.\begin{aligned} y_1 &= a\cos\omega t \\ y_2 &= a\cos(\omega t + \phi) \end{aligned}\right\} \quad (13.11)$$

then the resultant displacement would be

$$y = y_1 + y_2 = 2a\cos\phi/2\cos(\omega t + \phi/2) \quad (13.12)$$

The intensity (I) which is proportional to the square of the amplitude can be written in the form

$$I = 4I_0\cos^2\phi/2 \quad (13.13)$$

where I_0 is the intensity produced by each one of the source individually. Clearly if $\phi = \pm\pi, \pm 3\pi, \ldots$, the resultant intensity will be zero and we will have minima. On the other hand, when $\phi = 0, \pm 2\pi, \pm 4\pi, \ldots$, the intensity will be maximum ($= 4I_0$). However, if the phase difference between the sources S_1 and S_2 (i.e., ϕ) is changing with time, the observed intensity will be given by

$$I = 4I_0\left\langle\cos^2\frac{\phi}{2}\right\rangle \quad (13.14)$$

where $\langle ... \rangle$ denotes the time average of the quantity inside the angular brackets; the time average of a time dependent function is defined by the following relation:

$$\langle f(t) \rangle = \frac{1}{\tau} \int_{-\tau/2}^{+\tau/2} f(t)\, dt \qquad \textbf{(13.15)}$$

where τ represents the time over which the averaging is carried out. For example, if the interference pattern is viewed by a normal eye, this averaging will be over about 1/10th of a second; for a camera with exposure time 0.001 sec, τ = 0.001 sec. etc. Clearly, if ϕ varies in a random manner in times which are small compared to τ, then $\cos^2 \phi/2$ will randomly vary between 0 and 1 and $< \cos^2 \phi/2 >$ would be 1/2 [see also Sec. 13.6]. For such a case,

$$I = 2I_0 \qquad \textbf{(13.16)}$$

which implies that if the sources are incoherent then the resultant intensity is the sum of the two intensities and there is no variation of intensity! Thus, if one (or both) of the two vibrating sources are turned on and off in a random manner (such that the phase difference between the vibrations of the two sources varies rapidly) then the interference phenomenon will not be observed. We will discuss this point again in Sec. 13.6 and also in Chapter 16.

13.4 Interference of Light Waves

LO3

Till now we have considered interference of waves produced on the surface of water. We will now discuss the interference pattern produced by light waves; however, for light waves it is difficult to observe a stationary interference pattern. For example, if we use two conventional light sources (like two sodium lamps) illuminating two pinholes (see Fig. 13.5), we will not observe any interference pattern on the screen. This can be understood from the following reasoning: In a conventional light source, light comes from a large number of independent atoms; each atom emitting light for about 10^{-10} sec, i.e., light emitted by an atom is essentially a pulse lasting for only 10^{-10} seconds.* Even if the atoms were emitting under similar conditions, waves from different atoms would differ in their initial phases.

Consequently, light coming out from the holes S_1 and S_2 will have a fixed phase relationship for a period of about 10^{-10} seconds, hence the interference pattern will keep on changing every billionth of a second. Eye can notice intensity changes which last at least for a tenth of a second and hence we will observe a uniform intensity over the screen. However, if we have a camera whose time of shutter opening can be made less than 10^{-10} seconds then the film will record an interference pattern. This interference pattern will be a set of dark and bright bands only if the light waves have the same state of polarization. This can, however, be easily done by putting two polaroids in front of S_1 and S_2. We should mention here that by using two independent laser beams it has been possible to record the interference pattern (see Chapter 16). We summarise the above results by noting that light beams from two independent sources do not have any fixed phase relationship, as such they do not produce any stationary interference pattern. Such sources are termed as incoherent sources.

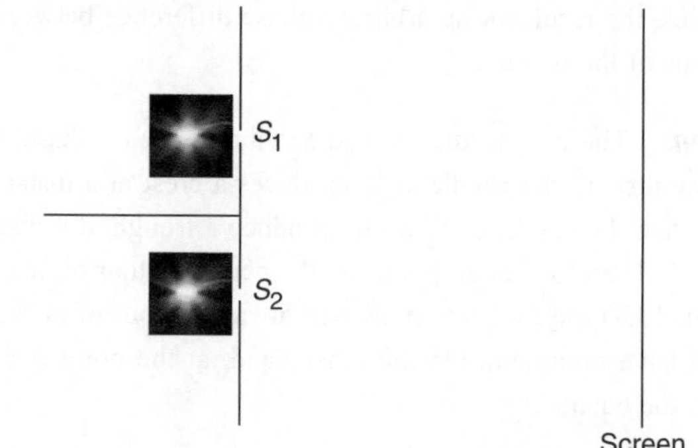

Figure 13.5
If two sodium lamps illuminate two pinholes S_1 and S_2, no interference pattern will be observed on the screen.

Thomas Young in 1801 devised an ingenious but simple method to lock the phase relationship between the two sources. The trick lies in the division of a single wavefront into two; these two split wavefronts act as if they emanated from two sources having a fixed phase relationship and, therefore, when these two waves were allowed to interfere, a stationary interference pattern was obtained. In the actual experiment, a light source illuminates the pinhole S (see Fig. 13.6). Light diverging from this pinhole fell on a barrier which contained two pinholes S_1 and S_2 which were very close to one another and were located equidistant from S. Spherical waves emanating from S_1 and S_2 (see Fig. 13.7) were coherent and on the screen beautiful interference fringes were obtained. In order to show that this was indeed an interference effect, Young showed that the fringes on the screen disappear when S_1 (or S_2) is covered up. Young explained the interference pattern by considering the principle of superposition, and by measuring the distance between the fringes he

* Since the optical frequencies are of the order of 10^{15} s^{-1}, such a short pulse consists of about a million oscillations; thus it is almost monochromatic (see Chapter 16).

calculated the wavelength. Figure 13.7 shows the section of the wavefront on the plane containing S, S_1 and S_2 (which is the x–z plane).

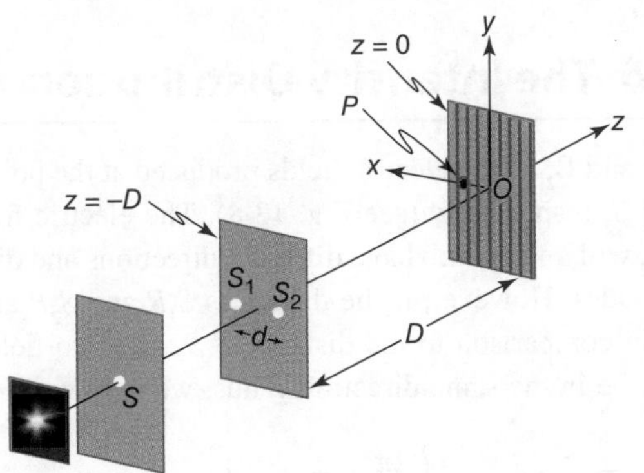

Figure 13.6
Young's arrangement to produce interference pattern.

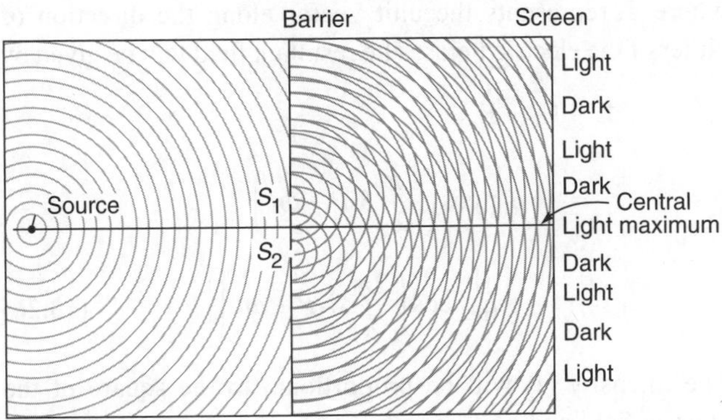

Figure 13.7
Sections of the spherical wavefronts emanating from S, S_1 and S_2 (Adapted from Ref. 13.9; used with permission).

13.5 The Interference Pattern 

In this section, we will first obtain an expression for the fringe width and then we will show that the fringes are strictly hyperbolic.

Let S_1 and S_2 represent the two pinholes of the Young's double hole arrangement. We would determine the positions of maxima and minima on the line LL' which is parallel to the x-axis and lies in the plane containing S_1 and S_2 (see Fig. 13.8). We will show that the interference pattern (around the point O) consists approximately of a series of dark and bright lines perpendicular to the plane of Fig. 13.8; O being the foot of the perpendicular from the point S on the screen.

For an arbitrary point P (on the line LL') to correspond to a maximum we must have

$$S_2P - S_1P = n\lambda;\ n = 0, 1, 2, 3, \ldots \quad \textbf{(13.17)}$$

Now,

$$(S_2P)^2 - (S_1P)^2 = \left[D^2 + \left(x_n + \frac{d}{2}\right)^2\right] - \left[D^2 + \left(x_n - \frac{d}{2}\right)^2\right]$$

$$= 2x_n d \quad \textbf{(13.18)}$$

where $S_1S_2 = d$ and $OP = x_n$. Thus,

$$S_2P - S_1P = \frac{2x_n d}{S_2P + S_1P} \approx \frac{x_n d}{D} \quad \textbf{(13.19)}$$

where in the last step we have replaced $S_2P + S_1P$ by $2D$ which will be valid when $D >>> d, x_n$. For example, for $d = 0.02$ cm, $D = 50$ cm, and $OP = 0.5$ cm (which corresponds to typical values in a light interference experiment) we will have

$$S_2P + S_1P = \sqrt{(50)^2 + (0.51)^2} + \sqrt{(50)^2 + (0.49)^2}$$
$$= 100.005 \text{ cm}$$

Thus, if we replace $S_2P + S_1P$ by $2D$, the error involved is about 0.005%. Using Eqs. (13.17) and (13.19) we obtain

$$x_n = \frac{n\lambda D}{d} \quad \textbf{(13.20)}$$

Thus, the bright (and dark) fringes are equally spaced and the distance between two consecutive bright (or dark) fringes is given by

$$\beta = x_{n+1} - x_n = \frac{\lambda D}{d} \quad \textbf{(13.21)}$$

which is the expression for the fringe width.

We will next determine the shape of the interference pattern on the screen LL' and show that the fringes are a set of hyperbolae. We assume the origin to be at the point O and the z-axis to be perpendicular to the plane of the screen LL' as shown in Fig. 13.8. The screen LL' corresponds to the plane

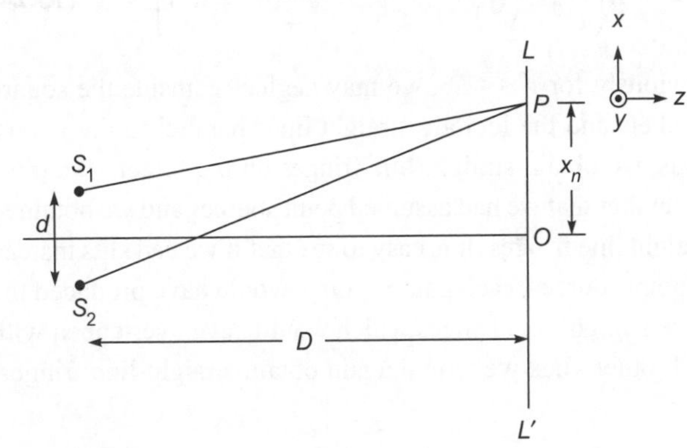

Figure 13.8
Arrangement for producing Young's interference pattern.

$z = 0$; thus the coordinates of an arbitrary point P on the screen will be $(x, y, 0)$. The coordinates of the point S_1 and S_2 would be $\left(+\frac{d}{2}, 0, -D\right)$ and $\left(-\frac{d}{2}, 0, -D\right)$, respectively. Thus,

$$S_2P - S_1P = \left[\left(x+\frac{d}{2}\right)^2 + y^2 + D^2\right]^{1/2} - \left[\left(x-\frac{d}{2}\right)^2 + y^2 + D^2\right]^{1/2}$$

$$= \Delta \text{ (say)}$$

or

$$\left(x+\frac{d}{2}\right)^2 + y^2 + D^2 = \left\{\Delta + \left[\left(x-\frac{d}{2}\right)^2 + y^2 + D^2\right]^{1/2}\right\}^2$$

Simple manipulations will give us

$$(d^2 - \Delta^2)x^2 - \Delta^2 y^2 = \Delta^2\left[D^2 + \frac{1}{4}(d^2 - \Delta^2)\right]$$

For $\Delta = 0$ (zero path difference) we must have $x = 0$ which implies that the central (bright) fringe is along the y-axis; this is rigorously true. In general, the above equation can always be written in the form

$$\frac{x^2}{a^2} - \frac{y^2}{b^2} = 1 \qquad \textbf{(13.22)}$$

where

$$a^2 = \frac{\Delta^2}{(d^2 - \Delta^2)}\left[D^2 + \frac{1}{4}(d^2 - \Delta^2)\right]$$

and $$b^2 = D^2 + \frac{1}{4}(d^2 - \Delta^2) \qquad \textbf{(13.23)}$$

Equation (13.22) represents a hyperbola; see Sec. 13.6(c) and Fig. 13.10. On rearranging, we get

$$x = \pm\left(\frac{\Delta^2}{d^2 - \Delta^2}\right)^{1/2}\left[y^2 + D^2 + \frac{1}{4}(d^2 - \Delta^2)\right]^{1/2} \qquad \textbf{(13.24)}$$

Obviously for $y^2 << D^2$, we may neglect y^2 inside the square brackets and the loci are straight lines parallel to the y-axis. Thus, we obtain straight line fringes on the screen. We must remember that we had assumed point sources and we obtained straight line fringes. It is easy to see that if we had slits instead of point sources, each pair of points would have produced the same straight line fringes which would have overlapped with each other–thus we would again obtain straight line fringes. The fringes so produced are said to be non-localized; they can be photographed by just placing a film on the screen; they can also be seen through an eyepiece.

13.6 The Intensity Distribution LO5

Let $\mathbf{E}_1$ and $\mathbf{E}_2$ be the electric fields produced at the point P by S_1 and S_2 respectively (see Fig. 13.8). The electric fields $\mathbf{E}_1$ and $\mathbf{E}_2$ will, in general, have different directions and different magnitudes. However, if the distances S_1P and S_2P are very large in comparison to the distance S_1S_2, the two fields will almost be in the same direction. Thus, we may write

$$\left.\begin{aligned}\mathbf{E}_1 &= \hat{\mathbf{i}}E_{01}\cos\left(\frac{2\pi}{\lambda}S_1P - \omega t\right)\\ \text{and}\quad \mathbf{E}_2 &= \hat{\mathbf{i}}E_{02}\cos\left(\frac{2\pi}{\lambda}S_2P - \omega t\right)\end{aligned}\right\} \qquad \textbf{(13.25)}$$

where $\hat{\mathbf{i}}$ represents the unit vector along the direction of either of the electric fields. The resultant field will be given by

$$\mathbf{E} = \mathbf{E}_1 + \mathbf{E}_2$$

$$= \hat{\mathbf{i}}\left[E_{01}\cos\left(\frac{2\pi}{\lambda}S_1P - \omega t\right) + E_{02}\cos\left(\frac{2\pi}{\lambda}S_2P - \omega t\right)\right] \qquad \textbf{(13.26)}$$

The intensity (I) will be proportional to the square of the electric field and will be given by

$$I = KE^2 \qquad \textbf{(13.27)}$$

or

$$I = K\left[E_{01}^2\cos^2\left(\frac{2\pi}{\lambda}S_1P - \omega t\right) + E_{02}^2\cos^2\left(\frac{2\pi}{\lambda}S_2P - \omega t\right) + E_{01}E_{02}\left\{\cos\left[\frac{2\pi}{\lambda}(S_2P - S_1P)\right] + \cos\left[2\omega t - \frac{2\pi}{\lambda}(S_2P + S_1P)\right]\right\}\right] \qquad \textbf{(13.28)}$$

where K is a proportionality constant.* For an optical beam the frequency is very large ($\omega \approx 10^{15}$ sec^{-1}) and all the terms depending on ωt will vary with extreme rapidity (10^{15} times in a second); consequently, any detector would record an average value of various quantities. Now,

* Equation (13.27) will be derived in Sec. 22.5. In free space, the constant K will be shown to be equal to $\varepsilon_0 c^2$ where ε_0 (= 8.854×10^{-12} Coul^2/N–m^2) represents the permittivity of free space and c, the speed of light in free space.

$$\langle \cos^2(\omega t - \theta)\rangle = \frac{1}{2\tau}\int_{-\tau}^{+\tau}\frac{1+\cos[2(\omega t-\theta)]}{2}\,dt$$

$$= \frac{1}{2} + \frac{1}{16\pi}\frac{T}{\tau}\left\{[\sin 2(\omega t - \theta)]_{-\tau}^{+\tau}\right\}$$

where $T = \frac{2\pi}{\omega}$ ($\approx 2\pi \times 10^{-15}$ sec for an optical beam). For any practical detector** $\frac{T}{\tau} <<< 1$ and since the quantity between the curly brackets will always be between −2 and +2, we may write

$$\langle \cos^2(\omega t - \theta)\rangle \approx \frac{1}{2} \tag{13.29}$$

The factor $\cos(2\omega t - \phi)$ will oscillate between +1 and −1 and its average will be zero as can indeed be shown mathematically. Thus the intensity, that a detector will record, will be given by

$$I = I_1 + I_2 + 2\sqrt{I_1 I_2}\cos\delta \tag{13.30}$$

where
$$\delta = \frac{2\pi}{\lambda}(S_2P - S_1P) \tag{13.31}$$

represents the phase difference between the displacements reaching the point P from S_1 and S_2. Further

$$I_1 = \frac{1}{2}KE_{01}^2$$

represents the intensity produced by the source S_1 if no light from S_2 is allowed to fall on the screen; similarly $I_2 = \frac{1}{2}KE_{02}^2$ represents the intensity produced by the source S_2 if no light from S_1 is allowed to fall on the screen. From Eq. (13.30) we may deduce the following:

(a) The maximum and minimum values of $\cos\delta$ are +1 and −1, respectively; as such the maximum and minimum values of I are given by

and
$$\left.\begin{aligned} I_{max} &= (\sqrt{I_1}+\sqrt{I_2})^2 \\ I_{min} &= (\sqrt{I_1}-\sqrt{I_2})^2 \end{aligned}\right\} \tag{13.32}$$

The maximum intensity occurs when

$$\delta = 2n\pi;\quad n = 0, 1, 2, \ldots$$

or $S_2P \sim S_1P = n\lambda$,

and the minimum intensity occurs when

$$\delta = (2n+1)\pi;\ n = 0, 1, 2, \ldots$$

or $S_2P \sim S_1P = \left(n + \frac{1}{2}\right)\lambda$

Notice that when $I_1 = I_2$, the intensity minimum is zero. In general, $I_1 \neq I_2$ and the minimum intensity is not zero.

(b) If the holes S_1 and S_2 are illuminated by different light sources (see Fig. 13.5), then the phase difference δ will remain constant for about 10^{-10} sec (see discussion in Sec. 13.3) and thus δ would also vary with time*** in a random way. If we now carry out the averaging over time scales which are of the order of 10^{-8} sec, then

$$\langle \cos\delta\rangle = 0$$

and we obtain

$$I = I_1 + I_2$$

Thus, for two incoherent sources, the resultant intensity is the sum of the intensities produced by each one of the sources independently and no interference pattern is observed.

(c) In the arrangement shown in Fig. 13.6, if the distances S_1P and S_2P are large in comparison to d, then

$$I_1 \approx I_2 = I_0 \text{ (say)}$$

and
$$I = 2I_0 + 2I_0\cos\delta = 4I_0\cos^2\frac{\delta}{2} \tag{13.33}$$

The intensity distribution (which is often termed as the cos² pattern) is shown in Fig. 13.9. The actual fringe pattern (as it will appear on the screen) is shown in Fig. 13.10. Figures 13.10(a) and (b) correspond to d = 0.005 mm ($\beta \approx 5$ mm) and d = 0.025 mm ($\beta \approx 1$ mm), respectively. Both figures correspond to D = 5 cm and $\lambda = 5 \times 10^{-5}$ cm. The values of the parameters are such that one can see the hyperbolic nature of the fringe pattern in Fig. 13.10(a).

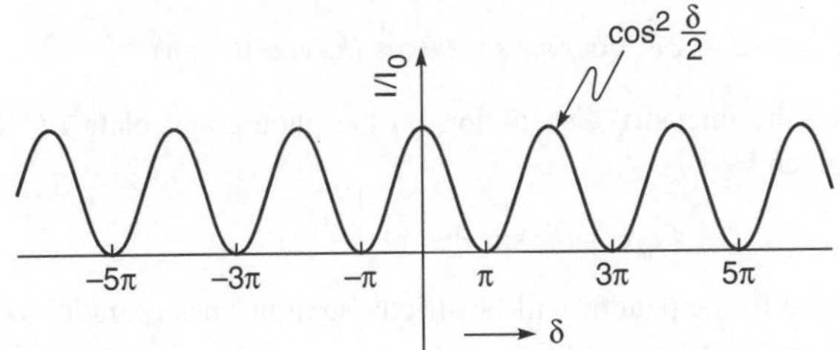

Figure 13.9
The variation of intensity with δ.

** For a normal eye, $\tau \approx 0.1$ s; thus $T/\tau \approx 6 \times 10^{-14}$; even for a detector having 1 nsec as the resolution time, $T/\tau \approx 6 \times 10^{-5}$.

*** Notice that this variation occurs in times of the order of 10^{-10} sec which is about a million times longer than the times for variation of the intensity due to the terms depending on ωt. Thus we are justified in first carrying out the averaging which leads to Eq. (13.30).

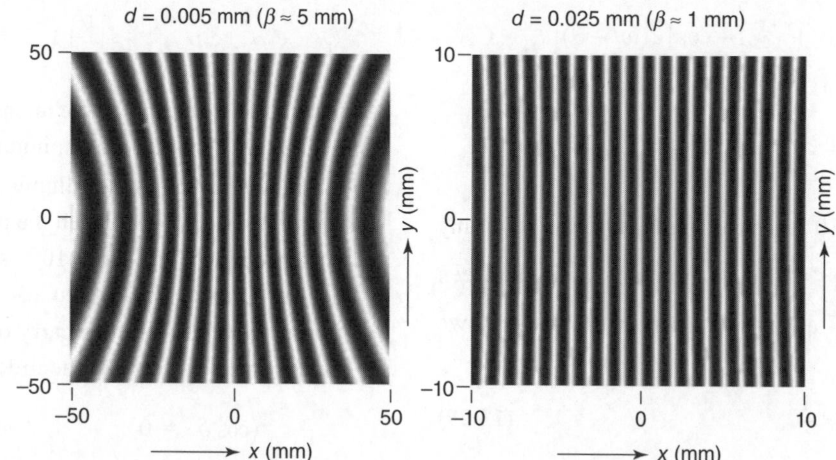

Figure 13.10

Computer generated fringe pattern produced by two point sources S_1 and S_2 on the screen LL' (see Fig. 13.8); (a) and (b) correspond to $d = 0.005$ mm and 0.025 mm, respectively (both figures correspond to $D = 5$ cm and $\lambda = 5 \times 10^{-5}$ cm).

EXAMPLE 13.5 Instead of considering two point sources, we consider the superposition of two plane waves as shown in Fig. 13.11(a). The wave vectors for the two waves are given by

$$\mathbf{k}_1 = -\hat{\mathbf{x}}\ k \sin\theta_1 + \hat{\mathbf{z}}\ k \cos\theta_1$$

and

$$\mathbf{k}_2 = +\hat{\mathbf{x}}\ k \sin\theta_2 + \hat{\mathbf{z}}\ k \cos\theta_2$$

where $k = 2\pi/\lambda$ and θ_1 and θ_2 are defined in Fig. 13.11(a). Thus the electric fields of the two waves are described by the following two equations:

$$\begin{aligned} E_1 &= E_{01} \cos [\mathbf{k}_1 \cdot \mathbf{r} - \omega t] \\ &= E_{01} \cos [-kx \sin \theta_1 + kz \cos \theta_1 - \omega t] \\ E_2 &= E_{02} \cos [\mathbf{k}_2 \cdot \mathbf{r} - \omega t] \\ &= E_{02} \cos [kx \sin \theta_2 + kz \cos \theta_2 - \omega t] \end{aligned}$$

where we have assumed both electric fields along the same direction (say along the y-axis); if we further assume $E_{01} = E_{02} = E_0$ and $\theta_1 = \theta_2 = \theta$ then the resultant field will be given by

$$E = 2E_0 \cos (kx \sin \theta) \cos (kz \cos \theta - \omega t)$$

Thus, the intensity distribution on the photograph plate LL' will be given by

$$I = 4 I_0 \cos^2(kx \sin \theta)$$

and the fringe pattern will be strictly straight lines (parallel to the y-axis) with fringe width given by

$$\beta = \frac{\lambda}{2 \sin \theta}$$

Figure 13.11(b) shows the computer generated interference pattern on the screen LL' for $\theta = \pi/6$ and $\lambda = 5000$ Å. Thus $\beta = \lambda = 0.0005$ mm.

EXAMPLE 13.6 In this example, we once again consider the interference pattern produced by 2 point sources S_1 and S_2 on a plane PP' which is perpendicular to the line joining S_1 and S_2 [see Fig. 13.12(a)]. Obviously, on the plane PP', the locus of the point P for which

$$S_1P - S_2P = \text{constant}$$

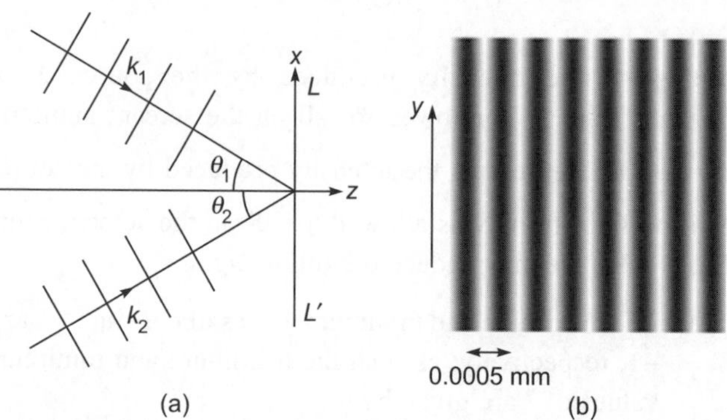

Figure 13.11

(a) The superposition of two plane waves on LL'. (b) Computer generated interference pattern on the screen LL' for $\theta_1 = \theta_2 = \pi/6$ and $\lambda = 5000$ Å. The fringes are parallel to the y-axis.

will be a circle. Figures 13.12(b) and (c) show the fringe patterns for $D = 20$ cm and $D = 10$ cm; for both figures $S_1S_2 = d = 0.05$ mm and $\lambda = 5000$ Å. Obviously, if O represents the centre of the fringe pattern then

$$S_1O - S_2O = d = 100\ \lambda$$

Thus (for this value of d) the central spot will be bright for all values of D and will correspond to $n = 100$. The first and second bright circles will correspond to a path difference of 99 λ and 98 λ, respectively. Similarly, the first and second dark rings in the interference pattern will correspond to a path difference of 99.5 λ and 98.5 λ, respectively. The radii of the fringes can be calculated by using the formula given in Problem 13.10.

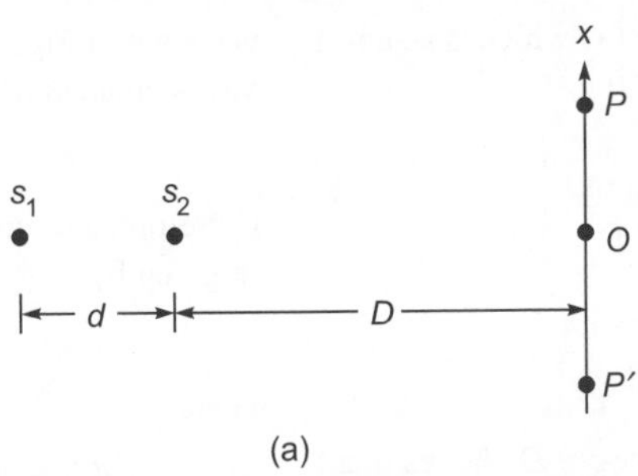

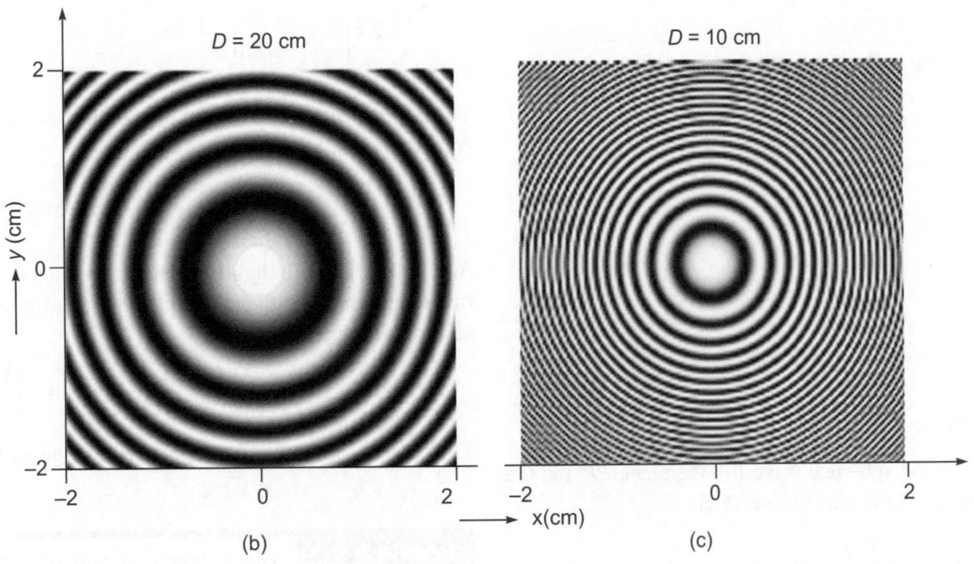

Figure 13.12

(a) S_1 and S_2 represent two coherent sources, (b) and (c) show the interference fringes observed on the screen PP' when $D = 20$ cm and $D = 10$ cm, respectively.

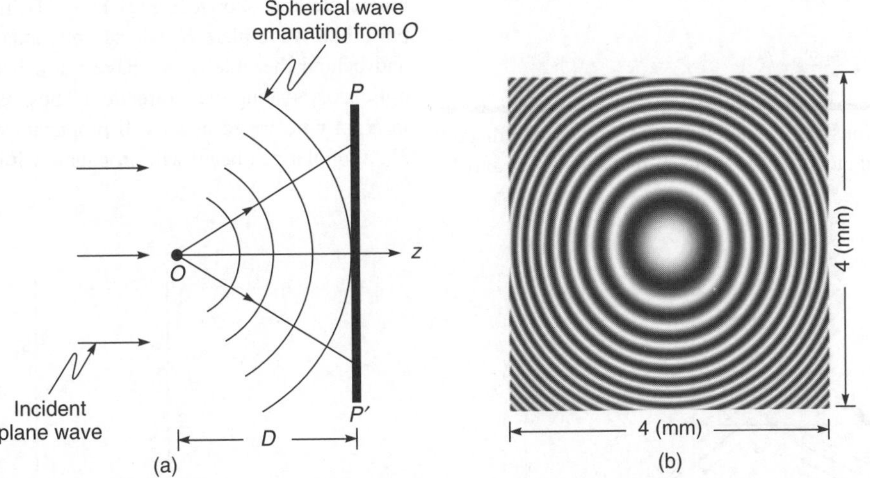

Figure 13.13

(a) Superposition of a plane wave and a spherical wave emanating from the point O; (b) shows the interference fringes observed on the screen PP'.

EXAMPLE 13.7 We finally consider the interference pattern produced on PP' by the superposition of a plane wave incident normally and a spherical wave emanating from the point O (see Fig. 13.13). The plane wave will be given by

$$E_1 = E_0 \cos(kz - \omega t + \phi)$$

and the spherical wave will be given by

$$E_2 = \frac{A_0}{r} \cos(kr - \omega t)$$

where r is the distance measured from the point O which is assumed to be the origin. Now, on the plane PP' ($z = D$)

$$r = (x^2 + y^2 + D^2)^{\frac{1}{2}} \approx D\left[1 + \frac{x^2 + y^2}{2D^2}\right]$$

$$\approx D + \frac{x^2 + y^2}{2D}$$

where we have assumed $x, y << D$. On the plane $z = D$, the resultant field will be given by

$$E = E_1 + E_2$$

$$\approx E_0 \cos(kD - \omega t + \phi)$$

$$+ \frac{A_0}{D}\cos\left[kD + \frac{k}{2D}(x^2 + y^2) - \omega t\right]$$

Thus, $$\langle E^2 \rangle = \frac{1}{2}E_0^2 + \frac{1}{2}\left(\frac{A_0}{D}\right)^2$$

$$+ E_0 \frac{A_0}{D}\cos\left[\frac{k}{2D}(x^2 + y^2) - \phi\right]$$

If we assume that

$$\frac{A_0}{D} \approx E_0$$

i.e., the amplitude of the spherical wave (on the plane PP') is the same as the amplitude of the plane wave, then

$$\langle E^2 \rangle \approx 2E_0^2 \cos^2\left(\frac{k}{4D}(x^2 + y^2) - \frac{1}{2}\phi\right)$$

and we would obtain circular interference fringes as shown in Fig. 13.13(b). If r_m and r_{m+p} denote the radii of mth and $(m + p)^{th}$ bright ring, then

$$r_{m+p}^2 - r_m^2 = 2p\lambda D$$

EXAMPLE 13.8 Consider a parallel beam of light (from a distant source S' like a star incident at an angle θ) on two slits S_1 and S_2 as shown in Fig. 13.14. Obviously, the path difference between the waves emanating from the slits S_1 and S_2 will be given by

$$XS_2 = d \sin\theta$$

Therefore, the intensity distribution on the screen due to S' will be given by

$$I = I_0 \cos^2 \frac{\delta}{2}$$

where

$$\delta = \frac{2\pi}{\lambda}[XS_2 + S_2P - S_1P] = \frac{2\pi}{\lambda}[S_2P - S_1P) + d\sin\theta]$$

$$= \frac{2\pi}{\lambda}\left[\frac{xd}{D} + d\sin\theta\right]$$

Thus, the intensity distribution (due to light coming from the distant source S') will be given by

$$I' = I_0 \cos^2\left(\frac{\pi}{\lambda}\left[\frac{xd}{D} + d\sin\phi\right]\right)$$

Similarly, if there is light incident from another distant source S'' (at an angle ϕ) then the corresponding intensity distribution on the screen will be given by

$$I'' = I_0 \cos^2\left(\frac{\pi}{\lambda}\left[\frac{xd}{D} - d\sin\phi\right]\right)$$

The resultant intensity distribution will be given by

$$I = I' + I''$$

EXAMPLE 13.9 This example presupposes the knowledge of half-wave plates (see Sec. 21.6) and therefore the reader may skip this example until he has gone through Chapter 21.

Consider a y-polarized beam light beam incident on a double hole system as shown in Fig. 13.15. Behind the hole S_1 we have put a half-wave plate H_1 whose optic axis is along the y direction and behind the hole S_2 we have put a half-wave plate H_2 whose optic axis is along the x direction. Thus, as discussed in Sec. 21.6, in H_1, a y-polarized beam will propagate with velocity c/n_e and in H_2, a y-polarized beam will propagate with velocity c/n_o. In calcite

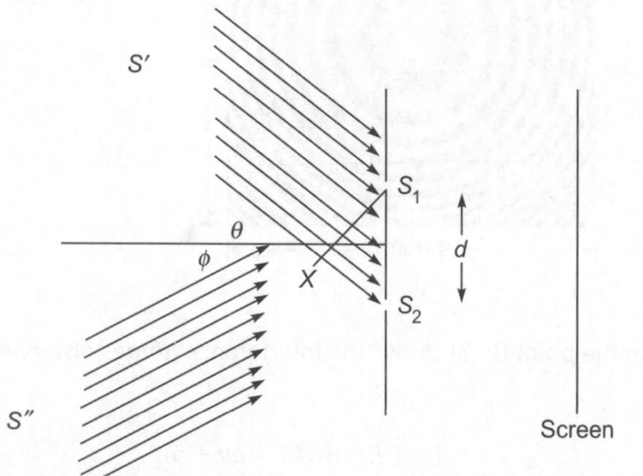

Figure 13.14

Two distant incoherent sources S' and S'' illuminate the slits S_1 and S_2.

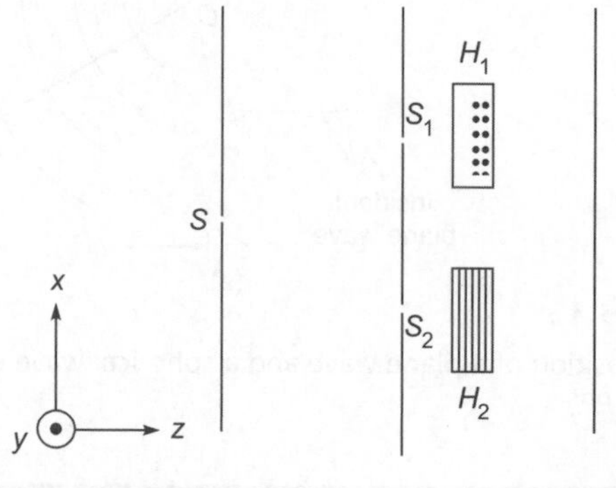

Figure 13.15

H_1 and H_2 are half-wave plates placed in front of the slits S_1 and S_2. The optic axis of H_1 and H_2 are along y and x directions, respectively.

$n_e < n_o$; and, in a half-wave plate a phase change of π is introduced between the *o*-wave and the *e*-wave. Thus, the whole fringe pattern will shift by $\beta/2$ where β is the fringe width.

13.7 Fresnel's Two-Mirror Arrangement

LO6

After Young's double hole interference experiment, Fresnel devised a series of arrangements to produce the interference pattern. One of the experimental arrangements, known as the **Fresnel two-mirror arrangement**, is shown in Fig. 13.16; it consists of two plane mirrors which are inclined to each other at a small angle θ and touching at the point *M*. *S* represents a narrow slit placed perpendicular to the plane of the paper.

A portion of the wavefront from *S* gets reflected from M_1M and illuminates the region *AD* of the screen. Another portion of the wavefront gets reflected from the mirror MM_2 and illuminates the region *BC* of the screen. Since these two wavefronts are derived from the same source they are coherent. Thus in the region *BC*, one observes interference fringes. The formation of the fringes can also be understood as being due to the interference of the wavefronts from the virtual sources S_1 and S_2 of *S* formed by the mirrors M_1 and M_2, respectively. From simple geometric considerations, it can be shown that the points S, S_1 and S_2 lie on a circle whose centre is at the point *M*. Further, if the angle between the mirrors is θ, then the angle S_1SS_2 is also θ and the angle S_1MS_2 is 2θ. Thus, S_1S_2 is $2R\theta$, where *R* is the radius of the circle.

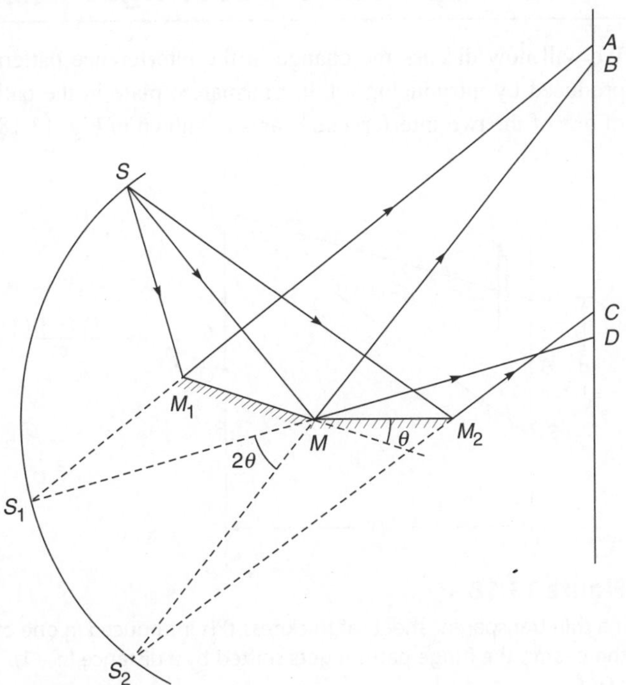

Figure 13.16

Fresnel's two-mirror arrangement.

13.8 Fresnel Biprism

LO6

Fresnel devised yet another simple arrangement for the production of interference pattern. He used a biprism, which was actually a simple prism, the base angles of which are extremely small (~20′). The base of the prism is shown in Fig. 13.17 and the prism is assumed to stand perpendicular to the plane of the paper. *S* represents the slit which is also placed perpendicular to the plane of the paper. Light from the slit *S* gets refracted by the prism and produces two virtual images S_1 and S_2. These images act as coherent sources and produce interference fringes on the right of the biprism. The fringes can be viewed through an eyepiece. If *n* represents the refractive index of the material of the biprism and α the base angle, then $(n - 1)\alpha$ is approximately the angular deviation produced by the prism and, therefore, the distance S_1S_2 is $2a(n - 1)\alpha$, where *a* represents the distance from *S* to the base of the prism. Thus, for $n = 1.5$, $\alpha \approx (20') \approx 5.8 \times 10^{-3}$ radians, $a \approx 2$ cm, one gets $d = 0.012$ cm.

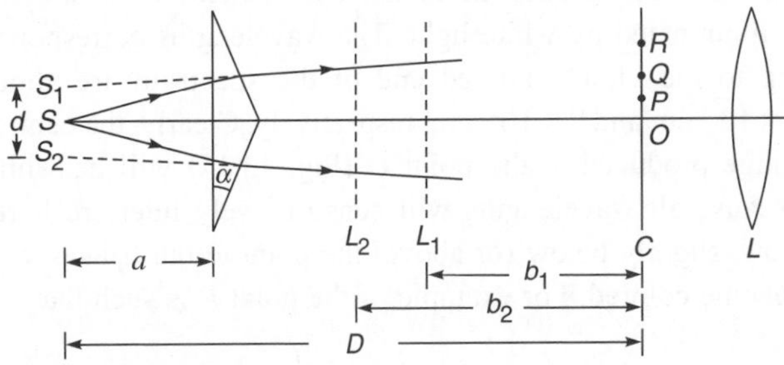

Figure 13.17

Fresnel's biprism arrangement. *C* and *L* represent the positions of the crosswires and the eyepiece, respectively. In order to determine *d* one introduces a lens between the biprism and the crosswires; L_1 and L_2 represent the two positions of the lens where the slits are clearly seen.

The biprism arrangement can be used for the determination of wavelength of an almost monochromatic light like the one coming from a sodium lamp. Light from the sodium lamp illuminates the slit *S* and interference fringes can be easily viewed through the eyepiece. The fringe width (β) can be determined by means of a micrometer attached to the eyepiece. Once β is known, λ can be determined by using the following relation:

$$\lambda = \frac{d\beta}{D} \tag{13.34}$$

It may be mentioned that in order to determine *d*, one need not measure the value of α. In fact the distances *d* and *D* can easily be determined by placing a convex lens between the biprism and the eyepiece. For a fixed position of the eyepiece there will be two positions of the lens (shown as L_1 and L_2 in Fig. 13.17) where the images of S_1 and S_2 can be seen at the eyepiece.* Let d_1 be the distance between the two images when the lens is at the position L_1 (at a distance b_1 from the eyepiece). Let d_2 and b_2 be the corresponding distances when the lens is at L_2. Then, it can easily be shown that

$$d = \sqrt{d_1 d_2}$$

and

$$D = b_1 + b_2$$

Typically for $d \approx 0.01$ cm, $\lambda \approx 6 \times 10^{-5}$ cm, $D \approx 50$ cm, $\beta \approx 0.3$ cm.

In the above arrangement we have considered a slit instead of a point source. Since each pair of points S_1 and S_2 produce (approximately) straight line fringes, the slit will also produce straight line fringes of increased intensity.

13.9 Interference with White Light LO7

We will now discuss the interference pattern when the slit is illuminated by white light. The wavelengths corresponding to the violet and red end of the spectrum are about 4×10^{-5} cm and 7×10^{-5} cm, respectively. Clearly, the central fringe produced at the point O (Fig. 13.17) will be white because all wavelengths will constructively interfere here. Now, slightly below (or above) the point O the fringes will become colored. For example, if the point P is such that

$$S_2P \sim S_1P = 2 \times 10^{-5} \text{ cm} \left(= \frac{\lambda_{\text{violet}}}{2}\right)$$

then complete destructive interference will occur only for the violet color. Partial destructive interference will occur for other wavelengths. Consequently, we will have a line devoid of the violet color and will appear reddish. The point Q which satisfies

$$S_2Q \sim S_1Q = 3.5 \times 10^{-5} \text{ cm} \left(= \frac{\lambda_{\text{red}}}{2}\right)$$

will be devoid of the red color. It will correspond to almost constructive interference for the violet color. No other wavelength (in the visible region) will neither constructively nor destructively interfere. Thus following the white central fringe we will have colored fringes; when the path difference is about 2×10^{-5} cm the fringe will be red in color, then the color will gradually change to violet. The colored fringes will soon disappear because at points far away from O there will be so many wavelengths (in the visible region) which will constructively interfere that we will observe uniform white illumination. For example, at a point R, such that $S_2R \sim S_1R = 30 \times 10^{-5}$ cm, wavelengths corresponding to $30 \times 10^{-5}/n$ ($n = 1, 2, \ldots$) will constructively interfere. In the visible region, these wavelengths will be 7.5×10^{-5} cm (red), 6×10^{-5} cm (yellow), 5×10^{-5} cm (greenish yellow) and 4.3×10^{-5} cm (violet). Further, wavelengths corresponding to $30 \times 10^{-5}/\left(n + \frac{1}{2}\right)$ will destructively interfere; thus, in the visible region, the wavelengths 6.67×10^{-5} cm (orange), 5.5×10^{-5} cm (yellow), 4.6×10^{-5} cm (indigo) and 4.0×10^{-5} cm (violet) will be absent. The color of such light, as seen by the unaided eye, will be white. Thus, with white light one gets a white central fringe at the point of zero path difference along with a few colored fringes on both the sides, the color soon fading off to white. While using a white light source, if we put a red (or green) filter in front of our eye, we will see the interference pattern corresponding to the red (or green) light.

In the usual interference pattern with a nearly monochromatic source (like a sodium lamp) a large number of interference fringes are obtained and it is extremely difficult to determine the position of the central fringe. In many interference experiments, it is necessary to determine the position of the central fringe and, as has been discussed above, this can easily be done by using white light as a source.

As discussed above, when we observe interference pattern using a white light source, we will see only few colored fringes. However, if we put a red filter in front of our eye, the fringe pattern (corresponding to the red color) will suddenly appear. If we replace the red filter by a green filter in front of our eye, the fringe pattern corresponding to the green color will appear.

13.10 Displacement of Fringes LO8

We will now discuss the change in the interference pattern produced by introducing a thin transparent plate in the path of one of the two interference beams as shown in Fig. 13.18.

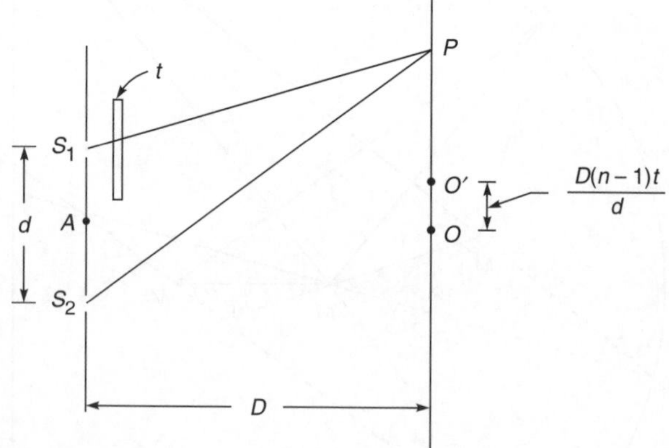

Figure 13.18

If a thin transparent sheet (of thickness t) is introduced in one of the beams, the fringe pattern gets shifted by a distance $(n - 1)$ $t\,D/d$.

* This method is similar to the displacement method for the determination of the focal length of a convex lens.

Let t be the thickness of the plate and let n be its refractive index. It is easily seen from the figure that light reaching the point P from S_1 has to traverse a distance t in the plate and a distance $S_1P - t$ in air. Thus the time required for the light to reach from S_1 to the point P is given by

$$\frac{S_1P - t}{c} + \frac{t}{v} = \frac{1}{c}[S_1P - t + nt]$$

$$= \frac{1}{c}[S_1P + (n - 1)t] \quad (13.35)$$

where $v \left(= \frac{c}{n}\right)$ represents the speed of light in the plate. Equation (13.35) shows that by introducing the thin plate the effective optical path increases by $(n - 1)t$. Thus, when the thin plate is introduced, the central fringe (which corresponds to equal optical path from S_1 and S_2) is formed at the point O' where

$$S_1O' + (n - 1)t = S_2O'$$

Since [see Eq. (13.19)]

$$S_2O' - S_1O' \approx \frac{d}{D}OO'$$

therefore, $$(n - 1)t = \frac{d}{D}OO' \quad (13.36)$$

Thus the fringe pattern gets shifted by a distance Δ which is given by the following equation:

$$\Delta = \frac{D(n-1)t}{d} \quad (13.37)$$

The above principle enables us to determine the thickness of extremely thin transparent sheets (like that of mica) by measuring the displacement of the central fringe. Further, if white light is used as a source, the displacement of the central fringe is easy to measure.

EXAMPLE 13.10 In a double-slit interference arrangement, one of the slits is covered by a thin mica sheet whose refractive index is 1.58. The distances S_1S_2 and AO (see Fig. 13.18) are 0.1 cm and 50 cm, respectively. Due to the introduction of the mica sheet the central fringe gets shifted by 0.2 cm. Determine the thickness of the mica sheet.

Solution: $\Delta = 0.2$ cm; $d = 0.1$ cm; $D = 50$ cm

Hence, $$t = \frac{d\Delta}{D(n-1)} = \frac{0.1 \times 0.2}{50 \times 0.58}$$

$$\approx 6.7 \times 10^{-4} \text{ cm}$$

EXAMPLE 13.11 In an experimental arrangement similar to the one discussed in the above example, one finds that by introducing the mica sheet the central fringe occupies the position that was originally occupied by the eleventh bright fringe. If the source of light is a sodium lamp ($\lambda = 5893$ Å) determine the thickness of the mica sheet.

Solution: The point O' (see Fig. 13.18) corresponds to the eleventh bright fringe, thus,

$$S_2O' - S_1O' = 11\lambda = (n - 1)t = 0.58t$$

$$\Rightarrow \quad t = \frac{11\lambda}{0.58} = \frac{11 \times 0.5893\ \mu\text{m}}{0.58} \approx 11.2\ \mu\text{m}$$

13.11 The Lloyd's Mirror Arrangement

LO9

In this arrangement, light from a slit S_1 is allowed to fall on a plane mirror at grazing incidence (see Fig. 13.19). The light directly coming from the slit S_1 interferes with the light reflected from the mirror forming an interference pattern in the region BC of the screen. One may thus consider the slit S_1 and its virtual image S_2 to form two coherent sources which produce the interference pattern. It should be noted that at grazing incidence one really need not have a mirror; even a dielectric surface has very high reflectivity (see Chapter 22).

As can be seen from Fig. 13.19, the central fringe cannot be observed on the screen unless the latter is moved to the position $L'_1L'_2$, where it touches the end of the reflector. Alternatively, one may introduce a thin mica sheet in the path of the direct beam so that the central fringe appears in the region BC. (This is discussed in detail in Problem 13.2) Indeed, if the central fringe is observed with white light, it is found to be dark. This implies that the reflected beam undergoes a sudden phase change of π on reflection. Consequently, when the point P on the screen is such that

$$S_2P - S_1P = n\lambda, n = 0, 1, 2, 3, \ldots$$

we will get minima (i.e., destructive interference). On the other hand, if

$$S_2P - S_1P = \left(n + \frac{1}{2}\right)\lambda$$

we will get maxima.

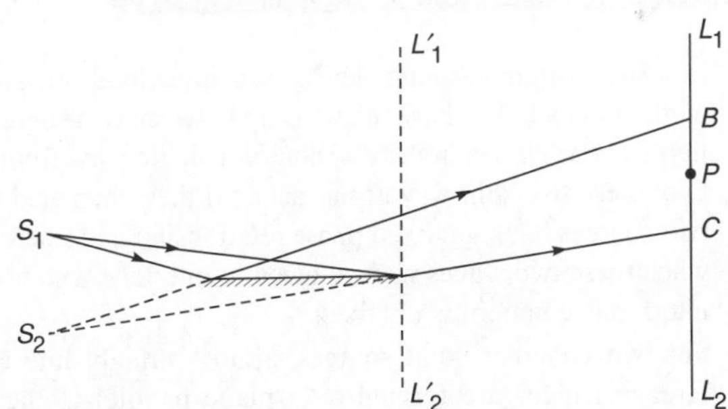

Figure 13.19
The Lloyd's mirror arrangement.

In the next section, using the principle of optical reversibility, we will show that if there is an abrupt phase change of π when light gets reflected by a denser medium, then no such abrupt phase change occurs when reflection takes place at a rarer medium.

13.12 Phase Change on Reflection

We will now investigate the reflection of light at an interface between two media using the principle of optical reversibility. According to this principle, in the absence of any absorption, a light ray that is reflected or refracted will retrace its original path if its direction is reversed.*

Consider a light ray incident on an interface of two media of refractive indices n_1 and n_2 as shown in Fig. 13.20(a). Let the amplitude reflection and transmission coefficients be r_1 and t_1, respectively. Thus, if the amplitude of the incident ray is a, then the amplitudes of the reflected and refracted rays would be ar_1 and at_1, respectively.

We now reverse the rays and we consider a ray of amplitude at_1 incident on medium 1 and a ray of amplitude ar_1 incident on medium 2 as shown in Fig. 13.20(b). The ray of amplitude at_1 will give rise to a reflected ray of amplitude at_1r_2 and a transmitted ray of amplitude at_1t_2 where r_2 and t_2 are the amplitude reflection and transmission coefficients when a ray is incident from medium 2 on medium 1. Similarly, the ray of amplitude ar_1 will give rise to a ray of amplitude ar_1^2 and a refracted ray of amplitude ar_1t_1. According to the principle of optical reversibility the two rays of amplitudes ar_1^2 and at_1t_2 must combine to give the incident ray of Fig. 13.20(a); thus,

$$ar_1^2 + at_1t_2 = a$$

or

$$t_1t_2 = 1 - r_1^2 \tag{13.38}$$

Further, the two rays of amplitudes at_1r_2 and ar_1t_1 must cancel each other, i.e.,

$$at_1r_2 + ar_1t_1 = 0$$

or

$$r_2 = -r_1 \tag{13.39}$$

Since we know from the Lloyd's mirror experiment that an abrupt phase change of π occurs when light gets reflected by a denser medium, we may infer from Eq. (13.39) that no such abrupt phase change occurs when light gets reflected by a rarer medium. This is indeed borne out by experiments. Equations (13.38) and (13.39) are known as **Stokes' relations**.

In Chapter 23, we will calculate the amplitude reflection and transmission coefficients for plane waves incident on a dielectric and also on a conductor. It will be shown that the coefficients satisfy Stokes' relations; the phase change on reflection will also be discussed there.

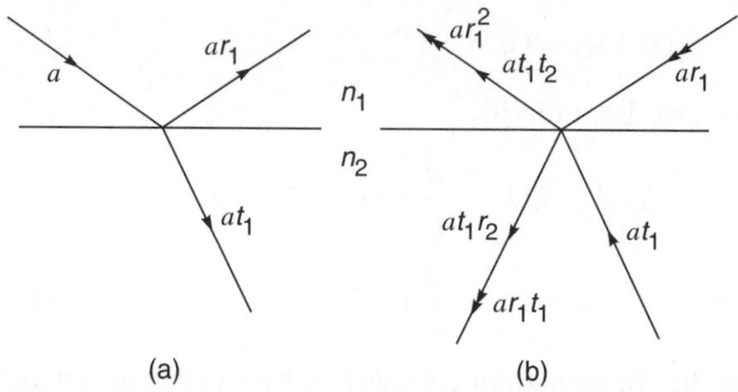

Figure 13.20

(a) A ray traveling in a medium of refractive index n_1 incident on a medium of refractive index n_2. (b) Rays of amplitude ar_1 and at_1 incident on a medium of refractive index n_1.

SUMMARY

- In 1801, Thomas Young devised an ingenious but simple method to lock the phase relationship between two sources of light. The trick lies in the division of a single wavefront into two; these two split wavefronts act as if they emanated from two sources having a fixed phase relationship and, therefore, when these two waves were allowed to interfere, a stationary interference pattern is obtained.
- For two coherent point sources, almost straight-line interference fringes are formed on a plane parallel to the line joining the two point sources and by measuring the fringe width (which represents the distance between two consecutive fringes) one can calculate the wavelength.
- On a plane which is normal to the line joining the two coherent point sources, the fringe pattern is circular.
- In the Young's double-slit interference pattern, if we use a white light source, one gets a white central fringe at the point of zero path difference along with a few colored fringes on both the sides, the color soon fading off to white. If we now introduce a very thin slice of transparent material (like mica) in the path of one of the interfering beams, the fringes get displaced and by measuring the displacement of fringes, one can calculate the thickness of the mica sheet.

* This principle is consequence of time reversal invariance according to which processes can run either way in time; for more details see Refs. 13.3 and 13.8.

PROBLEMS

13.1 In the Young's double-hole experiment (see Fig. 13.6), the distance between the two holes is 0.5 mm, $\lambda = 5 \times 10^{-5}$ cm and $D = 50$ cm. What will be the fringe width?

13.2 Figure 13.21 represents the layout of Lloyd's mirror experiment. S is a point source emitting waves of frequency $6 \times 10^{14}\ \text{s}^{-1}$. A and B represent the two ends of a mirror placed horizontally and LOM represents the screen. The distances SP, PA, AB and BO are 1 mm, 5 cm, 5 cm and 190 cm, respectively. (a) Determine the position of the region where the fringes will be visible and calculate the number of fringes. (b) Calculate the thickness of a mica sheet ($n = 1.5$) which should be introduced in the path of the direct ray so that the lowest fringe becomes the central fringe. The velocity of light is 3×10^{10} cm/s.

[**Ans:** (a) 2 cm, 40 fringes, (b) 38 μm]

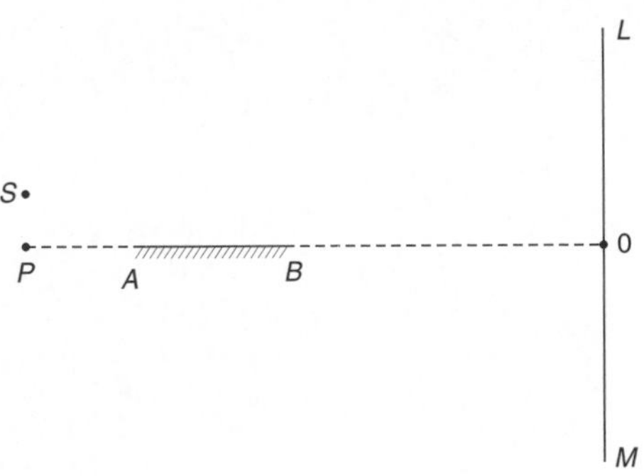

Figure 13.21

Figure for Problem 13.2.

13.3 **(a)** In the Fresnel's biprism arrangement, show that $d = 2(n - 1)\, a\alpha$ where a represents the distance from the source to the base of the prism (see Fig. 13.17), α is the angle of the biprism and n the refractive index of the material of the biprism.

(b) In a typical biprism arrangement $b/a = 20$, and for sodium light ($\lambda \simeq 5893$ Å) one obtains a fringe width of 0.1 cm; here b is the distance between the biprism and the screen. Assuming $n = 1.5$, calculate the angle α. [**Ans:** $\simeq 0.71°$]

13.4 In the Young's double-hole experiment a thin mica sheet ($n = 1.5$) is introduced in the path of one of the beams. If the central fringe gets shifted by 0.2 cm, calculate the thickness of the mica sheet. Assume $d = 0.1$ cm, and $D = 50$ cm.

13.5 In order to determine the distance between the slits in the Fresnel biprism experiment, one puts a convex lens in between the biprism and the eyepiece. Show that if $D > 4f$ one will obtain two positions of the lens where the image of the slits will be formed at the eyepiece; here f is the focal length of the convex lens and D is the distance between the slit and the eyepiece. If d_1 and d_2 are the distances between the images (of the slits) as measured by the eyepiece, then show that $d = \sqrt{d_1 d_2}$. What would happen if $D < 4f$?

13.6 In the Young's double hole experiment, interference fringes are formed using sodium light which predominantly comprises of two wavelengths (5890 Å and 5896 Å). Obtain the regions on the screen where the fringe pattern will disappear. You may assume $d = 0.5$ mm and $D = 100$ cm.

13.7 If one carries out the Young's double-hole interference experiment using microwaves of wavelength 3 cm, discuss the nature of the fringe pattern if $d = 0.1$ cm, 1 cm, and 4 cm. You may assume $D = 100$ cm. Can you use Eq. (13.21) for the fringe width?

13.8 In the Fresnel's two-mirror arrangement (see Fig. 13.16) show that the points S, S_1, and S_2 lie on a circle and $S_1S_2 = 2b\theta$ where $b = MS$ and θ is the angle between the mirrors.

13.9 In the double-hole experiment using white light, consider two points on the screen, one corresponding to a path difference of 5000 Å and the other corresponding to a path difference of 40000 Å. Find the wavelengths (in the visible region) which correspond to constructive and destructive interference. What will be the color of these points?

13.10 **(a)** Consider a plane which is normal to the line joining two point coherent sources S_1 and S_2 as shown in Fig. 13.12(a). If $S_1P - S_2P = \Delta$, then show that

$$x = \frac{1}{2\Delta}(d^2 - \Delta^2)^{\frac{1}{2}}\,[4D^2 + 4Dd + (d^2 - \Delta^2)]^{\frac{1}{2}}$$

$$\approx \frac{D}{\Delta}\sqrt{(d-\Delta)(d+\Delta)}$$

where the last expression is valid for $D >> d$.

(b) For $\lambda = 0.5$ μm, $d = 0.4$ mm and $D = 20$ cm; $S_1O - S_2O = 800\ \lambda$. Calculate the value of $S_1P - S_2P$ for the point P to be first dark ring and first bright ring.

[**Ans:** 0.39975 mm, 0.3995 mm]

13.11 In continuation of the above problem calculate the radii of the first two dark rings for

(a) $D = 20$ cm and **(b)** $D = 10$ cm.

[**Ans:** (a) ≈ 0.71 cm and 1.22 cm]

13.12 In continuation of Problem 13.10 assume that $d = 0.5$ mm, $\lambda = 5 \times 10^{-5}$ cm and $D = 100$ cm. Thus the central (bright) spot will correspond to $n = 1000$. Calculate the radii of the first, second and third bright rings which will correspond to $n = 999$, 998 and $n = 997$, respectively.

13.13 Using the expressions for the amplitude reflection and transmission coefficients (derived in Chapter 23), show that they satisfy Stokes' relations.

13.14 Assume a plane wave incident normally on a plane containing two holes separated by a distance d. If we place a convex lens behind the slits, show that the fringe width, as observed on the focal plane of the lens, will be $f\lambda/d$ where f is the focal length of the lens.

13.15 In Problem 13.14, show that if the plane (containing the holes) lies in the front focal plane of the lens, then the interference pattern will consist of exactly parallel straight lines. However, if the plane does not lie on the front focal plane, the fringe pattern will be hyperbolae.

13.16 In the Young's double-hole experiment calculate I/I_{max} where I represents the intensity at a point where the path difference is $\lambda/5$.

CHAPTER 14

Following a method suggested by Fizeau in 1868, Professor Michelson has produced what is perhaps the most ingenious and sensational instrument in the service of astronomy—the interferometer.

—Sir James Jeans in *The Universe Around Us*, Cambridge University Press, (1930)

Interference by Division of Amplitude

LEARNING OBJECTIVES

After reading this chapter, the reader should be able to:

LO 1: *describe the interference pattern observed when a plane parallel film is illuminated by a plane wave.*

LO 2: *derive the cosine law when reflection occurs by a plane parallel film.*

LO 3: *discuss the role of non-reflective films in reducing reflectivity of lens surfaces.*

LO 4: *demonstrate high reflectivity by deposition of a thin film.*

LO 5: *calculate the wavelength corresponding to peak reflectivity by a periodic structure.*

LO 6: *discuss interference by a plane parallel film illuminated by a point source.*

LO 7: *describe interference by a film with two non-parallel reflecting surfaces.*

LO 8: *analyse colors of thin films.*

LO 9: *explain the formation of Newton's rings.*

LO 10: *discuss the working of Michelson interferometer.*

Above Image: View of a rainbow against a background of clouds. Photograph courtesy McGraw Hill Digital Access Library.

Important Milestones

1665: In his treatise, Micrographia, the British physicist Robert Hooke described his observations with a compound microscope having a converging objective lens and a converging eye lens. In the same work, he described his observations of the colors produced in flakes of mica, soap bubbles and films of oil on water. He recognised that the color produced in mica flakes is related to their thickness but was unable to establish any definite relationship between thickness and color. Hooke advocated a wave theory for the propagation of light.

1704: "Newton's rings" were first observed by Boyle and Hooke—they are named after Newton because he had given an explanation using the corpuscular model which was later found to be unsatisfactory.

1802: Thomas Young gave a satisfactory explanation of 'Newton's rings' based on wave theory.

1881: A.A. Michelson invented the "Michelson interferometer". He was awarded the 1907 Nobel Prize in Physics "for his optical precision instruments and the spectroscopic and metrological investigations carried out with their aid" Michelson was America's first Nobel Prize winner in science and during the presentation ceremony of the Nobel prize, the President of the Royal Swedish Academy of Sciences said, "Professor Michelson, Your interferometer has rendered it possible to obtain a non-material standard of length possessed of a degree of accuracy never hitherto attained. By its means we are enabled to ensure that the prototype of the meter has remained unaltered in length, and to restore it with absolute infallibility, supposing it were to get lost….. "

1887: A.A. Michelson and E.W. Morley carried out the famous Michelson-Morley experiment using the Michelson interferometer to detect the motion of the earth with respect to the 'Luminiferous Aether'.

14.1 Introduction

In the previous chapter, we discussed the interference pattern produced by division of a wavefront; for example, light coming out of a pinhole was allowed to fall on two holes, and spherical waves emanating from these two holes produced the interference pattern. In this chapter, we will consider the formation of interference pattern by division of amplitude; for example, if a plane wave falls on a thin film then the wave reflected from the upper surface interferes with the wave reflected from the lower surface. Such studies have many practical applications and also explain phenomena like the formation of beautiful colors produced by a soap film illuminated by white light.

14.2 Interference by a Plane Parallel Film when Illuminated by a Plane Wave

LO1

If a plane wave is incident normally on a thin* film of uniform thickness d (see Fig. 14.1) then the waves reflected from the upper surface interfere with the waves reflected from the lower surface. In this section, we will study this interference pattern. In order to observe the interference pattern without obstructing the incident beam, we use a partially reflecting plate G as shown in Fig. 14.1. Such an arrangement also enables us to eliminate the direct beam from reaching the photographic plate P (or the eye). The plane wave may be produced by placing an illuminated pinhole at the focal point of a corrected lens; alternatively, it may just be a beam coming out of a laser.

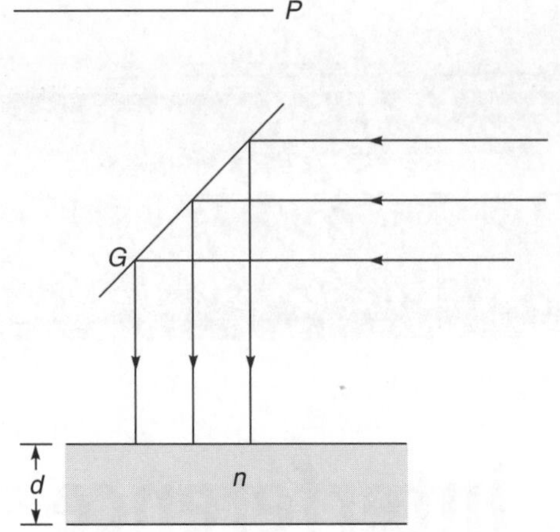

Figure 14.1
The normal incidence of a parallel beam of light on a thin film of refractive index n and thickness d. G denotes a partially reflecting plate and P represents a photographic plate.

Let the solid and the dashed lines in Fig. 14.2 represent the positions of the crests** (at any particular instant of time) corresponding to the waves reflected from the upper and lower surfaces of the film, respectively. In general, the wave reflected from the lower surface of the film will suffer multiple reflections. The effect of such multiple reflections is neglected (see Chapter 15). Clearly, the wave reflected from

Figure 14.2
The solid and the dashed lines represent the crests of the waves reflected from the upper surface and from the lower surface of the thin film. Notice that the distance between the consecutive crests inside the film is less than the corresponding distance in medium I.

* Why the film should be thin is explained in Sec. 14.7.

** Notice that the distance between consecutive crests in the film is less than the corresponding distance in air. This is because of the fact that the effective wavelength in a medium of refractive index n is λ/n.

the lower surface of the film traverses an additional optical path of $2nd$, where n represents the refractive index of the material of the film. Further, if the film is placed in air, then the wave reflected from the upper surface of the film will undergo a sudden change in phase of π (see Sec. 13.12) and as such the conditions for destructive or constructive interference will be given by

$$2nd = m\lambda \quad \text{destructive interference} \qquad \textbf{(14.1a)}$$

$$= \left(m+\frac{1}{2}\right)\lambda \quad \text{constructive interference} \qquad \textbf{(14.1b)}$$

where $m = 0, 1, 2, \ldots$ and λ represents the free space wavelength.

Thus, if we place a photographic plate at P (see Fig. 14.1), then the plate will receive uniform illumination; it will be dark when $2nd = m\lambda$ and bright when $2nd = \left(m+\frac{1}{2}\right)\lambda$; $m = 0, 1, 2,\ldots$ Instead of placing the photographic plate, if we try to view the film (from the top) with naked eye, then the film will appear to be uniformly illuminated.

It may be noted that the amplitudes of the waves reflected from the upper and lower surfaces will, in general, be slightly different; and as such the interference will not be completely destructive. However, with appropriate choice of the refractive indices of media II and III, the two amplitudes can be made very nearly equal (see Example 14.1).

For an air film between two glass plates (see Fig. 14.3) no phase change will occur on reflection at the glass-air interface, but a phase change of π will occur on reflection at the air-glass interface and the conditions for maxima and minima will remain the same. On the other hand, if the I medium is crown glass ($n = 1.52$), the II medium is an oil of refractive index 1.60 and the III medium is flint glass ($n = 1.66$) then a phase change of π will occur at both the reflections and the conditions for maxima and minima would be

$$2nd = \left(m+\frac{1}{2}\right)\lambda \quad \text{minima} \qquad \textbf{(14.2a)}$$

$$= m\lambda \quad \text{maxima} \qquad \textbf{(14.2b)}$$

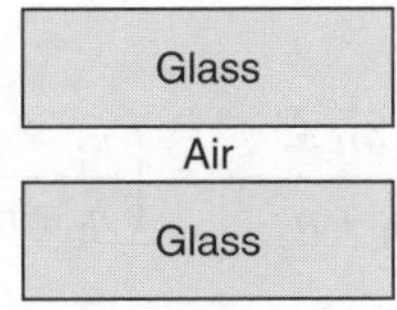

Figure 14.3
Thin film of air formed between two glass plates.

In general, whenever the refractive index of the II medium lies in between the refractive indices of the I and the III media, then the conditions of maxima and minima would be given by Eqs. (14.2a) and (14.2b).

We next consider the oblique incidence of the plane wave on the thin film (see Fig. 14.4). Once again, the wave reflected

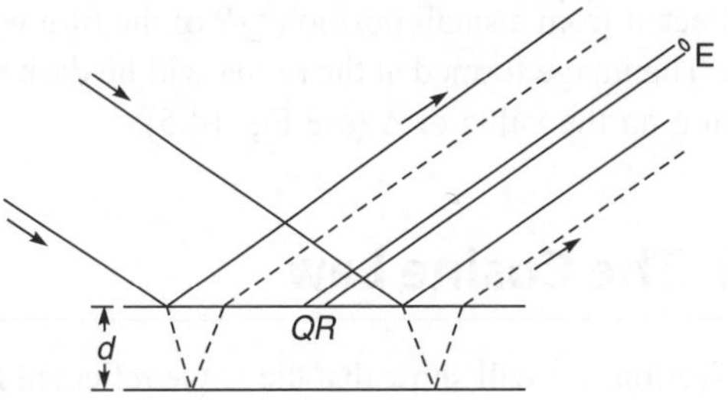

Figure 14.4
The oblique incidence of a plane wave on a thin film. The solid and dashed lines denote the boundary of the wave reflected from the upper surface and from the lower surface of the film. The eye E receives the light reflected from the region QR.

from the upper surface of the film interferes with the wave reflected from the lower surface of the film. The latter traverses an additional optical path Δ, which is given by (see Fig. 14.5):

$$\Delta = n_2(BD + DF) - n_1 BC \qquad \textbf{(14.3)}$$

where C is the foot of the perpendicular from the point F on BG. We will show in the next section that

$$\Delta = 2n_2 d \cos\theta' \qquad \textbf{(14.4)}$$

where θ' is the angle of refraction.

For a film placed in air, a phase change of π will occur when reflection takes place at the point B and as such, the conditions of destructive and constructive interference would be given by

$$\Delta = 2n_2 d \cos\theta' = m\lambda \quad \text{minima} \qquad \textbf{(14.5a)}$$

$$= \left(m+\frac{1}{2}\right)\lambda \quad \text{maxima} \qquad \textbf{(14.5b)}$$

If we place a photographic plate at P (see Fig. 14.5) it will receive uniform illumination; if we try to view the film with naked eye (at the position E — see Fig. 14.4) then only light

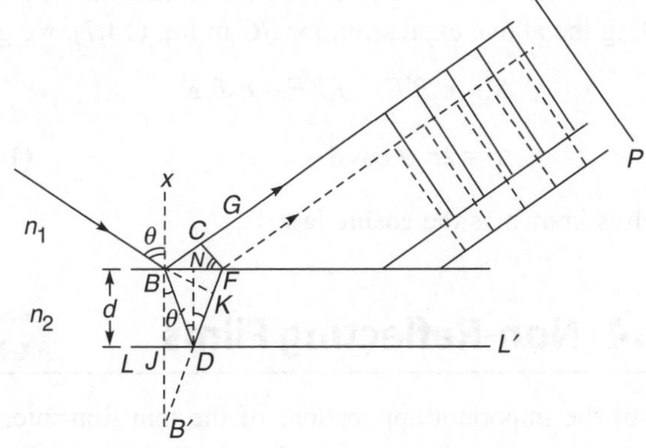

Figure 14.5
Calculation of the optical path difference between the waves reflected from the upper surface of the film and from the lower surface of the film. The solid and the dashed lines represent the corresponding positions of the crests. P denotes a photographic plate.

rays reflected from a small position QR of the film will reach the eye. The image formed at the retina will be dark or bright depending on the value of Δ (see Eq. 14.5).

14.3 The Cosine Law

LO2

In this section, we will show that the wave reflected from the lower surface of the film traverses an additional optical path which is given by the following expression:

$$\Delta = [n_2(BD + DF) - n_1BC] = 2n_2d \cos \theta' \quad (14.6)$$

Let θ and θ' denote the angles of incidence and refraction respectively. We drop a perpendicular BJ from the point B on the lower surface LL' and extend BJ and FD to the point B' where they meet (see Fig. 14.5). Clearly,

$$\angle JBD = \angle BDN = \angle NDF = \theta'$$

where N is the foot of the perpendicular drawn from the point D on BF. Now,

$$\angle BDJ = \frac{\pi}{2} - \theta'$$

and $$\angle B'DJ = \pi - \left[\left(\frac{\pi}{2} - \theta'\right) + \theta' + \theta'\right] = \frac{\pi}{2} - \theta' = \angle KFB$$

Thus, $BD = BD'$ and $BJ = JB' = d$

or $BD + DF = B'D + DF = B'F$

Hence, $$\Delta = n_2B'F - n_1BC \quad (14.7)$$

Now, $\angle CFB = \angle CBX = \theta$

$$BC = BF \sin \theta = \frac{KF}{\sin \theta'} \sin \theta = \frac{n_2}{n_1} KF \quad (14.8)$$

where K is the foot of the perpendicular from B on $B'F$. Substituting the above expression for BC in Eq. (14.7), we get

$$\Delta = n_2B'F - n_2KF = n_2B'K$$

or $$\Delta = 2n_2d \cos \theta' \quad (14.9)$$

which is known as the **cosine law**.

14.4 Non-Reflecting Films

LO3

One of the important applications of the thin film interference phenomenon discussed in Sec. 14.2 lies in reducing the reflectivity of lens surfaces; this we plan to discuss in this section. However, for a quantitative understanding of the

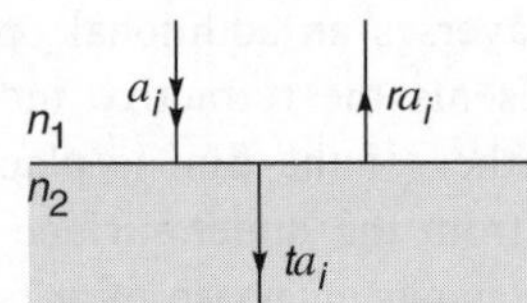

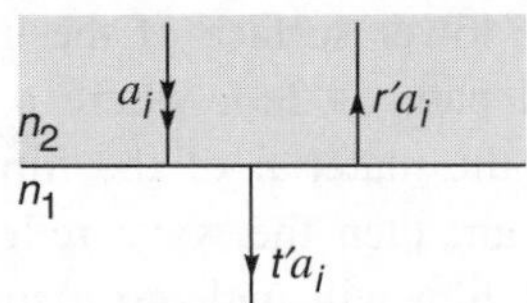

Figure 14.6

(a) If a plane wave of amplitude a_i, propagating in a medium of refractive index n_1, is incident normally on a medium of refractive index n_2, then the amplitudes of the reflected and the transmitted beams are a_r and a_t, respectively. Similarly, (b) corresponds to the case when the beam (propagating in a medium of refractive index n_2) is incident on a medium of refractive index n_1.

phenomenon, we will have to assume that when a light beam (propagating in a medium of refractive index n_1) is incident normally on a dielectric of refractive index n_2 then the amplitudes of the reflected and the transmitted beams are related to that of the incident beam through the following relations:

$$a_r = ra_i \quad \text{and} \quad a_t = ta_i \quad (14.10)$$

where a_i, a_r and a_t are the amplitudes of the incident beam, reflected beam and the transmitted beam respectively, and.

$$r = \frac{n_1 - n_2}{n_1 + n_2} \text{ and } t = \frac{2n_1}{n_1 + n_2} \quad (14.11)$$

amplitude reflection and transmission coefficients respectively [see Sec. 23.3 and Fig. 14.6(a)].

If r' and t' are the reflection and transmission coefficients where light propagating in a medium of refractive index n_2 is incident on a medium of refractive index n_1 [see Fig. 14.6(b)], then

$$r' = \frac{n_2 - n_1}{n_2 + n_1} = -r \quad (14.12)$$

$$t' = \frac{2n_2}{n_1 + n_2} \quad (14.13)$$

and

$$1 - tt' = 1 - \frac{4n_1n_2}{(n_1 + n_2)^2} = \left(\frac{n_1 - n_2}{n_1 + n_2}\right)^2 = r^2 \quad (14.14)$$

Equations (14.13) and (14.14) represent the Stokes' relations (see Sec. 13.12).

We will now discuss the application of the thin film interference phenomenon in reducing the reflectivity of lens surfaces. We all know that in many optical instruments (like a telescope) there are many interfaces and the loss of intensity due to reflections can be severe. For example, for near normal incidence, the reflectivity of crown glass surface in air is

$$\left(\frac{n-1}{n+1}\right)^2 = \left(\frac{1.5-1}{1.5+1}\right)^2 \simeq 0.04,$$

i.e., 4% of the incident light is reflected; in all what follows in this section, we will assume near normal incidence. For a dense flint glass $n \simeq 1.67$ and about 6% of light is reflected. Thus, if we have a large number of surfaces, the losses at the interfaces can be considerable. In order to reduce these losses, lens surfaces are often coated with a $\lambda/4n$ thick 'non-reflecting film'; the refractive index of the film being less than that of the lens. For example, glass (n = 1.5) may be coated with an MgF_2 film (see Fig. 14.7) and the film thickness d should be such that

$$2n_f d = \frac{1}{2}\lambda$$

or

$$d = \frac{\lambda}{4n_f} \qquad \textbf{(14.15)}$$

where we have assumed near normal incidence [i.e., $\cos\theta' \cong 1$; see Eq. (14.9)] and n_f represents the refractive index of the film; for MgF_2, $n_f = 1.38$. [Since the refractive index of the non-reflecting film is greater than that of air and less than that of the glass, abrupt phase change of π occurs at both the reflections. Consequently, when $2nd\cos\theta' = m\lambda$ there would be constructive interference and when $2nd\cos\theta' = \left(m+\frac{1}{2}\right)\lambda$ there would be destructive interference.] Thus, if we assume λ to be 5.0×10^{-5} cm (which roughly corresponds to the center of the visible spectrum), we will have

$$d = \frac{5.0\times10^{-5}\text{ cm}}{4\times1.38} \approx 0.9 \times 10^{-5}\text{ cm}$$

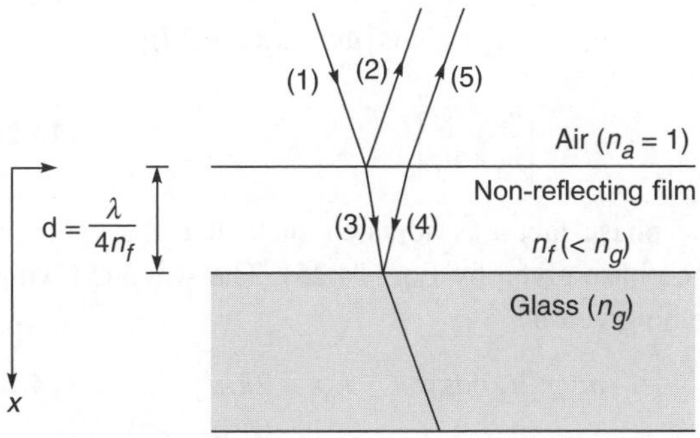

(1) (2) (5)
Air (n_a = 1)
$x = 0$
Non-reflecting film
$d = \frac{\lambda}{4n_f}$
(3) (4)
$n_f (< n_g)$
$x = d$
Glass (n_g)
x

Figure 14.7
If a film (having a thickness of $\lambda/4n_f$ and having refractive index less than that of the glass) is coated on the glass, then waves reflected from the upper surface of the film destructively interfere with the waves reflected from the lower surface of the film. Such a film is known as a non-reflecting film.

Figure 14.8 shows a comparison between a glasses lens without anti-reflective coating (top) and a lens with anti-reflective coating (bottom). Note the reflection of the photographer in the top lens and the tinted reflection in the bottom. We would like to emphasize the following points:

(a) Let n_a, n_f and n_g be the refractive indices of air, non-reflecting film and glass, respectively. If a is the amplitude of the incident wave then the amplitudes of the reflected and refracted waves (the corresponding rays shown as (2) and (3) in Fig. 14.7) would be

$$-\frac{n_f - n_a}{n_f + n_a}a \text{ and } \frac{2n_a}{n_f + n_a}a$$

respectively (we have assumed near normal incidence). The amplitudes of the waves corresponding to rays (4) and (5) would be

$$-\frac{2n_a}{n_f + n_a}\frac{n_g - n_f}{n_g + n_f}a$$

and

$$-\frac{2n_a}{n_f + n_a}\frac{n_g - n_f}{n_g + n_f}\frac{2n_f}{n_f + n_a}a$$

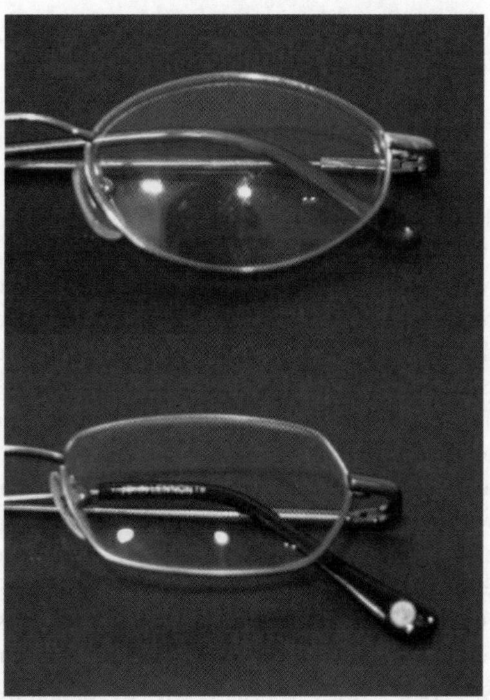

Figure 14.8
The top photograph is a glass lens without anti-reflective coating and the bottom photograph is of a lens with anti-reflective coating, Note the reflection of the photographer in the top lens and the tinted reflection in the bottom. [*Photograph taken by Justin Lebar; used with kind permission from Mr Lebar*].

respectively. Now, for complete destructive interference, the waves corresponding to rays (2) and (5) should have the same amplitude, i.e.,

$$-\frac{n_f - n_a}{n_f + n_a} a = -\frac{2n_a}{n_f + n_a} \frac{n_g - n_f}{n_g + n_f} \frac{2n_f}{n_f + n_a} a \quad \textbf{(14.16)}$$

or
$$\frac{n_f - n_a}{n_f + n_a} = \frac{n_g - n_f}{n_g + n_f} \quad \textbf{(14.17)}$$

where we have used the fact that $\frac{4n_a n_f}{(n_f + n_a)^2}$ is very nearly equal to unity; for $n_a = 1$ and $n_f = 1.4$,

$$\frac{4n_a n_f}{(n_f + n_a)^2} \approx 0.97$$

On simplification we obtain

$$n_f = \sqrt{n_a n_g} \quad \textbf{(14.18)}$$

If the first medium is air then $n_a = 1$ and with $n_g = 1.66$ (dense flint glass) n_f should be 1.29 and when $n_g = 1.5$ (light crown glass) n_f should be 1.22. We note that the refractive indices of magnesium fluoride and cryolite are 1.38 and 1.36, respectively. Now for a $\frac{\lambda}{4n}$ thick film, the reflectivity will be about

$$\left[\frac{n_f - n_a}{n_f + n_a} - \frac{n_g - n_f}{n_g + n_f}\right]^2 \quad \textbf{(14.19)}$$

Thus, for $n_a = 1$, $n_f = 1.38$ and $n_g = 1.5$ the reflectivity will be about 1.3%. In the absence of the film, the reflectivity would have been about 4%. The reduction of reflectivity is much more pronounced for the dense flint glass. This technique of reducing the reflectivity is known as **blooming**.

(b) The film is non-reflecting only for a particular value of λ; in Eq. (14.15) λ was assumed to be 5000 Å. For a polychromatic light, the film's non-reflecting property will be falling off when λ is greater or less than the above value. However, the effect is not serious. For example, for the MgF_2 film on crown glass at 5000 Å, the reflectivity rises by about 0.5% as one goes either to the red or the violet end of the visible spectrum. In Sec. 14.4.2, we will discuss why we should use a $\frac{\lambda}{4n}$ thick film and not $\frac{3\lambda}{4n}$ or $\frac{5\lambda}{4n}$ thick film, although the latter will also give destructive interference for the chosen wavelength.

(c) As in the case of Young's double slit experiment there is no loss of energy; there is merely a redistribution of energy. The energy appears mostly in the transmitted beam.

14.4.1 Mathematical Expressions for the Reflected Waves

It may be worthwhile to carry out a bit of mathematical analysis for the anti-reflecting film shown in Fig. 14.7. We assume $n_g > n_f > n_a$ and that the x-axis is pointing downwards with $x = 0$ at the upper surface of the film. The displacement associated with the incident wave (propagating in the $+x$ direction) is given by

$$y_1 = a\cos(\omega t - k_a x); \quad k_a = \frac{\omega}{c} n_a \quad \textbf{(14.20)}$$

Thus at $x = 0$, $y_1 = a \cos \omega t$. The reflected wave (shown as 2) would therefore be

$$y_2 = -a|r_1|\cos(\omega t + k_a x); \quad \textbf{(14.21)}$$

where

$$|r_1| = \left|\frac{n_f - n_a}{n_f + n_a}\right| \quad \textbf{(14.22)}$$

is a positive quantity. The minus sign in Eq. (14.21) represents the sudden phase change of π at $x = 0$. The transmitted wave (shown as 3) would be given by

$$y_3 = at_1\cos(\omega t - k_f x); \quad k_f = \frac{\omega}{c} n_f \quad \textbf{(14.23)}$$

where

$$t_1 = \frac{2n_a}{n_f + n_a} \quad \textbf{(14.24)}$$

Thus the displacement at $x = d$ [associated with wave (3)] is

$$y_3 = at_1\cos(\omega t - k_f d) \quad \textbf{(14.25)}$$

Therefore, the wave reflected from the lower surface [wave (4), which would be propagating in the negative x-direction] is given by

$$y_4 = -at_1|r_2|\cos[\omega t + k_f(x - 2d)]$$

$$|r_2| = \left|\frac{n_g - n_f}{n_g + n_f}\right| \quad \textbf{(14.26)}$$

where the phase factor is adjusted such that at $x = +d$ we obtain the phase given by Eq. (14.25). The wave (5) would therefore be given by

$$y_5 = -at_1|r_2|t_2\cos[\omega t + k_a x - 2k_f d] \quad \textbf{(14.27)}$$

Assuming the amplitudes of y_2 and y_5 to be approximately the same, destructive interference (between y_2 and y_5) would occur if

$$2k_f d = \pi, 3\pi, \ldots \quad \textbf{(14.28)}$$

or

$$d = \frac{\lambda_f}{4}, \frac{3\lambda_f}{4}, \frac{5\lambda_f}{4}, \ldots \quad \lambda_f = \frac{\lambda}{n_f} \quad \textbf{(14.29)}$$

14.4.2 Rigorous Expressions for Reflectivity

In the above section, we have considered two-beam interference and have neglected multiple reflections at the lower and upper surfaces. The effect of multiple reflections will be discussed in Sec. 15.2; however, such an effect is automatically taken into account when we solve Maxwell's equations incorporating the appropriate boundary conditions. In Sec. 23.4, we will carry out such an analysis and will show that the reflectivity (at normal incidence) of a dielectric film of the type shown in Fig. 14.7 is given by [see Sec. 23.10 and Eq. (23.94)]:*

$$R = \frac{r_1^2 + r_2^2 + 2r_1 r_2 \cos 2\delta}{1 + r_1^2 r_2^2 + 2r_1 r_2 \cos 2\delta} \tag{14.30}$$

where

$$r_1 = \frac{n_a - n_f}{n_a + n_f} \quad \text{and} \quad r_2 = \frac{n_f - n_g}{n_f + n_g}. \tag{14.31}$$

represent the Fresnel reflection coefficients at the first and second interface, respectively, and

$$\delta = \frac{2\pi}{\lambda} n_f d \tag{14.32}$$

d being the thickness of the film and, as before, λ represents the free space wavelength. Elementary differentiation shows us that $dR/d\delta = 0$ when $\sin 2\delta = 0$. Indeed for $r_1 r_2 > 0$,

$$\cos 2\delta = -1 \text{ (minima)} \tag{14.33}$$

represents the condition for minimum reflectivity and when this condition is satisfied, the reflectivity is given by

$$R = \left(\frac{r_1 - r_2}{1 - r_1 r_2}\right)^2 = \left(\frac{n_a n_g - n_f^2}{n_a n_g + n_f^2}\right)^2 \tag{14.34}$$

where we have used Eq. (14.18). Thus the film is non-reflecting when

$$n_f = \sqrt{n_a n_g}$$

consistent with Eq. (14.18). Now, the condition $\cos 2\delta = -1$ implies

$$2\delta = \frac{4\pi}{\lambda} n_f d = (2m + 1)\pi\,; \; m = 0, 1, 2, \ldots \tag{14.35}$$

or

$$d = \frac{\lambda}{4n_f}, \frac{3\lambda}{4n_f}, \frac{5\lambda}{4n_f}, \ldots \tag{14.36}$$

In Fig. 14.9, we have plotted the reflectivity as a function of δ for

$$n_a = 1 \qquad n_g = 1.5 \tag{14.37}$$

and

$$n_f = \sqrt{n_a n_g} \simeq 1.225$$

As expected, R is maximum ($\approx$ 4%) when $\delta = 0, \pi, 2\pi, \ldots$ and the film is anti-reflecting ($R = 0$) when $\delta = \pi/2, 3\pi/2, \ldots$ implying $d = \lambda/4n_f, 3\lambda/4n_f, \ldots$ As an example, let us suppose that we wish to make the film antireflecting at λ = 6000 Å; then from Eq. (14.26), the thickness of the film could be

1224.5 Å or 3673.5 Å or 6122.5 Å, …

In Fig. 14.9(b), we have plotted the reflectivity as a function of wavelength for d = 1224.5 Å and 3673.5 Å. As can be seen, for $d = \lambda/4n_f$, the minimum is broad and the reflectivity small for the entire range of the visible spectrum. Thus for antireflecting coating, the smallest film thickness is always preferred. For $n_a = 1$, $n_g = 1.5$ and $n_f = 1.38$, the reflectivity [according to Eq. (14.34)] comes out to be 1.4%, which is quite close to the result obtained by using the approximate theory described earlier [see Eq. (14.19)].

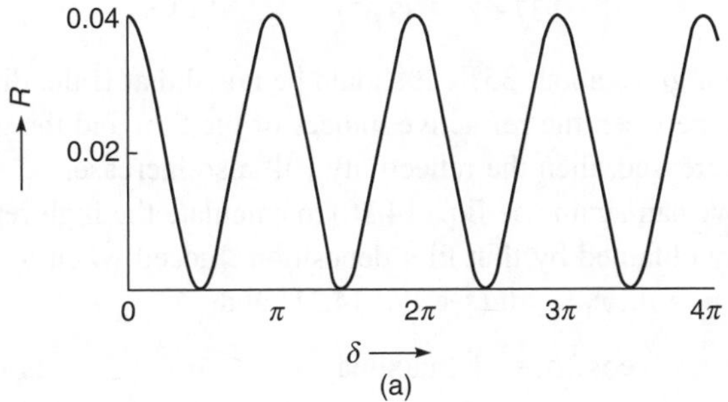

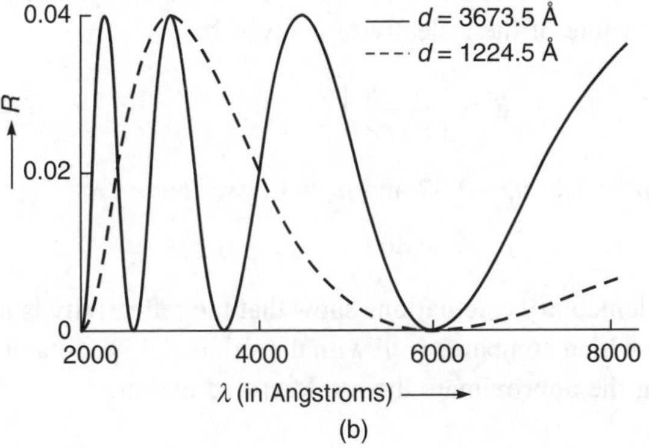

Figure 14.9
(a) Variation of the reflectivity of a film as a function of δ (= $2\pi n_f d/\lambda$) for $n_a = 1$, $n_g = 1.5$ and $n_f = \sqrt{n_a n_g} \simeq 1.225$. Notice that the reflectivity is zero for $\delta = \pi/2, 3\pi/2, 5\pi/2, \ldots$
(b) Wavelength variation of the reflectivity for a film of thickness 1224.5 Å (dashed curve) and of thickness 3673.5 Å (solid curve) with $n_a = 1$, $n_g = 1.5$ and $n_f = \sqrt{n_a n_g} \approx 1.225$. Notice that both films are non-reflecting at 6000 Å.

* Equation (14.30) is actually valid even for oblique incidence with r_1, r_2 and δ defined appropriately (see Sec. 23.10).

14.5 High Reflectivity by Thin Film Deposition

LO4

Another important application of the thin film interference phenomenon is the converse of the procedure just discussed, viz., the glass surface is coated by a thin film of suitable material to increase the reflectivity. The film thickness is again $\lambda/4n_f$ where n_f represents the refractive index of the film; however, the film is such that its refractive index is greater than that of the glass; consequently, an abrupt phase change of π occurs only at the air–film interface and the beams reflected from the air–film interface and the film–glass interface constructively interfere. For example, if we consider a film of refractive index 2.37 (zinc sulphide) then the reflectivity is $(2.37 - 1)^2/(2.37 + 1)^2$, i.e., about 16%. In the presence of a glass surface of refractive index 1.5 (light crown glass), the reflectivity will become [see the analysis in Sec. 14.4]:

$$\left[-\frac{2.37-1}{2.37+1}-\frac{4\times1\times2.37}{(3.37)^2}\times\frac{2.37-1.5}{2.37+1.5}\right]^2$$

which gives about 35%. It should be noted that if the difference between the refractive indices of the film and the glass is increased, then the reflectivity will also increase.

We can again use Eq. (14.30) to calculate the high reflectivity obtained by thin film deposition. Indeed when $n_a < n_f$ and $n_f > n_g$, $r_1r_2 < 0$ (see Eq. 14.31) and

$$\cos 2\delta = -1 \text{ (maxima)} \tag{14.38}$$

represents the condition for *maximum* reflectivity. The *maximum* value of the reflectivity is given by

$$R = \left(\frac{r_1 - r_2}{1 - r_1r_2}\right)^2 \tag{14.39}$$

For $n_a = 1.0$, $n_f = 2.37$ and $n_g = 1.5$, we have

$$r_1 \simeq -0.407, \qquad r_2 \simeq 0.225$$

Elementary calculations show that the reflectivity is about 33% which compares well with the value of 35% obtained by using the approximate theory described earlier.

14.6 Reflection by a Periodic Structure*

LO5

In Sec. 14.4, we had shown that a film of thickness $\lambda/4n_f$ where λ is the free space wavelength and n_f is the film refractive index (which lies between the refractive indices of the two surrounding media) acts like an antireflection layer. This happens due to the destructive interference occurring between the waves reflected from the top and bottom interfaces. In Sec. 14.5, we had shown that if the refractive index of the film was smaller (or greater) than both the surrounding media, then in such a case, in addition to the phase difference due to the additional path travelled by the wave reflected from the lower interface, there would also be an extra phase difference of π between the two reflected waves. Thus, in such a case a film of thickness $\lambda/4n_f$ would increase the reflectivity rather than reduce it.

We now consider a medium consisting of alternate layers of high and low refractive indices of $n_0 + \Delta n$ and $n_0 - \Delta n$ of equal thickness d [see Fig. 14.10(a)]. Such a medium is called a periodic medium and the spatial period of the refractive index variation is given by

$$\Lambda = 2d$$

Now if $\Delta n << n_0$, and if we choose the thickness of each layer to be

$$d = \frac{\lambda}{4n_0} \approx \frac{\lambda}{4(n_0 + \Delta n)} \approx \frac{\lambda}{4(n_0 - \Delta n)}$$

then the reflections arising out of individual reflections from the various interfaces would all be in phase and should result in a strong reflection. Thus for strong reflection at a chosen

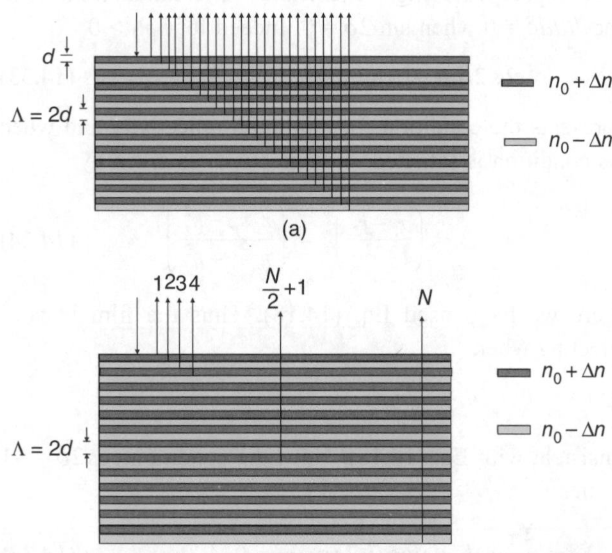

Figure 14.10

(a) Reflection from a periodic structure consisting of alternate layers of refractive indices $(n_0 + \Delta n)$ and $(n_0 - \Delta n)$, each of thickness $d = \lambda_B/4n_0$. (b) If we choose a wavelength $(\lambda_B + \Delta\lambda)$ such that reflections from layer 1 and layer $(N/2 + 1)$ are out of phase, reflections from layer 2 and layer $(N/2 + 2)$ are out of phase, etc., and finally reflection from layers $N/2$ and N are out of phase, then the reflectivity will be zero.

* A portion of this section has been very kindly written by Professor K. Thyagarajan.

(free space) wavelength λ_B, the period of the refractive index variation should be

$$\Lambda = 2d = \frac{\lambda_B}{2n_0} \quad \textbf{(14.40)}$$

This is referred to as the Bragg condition and is very similar to the Bragg diffraction of X-rays from various atomic layers (see Sec. 17.9). Equation (14.40) corresponds to the Bragg condition for normal incidence. The quantity λ_B is often referred to as the **Bragg wavelength**.

As an example, we consider a periodic medium comprising of alternate layers of refractive indices 1.51 and 1.49, i.e., $n_0 = 1.50$ and $\Delta n = 0.01$. If we require a strong reflectivity at $\lambda = \lambda_B = 5500$ Å then the required periodicity is

$$\Lambda = \frac{5500}{2 \times 1.5} \text{ Å} \approx 1833 \text{ Å}$$

If the periodic medium is made up of 100 layers (i.e., 50 periods) then we may approximate the total resultant amplitude to be

$$100 \times \frac{\Delta n}{n_0} \approx \frac{1}{1.5}$$

where $\Delta n/n_0$ is the amplitude reflection coefficient at each interface. The above estimation is only an approximation which is valid when $N \Delta n/n_0 << 1$, i.e., for small reflectivities; here we are just trying to obtain a crude estimate of the total reflectivity. Thus the reflectivity at 5500 Å should be

$$R \approx \left(\frac{1}{1.5}\right)^2 \Rightarrow R \approx 44\% \quad \textbf{(14.41)}$$

Figure 14.11 shows an actual calculated value of the reflectivity as a function of wavelength (using rigorous electromagnetic theory—see Ref. 14.6) for a periodic medium with $n_0 = 1.5$, $\Delta n = 0.01$, $d = \lambda_B/4n_0$ and consisting of 100 layers. Note that the actual calculation predicts a reflectivity of about 33% which compares well with our crude estimate of 44%!

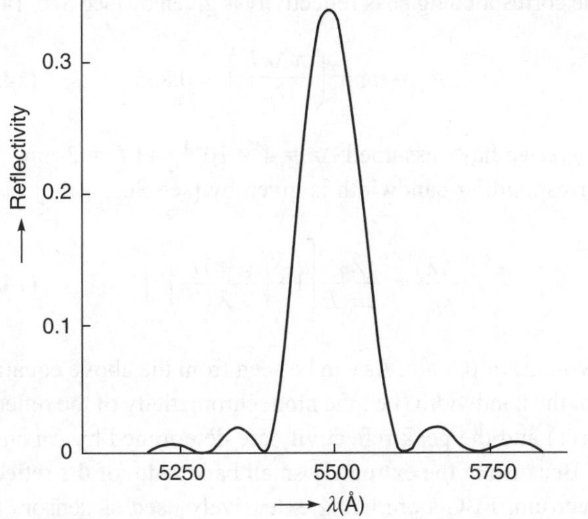

Figure 14.11
The exact variation of reflectivity with wavelength of a 100 layer periodic structure with $n_0 = 1.5$, $\Delta n = 0.01$, $\Lambda = 2d = 1833$ Å. The peak reflectivity appears at $\lambda = \lambda_B = 4n_0 d$. (Adapted from Ref. 14.6).

One notices from Fig. 14.11 that as we move away from the central wavelength ($\lambda_B = 2n_0\Lambda$) the reflectivity of the periodic medium falls off sharply. One can indeed obtain an approximate expression for the wavelength deviation $\Delta\lambda$ from λ_B which will produce a zero reflectivity. In order to do this, we first note that at λ_B (= $2n_0\Lambda$), the waves reflected from each of the N individual layers are all in phase leading to a strong reflection. If we move away from λ_B then the individual waves reflected from the various layers will not be in phase and thus the reflectivity reduces. If we choose a wavelength ($\lambda_B + \Delta\lambda$) such that the reflections from layer 1 and layer $\left(\frac{N}{2}+1\right)$, from layer 2 and $\left(\frac{N}{2}+2\right)$, and so on up to the reflections from layers $\frac{N}{2}$ and N are out of phase [see Fig. 14.10(b)], then the reflectivity will be zero. For reflection from each of the top $N/2$ layers, there is a reflection from a corresponding lower $N/2$ layer which is out of phase. (The argument is very similar to that used for obtaining the direction of minima in the diffraction pattern of a slit – see Sec. 17.2 and Fig. 17.5). Thus, when we move from λ_B to ($\lambda_B + \Delta\lambda$), the waves reflected from the first and $\left(\frac{N}{2}+1\right)$th layer should have an additional phase difference of π. Thus,

$$\frac{2\pi}{\lambda_B} n_0 \frac{N\Lambda}{2} - \frac{2\pi}{(\lambda_B + \Delta\lambda)} n_0 \frac{N\Lambda}{2} = \pi \quad \textbf{(14.42)}$$

where the first term on the LHS is simply the phase difference at λ_B between reflections 1 and $\left(\frac{N}{2}+1\right)$ due to the extra path travelled by the latter wave and the second term is that at ($\lambda_B + \Delta\lambda$). Assuming $\Delta\lambda << \lambda_B$, we have

$$\frac{2\pi}{\lambda_B^2} \frac{n_0 N\Lambda}{2} \Delta\lambda = \pi$$

or

$$\frac{\Delta\lambda}{\lambda_B} = \frac{\lambda_B}{n_0 N\Lambda} = \frac{\lambda_B}{2n_0 L} \quad \textbf{(14.43)}$$

where we have used Eq. (14.40) and $L = N\Lambda/2$ is the total thickness of the periodic medium. For the example shown in Fig. 14.11, we have

$$\Delta\lambda \approx 110 \text{ Å} \quad \textbf{(14.44)}$$

which compares very well with the actual value in Fig. 14.11. Thus if the incident wave is polychromatic (like white light) the reflected light may have a high degree of monochromaticity. This is indeed the principle used in white light holography.

The periodic medium discussed above finds wide applications in high reflectivity multilayer coatings, volume holography, fiber Bragg gratings etc. We will have a very brief discussion on fiber Bragg gratings below.

14.6.1 Fiber Bragg Gratings

A periodic structure discussed above has a very important application in the working of a fiber Bragg grating (usually abbreviated as FBG). We will discuss the optical fiber in Chapter 28; it may suffice here to mention that an optical fiber is a cylindrical structure consisting of a central dielectric core cladded by a material of slightly lower refractive index (see Fig. 28.7); the guidance of the light beam takes place because of total internal reflections at the core-cladding interface (see Chapters 28 and 30 for details). The cladding material is pure silica and the core is usually silica doped with germanium; the doping results in a slightly higher refractive index. Now, when a germanium-doped silica core fiber is exposed to ultraviolet radiation (with wavelength around 0.24 μm), the refractive index of the germanium-doped region increases; this is due to the phenomenon known as **photosensitivity** which was discovered by Kenneth Hill in 1974. The refractive index increase can be as large as 0.001 in the core of the fiber. If the fiber is exposed to a pair of interfering UV beams (see Fig. 14.12), then we would obtain an interference pattern similar to that shown in Fig. 14.13(b). In regions of constructive interference, the refractive index increases. Since the fringe width would depend on the angle between the interfering beams, the period of the grating can be controlled by choosing the angle between the interfering beams (see Example 13.5). Thus exposing a germanium doped silica fiber to the interference pattern formed between two UV beams leads to the formation of a periodic refractive index variation in the core of the fiber.

We consider a polychromatic beam incident on the fiber as shown in Fig. 14.13. As discussed above, the reflection from the periodic structure will add up in phase when

$$\lambda = \lambda_B = 2\Lambda n_0 \qquad \text{Bragg condition} \qquad \textbf{(14.45)}$$

which is the Bragg condition. Figure 14.13(a) shows the frequency spectrum of the incident polychromatic beam, the

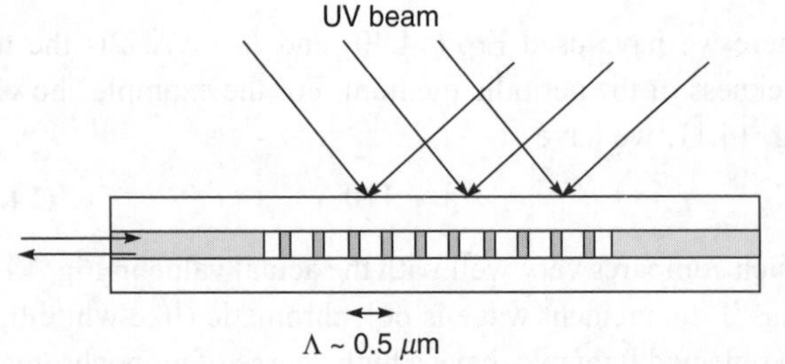

Figure 14.12

A Fiber Bragg Grating (usually abbreviated as FBG) is produced by allowing two beams to produce an interference pattern.

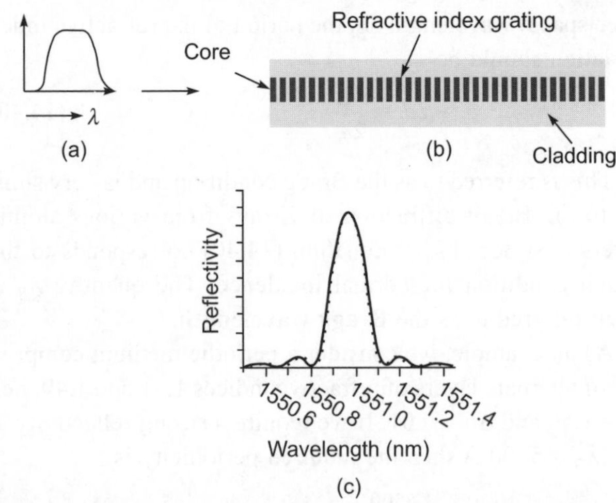

Figure 14.13

(a) The broad spectrum of the light wave incident on the FBG (Fiber Bragg Grating) shown in (b). (c) The spectrum of the reflected wave; solid line shows the calculated spectrum and the dotted curved show the experimentally measured values of the FBG fabricated at CGCRI, Kolkata. [*Figure courtesy Dr. S. Bhadra and Dr. S. Bandyopadhyay of CGCRI, Kolkata*].

Fiber Bragg grating is schematically shown in Fig. 14.13(b). Figure 14.13(c) shows a typical frequency spectrum of the reflected wave; solid line shows the calculated spectrum and the dashed curve show the experimentally measured values. For a silica fiber $n_0 \approx 1.46$ and for the periodic structure to be reflecting at $\lambda = 1550$ nm, we must have

$$\Lambda = \frac{\lambda_B}{2n_0} = \frac{1550 \text{ nm}}{2 \times 1.46} \approx 0.531 \text{ μm} \qquad \textbf{(14.46)}$$

The corresponding peak reflectivity is given by [see Sec. 14.12]

$$R_p = \tanh^2\left(\frac{\pi \Delta n L}{\lambda_B}\right) \approx 0.855 \qquad \textbf{(14.47)}$$

where we have assumed $\Delta n = 4 \times 10^{-4}$ and $L = 2$ mm. The corresponding bandwidth is given by [see Sec.14.12]

$$\frac{\Delta\lambda}{\lambda_B} \approx \frac{\lambda_B}{2n_0 L}\left[1+\left(\frac{(\Delta n)L}{\lambda_B}\right)^2\right]^{\frac{1}{2}} \qquad \textbf{(14.48)}$$

giving $\Delta\lambda \approx 0.5$ nm. As can be seen from the above equations that the bandwidth (i.e., the monochromaticity of the reflected wave) and the peak reflectivity are determined by Δn and L.

Because of the extremely small bandwidth of the reflected spectrum, FBG's are being extensively used as sensors (see Sec. 28.14.3). For example, a small increase in the temperature will increase the period of the grating which will result in an increase of the peak wavelength (see Fig. 28.25). Because silica is a dielectric material, FBG-based temperature sensors become particularly useful in places where there

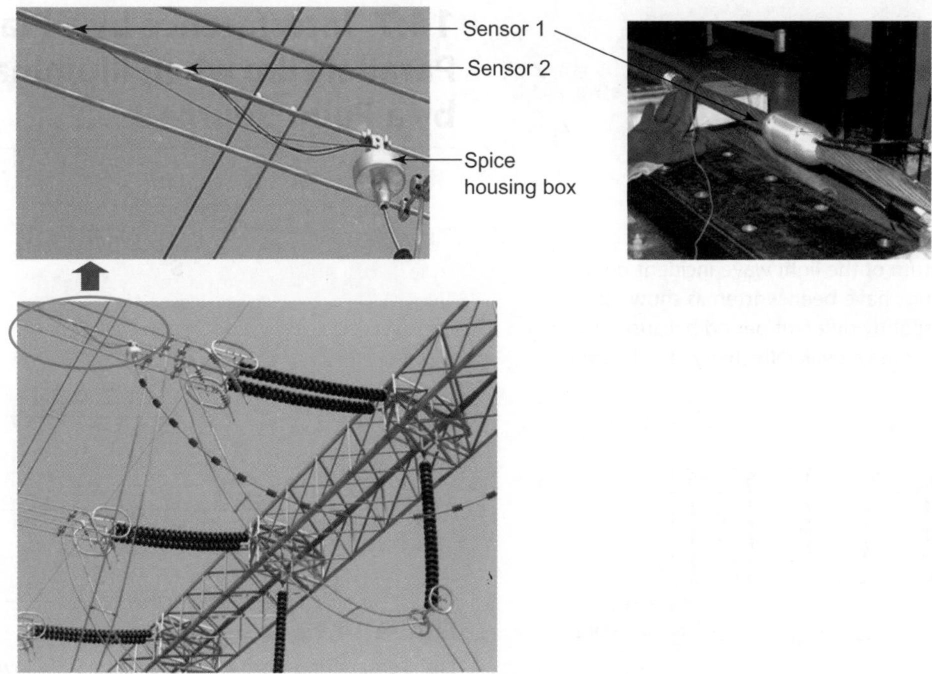

Figure 14.14

FBG based temperature sensor system on 400 KV power conductor at Subhashgram substation of Powergrid Corporation of India. Slide Courtesy: Dr Tarun Gangopadhyay and Mr. Kamal Dasgupta, CGCRI, Kolkata.

is high voltage. Figure 14.14 shows the FBG-based temperature sensor system on a 400 kV power conductor at an electric power substation (see Fig. 14.15). Figure 14.16 shows a typical reflection spectrum and the temperature recorded from the two FBG sensor shown in Fig. 14.14; for the two sensors, peak reflectivity occur at 1544.6438 nm and 1545.8789 nm, respectively.

Figure 14.15

The substation of Powergrid Corporation of India (near Kolkata, India) where the FBG temperature sensors have been installed. In the photograph, the author is with Dr. Tarun Gangopadhyay and Mr. Kamal Dasgupta. [*Slide Courtesy: Dr. Gangopadhyay and Mr. Dasgupta, CGCRI, Kolkata*].

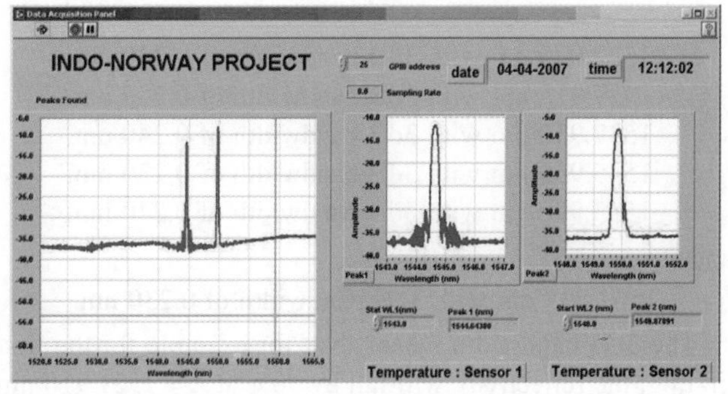

Figure 14.16

A typical reflection spectrum from the two FBG sensor shown in Fig. 14.14. [*Photo courtesy: Dr. Kamal Dasgupta and Dr. Tarun Gangopadhyay, CGCRI, Kolkata*].

One of the main advantages of the FBG sensor is the fact that several gratings can be written on a single fiber as shown in Fig. 14.17. Each grating has a different period and therefore a specific wavelength at which peak reflectivity occurs. If such a distributed sensor is put inside a bridge, one can measure the strain corresponding to the particular region. In fact, for many newly constructed bridges, FBG sensors are put at various places. Figure 14.18 shows the actual spectrum of the reflected light beam from a fiber on which six gratings have been written, each having a slightly different period. The wavelengths at which peak reflectivity occur are

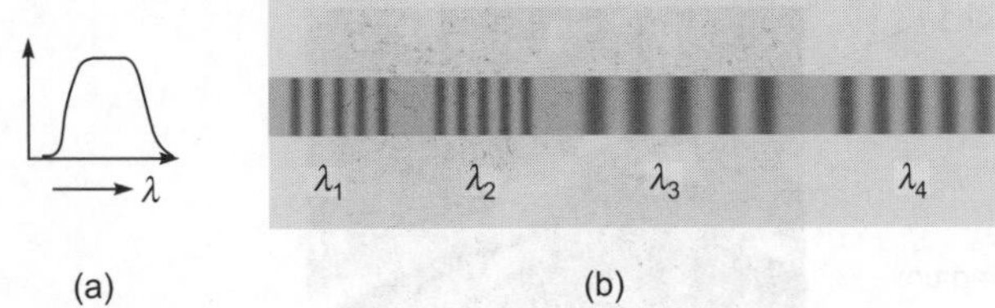

Figure 14.17

(a) The broad spectrum of the light wave incident on a fiber on which four gratings have been written as shown in (b). Each grating has a slightly different period because of which each one of them will have peak reflectivity at a different wavelength.

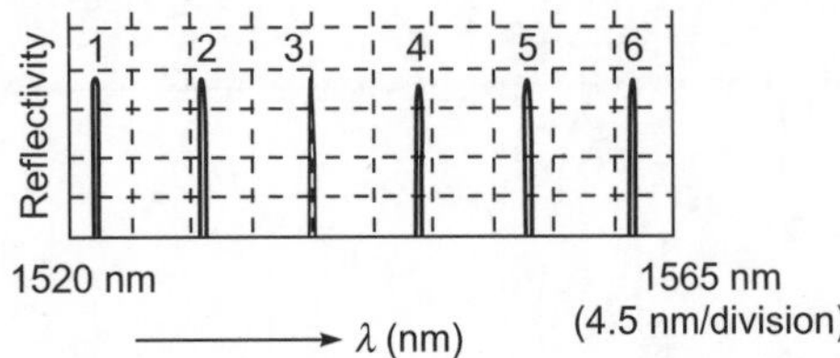

Figure 14.18

The actual spectrum of the reflected wave from a fiber on which six gratings have been written, each having a slightly different period. The wavelengths at which peak reflectivity occur are 1522.030 nm, 1529.915 nm, 1537.950 nm, 1545.955 nm, 1553.990 nm and 1561.895 nm. The gratings were fabricated at CGCRI, Kolkata. [*Figure courtesy: Dr. Kamal Dasgupta of CGCRI, Kolkata*].

1522.030 nm with 3dB bandwidth of 0.240 nm,
1529.915 nm with 3dB bandwidth of 0.230 nm,
1537.950 nm with 3dB bandwidth of 0.240 nm,
1545.955 nm with 3dB bandwidth of 0.230 nm,
1553.990 nm with 3dB bandwidth of 0.240 nm,

and

1561.895 nm with 3dB bandwidth of 0.230 nm.

The 3dB bandwidth means that, for example for the first grating, the reflectivity will fall by 50% at $\lambda \approx 1521.910$ nm and 1522.150 nm. Each grating has a length of 1 cm. Thus for the first grating with $\lambda_B = 1522.030$ nm, we get

$$\Lambda = \frac{\lambda_B}{2n_0} = \frac{1522.03 \text{ nm}}{2 \times 1.46} \approx 0.5212 \ \mu\text{m}$$

Further, assuming $L \approx 0.01$ m and $n_0 \approx 1.46$, Eq. (14.48) would give (one has to be careful with the units!)

$$\frac{0.240}{1522} \approx \frac{1.522 \times 10^{-6}}{1.46 \times 0.01}\left[1 + \left(\frac{(\Delta n) \times 0.01}{1.522 \times 10^{-6}}\right)^2\right]^{\frac{1}{2}}$$

giving $\Delta n \approx 1.7 \times 10^{-4}$.

14.7 Interference by a Plane Parallel Film when Illuminated by a Point Source

LO6

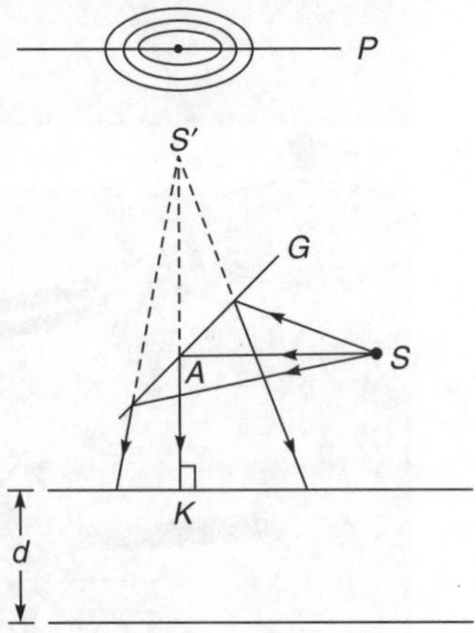

Figure 14.19

Light emanating from a point source *S* is allowed to fall on a thin film of thickness *d*. *G* is a partially reflecting plate and *P* represents the photographic plate. On the photographic plate circular fringes are obtained.

In Sec. 14.2, we had considered the incidence of a parallel beam of light on a thin film and had discussed the interference produced by the waves reflected from the upper and lower surfaces of the film. We will now consider the illumination of the film by a point source of light and, once again, in order to observe the film without obstructing the incident beam, we will use a partially reflecting plate *G* as shown in Fig. 14.19. However, in order to study the interference pattern we may *assume* the point source *S* to be right above the film (see Fig. 14.20) such that the distance *SK* (in Fig. 14.20) is equal to *SA* + *AK* (in Fig. 14.19); *KA* (in Fig. 14.19) and *KS* (in Fig. 14.20) being normal to the film. Obviously, the waves reflected from the upper surface of the film will appear to emanate from the point *S*′ where

$$KS' = KS \tag{14.49}$$

(see Fig. 14.20). Further, simple geometrical considerations will show that the waves reflected from the lower surface will appear to emanate from the point *S*″, where

$$KS'' \simeq KS + 2d/n_2 \tag{14.50}$$

(see Fig. 14.20). Equation (14.50) is valid only for near normal incidence.* Thus, at least for near normal incidence, the interference pattern produced in region I (see Fig. 14.20) will be very nearly** the same as produced by two point

* This is a consequence of the fact that the image of a point source produced by a plane refracting surface is not perfect.

** The fact that this is not identical to the Young's pattern is because of the fact that *S*″ is not a perfect image of the point *S*. For large angles of incidence, the waves reflected from the lower surface will appear to emanate from a point which will be displaced from *S*″.

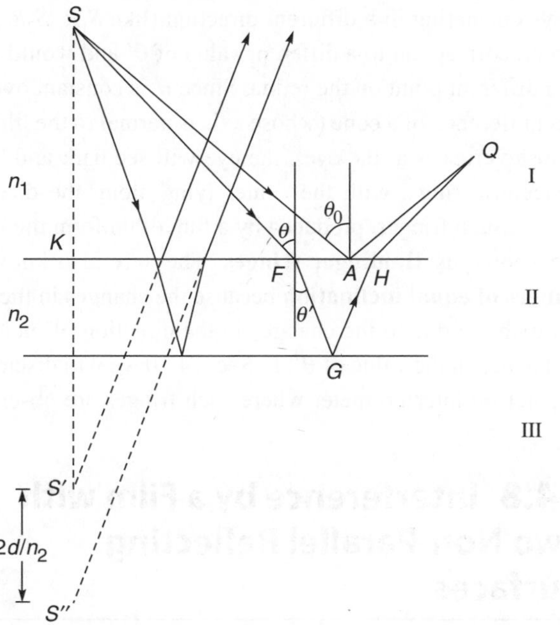

Figure 14.20
If light emanating from a point source S is incident on a thin film then the interference pattern produced in the region I is approximately the same as would have been produced by two coherent point sources S' and S'' (separated by a distance $2d/n_2$) where d represents the thickness of the film and n_2 represents the refractive index of the film.

coherent sources S' and S'' (which is the double hole experiment of Young discussed in the previous chapter). Thus, if we put a photographic plate P (see Fig. 14.19) we will, in general, obtain interference fringes. The intensity of an arbitrary point Q [in Fig. 14.20] will be determined by the following relations:

$$\Delta = \left(m + \frac{1}{2}\right)\lambda \qquad \text{maxima} \tag{14.51a}$$

$$= m\lambda \qquad \text{minima} \tag{14.51b}$$

where $$\Delta = [n_1 SF + n_2(FG + GH) + n_1 HQ] - [n_1(SA + AQ)] \tag{14.52}$$

represents the optical path difference and we have assumed that in one of the reflections, an abrupt phase change of π occurs; n_1 and n_2 are the refractive indices of media I and II respectively. The above conditions are rigorously correct; i.e., valid even for large angles of incidence. Further, it can be shown that for near normal incidence,

$$\Delta \simeq 2n_2 d\cos\theta' \tag{14.53}$$

A more rigorous calculation shows (see Ref. 14.7)

$$\Delta \simeq 2n_2 d\cos\theta' \left[1 - \frac{n_1^2 \sin\theta\cos\theta}{n_2^2 - n_1^2\sin^2\theta}\left(\frac{\theta_0 - \theta}{2}\right)\right] \tag{14.54}$$

where the angles θ, θ_0 and θ' are defined in Fig. 14.20.

Now, if we put a photographic plate (parallel to the surface of the film (see Fig. 14.20)) we will obtain dark and bright concentric rings (see Example 14.6).* On the other hand, if we view the film with naked eye then, for a given position of the eye, we will be able to see only a very small portion of the film; e.g., with eye at the position E and the point source at S only a portion of the film around the point B will be visible [see Fig. 14.21(a)], and this point will appear to be dark or bright as the optical path difference,

$$\Delta = n_1 SQ + n_2(QA + AB) - n_1 SB$$

is $m\lambda$ or $\left(m + \frac{1}{2}\right)\lambda$. Further, using a method similar to the one described in Sec. 14.3, we can obtain

$$\Delta \simeq 2n_2 d\cos\theta' \tag{14.55}$$

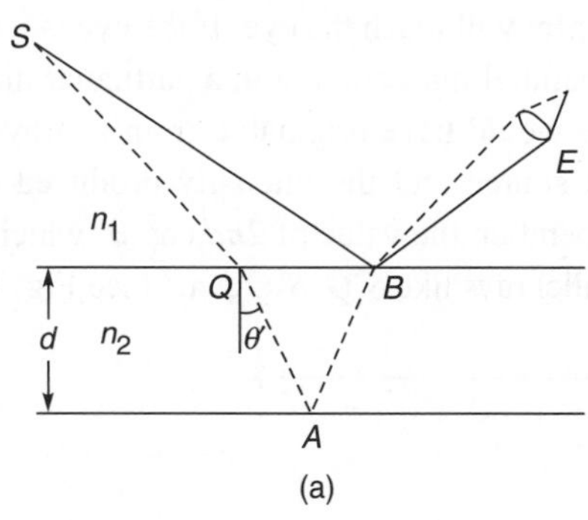

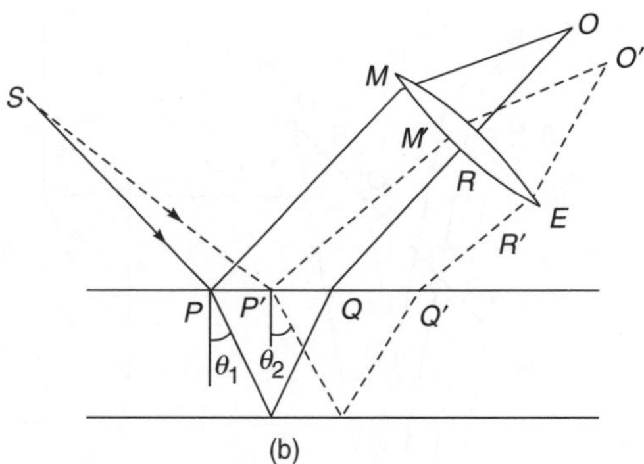

Figure 14.21
Light emanating from a point source S is incident on a thin film; (a) if the film is viewed by the naked eye E then the point B will appear to be dark if the optical path $[\{n_1 SQ + n_2(QA + AB)\} - n_1 SB]$ is $m\lambda$, and bright if the optical path is $\left(m + \frac{1}{2}\right)\lambda$. (b) If the eye is focused for infinity then it receives parallel rays from different directions corresponding to different values of the angles of refraction θ' (and hence different values of the optical path difference).

* If the point source is taken far away, then it can easily be seen that the rings will spread out and in the limit of the point source being taken to infinity (i.e., incidence of a parallel beam), the photographic plate will be uniformly illuminated.

Instead of looking at the film, if the eye is focussed at infinity, then the interference is between the rays which are derived from a single incident ray by reflection from the upper and the lower surfaces of the film [see Fig. 14.21(b)]. For example, the rays PM and QR, which focus at the point O of the retina, are derived from the single ray SP, and the rays $P'M'$ and $Q'R'$, which focus at a different point O' on the retina, are derived from the ray SP'. Since the angles of refraction θ_1' and θ_2' (for these two sets of rays) will be different, the points O and O' will, in general, not have the same intensity.

We next consider the illumination by an extended source of light S (see Fig. 14.22). Such an extended source may be produced by illuminating a ground glass plate by a sodium lamp. Each point on the extended source will produce its own interference pattern on the photographic plate P; these will be displaced with respect to one another; consequently, no definite fringe pattern will appear on the photographic plate. However, if we view the film with our eye, rays from all points of the film will reach the eye. If the eye is focussed at infinity then parallel light coming in a particular direction reaching the eye would have originated from nearby points of the extended source and the intensity produced on the retina would depend on the value of $2nd \cos \theta'$ which is the same for all parallel rays like S_1Q, S_2Q', etc. (see Fig. 14.22).

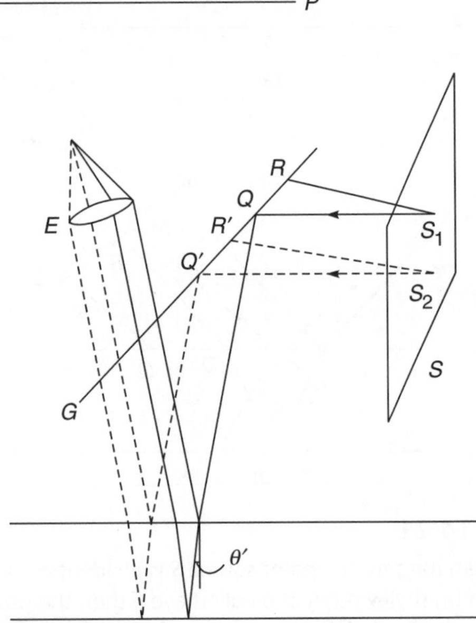

Figure 14.22
Light emanating from an extended source illuminates a thin film. G represents the partially reflecting plate and P represents the photographic plate. The eye E is focussed at infinity.

Rays emanating in a different direction (like S_1R, S_2R', etc.) would correspond to a different value of θ' and would focus at a different point on the retina. Since θ' is constant over the circumference of a cone (whose axis is normal to the film and whose vertex is at the eye), the eye will see dark and bright concentric rings, with the center lying along the direction $\theta' = 0$. Such fringes, produced by a film of uniform thickness, are known as **Haidinger fringes**. They are also known as **fringes of equal inclination** because the changes in the optical path are due to the changes in the direction of incidence and hence in the value of θ'. In Sec. 14.10 we will discuss the Michelson interferometer where such fringes are observed.

14.8 Interference by a Film with Two Non-Parallel Reflecting Surfaces

LO7

Till now we have assumed the film to be of uniform thickness. We will now discuss the interference pattern produced by a film of varying thickness. Such a film may be produced by a wedge which consists of two non-parallel plane surfaces [see Fig. 14.23(a)].

We first consider a parallel beam of light incident normally on the upper surface of the film [see Fig. 14.23(a)]. In Fig. 14.23(b) the successive positions of the crests (at a particular instant of time) reflected from the upper surface and from the lower surface of the film are shown by solid and dashed lines, respectively. Obviously, a photographic plate P will record straight line interference fringes which will be parallel to the edge of the wedge (the edge is the line passing through the point O and perpendicular to the plane of the paper). The dots in the figure indicate the positions of maxima. In order to find the distance between two consecutive fringes on the film we note that for the point A to be bright*

$$n(LM + MA) = \left(m + \frac{1}{2}\right)\lambda; \quad m = 0, 1, 2, \ldots \qquad \textbf{(14.56)}$$

[see Fig. 14.23(a)]. However, when the wedge angle ϕ is very small (which is indeed the case for practical systems)

$$LM + MA \approx 2AA'$$

where AA' represents the thickness of the film at A. Thus, the condition for the point A to be bright is

$$2nAA' \approx \left(m + \frac{1}{2}\right)\lambda \qquad \textbf{(14.57)}$$

* We are assuming here that the beam undergoes a sudden phase change of π when it gets reflected by the upper surface. The expression for the fringe width (Eq. 14.60) is, however, independent of this condition.

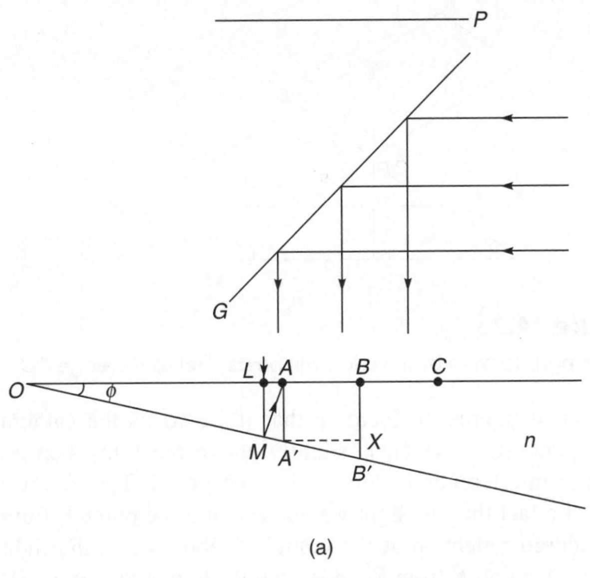

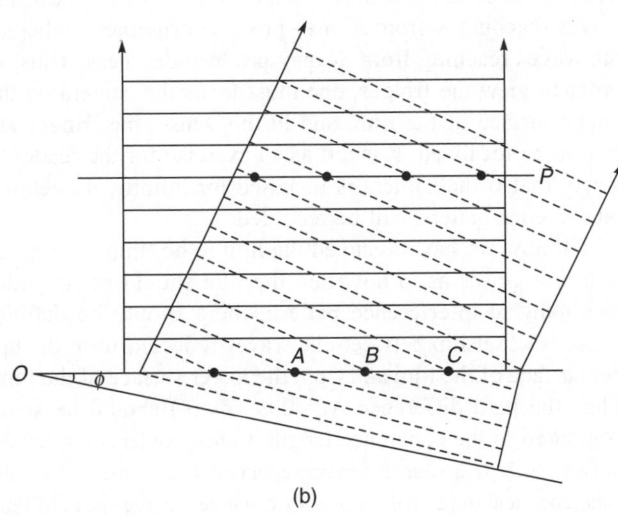

Figure 14.23

(a) A parallel beam of light incident on a wedge. (b) The solid and the dashed lines represent the positions of the crests (at a particular instant of time) corresponding to the waves reflected from the upper surface and from the lower surface respectively. The maxima will correspond to the intersection of the solid and dashed lines. The fringes will be perpendicular to the plane of the paper.

Similarly, the next bright fringe will occur at the point B where

$$2nBB' \approx \left(m + \frac{3}{2}\right)\lambda \tag{14.58}$$

Thus, $\quad 2n(BB' - AA') \approx \lambda$

or $\quad XB' \approx \lambda/2n \quad (14.59)$

But $\quad XB' = (A'X) \tan\phi$

or

$$A'X = \beta \approx \frac{\lambda}{2n\phi} \tag{14.60}$$

where β represents the fringe width and we have assumed ϕ to be small. Such fringes are commonly referred to as **fringes of equal thickness**.

On the other hand, for a point source, the fringe pattern will be similar to the parallel film case; i.e., for near normal incidence, the pattern will be very nearly the same as produced by two sources S' and S'' (Fig. 14.24). (Notice that the point S'' is not vertically below S'; this is a consequence of the fact that the two surfaces of the film are not parallel.) The intensity of an arbitrary point Q will be determined by the following equations:

$$[SA + n(AB + BC) + CQ] - [SD + DQ]$$

$$= \left(m + \frac{1}{2}\right)\lambda \quad \text{maxima} \tag{14.61}$$

$$= m\lambda \qquad \text{minima}$$

If we view the film with naked eye (say at the position E—see Fig. 14.24) then only a small portion of the film (around the point R) would be visible and the point R will be bright or dark as the optical path difference $[\{SN + n(NL + LR)\} - SR]$ is $\left(m + \frac{1}{2}\right)\lambda$ or $m\lambda$, respectively. One can similarly discuss the case when the eye is focussed for infinity.

We next consider the illumination by an extended source S as shown in Fig. 14.25. Since the extended source can be assumed to consist of a large number of independent point

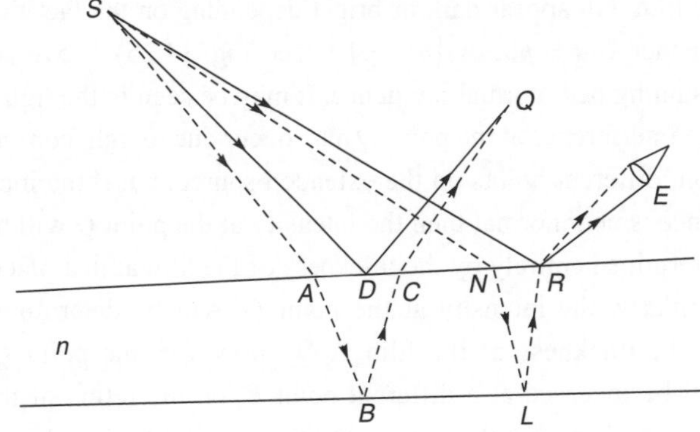

Figure 14.24

Light from a point source illuminating a wedge. E represents the lens of the eye.

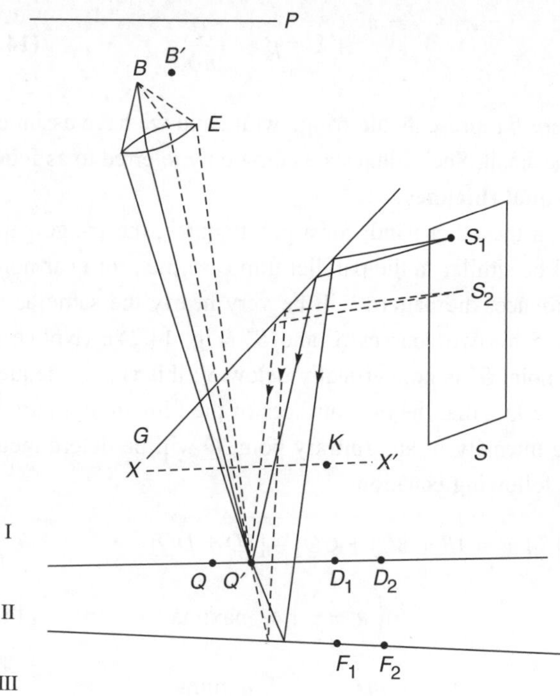

Figure 14.25
Localized interference fringes produced by an extended source *S*. Fringes will be seen only when the eye is focussed on the upper surface of the film.

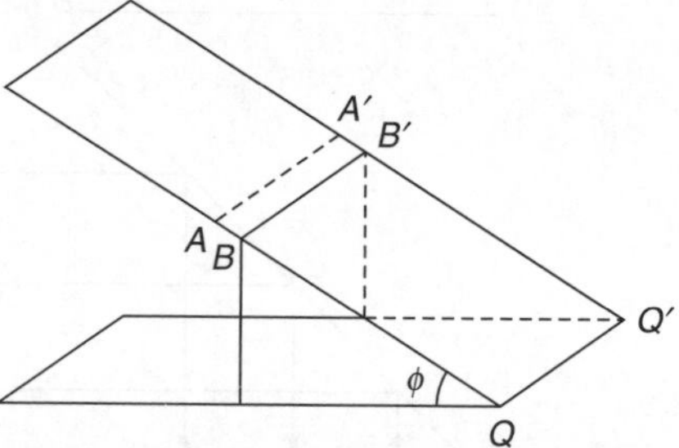

Figure 14.26
The fringes formed by a wedge will be parallel to the edge *OO*′.

sources, each point source will produce its own pattern on a photographic plate *P*. Consequently, no definite fringe pattern will be observed.* However, if we view the film with a camera (or with a naked eye) and if the camera is focussed on the upper surface of the film then a particular point on the film will appear dark or bright depending on the fact that whether $2nd$ is $m\lambda$ or $\left(m+\frac{1}{2}\right)\lambda$ (see Fig. 14.25) — we are assuming near normal incidence. It may be seen in the figure that interference at the point Q may occur due to light coming from different points on the extended source, but if the incidence is near normal then the intensity at the point Q will be determined entirely by the thickness of the film at that place. Similarly, the intensity at the point Q' will be determined by the thickness of the film at Q'; however, the point Q' will be focussed at a different point B' on the retina of the eye. The fringes will be straight lines parallel to the edge of the film OO' (Fig. 14.26). It should be emphasized that all along we are assuming near normal incidence and the fact that the wedge angle is extremely small. These assumptions are indeed valid for practical systems.

It is of interest to mention that if we focus the camera on a plane XX', which is slightly above the film, then no definite interference pattern will be observed. This follows from the fact that the light waves reaching the point K from S_2 undergo reflection at the points D_2 and F_2 and the light waves reaching K from S_1 undergo reflection at the points D_1 and F_1. Since the thickness of the film is not uniform, the waves reaching K from S_1 may produce brightness, whereas the waves reaching from S_2 may produce darkness. Thus, in order to view the fringes, one must focus the camera on the upper surface of the film, and in this sense, the fringes are said to be localized. It is left as an exercise for the reader to verify that if the camera is focussed for infinity, no definite interference pattern will be recorded.

Till now we have assumed the film to be 'thin'; the question now arises as to how thin the film should be. In order to obtain an interference pattern, there should be definite phase relationship between the waves reflected from the upper surface of the film and from the lower surface of the film. Thus the path difference $\Delta(= 2nd \cos\theta')$ should be small compared to the coherence length. Coherence length is defined in Sec. 16.1. If a source remains coherent for a time τ, then the coherence length (L) will be about $c\tau_c$ where c is the speed of light in free space. Thus for $\tau_c \sim 10^{-10}$ sec, $L \sim 3$ cm. For example, if we are using the D_1 line of an ordinary sodium lamp ($\lambda = 5.890 \times 10^{-5}$ cm), the coherence length is of the order of 1 cm and for fringes to be visible Δ should be much less than 1 cm. It should be pointed out that there is no particular value of Δ for which the fringes disappear; but as the value of Δ increases, the contrast of the fringes becomes poorer. A laser beam has a very high coherence length and fringes can be visible even for path differences much greater than 1 m. On the other hand, if we use a white light source no fringes will be visible for $\Delta \gtrsim 2 \times 10^{-4}$ cm (see Sec. 13.9).

It should be pointed out that interference also occurs in region III (see Fig. 14.27) between the directly transmitted beam and the beam which comes out of the film after suffering two reflections, first from the lower surface and then from

* There is, however, one exception to this, when the extended source is taken to a very large distance, then the light rays reaching the plate *G* will be approximately parallel and an interference pattern (of low contrast) will be formed on the plate *P*. The same phenomenon will also occur if instead of moving the extended source we take the plate *P* far away from the wedge.

the upper surface of the film. However, the two amplitudes will be very different and the fringes will have very poor contrast (see Example 14.1).

EXAMPLE 14.1 Consider a film of refractive index 1.36 in air. Assuming near normal incidence ($\theta \approx 0$), show that whereas the amplitudes of the reflected rays (1) and (5) (Fig. 14.27) are nearly equal, the amplitudes of the transmitted rays (4) and (7) are quite different. (This is the reason why the fringes observed in transmission have very poor contrast.)

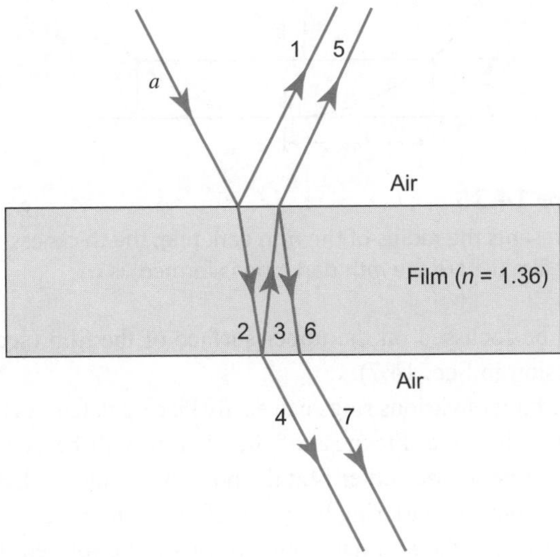

Figure 14.27
Near normal incidence of a light beam on a film (of refractive index 1.36) placed in air.

Solution: Let the amplitude of the incident ray be a and let the amplitudes of the rays (1), (2), (3), ... be denoted by a_1, a_2, ... etc. Using Eqs. (14.10a) and (14.10b), we get

$$a_1 = \frac{1-n}{1+n}a = -\frac{0.36}{2.36}a \approx -0.153a$$

$$a_2 = \frac{2}{1+n}a = \frac{2}{2.36}a \approx 0.847a$$

$$a_3 = \frac{n-1}{n+1}a_2 = \frac{0.36}{2.36} \times 0.874a \approx 0.129a$$

$$a_5 = \frac{2n}{n+1}a_3 = \frac{2 \times 1.36}{2.36} \times 0.129a \approx 0.149a$$

$$a_4 = \frac{2n}{1+n}a_2 = \frac{2 \times 1.36}{2.36} \times 0.847a \approx 0.977a$$

$$a_7 = \frac{2n}{n+1}a_6 = \frac{2n}{n+1} \cdot \frac{n-1}{n+1}a_3 = \frac{2 \times 1.36 \times .36}{(2.36)^2}a_3$$

$$\approx 0.023a$$

We first note that the sign of a_5 is opposite to that of a_1 which is a consequence of the fact that a sudden phase change of π occurs when the ray gets reflected at the point B. Further the magnitude of a_5 is nearly equal to that of a_1. On the other hand $|a_7| << |a_4|$. This is the reason why the interference fringes formed in transmission have poor contrast.

14.9 Colors of Thin Films

LO7

We have seen in the previous section that if light from an extended monochromatic source (like a sodium lamp) is incident normally on a wedge, then equally spaced dark and bright fringes will be observed. The distance between two consecutive bright (or dark) fringes is determined by the wedge angle, the wavelength of light and by the refractive index of the film. If we use a polychromatic source (like an incandescent lamp) we will observe colored fringes. Further, if instead of a wedge we have a film of arbitrarily varying thickness we will again observe fringes, each fringe representing the locus of constant film thickness (see Fig. 14.28). This is indeed what we see when sunlight falls on a soap bubble or on a thin film of oil on water. It should be mentioned that if the optical path difference between the waves reflected from the upper surface of the film and from the lower surface of the film exceeds a few wavelengths, the interference pattern will be washed out due to the overlapping of interference patterns of many colors and no fringes will be seen (see Sec. 13.9). Thus, in order to see the fringes with white light, the film should not be more than few wavelength thick.

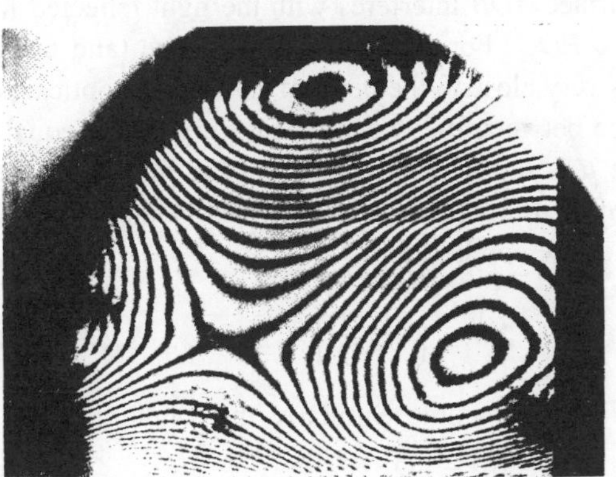

Figure 14.28
A typical fringe pattern produced by an airfilm formed between two glass surfaces (which are not optically flat) and placed in contact with each other. Whenever the thickness of the airfilm is $m\lambda/2$, we obtain a dark fringe and when the thickness is $\left(m+\frac{1}{2}\right)\lambda/2$, we obtain a bright fringe. Each fringe describes a focus of equal thickness of the film. [*Photograph courtesy: Prof. R.S. Sirohi*].

14.10 Newton's Rings

If we place a plano-convex lens on a plane glass surface, a thin film of air is formed between the curved surface of the lens (*AOB*) and the plane glass plate (*POQ*)—see Fig. 14.29.

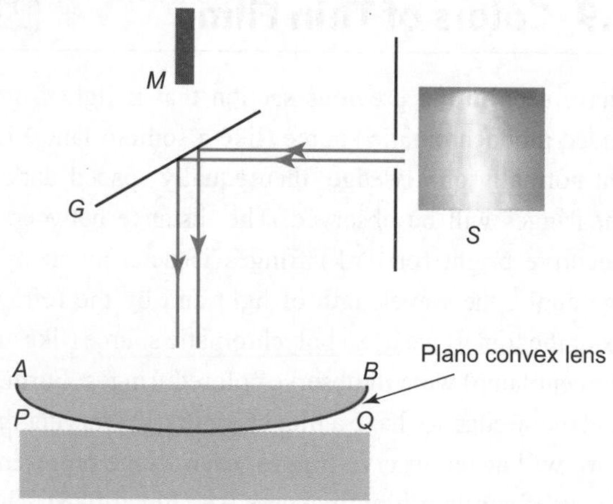

Figure 14.29
An arrangement for observing Newton's rings. Light from an extended source *S* is allowed to fall on a thin film formed between the plano-convex lens *AOB* and the plane glass plate *POQ*. *M* represents a traveling microscope.

The thickness of the air film is zero at the point of contact *O* and increases as one moves away from the point of contact. If we allow monochromatic light (such as from a sodium lamp) to fall on the surface of the lens, then the light reflected from the surface *AOB* interferes with the light reflected from the surface *POQ*. For near normal incidence (and considering points very close to the point of contact) the optical path difference between the two waves is very nearly equal to $2\mu t$, where μ is the refractive index of the film and t the thickness of the film. Thus, whenever the thickness of the air film satisfies the condition

$$2\mu t = \left(m + \frac{1}{2}\right)\lambda;\ m = 0, 1, 2, \ldots \tag{14.62}$$

we will have maxima. Similarly, the condition

$$2\mu t = m\lambda \tag{14.63}$$

will correspond to minima. Since the convex side of the lens is a spherical surface, the thickness of the air film will be constant over a circle (whose center will be at *O*) and we will obtain concentric dark and bright rings. These rings are known as **Newton's rings**. [Boyle and Hooke had independently observed the fringes earlier but Newton was the first to measure their radii and make an analysis. The proper explanation was given by Thomas Young. Also see 'Milestones' in the beginning of this chapter.] It should be pointed out that in order to observe the fringes, the microscope (or the eye) has to be focussed on the upper surface of the film (see the discussion in Sec. 14.7).

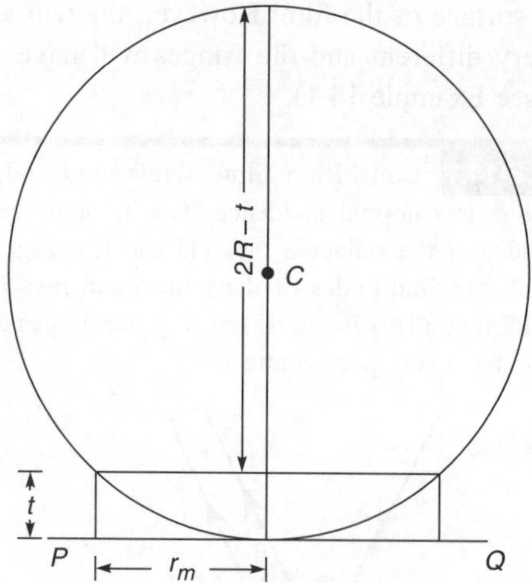

Figure 14.30
r_m represents the radius of the *m*th dark ring; the thickness of the air film (where the *m*th dark ring is formed) is *t*.

The radii of various rings can easily be calculated. As mentioned earlier, the thickness of the air film will be constant over a circle whose center is at the point of contact *O*. Let the radius of the *m*th dark ring be r_m and if t is the thickness of the air film where the *m*th dark ring appears to be formed, then

$$r_m^2 = t(2R - t) \tag{14.64}$$

where R represents the radius of curvature of the convex surface of the lens (see Fig. 14.30). Now $R \approx 100$ cm and $t \lesssim 10^{-3}$ cm, thus we may neglect t in comparison to $2R$ to obtain

$$r_m^2 \approx 2Rt$$

or

$$2t \approx \frac{r_m^2}{R} \tag{14.65}$$

Substituting this in Eq. (14.63), we get

$$r_m^2 \approx \frac{m\lambda R}{\mu};\ m = 0, 1, 2, \ldots \tag{14.66}$$

which implies that the radii of the rings vary as square root of natural numbers. Thus the rings will become close to each other as the radius increases (see Fig. 14.31). Between the two dark rings there will be a bright ring whose radius will be $\sqrt{\left(m + \frac{1}{2}\right)\frac{\lambda R}{\mu}}$.

Newton's rings can easily be observed in the laboratory by using an apparatus as shown in Fig. 14.29. Light from an extended source (emitting almost monochromatic light, like a sodium lamp) is allowed to fall on a glass plate which partially reflects the beam. This reflected beam falls on the plano-convex lens–glass plate arrangement and Newton's rings can easily be observed by viewing directly or through

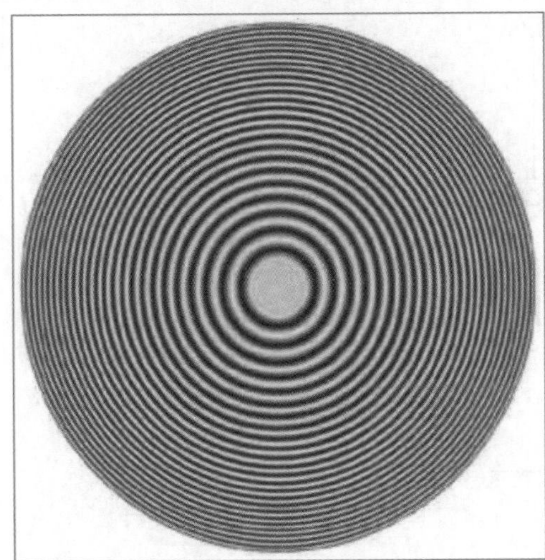

Figure 14.31
Newton's Rings against a white background. The optical phenomenon is named for Sir Isaac Newton, who studied the effect of the series of concentric rings appearing as bright and dark rings when viewed with monochromatic light and appearing as rainbow colors when viewed with white light. Photograph courtesy McGraw Hill Digital Access Library. Rings observed with transmitted light will be of much poorer contrast.

a travelling microscope M. Actually, one really need not have plano-convex lens; the rings would be visible even when a biconvex lens is used.

Typically for $\lambda = 6 \times 10^{-5}$ cm, $\mu = 1$ and $R = 100$ cm

$$r_m = 0.0774\ \sqrt{m}\ \text{cm} \qquad \textbf{(14.67)}$$

Thus the radii of the first, second and third dark rings would be approximately 0.0774 cm, 0.110 cm and 0.134 cm, respectively. Notice that the spacing between the second and third dark rings is smaller than the spacing between the first and second dark rings.

Equation (14.63) predicts that the central spot should be dark. Normally, with the presence of minute dust particles the point of contact is really not perfect and the central spot may not be perfectly dark. Thus, while carrying out the experiment one should measure the radii of the mth and the $(m+p)$th ring ($p \approx 10$) and take the difference in the squares of the radii ($r_{m+p}^2 - r_m^2 = p\lambda R$), which is indeed independent of m. Usually, the diameter can be more accurately measured and in terms of the diameters the wavelength is given by the following expression:

$$\lambda = \frac{D_{m+p}^2 - D_m^2}{4pR} \qquad \textbf{(14.68)}$$

The radius of curvature can be accurately measured with the help of a spherometer and therefore by carefully measuring the diameters of dark (or bright) rings one can experimentally determine the wavelength.

If a liquid of refractive index μ is introduced between the lens and the glass plate, the radii of the dark rings would be given by

$$r_m = \sqrt{\frac{m\lambda R}{\mu}};\ m = 1, 2, 3, \ldots \qquad \textbf{(14.69)}$$

Further, if the refractive indices of the material of the lens and of the glass plate are different and if the refractive index of the liquid lies in between the two values, the central spot will be bright as in Fig. 14.31 and Eq. (14.69) would give the radii of the bright rings.

An important practical application of the principle involved in the Newton's rings experiment lies in the determination of the optical flatness of a glass plate. Consider a glass surface placed on another surface whose flatness is known. If a monochromatic light beam is allowed to fall on this combination and the reflected light is viewed by a microscope, then, in general, dark and bright patches will be seen (Fig. 14.28). The space between the two glass surfaces forms an air film of varying thickness and whenever this thickness becomes $m\lambda/2$, we see a dark spot and when this thickness becomes $\left(m+\frac{1}{2}\right)\lambda/2$ we see a bright spot. Two consecutive dark fringes will be separated by the air film whose thickness will differ by $\lambda/2$. Consequently, by measuring the distance between consecutive dark and bright fringes one can calculate the optical flatness of a glass plate.

When we observe Newton's rings using a white light source, we will have situation similar to that discussed in Sec. 13.9, i.e., we will see only few colored fringes. However, if we put a red filter in front of our eye, the fringe pattern (corresponding to the red color) will suddenly appear. If we replace the red filter by a green filter in front of our eye, the fringe pattern corresponding to the green color will appear; this is similar to the discussion we had in Sec. 13.9.

EXAMPLE 14.2 Consider the formation of Newton's rings by monochromatic light of $\lambda = 6.4 \times 10^{-5}$ cm. Assume the point of contact to be perfect. Now slowly raise the lens vertically above the plate. As the lens moves gradually away from the plate, discuss the ring pattern as seen through the microscope. Assume the radius of the convex surface to be 100 cm.

Solution: Since the point of contact is perfect, the central spot will be dark, the first dark ring will form at P where $PA = \lambda/2$, and the radius of this ring, OA, will be $\sqrt{\lambda R}$ (= 0.080 cm) –see Fig. 14.32(a). Similarly, the radius of the second dark ring will be $OB = \sqrt{2\lambda R}$ (= 0.113 cm). If we now raise the lens by $\frac{\lambda}{4}$ ($=1.6 \times 10^{-5}$ cm) then $2t$ corresponding to the central spot would be $\lambda/2$ and instead of the dark spot at the centre we will now have a bright spot. The radii of the first and the second dark rings will be

$$OA_1 = \left(\frac{1}{2}\lambda R\right)^{1/2} = 0.0566 \text{ cm}$$

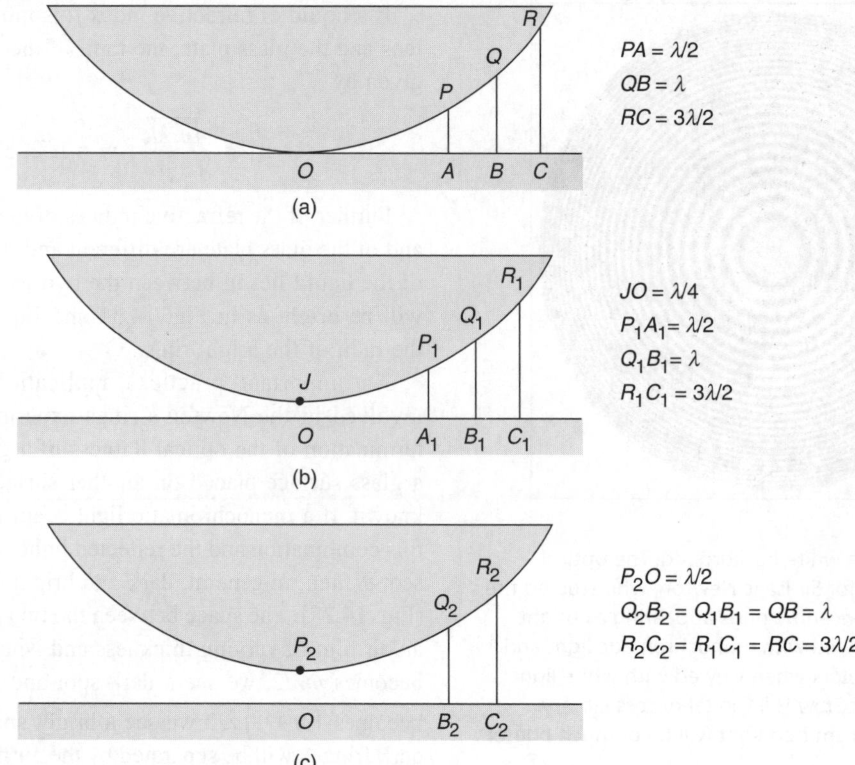

Figure 14.32
The rings collapse to the center as the lens is moved away from the plate.

and $$OB_1 = \left(\frac{3}{2}\lambda R\right)^{1/2} = 0.098 \text{ cm}$$

respectively [see Fig. 14.32(b)]. If the lens is further moved by $\lambda/4$ (see Fig. 14.32(c)], then the first dark ring collapses to the center and the central spot will be dark. The ring which was originally at Q now shifts to Q_2; similarly the ring at R [Fig. 14.32(a)] collapses to R_2 [Fig. 14.32(c)].

Thus, as the lens is moved upward the rings collapse to the centre. Hence if we can measure the distance by which the lens is moved upward and also count the number of dark spots that have collapsed to the center, we can determine the wavelength. For example, in the present case, if the lens is moved by 6.4×10^{-3} cm, 200 rings will collapse to the center. If one carries out this experiment it will be observed that the 200th dark ring will slowly converge to the center and when the lens has moved exactly by 6.4×10^{-3} cm it has exactly come to the center.

EXAMPLE 14.3 Consider the formation of Newton's rings when two closely spaced wavelengths are present; for example, the D_1 and D_2 lines of sodium (λ_1 = 5890 Å and λ_2 = 5896 Å). What will be the effect of the presence of these two wavelengths as the lens is gradually moved away from the plate? What will happen if the sodium lamp is replaced by a white light source?

Solution: We will first assume that the lens is in contact with the plane glass plate [see Fig. 14.32(a)]. Since the two wavelengths are very close, the bright and dark rings of λ_1 superpose on the bright and dark rings of λ_2, respectively. This can easily be seen by calculating the radii of the ninth dark and bright ring for each wavelength.

For $\lambda = 5.890 \times 10^{-5}$ cm,

$$\text{radius of the ninth bright ring} = \sqrt{\left(9+\frac{1}{2}\right)\lambda R}$$
$$= \sqrt{9.5 \times 5.890 \times 10^{-5} \times 100}$$
$$= 0.236548 \text{ cm}$$
$$\text{radius of the ninth dark ring} = \sqrt{9\lambda R}$$
$$= 0.230239 \text{ cm}$$

Similarly, for $\lambda = 5.896 \times 10^{-5}$ cm,

$$\text{radius of the ninth bright ring} = \sqrt{9.5 \times 5.896 \times 10^{-5} \times 100}$$
$$= 0.236669 \text{ cm}$$

and

$$\text{radius of the ninth dark ring} = \sqrt{9 \times 5.896 \times 10^{-3}}$$
$$= 0.230356 \text{ cm}$$

Thus the rings almost exactly superpose on each other. However, for large values of m, the two ring patterns may produce uniform illumination. To be more specific, when the air film thickness t is such that

$$2t = m\lambda_1 = \left(m+\frac{1}{2}\right)\lambda_2$$

or
$$\frac{2t}{\lambda_2} - \frac{2t}{\lambda_1} = \frac{1}{2} \tag{14.70}$$

then around that point the fringe system will completely disappear; i.e., the bright ring for the wavelength λ_1 will fall on the dark ring for the wavelength λ_2 and conversely. Thus the contrast will be zero and no fringe pattern will be visible. Rewriting Eq. (14.70) we get

$$2t\frac{\lambda_1 - \lambda_2}{\lambda_1\lambda_2} = \frac{1}{2}$$

or
$$2t = \frac{1}{2}\frac{\lambda_1\lambda_2}{\Delta\lambda} \approx \frac{1}{2}\frac{(5.893\times10^{-5})^2}{6\times10^{-8}}$$
$$\approx 3 \times 10^{-2} \text{ cm}$$

This will correspond to $m \approx 500$.

We shall see the effect of the same phenomenon if we slowly raise the convex lens in the upward direction as we had considered in Example 14.2. Let t_0 be the vertical distance through which the lens has been raised (see Fig. 14.33) and let t_0 be such that it satisfies the following equation:

$$\frac{2t_0}{\lambda_2} - \frac{2t_0}{\lambda_1} = \frac{1}{2}$$

or
$$t_0 = \frac{\lambda_1\lambda_2}{4(\lambda_1 - \lambda_2)}$$

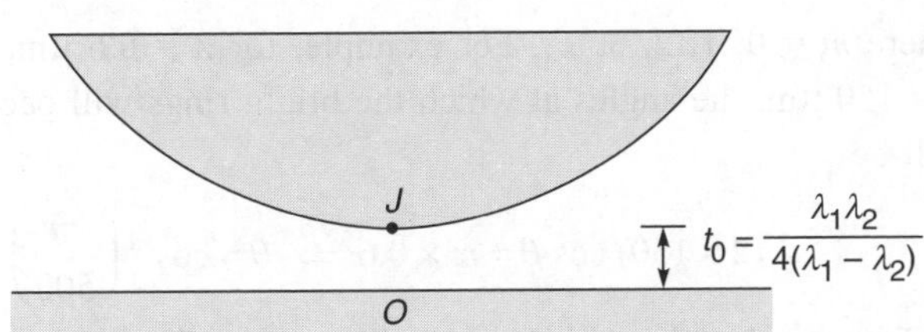

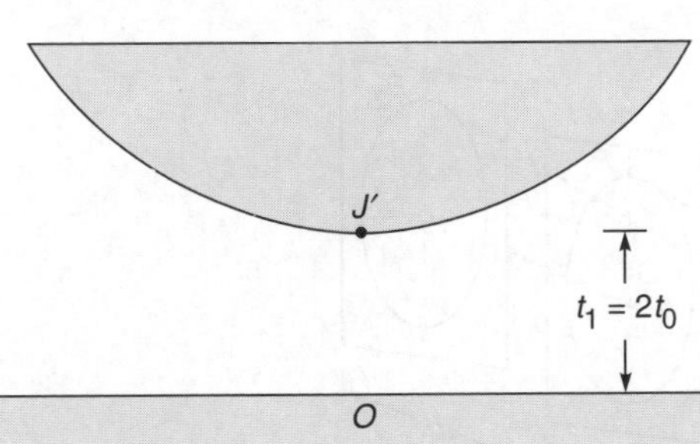

Figure 14.33

In the Newton's rings experiment, if the light consists of two closely spaced wavelengths λ_1 and λ_2 (like the D_1 and D_2 lines of sodium) then, if the lens is separated by a distance $t_0\left(= \frac{\lambda_1\lambda_2}{4(\lambda_1 - \lambda_2)}\right)$ interference fringes will be washed out. The fringes will reappear when the distance is $2t_0$.

Thus, if the point J (see Fig. 14.33) corresponds to a dark spot for λ_1 then it will correspond to a bright spot for λ_2 and conversely. Further, the nearby dark rings for λ_1, will almost fall at the same place as the bright rings for λ_2 and the interference pattern will be washed out. Thus viewing from a microscope we will not be able to see any ring pattern. Now, if the lens is further moved upwards by a distance t_0, then we will have

$$\frac{2t_1}{\lambda_2} - \frac{2t_1}{\lambda_1} = 1 \tag{14.71}$$

where $t_1 = 2t_0$. Consequently, if the point J' corresponds to a dark spot for λ_1 then it will also correspond to a dark spot for λ_2. The fringe pattern will reappear but now with a slightly weaker contrast (see also Chapter 16).

In this way if we continue to move the lens upwards the fringe system will reappear every time the lens is moved up by a distance $2t_0\left(\approx \frac{1}{2}\frac{\lambda_1\lambda_2}{\Delta\lambda}\right)$. This principle is used in a Michelson interferometer to measure the small wavelength difference $\Delta\lambda$, between two closely spaced lines (like the D_1 and D_2 lines of sodium).

It should be pointed out that for complete disappearance of the fringe pattern the intensities of the two lines λ_1 and λ_2 should be the same.

Another corollary of the above experiment consists in finding the change in the interference pattern (as we move up the convex lens) when we consider a single line of wavelength λ, but which has a width of $\Delta\lambda$. Thus we should assume all wavelengths between λ and $\lambda + \Delta\lambda$ to exist. By finding the approximate height at which the fringes disappear one can calculate $\Delta\lambda$. The coherence length (L) is related to $\Delta\lambda$ through the following relation (see Sec. 16.2):

$$L \sim \frac{\lambda^2}{\Delta\lambda} \tag{14.72}$$

14.11 The Michelson Interferometer*

LO10

A schematic diagram of the Michelson interferometer is shown in Fig. 14.34. S represents a light source (which may be a sodium lamp) and L represents a ground glass plate so that an extended source of almost uniform intensity is formed. G_1 is a beam splitter; i.e., a beam incident on G_1 gets partially reflected and partially transmitted. M_1 and M_2 are good quality plane mirrors having very high reflectivity. One of the mirrors (usually M_2) is fixed and the other (usually M_1) is capable of moving away or towards the glass plate G_1 along an accurately machined track by means of a screw. In the normal adjustment of the interferometer, the mirrors M_1 and M_2 are perpendicular to each other and G_1 is at 45° to the mirror.

* The Michelson–Morley experiments using the Michelson interferometer to detect the motion of the earth with respect to the "ether" is discussed in Chapter 31.

Waves emanating from a point P get partially reflected and partially transmitted by the beam splitter G_1, and the two resulting beams are made to interfere in the following manner: The reflected wave [shown as (1) in Fig. 14.34] undergoes a further reflection at M_1 and this reflected wave gets (partially) transmitted through G_1; this is shown as (5) in the figure. The transmitted wave [shown as (2) in Fig. 14.34] gets reflected by M_2 and gets (partially) reflected by G_1 and results in the wave shown as (6) in the figure. Waves (5) and (6) interfere in a manner exactly similar to that shown in Fig. 14.22. This can easily be seen from the fact that if x_1 and x_2 are the distances of the mirrors M_1 and M_2 from the plate G_1, then to the eye the waves emanating from the point P will appear to get reflected by two parallel mirrors [M_1 and M_2' – see Fig. 14.34] separated by a distance ($x_1 \sim x_2$). As discussed in Sec. 14.7, if we use an extended source, then no definite interference pattern will be obtained on a photographic plate placed at the position of the eye. Instead, if we have a camera focused for infinity, then on the focal plane we will obtain circular fringes, each circle corresponding to a definite value of θ (see Figs. 14.22 and 14.35); the circular fringes will look like the ones shown in Fig. 14.36.

We will show in Sec. 14.11.1 that for a symmetric beam splitter without any losses, the waves reflected and transmitted by a beam splitter differ in phase by $\pi/2$ Since the extra path that one of the beams will traverse will be $2(x_1 \sim x_2)$, the condition for constructive interference will be

$$2d \cos \theta = m\lambda \tag{14.73}$$

where $d = x_1 \sim x_2$, the angle θ represents the angle that the rays make with the axis (which is normal to the mirrors as

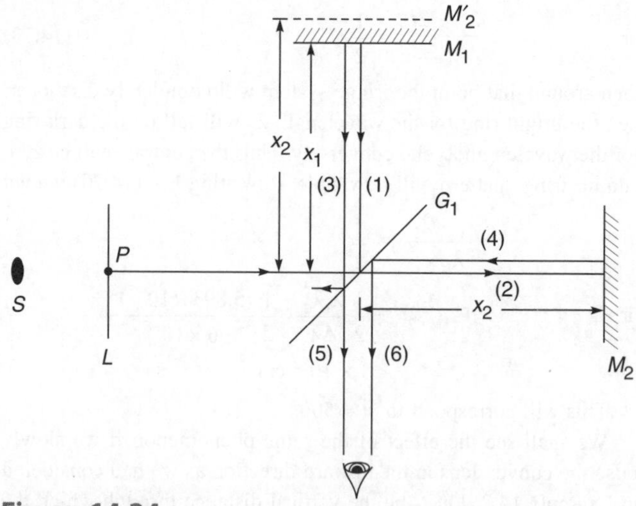

Figure 14.34
Schematic of the Michelson interferometer.

shown in Fig. 14.35) and $m = 0, 1, 2, 3, \ldots$. Similarly, the condition for destructive interference is

$$2d \cos\theta = \left(m + \frac{1}{2}\right)\lambda \tag{14.74}$$

where $m = 0, 1, 2, 3, \ldots$. For example, for $\lambda = 0.6$ μm, if $d = 150$ μm, the angles at which the bright rings will occur will be

$$(2 \times 150) \cos \theta = m \times 0.6 \Rightarrow \theta = \cos^{-1}\left(\frac{m}{500}\right)$$

Thus bright (circular) fringes will appear when

$$\theta = 0°(m = 500),\ 3.62°(m = 499),\ 5.13°(m = 498),\ 6.28°(m = 497), \ldots$$

[Bright rings when $d = 150$ μm]

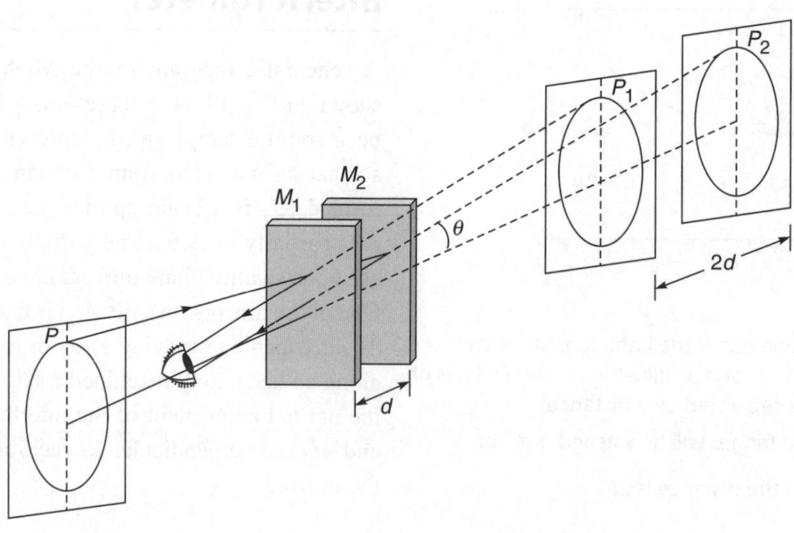

Figure 14.35
A schematic of the formation of circular fringes [Adapted from Ref. 14.7].

[see Fig. 14.36(a)]. The dark (circular) fringes will appear when

$$\theta = \cos^{-1}\left(\frac{m+\frac{1}{2}}{500}\right)$$

$$= 2.56°(m = 499), 4.43°(m = 498), 5.73°(m = 497), ...$$

[Dark rings when d = 150 μm]

If we reduce the distance between 2 mirrors and assume d = 149.85 μm, the angles at which bright rings will occur will be

$$(2 \times 149.85) \cos\theta = m \times 0.6 \Rightarrow \theta = \cos^{-1}\left(\frac{m}{499.5}\right)$$

Thus, when d = 149.85 μm, the angles at which the bright rings will occur will be [see Fig. 14.36(b)]:

$$\theta = \cos^{-1}\left(\frac{m}{499.5}\right)$$

$$= 2.56°(m = 499), 4.44°(m = 498), 5.73°(m = 497), ...$$

[Bright rings when d = 149.85 μm]

The corresponding angles at which the dark rings will occur will be

$$\theta = \cos^{-1}\left(\frac{m+\frac{1}{2}}{499.5}\right)$$

$$= 0°(m = 499), 3.63°(m = 498), 5.13°(m = 497), ...$$

[Dark rings when d = 149.85 μm]

Thus, when d is decreased from 150 μm to d = 149.85 μm, the bright ring at $\theta = 0$ (m = 500) will disappear and the bright rings at θ = 3.62 (m = 499), 5.13 (m = 498), 6.28 (m = 497),… will collapse to θ = 2.56°(m = 499), 4.44°(m = 398), 5.73° (m = 497),…. On the other hand, the first dark ring will collapse to the center and the other dark rings will appear at smaller angles given by θ = 3.63°(m = 498), 5.13° (m = 497), …

If we increase the distance between 2 mirrors and assume d = 299.85 μm, the angles at which bright rings will occur will be [see Fig. 14.36(c)]:

$$(2 \times 299.85) \cos\theta = m \times 0.6$$

$$\Rightarrow \quad \theta = \cos^{-1}\left(\frac{m}{999.5}\right)$$

$$= 1.81°(m = 999), 3.14°(m = 998), 4.05°(m = 997), ...$$

[Bright rings when d = 299.85 μm]

On the other hand, the angles at which dark rings will occur will be given by

$$\theta = \cos^{-1}\left(\frac{m+\frac{1}{2}}{999.5}\right)$$

$$= 0°(m = 999), 2.56°(m = 998), 4.05°(m = 997), ...$$

[Dark rings when d = 299.85 μm]

Thus, as d decreases, the fringe pattern tends to collapse and conversely, if d is increased, the fringe pattern will expand. Indeed, if N fringes collapse to the center as mirror M_1 moves by a distance d_0, then we must have

$$2d = m\lambda$$

$$2(d - d_0) = (m - N)\lambda$$

where we have put $\theta' = 0$ because we are looking at the central fringe. Thus,

$$\lambda = \frac{2d_0}{N} \quad \textbf{(14.75)}$$

This provides us with a method for the measurement of the wavelength. For example, in a typical experiment, if one finds

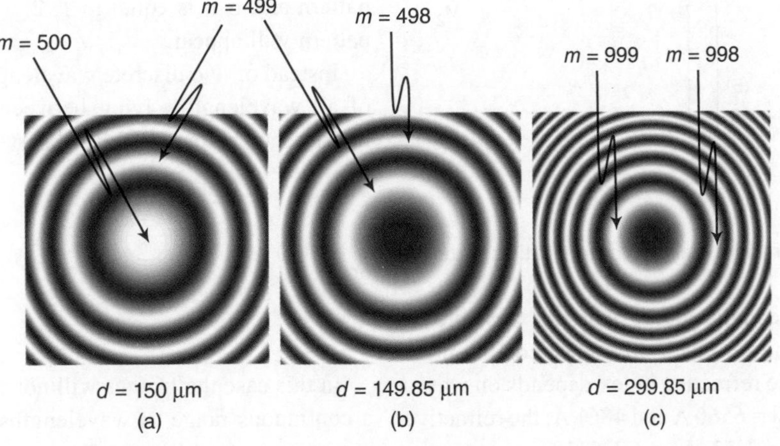

Figure 14.36

Computer generated interference pattern produced by a Michelson interferometer. As the value of d decreases, fringe pattern tends to collapse towards the center.

1000 fringes collapse to the center as the mirror is moved through a distance of 2.90×10^{-2} cm, then

$$\lambda = 5800 \text{ Å}$$

The above method was used by Michelson for the standardization of the meter. He had found that the red cadmium line (λ = 6438.4696 Å) is one of the ideal monochromatic sources and as such this wavelength was used as a reference for the standardization of the meter. In fact, he defined the meter by the following relation:

$$1 \text{ meter} = 1553164.13 \text{ red cadmium wavelengths,}$$

the accuracy is almost one part in 10^9.

In an actual Michelson interferometer, the beam splitter G_1 consists of a plate (which may be about 1/2 cm thick), the back surface of which is partially silvered and the reflections occur at the back surface as shown in Fig. 14.37. It is immediately obvious that the beam (5) traverses the glass plate thrice and in order to compensate for this additional path, one introduces a 'compensating plate' G_2 which is exactly of the same thickness as G_1. The compensating plate is not really necessary for a monochromatic source because the additional path $2(n - 1)t$ introduced by G_1 can be compensated by moving the mirror M_1 by a distance $(n - 1)t$ where n is the refractive index of the material of the glass plate G_1.

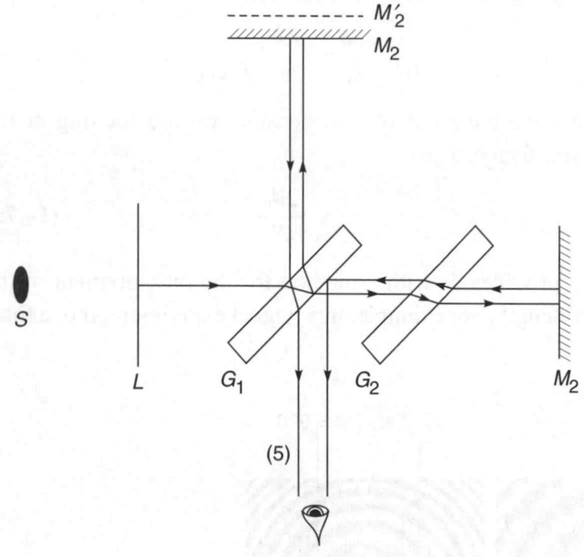

Figure 14.37
In an actual interferometer there is also a compensating plate G_2.

However, for a white light source it is not possible to simultaneously satisfy the zero path-difference condition for all wavelengths, since the refractive index depends on wavelength. For example, for λ = 6560 Å and 4861 Å, the refractive index of crown glass is 1.5244 and 1.5330 respectively. If we are using a 0.5 cm thick crown glass plate as G_1, then M_1 should be moved by 0.2622 cm for λ = 6560 Å and by 0.2665 cm for λ = 4861 Å, the difference between the two positions corresponding to over hundred wavelengths! Thus, if we have a continuous range of wavelengths from 4861 Å to 6560 Å, the path difference between any pair of interfering rays (see Fig. 14.34) will vary so rapidly with wavelength that we would observe only a uniform white light illumination. However, in the presence of the compensating plate G_2, one would observe a few colored fringes around the point corresponding to zero path difference (see Sec. 13.9).

Michelson interferometer can also be used in the measurement of two closely spaced wavelengths. Let us assume that we have a sodium lamp which emits predominantly two closely spaced wavelengths 5890 Å and 5896 Å. The interferometer is first set corresponding to the zero path difference.* Near $d = 0$, both the fringe patterns will overlap. If the mirror M_1 is moved away (or towards) the plate G_1 through a distance d, then the maxima corresponding to the wavelength λ_1 will not, in general, occur at the same angle as λ_2. Indeed, if the distance d is such that

$$\frac{2d}{\lambda_1} - \frac{2d}{\lambda_2} = \frac{1}{2} \qquad \textbf{(14.76)}$$

and if $2d \cos\theta' = m\lambda_1$, then $2d \cos\theta' = \left(m + \frac{1}{2}\right)\lambda_2$. Thus, the maxima of λ_1 will fall on the minima of λ_2 and conversely, and the fringe system will disappear. It can easily be seen that if

$$\frac{2d}{\lambda_1} - \frac{2d}{\lambda_2} = 1 \qquad \textbf{(14.77)}$$

then interference pattern will again reappear. In general, if

$$\frac{2d}{\lambda_1} - \frac{2d}{\lambda_2}$$

is 1/2, 3/2, 5/2, ... we will have disappearance of the fringe pattern and if it is equal to 1, 2, 3, ... then the interference pattern will appear.

Instead of two discrete wavelengths, if the source consists of all wavelengths, lying between λ and $\lambda + \Delta\lambda$, then no interference pattern will be observed if

$$\frac{2d}{\lambda} - \frac{2d}{\lambda + \frac{\Delta\lambda}{2}} \gtrsim \frac{1}{2}$$

or

$$2d \gtrsim \frac{\lambda^2}{\Delta\lambda} \qquad \textbf{(14.78)}$$

In this case the fringes will not reappear because we have a continuous range of wavelengths rather than two discrete wavelengths (see Sec. 16.2).

* The zero path difference is easily obtained by using white light where only a few coloured fringes, around $d = 0$, will be visible.

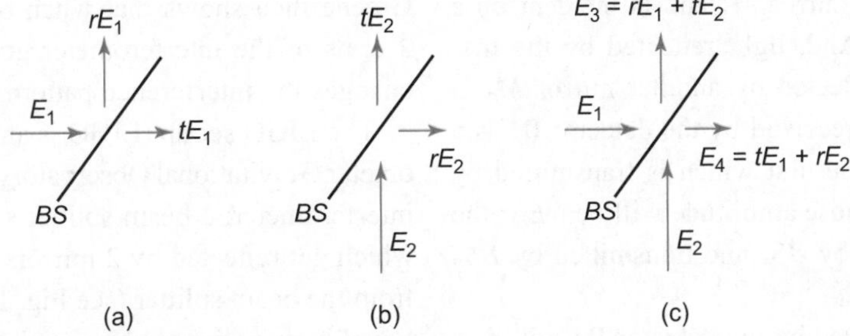

Figure 14.38
Reflection and transmission of a light beam by a beam splitter shown as *BS*.

EXAMPLE 14.4 For a sodium lamp, the distance traversed by the mirror between two successive disappearances is 0.289 mm. Calculate the difference in the wavelengths of the D_1 and the D_2 lines. Assume $\lambda = 5890$ Å.

Solution: When the mirror moves through a distance 0.289 mm, the additional path introduced is 0.578 mm. Thus,

$$\frac{0.578}{\lambda} - \frac{0.578}{\lambda + \Delta\lambda} = 1$$

or

$$\Delta\lambda \simeq \frac{\lambda^2}{0.578} = \frac{(5890 \times 10^{-7})^2}{0.578} \text{ mm}$$

$$\simeq 6 \text{Å}$$

14.11.1 Phase Shift between Transmitted and Reflected Beams

One of the very important components of a Michelson interferometer is the beam splitter shown as *BS* in Fig. 14.38. We consider a symmetric beam splitter without any losses; by symmetric we imply that the amplitude reflection coefficient and amplitude transmission coefficients of the beam splitter are the same from both directions [see Figs. 14.38(a) and 14.38(b)]. Thus, if E_1 and E_2 are the amplitudes of the incident beam [see Fig. 14.38(c)], then

$$E_3 = rE_1 + tE_2 \quad (14.79)$$

$$E_4 = tE_1 + rE_2 \quad (14.80)$$

where E_3 and E_4 are the amplitudes of the beams shown in Fig. 14.38(a); *r* and *t* are amplitude reflection coefficient and amplitude transmission coefficients respectively. Now,

$$\begin{aligned}|E_3|^2 + |E_4|^2 &= |rE_1 + tE_2|^2 + |tE_1 + rE_2|^2 \\ &= (rE_1 + tE_2)(r^*E_1^* + t^*E_2^*) \\ &\quad + (tE_1 + rE_2)(t^*E_1^* + r^*E_2^*) \\ &= |r|^2|E_1|^2 + |t|^2|E_2|^2 + rt^*E_1E_2^* \\ &\quad + tr^*E_2E_1^* + |t|^2|E_1|^2 + |r|^2|E_2|^2 \\ &\quad + tr^*E_1E_2^* + rt^*E_2E_1^*\end{aligned}$$

$$\begin{aligned}|E_3|^2 + |E_4|^2 &= [|r|^2 + |t|^2][|E_1|^2 + |E_2|^2] \\ &\quad + [rt^* + tr^*] + [E_1E_2^* + E_1^*E_2] \quad (14.81)\end{aligned}$$

Energy conservation tells us that $|E_3|^2 + |E_4|^2$ must be equal to $|E_1|^2 + |E_2|^2$. Thus, we must have

$$|r|^2 + |t|^2 = 1 \quad (14.82)$$

and

$$rt^* + tr^* = 0 \quad (14.83)$$

We write $r = |r|e^{i\phi_r}$ and $t = |t|e^{i\phi_t}$ (14.84)

For a perfect beam splitter

$$|r| = \frac{1}{\sqrt{2}} \text{ and } |t| = \frac{1}{\sqrt{2}} \quad (14.85)$$

Now $rt^* + tr^* = 0$

$$\Rightarrow \quad |r||t|[\exp\{i(\phi_r - \phi_t)\} + \exp\{-i(\phi_r - \phi_t)\}] = 0 \quad (14.86)$$

Thus $2|r||t| \cos(\phi_r - \phi_t) = 0$

$$\Rightarrow \quad (\phi_r - \phi_t) = \pm\frac{\pi}{2} \quad (14.87)$$

The above equation tells us (from energy conservation condition) that the waves reflected and transmitted by a beam splitter differ in phase by $\pi/2$.

Figure 14.39 shows the Mach Zehnder interferometer in which a light beam transmitted by the first beam splitter

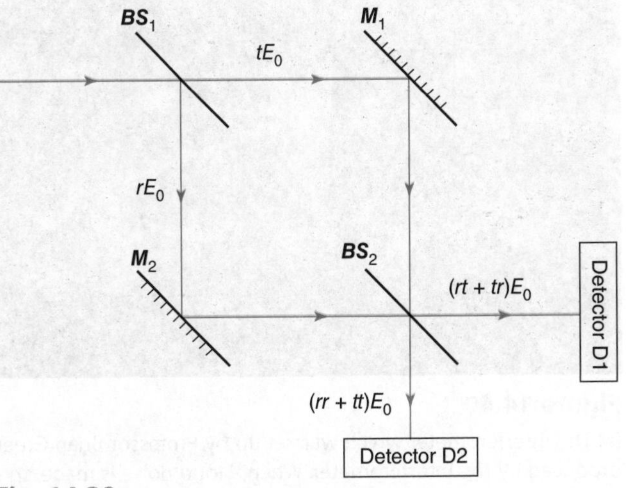

Fig. 14.39
The Mach Zehnder interferometer; BS_1 and BS_2 denote beam splitters and M_1 and M_2 denote mirrors.

(**$BS1$**) gets reflected by the mirror M_1 and is incident on a second beam splitter BS_2. And, light reflected by the first beam splitter (BS_1) gets reflected by another mirror M_2 is also incident on BS_2. Light received by the detector **D1** is a superposition of 2 beams: the first which is transmitted by BS_1 and reflected by BS_2 whose amplitude will be trE_0 ; the second one that is reflected by BS_1 and transmitted by BS_2 whose amplitude will be rtE_0.

Thus the amplitude received by the detector **D1** will be

$$(rt + tr)E_0$$

On the other hand, light received by the detector **D2** is also a superposition of 2 beams: the first which is reflected by BS_1 and also by BS_2 whose amplitude will be rrE_0; the second one that is transmitted by BS_1 and also by BS_2 whose amplitude will be ttE_0. Thus the amplitude received by the detector **D2** will be

$$(rr + tt)E_0$$

The two beams will be out of phase by π because (as discussed above) waves reflected and transmitted by a beam splitter differ in phase by $\pi/2$ Thus if the beam splitters are perfect and the mirrors are properly adjusted, the amplitude received by the detector **D2** will be zero.

In the Michelson interferometer, for zero path difference between the two waves interfering in the transmitted arm, the interference will be constructive and there will be a maximum interference.

If you go to You Tube and search for *Gravitation Waves Hit Late Show*, you will be able to reach the website https://www.youtube.com/watch?v=ajZojAwfEbs where Professor Brian Greene demonstrates the interference pattern produced by an interferometer[see Figs. 14.40 (a) and (b)]. Professor Greene then shows that when one makes a loud noise, the 2 arms of the interferometer get affected differently which changes the interference pattern.

The LIGO set up (LIGO is an acronym for Laser Interferometer Gravitational Observatory) is just a gigantic Michelson interferometer: a beam splitter splits the light from the laser which get reflected by 2 mirrors at a distance of about 4 km from the beam splitter (see Fig. 16 in the Prologue). Gravitational waves (created by a violent collision of 2 black holes 1.3 billion light years away) are detected from a study of the interference pattern; see Fig. 15 in the Prologue. We urge the students to go to the website mentioned above where Professor Greene explains the LIGO experiment.

14.12 Expression for Reflectivity of a FBG

Detailed theory tells us that the Reflectivity of a Fiber Bragg Grating is approximately given by (see e.g., Ref. 14.12):

$$R \approx \frac{\kappa^2 \sinh^2 \alpha L}{\kappa^2 \cosh^2 \alpha L - \dfrac{\Gamma^2}{4}} \qquad (14.88)$$

where L is the length of the FBG,

$$\Gamma = 4\pi n_0 \left[\frac{1}{\lambda_0} - \frac{1}{\lambda_B}\right], \quad \alpha = \sqrt{\kappa^2 - \frac{\Gamma^2}{4}},$$

$$\lambda_B = 2\,\Lambda\, n_0 \quad \text{and} \quad \kappa = \frac{\pi\, \Delta n}{\lambda_0} \qquad (14.89)$$

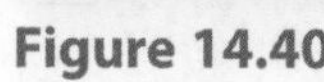

Figure 14.40

(a) The interferometer which was set up by Professor Brian Green to explain the LIGO experiment. (b) The interference pattern produced by the interferometer. When a loud noise is made, the interference pattern changes. Diagrams adapted from the experiment demonstrated by Professor Green - see https://www.youtube.com/watch?v=ajZojAwfEbs

The maximum reflectivity occurs when $\lambda_0 = \lambda_B$ (thus $\Gamma = 0$) and one obtains the following expression for the peak reflectivity

$$R = \tanh^2 \frac{\pi \Delta n L}{\lambda_B} \tag{14.90}$$

When $\Gamma > 2\kappa$, α would become imaginary and we have

$$R = \frac{\kappa^2 \sin^2 \gamma L}{\kappa^2 \cos^2 \gamma L + \dfrac{\Gamma^2}{4}} \quad \text{with} \quad \gamma = \sqrt{\frac{\Gamma^2}{4} - \kappa^2} \tag{14.91}$$

Thus $R = 0$ when $\gamma L = n\pi$ (n = 1, 2, 3, …). The wavelengths at which $R = 0$ [see Fig. 14.13(c)] will be given by

$$\lambda_0 \approx \lambda_B \pm \frac{\lambda_B^2}{2\pi n_0 L}\sqrt{\kappa^2 L^2 + n^2\pi^2} \tag{14.92}$$

Thus the bandwidth will be given by

$$\Delta\lambda_0 = \frac{\lambda_B^2}{n_0 L}[1 + \kappa^2 L^2]^{1/2} = \frac{\lambda_B^2}{n_0 L}\sqrt{1 + \left(\frac{(\Delta n)L}{\lambda_B}\right)^2}$$

or

$$\frac{\Delta\lambda_0}{\lambda_B} = \frac{\lambda_B}{n_0 L}\sqrt{1 + \left(\frac{(\Delta n)L}{\lambda_B}\right)^2} \tag{14.93}$$

SUMMARY

- If a plane wave is incident normally on a thin film of uniform thickness d then the waves reflected from the upper surface interfere with the waves reflected from the lower surface. Indeed, for a film of thickness $\lambda/4n_f$ [where λ is the free space wavelength and n_f is the film refractive index which lies between the refractive indices of the two surrounding media], the wave reflected from the upper surface interferes destructively with the wave reflected from the lower surface and therefore the film acts like an anti-reflection layer.
- A medium consisting of a large number of alternate layers of high and low refractive indices of $n_0 + \Delta n$ and $n_0 - \Delta n$ of equal thickness d is called a periodic medium and the spatial period of the refractive index variation is denoted by Λ (=2d). For $\Delta n << n_0$, if $d \approx \dfrac{\lambda}{4n_0}$ (where λ is the free space wavelength), the reflections arising out of the individual reflections from the various interfaces would all be in phase and would result in a strong reflection. Thus for strong reflection at a chosen (free space) wavelength λ_B, the period of the refractive index variation should be

$$\Lambda = 2d = \frac{\lambda_B}{2n_0}$$

  This is referred to as the Bragg condition. This is the principle of operation of Fiber Bragg gratings.
- If we place a plano-convex lens on a plane glass surface, a thin film of air is formed between the curved surface of the lens and the plane glass plate. If we allow monochromatic light (such as from a sodium lamp) to fall (almost normally) on the surface of the lens, then the light reflected from the curved surface interferes with the light reflected from the plane surface. Since the convex side of the lens is a spherical surface, the thickness of the air film will be constant over a circle and we will see concentric dark and bright rings. These rings are known as Newton's rings. The radii of the concentric rings are such that the difference between the square of the radii of successive fringes is very nearly a constant.
- The Michelson interferometer was used by Michelson for the standardization of the meter. He had found that the red cadmium line (λ = 6438.4696 Å) is one of the ideal monochromatic sources and as such this wavelength was used as a reference for the standardization of the meter. In fact, he defined the meter by the following relation:

  1 meter = 1553164.13 red cadmium wavelengths,

  the accuracy is almost one part in 10^9.
- Michelson interferometer can also be used in the measurement of two closely spaced wavelengths.

PROBLEMS

14.1 A glass plate of refractive index 1.6 is in contact with another glass plate of refractive index 1.8 along a line such that a wedge of 0.5° is formed. Light of wavelength 5000 Å is incident vertically on the wedge and the film is viewed from the top. Calculate the fringe spacing. The whole apparatus is immersed in an oil of refractive index 1.7. What will be the qualitative difference in the fringe pattern and what will be the new fringe width?

14.2 Two plane glass plates are placed on top of one another and on one side a cardboard is introduced to form a thin wedge of air. Assuming that a beam of wavelength 6000 Å is incident normally, and that there are 100 interference fringes per centimeter, calculate the wedge angle.

14.3 Consider a non-reflecting film of refractive index 1.38. Assume that its thickness is 9×10^{-6} cm. Calculate the wavelengths (in the visible region) for which the film will be non-reflecting. Repeat the calculations for the thickness of the film to be 45×10^{-6} cm. Show that both the films will be non-reflecting for a particular wavelength but only the former one will be suitable. Why?

14.4 In the Newton's rings arrangement, the radius of curvature of the curved side of the plano-convex lens is 100 cm. For $\lambda = 6 \times 10^{-5}$ cm what will be the radii of the 9th and 10th bright rings?

14.5 In the Newton's rings arrangement, the radius of curvature of the curved surface is 50 cm. The radii of the 9th and 16th dark rings are 0.18 cm and 0.2235 cm. Calculate the wavelength.
(**Hint:** The use of Eq. (14.66) will give wrong results, why?)

[**Ans.** 5015 Å]

14.6 In the Newton's rings arrangement if the incident light consists of two wavelengths 4000 Å and 4002 Å calculate the distance (from the point of contact) at which the rings will disappear. Assume that the radius of curvature of the curved surface is 400 cm.

[**Ans.** 4 cm]

14.7 In Problem 14.6, if the lens is slowly moved upward, calculate the height of the lens at which the fringe system (around the center) will disappear.

[**Ans.** 0.2 mm]

14.8 An equiconvex lens is placed on another equiconvex lens. The radii of curvatures of the two surfaces of the upper lens are 50 cm and those of the lower lens are 100 cm. The waves reflected from the upper and lower surface of the air film (formed between the two lenses) interfere to produce Newton's rings. Calculate the radii of the dark rings. Assume $\lambda = 6000$ Å.

[**Ans.** $0.0447\sqrt{m}$ cm]

14.9 In the Michelson interferometer arrangement, if one of the mirrors is moved by a distance 0.08 mm, 250 fringes cross the field of view. Calculate the wavelength.

[**Ans.** 6400 Å]

14.10 The Michelson interferometer experiment is performed with a source which consists of two wavelengths 4882 Å and 4886 Å. Through what distance does the mirror have to be moved between two positions of the disappearance of the fringes?

[**Ans.** 0.298 mm]

14.11 In the Michelson interferometer experiment, calculate the various values of θ' (corresponding to bright rings) for $d = 5 \times 10^{-3}$ cm. Show that if d is decreased to 4.997×10^{-3} cm the fringe corresponding to $m = 200$ disappears. What will be the corresponding values of θ'? Assume $\lambda = 5 \times 10^{-5}$ cm.

CHAPTER 15

Multiple Beam Interferometry

When two Undulations ... coincide either perfectly or very nearly in Direction, their joint effect is a Combination of the Motions belonging to each. *

—Thomas Young (1801)

Important Milestone

1899: Marie Fabry and Jean Perot invented the Fabry–Perot interferometer which is characterized by a very high resolving power.

LEARNING OBJECTIVES

After reading this chapter, the reader should be able to:

LO 1: *derive the interference pattern using multiple reflection system.*

LO 2: *understand the working of the Fabry-Perot interferometer.*

LO 3: *obtain the resolving power of Fabry-Perot interferometer.*

LO 4: *discuss usefulness of Lummer-Gehrcke plate.*

LO 5: *understand the working of inteference filters.*

15.1 Introduction

In the last two chapters, we have been discussing interference between two beams which are derived from a single beam either by division of wavefront or by division of amplitude. In this chapter, we will discuss interference involving many beams which are derived from a single beam by multiple reflections (division of amplitude). Thus, for example, if a plane wave falls on a plane parallel glass plate, then the beam would undergo multiple reflections at the two surfaces and a large number of beams of successively diminishing amplitude will emerge on both sides of the plate. These beams (on either side) interfere to produce an interference pattern at infinity. We will show that the fringes so formed are much sharper than those by two beam interference and, therefore, the interferometers involving multiple beam interference have a high resolving power and hence find applications in high resolution spectroscopy.

* The author found this quotation in Ref. 15.1.

Above Image: View of a rainbow against a background of clouds. Photograph courtesy McGraw Hill Digital Access Library.

15.2 Multiple Reflections from a Plane Parallel Film

LO1

We consider the incidence of a plane wave on a plate of thickness h (and of refractive index n_2) surrounded by a medium of refractive index n_1 as shown in Fig. 15.1; as we will discuss later, the Fabry–Perot interferometer consists of two partially reflecting mirrors (separated by a fixed distance h) placed in air so that $n_1 = n_2 = 1$.

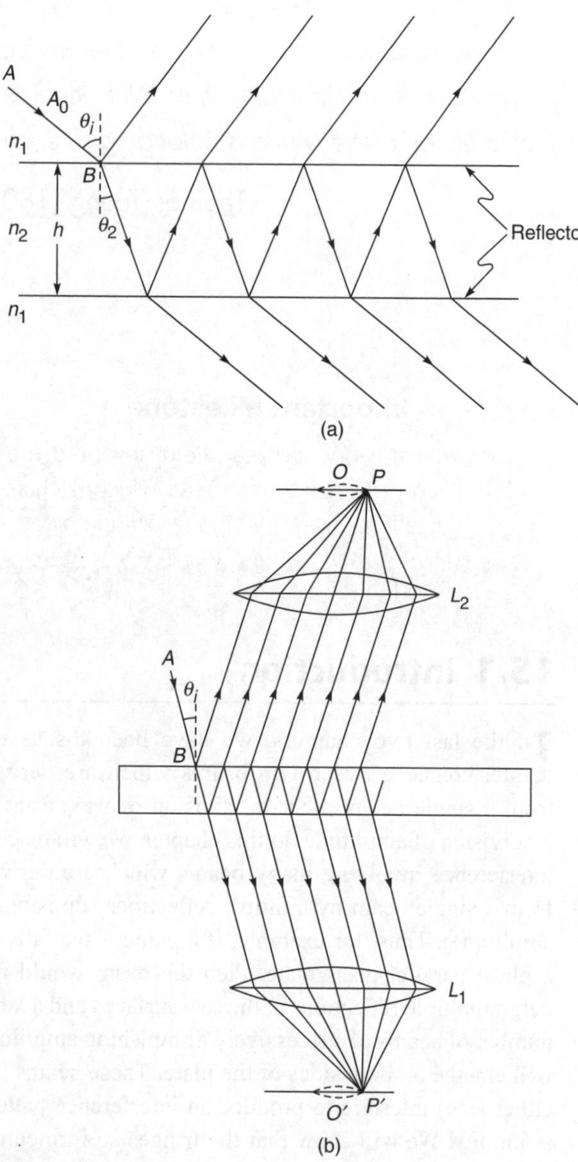

Figure 15.1
(a) Reflection and transmission of a beam of amplitude A_0 incident at an angle θ_i on a film of refractive index n_2 and thickness h. (b) Any ray parallel to AB will focus at the same point P. If the ray AB is rotated about the normal at B, then the point P will rotate on the circumference of a circle centred at the point O; this circle will be bright or dark depending on the value of θ_i. Rays incident at different angles will focus at different distances from the point O and one will obtain concentric bright and dark rings for an extended source.

Let A_0 be the (complex) amplitude of the incident wave. The wave will undergo multiple reflections at the two interfaces as shown in Fig. 15.1(a). Let r_1 and t_1 represent the amplitude reflection and transmission coefficients when the wave is incident from n_1 towards n_2 and let r_2 and t_2 represent the corresponding coefficients when the wave is incident from n_2 towards n_1. Thus the amplitude of the successive reflected waves will be

$$A_0 r_1,\ A_0 t_1 r_2 t_2 e^{i\delta},\ A_0 t_1 r_2^3 e^{2i\delta},\ \ldots$$

where
$$\delta = \frac{2\pi}{\lambda_0}\Delta = \frac{4\pi n_2\, h\cos\theta_2}{\lambda_0} \tag{15.1}$$

represents the phase difference (between two successive waves emanating from the plate) due to the additional path traversed by the beam in the film (see Sec. 15.1) and in Eq. (15.1), θ_2 is the angle of refraction inside the film (of refractive index n_2), h the film thickness and λ_0 is the free space wavelength. Thus the resultant (complex) amplitude of the reflected wave will be

$$A_r = A_0\,[r_1 + t_1 t_2 r_2 e^{i\delta}(1 + r_2^2 e^{i\delta} + r_2^4 e^{2i\delta} + \ldots)]$$

$$= A_0\left[r_1 + \frac{t_1 t_2 r_2 e^{i\delta}}{1 - r_2^2 e^{i\delta}}\right] \tag{15.2}$$

Now, if the reflectors are lossless, the reflectivity and the transmittivity at each interface are given by (see Sec. 13.12)

$$R = r_1^2 = r_2^2$$
$$\tau = t_1 t_2 = 1 - R$$

(We are reserving the symbol T for the transmittivity of the Fabry–Perot etalon.) Thus,

$$\frac{A_r}{A_0} = r_1\left[1 - \frac{(1-R)e^{i\delta}}{1 - Re^{i\delta}}\right]$$

where we have used the fact that $r_2 = -r_1$. Thus, the reflectivity of the Fabry–Perot etalon is given by

$$\mathcal{R} = \left|\frac{A_r}{A_0}\right|^2 = R\left|\frac{1 - e^{i\delta}}{1 - Re^{i\delta}}\right|^2$$

$$= R\,\frac{(1-\cos\delta)^2 + \sin^2\delta}{(1 - R\cos\delta)^2 + R^2\sin^2\delta}$$

$$= \frac{4R\sin^2\dfrac{\delta}{2}}{(1-R)^2 + 4R\sin^2\dfrac{\delta}{2}}$$

or,
$$\mathcal{R} = \frac{F\sin^2\dfrac{\delta}{2}}{1 + F\sin^2\dfrac{\delta}{2}} \tag{15.3}$$

where $$F = \frac{4R}{(1-R)^2} \tag{15.4}$$

is called the **coefficient of Finesse**. One can immediately see that when $R << 1$, F is small and the reflectivity is proportional to $\sin^2 \delta/2$. The same intensity distribution is obtained in the two beam interference pattern (see Sec. 13.6); we may mention here that we have obtained $\sin^2 \delta/2$ instead of $\cos^2 \delta/2$ because of the additional phase change of π in one of the reflected beams.

Similarly, the amplitude of the successive transmitted waves will be

$$A_0 t_1 t_2,\ A_0 t_1 t_2 r_2^2 e^{i\delta},\ A_0 t_1 t_2 r_2^4 e^{2i\delta}, \ldots$$

where, without any loss of generality, we have assumed the first transmitted wave to have zero phase. Thus the resultant amplitude of the transmitted wave will be given by

$$A_t = A_0 t_1 t_2 [1 + r_2^2 e^{i\delta} + r_2^4 e^{2i\delta} + \ldots]$$

$$= A_0 \frac{t_1 t_2}{1 - r_2^2 e^{i\delta}} = A_0 \frac{1-R}{1 - Re^{i\delta}}$$

Thus, the transmittivity T of the film is given by

$$T = \left| \frac{A_t}{A_0} \right|^2 = \frac{(1-R)^2}{(1 - R\cos\delta)^2 + R^2 \sin^2 \delta}$$

or $$T = \frac{1}{1 + F \sin^2 \dfrac{\delta}{2}} \tag{15.5}$$

It is immediately seen that the reflectivity and the transmittivity of the Fabry–Perot etalon add up to unity. Further,

$$T = 1$$

when $$\delta = 2m\pi \ ; \quad m = 1, 2, 3, \ldots \tag{15.6}$$

In Fig. 15.2, we have plotted the transmittivity as a function of δ for different values of F. In order to get an estimate of the width of the transmission resonances, let

$$T = \frac{1}{2} \quad \text{for} \quad \delta = 2m\pi \pm \frac{\Delta\delta}{2}$$

Thus, $$F \sin^2 \frac{\Delta\delta}{4} = 1 \tag{15.7}$$

The quantity $\Delta\delta$ represents the FWHM (Full Width at Half Maximum). In almost all cases, $\Delta\delta <<< 1$ and therefore, to a very good approximation, it is given by

$$\Delta\delta \approx \frac{4}{\sqrt{F}} = \frac{2(1-R)}{\sqrt{R}} \tag{15.8}$$

Thus the transmission resonances become sharper as the value of F increases (see Fig. 15.2).

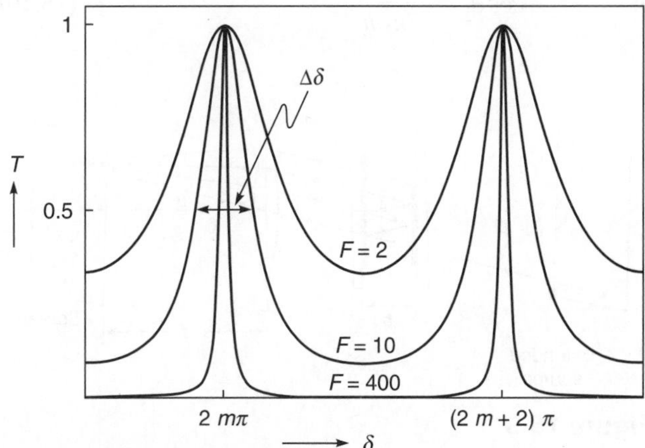

Figure 15.2
The transmittivity of a Fabry–Perot etalon as a function of δ for different values of F; the value of m is usually large. The transmission resonances become sharper as we increase the value of F. The FWHM (Full Width at Half Maximum) is denoted by $\Delta\delta$.

15.3 The Fabry–Perot Etalon

LO2

In this section, we will discuss the Fabry–Perot interferometer which is based on the principle of multiple beam interferometry discussed in the last section. The interferometer (as shown in Fig. 15.3) consists of two plane glass (or quartz) plates which are coated on one side with a partially reflecting metallic film* (of aluminum or silver) of about 80% reflectivity. These two plates are kept in such a way that they enclose a plane parallel slab of air between their coated surfaces. If the reflecting glass plates are held parallel to each other at a fixed separation, we have what is known as a **Fabry–Perot etalon.** In fact, we may neglect the presence of the plates and consider only the reflection (and transmission) by the metallic film; further, if the plates are parallel, the rays will not undergo any deviation.

In a typical experiment, light from a broad source is collimated by a lens and is passed through the Fabry–Perot etalon as shown in Fig. 15.3. Thus, if we consider light of a specific

* In the visible region of the spectrum, silver is the best metal to coat with (the reflectivity is about 0.97 in the red region and decrease to about 0.90 in the blue region). But beyond the blue region, the reflectivity falls rapidly. Aluminum is usually employed below 4000 Å.

wavelength λ_0, the incident light will be completely transmitted (i.e., $T = 1$) if the angle of incidence is such that

$$\delta = \frac{4\pi}{\lambda_0} n_2 h \cos\theta_2 = 2m\pi \quad \textbf{(15.9)}$$

or

$$\cos\theta_2 = \frac{m\lambda_0}{2n_2 h} \quad \textbf{(15.10)}$$

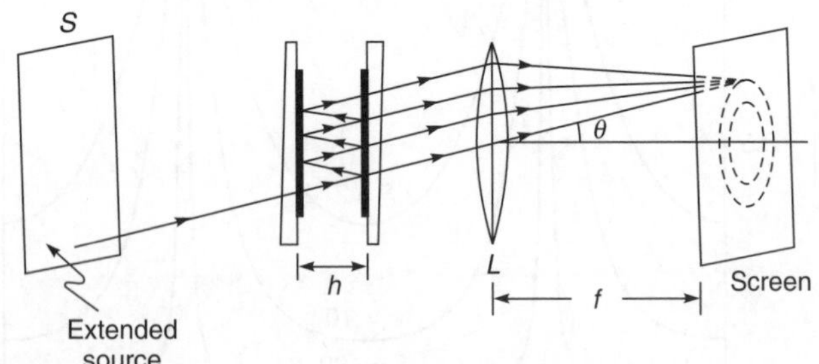

Figure 15.3
The Fabry–Perot etalon.

For large values of F, when θ_2 is slightly different from the value given by the above equation, the transmittivity will be very small. Hence, for a given wavelength, at the focal plane of the lens L, we will obtain a fringe pattern consisting of concentric rings—each bright ring will correspond to a particular value of m. The sharpness of the bright rings (and hence the resolving power of the etalon) will increase with the value of F.

EXAMPLE 15.1 As an example, we assume an etalon with $n_2 = 1$, $h = 1$ cm and $F = 400$ ($F = 400$ implies $R \approx 0.905$; i.e., each mirror of the etalon has about 90% reflectivity). In Fig. 15.4 we have plotted the intensity variation with θ for $\lambda_0 = 5000$ Å and 4999.98 Å. The actual fringe pattern (as obtained on the focal plane of a lens of focal length 25 cm) is shown in Fig. 15.5. Now, for

$$\lambda_0 = \lambda_1 = 5000 \text{ Å}$$

Equation (15.9) gives us

$$\theta_2 = \cos^{-1}\left(\frac{m}{40000}\right)$$

Thus bright rings will form at

$$\theta_2 = 0°, 0.405°, 0.573°, 0.702°, \ldots$$

corresponding to $m = 40000, 39999, 39998, 39997, \ldots$ respectively. This is shown as the thick curve in Fig. 15.4. On the other hand, for

$$\lambda_0 = \lambda_2 = 4999.98 \text{ Å}$$

we get

$$\theta_2 = \cos^{-1}\left(\frac{m}{40000.16}\right)$$

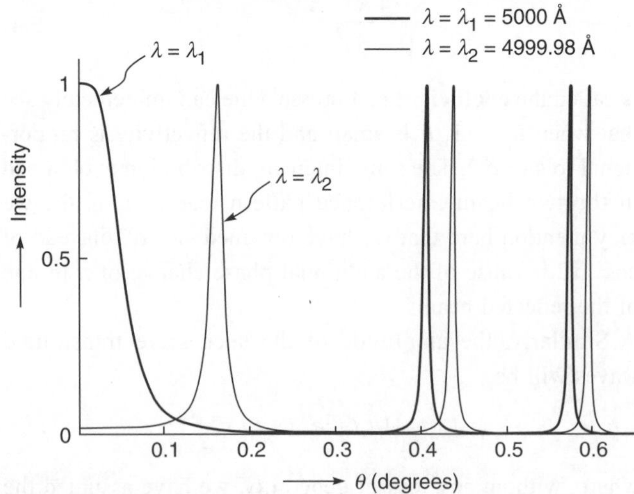

Figure 15.4
The variation of intensity with θ for a Fabry–Perot interferometer with $n_2 = 1$, $h = 1.0$ cm and $F = 400$, corresponding to $\lambda_0 = 5000$ Å ($=\lambda_1$) and $\lambda_0 = 4999.98$ Å ($=\lambda_2$).

Thus, bright rings will form at

$$\theta_2 = 0.162°, 0.436°, 0.595°, \ldots$$

corresponding to $m = 40000$, 39999, and 39998, respectively. This is shown as the thin curve in Fig. 15.4. The corresponding ring patterns as obtained on the focal plane of the lens is shown in Fig. 15.5. From the figure we can see that the two spectral lines having a small wavelength difference of 0.02 Å are quite well resolved by the etalon. In the figure, the central bright spot and the first ring corresponds respectively to $\lambda_0 = 5000$ Å and $\lambda_0 = 4999.98$ Å; both corresponding to $m = 40000$. The next two closely spaced rings correspond to $m = 39999$ for the two wavelengths.

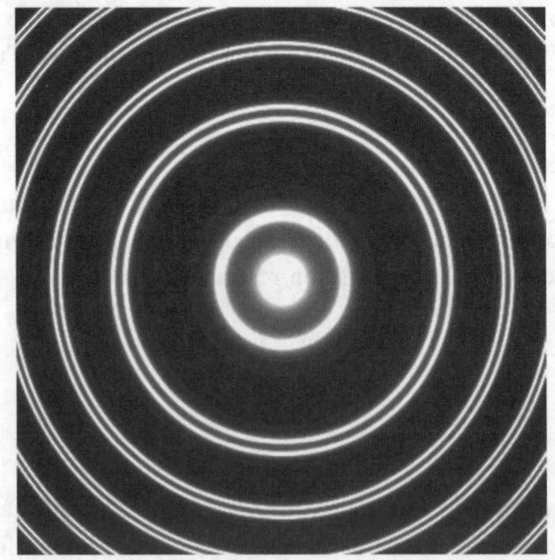

Figure 15.5
The (computer generated) ring pattern as obtained (on the focal plane of a lens) in a Fabry–Perot etalon with $n_2 = 1$, $h = 1.0$ cm and $F = 400$, corresponding to $\lambda_0 = 5000$ Å ($=\lambda_1$) and $\lambda_0 = 4999.98$ Å ($=\lambda_2$).

15.3.1 Flatness of the Coated Surfaces

In order to have sharp fringes, the coated surfaces should be parallel to a very high degree of accuracy. Indeed, the coated surfaces should be flat within about $\lambda/50$ where λ is the wavelength of light. In order to see this, we assume that in the above example, h is increased by $\lambda/20$ (= 250 Å = 2.5 × 10^{-6} cm):

$$h = 1 + 2.5 \times 10^{-6} = 1.0000025 \text{ cm}$$

For λ_0 = 5000 Å, we will have

$$\theta_2 = \cos^{-1}\left(\frac{m}{40000.1}\right)$$

and bright rings will form at

$$\theta_2 = 0.128°, 0.425°, 0.587°, \ldots$$

If we compare the results obtained in Example 15.1, we will find that if there is a variation in the spacing by about $\lambda/20$, the fringes corresponding to the wavelengths 5000 Å and 4999.98 Å will start overlapping. Thus the coated surfaces should be parallel within a very small fraction of the wavelength. Further, the two non-coated surfaces of each plate are made to have a slight angle between them (~1 to 10 minutes – see Fig. 15.3) so that one could avoid the unwanted fringes formed due to multiple reflections in the plate itself.

15.3.2 Modes of the Fabry–Perot Cavity

We consider a polychromatic beam incident normally ($\theta_2 = 0$) on a Fabry–Perot etalon with air between the reflecting plates ($n_2 = 1$) – see Fig. 15.6. In terms of the frequency

$$\nu = \frac{c}{\lambda_0}$$

Equation (15.9) tells us that transmission resonance will occur when

$$\nu = \nu_m = m\frac{c}{2h} \tag{15.11}$$

where m is an integer. The above equation represents the different (longitudinal) modes of the (Fabry–Perot) cavity. For h = 10 cm, the frequency spacing of two adjacent modes would be given by

$$\delta\nu = \frac{c}{2h} = 1500 \text{ MHz}$$

For an incident beam having a central frequency of

$$\nu = \nu_0 = 6 \times 10^{14} \text{ Hz}$$

and a spectral width* of 7000 MHz the output beam will have frequencies

$$\nu_0,\ \nu_0 \pm \delta\nu \quad \text{and} \quad \nu_0 \pm 2\delta\nu$$

as shown in Fig. 15.6. One can readily calculate from Eq. (15.11) that the five lines correspond to

$$m = 399998, 399999, 400000, 400001 \text{ and } 400002$$

Figure 15.7 shows a typical output of a multi-longitudinal (MLM) laser diode. The wavelength spacing between two modes is about 0.005 μm; the corresponding $\delta\nu \approx$ 620 GHz.

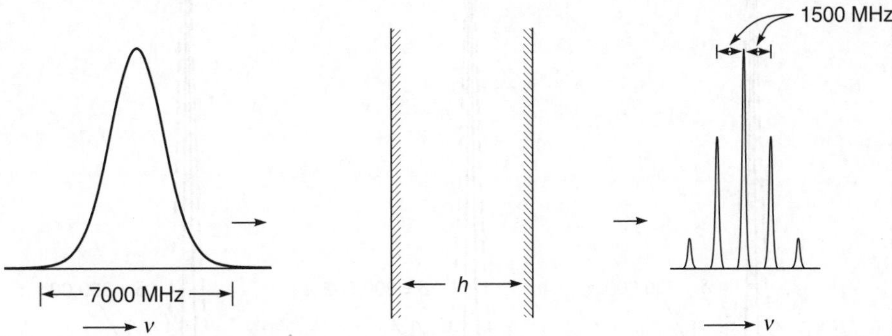

Figure 15.6
A beam having a spectral width of about 7000 MHz (around $\nu_0 = 6 \times 10^{14}$ Hz) is incident normally on a Fabry–Perot etalon with h = 10 cm and n_2 = 1. The output has five narrow spectral lines.

---

* For $\nu_0 = 6 \times 10^{14}$ Hz, λ_0 = 5000 Å and a spectral width of 7000 MHz would imply $\left|\frac{\Delta\lambda_0}{\lambda_0}\right| = \left|\frac{\Delta\nu}{\nu_0}\right| = \frac{7\times10^9}{6\times10^{14}} \approx 1.2 \times 10^{-5}$ giving $\Delta\lambda_0 \approx$ 0.06 Å. Thus a frequency spectral width of 7000 MHz (around $\nu_0 = 6 \times 10^{14}$ Hz) implies a wavelength spread of only 0.06 Å.

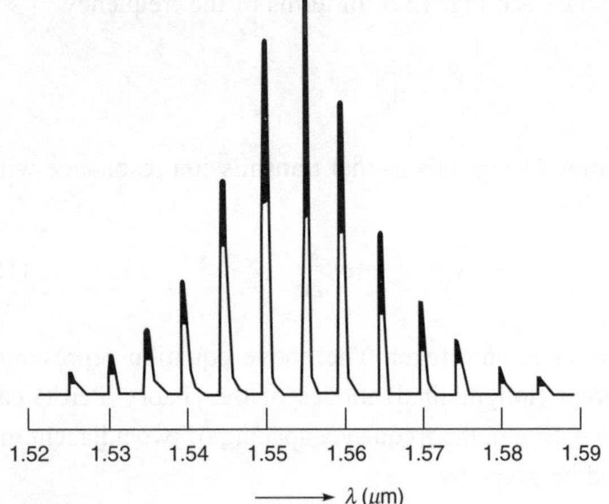

Figure 15.7
Typical output spectrum of a Fabry–Perot multilongitudinal mode (MLM) laser diode; the wavelength spacing between two modes is about 0.005 μm (Refs. 15.10, 15.11, 15.12).

15.4 The Fabry–Perot Interferometer

If one of the mirrors is kept fixed while the other is capable of moving to change the separation between the two mirrors, the system is called a **Fabry–Perot interferometer**. For a beam incident normally on the interferometer, we vary the separation h and measure the intensity variation on the focal plane of the lens L as shown in Fig. 15.8. Such an arrangement is usually referred as a scanning Fabry–Perot interferometer. Since the separation h is varied, we write it as

$$h = h_0 + x \quad \textbf{(15.12)}$$

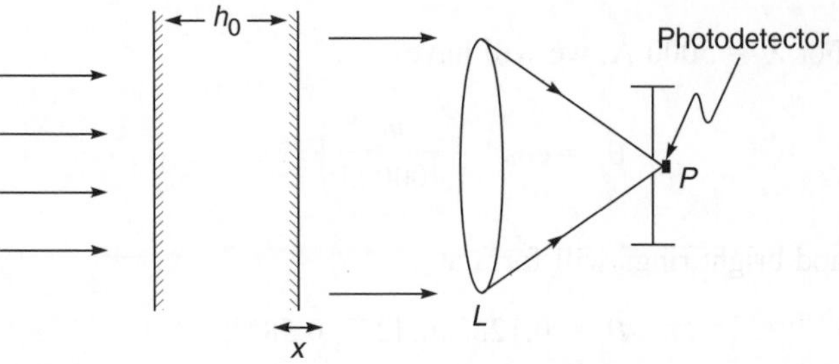

Figure 15.8
A scanning Fabry–Perot interferometer. The intensity variation is recorded (by a photodetector) on the focal plane of the lens L.

If the incident beam is monochromatic, a typical variation of intensity at the point P is shown in Fig. 15.9. The figure corresponds to the frequency of the incident beam being

$$\nu = \nu_0 = 6 \times 10^{14} \text{ Hz}$$

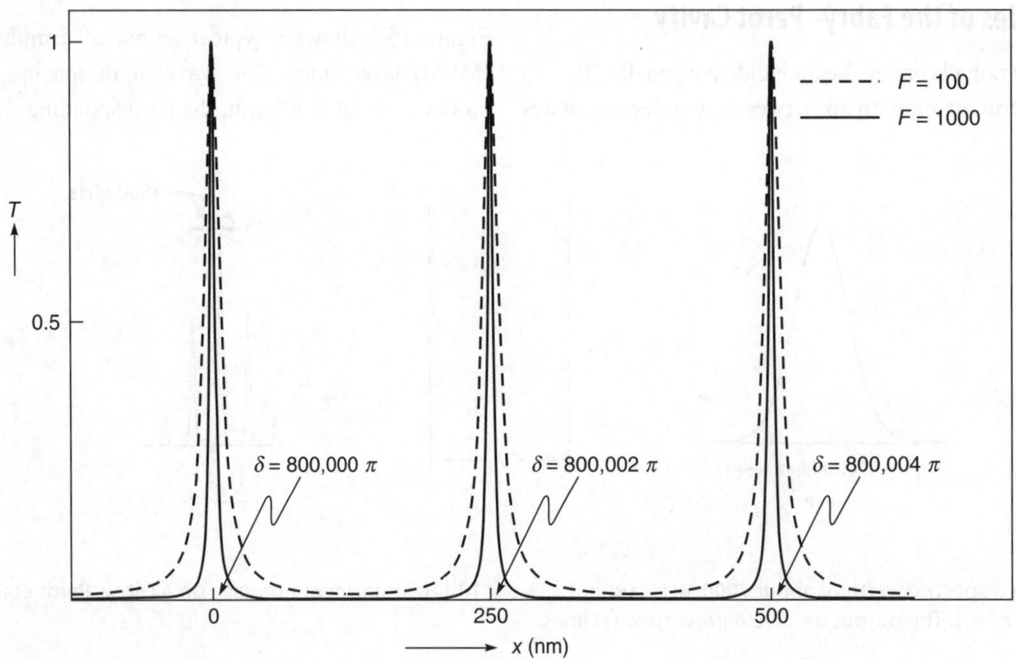

Figure 15.9
Variation of intensity at the point P with x (see Fig. 15.8) for a monochromatic beam incident normally on a scanning Fabry–Perot interferometer; the solid curve corresponds to $F = 1000$ and the dashed curve corresponds to $F = 100$.

For $h_0 = 10$ cm, $n_2 = 1$ and $\cos\theta_2 = 1$, we get

$$\delta = \frac{4\pi\,\nu_0\,(h_0 + x)}{c}$$

$$= 800000\,\pi\left(1+\frac{x}{h_0}\right)$$

Thus, transmittivity resonances will occur for

$$\delta = 800000\pi,\ 800002\pi,\ 800004\pi,\ \ldots$$

which will occur when

$$x = 0,\ 250\text{ nm},\ 500\text{ nm},\ \ldots$$

respectively. The two curves in Fig. 15.9 correspond to $F = 100$ and $F = 1000$. Notice that the transmission resonances become sharper if we increase the value of F. Fig. 15.10 shows variation of intensity at the point P when the incident beam has two frequencies separated by 300 MHz. Obviously, the two frequencies are well resolved.

We may mention here that if the frequency of the incident beam is increased by $c/2h_0$, i.e., if

$$\nu = \nu_0 + \frac{c}{2h_0}$$

then one can easily show that transmission resonances will occur at the same values of x, the corresponding values of δ will be 800002π (corresponding to $x = 0$), 800004π (corresponding to $x = 250$ nm) etc. Indeed, if

$$\nu = \nu_0 \pm p\frac{c}{2h_0};\quad p = 1, 2, 3, \ldots$$

we will have the same T vs. x curve. The quantity

$$\Delta\nu_s = \frac{c}{2h_0} \tag{15.13}$$

is known as the **free spectral range** (FSR) of the interferometer. Thus when the spectrum has widely separated wavelength components, we will have overlapping of orders.

15.5 Resolving Power

LO3

We will first consider the resolving power corresponding to a beam incident normally on a scanning Fabry–Perot interferometer. This will be followed by the case corresponding to the Fabry–Perot etalon.

15.5.1 Resolving Power of a Scanning Fabry–Perot Interferometer

We consider the presence of two frequencies ν_1 and ν_2 of equal intensity in the beam incident normally on a scanning Fabry–Perot interferometer. For the two frequencies to be just resolved, we assume that the half intensity point of n_1 falls on the half intensity point of ν_2 as shown in Fig. 15.11. When this happens, the minimum of the resultant intensity distribution (shown as the dashed curve in Fig. 15.11) is about 74% of the corresponding maximum value. Now, as discussed in Sec. 15.2, if the half intensity point occurs at

$$\delta = \delta_{1/2} = 2m\pi \pm \frac{\Delta\delta}{2} \tag{15.14}$$

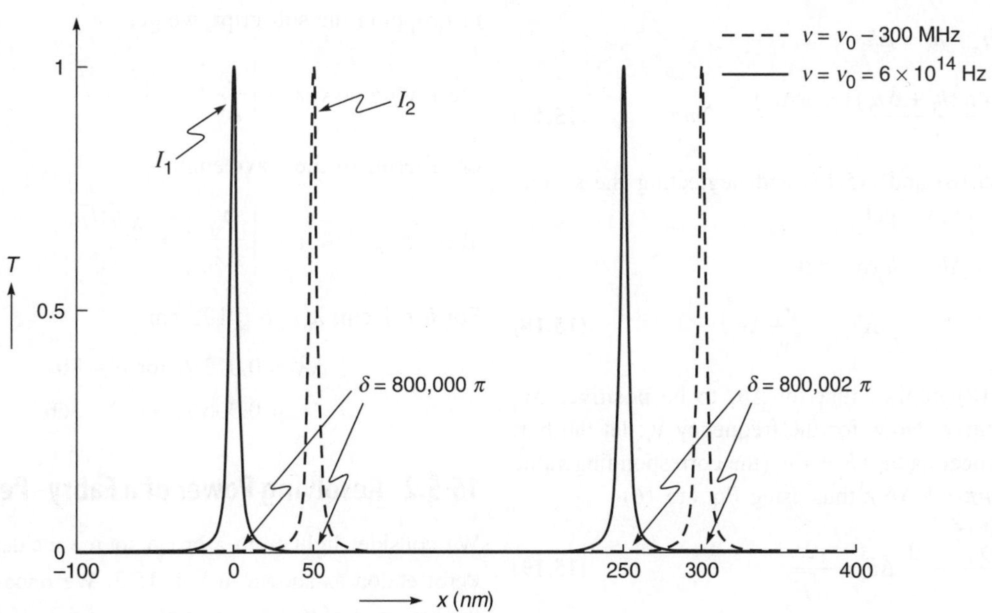

Figure 15.10
Variation of intensity at the point P with x (see Fig. 15.8) when the incident beam has two frequencies separated by 300 MHz.

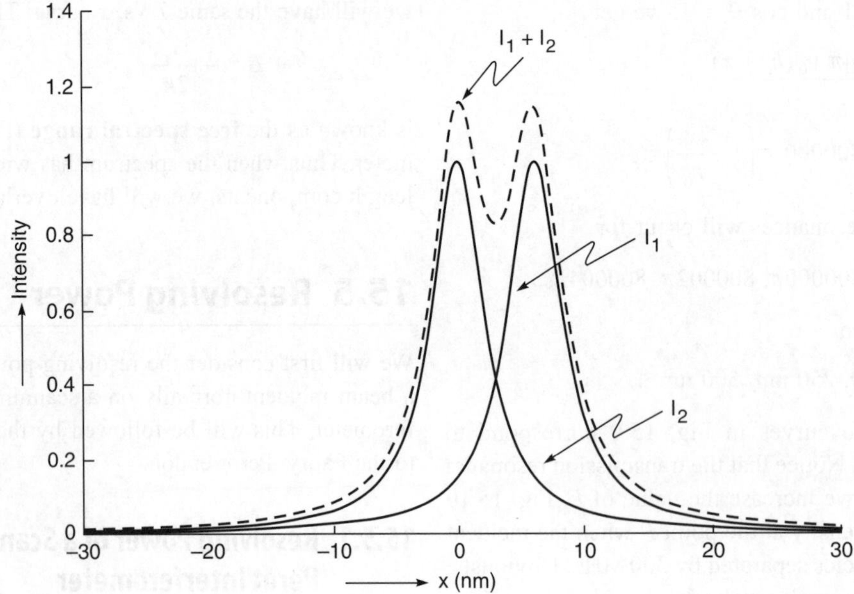

Figure 15.11
The individual intensity variations I_1 and I_2 in the presence of two frequencies ν_1 and ν_2 and the total intensity variation $(I_1 + I_2)$ when the two frequencies are just resolved.

then $$\Delta\delta \approx \frac{4}{\sqrt{F}} \qquad \textbf{(15.15)}$$

[see Eq. (15.8)]. Consider the frequency ν_1. If the maximum intensity occurs at $h = h_1$ then

$$\delta_1 = \frac{4\pi h_1 \nu_1}{c} = 2m\pi \qquad \textbf{(15.16)}$$

Let the intensity maximum for $\nu = \nu_2$ $(= \nu_1 + \Delta\nu_1)$ occur at

$$h = h_2 = h_1 + \Delta h_1$$

Thus, $$\delta_2 = \frac{4\pi (h_1 + \Delta h_1)(\nu_1 + \Delta\nu_1)}{c} = 2m\pi \qquad \textbf{(15.17)}$$

Using Eqs. (15.16) and (15.17) and neglecting the second order term $\Delta h_1 \Delta\nu_1$, we get

$$\nu_1 \Delta h_1 + h_1 \Delta\nu_1 = 0$$

or $$\Delta h_1 = -\frac{h_1}{\nu_1}\Delta\nu_1 \qquad \textbf{(15.18)}$$

Equation (15.18) implies that for Δh_1 to be positive, $\Delta\nu_1$ should be negative. Now, for the frequency ν_1, let the half intensity point occur at $h = h_1 + \delta h_1$ (the corresponding value of δ will be $2m\pi + \frac{1}{2}\Delta\delta_1$); thus using Eq. (15.16)

$$\frac{4\pi \nu_1 \delta h_1}{c} = \frac{1}{2}\Delta\delta_1 \approx \frac{2}{\sqrt{F}} \qquad \textbf{(15.19)}$$

or $$\delta h_1 \approx \frac{c}{2\pi \nu_1 \sqrt{F}} \qquad \textbf{(15.20)}$$

For the two frequencies to be just resolved

$$\Delta h_1 = 2\delta h_1 \approx \frac{c}{\pi \nu_1 \sqrt{F}} \qquad \textbf{(15.21)}$$

Using Eq. (15.18), we get for the resolving power

$$\left|\frac{\nu_1}{\Delta\nu}\right| = \frac{h_1}{\Delta h_1} = \frac{\pi h_1 \nu_1 \sqrt{F}}{c}$$

or dropping the subscript, we get

$$\text{Resolving power} = \left|\frac{\nu}{\Delta\nu}\right| = \frac{\pi h \nu \sqrt{F}}{c} \qquad \textbf{(15.22)}$$

or in terms of the wavelength

$$\text{Resolving power} = \left|\frac{\lambda_0}{\Delta\lambda_0}\right| = \frac{\pi h \sqrt{F}}{\lambda_0} \qquad \textbf{(15.23)}$$

For $h = 1$ cm, $\lambda_0 = 6 \times 10^{-5}$ cm

$$\Delta\lambda \approx 0.013 \text{ Å for } F = 80$$
$$\approx 0.006 \text{ Å for } F = 360$$

15.5.2 Resolving Power of a Fabry–Perot Etalon

We consider light from a broad source incident on a Fabry–Perot etalon as shown in Fig. 15.3. We once again consider the presence of two wavelengths λ_1 and λ_2 of equal intensity. Now, $T = 1$ if the angle of incidence is such that [see Eq. (15.9)]

$$\delta = \frac{4\pi\nu}{c} h\mu = 2m\pi \tag{15.24}$$

where $\mu = \cos\theta$, and for the sake of simplicity, we have dropped the subscript on μ and θ. We can now have arguments very similar to that in Sec. 15.5.1 except now h is fixed and μ (= cos θ) is varied. Thus, if the mth order intensity maxima for $\nu = \nu_1$ and $\nu = \nu_2$ (= $\nu_1 + \Delta\nu_1$) occur at $\mu = \mu_1$ and $\mu = \mu_2$ (= $\mu_1 + \Delta\mu_1$), then

$$\delta_1 = \frac{4\pi\nu_1 h\mu_1}{c} = 2m\pi \tag{15.25}$$

and

$$\delta_2 = \frac{4\pi h(\nu_1 + \Delta\nu_1)(\mu_1 + \Delta\mu_1)}{c} = 2m\pi \tag{15.26}$$

Thus, neglecting the second order term we get

$$\Delta\mu_1 = -\frac{\mu_1}{\nu_1}\Delta\nu_1 \tag{15.27}$$

Now, for the frequency ν_1, let the half intensity point occur at $\mu = \mu_1 + \delta\mu_1$ (the corresponding value of δ will be $2m\pi + \frac{1}{2}\Delta\delta_1$); thus using Eq. (15.24)

$$\frac{4\pi\nu_1 h\delta\mu_1}{c} = \frac{1}{2}\Delta\delta_1 \approx \frac{2}{\sqrt{F}} \tag{15.28}$$

or

$$\delta\mu_1 \approx \frac{c}{2\pi\nu_1 h\sqrt{F}} \tag{15.29}$$

As discussed earlier, for the two frequencies to be just resolved, we assume that the half intensity point of ν_1 falls on the half intensity point of ν_2 giving

$$\Delta\mu_1 = 2\delta\mu_1 \approx \frac{c}{\pi\nu_1 h\sqrt{F}} \tag{15.30}$$

Using Eq. (15.27) we get

$$\text{Resolving power} = \left|\frac{\nu_1}{\Delta\nu_1}\right| = \frac{\mu_1}{\Delta\mu_1} = \frac{\pi\nu_1 h\sqrt{F}\mu_1}{c} \tag{15.31}$$

or in terms of the wavelength

$$\text{Resolving power} = \left|\frac{\lambda_0}{\Delta\lambda_0}\right| = \frac{\pi h\sqrt{F}\cos\theta}{\lambda_0} \tag{15.32}$$

Thus for $F = 360$ ($R = 0.9$), $h = 1$ cm, $\lambda_0 = 5000$ Å

$$\left|\frac{\lambda_0}{\Delta\lambda_0}\right| \approx 1.2 \times 10^6$$

where we have assumed normal incidence. The above equation gives

$$\Delta\lambda_0 \approx 0.004 \text{ Å}$$

Thus a Fabry–Perot instrument can resolve wavelengths differing by about 10^{-3} Å. This is in contrast to that of a grating (say having 25000 grooves) which resolves up to about 0.1 Å at $\lambda = 5000$ Å and that of a prism (made of dense flint glass with 5 cm base) which resolves only up to about 1 Å at 5000 Å. It must be noted that in the above analysis, we have considered two monochromatic lines at λ and $\lambda + \Delta\lambda$. In general, the lines at the two wavelengths λ and $\lambda + \Delta\lambda$ themselves will have a wavelength spread and this restricts the use of such high resolving powers.

When the Fabry–Perot interferometer is used to analyze spectra with closely spaced lines, then the distance between the adjacent maxima would be greater than the displacement between the system of rings of the spectral lines. But when the spectrum has widely separated wavelength components, then it might happen that the displacement between the rings is greater than the separation between adjacent maxima. The results in the 'overlapping' of orders (see also the discussion at the end of Sec. 15.4). The difference in wavelength ($\Delta\lambda_s$) which corresponds to a displacement of one order, is called the spectral range of the interferometer. Thus we can write

$$\Delta\lambda_s = \frac{\lambda^2}{2nh\cos\theta} \tag{15.33}$$

This becomes, for near normal incidence ($\theta \approx 0$),

$$\Delta\lambda_s = \frac{\lambda^2}{2nh} \tag{15.34}$$

which is found to be inversely proportional to h. This is in contrast to the resolving power which depends directly on h [see Eqs. (15.31) and (15.32)].

When the spectrum is complex consisting of a number of widely separated wavelength components, each with a hyperfine structure, then one can separate the different wavelength components by employing the Fabry–Perot interferometer along with a spectrograph as shown in Fig. 15.12(a). The light emerging from the source S is rendered parallel by the lens L_1. The interference pattern formed by the Fabry–Perot interferometer (marked by FP in the figure) is made to fall on the slit of the spectrograph. The spectrograph separates the spectral components and one obtains in the plane P images of the slit, each crossed by fringes as shown in Fig. 15.12(b).

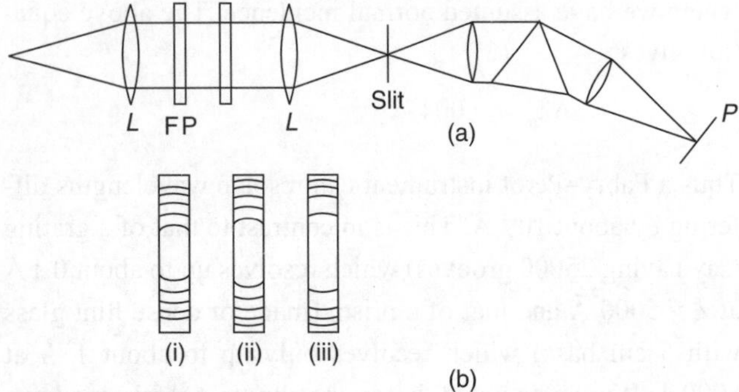

Figure 15.12

(a) A Fabry–Perot interferometer used in conjunction with a spectrograph. (b) The interlaced fringes formed in the plane of the slit are separated by the prism. For example, (i), (ii) and (iii) may correspond to the lines in the red, yellow and green regions, respectively as observed on plane *P*.

15.6 The Lummer–Gehrcke Plate*

LO4

We saw in Sec. 15.2 that the sharpness of fringes (and hence the resolving power) of a multiple beam interferometer increases as the reflectivity *R* of the plate increases. But one cannot use every thick coating of metals to increase the reflectivity as the intensity of the beam would be reduced considerably due to absorption in metallic coatings. This difficulty can be overcome by the use of the phenomenon of total internal reflection (instead of metallic reflection); this is used in the Lummer–Gehrcke plate which will be discussed in this section.

A **Lummer-Gehrcke plate** is a plane parallel made of glass (or quartz), on one end of which a small right-angled prism of the same material is fixed (see Fig. 15.13). The angle of the prism is chosen in such a way that the rays incident normally on the surface of the prism hit the two surfaces of the plate at an angle slightly less than the critical angle.** Since the two surfaces are parallel, all successive reflections will occur at the same (near critical) angle. Most of the light will be reflected with a little fraction being transmitted at each reflection. Thus, there will emerge from the upper and lower surfaces of the plate a series of waves which would finally interfere to produce interference fringes in the plane *P* (see Fig. 15.13). Notice that the prism suppresses the externally reflected beam. In the plane *P*, one obtains fringe patterns on either side of the plate. The fringes are approximately straight lines parallel to the plate surfaces.

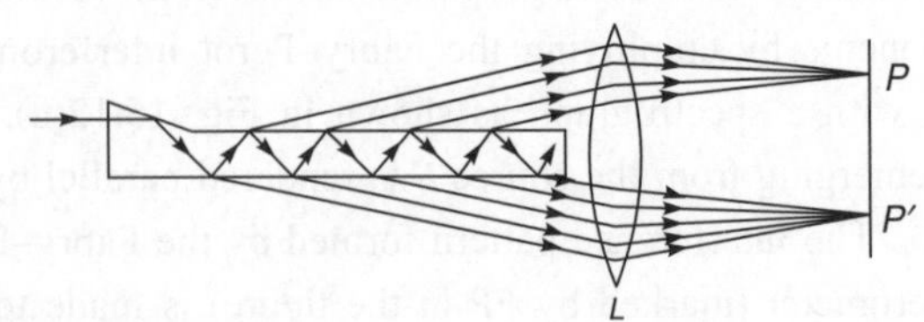

Figure 15.13

The Lummer–Gehrcke plate.

We will not go into the details of the theory of the Lummer–Gehrcke plate but two points may be noted:

(a) Unlike in the case of Fabry–Perot interferometer, the space between the reflecting surfaces is a dispersive medium, and

(b) The number of reflections is also not very large as in the case of the Fabry–Perot interferometer; the number of reflections depends on the length of the plate and the angle θ, (see Fig. 15.13). Thus, the resolving power of the instrument depends on the length of the plate.

Earlier, Lummer–Gehrcke plates were used in high resolution spectroscopy. However, it has been replaced by the more flexible Fabry–Perot interferometer.

15.7 Interference Filters

LO5

When a Fabry–Perot interferometer is illuminated by a monochromatic (uncollimated) beam, we get a spectrum consisting of different intensity maxima which satisfy the following relation:

$$2nh \cos \theta_r = m\lambda \tag{15.35}$$

Now if a Fabry–Perot interferometer is illuminated with a collimated white light incident normally ($\theta_r \approx 0$), maxima of different orders are formed in the transmitted light corresponding to wavelengths given by

$$\lambda = \frac{2nh}{m} \tag{15.36}$$

If *h* is large, a large number of maxima will be observed in the visible region; for example, about 23,000 maxima are observed if $h = 1$ cm. But, if we go on reducing *h*, we reach a situation in which only one or two maxima are obtained in the visible region. For example, if $n = 1.5$ and $h = 6 \times 10^{-5}$ cm, there are only two maxima in the visible region, corresponding to $\lambda = 6000$ Å ($m = 3$) and $\lambda = 4500$ Å ($m = 4$). They are widely separated and one of them can be masked so as to transmit only one wavelength. In this way, it is possible to filter a particular wavelength out of a white light beam. Such a structure is known as an **interference filter**.*** Interference filters using this principle can be obtained by

* Sections 15.6 and 15.7 have been very kindly written by Professor Anurag Sharma.

** Beyond the critical angle, the reflection is total while slightly below the critical angle, the reflectivity is high (see Sec. 23.2).

*** The Fabry–Perot structure also behaves as a resonator and supports the oscillation of what are known as *modes*.

modern vacuum deposition techniques. A thin metallic film (usually, of aluminum or silver) is deposited on a substrate (generally, a glass plate) by vacuum deposition techniques. Then a thin layer of a dielectric material such as cryolite ($3NaF.AlF_3$) is deposited over this. This structure is again covered by another metallic film (see Fig. 15.14). To protect this film structure from any damage, another glass plate is placed over it. Thus, a Fabry–Perot structure is formed between the two glass plates. By varying the thickness of the dielectric film, one can filter out any particular wavelength. However, the filtered light will have a finite width, that is, it will have a narrow spectrum sharply peaked about one wavelength. The sharpness of the transmitted spectrum is determined by the resolving power of the formed Fabry–Perot structure, and hence by the reflectivity of the surfaces. The larger the reflectivity, the narrower is the transmitted spectrum. But it is not possible to increase the thickness of the metallic films indefinitely as absorption will reduce the intensity of the transmitted light. To overcome this difficulty, metallic films are replaced by all dielectric structures.

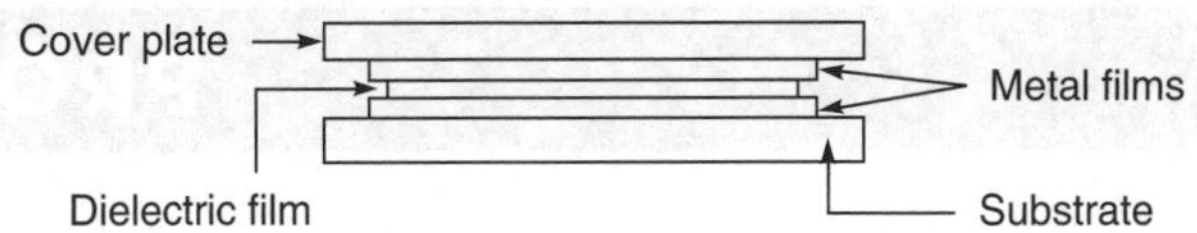

Figure 15.14
The interference filter.

In an all-dielectric structure, layers of dielectric materials of appropriate refractive indices are deposited. It was shown in Chapter 14 how dielectric films can be used to enhance the reflectivity of a surface. If, on a glass-plate, a $\lambda/4$ thick film of a dielectric material whose refractive index is more than that of glass, is deposited, the reflectivity of the glass plate increases. Larger the difference between the refractive indices, greater will be the reflectivity. The materials generally used in interference filters are titanium oxide ($n = 2.8$) or zinc sulphide ($n = 2.3$). To obtain interference filters, a $\lambda/4$ thick film of titanium oxide is deposited on a glass substrate. Then a thin layer of dielectric material with lower refractive index (such as cryolite or magnesium fluoride) is deposited. On this is again deposited a $\lambda/4$ thick layer of a material of higher refractive index. To increase the reflectivity, multi-layer structures of alternate higher and lower refractive index materials are used. In this way, it is possible to achieve a reflectivity of more than 90% for any particular wavelength (see Sec. 14.6 for a more detailed account). Thus if the incident wave is polychromatic (like white light), the reflected light may have a high degree of monochromaticity.

SUMMARY

- If a plane wave falls on a plane parallel film, then the beam would undergo multiple reflections at the two surfaces and a large number of beams of successively diminishing amplitude will emerge on both sides of the plate. These beams (on either side) interfere to produce an interference pattern at infinity. If the reflectivity R at each surface is close to unity, then the fringes so formed are much sharper than those by two beam interference and, therefore, the interferometers involving multiple beam interference have a high resolving power and hence find applications in high resolution spectroscopy. The transmittivity of such a film is given by

$$T = \frac{1}{1 + F\sin^2\frac{\delta}{2}}$$

where $F = \dfrac{4R}{(1-R)^2}$ is known as coefficient of Finesse and

$$\delta = \frac{4\pi n_2 h\cos\theta_2}{\lambda_0}$$

represents the phase difference (between two consecutive waves emanating from the film) due to the additional path traversed by the beam in the film; θ_2 is the angle of refraction inside the film (of refractive index n_2), h the film thickness and λ_0 is the free space wavelength. The transmittivity $T = 1$ when $\delta = 2m\pi$; $m = 1, 2, 3, \ldots$ For $R \approx 1$, the value of F is very large and the transmission resonances become very sharp. This is the principle used in the Fabry–Perot interferometer which is characterized by a high resolving power.

- For a given wavelength, at the focal plane of the lens L, we will obtain a fringe pattern consisting of concentric rings—each bright ring will correspond to a particular value of m. The sharpness of the bright rings (and hence the resolving power of the etalon) will increase with the value of F.
- When the Fabry–Perot interferometer is used to analyze spectra with closely spaced lines, then the distance between the adjacent maxima would be greater than the displacement between the system of rings of the spectral lines.
- The number of reflections is also not very large as in the case of the Fabry–Perot interferometer; the number of reflections depends on the length of the plate and the angle q, (see Fig. 15.13). Thus, the resolving power of the instrument depends on the length of the plate.
- The larger the reflectivity, the narrower is the transmitted spectrum. Dielectric structures have replaced metallic films these days.

PROBLEMS

15.1 Calculate the resolving power of a Fabry–Perot interferometer made of reflecting surfaces of reflectivity 0.85 and separated by a distance 1 mm at $\lambda = 4880$ Å.

15.2 Calculate the minimum spacing between the plates of a Fabry–Perot interferometer which would resolve two lines with $\Delta\lambda = 0.1$ Å at $\lambda = 6000$ Å. Assume the reflectivity to be 0.8.

15.3 Consider a monochromatic beam of wavelength 6000 Å incident (from an extended source) on a Fabry–Perot etalon with $n_2 = 1$, $h = 1$ cm and $F = 200$. Concentric rings are observed on the focal plane of a lens of focal length 20 cm

(a) Calculate the reflectivity of each mirror.

(b) Calculate the radii of the first four bright rings. What will be the corresponding values of m?

(c) Calculate the angular width of each ring where the intensity falls by half and the corresponding FWHM (in mm) of each ring.

15.4 Consider now two wavelengths 6000 Å and 5999.9 Å incident on a Fabry–Perot etalon with the same parameters as given in the previous problem. Calculate the radii of the first three bright rings corresponding to each wavelength. What will be the corresponding values of m? Will the lines be resolved?

15.5 Consider a monochromatic beam of wavelength 6000 Å incident normally on a scanning Fabry–Perot interferometer with $n_2 = 1$ and $F = 400$. The distance between the two mirrors is written as $h = h_0 + x$. With $h_0 = 10$ cm, calculate

(a) The first three values of x for which we will have unit transmittivity and the corresponding values of m.

(b) Also calculate the FWHM Δh for which the transmittivity will be half.

(c) What would be the value of Δh if F was 200?

[**Ans.** (a) $x \approx 200$ nm ($m = 333334$), 500 nm ($m = 333335$); (b) $\Delta h \approx 9.5$ nm].

15.6 In continuation of Problem 15.5, consider now two wavelengths λ_0 (= 6,000 Å) and $\lambda_0 + \Delta\lambda$ incident normally on the Fabry–Perot interferometer with $n_2 = 1$, $F = 400$ and $h_0 = 10$ cm. What will be the value of $\Delta\lambda$ so that $T = \frac{1}{2}$ occurs at the same value of h for both the wavelengths?

15.7 Consider a laser beam incident normally on the Fabry–Perot interferometer as shown in Fig. 15.15.

(a) Assume $h_0 = 0.1$ m, $c = 3 \times 10^8$ m/s, $\nu = \nu_0 = 5 \times 10^{14}$ s^{-1}. Plot T as a function of x (-100 nm $< x < 400$ nm) for $F = 200$ and $F = 1000$.

(b) Show that if $\nu = (\nu_0 \pm p$ 1500 MHz; $p = 1, 2, \ldots)$ we will have the same T vs. x curve; 1500 MHz is known as the free spectral range (FSR). What will be the corresponding values of δ?

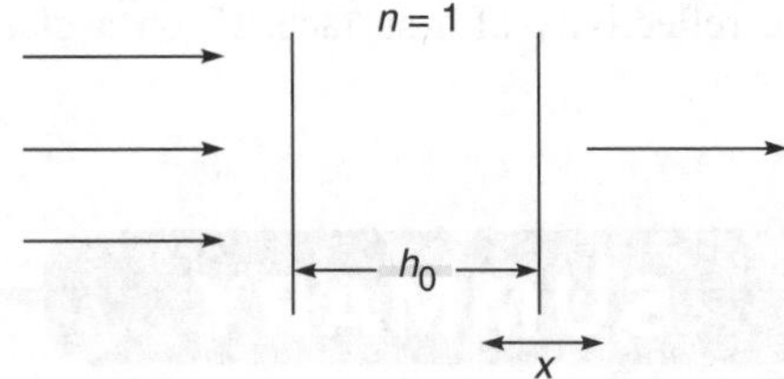

Figure 15.15

CHAPTER

16

Coherence

Light which is capable of interference is called 'coherent', and it is evident that in order to yield many interference fringes, it must be very monochromatic. Coherence is conveniently measured by the path difference between two rays of the same source, by which they can differ while still giving observable interference contrast. This is called the coherence length...... Lord Rayleigh and Albert Michelson were the first to understand that it is a reciprocal measure of the spectroscopic line width. Michelson used it for ingenious methods of spectral analysis and for the measurement of the diameter of stars.

—Dennis Gabor in his Nobel Lecture on Holography, December 11, 1971

LEARNING OBJECTIVES

After reading this chapter, the reader should be able to:

LO 1: *understand coherence time of a source*

LO 2: *discuss the linewidth of a source.*

LO 3: *understand the basic physics of spatial coherence.*

LO 4: *determine angular diameter of star by Michelson Stellar Interfermometer.*

LO 5: *discuss optical beats.*

LO 6: *understand coherence time and linewidth via Fourier analysis.*

LO 7: *discuss the complex degree of coherence in Young's double-hole experiment.*

LO 8: *explain principle of Fourier transform spectroscopy and its applications.*

16.1 Introduction LO1

In earlier chapters on interference, we had assumed that the displacement associated with a wave remained sinusoidal for all values of time. Thus, the displacement (which we denote by E) was assumed to be given by

$$E = A\cos(kx - \omega t + \phi)$$

The above equation predicts that at any value of x, the displacement is sinusoidal for $-\infty < t < \infty$. For example, at $x = 0$ we have [see Fig. 16.1(a)].

$$E = A\cos(\omega t - \phi), -\infty < t < \infty \quad \textbf{(16.1)}$$

Obviously this corresponds to an idealised situation because the radiation from an ordinary light source consists of finite size wavetrains, a typical variation of which is shown in Fig. 16.1(b). Since we will be considering only light waves, the quantity E represents the electric field associated with the light wave. Now, in Fig. 16.1(b), τ_c represents the average duration of the wavetrains, i.e., the electric field remains sinusoidal for

Above Image: View of a rainbow against a background of clouds. Photograph courtesy McGraw Hill Digital Access Library.

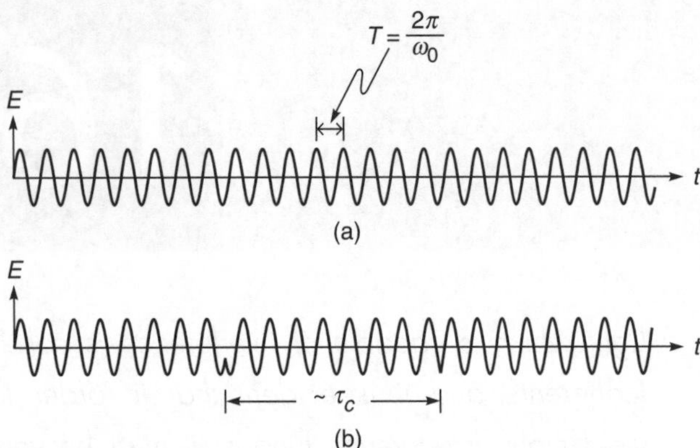

Figure 16.1

(a) For a perfectly monochromatic beam, the displacement remains sinusoidal for $-\infty < t < +\infty$. (b) For an actual source, a definite phase relationship exists for times of the order of τ_c, which is known as the *temporal coherence of the beam*. For $\nu \sim 5 \times 10^{14}$ Hz and $\tau_c \sim 10^{-10}$ sec, one has about 50,000 oscillations in the time τ_c.

times of the order of τ_c. Thus, at a given point, the electric fields at times t and $t + \Delta t$ will, in general, have a definite phase relationship if $\Delta t \ll \tau_c$ and will (almost) never have any phase relationship if $\Delta t \gg \tau_c$. The time duration τ_c is known as the **coherence time** of the source and the field is said to remain coherent for times $\sim\tau_c$. The length of the wavetrain, given by

$$L = c\,\tau_c \tag{16.2}$$

(where c is the speed of light in free space) is referred to as **coherence length**. For example, for the neon line (λ = 6328 Å), $\tau_c \sim 10^{-10}$ sec and for the red cadmium line (λ = 6438 Å), $\tau_c \sim 10^{-9}$ sec; the corresponding coherence lengths are 3 cm and 30 cm, respectively. The finite value of the coherence time τ_c could be due to many factors; for example, if a radiating atom undergoes collision with another atom, then the wavetrain undergoes an abrupt phase shift of the type shown in Fig. 16.1(b). The finite coherence time could also be on account of the random motion of atoms or due to the fact that an atom has a finite lifetime in the energy level from which it drops to the lower energy level while radiating; for more details, see Ref. 16.17.

In order to understand the concept of coherence time (or of coherence length) we consider Young's double hole experiment as shown in Fig. 16.2; the interference pattern produced by this experimental arrangement was discussed in considerable detail in Sec. 13.4. Now, the interference pattern observed around the point P at time t is due to the superposition of waves emanating from S_1 and S_2 at times $t - r_1/c$ and $t - r_2/c$, respectively, where r_1 and r_2 are the distances S_1P and S_2P, respectively. Obviously, if

$$\frac{r_2 - r_1}{c} \ll \tau_c$$

then the waves arriving at P from S_1 and S_2 will have a definite phase relationship and an interference pattern of good contrast will be obtained. On the other hand, if the path difference $(r_2 - r_1)$ is large enough such that

$$\frac{r_2 - r_1}{c} \gg \tau_c$$

then the waves arriving at P from S_1 and S_2 will have no fixed phase relationship and no interference pattern will be observed. Thus the central fringe (for which $r_1 = r_2$) will, in general, have a good contrast and as we move towards higher order fringes the contrast of the fringes will gradually become poorer. This point is discussed in greater detail in Sec. 16.7.

We next consider the Michelson interferometer experiment (see Sec. 14.11). A light beam falls on a beam splitter G (which is usually a partially silvered plate) and the waves reflected from the mirrors M_1 and M_2 interfere (see Fig. 16.3). Let M_2' represent the image of the mirror M_2 (formed by the plate G) as seen by the eye. If the distance M_1M_2' is denoted by d, then the beam which gets reflected by mirror M_2 travels an additional path equal to $2d$. Thus, the beam reflected from M_1 interferes with the beam reflected by M_2 which had originated $2d/c$ seconds earlier. If the distance d is such that

$$\frac{2d}{c} \ll \tau_c$$

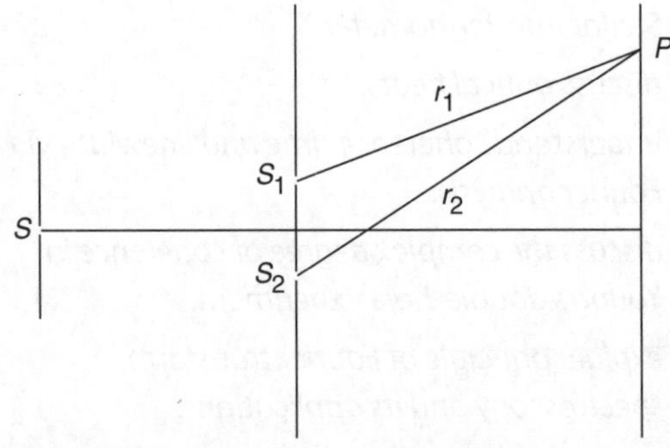

Figure 16.2

Young's double-hole experiment. The interference pattern observed around the point P at time t is due to the superposition of waves emanating from S_1 and S_2 at times $t - \frac{r_1}{c}$ and $t - \frac{r_2}{c}$, respectively; thus interference fringes of good contrast will be observed at P if $(r_2 - r_1)/c << \tau_c$.

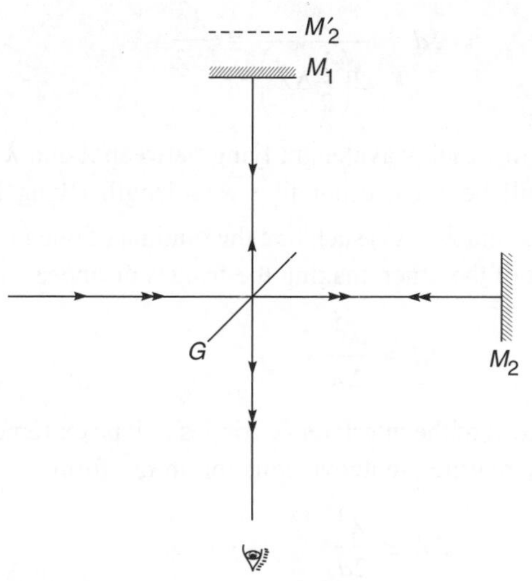

Figure 16.3
The Michelson interferometer arrangement. G represents the beam splitter. M_2' represents the image of M_2 as formed by G.

then a definite phase relationship exists between the two beams and well-defined interference fringes are observed. On the other hand, if

$$\frac{2d}{c} >> \tau_c$$

then, in general, there is no definite phase relationship between the two beams and no interference pattern is observed. It may be mentioned that there is no definite distance at which the interference pattern disappears; as the distance increases, the contrast of the fringes becomes gradually poorer and eventually the fringe system disappears. For the neon line

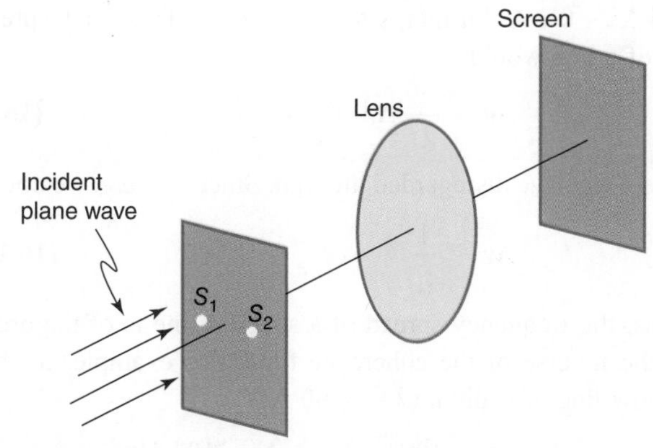

Figure 16.4
A parallel beam of light is incident normally on a pair of circular holes and the Fraunhofer diffraction pattern is observed on the focal plane of a convex lens.

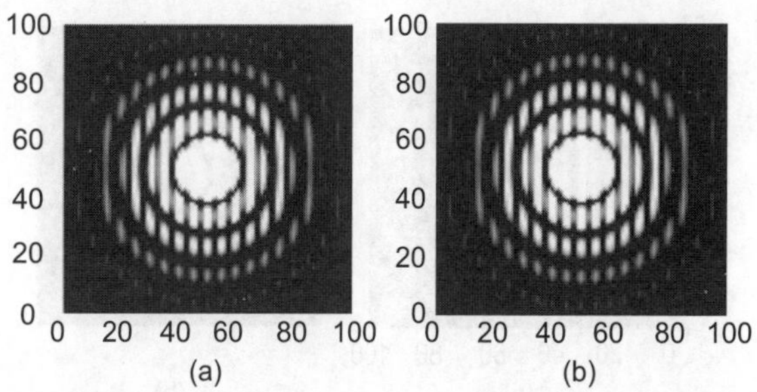

Figure 16.5
(a) The interference pattern produced for the arrangement shown in Fig. 16.4 using a helium–neon laser beam. (b) The interference pattern produced by the same arrangement with 1 mm thick glass plate in front of one of the holes. (The above figures are computer-generated; the experimentally obtained photographs are very similar—see Ref. 16.16.)

(λ = 6328 Å), the disappearance occurs when the path difference is about a few centimetres giving $\tau_c \sim 10^{-10}$ s. On the other hand, for the red cadmium line (λ = 6438 Å), the coherence length is of the order of 30 cm giving $\tau_c \sim 10^{-9}$ sec.

The coherence time for a laser beam is usually much large in comparison to ordinary light sources. Indeed, for helium–neon laser, coherence times as large as 50 milliseconds have been obtained Ref. 16.9]; this would imply a coherence length of 15,000 km! Commercially available helium–neon lasers have $\tau_c \sim 50$ nsec implying coherence lengths of about 15 m. Thus using such a laser beam, high contrast interference fringes can be obtained even for a path difference of a few metres.

In order to demonstrate the large coherence length of the laser beam we consider an experimental arrangement shown in Fig. 16.4. A parallel beam of light is incident normally on a pair of circular holes. The Fraunhofer diffraction pattern is observed on the focal plane of a convex lens. We first use a helium neon laser beam, the resulting interference pattern is shown in Fig. 16.5(a) which is simply the product of the Airy pattern and the interference pattern produced by two point sources (see Sec. 18.8). We next introduce a $\frac{1}{2}$ mm thick glass plate in front of one of the circular holes; there is almost no change in the interference pattern as can be seen from Fig. 16.5(b). Clearly, the extra path introduced by the plate [= $(\mu - 1)t$, see Sec. 13.10] is very small in comparison to the coherence length associated with the laser beam. If we repeat the experiment with a collimated mercury arc beam, we would find that with the introduction of the glass plate the interference pattern disappears (Fig. 16.6). This implies that the extra path length introduced by the glass plate is so large that there is no definite phase relationship between the waves arriving on the screen from the two circular apertures.

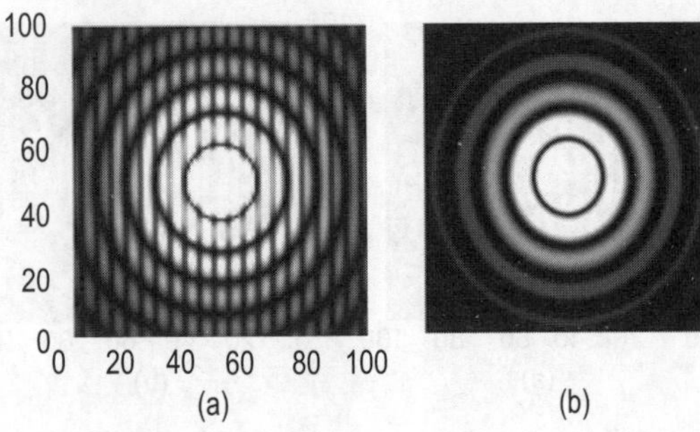

Figure 16.6
(a) The interference pattern produced for the arrangement shown in Fig. 16.4 using a collimated mercury arc. (b) The interference pattern is washed out when 0.5 mm thick glass plate is introduced in front of one of the holes. (The above figures are computer-generated; the experimentally obtained photographs are very similar—see Ref. 16.16.)

16.2 The Linewidth

LO2

In the Michelson interferometer experiment discussed in the previous section, the decrease in the contrast of the fringes can also be interpreted as being due to the fact that the source is not emitting at a single frequency but over a narrow band of frequencies. When the path difference between the two interfering beams is zero or very small, the different wavelength components produce fringes superimposed on one another and the fringe contrast is good. On the other hand, when the path difference is increased, different wavelength components produce fringe patterns which are slightly displaced with respect to one another, and the fringe contrast becomes poorer. One can equally well say that the poor fringe visibility for a large optical path difference is due to the non-monochromaticity of the light source.

The equivalence of the above two approaches can be easily understood if we consider the Michelson interferometer experiment using two closely spaced wavelengths λ_1 and λ_2. Indeed in Sec. 14.10 we had shown that for two closely spaced wavelengths λ_1 and λ_2 (like the D_1 and D_2 lines of sodium), the interference pattern will disappear if

$$\frac{2d}{\lambda_2} - \frac{2d}{\lambda_1} = \frac{1}{2} \tag{16.3}$$

where $2d$ represents the path difference between the two beams. Thus,

$$2d = \frac{\lambda_1 \lambda_2}{2(\lambda_1 - \lambda_2)} \simeq \frac{\lambda^2}{2(\lambda_1 - \lambda_2)} \tag{16.4}$$

Instead of two discrete wavelengths, if we assume that the beam consists of all wavelengths lying between λ and $\lambda + \Delta\lambda$, then the interference pattern produced by the wavelengths λ and $\lambda + \frac{1}{2}\Delta\lambda$ will disappear if

$$2d = \frac{\lambda^2}{2\left(\frac{1}{2}\Delta\lambda\right)} = \frac{\lambda^2}{\Delta\lambda} \tag{16.5}$$

Further, for each wavelength lying between λ and $\lambda + \frac{1}{2}\Delta\lambda$, there will be a corresponding wavelength (lying between $\lambda + \frac{1}{2}\Delta\lambda$ and $\lambda + \Delta\lambda$) such that the minima of one falls on the maxima of the other, making the fringes disappear. Thus, for

$$2d \geq \frac{\lambda^2}{\Delta\lambda} \tag{16.6}$$

the contrast of the interference fringes will be extremely poor. We may rewrite the above equation in the form

$$\Delta\lambda \geq \frac{\lambda^2}{2d} \tag{16.7}$$

implying that if the contrast of the interference fringes becomes very poor when the path difference is $\sim d$, then the spectral width of the source would be $\sim \lambda^2/2d$.

Now, in Sec. 16.1 we had observed that if the path difference exceeds the coherence length L, the fringes are not observed. From the above discussion it therefore follows that the spectral width of the source $\Delta\lambda$, will be given by

$$\Delta\lambda \sim \frac{\lambda^2}{L} = \frac{\lambda^2}{c\tau_c} \tag{16.8}$$

Thus the temporal coherence τ_c of the beam is directly related to the spectral width $\Delta\lambda$. For example, for the red cadmium line, $\lambda = 6438$ Å, $L \simeq 30$ cm ($\tau_c \simeq 10^{-9}$ sec) giving

$$\Delta\lambda \sim \frac{\lambda^2}{c\tau_c} = \frac{(6.438 \times 10^{-5})^2}{3 \times 10^{10} \times 10^{-9}}$$
$$\sim 0.01 \text{ Å}$$

For the sodium line, $\lambda \simeq 5890$ Å, $L \simeq 3$ cm ($\tau_c \simeq 10^{-10}$ sec) and $\Delta\lambda \sim 0.1$ Å. Further, since $\nu = c/\lambda$, the frequency spread $\Delta\nu$ of a line would be

$$\Delta\nu \sim \frac{c}{\lambda^2}\Delta\lambda \sim \frac{c}{L} \tag{16.9}$$

where we have disregarded the sign. Since $\tau_c = L/c$, we obtain

$$\Delta\nu \sim \frac{1}{\tau_c} \tag{16.10}$$

Thus, the frequency spread of a spectral line is of the order of the inverse of the coherence time. For example, for the yellow line of sodium ($\lambda = 5890$ Å),

$$\tau_c \sim 10^{-10} \text{ s} \Rightarrow \Delta\nu \sim 10^{10} \text{ Hz}$$

$$\nu = \frac{c}{\lambda} = \frac{3 \times 10^{10}}{5.89 \times 10^{-5}} \simeq 5 \times 10^{14} \text{ Hz}$$

we get

$$\frac{\Delta\nu}{\nu} \sim \frac{10^{10}}{5 \times 10^{14}} = 2 \times 10^{-5}$$

The quantity $\Delta\nu/\nu$ represents the monochromaticity (or the spectral purity) of the source and one can see that even for an ordinary light source it is very small. For a commercially available laser beam, $\tau_c \sim 50$ nsec implying $\Delta\nu/\nu \sim 4 \times 10^{-8}$. The fact that the finite coherence time is directly related to the spectral width of the source can also be seen using Fourier analysis; this is discussed in Sec. 16.6.

16.3 The Spatial Coherence

LO3

Till now we have considered the coherence of two fields arriving at a particular point in space from a point source through two different optical paths. In this section, we will discuss the coherence properties of the field associated with the finite dimension of the source.

We consider the Young's double-hole experiment with the point source S being equidistant from S_1 and S_2 [see Fig. 16.7(a)]. We assume S to be nearly monochromatic so that it produces interference fringes of good contrast on the screen PP'. The point O on the screen is such that $S_1O = S_2O$. Clearly, the point source S will produce an intensity maximum around the point O. We next consider another similar source S' at a distance l from S. We assume that the waves from S and S' have no definite phase relationship. Thus the interference pattern observed on the screen PP' will be a superposition of the intensity distributions of the interference patterns formed due to S and S' (see Sec. 16.5). If the separation l is slowly increased from zero, the contrast of the fringes on the screen PP' becomes poorer because of the fact that the interference pattern produced by S' is slightly shifted from that produced by S. Clearly, if

$$S'S_2 - S'S_1 = \frac{\lambda}{2} \tag{16.11}$$

the minima of the interference pattern produced by S will fall on the maxima of the interference pattern produced by S' and no fringe pattern will be observed. It can be easily seen that

$$S'S_2 = \left[a^2 + \left(\frac{d}{2} + l\right)^2\right]^{1/2} \simeq a + \frac{1}{2a}\left(\frac{d}{2} + l\right)^2$$

and $$S'S_1 = \left[a^2 + \left(\frac{d}{2} - l\right)^2\right]^{1/2} \simeq a + \frac{1}{2a}\left(\frac{d}{2} - l\right)^2$$

where $a = a_1 + a_2$

and we have assumed $a >> d, l$. Thus,

$$S'S_2 - S'S_1 \simeq \frac{ld}{a}$$

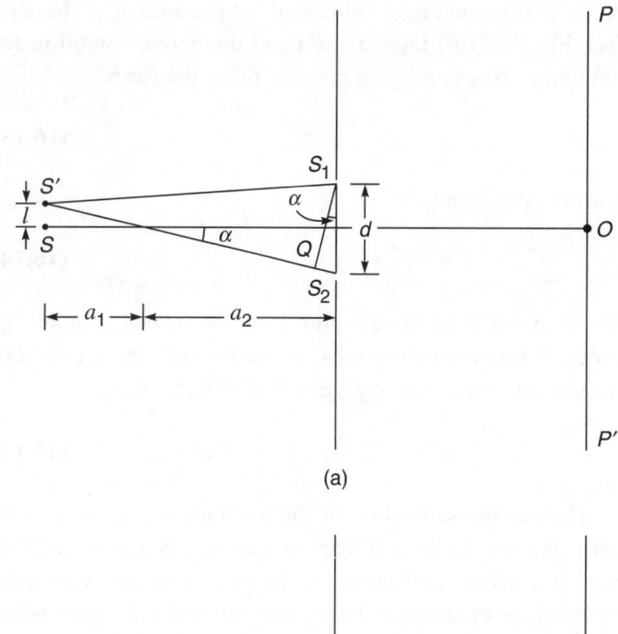

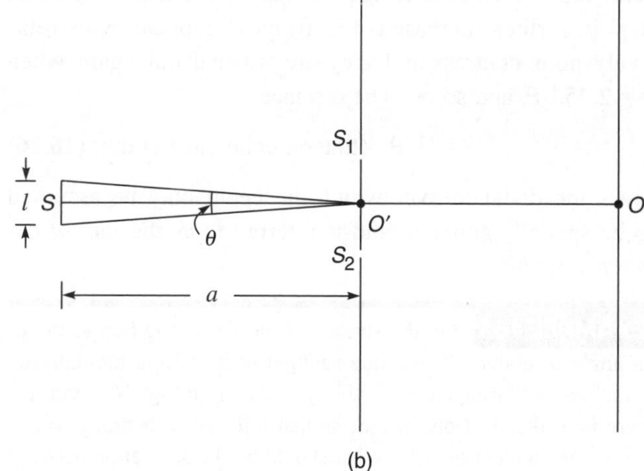

Figure 16.7

(a) Young's double-hole interference experiment with two independent point sources S and S′. (b) The same experiment with an extended source.

Thus for the fringes to disappear, we must have

$$\frac{\lambda}{2} = S'S_2 - S'S_1 \simeq \frac{ld}{a}$$

or $$l \simeq \frac{\lambda a}{2d}$$

Now, if we have an extended incoherent source whose linear dimension is $\sim\lambda a/d$ then for every point on the source, there is a point at a distance of $\lambda a/2d$ which produces fringes which are shifted by half a fringe width. Therefore, the interference pattern will not be observed. Thus for an extended incoherent source, interference fringes of good contrast will be observed only when

$$l << \frac{\lambda a}{d} \tag{16.12}$$

Now, if θ is the angle subtended by the source at the slits [see Fig. 16.7(b)] then $\theta \simeq l/a$ and the above condition for obtaining fringes of good contrast takes the form

$$d << \frac{\lambda}{\theta} \tag{16.13}$$

On the other hand, if

$$d \sim \frac{\lambda}{\theta} \tag{16.14}$$

the fringes will be of very poor contrast. Indeed, a more rigorous diffraction theory tells us that the interference pattern disappears when (see, e.g., Sec. 4.5 of Ref. 16.7.)

$$d = 1.22\frac{\lambda}{\theta}, 2.25\frac{\lambda}{\theta}, 3.24\frac{\lambda}{\theta}, ... \tag{16.15}$$

Thus as the separation of the pinholes is increased from zero, the interference fringes disappear when $d = 1.22\lambda/\theta$; if d is further increased, the fringes reappear with relatively poor contrast and they are washed out again when $d = 2.25\lambda/\theta$, and so on. The distance

$$l_w = \lambda/\theta \quad \text{(Lateral coherence width)} \tag{16.16}$$

gives the distance over which the beam may be assumed to be spatially coherent and is referred to as the *lateral coherence width*.

EXAMPLE 16.1 On the surface of the Earth, the Sun subtends an angle of about 32′. Assume sunlight to be falling normally on a double-hole arrangement of the type shown in Fig. 16.7 and that there is a filter in front of S_1S_2 so that light corresponding to $\lambda \approx$ 5000 Å is incident on S_1S_2. What should be the separation between S_1 and S_2 so that fringes of good contrast are observed on the screen?

Solution:

$$\theta \approx 32' = \frac{32\pi}{180 \times 60} \text{ rad} \simeq 0.01 \text{ rad}$$

Thus the lateral coherence length

$$l_w \approx \frac{5 \times 10^{-5}}{10^{-2}} = 0.005 \text{ cm}$$

Therefore, if the pin holes are separated by a distance which is small compared to 0.005 cm, interference fringes of good contrast should be observed.

16.4 Michelson Stellar Interferometer

LO4

Using the concept of spatial coherence, Michelson developed an ingenious method for determining the angular diameter of stars. The method is based on the result that for a distant circular source, the interference fringes will disappear if the distance between the pinholes S_1 and S_2 (see Fig. 16.8) is given by [see Eq. (16.15)]:

$$d = 1.22\frac{\lambda}{\theta} \tag{16.17}$$

where θ is the angle subtended by the circular source as shown in Fig. 16.8. For a star whose angular diameter is 10^{-7} radians, the distance d for which the fringes will disappear would be

$$d \sim \frac{1.22 \times 5 \times 10^{-5}}{10^{-7}} \simeq 600 \text{ cm}$$

where we have assumed $\lambda \simeq 5000$ Å. Obviously, for such a large value of d, the fringe width will become extremely small. Further, one has to use a big lens, which is not only difficult to make, but only a small portion of which will be used. In order to overcome this difficulty, Michelson used two movable mirrors M_1 and M_2 as shown in Fig. 16.9, and thus he effectively got a large value of d. The apparatus is known as Michelson's stellar interferometer. In a typical experiment the first disappearance occurred when the distance M_1M_2 was about 24 feet, which gave

$$\theta \simeq \frac{1.22 \times 5 \times 10^{-5}}{24 \times 12 \times 2.54} \text{ radians} \simeq 0.02''$$

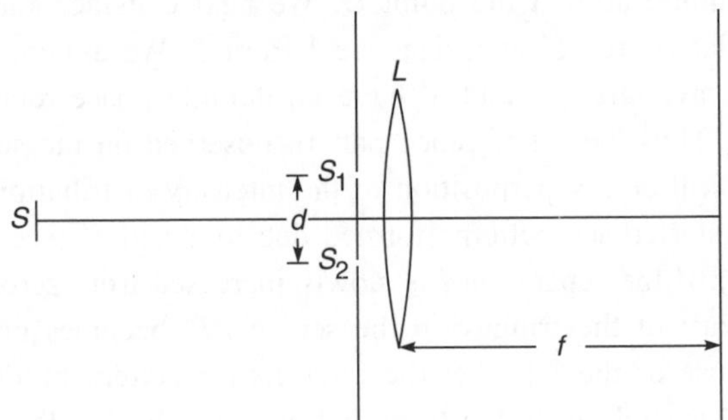

Figure 16.8
S is a source of certain spatial extent; S_1 and S_2 are two slits separated by a distance d which can be varied. The fringes are observed on the focal plane of the lens L.

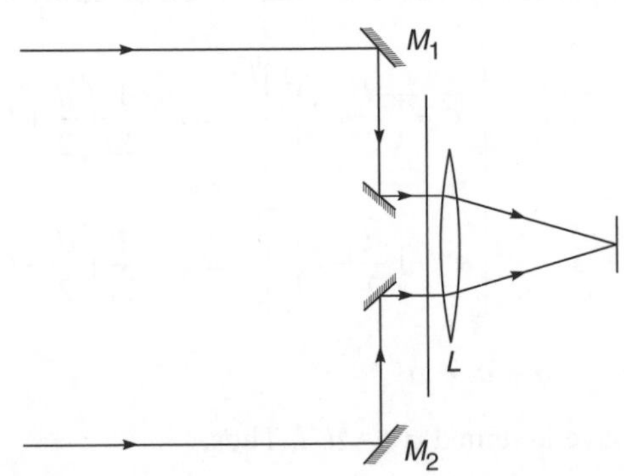

Figure 16.9
Michelson's stellar interferometer.

for the angular diameter of the star. This star is known as **Arctures**. From the known distance of the star, one can estimate that the diameter of the star is about 27 times that of the sun.

We should point out that a laser beam is spatially coherent across the entire beam. Thus, if a laser beam is allowed to fall directly on a double-slit arrangement (see Fig. 16.10), then as long as the beam falls on both the slits, a clear interference pattern is observed on the screen. This shows that the laser beam is spatially coherent across the entire wavefront.

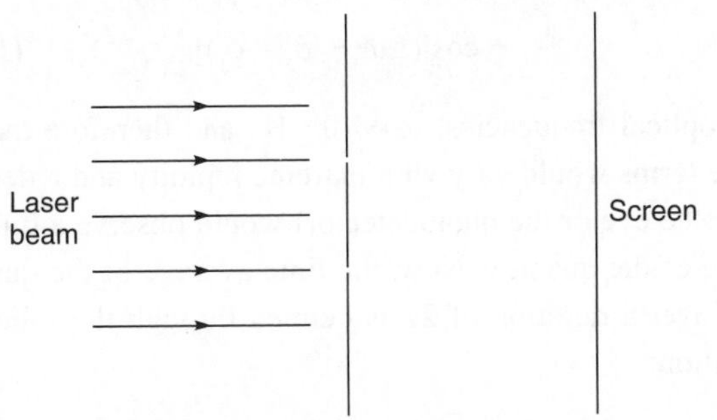

Figure 16.10
If a laser beam falls on a double-slit arrangement, interference fringes are observed on the screen. This shows that the laser beam is spatially coherent across the entire wavefront.

Figure 16.11 shows the interference pattern obtained by Nelson and Collins (Ref. 16.14) by placing a pair of slits of width 7.5 μm separated by a distance 54.1 μm on the end of the ruby rod in a ruby laser. The interference pattern agrees with the theoretical calculation to within 20%. To show that the spatial coherence is indeed due to laser action, they showed that below threshold (of the laser) no regular interference pattern was observed; only a uniform darkening of the photographic plate was obtained.

16.5 Optical Beats

LO5

When two tuning forks, one having a frequency of 256 Hz and the other a frequency of 260 Hz, are made to vibrate at the same time, we hear a frequency of about 258 Hz whose intensity varies from zero to maximum and back with a frequency of 4 Hz. This phenomenon is known as **beats**. It can be easily understood by considering the superposition of two waves having frequencies ω and $\omega + \Delta\omega$:

$$y_1 = a \sin(\omega t + \phi_1)$$
$$y_2 = a \sin[(\omega + \Delta\omega)t + \phi_2] \tag{16.18}$$

where we are assuming (for the sake of simplicity) that both the waves have the same amplitude. The resultant displacement would be given by

$$\begin{aligned} y &= y_1 + y_2 \\ &= 2a \sin\left[\left(\omega + \frac{1}{2}\Delta\omega\right)t + \frac{1}{2}(\phi_1 + \phi_2)\right] \\ &\quad \times \cos\left[\frac{1}{2}(\Delta\omega)t + \frac{1}{2}(\phi_2 - \phi_1)\right] \\ &= 2a \sin\left[\left(\omega + \frac{1}{2}\Delta\omega\right)t\right] \sin\left(\frac{1}{2}\Delta\omega t\right) \end{aligned} \tag{16.19}$$

where we have assumed, without any loss of generality, $\phi_1 = \pi/2 = -\phi_2$. Figures 16.12(a) and (b) show the time variation of the terms

$$\sin\left(\omega + \frac{1}{2}\Delta\omega\right)t \quad \text{and} \quad \sin\left(\frac{1}{2}\Delta\omega\right)t$$

respectively. In Fig. 16.12(c), we have plotted their product which represents the resultant displacement. Notice that

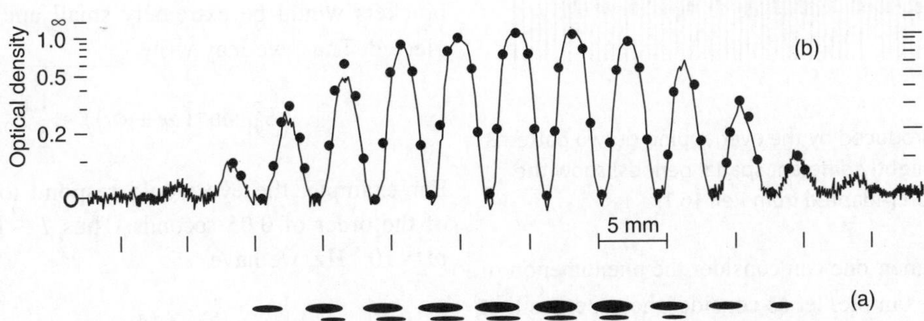

Figure 16.11
The double-slit interference pattern obtained by placing a pair of slits each 7.5 μm wide and separated by a distance of 54.1 μm across the diameter of a ruby rod. (a) shows the actual interference pattern, and (b) shows a densitometer trace of the interference pattern. The dots correspond to a theoretical calculation assuming that a plane wave strikes the pair of slits. Ref. 16.14. [*Photograph courtesy: Dr D.F. Nelson*].

although the envelope has a frequency of $\frac{\Delta\omega}{4\pi}\left(=\frac{1}{2}\Delta\nu\right)$ [see Fig. 16.12(b)] the intensity repeats itself after every $1/\Delta\nu$ seconds. This waxing and waning of sound is known as *beats*.

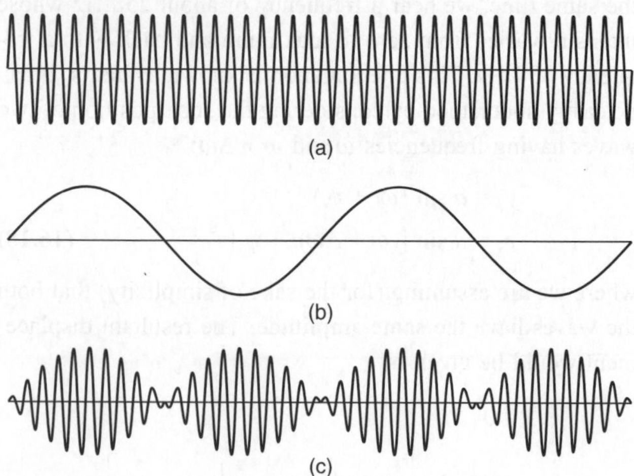

Figure 16.12

(a) and (b) show typical time variation of sin $\left[\left(\omega+\frac{1}{2}\Delta\omega\right)t\right]$ and sin $\left[\frac{1}{2}\Delta\omega t\right]$, respectively and (c) shows the time dependence of their product.

The beat phenomenon can be easily understood by observing the Moiré fringes obtained by the overlapping of two patterns of slightly different spatial frequency (see Fig. 16.13). Whenever the dark line of one of the patterns falls on the bright region of the other, then the two waves can be considered to be 'out of phase' and we have a broad 'dark region' which appears periodically.

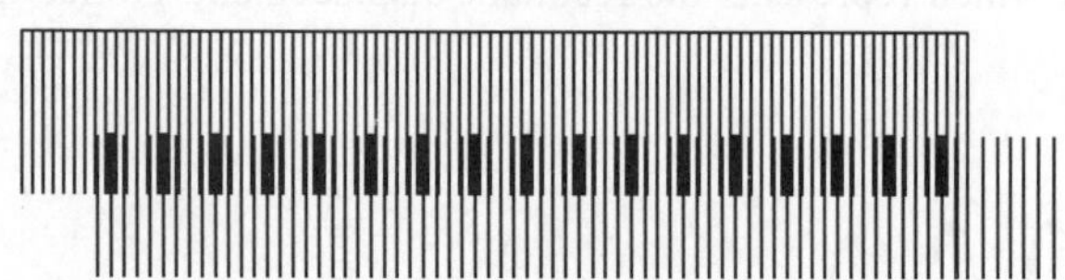

Figure 16.13

The Moiré pattern produced by the overlapping of two patterns of parallel lines (of slightly different spatial periods) show the beating phenomenon [Adapted from Ref. 16.1].

In a similar manner, one can consider the phenomenon of optical beats. For example, let us consider the superposition of two fields $\mathbf{E}_1$ and $\mathbf{E}_2$ having frequencies ω and $\omega + \Delta\omega$:

$$\mathbf{E}_1 = \mathbf{E}_{01} \sin(\omega t + \phi_1) \tag{16.20}$$

and

$$\mathbf{E}_2 = \mathbf{E}_{02} \sin[(\omega + \Delta\omega)t + \phi_2] \tag{16.21}$$

If we assume that both the fields are linearly polarized in the same direction then in order to calculate the resultant field, we may simply algebraically add E_1 and E_2. Thus, the resultant would be given by

$$E = E_1 + E_2$$
$$= E_{01} \sin(\omega t + \phi_1) + E_{02} \sin([\omega + \Delta\omega]t + \phi_2)$$

Now

$$E^2(t) = E_{01}^2 \sin^2(\omega t + \phi_1) + E_{02}^2 \sin^2([\omega + \Delta\omega]t + \phi_2)$$
$$+ E_{01}E_{02}[-\cos(2\omega t + \Delta\omega t + \phi_1 + \phi_2)$$
$$+ \cos(\Delta\omega t + \phi_2 - \phi_1)] \tag{16.22}$$

For optical frequencies, $\omega \approx 10^{15}$ Hz and therefore the first three terms would vary with extreme rapidity and a detector (like the eye or the photodetector) would observe a time average of the quantity. Now, the time average of the quantity $F(t)$ over a duration of $2T$ is defined through the following equation:

$$\langle F(t)\rangle = \frac{1}{2T}\int_{-T}^{+T} F(t)\,dt \tag{16.23}$$

Thus,

$$\left\langle E_{01}^2 \sin^2(\omega t + \phi_1)\right\rangle$$
$$= E_{01}^2 \frac{1}{2T}\int_{-T}^{+T} \sin^2(\omega t + \phi_1)\,dt$$
$$= E_{01}^2\left[\frac{1}{2} - \frac{1}{2\omega T}\{\sin 2(\omega t + \phi_1)\}_{-T}^{+T}\right]$$
$$= \frac{1}{2}E_{01}^2\left[1 - \frac{1}{2\omega T}\sin 2\omega T \cos 2\phi_1\right] \tag{16.24}$$

For averaging times $T >> 1/\omega$, the second term inside the brackets would be extremely small and hence can be neglected. Thus, we may write

$$\left\langle E_{01}^2 \sin^2(\omega t + \phi_1)\right\rangle \simeq \frac{1}{2}E_{01}^2 \tag{16.25}$$

For example, the eye would respond to changes in times of the order of 0.05 seconds. Thus $T \sim 0.05$ sec and since $\omega \simeq 10^{15}$ Hz, we have

$$\frac{1}{\omega T} \simeq 2 \times 10^{-14}$$

which is an extremely small quantity in comparison to unity. It is for this reason that the eye does not see any intensity variations. Even for a fast photodetector with response times $\sim 10^{-9}$ sec, $1/(\omega T) \sim 10^{-6}$ which can also be neglected.

Returning to Eq. (16.22), if we carry out an averaging over times which are long compared to $2\pi/\omega$ but short compared to $2\pi/\Delta\omega$ then we would obtain

$$\left\langle E^2(t)\right\rangle = \frac{1}{2}E_{01}^2 + \frac{1}{2}E_{02}^2 + E_{01}E_{02}\cos[(\Delta\omega)t + \phi_2 - \phi_1] \quad \textbf{(16.26)}$$

For example, if $\Delta\omega \simeq 10^7$ Hz and the photodetector resolution is about 10^{-9} s, then the detector will record only the average values of the first three terms on the RHS of Eq. (16.22); however, it will be able to record the time variation of the last term. This is what is shown in the above equation leading to the familiar phenomenon of beats.

As an example, we consider the beating of the D_1 and D_2 lines of sodium for which

$$\lambda_1 = 5890 \text{ Å } (\Rightarrow \omega_1 \simeq 3.2003 \times 10^{15} \text{ Hz})$$

$$\lambda_2 = 5896 \text{ Å } (\Rightarrow \omega_2 \simeq 3.1970 \times 10^{15} \text{ Hz})$$

Thus $\Delta\omega \simeq 3.3 \times 10^{12}$ Hz

In order to observe the beating, the detector should have a response time much smaller than $1/\Delta\omega$, thus the photodetector response time should be $\lesssim 10^{-13}$ s which is a practical impossibility. Therefore, in order to observe the beats, we must decrease the value of $\Delta\omega$. Indeed the first experiment on optical beats was carried out by Forrester *et al.* (Ref. 16.6) in which they used two closely spaced frequencies by splitting a spectral line using a magnetic field (this splitting is known as Zeeman effect). The weaker the magnetic field, the smaller is the value of $\Delta\omega$. In the experiment of Forrester and his coworkers, $\Delta\nu$ was of the order of 10^{10} Hz and they were able to observe optical beats.

Obviously, in order that the beats occur very slowly (so that we may use photodetectors of much longer response times) $\Delta\omega$ should be made even smaller—but then we may have the coherence problem. In the above analysis we have assumed the phase ϕ_1 and ϕ_2 to remain constant in time. Now for an incoherent source, ϕ_1 and ϕ_2 will randomly change in times $\sim 10^{-9}$ s; thus if the detector response time is $\gtrsim 10^{-8}$ s, we will observe the average of the $\cos[(\Delta\omega)t + \phi_2 - \phi_1]$ term in Eq. (16.26). Obviously, the average value of the 'cosine term' is zero and we will have

$$\left\langle E^2(t)\right\rangle = \frac{1}{2}E_{01}^2 + \frac{1}{2}E_{02}^2$$

implying that the resultant intensity will be just the sum of the independent intensities:

$$I = I_1 + I_2 \quad \textbf{(16.27)}$$

With the advent of laser beams, the beating experiments have become much easier; a typical arrangement (which resembles a Michelson interferometer) is shown in Fig. 16.14. A typical beat note of the experiment of Lipsett and Mandel (Ref. 16.11) is shown in Fig. 16.15. It was observed that the beat note changed in frequency from about 33 to approximately 21 MHz in a time of about 0.7 μs. The coherence time is ~0.5 μsec which is consistent with the duration of the spike.

We conclude this section by quoting Feynman: "With the availability of laser sources, someone will be able to demonstrate two sources shining on a wall, in which the beats are so slow that one can see the wall get bright and dark".

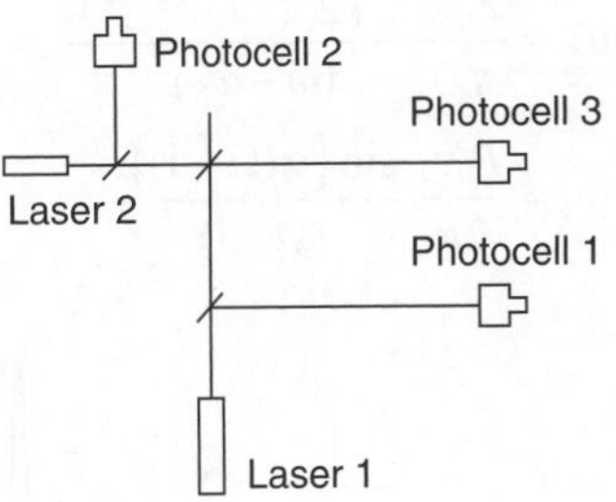

Figure 16.14
The experimental arrangement of Lipsett and Mandel (Ref. 16.11) to observe optical beats using two laser beams.

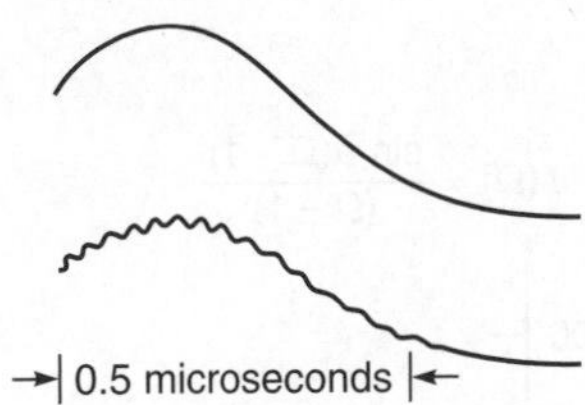

Figure 16.15
Oscilloscope trace of the sum of the intensities of the laser beams (upper curve) and the intensity of the superposed laser beam (lower curve) [Adapted from Ref. 16.11].

16.6 Coherence Time and Linewidth via Fourier Analysis

LO6

That the frequency spread of a line is of the order of the inverse of the coherence time [see Eq. (10)] can also be shown by Fourier analysis. As an example, we consider a sinusoidal pulse of duration τ_c. Thus, we may write

$$E(t) = E_0\, e^{+i\omega_0 t} \quad \text{for} \quad -\frac{1}{2}\tau_c < t < \frac{1}{2}\tau_c \qquad (16.28)$$

$$= 0 \quad \text{for} \quad |t| > \frac{1}{2}\tau_c$$

We will assume that τ_c is long enough so that the disturbance consists of many oscillations. For example, for $\nu_0 \approx 5 \times 10^{14}$ Hz a 2 ns pulse will imply $\tau_c \approx 2 \times 10^{-9}$ s and the number of oscillations will be $\nu_0\tau_c \approx (5 \times 10^{14}) \times (2 \times 10^{-9}) = 10^6$; i.e., the pulse will consist of about a million oscillations! Now, while discussing the Fourier transform theory, we had shown that for a time-dependent function, its Fourier transform will be given by (see Example 8.2):

$$A(\omega) = \frac{1}{2\pi}\int_{-\infty}^{+\infty} E(t)\, e^{-i\omega t}\, dt = \frac{E_0}{2\pi}\int_{-\tau_c/2}^{+\tau_c/2} e^{-i(\omega-\omega_0)t}\, dt \qquad (16.29)$$

Evaluating the integral we get

$$\begin{aligned} A(\omega) &= \frac{E_0}{\pi}\,\frac{\sin\left\{\frac{1}{2}(\omega-\omega_0)\tau_c\right\}}{(\omega-\omega_0)} \\ &= \frac{E_0\tau_c}{2\pi}\,\frac{\sin\{\alpha(\Omega-1)\}}{(\Omega-1)} \end{aligned} \qquad (16.30)$$

where $\Omega \equiv \dfrac{\omega}{\omega_0}$ and $\alpha \equiv \dfrac{1}{2}\omega_0\tau_c$. In Fig. 16.16, we have plotted the function $\dfrac{\sin\{\alpha(\Omega-1)\}}{(\Omega-1)}$ as a function of Ω for $\alpha = 200$ ($\Rightarrow \omega_0 t_c = 400$). One can see that the function is very sharply peaked at $\Omega = 1$ the function has a value equal to α, and that the first zero on either side occurs at

$$\Omega = 1 \pm \frac{\pi}{\alpha} \qquad (16.31)$$

For larger values of α (implying larger coherence times), the function will become more sharply peaked; the width of the peak being given by

$$\Delta\Omega\left(=\frac{\Delta\omega}{\omega_0}\right) \sim \frac{\pi}{\alpha} \quad \Rightarrow \quad \Delta\omega \sim \frac{\pi\omega_0}{\alpha} = \frac{2\pi}{\tau_c}$$

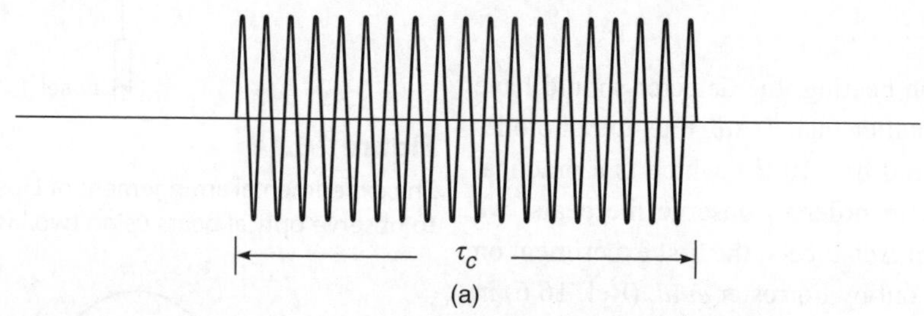

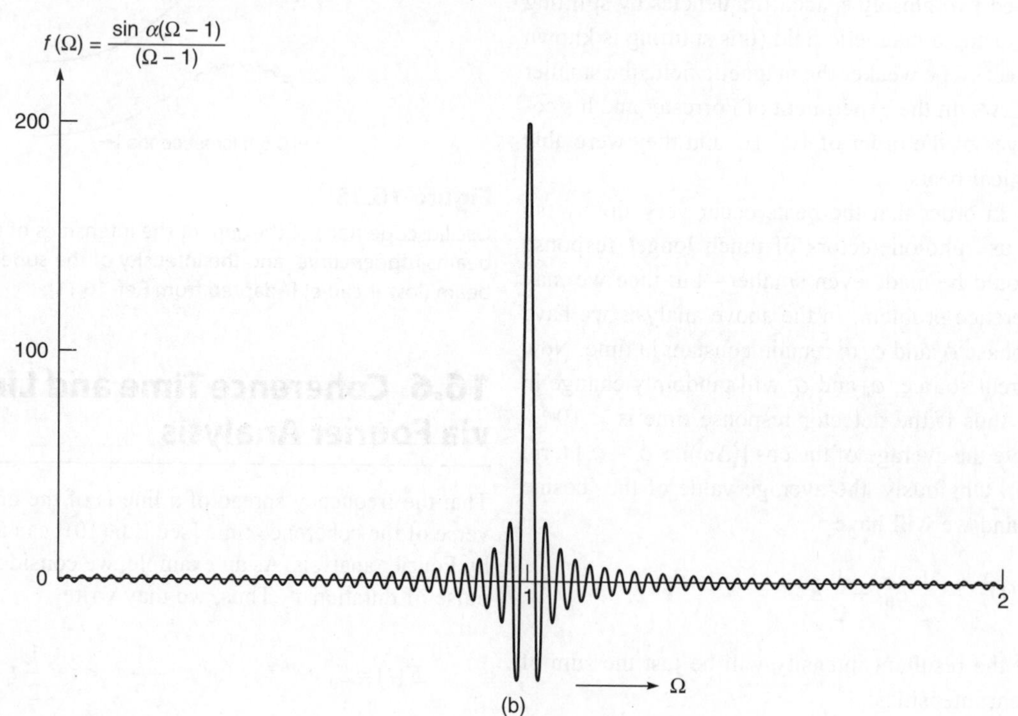

Figure 16.16
(a) A sinusoidal displacement of duration τ_c. (b) The variation of the function $[\sin(\Omega - 1)\alpha]/(\Omega - 1)$ as a function of Ω for $\alpha = 200$. Notice that the function is sharply peaked around $\Omega = 1$.

$$\text{Thus } \Delta\nu \sim \frac{1}{\tau_c} \quad (16.32)$$

consistent with Eq. (16.10). The above analysis shows that a wave having a coherence time $\sim \tau_c$ is essentially a superposition of harmonic waves having frequencies in the region

$$\nu_0 - \frac{1}{2}\Delta\nu \le \nu_0 \le \nu_0 + \frac{1}{2}\Delta\nu \quad (16.33)$$

We should mention that the condition expressed by Eq. (16.33) is quite general in the sense that it is valid for a pulse of arbitrary shape. For example, for a Gaussian pulse having a duration $\sim \tau_0$, the corresponding frequency spread will be given by [see Example 11.4]

$$\text{FWHM} = \Delta\omega \approx \frac{2.35}{\tau_0} \quad (16.34)$$

Thus we have the "uncertainty product":

$$\Delta\omega\Delta t \approx \Delta\omega t_0 \sim 1 \quad (16.35)$$

16.7 Complex Degree of Coherence and Fringe Visibility in Young's Double-Hole Experiment

LO7

In this section, we will introduce the complex degree of coherence and will show how it can be related to the contrast of the fringes in the Young's double hole interference experiment. We refer back to Fig. 16.2. Let $\Psi_1(P, t)$ and $\Psi_2(P, t)$ represent the complex fields at the point P due to the waves emanating from S_1 and S_2 respectively. The resultant displacement would be given by

$$\Psi = \Psi_1(P, t) + \Psi_2(P, t) \quad \textbf{(16.36)}$$

Now, the intensity at the point P will be proportional to $|\Psi|^2$ which is given by the following equation:

$$|\Psi|^2 = \Psi_1^*\Psi_1 + \Psi_2^*\Psi_2 + \Psi_1^*\Psi_2 + \Psi_1\Psi_2^*$$
$$= |\Psi_1|^2 + |\Psi_2|^2 + 2\,\text{Re}\,(\Psi_1^*\Psi_2)$$

Since Ψ_1 and Ψ_2 vary with extreme rapidity, we can observe only the average values of $|\Psi_1|^2$ and $|\Psi_2|^2$. Thus, if we write

$$I_1 = \langle|\Psi_1(P, t)|^2\rangle$$

and $$I_2 = \langle|\Psi_2(P, t)|^2\rangle$$

then $$I = I_1 + I_2 + 2\sqrt{I_1 I_2}\,\text{Re}\,\gamma_{12} \quad \textbf{(16.37)}$$

where $$\gamma_{12} = \frac{\langle\Psi_1^*(P,t)\Psi_2(P,t)\rangle}{[\langle|\Psi_1(P,t)|^2\rangle\langle|\Psi_2(P,t)|^2\rangle]^{1/2}} \quad \textbf{(16.38)}$$

is known as the **complex degree of coherence** and $\langle\ldots\rangle$ denotes the time average of the quantity inside the triangular brackets [see Eq. (16.23)]. The field $\Psi_1(P, t)$ is due to the waves emanating from the point S_1 at $t - \frac{r_1}{c}$ where $r_1 = S_1P$. Thus, $\Psi_1(P, t)$ will be proportional to $\Psi\left(S_1, t - \frac{r_1}{c}\right)$ where $\Psi(S_1, t)$ denotes the field at S_1 at time t. Similarly $\Psi_2(P, t)$ will be proportional to $\left(S_2, t - \frac{r_2}{c}\right)$. Thus

$$\gamma_{12} = \frac{\left\langle\Psi^*\left(S_1, t - \frac{r_1}{c}\right)\Psi\left(S_2, t - \frac{r_2}{c}\right)\right\rangle}{\left[\left\langle\left|\Psi\left(S_1, t - \frac{r_1}{c}\right)\right|^2\right\rangle\left\langle\left|\Psi\left(S_2, t - \frac{r_2}{c}\right)\right|^2\right\rangle\right]^{1/2}}$$

Since the overall intensity distribution in the fringe pattern does not change with time, we may write

$$\gamma_{12} = \frac{\langle\Psi^*(S_1, t+\tau)\,\Psi(S_2, t)\rangle}{[\langle|\Psi^*(S_1, t)|^2\rangle\langle|\Psi(S_2, t)|^2\rangle]^{1/2}} \quad \textbf{(16.39)}$$

where $\tau = (r_2 - r_1)/c$. In order to discuss the effect of temporal coherence, we assume S, S_1 and S_2 to be of negligible spatial dimensions. Further, if S_1 and S_2 are equidistant from S, then we may assume that

$$\Psi(S_1, t) = \Psi(S_2, t) = \Psi(t) \quad \textbf{(16.40)}$$

Thus, for such a case

$$\gamma_{12}(\tau) = \frac{\langle\Psi^*(t+\tau)\,\Psi(t)\rangle}{\langle|\Psi(t)|^2\rangle} \quad \textbf{(16.41)}$$

Now, for an actual field, we may write

$$\Psi(t) = A(t)e^{-i[\omega t + \phi(t)]} \quad \textbf{(16.42)}$$

where $A(t)$ and $\phi(t)$ are slowly varying real functions of time. For a perfectly monochromatic beam (i.e., infinite coherence time) $A(t)$ and $\phi(t)$ are constants so that

$$\Psi^*(t+\tau)\Psi(t) = A^2 e^{i\omega\tau}$$

Consequently,

$$\gamma_{12}(\tau) = e^{i\omega\tau} \quad \textbf{(16.43)}$$

Thus, for such a case

$$I = I_1 + I_2 + 2\sqrt{I_1 I_2}\cos\omega\tau \quad \textbf{(16.44)}$$

and the visibility V, which is defined by

$$V = \frac{I_{\max} - I_{\min}}{I_{\max} + I_{\min}} \quad \textbf{(16.45)}$$

would be given by

$$V = \frac{2\sqrt{I_1 I_2}}{I_1 + I_2} \tag{16.46}$$

For $I_1 = I_2$ we have $V = 1$ implying that, for a perfectly monochromatic beam, the contrast of the fringes is perfect. On the other hand, for an ordinary light source having $\tau_c \sim 10^{-10}$ s, the functions $A(t)$ and $\phi(t)$ can be assumed to be constants in times $\lesssim 10^{-10}$ s. Thus, if $\tau_c \gtrsim 10^{-10}$ s, $\Psi(t + \tau)$ will have no phase relationship with $\Psi(t)$ and the time average $\langle \Psi^*(t + \tau)\Psi(t)\rangle$ will be zero. Thus, if the path difference $S_2P \sim S_1P$ is such that

$$\frac{S_2P \sim S_1P}{c} \gtrsim \tau_c \tag{16.47}$$

the fringe pattern will not be observed.

In general, we may write

$$\gamma_{12} = |\gamma_{12}| e^{i(\omega\tau+\beta)} \tag{16.48}$$

where $|\gamma_{12}|$ and β may be assumed to be constants around the observation point. This gives us

$$I = I_1 + I_2 + 2\sqrt{I_1 I_2}\,|\gamma_{12}| \cos\alpha \tag{16.49}$$

where $\alpha = \omega\tau + \beta$. Thus,

$$I_{\max} = I_1 + I_2 + 2\sqrt{I_1 I_2}\,|\gamma_{12}| \tag{16.50}$$

and

$$I_{\min} = I_1 + I_2 - 2\sqrt{I_1 I_2}\,|\gamma_{12}| \tag{16.51}$$

Hence, the visibility becomes

$$V = \frac{I_{\max} - I_{\min}}{I_{\max} + I_{\min}} = \frac{2\sqrt{I_1 I_2}}{I_1 + I_2}\,|\gamma_{12}| \tag{16.52}$$

Thus, the visibility (or the contrast) of the fringes is a direct measure of $|\gamma_{12}|$. If $I_1 = I_2$ then $V = |\gamma_{12}|$. In the present case, since S, S_1 and S_2 have been assumed to be points $|\gamma_{12}|$ depends only on the temporal coherence of the beam. For $\tau \ll \tau_c$, $|\gamma_{12}|$ is very close to unity and the contrast of the fringes will be very good; for $\tau \gg \tau_c$, $|\gamma_{12}|$ will be close to zero and the contrast will be extremely poor.

It may be noted from Eq. (16.43) that for a perfectly monochromatic beam $|\gamma_{12}| = 1$ and $\alpha = \omega\tau = \omega(S_2P \sim S_1P)/c$. In general, it can be shown that $0 < |\gamma_{12}| < 1$; $|\gamma_{12}| = 0$ implies complete incoherence and $|\gamma_{12}| = 1$ implies complete coherence. In practice, if $|\gamma_{12}| > 0.88$, the light is said to be 'almost coherent'. Further, since

$$\langle \Psi^*(t + \tau)\Psi(t)\rangle = e^{i\omega\tau}\langle A(t + \tau)A(t)e^{i[\phi(t+\tau)-\phi(t)]}\rangle$$

and for a nearly monochromatic source $A(t)$ and $\phi(t)$ are already slowly varying functions of time, the quantity inside the angular brackets (on the RHS of the above equation) will not vary rapidly with τ. Thus, we may write

$$\gamma_{12} = |\gamma_{12}| e^{i\beta} e^{i\omega\tau} \tag{16.53}$$

where both $|\gamma_{12}|$ and β are slowly varying functions of

$$\tau = \frac{S_2P \sim S_1P}{c} \tag{16.54}$$

For a more detailed theory of spatial and temporal coherence, you may look in Refs. 16.2, 16.3, 16.7 and 16.20.

16.8 Fourier Transform Spectroscopy*

LO8

In the previous section, we have shown that the contrast in an interference pattern depends on the relative magnitudes of the optical path difference Δ, vis-à-vis the coherence length of the source L_c ($= c\tau_c$). For a given source, the contrast varies as the optical path difference Δ is varied, beginning from an extremely good contrast for $\Delta \ll L_c$ to a very poor contrast for $\Delta \gg L_c$. Indeed Fizeau in 1862 interpreted the periodic variation in contrast in Newton's rings under illumination with a sodium lamp as the lens is moved up, as being due to the presence of two lines separated by 6 Å (see Example 14.4). Michelson in the years 1890–1900 performed various experiments with a number of spectral lines. Using the Michelson interferometer, he measured visibility as a function of optical path difference and using a mechanical device he himself had built, he could obtain the spectra. It is the purpose of this section to show that from a knowledge of variation of intensity with optical path difference one can obtain the source spectral distribution by a Fourier transformation.

The use of the Michelson interferometer for spectroscopy was revived in the 1950s for application, specially for the relatively complex spectra in the infrared region.

We will derive expressions for the variation of visibility with optical path difference for a source having a certain spectral distribution and we will show that from the interference pattern one can obtain the spectral intensity distribution of the given source.

16.8.1 Principle of Fourier Transform Spectroscopy

Figure 16.17 shows the arrangement used in a Fourier transform spectrometer. Light from the given source is collimated and enters the Michelson interferometer and in the transmitted arm we measure the intensity at the focus of the lens as a function of the path difference Δ. Now, if a monochromatic beam of intensity I_0 is split into two beams (each of intensity $\frac{1}{2}I_0$) and are made to interfere, then the resultant intensity is given by

$$I = I_0(1 + \cos\delta) \tag{16.55}$$

* This section was kindly written by Professor K. Thyagarajan.

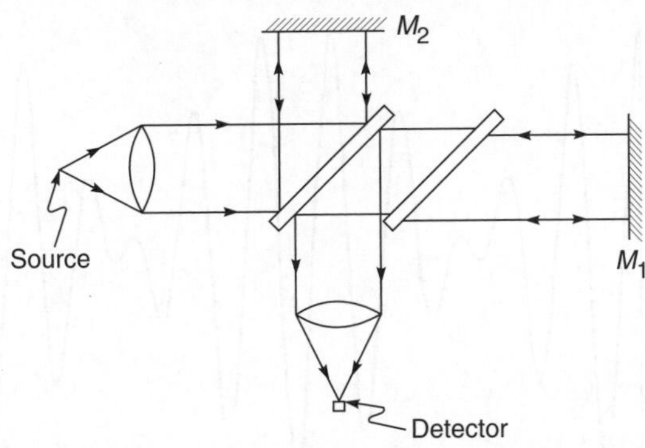

Figure 16.17
The arrangement used in a Fourier transform spectrometer.

where

$$\delta = \frac{2\pi}{\lambda}\Delta = \frac{2\pi\nu}{c}\Delta \quad \textbf{(16.56)}$$

represents the phase difference between the interfering beams, and in writing Eq. (16.55), we have used Eq. (16.30) of Chapter 13 with

$$I_1 = I_2 = \frac{1}{2}I_0$$

Thus if $I(\nu)\,d\nu$ represents the intensity emitted by the source between ν and $\nu + d\nu$ then the intensity at O lying between ν and $\nu + d\nu$ is given by

$$I_t(\nu)\,d\nu = I(\nu)\,d\nu\left[1 + \cos\frac{2\pi\nu\Delta}{c}\right] \quad \textbf{(16.57)}$$

Hence, the total intensity at O corresponding to a path difference Δ is

$$I_t(\Delta) = \int_0^\infty I_t(\nu)\,d\nu$$

$$= \int_0^\infty I(\nu)\,d\nu + \int_0^\infty I(\nu)\cos\frac{2\pi\nu\Delta}{c}\,d\nu \quad \textbf{(16.58)}$$

The quantity

$$I_T = \int_0^\infty I(\nu)\,d\nu = \frac{1}{2}I_t(0) \quad \textbf{(16.59)}$$

represents the total intensity of the source. We define normalized transmission as

$$\gamma(\Delta) = \frac{I_t(\Delta) - I_T}{I_T}$$

$$= \frac{1}{I_T}\int_0^\infty I(\nu)\cos\frac{2\pi\nu\Delta}{c}\,d\nu \quad \textbf{(16.60)}$$

It is the quantity $I_t(\Delta)$ which is measured as a function of Δ from which $\gamma(\Delta)$ is evaluated. We first consider some examples giving explicit expressions for $I_t(\Delta)$ and $\gamma(\Delta)$ for some specific cases.

(i) Monochromatic Source For a monochromatic source of intensity I_0 emitting at a frequency ν_0, we have

$$I(\nu)\,d\nu = I_0\,\delta(\nu - \nu_0)\,d\nu \quad \textbf{(16.61)}$$

where $\delta(\nu - \nu_0)$ represents the Dirac–delta function. Hence,

$$\gamma(\Delta) = I_0\frac{\int_0^\infty \delta(\nu - \nu_0)\cos\frac{2\pi\nu\Delta}{c}\,d\nu}{\int_0^\infty \delta(\nu - \nu_0)\,d\nu}$$

$$= \cos\left(\frac{2\pi\nu_0\Delta}{c}\right) \quad \textbf{(16.62)}$$

and

$$I_t(\Delta) = I_0\left(1 + \cos\frac{2\pi\nu_0\Delta}{c}\right) \quad \textbf{(16.63)}$$

Hence $I_t(\Delta)$ and γ vary sinusoidally for all values of path difference Δ [see Figs. 16.18(a) and (b)] implying that the coherence length of the source is infinite.

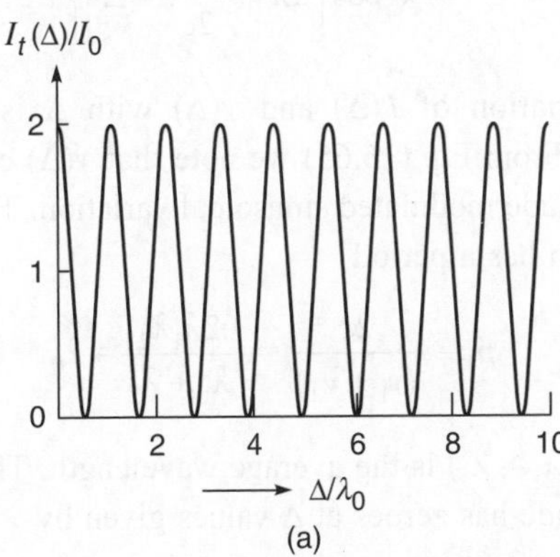

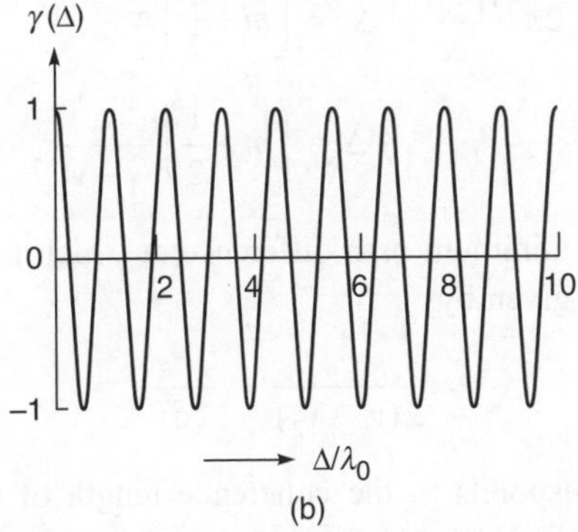

Figure 16.18
(a) The variation of the total intensity at O as a function of the path difference Δ for a monochromatic source. (b) The corresponding cosinusoidal variation of γ(Δ) with Δ.

(ii) Source Emitting Two Monochromatic Lines We now consider a source emitting two monochromatic lines at frequencies ν_1 and ν_2, each characterized by an intensity $\frac{1}{2}I_0$. Thus,

$$I(\nu)d\nu = \frac{1}{2}I_0[\delta(\nu - \nu_1) + \delta(\nu - \nu_2)] \tag{16.64}$$

and

$$\begin{aligned}\gamma(\Delta) &= \frac{1}{2}\left[\int_0^\infty \delta(\nu-\nu_1)\cos\frac{2\pi\nu\Delta}{c}\,d\nu + \int_0^\infty \delta(\nu-\nu_2)\cos\frac{2\pi\nu\Delta}{c}\,d\nu\right] \\ &= \frac{1}{2}\left[\cos\frac{2\pi\nu_1\Delta}{c} + \cos\frac{2\pi\nu_2\Delta}{c}\right] \\ &= \cos\left[2\pi\frac{(\nu_1+\nu_2)}{2c}\Delta\right] \times \cos\left[2\pi\frac{(\nu_1-\nu_2)}{2c}\Delta\right]\end{aligned} \tag{16.65}$$

and

$$I_t(\Delta) = I_0\left\{1 + \cos\left[2\pi\frac{(\nu_1-\nu_2)}{2c}\Delta\right] \times \cos\left[2\pi\frac{(\nu_1+\nu_2)}{2c}\Delta\right]\right\} \tag{16.66}$$

Such a variation of $I_t(\Delta)$ and $\gamma(\Delta)$ with Δ is shown in Fig. 16.19. From Eq. (16.65) we note that $\gamma(\Delta)$ corresponds to an amplitude modulated sinusoidal variation. The sinusoidal variation has a period

$$p = \frac{2c}{(\nu_1+\nu_2)} = \frac{2\lambda_1\lambda_2}{\lambda_1+\lambda_2} \simeq \lambda_0 \tag{16.67}$$

where $\lambda_0(\simeq\lambda_1\simeq\lambda_2)$ is the average wavelength. The modulation amplitude has zeroes at Δ values given by

$$2\pi\frac{(\nu_1-\nu_2)}{2c}\Delta = \left(m+\frac{1}{2}\right)\pi$$

or

$$\Delta = \left(m+\frac{1}{2}\right)\frac{c}{\nu_1-\nu_2} \tag{16.68}$$

Hence, the minimum path difference at which the visibility vanishes is given by

$$\Delta_m = \frac{c}{2(\nu_1-\nu_2)} = \frac{c}{2\delta\nu} \tag{16.69}$$

which corresponds to the coherence length of the source. Expressing $\delta\nu$ in terms of $\delta\lambda$, we have

$$L_c = \Delta_m = \frac{\lambda^2}{2\delta\lambda} \tag{16.70}$$

consistent with Eq. (16.2).

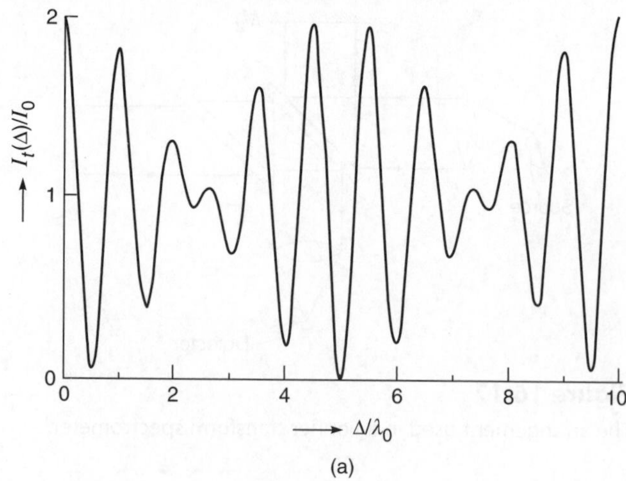

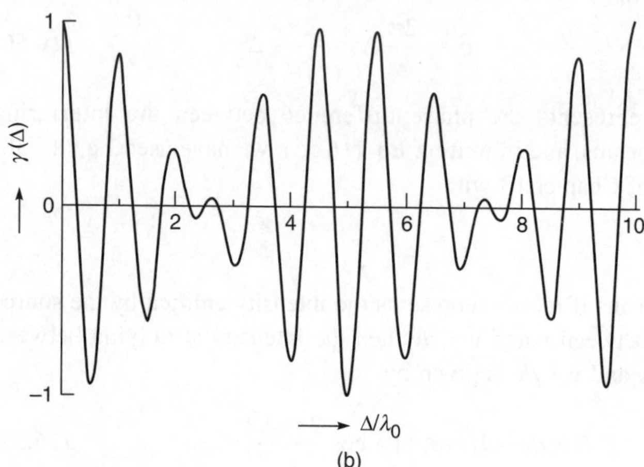

Figure 16.19

(a) The variation of the total intensity at O as a function of the path difference Δ for a source emitting two monochromatic lines. (b) The corresponding variation of $\gamma(\Delta)$ with Δ.

The difference in path difference between two consecutive positions of the disappearance of the fringes is $c/\delta\nu = \lambda^2/\delta\lambda$. As a simple consequence of this, we may consider the Newton's rings experiment with a sodium lamp. If we assume that the sodium lamp emits two discrete wavelengths λ_1 and λ_2, then as we raise the convex lens above the glass plate we should have a periodic appearance of fringes as we had discussed in Example 14.3.

16.8.2 Inversion to Recover $I(\nu)$ from $\gamma(\Delta)$

In an actual experiment, we measure $I_t(\Delta)$ and I_T. Thus, Eq. (16.60) has to be inverted to obtain the source spectral distribution $I(\nu)$ from the measured $\gamma(\Delta)$. To do this, we just multiply Eq. (16.60) by $\cos\frac{2\pi\nu'\Delta}{c}$ and integrate over Δ. Thus

$$\int_0^\infty \gamma(\Delta) \cos \frac{2\pi\nu'\Delta}{c} d\Delta$$

$$= \frac{1}{I_T} \int_0^\infty d\Delta \int_0^\infty d\nu\, I(\nu) \cos \frac{2\pi\nu\Delta}{c} \cos \frac{2\pi\nu'\Delta}{c}$$

$$= \frac{1}{I_T} \int_0^\infty d\nu\, I(\nu) \int_0^\infty \cos \frac{2\pi\nu\Delta}{c} \cos \frac{2\pi\nu'\Delta}{c} d\Delta$$

Now,

$$\int_0^\infty \cos \frac{2\pi\nu\Delta}{c} \cos \frac{2\pi\nu'\Delta}{c} d\Delta$$

$$= \frac{1}{2} \int_{-\infty}^{+\infty} \cos \frac{2\pi\nu\Delta}{c} \cos \frac{2\pi\nu'\Delta}{c} d\Delta$$

since the integrand is an even function of Δ. Writing the two cosine terms in terms of exponentials and using

$$\int_{-\infty}^{+\infty} e^{\pm 2\pi i(\nu-\nu')\Delta/c} d\Delta = \delta\left(\frac{\nu-\nu'}{c}\right) = c\delta(\nu-\nu') \quad \textbf{(16.71)}$$

and

$$\int_{-\infty}^{+\infty} e^{\pm 2\pi i(\nu+\nu')\Delta/c} d\Delta = 0 \quad \textbf{(16.72)}$$

(since ν and ν' are positive), we obtain

$$\int_0^\infty \gamma(\Delta) \cos \frac{2\pi\nu'\Delta}{c} d\Delta = \frac{c}{4I_T} \int_0^\infty \delta(\nu-\nu')\, I(\nu)\, d\nu$$

$$= \frac{c}{4I_T} I(\nu') \quad \textbf{(16.73)}$$

$$\text{Hence, } I(\nu) = \frac{4I_T}{c} \int_0^\infty \gamma(\Delta) \cos \frac{2\pi\nu\Delta}{c} d\Delta \quad \textbf{(16.74)}$$

Thus one can obtain the source spectral distribution $I(\nu)$ from the measured $\gamma(\Delta)$ just by a cosine transformation. Such an inversion from $\gamma(\Delta)$ to $I(\nu)$ is usually performed using a computer.

16.8.3 Resolution

From Eq. (16.74), it follows that to obtain $I(\nu)$ one must measure $\gamma(\Delta)$ for all values of path difference Δ lying between 0 and ∞. Since in an actual experiment, there is a maximum limit to path differences that can be introduced, this maximum path difference determines the resolution obtainable in the estimated $I(\nu)$. To estimate the resolution, we consider a perfectly monochromatic beam of frequency ν_0 incident on the interferometer. We have seen that for such a case $\gamma(\Delta)$ varies with Δ as given by Eq. (16.62). Now in the experiment if Δ_m is the maximum path difference measured, then $\gamma(\Delta)$ would be

$$\begin{aligned} \gamma(\Delta) &= \cos \frac{2\pi\nu_0\Delta}{c} \qquad 0 < \Delta < \Delta_m \\ &= 0 \qquad \text{otherwise} \end{aligned} \quad \textbf{(16.75)}$$

Hence using Eq. (16.74), we have

$$I(\nu) = \frac{4I_T}{c} \int_0^{\Delta_m} \cos\left(\frac{2\pi\nu_0\Delta}{c}\right) \cos\left(\frac{2\pi\nu\Delta}{c}\right) d\Delta$$

$$= \frac{2I_T}{c} \int_0^{\Delta_m} \left[\cos \frac{2\pi(\nu+\nu_0)\Delta}{c} + \cos \frac{2\pi(\nu-\nu_0)\Delta}{c}\right] d\Delta$$

$$= \frac{2I_T}{c} \left[\frac{\sin\left(\frac{2\pi(\nu+\nu_0)\Delta_m}{c}\right)}{\frac{2\pi}{c}(\nu+\nu_0)} + \frac{\sin\left(\frac{2\pi(\nu-\nu_0)\Delta_m}{c}\right)}{\frac{2\pi}{c}(\nu-\nu_0)}\right]$$

Since ν and ν_0 are both positive and much much greater than c/Δ, the first term in the RHS within brackets is negligible and we obtain

$$I(\nu) \simeq \frac{2I_T}{c} \left[\frac{\sin \frac{2\pi(\nu-\nu_0)\Delta_m}{c}}{\frac{2\pi}{c}(\nu-\nu_0)}\right] \quad \textbf{(16.76)}$$

The above estimated source spectrum is similar to that shown in Fig. 16.16. The spectrum is peaked at ν_0 and the first zero appears at

$$\frac{2\pi(\nu-\nu_0)}{c} \Delta_m = \pm\pi$$

or

$$\nu = \nu_0 \pm \frac{c}{2\Delta_m} \quad \textbf{(16.77)}$$

Thus although the incident beam is monochromatic, the inversion process gives us a finite spectral width due to a finite value of Δ_m.

If the incident source contains two frequencies, then we may use the Rayleigh criterion and define the minimum resolvable frequency separation to be the frequency width from the peak to the first zero in $I(\nu)$. Hence,

$$\delta\nu = \frac{c}{2\Delta_m} \quad \textbf{(16.78)}$$

Hence, the larger the maximum path difference Δ_m over which γ is measured, the higher will be the resolution.

As an example if $\Delta_m = 5$ cm, then

$$\delta\nu = \frac{3\times10^{10}}{2\times5} = 3 \text{ G Hz}$$

At $\lambda = 1$ μm, this corresponds to $\delta\lambda = 0.1$ Å.

EXAMPLE 16.2 We consider a quasi-monochromatic source characterized by a Gaussian spectral distribution given by

$$I(\nu) = \frac{1}{\sqrt{\pi}\,(\delta\nu)} I_0 e^{-(\nu-\nu_0)^2/(\delta\nu)^2}$$
$$= \frac{I_0}{\sqrt{\pi}} \tau e^{-(\nu-\nu_0)^2\tau^2} \quad (16.79)$$

Here $\delta\nu = 1/\tau$ characterizes the width of the spectrum since $I(\nu)$ drops to $1/e$ of the value at $\nu = \nu_0$ at $\nu = \nu_0 \pm \delta\nu$. For a quasi-monochromatic source $\delta\nu/\nu_0 << 1$. Thus,

$$I_T = \int_0^\infty I(\nu)\,d\nu = \frac{I_0\tau}{\sqrt{\pi}} \int_0^\infty e^{-(\nu-\nu_0)^2\tau^2} d\nu$$
$$\simeq \frac{I_0}{\sqrt{\pi}} \tau \int_{-\infty}^{+\infty} e^{-(\nu-\nu_0)^2\tau^2} d\nu \quad (16.80)$$

where in the last step we have used the condition $1/\tau = \delta\nu << \nu_0$. If we now use the integral

$$\int_{-\infty}^{+\infty} e^{-\alpha x^2 + \beta x} dx = \left(\frac{\pi}{\alpha}\right)^{1/2} \exp\left(\frac{\beta^2}{4\alpha}\right); \quad \text{Re}\,\alpha > 0 \quad (16.81)$$

we would obtain

$$I_T = I_0 \quad (16.82)$$

Now,

$$\int_0^\infty I(\nu) \cos\frac{2\pi\nu\Delta}{c} d\nu$$
$$= \frac{I_0\tau}{\sqrt{\pi}} \int_0^\infty e^{-(\nu-\nu_0)^2\tau^2} \cos\frac{2\pi\nu\Delta}{c} d\nu$$
$$\simeq \frac{\tau}{\sqrt{\pi}} I_0 \int_{-\infty}^{+\infty} e^{-(\nu-\nu_0)^2\tau^2} \cos\frac{2\pi\nu\Delta}{c} d\nu$$
$$= \frac{\tau}{\sqrt{\pi}} I_0 \,\text{Re} \int_{-\infty}^{+\infty} e^{-(\nu-\nu_0)^2\tau^2} e^{i2\pi\nu\Delta/c} d\nu$$
$$= \frac{\tau}{\sqrt{\pi}} I_0 \,\text{Re}\, e^{2\pi i\nu_0\Delta/c} \int_{-\infty}^{+\infty} e^{-\xi^2\tau^2} e^{i2\pi\xi\Delta/c} d\xi, \quad \xi = \nu - \nu_0$$
$$= I_0 \,\text{Re} \left\{ e^{2\pi i\nu_0\Delta/c} \exp\left[-\frac{\pi^2\Delta^2}{c^2\tau^2}\right]\right\}$$

where we have used Eq. (16.81) with $\alpha = \tau$ and $\beta = i2\pi\Delta/c$. Thus,

$$\int_0^\infty I(\nu) \cos\frac{2\pi\nu\Delta}{c} d\nu = I_0 \exp\left(-\frac{\pi^2\Delta^2}{c^2\tau^2}\right) \cos\frac{2\pi\nu_0\Delta}{c} \quad (16.83)$$

Hence,

$$\gamma(\Delta) = \exp\left(-\frac{\pi^2\Delta^2}{c^2\tau^2}\right) \cos\frac{2\pi\nu_0\Delta}{c} \quad (16.84)$$

Figure 16.20 shows the source spectral distribution as well as the variation of $\gamma(\Delta)$ with Δ. Notice that in this case for path differences $\Delta << c/\delta\nu$, $\gamma(\Delta) \simeq \cos(2\pi\nu_0\Delta/c)$ much like that for a monochromatic source. But as the path difference increases, the modulation amplitude of $\gamma(\Delta)$ is reduced. For good contrast, one must have

$$\Delta << c\tau = c/\delta\nu \quad (16.85)$$

We may thus define the coherence length as

$$L_c = c\tau = \frac{c}{\delta\nu} \quad (16.86)$$

consistent with Eq. (16.2).

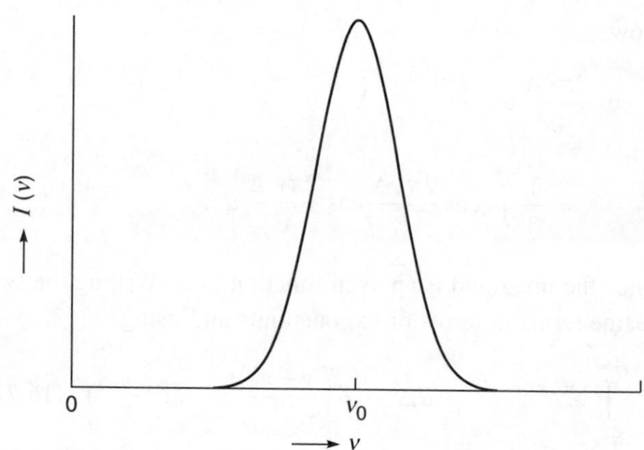

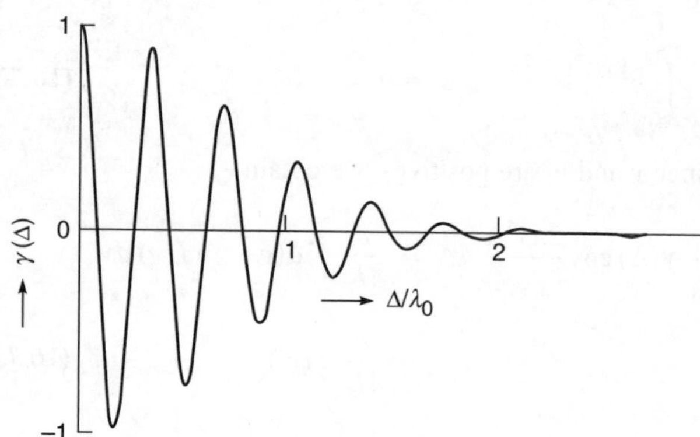

Figure 16.20
Spectral distribution and the variation of $\gamma(\Delta)$ with Δ for a source characterized by Eq.(16.79).

EXAMPLE 16.3 Consider a quasi-monochromatic source characterized by a spectral distribution

$$I(\nu) = \frac{1}{\delta\nu} I_0; \qquad \nu_0 - \frac{1}{2}\delta\nu < \nu < \nu_0 + \frac{1}{2}\delta\nu \quad (16.87)$$
$$= 0 \qquad \text{otherwise}$$

Calculate $\gamma(\Delta)$ and show that again for path differences $\Delta >> c/\delta\nu$, the contrast will be very poor.

Solution:

$$I_T = \frac{1}{\delta\nu} I_0 \int_{\nu_0-\frac{1}{2}\delta\nu}^{\nu_0+\frac{1}{2}\delta\nu} d\nu = I_0 \quad (16.88)$$

$$\int_0^\infty I(\nu)\cos\frac{2\pi\nu\Delta}{c}\,d\nu = \frac{I_0}{(\delta\nu)}\cos\frac{2\pi\nu_0\Delta}{c}\left(\frac{\sin\left(\frac{\pi\delta\nu\Delta}{c}\right)}{\pi\Delta/c}\right)$$

Thus,

$$\gamma(\Delta) = \frac{1}{I_T}\int_0^\infty I(\nu)\cos\frac{2\pi\nu\Delta}{c}\,d\nu$$

$$= \left[\frac{\sin\frac{\pi\delta\nu\Delta}{c}}{\frac{\pi\delta\nu\Delta}{c}}\right]\cos\left(\frac{2\pi\nu_0\Delta}{c}\right) \quad \textbf{(16.89)}$$

For $\Delta << c/\delta\nu$, $\gamma(\Delta) \simeq \cos(2\pi\nu_0\Delta/c)$ and the contrast vanishes for

$$\Delta = c/\delta\nu \quad \textbf{(16.90)}$$

which represents the coherence length. Plot $\gamma(\Delta)$ as a function of Δ and notice that unlike in the earlier example, in this case $\gamma(\Delta)$ does not monotonically reduce to zero.

For more details on Fourier transform spectroscopy, one may look at Refs. 16.10, 16.12 and 16.18.

SUMMARY

- The coherence time τ_c represents the average duration of the wavetrains, i.e., the electric field remains sinusoidal for times of the order of τ_c.
- The length of the wavetrain, given by

$$L_c = c\tau_c$$

(where c is the speed of the light in free space) is referred to as coherence length. For example, for the red cadmium line (λ = 6438 Å), $\tau_c \sim 10^{-9}$ sec; the corresponding coherence length is ~30 cm.

- The lateral coherence width (l_w) of an extended incoherent source represents the distance over which the beam may be assumed to be spatially coherent; it is given by

$$l_w \approx \frac{\lambda}{\theta}$$

where θ is the angle subtended by the source at the point of observation.

- Using the concept of spatial coherence, Michelson developed an ingenious method for determining the angular diameter of stars. The method is based on the result that for a distant circular source, the interference fringes (formed by two pin-holes) will disappear if the distance between the two pinholes is given by

$$d = 1.22\frac{\lambda}{\theta}$$

where θ is the angle subtended by the circular source.

- Using two laser beams it is possible to observe optical beats.
- In the two beam interference pattern, the contrast of the interference fringes varies as the optical path difference Δ is varied, beginning from an extremely good contrast for $\Delta << L_c$ to a very poor contrast for $\Delta >> L_c$.
- Indeed from a knowledge of variation of intensity with optical path difference one can obtain the source spectral distribution by a Fourier transformation.

PROBLEMS

16.1 The orange Krypton line (λ = 6058 Å) has a coherence length of ~20 cm. Calculate the line width and the frequency stability.

[**Ans:** ~0.018 Å, ~3 × 10^{-6}]

16.2 Laser linewidths as low as 20 Hz have been obtained. Calculate the coherence length and the frequency stability. Assume λ = 6328 Å.

16.3 In Sec. 16.4, we had mentioned that the lateral coherence width of a circular source is 1.22 λ/θ. It can be shown that for good coherence (i.e., for a visibility of 0.88 or better), the coherence width should be $\leq 0.3\lambda/\theta$. Assuming that the angular diameter of the sun is about 30′, calculate the distance between two pinholes which would produce a clear interference pattern.

[**Ans.** ~ 0.02 mm]

16.4 Calculate the distance at which a source of diameter 1 mm should be kept from a screen so that two points separated by a distance of 0.5 mm may be said to be coherent. Assume $\lambda = 6 \times 10^{-5}$ cm.

16.5 In a Michelson interferometer experiment, it is found that for a source S, as one of the mirrors is moved away from the equal path length position by a distance of about 5 cm, the fringes disappear. What is the coherence time of the radiation emerging from the source?

16.6 If we perform the Young's double-hole experiment using white light, then only a few coloured fringes are visible. Assuming that the visible spectrum extends from 4000 to 7000 Å, explain this phenomenon qualitatively on the basis of coherence length.

16.7 Using the stellar interferometer, Michelson observed for the star Betelgeuse, that the fringes disappear when the distance between the movable mirrors is 25 inches. Assuming $\lambda \simeq 6 \times 10^{-5}$ cm, calculate the angular diameter of the star.

16.8 Consider Young's double-hole experiment as shown in Fig. 16.2. The distance $SS_1 \simeq 1$ m and $S_1S_2 \approx 0.5$ mm. Calculate the angular diameter of the hole S which will produce a good interference pattern on the screen. Assume $\lambda = 6000$ Å.

16.9 Assume a Gaussian pulse of the form

$$\Psi(x = 0, t) = E_0 \exp\left[-\frac{t^2}{2\tau^2}\right] e^{i\omega_0 t}$$

Show that the Fourier transform is given by

$$A(\omega) = E_0 \tau \exp\left[-\frac{1}{2}(\omega - \omega_0)^2 \tau^2\right]$$

Show that the temporal coherence is $\sim \tau$. Assume $\tau >> (1/\omega_0)$, plot the Fourier transform $A(\omega)$ [as a function of ω] and interpret it physically. Show that the frequency spread $\Delta\omega \sim 1/\tau$.

16.10 In Problem 16.9, assume $\lambda_0 = 6 \times 10^{-5}$ cm and $\tau \sim 10^{-9}$ s. Calculate the frequency components predominantly present in the pulse and compare it with the case corresponding to $\tau \sim 10^{-6}$ s.

CHAPTER 17

Fraunhofer Diffraction I

No one has ever been able to define the difference between interference and diffraction satisfactorily. It is just a question of usage, and there is no specific, important physical difference between them. The best we can do is, roughly speaking, is to say that when there are only a few sources, say two, interfering, then the result is usually called interference, but if there is a large number of them, it seems that the word diffraction is more often used.

—Richard Feynman in *Feynman Lectures on Physics*, Vol. 1

LEARNING OBJECTIVES

After reading this chapter, the reader should be able to:

LO 1: *describe diffraction phenomenon.*

LO 2: *derive the intensity distribution associated with the single-slit diffraction pattern.*

LO 3: *analyse diffraction by circular aperture.*

LO 4: *discuss the directionality of laser beams.*

LO 5: *discuss the limit of resolution.*

LO 6: *derive the intensity distributions associated with the 2 slit and N-slit Fraunhofer diffraction patterns.*

LO 7: *discuss the grating spectrun.*

LO 8: *discuss the diffraction of a plane wave incident obliquely on a grating.*

LO 9: *analyse X-ray diffraction and its experimental methods.*

LO 10: *discuss self-focussing of laser beams.*

Above Image: Close-up view of a red laser on a cutting machine in a college physics laboratory. Photograph courtesy McGraw Hill Digital Access Library.

Important Milestones

1819: Joseph Fraunhofer demonstrated the diffraction of light by gratings which were initially made by winding fine wires around parallel screws.

1823: Fraunhofer published his theory of diffraction.

1835: George Airy calculated the (Fraunhofer) diffraction pattern produced by a circular aperture.

17.1 Introduction

LO1

Consider a plane wave incident on a long narrow slit of width b (see Fig. 17.1). According to geometrical optics one expects the region AB of the screen SS' to be illuminated and the remaining portion (known as the *geometrical shadow*) to be absolutely dark. However, if the observations are made carefully then one finds that if the width of the slit is not very large compared to the wavelength, then the light intensity in the region *AB* is not uniform and there is also some intensity inside the geometrical shadow. Further, if the width of the slit is made smaller, larger amounts of energy reach the geometrical shadow. This spreading out of a wave when it passes through a narrow opening is usually referred to as diffraction and the intensity distribution on the screen is known as the **diffraction pattern**. We will discuss the phenomenon of diffraction in this chapter and will show that the spreading out decreases with decrease in wavelength. Indeed, since the light wavelengths are very small ($\lambda \sim 5 \times 10^{-5}$ cm), the effects due to diffraction are not readily observed.

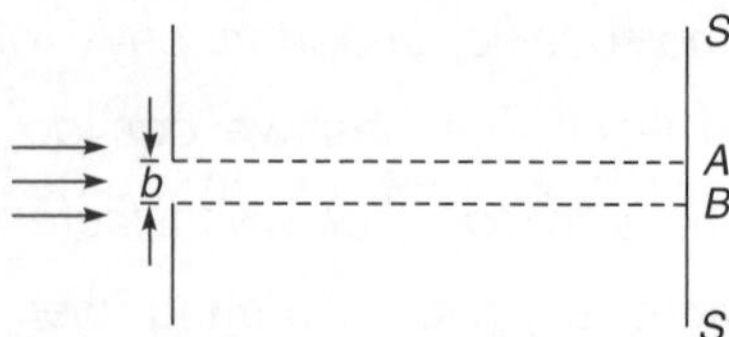

Figure 17.1
If a plane wave is incident on an aperture then according to geometrical optics a sharp shadow will be cast in the region *AB* of the screen.

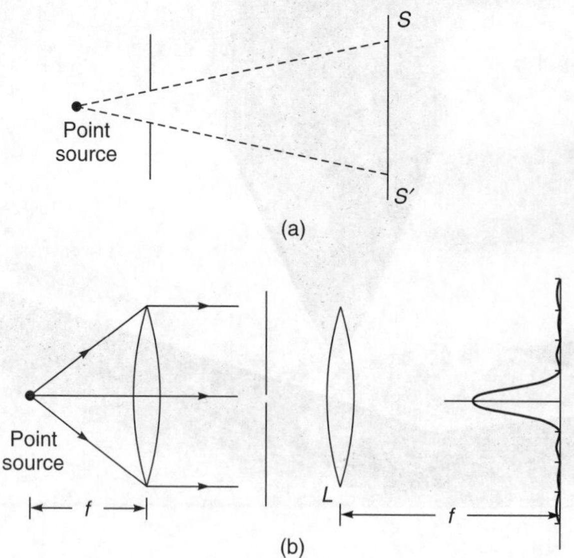

Figure 17.2
(a) When either the source or the screen (or both) are at finite distances from the aperture, the diffraction pattern corresponds to the Fresnel class. (b) In the Fraunhofer class both the source and the screen are at infinity.

We should point out that there is not much of a difference between the phenomena of interference and diffraction, indeed, interference corresponds to the situation when we consider the superposition of waves coming out from a number of point sources and diffraction corresponds to the situation when we consider waves coming out from an area source like a circular or rectangular aperture or even a large number of rectangular apertures (like the diffraction grating).

The diffraction phenomena are usually divided into two categories: (i) Fresnel diffraction, and (ii) Fraunhofer diffraction.

In the Fresnel class of diffraction, the source of light and the screen are, in general, at a finite distance from the diffracting aperture [see Fig. 17.2(a)]. In the Fraunhofer class of diffraction, the source and the screen are at infinite distances from the aperture; this is easily achieved by placing the source on the focal plane of a convex lens and placing the screen on the focal plane of another convex lens [see Fig. 17.2(b)]. The two lenses effectively moved the source and the screen to infinity because the first lens makes the light beam parallel and the second lens effectively makes the screen receive a parallel beam of light. It turns out that it is much easier to calculate the intensity distribution of a Fraunhofer diffraction pattern which we plan to do in this chapter. Further, the Fraunhofer diffraction pattern is not difficult to observe; all that one needs is an ordinary laboratory spectrometer; the collimator renders a parallel beam of light and the telescope receives parallel beams of light on its focal plane. The diffracting aperture is placed on the prism table. In Chapter 19, we will study the Fresnel class of diffraction and will discuss the transition from the Fresnel region to the Fraunhofer region.

17.2 Single-Slit Diffraction Pattern

LO2

We will first study the Fraunhofer diffraction pattern produced by an infinitely long slit of width *b*. A plane wave is assumed to fall normally on the slit and we wish to calculate the intensity distribution on the focal plane of the lens *L* [see Fig. 17.3(a)]. We assume that the slit consists of a large number of equally spaced point sources and that each point on the slit is a source of Huygens' secondary wavelets which interfere with the wavelets emanating from other points. Let the point sources be at $A_1, A_2, A_3, \ldots$ and let the distance between two consecutive points be Δ [see Fig. 17.3(b)]. Thus, if the number of point sources be *n*, then

$$b = (n - 1)\Delta \qquad \textbf{(17.1)}$$

We will now calculate the resultant field produced by these *n* sources at the point *P*, *P* being an arbitrary point (on the focal plane of the lens) receiving parallel rays making an angle θ with the normal to the slit [see Fig. 17.3(b)]. Since the slit actually consists of a continuous distribution of sources, we will, in the final expression, let *n* go to infinity and Δ go to zero such that $n\Delta$ tends to *b*.

Now, at the point *P*, the amplitudes of the disturbances reaching from $A_1, A_2, \ldots$ will be very nearly the same because the point *P* is at a distance which is very large in comparison to *b* [see Fig. 17.3(b)]. However, because of even slightly different path lengths to the point *P*, the field produced by A_1 will differ in phase from the field produced by A_2.

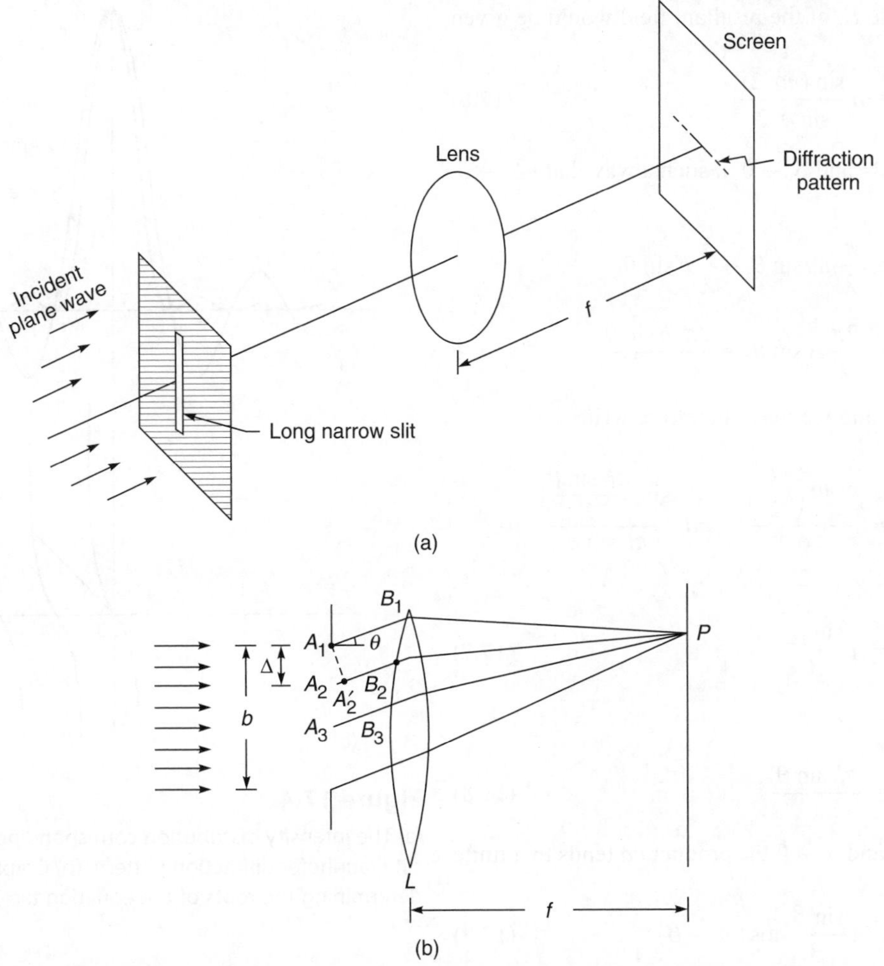

Figure 17.3
(a) Diffraction of a plane wave incident normally on a long narrow slit of width *b*. Notice that the spreading occurs along the width of the slit. (b) In order to calculate the diffraction pattern, the slit is assumed to consist of a large number of equally spaced points.

For an incident plane wave, the points A_1, A_2, … are in phase and, therefore, the additional path traversed by the disturbance emanating from the point A_2 will be A_2A_2' where A_2' is the foot of the perpendicular drawn from A_1 on A_2B_2. This follows from the fact that the optical paths A_1B_1P and $A_2'B_2P$ are the same. If the diffracted rays make an angle θ with the normal to the slit then the path difference would be

$$A_2A_2' = \Delta \sin \theta$$

The corresponding phase difference, ϕ, would be given by

$$\phi = \frac{2\pi}{\lambda} \Delta \sin \theta \qquad \textbf{(17.2)}$$

Thus, if the field at the point P due to the disturbance emanating from the point A_1 is $a \cos \omega t$ then the field due to the disturbance emanating from A_2 would be $a \cos(\omega t - \phi)$. Now the difference in the phases of the disturbance reaching from the points A_2 and A_3 will also be ϕ and thus the resultant field at the point P would be given by

$$E = a[\cos \omega t + \cos(\omega t - \phi) + \ldots + \cos(\omega t - (n-1)\phi)] \qquad \textbf{(17.3)}$$

where $\phi = \dfrac{2\pi}{\lambda} \Delta \sin \theta$

Now, we had shown in Sec. 9.7 that

$$\cos \omega t + \cos(\omega t - \phi) + \ldots + \cos[\omega t - (n-1)\phi] = \frac{\sin n\phi/2}{\sin \phi/2} \cos\left[\omega t - \frac{1}{2}(n-1)\phi\right] \qquad \textbf{(17.4)}$$

Thus,
$$E = E_0 \cos\left[\omega t - \frac{1}{2}(n-1)\phi\right] \qquad \textbf{(17.5)}$$

where the amplitude E_θ of the resultant field would be given by

$$E_\theta = a\frac{\sin (n\phi/2)}{\sin \phi/2} \quad (17.6)$$

In the limit of $n \to \infty$ and $\Delta \to 0$ in such a way that $n\Delta \to b$, we have

$$\frac{n\phi}{2} = \frac{\pi}{\lambda} n\Delta \sin \theta \to \frac{\pi}{\lambda} b \sin \theta$$

Further, $$\phi = \frac{2\pi}{\lambda}\Delta \sin \theta = \frac{2\pi}{\lambda}\frac{b \sin \theta}{n}$$

would tend to zero and we may, therefore, write

$$E_\theta \approx \frac{a \sin\left(\frac{n\phi}{2}\right)}{\frac{\phi}{2}} = na\frac{\sin \frac{\pi b \sin \theta}{\lambda}}{\frac{\pi b \sin \theta}{\lambda}}$$

$$= A\frac{\sin \beta}{\beta} \quad (17.7)$$

where $A = na$

and $$\beta = \frac{\pi b \sin \theta}{\lambda} \quad (17.8)$$

In the limit $n \to \infty$ and $a \to 0$ the product na tends to a finite limit. Thus,

$$E = A\frac{\sin \beta}{\beta}\cos (\omega t - \beta) \quad (17.9)$$

The corresponding intensity distribution is given by

$$I = I_0\frac{\sin^2 \beta}{\beta^2} \quad (17.10)$$

where I_0 represents the intensity at $\theta = 0$. We may mention here that Eq. (17.6) represents the amplitude distribution due to the interference of n point sources. Thus, for $n = 2$, the amplitude E_θ becomes $\cos \phi/2$ giving rise to $\cos^2 \phi/2$ intensity distribution [cf. Eq. (13.13)]. Notice that if we have a large number of equidistant sources oscillating in phase, then the propagation is only in certain directions where the displacements add up in phase.

17.2.1 Positions of Maxima and Minima

The variation of the intensity with β is shown in Fig. 17.4(a). It is obvious from Eq. (17.10) that the intensity is zero when

$$\beta = m\pi, m \neq 0 \quad (17.11)$$

[When $\beta = 0$, $\frac{\sin \beta}{\beta} = 1$ and $I = I_0$ which corresponds to the maximum of the intensity.] Substituting the value of β one obtains

$$b \sin \theta = m\lambda;\ m = \pm1, \pm2, \pm3, \ldots \text{ (minima)} \quad (17.12)$$

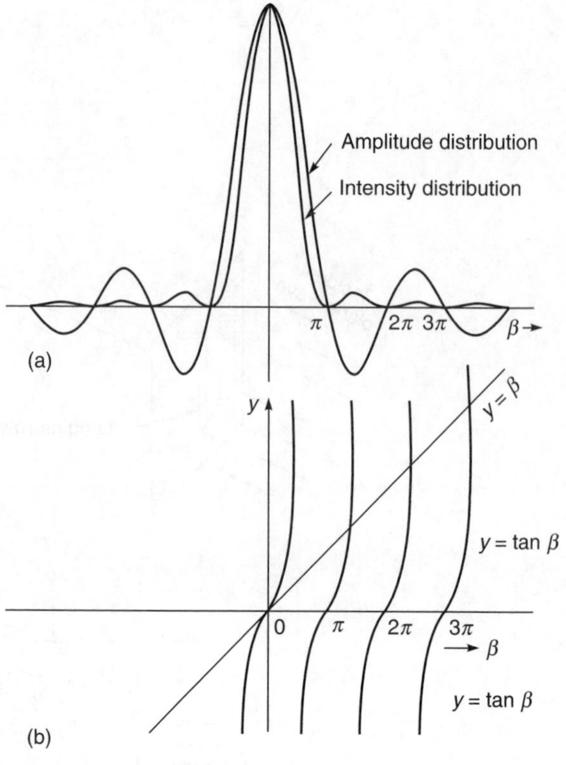

Figure 17.4
(a) The intensity distribution corresponding to the single slit Fraunhofer diffraction pattern. (b) Graphical method for determining the roots of the equation $\tan \beta = \beta$.

as the conditions for minima. The first minimum occurs at $\theta = \pm\sin^{-1}\left(\frac{\lambda}{b}\right)$; the second minimum at $\theta = \pm\sin^{-1}\left(\frac{2\lambda}{b}\right)$, etc. Since $\sin \theta$ cannot exceed unity, the maximum value of m is the integer which is less than (and closest to) b/λ.

The positions of minima can directly be obtained by simple qualitative arguments. Let us consider the case $m = 1$. The angle θ satisfies the equation

$$b \sin \theta = \lambda \quad (17.13)$$

We divide the slit into two halves as shown in Fig. 17.5. Consider two points A and A' separated by a distance $b/2$. Clearly the path difference between the disturbances (reaching the point P) emanating from A and A' is $\frac{b}{2}\sin \theta$ which in this case is $\frac{\lambda}{2}$. The corresponding phase difference will be π and the resultant disturbance will be zero. Similarly, the disturbance from the point B will be cancelled by the disturbance reaching from the point B'. Thus, the resultant disturbance due to the upper half of the slit will be canceled by the disturbances reaching from the lower half and the resultant intensity will be zero. In a similar manner when

$$b \sin \theta = 2\lambda \quad (17.14)$$

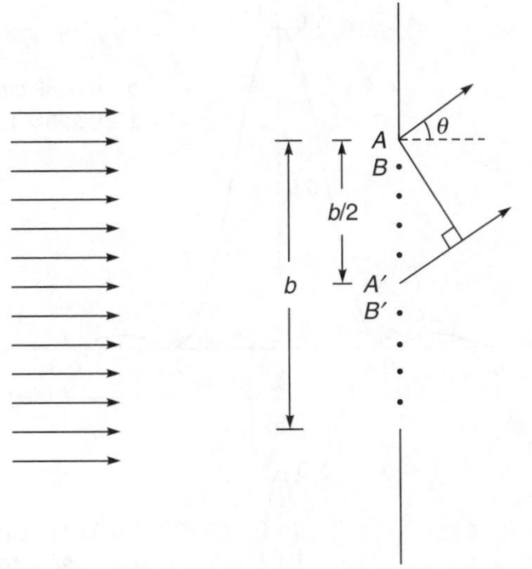

Figure 17.5
The slit is divided into two halves for deriving the condition for the first minimum.

we divide the slit into four parts; the first and second quarters cancelling each other and the third and fourth quarters cancelling each other. Similarly when $m = 3$, the slit is divided into six parts and so on.

In order to determine the positions of maxima, we differentiate Eq. (17.10) with respect to β and set it equal to zero. Thus

$$\frac{dI}{d\beta} = I_0\left[\frac{2\sin\beta\cos\beta}{\beta^2} - \frac{2\sin^2\beta}{\beta^3}\right] = 0$$

or
$$\sin\beta[\beta - \tan\beta] = 0 \tag{17.15}$$

The condition $\sin\beta = 0$, or $\beta = m\pi$ ($m \neq 0$) correspond to minima. The conditions for maxima are roots of the following transcendental equation

$$\tan\beta = \beta \quad \text{(maxima)} \tag{17.16}$$

The root $\beta = 0$ corresponds to the central maximum. The other roots can be found by determining the points of intersections of the curves $y = \beta$ and $y = \tan\beta$ [see Fig. 17.4(b)]. The intersections occur at $\beta = 1.43\pi$, $\beta = 2.46\pi$, etc., and are known as the first maximum, the second maximum, etc. Since

$$\left[\frac{\sin(1.43\pi)}{1.43\pi}\right]^2$$

is about 0.0496, the intensity of the first maximum is about 4.96% of the central maximum. Similarly, the intensities of the second and third maxima are about 1.68% and 0.83% of the central maximum, respectively.

EXAMPLE 17.1 A parallel beam of light is incident normally on a narrow slit of width 0.2 mm. The Fraunhofer diffraction pattern is observed on a screen which is placed at the focal plane of a convex lens whose focal length is 20 cm. Calculate the distance between the first two minima and the first two maxima on the screen. Assume $\lambda = 5 \times 10^{-5}$ cm and that the lens is placed very close to the slit.

Solution:

$$\frac{\lambda}{b} = \frac{5\times10^{-5}}{2\times10^{-2}} = 2.5 \times 10^{-3}$$

Now, the conditions for diffraction minima are given by $\sin\theta = m\lambda/b$. We assume θ to be small (measured in radians) so that we may write $\sin\theta \approx \theta$ (an assumption which will be justified by subsequent calculations); thus, on substituting the value of λ/b, we get

$$\theta \simeq 2.5 \times 10^{-3} \text{ and } 5 \times 10^{-3} \text{ radians}$$

as the angles of diffraction corresponding to the first and second minima, respectively. Notice that since

$$\sin(2.5 \times 10^{-3}) = 2.4999973 \times 10^{-3}$$

the error in the approximations $\sin\theta \simeq \theta$ is about 1 part in a million! These minima will be separated by a distance $(5 \times 10^{-3} - 2.5 \times 10^{-3}) \times 20 = 0.05$ cm on the focal plane of the lens. Similarly, the first and second maxima occur at

$$\beta = 1.43\pi \quad \text{and} \quad 2.46\pi$$

respectively. Thus,

$$b\sin\theta = 1.43\lambda \quad \text{and} \quad 2.46\lambda$$

or

$$\sin\theta = 1.43 \times 2.5 \times 10^{-3} \quad \text{and} \quad 2.46 \times 2.5 \times 10^{-3}$$

Consequently, the maxima will be separated by the distance given by

$$(2.46 - 1.43) \times 2.5 \times 10^{-3} \times 20 \simeq 0.05 \text{ cm}$$

EXAMPLE 17.2 Consider, once again, a parallel beam of light ($\lambda = 5 \times 10^{-5}$ cm) to be incident normally on a long narrow slit of width 0.2 mm. A screen is placed at a distance of 3 m from the slit. Assuming that the screen is so far away that the diffraction is essentially of the Fraunhofer type, calculate total width of the central maximum.

Solution: As in Example 17.1, the first minimum occurs at $\theta \simeq 2.5 \times 10^{-3}$ radians; thus the total width of the central maximum is approximately given by

$$2 \times 3 \times \tan(2.5 \times 10^{-3}) \simeq 0.015 \text{ m}$$

In Fig. 17.6, we have given the actual single slit diffraction pattern (as seen on a screen) for the following values of slit widths: 8.8×10^{-3} cm, 1.76×10^{-2} cm, 3.5×10^{-2} cm and 7.0×10^{-2} cm. The light wavelength used was 6328 Å = 6.328×10^{-5} cm. We may note the following two points:

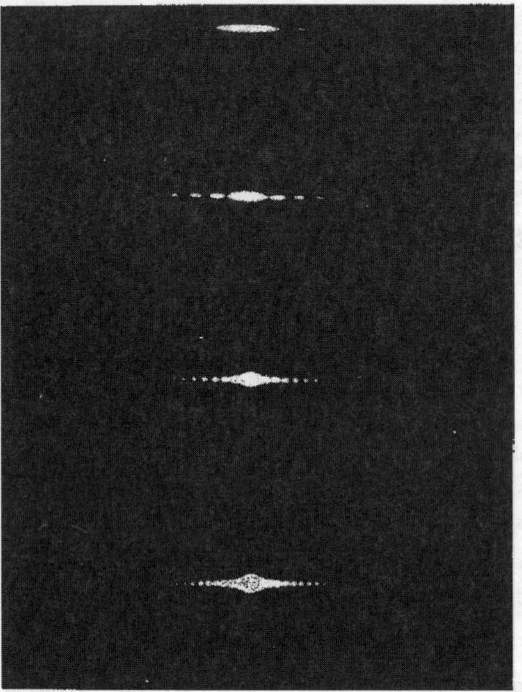

Figure 17.6
The single-slit diffraction patterns corresponding to b = 0.0088, 0.0176, 0.035 and 0.070 cm, respectively. The wavelength of the light used is 6.328×10^{-5} cm. [Adapted from Ref. 17.17; used with permission]

(i) The spreading is only in the direction of the width of the slit. This is because of the fact that the lengths of the slits were very large compared to their widths.

(ii) The values of λ/b corresponding to the four slit widths are 7.191×10^{-3}, 3.595×10^{-3}, 1.808×10^{-3} and 0.904×10^{-3}. Thus, the diffraction angle at which the first minimum will occur will be

$$\theta \simeq \sin\theta = 7.191 \times 10^{-3}, 3.595 \times 10^{-3},$$
$$1.808 \times 10^{-3} \text{ and } 0.904 \times 10^{-3};$$

where the angles are measured in radians. Figure 17.6 corresponds to the photographic film being 15 feet away from the slit. Thus it records the Fraunhofer pattern (see also Sec. 19.7) and for $b = 8.8 \times 10^{-3}$ cm, 1.76×10^{-2} cm, 3.5×10^{-2} cm and 7.0×10^{-2} cm, the first minima occur at distances of 3.288 cm, 1.644 cm, 0.827 cm and 0.413 cm, respectively, from the central maximum.

The intensity distributions predicted by Eq. (17.10) are given in Fig. 17.7 for $b = 8.8 \times 10^{-3}$ cm and 1.76×10^{-2} cm. For $b >> \lambda$, most of the energy (of the diffracted beam) is contained between the first two minima, i.e., for

$$-\frac{\lambda}{b} \lesssim \theta \lesssim \frac{\lambda}{b} \quad \textbf{(17.17)}$$

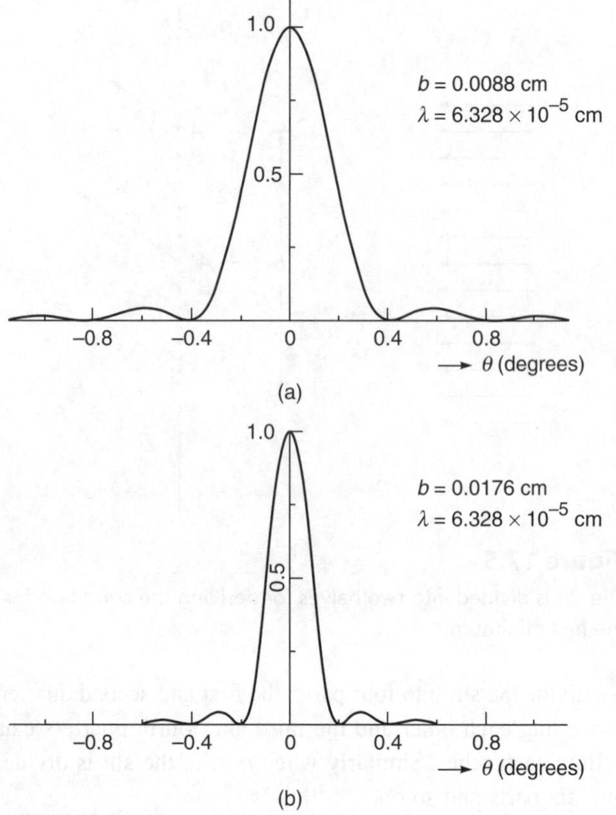

Figure 17.7
The intensity distribution as calculated by using Eq. (17.10) for b = 0.0088 cm and 0.0176 cm ($\lambda = 6.328 \times 10^{-5}$ cm).

(where θ is measured in radians). Thus the divergence angle (which would contain most of the energy) would be given by

$$\Delta\theta \sim \frac{\lambda}{b} \quad \textbf{(17.18)}$$

For very small values of b, the light almost uniformly spreads out from the slit. We should also mention that in the limit of $\lambda \to 0$, $\Delta\theta \to 0$ and the diffraction effects are absent.

17.3 Diffraction by a Circular Aperture

LO3

In the previous section, we have shown that when a plane wave is incident on a long narrow slit (of width b), then the emergent wave spreads out (along the width of the slit) with angular divergence $\sim \lambda/b$. In a similar manner, one can discuss the diffraction of a plane wave by a circular aperture.

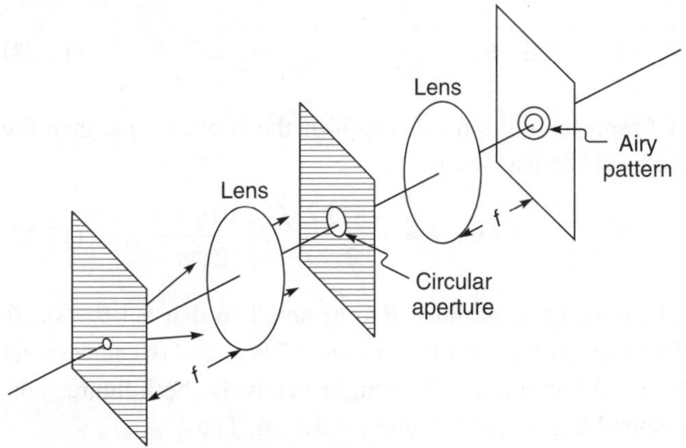

Figure 17.8
Experimental arrangement for observing the Fraunhofer diffraction pattern by a circular aperture.

Figure 17.8 shows the arrangement for observing the diffraction pattern; a plane wave is incident normally on the circular aperture and a lens whose diameter is much larger than that of the aperture is placed close to the aperture and the Fraunhofer diffraction pattern is observed on the focal plane of the lens. Because of the rotational symmetry of the system, the diffraction pattern will consist of concentric dark and bright rings; this diffraction pattern (as observed on the back focal plane of the lens) is known as the **Airy pattern**. In Figs. 17.9(a) and (b), we have shown the Airy patterns corresponding to the radius of the circular aperture being 0.5 mm and 0.25 mm, respectively. The detailed derivation of the diffraction pattern for a circular aperture is somewhat complicated (see Sec. 18.7); we give here the final result: the intensity distribution is given by

$$I = I_0 \left[\frac{2J_1(v)}{v}\right]^2 \tag{17.19}$$

where
$$v = \frac{2\pi}{\lambda} a \sin\theta \tag{17.20}$$

a being the radius of the circular aperture, λ the wavelength of light and θ the angle of diffraction; I_0 is the intensity at $\theta = 0$ (which represents the central maximum) and $J_1(v)$ is known as the **Bessel function of the first order**. On the focal plane of the convex lens

$$v \approx \frac{2\pi}{\lambda} a \frac{(x^2 + y^2)^{\frac{1}{2}}}{f} \tag{17.21}$$

where f is the focal length of the lens. For those not familiar with Bessel functions, we may mention that the variation of $J_1(v)$ is somewhat like a damped sine curve (see Fig. 17.10) and although $J_1(0) = 0$, we have

$$\underset{v\to 0}{Lt} \frac{2J_1(v)}{v} = 1$$

similar to the relation

$$\underset{x\to 0}{Lt} \frac{\sin x}{x} = 1$$

Other zeros of $J_1(v)$ occur at

$$v = 3.832,\ 7.016,\ 10.174,\ \ldots$$

In Fig. 17.11, we have plotted the function

$$\left[\frac{2J_1(v)}{v}\right]^2$$

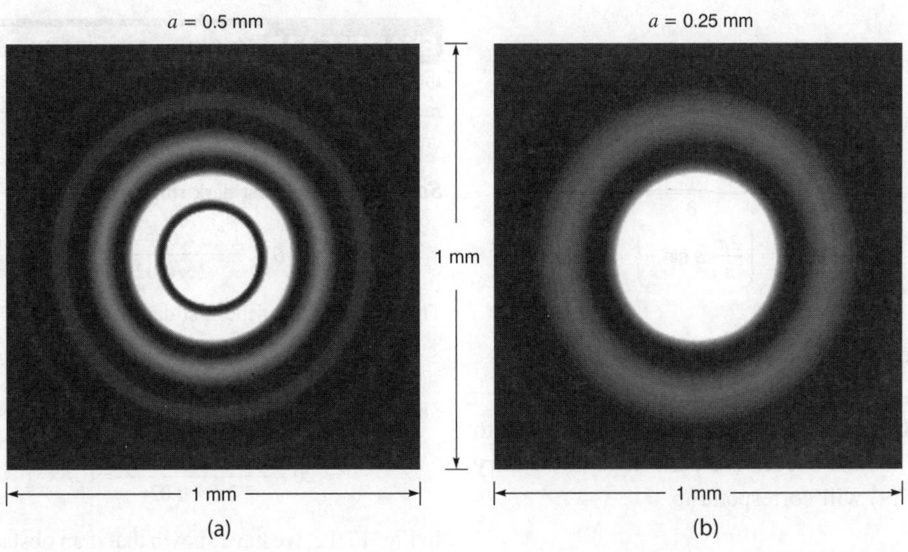

Figure 17.9
Computer generated Airy patterns; (a) and (b) correspond to $a = 0.5$ mm and $a = 0.25$ mm, respectively at the focal plane of a lens of focal length 20 cm ($\lambda = 0.5$ μm).

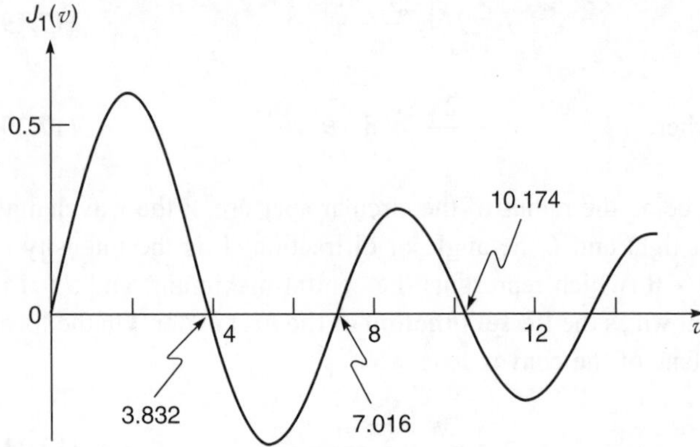

Figure 17.10
The variation of $J_1(v)$ with v.

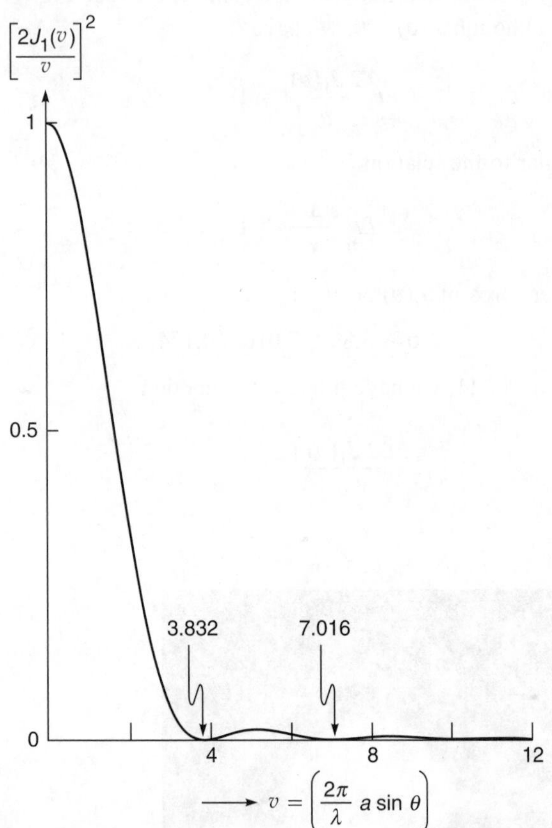

Figure 17.11
The intensity variation associated with the Airy pattern.

which represents the intensity distribution corresponding to the Airy pattern. Thus the successive dark rings in the Airy pattern (see Fig. 17.9) will correspond to

$$v = \frac{2\pi}{\lambda} a \sin\theta = 3.832,\ 7.016,\ 10.174,\ \ldots \quad \textbf{(17.22)}$$

or

$$\sin\theta = \frac{3.832\,\lambda}{2\pi a},\ \frac{7.016\,\lambda}{2\pi a},\ \ldots \quad \textbf{(17.23)}$$

If f represents the focal length of the convex lens, then the Radii of the dark rings

$$= f\tan\theta \approx \frac{3.832\,\lambda f}{2\pi a},\ \frac{7.016\,\lambda f}{2\pi a},\ \ldots \quad \textbf{(17.24)}$$

where we have assumed θ to be small so that $\tan\theta \approx \sin\theta$. The Airy patterns shown in Figs. 17.9(a) and (b) correspond to a = 0.5 mm and 0.25 mm, respectively; both figures correspond to λ = 5000 Å and f = 20 cm. Thus

Radius of the first dark ring ≈ 0.12 mm and 0.24 mm

corresponding to a = 0.5 mm and 0.25 mm, respectively. Detailed mathematical analysis shows that about 84% of the energy is contained within the first dark ring (see Sec. 18.7); thus we may say that the angular spread of the beam is approximately given by

$$\Delta\theta \approx \frac{0.61\,\lambda}{a} \approx \frac{\lambda}{D} \quad \textbf{(17.25)}$$

where D (= 2a) represents the diameter of the aperture. Comparing Eqs. (17.18) and (17.25), we may say that the angular divergence associated with the diffraction pattern can be written in the following general form:

$$\Delta\theta \sim \frac{\lambda}{\text{Linear dimension of the aperture}} \quad \textbf{(17.26)}$$

In a dark room, if we make a laser beam incident normally on a pin-hole, we will be able to see the Airy Pattern on the wall.

EXAMPLE 17.3 Calculate the radii of the first two dark rings of the Fraunhofer diffraction pattern produced by a circular aperture of radius 0.02 cm at the focal plane of a convex lens of focal length 20 cm. Assume $\lambda = 6 \times 10^{-5}$ cm.

Solution: The first dark ring occurs at

$$\theta \approx \sin\theta = \frac{1.22 \times 6 \times 10^{-5}}{2 \times 0.02} \approx 1.8 \times 10^{-3} \text{ radians}$$

Thus, the radius of the first dark ring is

$$\approx 20 \times 1.8 \times 10^{-3} = 3.6 \times 10^{-2} \text{ cm}$$

Similarly, the radius of the second dark ring is

$$\approx 20 \times \frac{7.016 \times 6 \times 10^{-5}}{2\pi \times 0.02} \approx 6.7 \times 10^{-2} \text{ cm}$$

In Fig. 17.12, we have shown that if an obstacle with a small gap is placed in the tank the ripples emerge in an almost semicircular pattern; the small gap acting almost like a point source. If the gap is large, the diffraction is much more limited. *Small*, in this context, means that the size of the obstacle is comparable to the wavelength of the ripples.

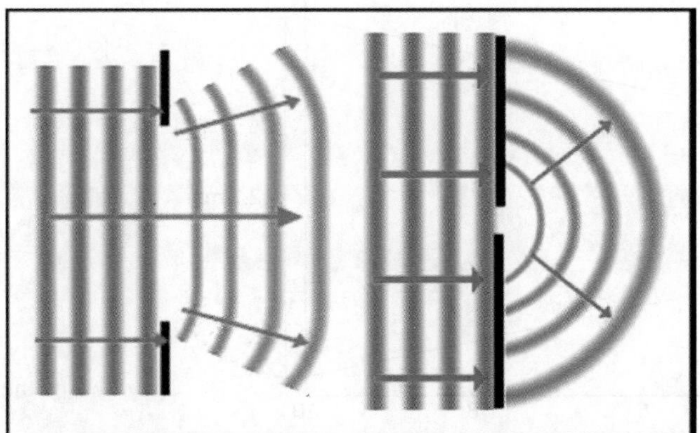

Figure 17.12
If an obstacle with a small gap is placed in the tank the ripples emerge in an almost semicircular pattern; the small gap acting almost like a point source. If the gap is large however, the diffraction is much more limited. *Small*, in this context, means that the size of the obstacle is comparable to the wavelength of the ripples. [Drawing by Ms. Theresa Knott; used with her kind permission].

17.4 Directionality of Laser Beams

LO4

An ordinary source of light (like a sodium lamp) radiates in all directions. On the other hand, the divergence of a laser beam is primarily due to diffraction effects. For most laser beams, the transverse amplitude distribution is approximately Gaussian; indeed just when the beam is leaving the laser (which we assume to be $z = 0$), the amplitude distribution can be assumed to be given by

$$A(x, y) = a \exp\left[-\frac{x^2 + y^2}{w_0^2}\right] \tag{17.27}$$

where we have assumed that the phase front is plane at $z = 0$. From the above equation it follows that at a distance w_0 from the z-axis, the amplitude falls by a factor $1/e$ (i.e., the intensity reduces by a factor $1/e^2$). This quantity w_0 is called the *spot size* of the beam. In Sec. 19.5 (and Appendix B) we will show that as the beam propagates in the z-direction, the intensity distribution is given by

$$I(x, y, z) = \frac{I_0}{1+\gamma^2} \exp\left[-\frac{2(x^2 + y^2)}{w^2(z)}\right] \tag{17.28}$$

where $\gamma = \dfrac{\lambda z}{\pi w_0^2}$ and

$$w(z) = w_0\sqrt{1+\gamma^2} = w_0\left[1+\frac{\lambda^2 z^2}{\pi^2 w_0^4}\right]^{1/2} \tag{17.29}$$

Thus the transverse intensity distribution remains Gaussian with the beam-width increasing with z. For large values of $z\left(>> \dfrac{w_0^2}{\lambda}\right)$, we obtain

$$w(z) \approx w_0 \frac{\lambda z}{\pi w_0^2} = \frac{\lambda z}{\pi w_0} \tag{17.30}$$

which shows that the width increases linearly with z. We define the diffraction angle as

$$\tan\theta = \frac{w(z)}{z} \approx \frac{\lambda}{\pi w_0} \tag{17.31}$$

showing that the rate of increase in the width is proportional to the wavelength and inversely proportional to the initial width of the beam; the above equation is consistent with Eq. (17.26).

We consider the propagation of a Gaussian beam with $\lambda = 0.5$ µm. If the initial spot size is given by $w_0 = 1$ mm, then

$$2\theta \approx 0.018° \text{ and at } z = 10 \text{ m, we get } w \approx 1.88 \text{ mm.}$$

[We must use Eq. (17.28) and not Eq. (17.31) — why??]. Similarly, for $w_0 = 0.25$ mm,

$$2\theta \approx 0.073° \text{ and at } z = 10 \text{ m, we get } w \approx 6.35 \text{ mm.}$$

(see Fig. 17.13). Notice that θ increases with decrease in w_0 (smaller the size of the aperture, greater is the diffraction).

From Eq. (17.31) we find that

(a) For a given value of λ, θ increases with a decrease in the value of w_0; this implies that smaller the initial spot size of the beam greater will be the diffraction divergence.

(b) For a given value of w_0, the value of θ (and hence the diffraction divergence) decreases with decrease in the value of λ. In Fig. 17.14, we have shown decrease in diffraction divergence for $w_0 = 0.25$ mm as the wavelength is decreased from 5000 Å to 500 Å; indeed as $\lambda \to 0$, $\theta \to 0$ and there is no diffraction which is the geometric optics limit.

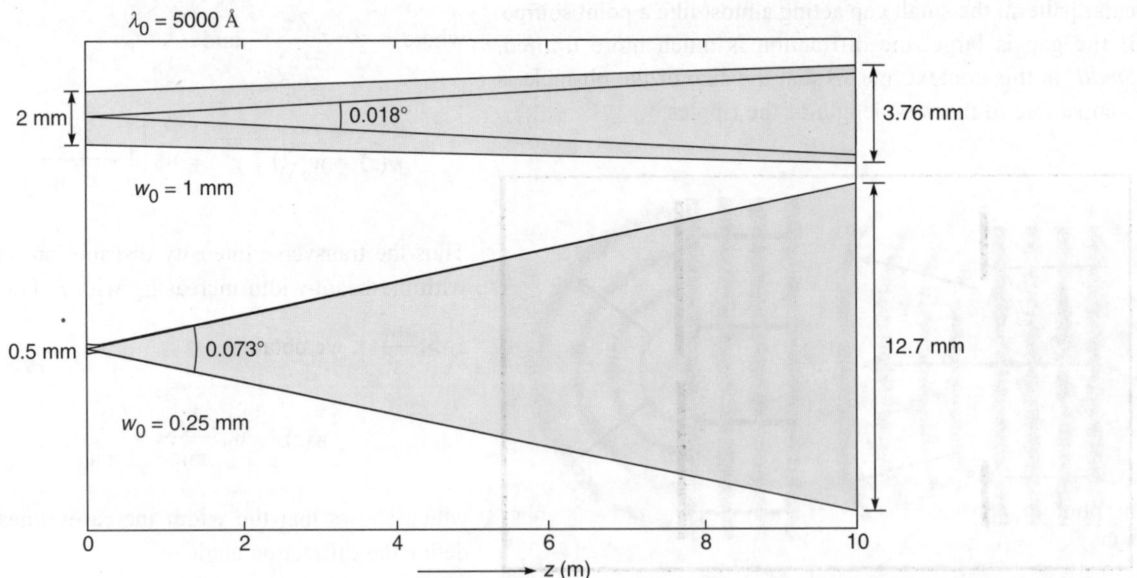

Figure 17.13

Diffraction divergence of a Gaussian beam whose phase front is plane at $z = 0$. The figure shows the increase in the diffraction divergence as the initial spot size is decreased from 1 mm to 0.25 mm; the wavelength is assumed to be 5000 Å.

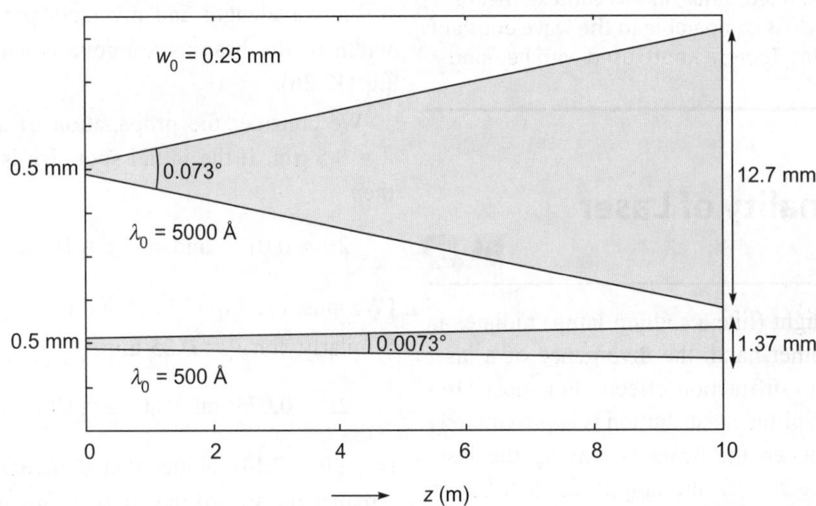

Figure 17.14

Diffraction divergence of a Gaussian beam whose phase front is plane at $z = 0$. The figure shows the decrease in divergence as the wavelength is decreased from 5000 Å to 500 Å; the initial spot size (w_0) is assumed to be 0.25 mm.

In Fig. 17.15, we have shown a laser beam propagating through the atmosphere. Notice the small divergence of the beam. From Eq. (17.27) one can readily show that

$$\iint_{-\infty}^{+\infty} I(x, y, z)\, dx\, dy = \frac{\pi w_0^2}{2} I_0$$

which is independent of z. This is to be expected, as the total energy crossing the entire x-y plane will not change with z.

EXAMPLE 17.4 The output from a single-mode fiber operating at the He–Ne laser wavelength ($\lambda_0 = 0.6328$ µm) is approximately Gaussian with $w_0 = 5$ µm. Thus, the corresponding divergence is

$$\theta \approx \tan^{-1}\left(\frac{\lambda_0}{\pi w_0}\right) \approx 2.3°$$

Thus, if a screen is placed at a distance of about 50 cm from the fiber, the radius of the beam is about 2 cm.

Figure 17.15

This photograph shows the Laser Ranging Facility at the Geophysical and Astronomical Observatory at NASA's Goddard Space Flight Center in Greenbelt, Maryland, USA. The observatory helps NASA keep track of orbiting satellites. In this image, the lower of the two green beams is from the Lunar Reconnaissance Orbiter's dedicated tracker. The other laser originates from another ground system at the facility. Both beams are pointed at the moon -- specifically at LRO in orbit around the Moon. Notice the small spreading of the beams. Photograph courtesy McGraw Hill Digital Access Library.

A beam is said to be *diffraction limited* if it diverges only due to diffraction. Usually laser beams are diffraction limited. On the other hand, if we have a tiny filament at the focal plane of a lens, the beam will diverge primarily due to the finite size of the filament (see Fig. 17.16). The angular spread of the beam is given by (see Fig. 17.16)

$$\Delta\theta \approx \frac{l}{f} \tag{17.32}$$

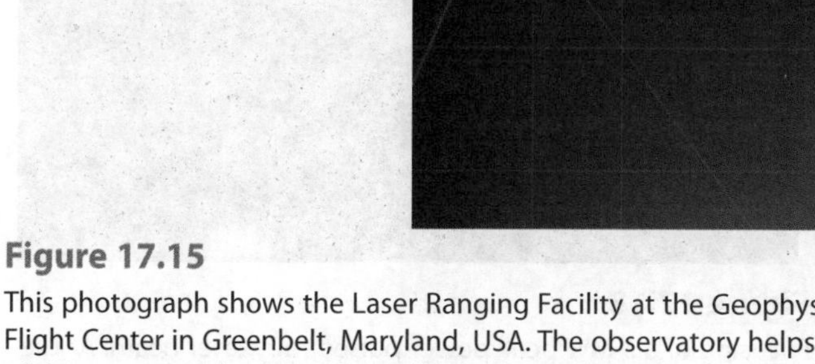

Figure 17.16

A filament placed at the focal plane of a convex lens.

where l is the length of the filament and f the focal length of the lens. If the linear dimension of the filament is about 2 mm (placed on the focal plane of a convex lens of focal length 10 cm) then the angular divergence of the beam (due to the finite size of the filament) is approximately given by

$$\Delta\theta \approx \frac{2\text{ mm}}{100\text{ mm}} = 0.02 \text{ radians}$$

If the diameter of the aperture of the lens is 5 cm then the angular divergence due to diffraction would be

$$\Delta\theta \approx \frac{\lambda}{D} \approx \frac{5\times10^{-5}\text{ cm}}{5\text{ cm}} = 0.00001 \text{ radians}$$

which is much much smaller than the angular divergence of the beam due to the finite size of the filament. Only if the size of the filament is smaller than 10^{-3} mm would the beam divergence be determined by diffraction. Thus for most practical sources, the beam divergence is due to the finite size of the filament rather than by diffraction.

17.4.1 Focusing of Laser Beams

As mentioned earlier, laser beams are usually diffraction limited. If such a diffraction limited beam is allowed to fall on a convex lens then

$$\text{Radius of the focussed spot} \approx \frac{\lambda_0 f}{a} \tag{17.33}$$

(see Fig. 17.17). In Eq. (17.32), f represents the focal length of the lens and a represents the beam radius or the radius of the aperture of the lens (whichever is smaller). Thus,

$$\text{Area of the focussed spot } A \approx \pi\left(\frac{\lambda_0 f}{a}\right)^2$$

We illustrate the effects of this focusing through some examples.

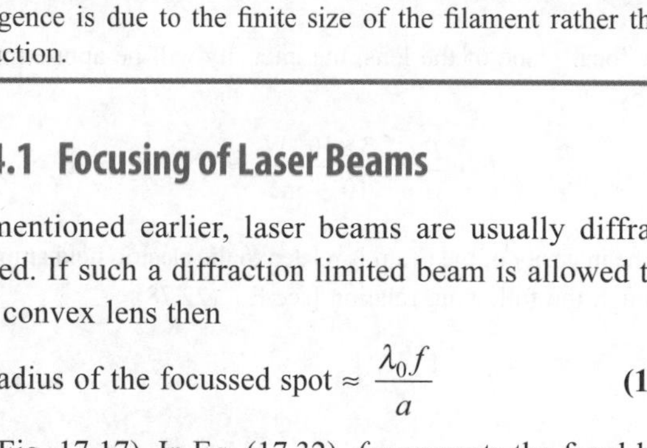

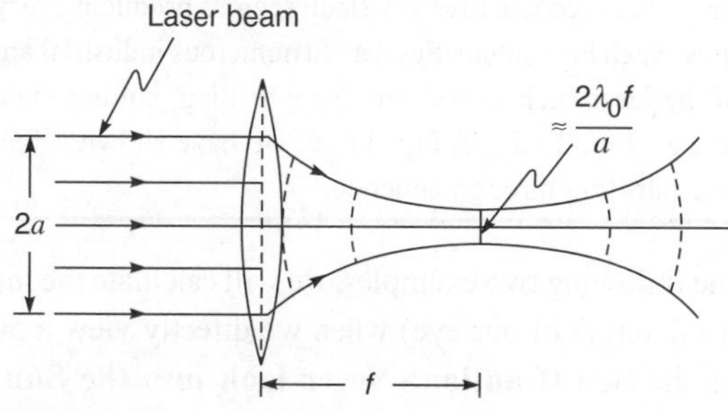

Figure 17.17

If a truncated plane wave (of diameter $2a$) is incident on an aberrationless lens of focal length f, then the wave emerging from the lens will get focused to spot of radius $\approx \lambda_0 f/a$; the area of the focused spot size is $\approx \pi(\lambda_0 f/a)^2$.

EXAMPLE 17.5 We consider a 2 mW laser beam ($\lambda_0 \approx 6 \times 10^{-5}$ cm) incident on the eye whose focal length is given by $f \approx 2.5$ cm. If the pupil diameter (= $2a$) is taken to be 2 mm, then

$$\text{Area of the focused spot } A = \pi\left(\frac{\lambda_0 f}{a}\right)^2 \approx 7 \times 10^{-6} \text{ cm}^2$$

On the retina, the intensity will be approximately given by

$$I \approx \frac{P}{A} \approx \frac{2\times10^{-3}\text{ W}}{7\times10^{-10}\text{ m}^2} \approx 3 \times 10^6 \text{ W/m}^2$$

Such high intensities will damage the retina!!!! **So never look into a (seemingly innocent) low power laser beam.**

EXAMPLE 17.6 We next consider a 3 MW laser beam ($\lambda_0 \approx 6 \times 10^{-5}$ cm and beam width $2a \approx 1$ cm) incident on a lens of focal length of 5 cm, then

Area of the focused spot

$$A = \pi\left(\frac{\lambda_0 f}{a}\right)^2 \approx 10^{-6} \text{ cm}^2 = 10^{-10} \text{ m}^2$$

On the focal plane of the lens, the intensity will be approximately given by

$$I \approx \frac{P}{A} \approx \frac{3\times10^6\text{ W}}{10^{-10}\text{ m}^2} \approx 3 \times 10^{16} \text{ W/m}^2$$

Now, the intensity of the beam is related to the electric field amplitude E_0 through the following relation [see Eq. (22.78)

$$I = \frac{1}{2}\varepsilon_0 c E_0^2 \tag{17.34}$$

where $\varepsilon_0 \approx 8.854 \times 10^{-12}$ MKS units represents the dielectric permittivity of free space and $c \approx 3 \times 10^8$ m/s represents the speed of light in free space. Substituting $I \approx 3 \times 10^{16}$ W/m² in Eq. (17.34) we readily get

$$E_0 \approx 5 \times 10^9 \text{ V/m}$$

Such high electric fields results in the creation of spark in air (see Fig. 17.18). Thus laser beams (because of their high directionality) can be focused to extremely small regions producing very high intensities. Such high intensities lead to numerous industrial applications of the laser such as welding, hole drilling, cutting materials, etc (see e.g., Ref. 17.5). In Fig. 17.19, we have shown a focussed laser beam drilling through concrete.

In the following two examples, we will calculate the intensities (at the retina of our eye) when we directly view a 500 W bulb or the Sun **(Caution: Never look into the Sun; the retina will be damaged not only because of high intensities but also because of large ultraviolet content of the sunlight).**

Figure 17.18

Focusing of a 3 MW peak power pulsed ruby laser beam. At the focus, the electric field strengths are of the order of 10^9 V/m which results in the creation of a spark in the air. [*Photograph courtesy: Dr. R. W. Terhune*]

Figure 17.19

A focussed laser beam drilling through concrete. *Photograph courtesy: Dr. Brahma Nand Upadhyay, RRCAT, Indore.*

EXAMPLE 17.7 We consider a 6 cm diameter incandescent source (like a 500 W bulb) at a distance of about 5 m from the eye (see Fig. 17.20). We assume the pupil diameter to be about 2 mm. Thus,

Area of the pupil of the eye $\approx \pi(1 \times 1)$ mm² $\approx 3 \times 10^{-6}$ m²

$$\text{Power entering eye} \approx (500\text{ W}) \times \frac{\pi r^2}{4\pi R^2} \approx 5 \times 10^{-6}\text{ W}$$

$$\begin{aligned}\text{Radius of image} &= \text{Radius of source} \times \text{demagnification}\\ &\approx 3\text{ cm} \times \frac{2.5}{500} \approx 1.5 \times 10^{-4}\text{ m}\end{aligned}$$

where we have assumed the image to be formed at a distance of about 2.5 cm from the pupil of the eye. Thus,

The power density in image

$$= \frac{(5\times10^{-6}\ \text{W})}{\pi\times(1.5\times10^{-4})^2\ \text{m}^2} \approx 70\ \text{W/m}^2$$

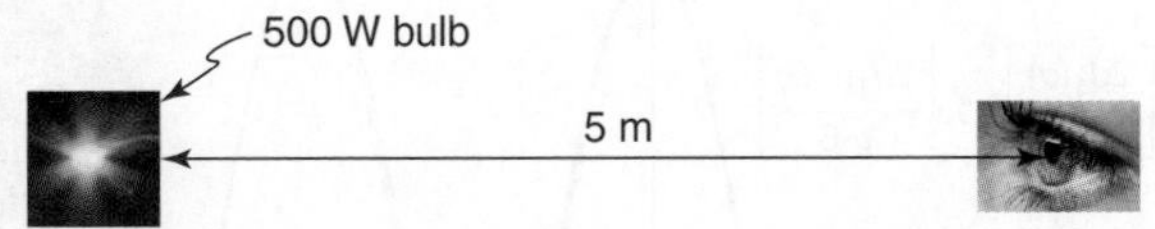

Figure 17.20
A 500 W bulb at a distance of about 5 m from the eye.

EXAMPLE 17.8 We next calculate the intensity at the retina if we are directly looking at the Sun (see Fig. 17.21). Now

The intensity of solar energy on earth ≈ 1.35 kW/m²

Thus, the energy entering the eye

$$\approx 1.35 \times 10^3 \times \pi \times 10^{-6} \approx 4\ \text{mW}$$

The Sun subtends about 0.5° on the earth. Thus,

The diameter of the image of the Sun

$$\approx 0.5 \times \frac{\pi}{180} \times 25 \approx 0.2\ \text{mm} = 2 \times 10^{-4}\ \text{m}$$

and, the power density in image

$$\approx \frac{4\times10^{-3}\ \text{W}}{\pi\times(10^{-4})^2\ \text{m}^2} \approx 100\ \text{kW/m}^2$$

To summarize, a 2 mW diffraction limited laser beam incident on the eye can produce an intensity of about 10^6 W/m² at the retina—this would certainly damage the retina. Thus, whereas it is quite safe to look at a 500 W ordinary light bulb, it is very dangerous to look directly into a 2 mW laser beam. Indeed, because a laser beam can be focused to very narrow areas, it has found important applications in areas like eye surgery, welding, etc.

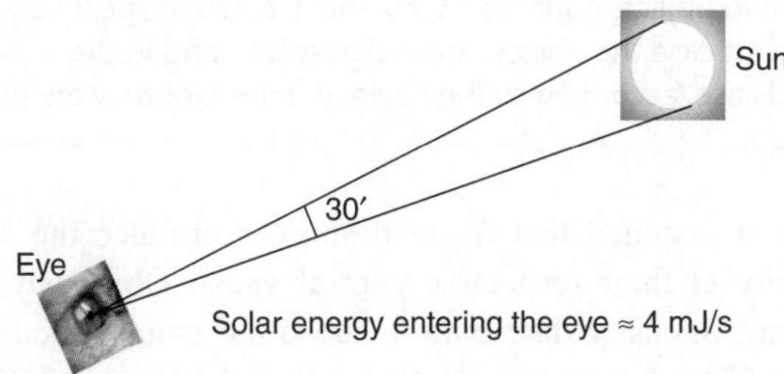

Figure 17.21
If we look directly at the sun, intensities as high as 100 kW/m² are produced; this can damage the retina of the eye!

From the above discussion it immediately follows that greater the radius of the beam, the smaller will be the size of the focused spot and hence greater will be the intensity at the focused spot. Indeed, one may use a beam expander (see Fig. 17.22) to produce a beam of greater size and hence a smaller focused spot size. However, after the focused spot, the beam would have a greater divergence and would therefore expand within a very short distance. One usually defines a *depth of focus* as the distance over which the intensity of the beam (on the axis) decreases by a certain factor of the value at the focal point. Thus, a small focused spot would lead to a small depth of focus. We may mention here that the intensity distribution at the focal plane of the lens is given by Eq. (17.19) where the parameter v is given by Eq. (17.21). On the other hand, the intensity along the axis is given by

$$I = I_0\left[\frac{\sin(w/4)}{w/4}\right]^2 \qquad \textbf{(17.35)}$$

where
$$w = \frac{2\pi}{\lambda}\left(\frac{a}{f}\right)^2 z \qquad \textbf{(17.36)}$$

and $z = 0$ represents the focal plane; the derivation of Eq. (17.35) has been given at many places—see, e.g., Sec. 5.5 of Ref. 17.6.

It can be readily seen that the intensity would drop by about 20% at

$$z \approx \pm 0.5\lambda\,(f/a)^2 \qquad \textbf{(17.37)}$$

which is usually referred to as the depth of the focus or focal tolerance. Notice that larger the value of a, smaller will be the focal tolerance. For $\lambda \approx 6 \times 10^{-5}$ cm, $f \approx 10$ cm and $a \approx 1$ cm, the focal tolerance is about 3×10^{-3} cm.

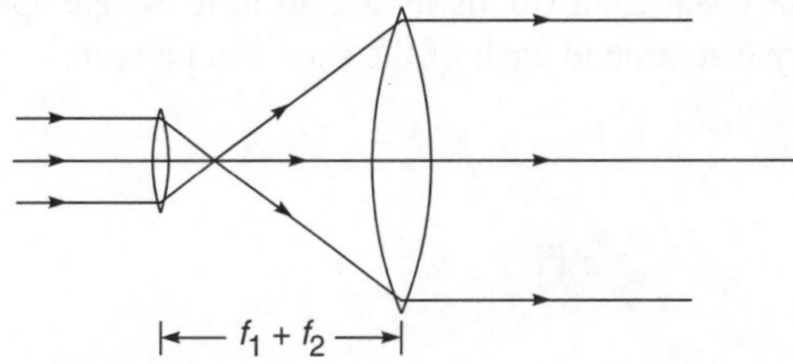

Figure 17.22
Two convex lenses separated by a distance equal to the sum of their focal lengths act like a beam expander.

17.5 Limit of Resolution

LO5

Consider two point sources, such as stars (so that we can consider plane waves entering the aperture) being focused by a telescope objective of diameter D (see Fig. 17.23). As discussed in the previous section, the system can be thought of as being equivalent to a circular aperture of diameter D, followed by a converging lens of focal length f, as shown in Fig. 17.8. As such, each point source will produce its Airy pattern as schematically shown in Fig. 17.23. The diameters of the Airy rings will be determined by the diameter of the objective, its focal length and the wavelength of light (see Example 17.3).

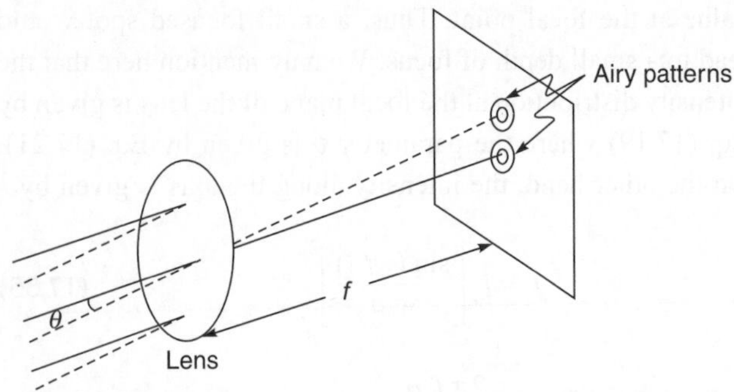

Figure 17.23
The image of two distant objects on the focal plane of a convex lens. If the diffraction patterns are well separated, they are said to be resolved.

In Fig. 17.23 the Airy patterns are shown to be quite far away from each other and, therefore, the two objects are said to be well resolved. Since the radius of the first ring is $1.22\, \lambda f/D$ the Airy patterns will overlap more for smaller values of D and hence for better resolution one requires a larger diameter of the objective. It is for this reason that a telescope is usually characterized by the diameter of the objective; for example, a 40 inch telescope implies that the diameter of the objective is 40″. In Fig. 17.24 we have shown the image of the binary star Zeta Bootis by a 2.56 m telescope aperture; the Airy disc around each of the stars can be seen.

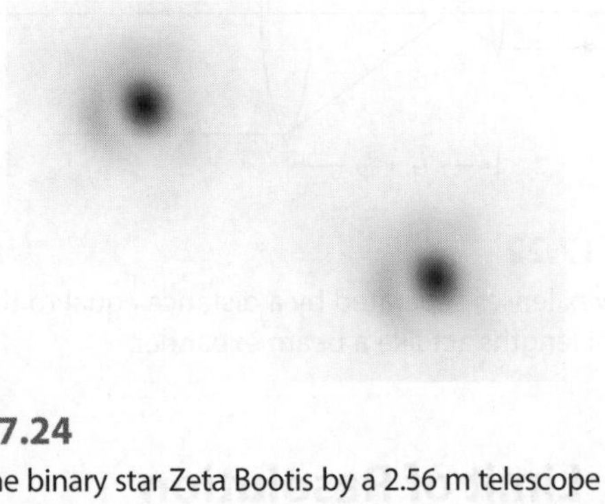

Figure 17.24
Image of the binary star Zeta Bootis by a 2.56 m telescope aperture; the Airy disc around each of the stars can be seen. The photograph is by Dr. Bob Tubbs; used with permission from Dr. Tubbs.

In Figs. 17.25 and 17.26, we have plotted the independent intensity distributions and their resultant produced by two distant objects for various angular separations; in each case

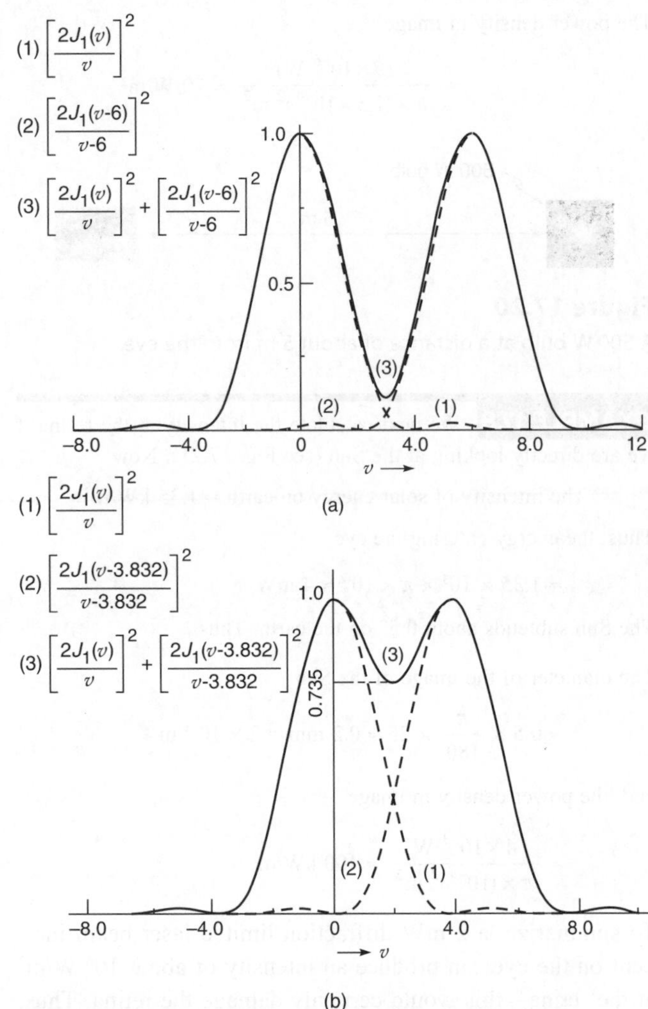

Figure 17.25
The dashed curves correspond to the intensity distribution produced by two point sources (producing the same intensity at the central spot) independently; the solid curves represent the resultant. (a) and (b) correspond to the angular separation of the two objects equal to $6\lambda/\pi D$ and $1.22\lambda/D$, respectively. In the first case the objects are well resolved and in the second case (according to the Rayleigh criterion) they are just resolved.

we have assumed that the two sources produce the same intensity at their respective central spots. Obviously, the resultant intensity distributions are quite complicated (see Fig. 17.27); what we have plotted in Figs. 17.25 and 17.26 are the intensity distributions on the line joining the two centers of the Airy patterns; we should mention here that since the point sources are independent sources, their intensity distributions (Airy patterns) will add. If we choose this line as x-axis then the parameter v in Figs. 17.25 and 17.26 is given by

$$v = \frac{2\pi a}{\lambda f} x \tag{17.38}$$

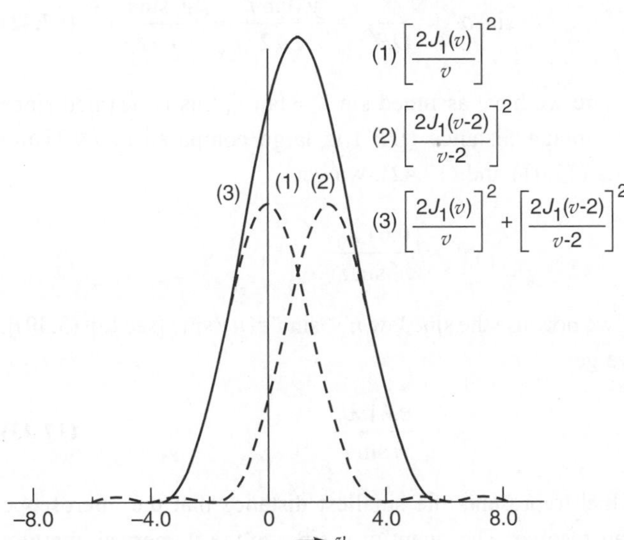

Figure 17.26
The dashed curves correspond to the intensity distribution produced independently by two distant point objects having an angular separation of $2\lambda/\pi D$. The resultant intensity distribution (shown as a solid curve) has only one peak and hence the objects are unresolved.

Now, the intensity distributions given in Fig. 17.25(a) correspond to two distant point objects having an angular separation of $6\lambda/\pi D$ and as can be seen the two images are clearly resolved. Figure 17.26 corresponds to

$$\Delta\theta \simeq \frac{2}{\pi}\frac{\lambda}{D} \tag{17.39}$$

and as can be seen, the resultant intensity distribution has only one peak and therefore the two points cannot be resolved at all. Finally, if the angular separation of the two objects is $1.22\,\lambda/D$ then the central spot of the one pattern falls on the first minimum of the second and the objects are said to be just resolved. This criterion of limit of resolution is called the Rayleigh criterion of resolution and the intensity distribution corresponding to this is plotted in Fig. 17.25(b). The actual diffraction patterns are shown in Fig. 17.27.

In order to get a numerical appreciation of the above results we consider a telescope objective whose diameter and focal length are 5 cm and 30 cm, respectively. Assuming the light wavelength to be 6×10^{-5} cm, one finds that the minimum angular separation of two distant objects which can just be resolved will be

$$\frac{1.22\lambda}{D} = \frac{1.22 \times 6 \times 10^{-5}}{5} \simeq 1.5 \times 10^{-5} \text{ radians}$$

Further, the radius of the first dark ring (of the Airy pattern) will be

$$\frac{1.22\lambda}{D} \times \text{focal length} = \frac{1.22 \times 6 \times 10^{-5}}{5} \times 30$$

$$\simeq 4.5 \times 10^{-4} \text{ cm}$$

It is immediately obvious that the larger the diameter of the objective, the better will be its resolving power. For example, the diameter of the largest telescope objective is about 80″ and the corresponding angular separation of the objects that it can resolve is $\simeq$0.07 sec of arc. This very low limit of resolution is never achieved in ground based telescopes due to the turbulence of the atmosphere. However, a larger aperture still provides a larger light gathering power and hence the ability to see deeper in space.

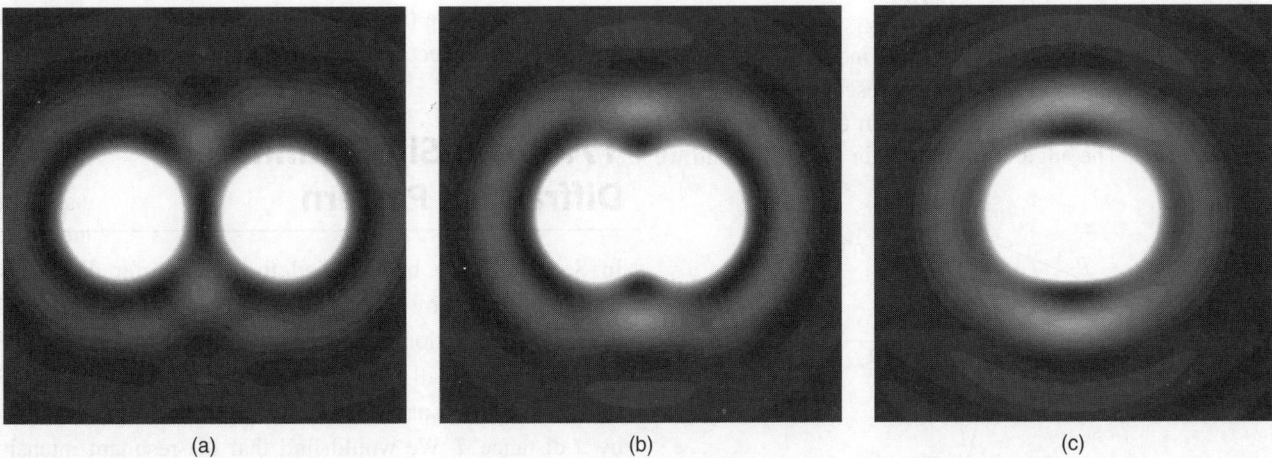

Figure 17.27
Computer generated intensity distributions corresponding to two point sources when they are: (a) well resolved, (b) just resolved, and (c) unresolved.

It is of interest to note that if we assume that the angular resolution of the human eye is primarily due to diffraction effects then it will be given by

$$\Delta\theta \sim \frac{\lambda}{D} \approx \frac{6\times10^{-5}}{2\times10^{-1}} = 3 \times 10^{-4} \text{ rad.} \qquad \textbf{(17.40)}$$

where we have assumed the pupil diameter to be 2 mm. Thus, at a distance of 20 m, the eye should be able to resolve two points which are separated by a distance

$$3 \times 10^{-4} \times 20 = 6 \times 10^{-3} \text{ m} = 6 \text{ mm}$$

One can indeed verify that this result is qualitatively valid by finding the distance at which the millimetre scale will become blurred.

In the above discussion, we have assumed that the two object points produce identical (but displaced) Airy patterns. If that is not the case then the two central maxima will have different intensities; accordingly one has to set up a modified criterion for the limit of resolution such that the two maxima stand out.

17.5.1 Resolving Power of a Microscope

We next consider the resolving power of a microscope objective of diameter D as shown in Fig. 17.28. Let P and Q represent two closely spaced self-luminous point objects which are to be viewed through the microscope. Assuming the absence of any geometrical aberrations, rays emanating from the points P and Q will produce spherical wavefronts (after refraction through the lens) which will form Airy patterns around their paraxial image points P' and Q'. For the points P and Q to be just resolved, the point Q' should lie on the first dark ring surrounding the point P' and, therefore, we must have

$$\sin\alpha' \approx \frac{1.22\,\lambda}{D} = \frac{1.22\,\lambda_0}{n'D} \qquad \textbf{(17.41)}$$

where n and n' represent the refractive indices of the object and image spaces, λ_0 and $\lambda(=\lambda_0/n')$ represent the wave-length of light in free space and in the medium of refractive index n' respectively. The angle α' is defined in Fig. 17.28 and we have

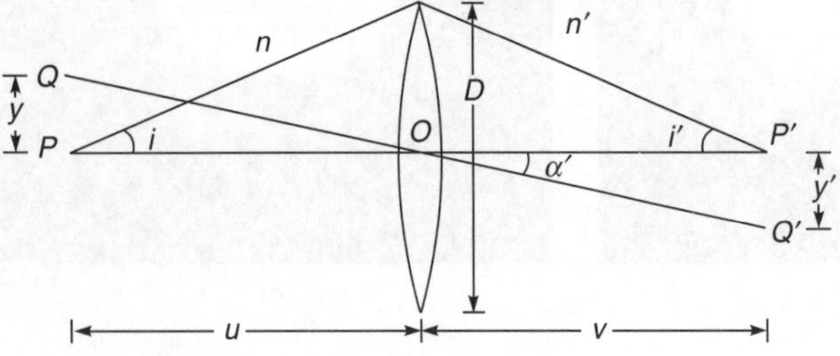

Figure 17.28
The resolving power of a microscope objective.

$$\sin\alpha' \approx \frac{y'}{OP'} = \frac{y'\tan i'}{D/2} \approx \frac{y'\sin i'}{D/2} \qquad \textbf{(17.42)}$$

where we have assumed $\sin i' \approx \tan i'$, this is justified since the image distance (OP') is large compared to D. Using Eqs. (17.41) and (17.42), we get

$$y' \approx \frac{0.61\,\lambda_0}{n'\sin i'}$$

If we now use the sine law $n'y'\sin i' = ny\sin i$ [see Eq. (3.39)], we get

$$y \approx \frac{0.61\,\lambda_0}{n\sin i} \qquad \textbf{(17.43)}$$

which represents the smallest distance that the microscope can resolve. The quantity $n \sin i$ is the numerical aperture of the optical system and the resolving power increases with increase in the numerical aperture. It is for this reason that in some microscopes the space between the object and the objective is filled with an oil—and they are referred to as 'oil immersion objectives'. Equation (17.43) also tells us that the resolving power increases with decrease in λ. As such, one often uses blue light (or even ultraviolet light) for the illumination of the object. For example, in an electron microscope the de Broglie wavelength of electrons accelerated to 100 keV is about 0.03×10^{-8} cm and therefore such a microscope has a very high resolving power.

In the above analysis, we have assumed that the two object points are self-luminous so that the intensities can be added up. However, in actual practice, the objects are illuminated by the same source and, therefore, in general, there is some phase relationship between the waves emanating from the two object points; for such a case the intensities will not be strictly additive (see Sec. 13.6), nevertheless Eq. (17.43) will give the correct order for the limit of resolution.

17.6 Two-Slit Fraunhofer Diffraction Pattern

LO6

In Sec. 17.3, we had studied the Fraunhofer diffraction pattern produced by a slit of width b and had found that the intensity distribution consisted of maxima and minima. In this section, we will study the Fraunhofer diffraction pattern produced by two parallel slits (each of width b) separated by a distance d. We would find that the resultant intensity distribution is a product of the single-slit diffraction pattern and the interference pattern produced by two point sources separated by a distance d.

In order to calculate the diffraction pattern we use a method similar to that used for the case of a single slit and assume that the slits consist of a large number of equally spaced point sources and that each point on the slit is a source of Huygens' secondary wavelets. Let the point sources be at $A_1, A_2, A_3, \ldots$ (in the first slit) and at $B_1, B_2, B_3, \ldots$ (in the second slit) [see Fig. 17.29]. As before, we assume that the distance between two consecutive points in either of the slits is Δ. If the diffracted rays make an angle θ with the normal to the plane of the slits, then the path difference between the disturbances reaching the point P from two consecutive points in a slit will be $\Delta \sin \theta$. The field produced by the first slit at the point P will, therefore, be given by [see Eq. (17.9)]

$$E_1 = A \frac{\sin \beta}{\beta} \cos(\omega t - \beta)$$

Similarly, the second slit will produce a field

$$E_2 = A \frac{\sin \beta}{\beta} \cos(\omega t - \beta - \Phi_1)$$

at the point P, where

$$\Phi_1 = \frac{2\pi}{\lambda} d \sin \theta$$

represents the phase difference between the disturbances (reaching the point P) from two corresponding points on the slits; by corresponding points we imply pairs of points like $(A_1, B_1), (A_2, B_2), \ldots$ which are separated by a distance d. Hence the resultant field will be

$$E = E_1 + E_2 = A \frac{\sin \beta}{\beta} [\cos(\omega t - \beta) + \cos(\omega t - \beta - \Phi_1)]$$

which represents the interference of two waves, each of amplitude $A \frac{\sin \beta}{\beta}$ and differing in phase by Φ_1. The above equation can be rewritten in the form

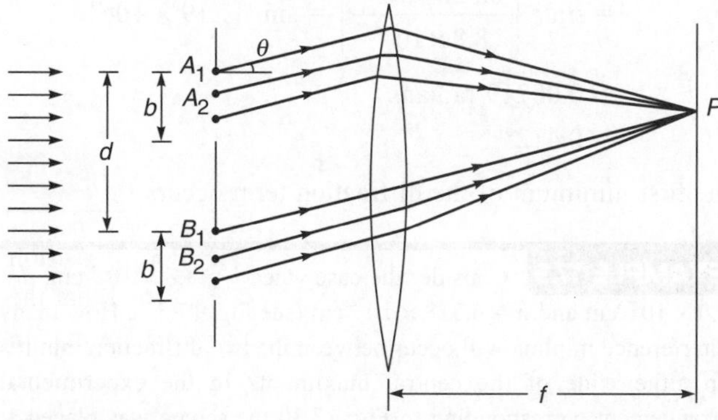

Figure 17.29

Fraunhofer diffraction of a plane wave incident normally on a double slit.

$$E = A \frac{\sin \beta}{\beta} \cos \gamma \cos\left(\omega t - \frac{1}{2}\beta - \frac{1}{2}\Phi_1\right)$$

$$\text{where } \gamma = \frac{\Phi_1}{2} = \frac{\pi}{\lambda} d \sin \theta \qquad \textbf{(17.44)}$$

The intensity distribution will be of the form

$$I = 4I_0 \frac{\sin^2 \beta}{\beta^2} \cos^2 \gamma \qquad \textbf{(17.45)}$$

where $I_0 \sin^2 \beta/\beta^2$ represents the intensity distribution produced by one of the slits. As can be seen, the intensity distribution is a product of two terms; the first term $(\sin^2 \beta/\beta^2)$ represents the diffraction pattern produced by a single slit of width b and the second term $(\cos^2 \gamma)$ represents the interference pattern produced by two point sources separated by a distance d. Indeed, if the slit widths are very small (so that there is almost no variation of the $\sin^2 \beta/\beta^2$ term with θ) then one simply obtains the Young's interference pattern (see Sec. 13.6).

In Fig. 17.30, we have shown the two slit diffraction patterns corresponding to $d = 0, 0.0176, 0.035$ and 0.070 cm with $b = 0.0088$ cm and $\lambda = 6.328 \times 10^{-5}$ cm. The intensity distribution as predicted by Eq. (17.45) is shown in Fig. 17.31.

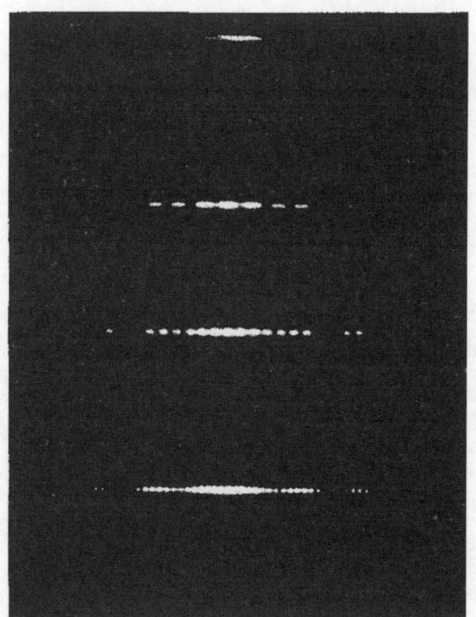

Figure 17.30

The double-slit Fraunhofer diffraction pattern corresponding to $b = 0.0088$ cm and $\lambda = 6.328 \times 10^{-5}$ cm. The values of d are 0, 0.0176, 0.035 and 0.070 cm respectively [Adapted from Ref. 17.17; used with permission].

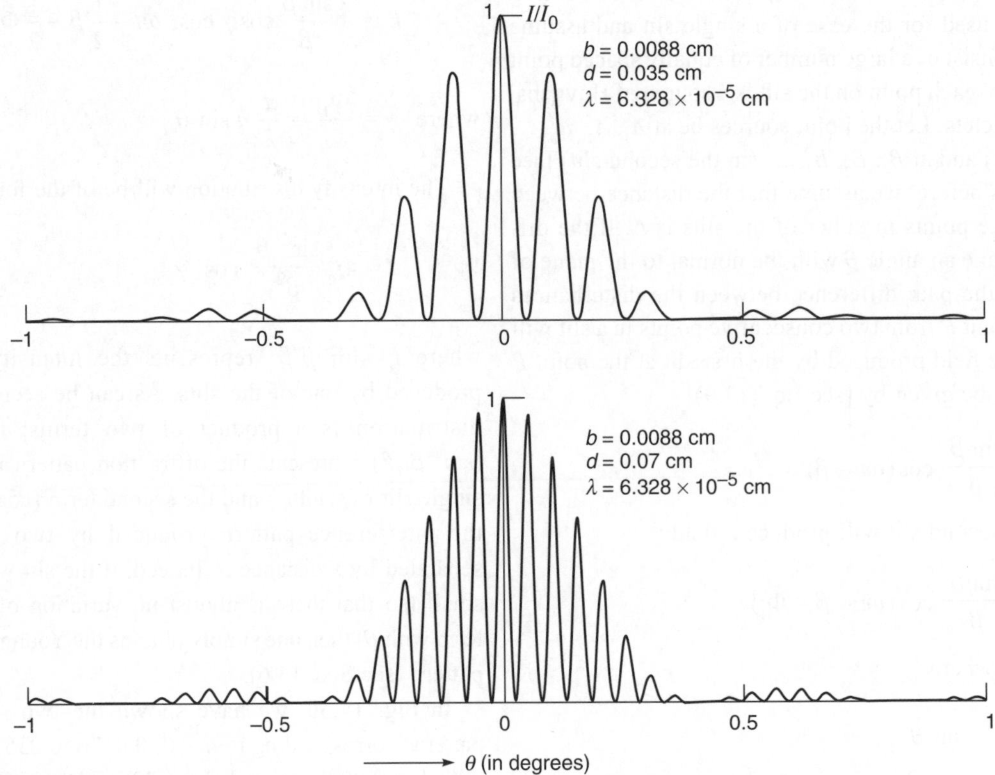

Figure 17.31
The double-slit intensity distribution as predicted by Eq. (17.45) corresponding to $d = 0.035$ and 0.070 cm, respectively ($b = 0.0088$ cm and $\lambda = 6.328 \times 10^{-5}$ cm).

17.6.1 Positions of Maxima and Minima

Equation (17.45) tells us that the intensity is zero wherever

$$\beta = \pi, 2\pi, 3\pi, \ldots$$

or when

$$\gamma = \frac{\pi}{2}, \frac{3\pi}{2}, \frac{5\pi}{2}, \ldots$$

The corresponding angles of diffraction will be given by the following equation:

$$\left.\begin{aligned} & b \sin\theta = m\lambda; && (m = 1, 2, 3, \ldots) \\ \text{and} \quad & d \sin\theta = \left(n + \frac{1}{2}\right)\lambda; && (n = 1, 2, 3, \ldots) \end{aligned}\right\} \quad \textbf{(17.46)}$$

The interference maxima occur when

$$\gamma = 0, \pi, 2\pi, \ldots$$

or when,

$$d \sin\theta = 0, \lambda, 2\lambda, 3\lambda, \ldots \quad \textbf{(17.47)}$$

The actual positions of the maxima will approximately occur at the above angles provided the variation of the diffraction term is not too rapid. Further, a maximum may not occur at all if θ corresponds to a diffraction minimum, i.e., if $b \sin\theta = \lambda, 2\lambda, 3\lambda, \ldots$ These are usually referred to as missing orders. For example, in Fig. 17.31 we can see that for $b = 0.0088$ cm, the interference maxima are extremely weak around $\theta \simeq 0.41°$; this is because of the fact that at

$$\theta = \sin^{-1}\left(\frac{\lambda}{b}\right)$$

$$= \sin^{-1}\left[\frac{6.328\times10^{-5}}{8.8\times10^{-3}}\right] = \sin^{-1}[7.19 \times 10^{-3}]$$

$$\simeq 0.00719 \text{ radians}$$

$$\simeq 0.412°$$

the first minimum of the diffraction term occurs.

EXAMPLE 17.9 Consider the case when $b = 8.8 \times 10^{-3}$ cm, $d = 7.0 \times 10^{-2}$ cm and $\lambda = 6.328 \times 10^{-5}$ cm (see Fig. 17.31). How many interference minima will occur between the two diffraction minima on either side of the central maximum? In the experimental arrangement corresponding to Fig. 17.30 the screen was placed at a distance of 15′. Calculate the fringe width.

Solution: The interference minima will occur when Eq. (17.46) is satisfied, i.e., when

$$\sin\theta = \left(n+\frac{1}{2}\right)\frac{\lambda}{d} = 0.904 \times 10^{-3}\left(n+\frac{1}{2}\right);$$
$$n = 0, 1, 2, \ldots$$
$$= 0.452 \times 10^{-3}, 1.356 \times 10^{-3}, 2.260 \times 10^{-3}, 3.164 \times 10^{-3}, 4.068 \times 10^{-3}, 4.972 \times 10^{-3}, 5.876 \times 10^{-3}, 6.780 \times 10^{-3}$$

Thus, there will be sixteen minima between the two first order diffraction minima.

The angular separation between two interference maxima is approximately given by (see Eq. 17.47)

$$\Delta\theta \simeq \frac{\lambda}{d} = 0.904 \times 10^{-4}$$

Thus, the fringe width will be

$$15 \times 12 \times 2.54 \times 0.904 \times 10^{-4} \simeq 0.0413 \text{ cm}$$

17.7 N-Slit Fraunhofer Diffraction Pattern

LO6

We next consider the diffraction pattern produced by N parallel slits, each of width b; the distance between two consecutive slits is assumed to be d.

As before, we assume that each slit consists of n equally spaced point sources with spacing Δ (see Fig. 17.32). Thus, the field at an arbitrary point P will essentially be a sum of N terms:

$$E = A\frac{\sin\beta}{\beta}\cos(\omega t - \beta) + A\frac{\sin\beta}{\beta}\cos(\omega t - \beta - \Phi_1)$$
$$+\ldots+ A\frac{\sin\beta}{\beta}\cos(\omega t - \beta - (N-1)\Phi_1) \quad (17.48)$$

where the first term represents the amplitude produced by the first slit, the second term by the second slit, etc., and the various symbols have the same meaning as in Sec. 17.5. Rewriting Eq. (17.48) we get

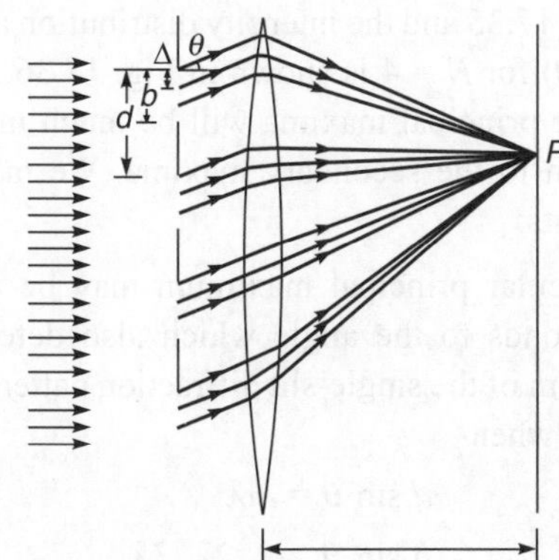

Figure 17.32

Fraunhofer diffraction of a plane wave incident normally on a multiple slit.

$$E = \frac{A\sin\beta}{\beta}\,[\cos(\omega t - \beta) + \cos(\omega t - \beta + \Phi_1) +\ldots+ \cos(\omega t - \beta - (N-1)\Phi_1)]$$
$$= \frac{A\sin\beta}{\beta}\frac{\sin N\gamma}{\sin\gamma}\cos\left[\omega t - \beta - \frac{1}{2}(N-1)\Phi_1\right] \quad (17.49)$$

where $\gamma = \dfrac{\Phi_1}{2} = \dfrac{\pi}{\lambda}d\sin\theta$

The corresponding intensity distribution will be

$$I = I_0\frac{\sin^2\beta}{\beta^2}\frac{\sin^2 N\gamma}{\sin^2\gamma} \quad (17.50)$$

where $I_0 \sin^2\beta/\beta^2$ represents the intensity distribution produced by a single slit. As can be seen, the intensity distribution is a product of two terms; the first term $\left(\frac{\sin^2\beta}{\beta^2}\right)$ represents the diffraction pattern produced by a single slit and the second term $\left(\frac{\sin^2 N\gamma}{\sin^2\gamma}\right)$ represents the interference pattern produced by N equally spaced point sources. For $N = 1$, Eq. (17.50) reduces to the single-slit diffraction pattern [see Eq. (17.10)] and for $N = 2$, to the double slit diffraction pattern [see Eq. (17.45)]. In Figs. 17.33 and 17.34, we have given a plot of the function

$$\frac{\sin^2 N\gamma}{\sin^2\gamma}$$

as a function of γ for $N = 5$ and $N = 12$. One can immediately see that as the value of N becomes very large, the above function would become very sharply peaked at $\gamma = 0, \pi, 2\pi, \ldots$ Between the two peaks, the function vanishes when

$$\gamma = \frac{p\pi}{N}; \quad p = \pm 1, \pm 2, \ldots \quad \text{but} \quad p \neq 0, \pm N, \pm 2N$$

which are referred to as secondary minima.

17.7.1 Positions of Maxima and Minima

When the value of N is very large, one obtains intense maxima at $\gamma \simeq m\pi$, i.e., when

$$d\sin\theta = m\lambda \quad (m = 0, 1, 2, \ldots) \quad (17.51)$$

This can be easily seen by noting that

$$\underset{\gamma\to m\pi}{Lt}\frac{\sin N\gamma}{\sin\gamma} = \underset{\gamma\to m\pi}{Lt}\frac{N\cos N\gamma}{\cos\gamma} = \pm N;$$

thus, the resultant amplitude and the corresponding intensity distributions are given by

$$E = N\frac{A\sin\beta}{\beta} \quad (17.52)$$

and

$$I = N^2 I_0\frac{\sin^2\beta}{\beta^2} \quad (17.53)$$

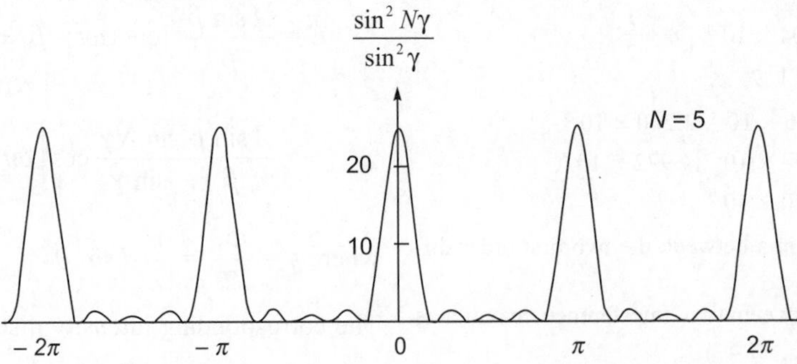

Figure 17.33
The variation of the function $\sin^2(N\gamma)/\sin^2\gamma$ with γ for $N = 5$.

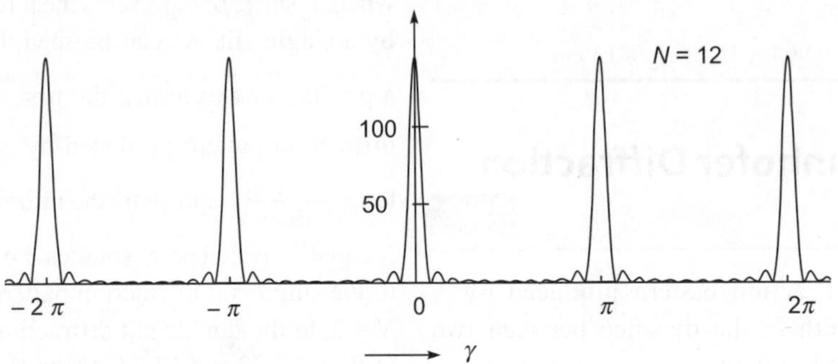

Figure 17.34
The variation of the function $\sin^2(N\gamma)/\sin^2\gamma$ with γ for $N = 12$. As N becomes larger, the function would become more and more sharply peaked at $\gamma = 0, \pm\pi, \pm 2\pi, \pm 3\pi, \ldots$.

where
$$\beta = \frac{\pi b \sin\theta}{\lambda} = \frac{\pi b}{\lambda}\frac{m\lambda}{d} = \frac{\pi b m}{d} \qquad (17.54)$$

Such maxima are known as **principal maxima**. Physically, at these maxima the fields produced by each of the slits are in phase and, therefore, they add up and the resultant field is N times the field produced by each of the slits; consequently, the intensity has a large value unless $\frac{\sin^2\beta}{\beta^2}$ itself is very small. Since $|\sin\theta| \le 1$, m cannot be greater than d/λ [see Eq. (17.51)]; thus, there will only be a finite number of principal maxima.

From Eq. (17.50) it can easily be seen that the intensity is zero when either

$$b \sin\theta = n\lambda,\ n = 1, 2, 3, \ldots \qquad (17.55)$$

or

$$N\gamma = p\pi,\ p \ne N, 2N, \ldots \qquad (17.56)$$

Equation (17.55) gives us the minima corresponding to the single slit diffraction pattern. The angles of diffraction corresponding to Eq. (17.56) are

$$d\sin\theta = \frac{\lambda}{N}, \frac{2\lambda}{N}, \ldots, \frac{(N-1)\lambda}{N}, \frac{(N+1)\lambda}{N}, \frac{(N+2)\lambda}{N},$$

$$\ldots, \frac{(2N-1)\lambda}{N}, \frac{(2N+1)\lambda}{N}, \frac{(2N+2)\lambda}{N}, \ldots \qquad (17.57)$$

Thus, between two principal maxima we have $(N-1)$ minima. Between two such consecutive minima the intensity has to have a maximum; these maxima are known as secondary maxima. Typical diffraction patterns for $N = 1, 2, 3$, and 4 are shown in Fig. 17.35 and the intensity distribution as predicted by Eq. (17.50) for $N = 4$ is shown in Fig. 17.36. When N is very large the principal maxima will be much more intense in comparison to the secondary maxima. We may mention here two points:

(a) A particular principal maximum may be absent if it corresponds to the angle which also determines the minimum of the single-slit diffraction pattern. This will happen when

$$d\sin\theta = m\lambda \qquad (17.58)$$

and

$$b\sin\theta = \lambda, 2\lambda, 3\lambda, \ldots \qquad (17.59)$$

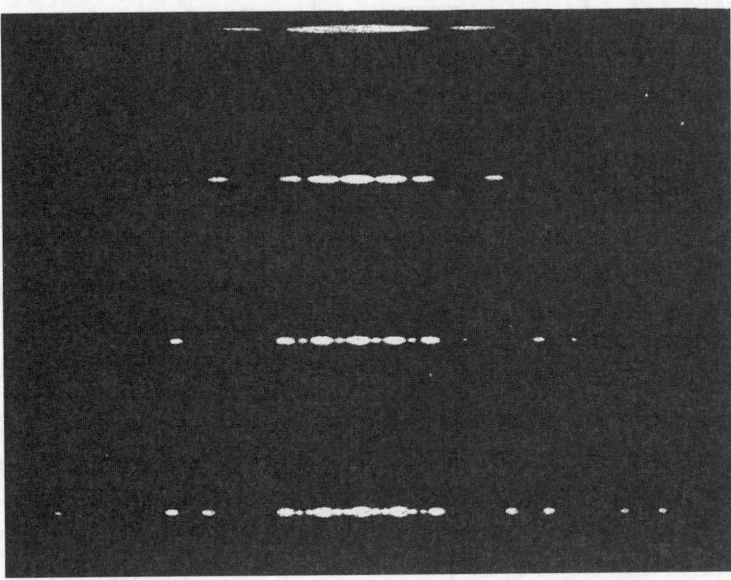

Figure 17.35
The multiple-slit Fraunhofer diffraction patterns corresponding to $b = 0.0044$ cm, $d = 0.0132$ cm and $\lambda = 6.328 \times 10^{-5}$ cm. The number of slits are 1, 2, 3 and 4 respectively (Adapted from Ref. 17.17; used with permission).

are satisfied simultaneously and is usually referred to as a missing order. Even when Eq. (17.59) does not hold exactly (i.e., if $b \sin \theta$ is close to an integral multiple of λ), the intensity of the corresponding principal maximum will be very weak (see, for example, Fig. 17.36 around $\theta \approx 0.8°$).

(b) In addition to the minima predicted by Eq. (17.56), we will also have the diffraction minima (see Eq. 17.55); however, when N is very large, the number of such minima will be very small.

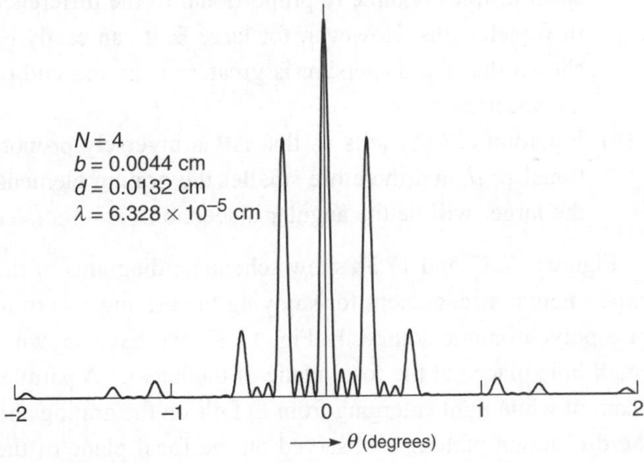

Figure 17.36
The intensity distribution corresponding to the four-slit Fraunhofer diffraction pattern as predicted by Eq. (17.50) corresponding to $b = 0.0044$ cm, $d = 0.0132$ cm and $\lambda = 6.328 \times 10^{-5}$ cm. The principle maxima occur at $\theta \approx 0.275°$, 0.55°, 0.82°, 1.1°, ... Notice the (almost) absent third order.

17.7.2 Width of the Principal Maxima

We have shown above that in the diffraction pattern produced by N slits, the mth order principal maximum occurs at

$$d \sin \theta_m = m\lambda,\ m = 0, 1, 2, \ldots \tag{17.60}$$

Further, the minima occur at the angles given by Eq. (17.57). If $\theta_m + \Delta\theta_{1m}$ and $\theta_m - \Delta\theta_{2m}$ represent the angles of diffraction corresponding to the first minimum on either side of the principal maximum, then $\frac{1}{2}(\Delta\theta_{1m} + \Delta\theta_{2m})$ is known as the **angular half width of the mth order principal maximum.** For a large value of N, $\Delta\theta_{1m} \simeq \Delta\theta_{2m}$ which we write as $\Delta\theta_m$. Clearly,

$$d \sin (\theta_m \pm \Delta\theta_m) = m\lambda \pm \frac{\lambda}{N} \tag{17.61}$$

But $$\sin(\theta_m \pm \Delta\theta_m) = \sin\theta_m \cos\Delta\theta_m \pm \cos\theta_m \sin\Delta\theta_m$$

$$\simeq \sin\theta_m \pm \Delta\theta_m \cos\theta_m \tag{17.62}$$

Thus Eq. (17.61) gives us

$$\Delta\theta_m \simeq \frac{\lambda}{Nd \cos\theta_m} \tag{17.63}$$

which shows that the principal maximum becomes sharper as N increases.

17.8 The Diffraction Grating

LO7

In Sec. 17.6, we have discussed the diffraction pattern produced by a system of parallel equidistant slits. An arrangement which essentially consists of a large number of equidistant slits is known as a **diffraction grating**; the corresponding diffraction pattern is known as the grating spectrum. Since the exact positions of the principal maxima in the diffraction pattern depend on the wavelength, the principal maxima corresponding to different spectral lines (associated with a source) will correspond to different angles of diffraction. Thus the grating spectrum provides us with an easily obtainable experimental set up for determination of wavelengths. From Eq. (17.63) we see that for narrow principal maxima (i.e., sharper spectral lines), a large value of N is required. A good quality grating, therefore, requires a large number of slits (typically about 15,000 per inch). This is achieved by ruling grooves with a diamond point on an optically transparent sheet of material; the grooves act as opaque spaces. After each groove is ruled, the machine lifts the diamond point and moves the sheet forward for the ruling of the next groove. Since the distance between two consecutive grooves is extremely small, the movement of the sheet is obtained with the help of the rotation of a screw which drives the carriage carrying it. Further, one of the important requirements of a good quality grating is that the lines should be as equally spaced as possible; consequently, the pitch of the screw must be constant, and it was not until the manufacture of a nearly perfect screw (which was achieved by Rowland in 1882) that the problem of construction of gratings was successfully solved. Rowland's arrangement gave 14,438 lines per inch, corresponding to $d = 2.54/14438 = 1.759 \times 10^{-4}$ cm. For such a grating, for $\lambda = 6 \times 10^{-5}$ cm, the maximum value of m would be 2, and, therefore, only the first two orders of the spectrum will be observed. However, for $\lambda = 5 \times 10^{-5}$ cm, the third order spectrum will also be visible.

Commercial gratings are produced by taking the cast of an actual grating on a transparent film like that of cellulose acetate. An appropriate strength solution of cellulose acetate is poured on the ruled surface and allowed to dry to form a strong thin film, detachable from the parent grating. These impressions of a grating are preserved by mounting the film between two glass sheets. Nowadays, gratings are also produced holographically, where one records the interference pattern between two plane or spherical waves (see Example 13.5). In contrast to ruled gratings, holographic gratings have a much larger number of lines/cm.

17.8.1 The Grating Spectrum

In Sec. 17.6, we have shown that the positions of the principal maxima are given by

$$d \sin \theta = m\lambda; \quad m = 0, 1, 2, \ldots \tag{17.64}$$

This relation, which is also called the **grating equation**, can be used to study the dependence of the angle of diffraction θ on the wavelength λ. The zeroeth order principal maximum occurs at $\theta = 0$ irrespective of the wavelength. Thus, if we are using a polychromatic source (e.g., white light) then the central maximum will be of the same colour as the source itself. However, for $m \neq 0$, the angles of diffraction are different for different wavelengths and, therefore, various spectral components appear at different positions. Thus, by measuring the angles of diffraction for various colors one can (knowing the value of m) determine the values of the wavelengths. It may be mentioned that the intensity is maximum for the zeroeth order spectrum (where no dispersion occurs) and it falls off as the value of m increases.

If we differentiate Eq. (17.64), we would obtain

$$\frac{\Delta\theta}{\Delta\lambda} = \frac{m}{d \cos \theta} \tag{17.65}$$

From this result we can deduce the following conclusions:

(a) Assuming θ to be very small (i.e., $\cos \theta \simeq 1$) we can see that the angle $\Delta\theta$ is directly proportional to the order of spectrum (m) for a given $\Delta\lambda$, so that for a given m, $\Delta\theta/\Delta\lambda$ is a constant. Such a spectrum is known as a **normal spectrum** and in this the difference in angle for two spectral lines is directly proportional to the difference in wavelengths. However, for large θ, it can easily be shown that the dispersion is greater at the red end of the spectrum.

(b) Equation (17.65) tells us that $\Delta\theta$ is inversely proportional to d, and therefore smaller the grating element, the larger will be the angular dispersion.

Figures 17.37 and 17.38 show schematic diagrams of the experimental arrangement for studying the grating spectrum of a polychromatic source. In Fig. 17.37, we have shown a small hole placed at the focal plane of the lens L_1. A parallel beam of white light emerging from L_1 falls on the grating and the diffraction pattern is observed on the focal plane of the lens L_2. If instead of a hole we have a slit at the focal plane of L_1 (see Fig. 17.38) — as it is indeed the case in a typical laboratory set up — we would have parallel beams propagating in different directions, and in the focal plane of the lens L_2 we will have a band spectrum as shown in Fig. 17.38.

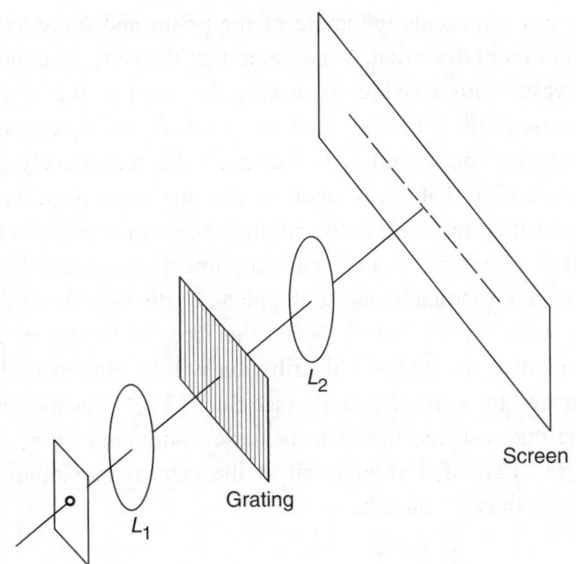

Figure 17.37
Fraunhofer diffraction of a plane wave incident normally on a grating.

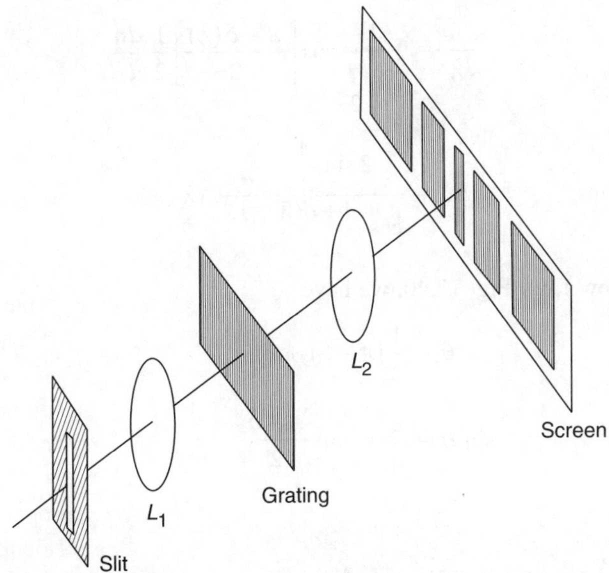

Figure 17.38
If instead of a point source we have a slit in the focal plane of L_1 then one will obtain bands on the focal plane of L_2.

The lens L_2 is the objective of a telescope and the diffraction pattern is viewed through an eyepiece. The angles of diffraction for various orders of the grating spectrum can be measured and knowing the value of d, one can calculate the wavelength of different spectral lines.

EXAMPLE 17.10 Consider a diffraction grating with 15,000 lines per inch. **(a)** Show that if we use a white light source the second and third order spectra overlap. **(b)** What will be the angular separation of the D_1 and D_2 lines of sodium in the second order spectra?

Solution: (a) The grating element is

$$d = \frac{2.54}{15000} = 1.69 \times 10^{-4} \text{ cm}$$

Let θ_{mv} and θ_{mr} represent the angles of diffraction for the mth order spectrum corresponding to the violet and red colors, respectively. Thus,

$$\theta_{2v} = \sin^{-1}\frac{2\times 4\times 10^{-5}}{1.69\times 10^{-4}} \simeq \sin^{-1} 0.473 \simeq 28.2°$$

$$\theta_{2r} = \sin^{-1}\frac{2\times 7\times 10^{-5}}{1.69\times 10^{-4}} \simeq \sin^{-1} 0.828 \simeq 55.90°$$

and

$$\theta_{3v} = \sin^{-1}\frac{3\times 4\times 10^{-5}}{1.69\times 10^{-4}} \simeq \sin^{-1} 0.710 \simeq 45.23°$$

where we have assumed the wavelengths of the violet and red colours to be 4×10^{-5} cm, and 7×10^{-5} cm, respectively. Since $\theta_{2r} > \theta_{3v}$, the second and third order spectra will overlap. Further since $\sin\theta_{3r} > 1$, the third order spectrum for the red colour will not be observed.

(b) Since $d \sin\theta = m\lambda$, we have for small $\Delta\lambda$:

$$(d \cos\theta)\, \Delta\theta = m(\Delta\lambda)$$

or $$\Delta\theta = \frac{m\Delta\lambda}{d\left\{1-\left(\frac{m\lambda}{d}\right)^2\right\}^{1/2}}$$

$$\simeq \frac{2\times 6\times 10^{-8}}{1.69\times 10^{-4}\left[1-\left(\frac{2\times 6\times 10^{-5}}{1.69\times 10^{-4}}\right)^2\right]^{1/2}}$$

$$\simeq 0.0010 \text{ radians} \simeq 3.47'$$

Thus, if we are using telescope of angular magnification 10, the two lines will appear to have an angular separation of 34.7′.

17.8.2 Resolving Power of a Grating

In the case of a grating the resolving power refers to the power of distinguishing two nearby spectral lines and is defined by the following equation:

$$R = \frac{\lambda}{\Delta\lambda} \tag{17.66}$$

where $\Delta\lambda$ is the separation of two wavelengths which the grating can just resolve; the smaller the value of $\Delta\lambda$, the larger the resolving power.

The Rayleigh criterion (see Sec. 17.4) can again be used to define the limit of resolution. According to this criterion, if the principal maximum corresponding to the wavelength

$\lambda + \Delta\lambda$ falls on the first minimum (on the either side of the principal maximum) of the wavelength λ, then the two wavelengths λ and $\lambda + \Delta\lambda$ are said to be just resolved (see Fig. 17.39). If this common diffraction angle is represented by θ and if we are looking at the mth order spectrum, then the two wavelengths λ and $\lambda + \Delta\lambda$ will be just resolved if the following two equations are simultaneously satisfied:

$$d \sin \theta = m(\lambda + \Delta\lambda) \tag{17.67}$$

and

$$d \sin \theta = m\lambda + \frac{\lambda}{N} \tag{17.68}$$

Thus,

$$R = \frac{\lambda}{\Delta\lambda} = mN \tag{17.69}$$

which implies that the resolving power depends on the total number of lines in the grating—obviously on only those lines which are exposed to the incident beam (see the derivation in Sec. 17.6). Further, the resolving power is proportional to the order of the spectrum. Thus, to resolve the D_1 and D_2 lines of sodium ($\Delta\lambda$ = 6 Å) in the first order, N must be at least $(5.89 \times 10^{-5})/(6 \times 10^{-8}) \approx 1000$.

From Eq. (17.69) it appears that the resolving power of the grating would increase indefinitely if N is increased; however, for a given width of the grating $D(= Nd)$, as N is increased, d decreases and therefore the maximum value of m also decreases. Thus if d becomes 2.5λ, only first and second order spectra will be seen and if it is further reduced to about 1.5λ then only the first order spectrum will be seen.

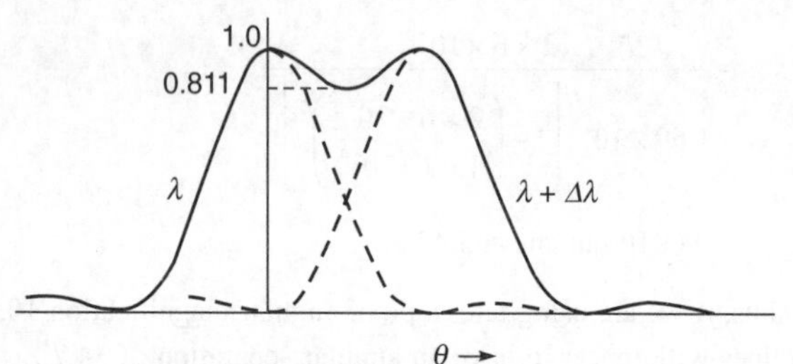

Figure 17.39

The Rayleigh criterion for the resolution of two spectral lines.

17.8.3 Resolving Power of a Prism

We conclude this section by calculating the resolving power of a prism. Figure 17.40 gives a schematic description of the experimental arrangement for observing the prism spectrum which is determined through the following formula:

$$n(\lambda) = \frac{\sin \dfrac{A + \delta(\lambda)}{2}}{\sin \dfrac{A}{2}} \tag{17.70}$$

where A represents the angle of the prism and δ the angle of minimum deviation. We assume that the refractive index decreases with λ (which is usually the case) so that δ also decreases with λ. In Fig. 17.40, the points P_1 and P_2 represent the images corresponding to λ and $\lambda + \Delta\lambda$, respectively. We are assuming that $\Delta\lambda$ is small so that the same position of the prism corresponds to the minimum deviation position for both wavelengths. In an actual experiment one usually has a slit source (perpendicular to the plane of the paper) forming line images at P_1 and P_2. Since the faces of the prism are rectangular, the intensity distribution will be similar to that produced by a slit of width b (see Sec. 17.2)*. For the lines to be just resolved the first diffraction minimum [m = 1 in Eq. (17.12)] of λ should fall at the central maximum of $\lambda + \Delta\lambda$, thus we must have

$$\Delta\delta \approx \frac{\lambda}{b} \tag{17.71}$$

In order to express $\Delta\delta$ in terms of $\Delta\lambda$, we differentiate Eq. (17.70):

$$\frac{dn}{d\lambda} = \frac{1}{\sin \dfrac{A}{2}} \cos\left[\frac{A + \delta(\lambda)}{2}\right] \frac{1}{2}\frac{d\delta}{d\lambda}$$

Thus,

$$\Delta\delta = \frac{2 \sin \dfrac{A}{2}}{\cos \dfrac{A + \delta(\lambda)}{2}} \frac{dn}{d\lambda} \Delta\lambda$$

Now from Fig. 17.40, we have

$$\theta = \frac{1}{2}[\pi - (A + \delta)]$$

or

$$\sin \theta = \frac{b}{a} = \cos \frac{A + \delta}{2}$$

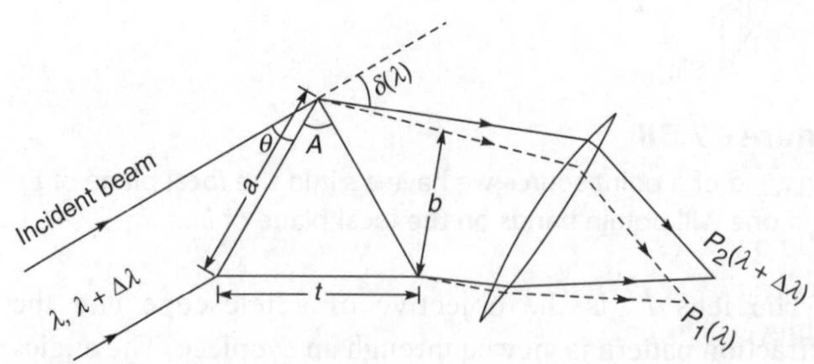

Figure 17.40

The schematic of the experimental arrangement to observe the prism spectrum. P_1 and P_2 represent the images corresponding to λ and $\lambda + \Delta\lambda$, respectively.

* Since we have a slit source we need not consider the diffraction in a direction perpendicular to the plane of the diagram.

where the length a is shown in the figure. Further

$$\sin\frac{A}{2} = \frac{t/2}{a}$$

where t is the length of the base of the prism. Thus,

$$\Delta\delta \approx \frac{t}{b}\frac{dn}{d\lambda}\Delta\lambda \tag{17.72}$$

Substituting in Eq. (17.71) we get for the resolving power

$$R = \frac{\lambda}{\Delta\lambda} = t\frac{dn}{d\lambda} \tag{17.73}$$

Now, for most glasses, the wavelength dependence of the refractive index (in the visible region of the spectrum) can be accurately described by the Cauchy formula

$$n = A + \frac{B}{\lambda^2} + \frac{C}{\lambda^4} + \ldots \tag{17.74}$$

Thus,

$$\frac{dn}{d\lambda} = -\left[\frac{2B}{\lambda^3} + \frac{4C}{\lambda^5} + \ldots\right] \tag{17.75}$$

the negative sign implying that the refractive index decreases with increase in wavelength. As an example, we consider telescope crown glass for which*

$A = 1.51375$, $B = 4.608 \times 10^{-11}$ cm^2, $C = 6.88 \times 10^{-22}$ cm^4

For $\lambda = 6 \times 10^{-5}$ cm, we have

$$\frac{dn}{d\lambda} \simeq -[4.27 \times 10^2 + 3.54]$$
$$\simeq -4.30 \times 10^2 \text{ cm}^{-1}$$

Thus, for $t \simeq 2.5$ cm we have

$$R = \frac{\lambda}{\Delta\lambda} \simeq 1000$$

which is an order of magnitude less than for typical diffraction gratings with 15,000 lines.

17.9 Oblique Incidence

LO9

Till now we have assumed plane waves incident normally on the grating. For experimental setting, it is quite difficult to achieve the condition of normal incidence to a great precision and it is easily seen that slight deviations from normal incidence will introduce considerable errors. It is, therefore, more practical to consider the more general oblique incidence case (see Fig. 17.41). The wavelength measurement can be carried out by using the method of minimum deviation as we do for prisms.

* Data quoted from Ref. 17.2.

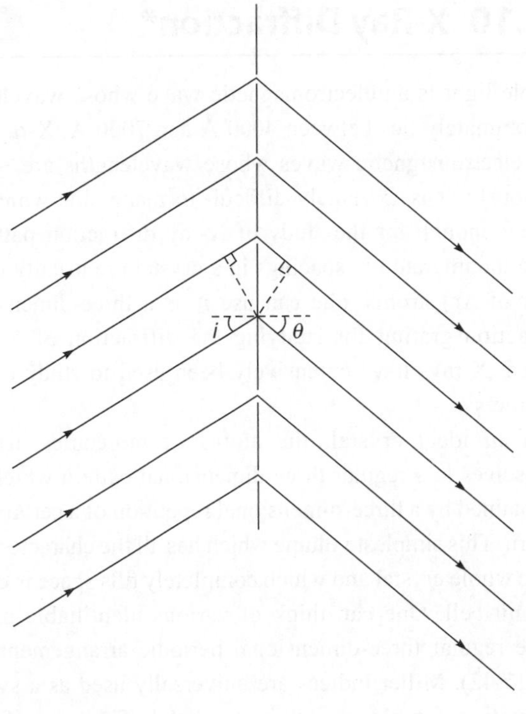

Figure 17.41
Diffraction of a plane wave incident obliquely on a grating.

If the angle of incidence is i, then the path difference of the diffracted rays from two corresponding points in adjacent slits will be $d \sin\theta + d\sin i$ (see Fig. 17.41). Thus, principal maxima will occur when

$$d(\sin\theta + \sin i) = m\lambda \tag{17.76}$$

or

$$d[\sin(\delta - i) + \sin i] = m\lambda \tag{17.77}$$

when $\delta = i + \theta$ is the angle of deviation. For δ to be minimum we must have

$$\frac{d}{di}[\sin(\delta - i) + \sin i] = 0 \tag{17.78}$$

$$-\cos(\delta - i) + \cos i = 0$$

i.e.,

$$i = \delta - i = \theta \tag{17.79}$$

or

$$i = \frac{\delta}{2} = \theta \tag{17.80}$$

Hence, at the position of minimum deviation, the grating condition becomes

$$2d\sin\frac{\delta}{2} = m\lambda \tag{17.81}$$

The minimum deviation position can be obtained in a manner similar to that used in the case of a prism and since the adjustments are relatively simpler, this provides a more accurate method for the determination of λ.

17.10 X-Ray Diffraction*

LO9

Visible light is an electromagnetic wave whose wavelength approximately lies between 4000 Å and 7000 Å. X-rays are also electromagnetic waves whose wavelengths are ~1 Å. Obviously, it is extremely difficult to make slits which are narrow enough for the study of X-ray diffraction patterns. Since the interatomic spacings in a crystal are usually of the order of Angstroms, one can use it as a three-dimensional diffraction grating for studying the diffraction of X-rays. Indeed, X-rays have extensively been used to study crystal structures[7].

In an ideal crystal, the atoms or molecules arrange themselves in a regular three-dimensional pattern which can be obtained by a three-dimensional repetition of a certain unit pattern. This simplest volume which has all the characteristics of the whole crystal and which completely fills space is called the unit cell. One can think of various identifiable planes in the regular three-dimensional periodic arrangement (see Fig. 17.42). Miller indices are universally used as a system of notation for planes within a crystal. They specify the orientation of planes relative to the crystal axis without giving the position of the plane in space with respect to the origin. These indices are based on the intercepts of a plane with the three crystal axes, each intercept with an axis being measured in terms of unit cell dimensions (a, b or c) along that axis. To determine the Miller indices of a plane, the following procedure is used:

(a) Find the intercepts (of the plane nearest to the origin) on the three axes and express them as multiple or fractions of the unit cell dimension.

(b) Take the reciprocals of these numbers and multiply by the LCM of the denominators.

(c) Enclose in parentheses.

For example, a (111) plane intercepts all three axes at one unit distance (see Fig. 17.43(a); a (211) plane intercepts the three axes at $\frac{1}{2}$, 1 and 1 unit distances (see Fig. 17.43(b)). Similarly, a (110) plane intercepts the z-axis at ∞. Miller indices can also be negative, the minus sign is shown above the digit like $(\bar{1}1\bar{1})$. Figure 17.44 shows the planes characterized by the Miller indices $(\bar{1}11)$ in a simple cubic lattice.

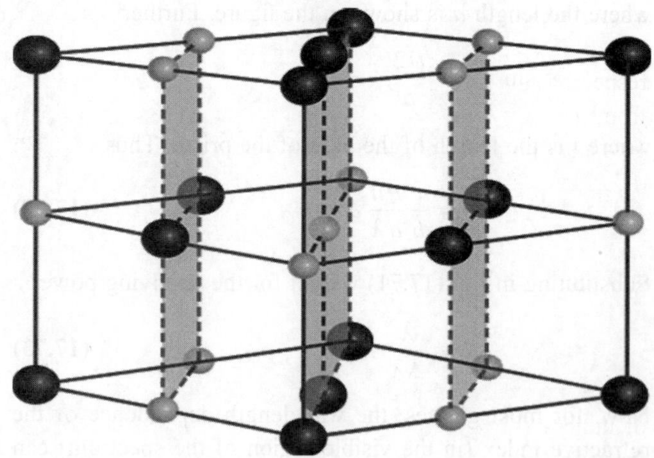

Figure 17.42
Planes in a NaCl crystal.

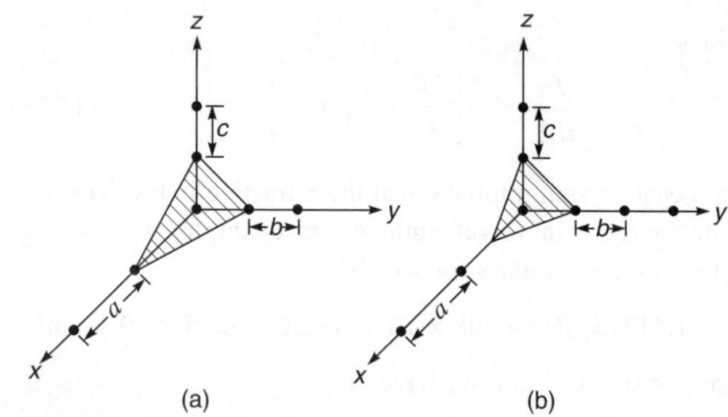

Figure 17.43
(a) The (111) plane intercepts all three axes at one unit distance of each axial dimension. (b) The (211) plane intercepts the three axes at ½, 1 and 1 unit distances.

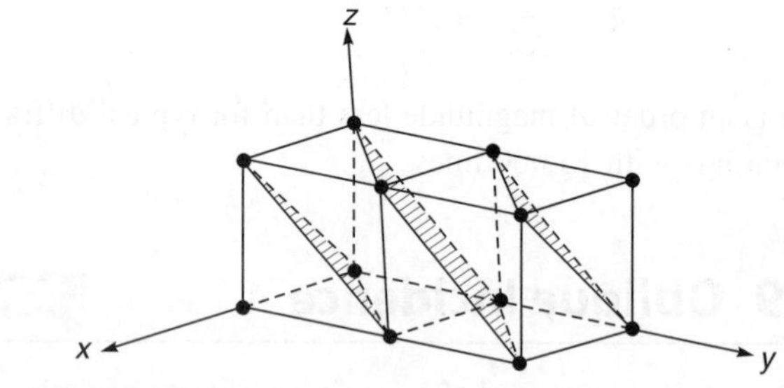

Figure 17.44
Planes characterized by the Miller indices $(\bar{1}\,1\,1)$ in a simple cubic lattice.

Consider a monochromatic beam of X-rays to be incident on a crystal. In Fig. 17.45 the horizontal dotted lines represent

* The author is grateful to Professor Lalit K. Malhotra for his help in writing this section.

a set of parallel crystal planes with Miller indices (*hkl*). W_1W_2 and W_3W_4 represent the incident and reflected wavefronts, respectively. Obviously, the secondary wavelets emanating from the points *A*, *B* and *C* are in phase on W_3W_4 (see Sec. 10.4 and Fig. 10.7); and the waves emanating from the points A_1, B_1 and C_1 will also be in phase on W_3W_4 if

$$XB_1 + B_1Y = m\lambda,\ m = 1, 2, 3, \ldots \tag{17.82}$$

or when

$$2d_{hkl} \sin \theta = m\lambda \tag{17.83}$$

where d_{hkl} is the interplanar spacing between crystal planes of indices (*hkl*), m = 1, 2, 3, ... is called the **order of diffraction** and θ is known as the **glancing angle**. This equation is known as Bragg's law and gives the angular positions of the reinforced diffracted beams in terms of the wavelength λ of the incoming X-rays and of the interplanar spacings d_{hkl} of the crystal planes. When the condition expressed by Eq. (17.83) is not satisfied, destructive interference occurs and no reinforced beam will be produced. Constructive interference occurs when the condition given by Eq. (17.83) is satisfied leading to peaks in the intensity distribution. For solids which crystallize in cubic structures (which are discussed later), the interplanar spacing d_{hkl} between two closest parallel planes with Miller indices (*hkl*) is given by

$$d_{hkl} = \frac{a}{\sqrt{h^2 + k^2 + l^2}} \tag{17.84}$$

where a represents the lattice constant. Thus knowing the Miller indices, we can find d_{hkl} and from Bragg's law, we can determine the value of θ at which Bragg's equation can be satisfied.

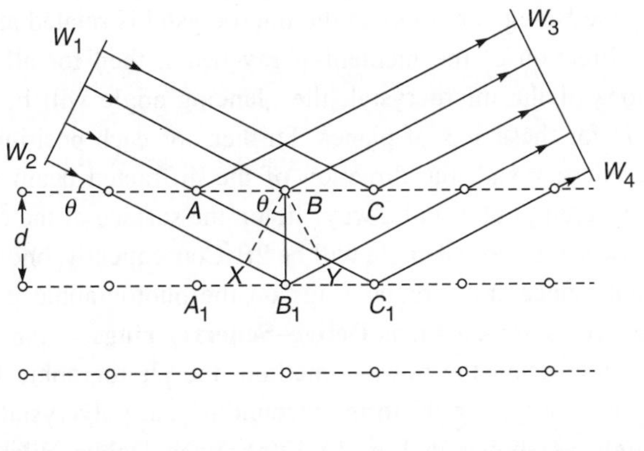

Figure 17.45

Reflection of a plane wave by a set of parallel crystal planes characterized by the Miller indices (*hkl*). When the Bragg condition $2d \sin \theta = m\lambda$ is satisfied, the waves scattered from different rows will be in phase.

There are three types of cubic structures: simple cubic, body centred cubic (BCC) and face centred cubic (FCC). Figure 17.45 shows a simple cubic structure (abbreviated as SC) in which the atoms are at the corners of a cube which forms what is known as a **unit cell**. The crystal is built up by the repetition of this unit cell in three dimensions. In addition, if there is an atom at the centre of each cube (shown as 9, 10, 11 and 12 in Fig. 17.46), the arrangement is known as a **BCC structure**. The distance between two adjacent planes characterized by the Miller indices $(\bar{1}10)$ is $a/\sqrt{2}$ which can be verified by simple geometry. On the other hand, if instead of having an atom at the center of the cube there is an atom at the center of each of the six faces of the cube (see Fig. 17.47) we will have the FCC structure. Copper, silver and gold crystallize in the FCC form with the lattice parameter a = 3.61 Å, 4.09 Å and 4.08 Å, respectively. Metals like sodium, barium and tungsten crystallize in the BCC form with a = 4.29 Å, 5.03 Å and 3.16 Å, respectively.

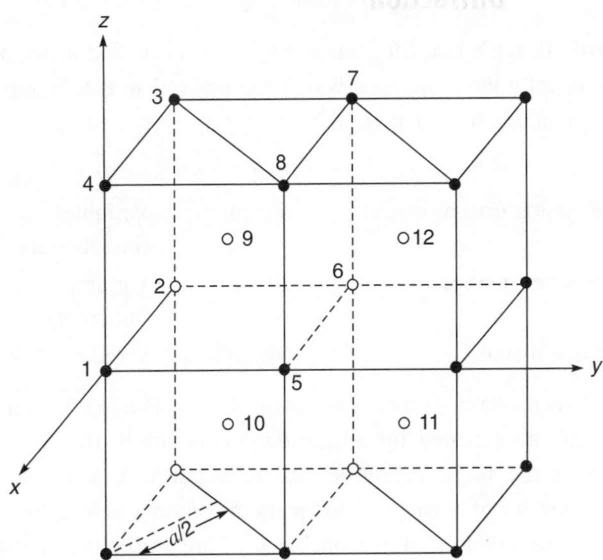

Figure 17.46

A body centered cubic (bcc) lattice. The $(\bar{1}10)$ planes are separated by $a/\sqrt{2}$.

Just as there are optical missing orders of a diffraction grating, there are structural extinctions of X-ray reflection from a crystal. For simple cubic structures, reflections from all (*hkl*) planes are possible. However for the BCC structure, diffraction occurs only on planes whose Miller indices when added together total to an even number. Thus for the BCC structure, the principal diffracting planes for a first order diffraction are (110), (200), (211) (and other similar planes), etc. where $h + k + l$ is an even number. In the case of the FCC crystal structure, the principal diffracting planes are those whose Miller indices are either all even or all odd, e.g., (111), (200), (220), etc.

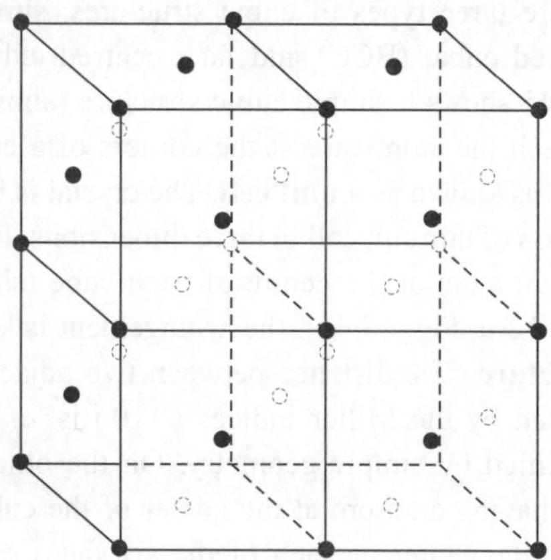

Figure 17.47
A face centered cubic (fcc) lattice.

17.10.1 Experimental Methods of X-ray Diffraction

From Bragg's law, $2d_{hkl} \sin \theta = m\lambda$, it is clear that there are essentially three methods which can be used so that Bragg's formula can be satisfied:

	λ	θ
Rotating crystal method	Fixed	Variable (intentional)
Powder method	Fixed	Variable (inherent)
Laue method	Variable	Fixed

When one uses monochromatic X-rays, Bragg's formula cannot be satisfied for an arbitrary value of θ. Hence one rotates the single crystal so that reflection can occur for a discrete set of θ values. This method can only be employed if single crystals of reasonable size are available. If this is not the case, one can still use monochromatic X-rays provided the sample is in the powder form so that there are always enough crystallites of the right orientation available to satisfy the Bragg relation. A powder will consist of a large number of randomly oriented micro-crystals; each micro-crystal is essentially a single crystal. As the X-ray beam passes through such a polycrystalline material, the orientation of any given set of planes, with reference to the X-ray beam, changes from one micro-crystal to the other. Thus, corresponding to any given set of planes there will be a large number of crystals for which Bragg's condition will be satisfied, and on the photographic plate one will obtain concentric rings [see Fig. 17.48(a)]; each ring will correspond to a particular value of d_{hkl} and a particular value of m. The appearance of the circular rings can be understood as follows. Consider a set of planes parallel to AB

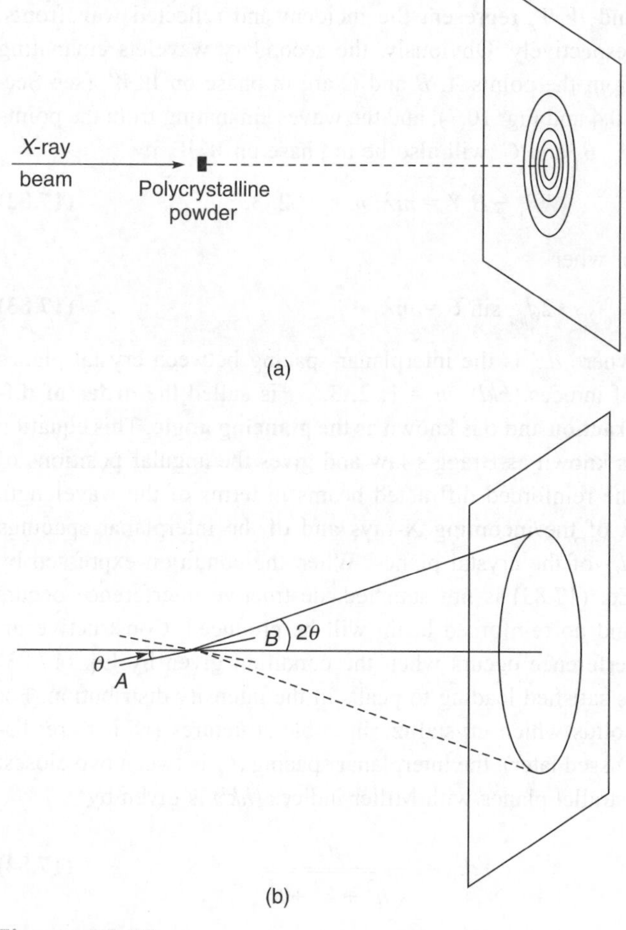

Figure 17.48
(a) When a monochromatic X-ray beam falls on a polycrystalline sample one obtains the Debye–Scherrer rings. (b) Diffraction from a polycrystalline sample.

[see Fig. 17.48(b)]. The glancing angle θ is assumed to satisfy the Bragg condition. If the microcrystal is rotated about the direction of the incident X-ray beam, then for all positions of the microcrystal, the glancing angle will be the same for these sets of planes. Further, for each position of the microcrystal, the direction of the diffracted beam will be different, but it will always lie on the surface of the cone whose semi-vertical angle will be 2θ. Consequently, one will obtain concentric circular rings on the photographic plate; these rings are known as **Debye–Scherrer rings**.

While using the powder method, the photographic film is put in a cylindrical form surrounding the polycrystalline sample as shown in Fig. 17.49(a). Each Debye–Scherrer ring will produce an arc on the film, and when the film is unrolled, one obtains a pattern as shown in Figs. 17.49(b) and (c). From the position of these arcs, one can calculate θ and thus determine the interplanar spacing. From a study of the interplanar spacings one can determine the crystal structure*. Although a powder camera with an enclosed film strip has been extensively used in the past, modern X-ray crystal analysis uses an X-ray diffractometer which has a radiation counter to detect the angle and intensity of the diffracted beam.

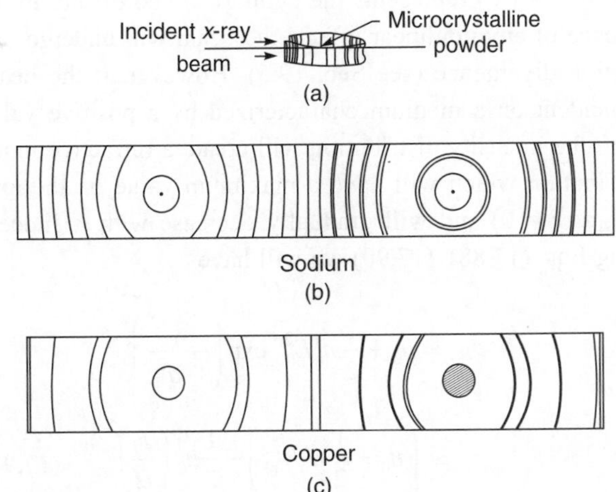

Figure 17.49
(a) While using the powder method the photographic film is kept in a cylindrical form as shown in the figure. (b) and (c) represent schematic diffraction patterns for sodium and copper, respectively.

Finally there is the Laue method in which the single crystal is held stationary in a beam of white X-rays. Each set of planes then chooses its own wavelength to satisfy the Bragg relation (see Fig. 17.50).

In order to calculate the angles of diffraction we substitute Eq. (17.84) in the Bragg's law [Eq. (17.83)] to obtain

$$\frac{2a}{\sqrt{h^2 + k^2 + l^2}} \sin \theta = m\lambda \tag{17.85}$$

We restrict ourselves only to first order reflections ($m = 1$); higher order reflections are usually rather weak (see also Problem 17.22). Thus Eq. (17.85) can be written in the form:

$$\sin \theta = \frac{\lambda}{2a} \sqrt{N} \tag{17.86}$$

where $N = h^2 + k^2 + l^2$

Now, for a simple cubic lattice, all values of (hkl) are possible implying the following possible values of N:

$$N = 1, 2, 3, 4, 5, 6, 7, \ldots \text{ (SC)} \tag{17.87a}$$

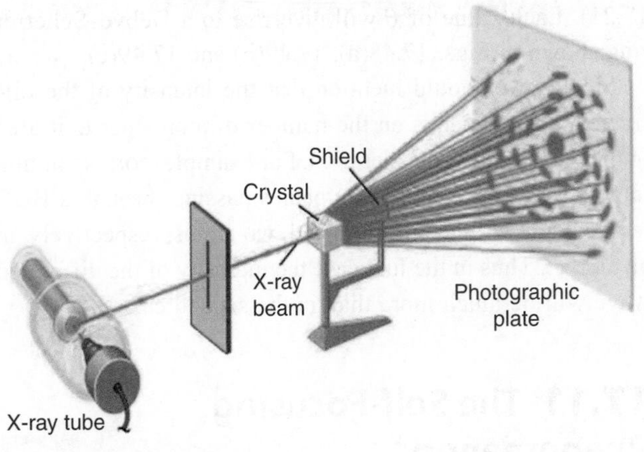

Figure 17.50
When a polychromatic X-ray beam falls on a single crystal, one obtains Laue spots. Each set of planes chooses its own wavelength to satisfy the Bragg relation given by Eq. (17.84). *Figure courtesy: McGraw Hill digital Access Library*

Similarly, for a BCC lattice $h + k + l$ must be even implying

$$N = h^2 + k^2 + l^2$$
$$= 2, 4, 6, 8, 10, 12, 14, 16, 18, 20, 22, \ldots \text{ (BCC)} \tag{17.87b}$$

Finally, for an FCC lattice, Miller indices are either all even or all odd implying

$$N = h^2 + k^2 + l^2$$
$$= 3, 4, 8, 11, 12, 16, 19, 20, 24, 27, \ldots \text{ (FCC)} \tag{17.87c}$$

For a given structure and for given values of λ and a one can now easily calculate the different values of θ. For example, if we consider λ = 1.540 Å and 1.544 Å (corresponding to the $\text{CuK}_{\alpha 1}$ and $\text{CuK}_{\alpha 2}$ lines) then for sodium (which is a BCC structure with a = 4.2906 Å), the various values of θ are

(14.70°, 14.74°), (21.03°, 21.09°), (26.08°, 26.15°),
(30.50°, 30.59°), (34.58°, 34.68°), (38.44°, 38.56°),
(42.18°, 42.32°), (45.88°, 46.03°), (49.59°, 49.76°),
(53.38°, 53.58°), (57.33°, 57.56°), (61.54°, 61.82°),
(66.22°, 66.56°), (79.41°, 80.23°),

The two values inside the parentheses correspond to the two wavelengths 1.540 Å and 1.544 Å, respectively. Because of the presence of two wavelengths one obtains double lines for each family of planes which become resolvable only at higher scattering angles. Similarly one can consider reflections from other structures (see Problems 17.19, 17.20 and

* Crystal structures other than cubic are also common; for example, zinc crystallizes into a hexagonal structure and carbon forms a diamond structure. However, the most important fact is that in all these structures there is a definite periodicity of atoms.

17.21). Each value of θ will give rise to a Debye–Scherrer ring shown in Figs. 17.48(a), 17.49(b) and 17.49(c).

Finally, we should mention that the intensity of the diffracted wave depends on the number of atoms per unit area in the plane under consideration. For example, corresponding to the $(\bar{1}10)$ and the $(\bar{2}22)$ planes passing through a BCC lattice, there will be one atom and two atoms, respectively, in an area a^2. Thus in the first case the intensity of the diffracted wave will be much more than in the second case.

17.11 The Self-Focusing Phenomenon*

LO10

With the availability of intense laser beams, a large number of interesting non-linear optical phenomena have been investigated. One such non-linear phenomenon is the effect on the propagation of a light beam due to the dependence of the refractive index on the intensity of the beam. This leads to the self-focusing (or defocusing) of the beam. In order to physically understand the self-focusing phenomenon we assume the non-linear dependence of the refractive index on the intensity to be of the form

$$n = n_0 + \frac{1}{2} n' E_0^2 \tag{17.88}$$

where n_0 is the refractive index of the medium in the absence of the electromagnetic field, n' is a constant representing the non-linear effect** and E_0 representing the amplitude of the electric field. As an example, we consider the incidence of a laser beam (propagating in the z-direction) having Gaussian intensity distribution in the transverse direction, i.e., we assume

$$E(x, y, z, t) \approx E_0 \cos(kz - \omega t) \tag{17.89}$$

with

$$E_0 = E_{00} \exp\left(-\frac{r^2}{a^2}\right) \tag{17.90}$$

where a represents the width of the Gaussian beam and $r\ (= \sqrt{x^2 + y^2}\ )$ represents the cylindrical coordinate. In the absence of any nonlinear effects the beam will undergo diffraction divergence (see Sec. 19.5). However, if the beam is incident on a medium characterized by a positive value of n', the intensity distribution will create a refractive index distribution which will have a maximum value on the axis (i.e., at $r = 0$) and will gradually decrease with r. Indeed, using Eqs. (17.88)–(17.90) we will have

$$n \simeq n_0 + \frac{1}{2} n' E_{00}^2 \exp\left(-\frac{2r^2}{a^2}\right)$$

$$\simeq \left(n_0 + \frac{1}{2} n' E_{00}^2\right) - \frac{1}{2} n_0 \left(\frac{r}{\alpha}\right)^2 \tag{17.91}$$

where

$$\alpha^2 = \frac{n_0 a^2}{2n' E_{00}^2} \tag{17.92}$$

and in writing Eq. (17.91) we have expanded the exponential term and have retained only the first two terms. In other words, we are restricting ourselves to small values of r, which is the paraxial approximation. The term $\frac{1}{2} n' E_{00}^2$ is usually very small compared to n_0; so we may write (after squaring)

$$n^2 \simeq n_0^2 \left[1 - \left(\frac{r}{\alpha}\right)^2\right] \tag{17.93}$$

We may recall that in Sec. 2.4.1 we had considered propagation in a medium whose refractive index decreased parabolically from the axis and had shown that the beam

* Based on Ref. 17.8; for a rigorous account, e.g., Ref. 17.9.

** This dependence may arise from a variety of mechanisms, such as the Kerr effect, electrostriction, thermal effect, etc. The simplest to understand is the thermal effect which is due to the fact that when an intense optical beam having a transverse distribution of intensity propagates through an absorbing medium, a temperature gradient is set up. For example, if the beam has a Gaussian transverse intensity variation (i.e., of the form $\exp(-r^2/a^2)$; the direction of propagation being along the z-axis), then the temperature will be maximum on the axis (i.e., $r = 0$) and will decrease with increase in the value of r. If $dn/dT > 0$, the refractive index will be maximum on the axis and the beam will undergo focusing; on the other hand if $dn/dT < 0$, the beam will undergo defocusing (see, e.g., Ref. 17.9).

The Kerr effect arises due to the anisotropic polarizability of liquid molecules (like CS_2). An intense light wave will tend to orient the anisotropically polarized molecules such that the direction of maximum polarizability is along the direction of the electric vector; this changes the dielectric constant of the medium. On the other hand, electrostriction (which is important in solids) is the force which a non-uniform electric field exerts on a material medium; this force affects the density of the material, which in turn affects the refractive index. Thus, a beam having nonuniform intensity distribution along its wavefront will give rise to a refractive index variation leading to the focusing (or defocusing) of the beam. For a detailed discussion on electrostriction and Kerr effect, refer to Refs. 17.9–17.11.

could undergo periodic focusing (see Fig. 2.25). Indeed we had shown that the medium behaved like a converging lens of focal length $\pi\alpha/2$ [see Eq. (2.48) of Chapter 2]. In the present case also because of nonlinear effects (with $n' > 0$), the medium will act as a converging lens of focal length approximately given by

$$f_{nl} \simeq \frac{\pi}{2}\alpha \simeq \frac{\pi}{2}\left[\frac{n_0}{2n' E_{00}^2}\right]^{1/2} a \qquad \textbf{(17.94)}$$

the subscript (nl) signifying that the effect is due to a non-linear phenomenon. Thus, because of non-linear effects the beam is said to undergo *self-focusing;* the word *self* signifies the fact that the beam creates its own refractive index gradient resulting in the focusing of the beam*.

Our analysis in Sec. 2.4.1 for the calculation of the focal length was based on ray optics and neglected diffraction effects. Now, in the absence of any non-linear effects, the beam will spread out due to diffraction and the angle of divergence will approximately be given by (see Fig. 17.14)

$$\theta_d \simeq \frac{\lambda}{\pi a} = \frac{(\lambda_0/n_0)}{\pi a} \qquad \textbf{(17.95)}$$

where λ_0 is the free space wavelength. Thus the phenomenon of diffraction can be approximated by a diverging lens of focal length (see Fig. 17.51).

$$f_d \simeq \frac{a}{\theta_d} \simeq \frac{1}{2}ka^2 \qquad \textbf{(17.96)}$$

where $$k = \frac{2\pi}{\lambda} = \frac{2\pi}{\lambda_0}n_0 \qquad \textbf{(17.97)}$$

Clearly if $f_d < f_{nl}$, the diffraction divergence will dominate and the beam will diverge. On the other hand, if $f_{nl} < f_d$, the non-linear focusing effects will dominate and the beam will undergo self-focusing. For $f_d \approx f_{nl}$, the two effects will cancel each other and the beam will propagate without any focusing or defocusing. This is the condition of *uniform waveguide like propagation*. In order to determine the critical power of the beam we note that the condition $f_d \approx f_{nl}$ implies

$$\frac{1}{2}ka^2 \approx \frac{\pi}{2}\left[\frac{n_0}{2n'E_{00}^2}\right]^{1/2} a$$

or $$E_{00}^2 \simeq \frac{1}{n_0 n'}\frac{\lambda_0^2}{8a^2} \qquad \textbf{(17.98)}$$

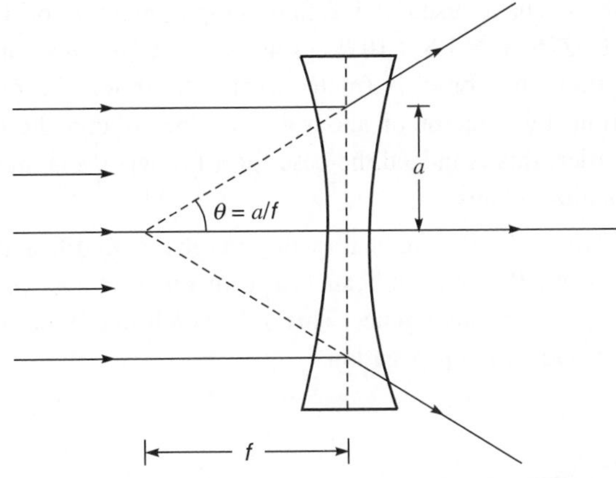

Figure 17.51
When a plane wave is incident on a diverging lens, the transmitted rays diverge making an angle $\theta \approx a/f$ with the axis.

Now the total power of the beam is given by

$$P = \int_0^\infty \text{velocity} \times (\text{energy/unit volume}) \times 2\pi r\, dr$$

$$\simeq \int_0^\infty \left(\frac{c}{n_0}\right)\times\left(\frac{1}{2}\varepsilon E_0^2\right)\times 2\pi r\,dr$$

$$\simeq \frac{c}{n_0}\left(\frac{1}{2}n_0^2\,\varepsilon_0\,E_{00}^2\right)\int_0^\infty \exp\left(-\frac{2r^2}{a^2}\right)2\pi r\,dr$$

$$\simeq \frac{\pi}{4}n_0 c\varepsilon_0 E_{00}^2 a^2 \qquad \textbf{(17.99)}$$

where $\varepsilon\ (= n_{00}^2\varepsilon_0)$ is the dielectric permittivity of the medium and ε_0 ($= 8.85 \times 10^{-12}$ C^2/N–m^2) is the dielectric permittivity of free space. Substituting the expression for E_{00}^2 from Eq. (17.98) in Eq. (17.99) we obtain the following expression for the critical power:

$$P_{cr} \simeq \frac{\pi}{32}(c\varepsilon_0)\frac{\lambda_0^2}{n'} \qquad \textbf{(17.100)}$$

Garmire, Chiao and Townes (Ref. 17.12) carried out experiments on the self-focusing of a ruby laser beam ($\lambda_0 = 0.6943$ µm) in CS_2 and found that the critical power was 25 ± 5 kW. Equation (17.100) gives us

$$P_{cr} \simeq \frac{3.14}{32}\times 3\times 10^8 \times 8.85\times 10^{-12}\times\frac{(0.6943\times 10^{-6})^2}{2\times 10^{-20}}$$

$$\simeq 6.3 \text{ kW} \qquad \textbf{(17.101)}$$

* It should be mentioned that if n' were a negative quantity, the refractive index would have increased as we move away from the axis and the beam would have undergone defocusing. For example, if the refractive index decreases with increase in temperature, the beam may undergo what is known as *thermal defocusing*.

where we have used the following parameters for CS_2: $n_0 \simeq 1.6276$, $n' \simeq 1.8 \times 10^{-11}$ cgs units $\simeq 2 \times 10^{-20}$ mks units. [The mks unit for n' is (meter/volt)^2.] Although the result is wrong by a factor of about 4, one does obtain the correct order; this is indeed the case for all order-of-magnitude calculations. Thus,

(a) when $P < P_{cr}$, the beam will diverge due to diffraction.

(b) when $P = P_{cr}$, the beam will propagate without divergence or convergence. This is the condition for uniform waveguide propagation.

(c) when $P > P_{cr}$, we may extrapolate that the beam will undergo focusing, which is indeed borne out by more rigorous analysis. This is known as the **self-focusing of the beam.**

We may mention that a detailed study of the self-focusing phenomenon is of considerable importance in laser induced fusion experiments where there is a non-linear interaction of the laser beam with the plasma.

SUMMARY

- Interference corresponds to the situation when we consider the superposition of waves coming out from two point sources and diffraction corresponds to the situation when we consider waves coming out from an area source like a circular or rectangular aperture or even a large number of rectangular apertures (like the diffraction grating).
- When a plane wave is incident normally on N parallel slits, the Fraunhofer diffraction pattern is given by

$$I = I_0 \frac{\sin^2 \beta}{\beta^2} \cdot \frac{\sin^2 N\gamma}{\sin^2 \gamma}$$

where

$$\beta = \frac{\pi b \sin\theta}{\lambda}, \quad \gamma = \frac{\pi d \sin\theta}{\lambda}$$

λ is the wavelength of light, θ the angle of diffraction, b represents the width of each slit and d the separation between two slits. When $N = 1$, we have the single slit diffraction pattern producing a central maximum at $\theta = 0$ and minima when $b \sin\theta = m\lambda$; $m = \pm1, \pm2, ...$ When $N \geq 2$, the intensity distribution is the product of the single slit diffraction pattern and the interference pattern produced by N point sources separated by a distance d. For $N = 2$, we obtain the Young's double slit interference pattern. For large values of N, the principle maxima occur when $\gamma = m\pi$ implying

$$d \sin\theta = m\lambda;\ m = 0, 1, 2, ...$$

which is usually referred to as the grating condition.

- The resolving power of the grating is given by

$$R = \frac{\lambda}{\Delta\lambda} = mN$$

where N represents the total number of lines in the grating. For example, in the first order spectrum ($m = 1$) of a diffraction grating with $N = 10000$, for $\lambda \approx 5000$ Å we get $\Delta\lambda \approx 0.5$ Å.

- Consider a monochromatic beam of X–rays incident on a crystal. The glancing angle θ for which we have reinforced diffracted beams is given by

$$2d_{hkl} \sin\theta = m\lambda$$

where d_{hkl} is the interplanar spacing between crystal planes having Miller indices (hkl); $m = 1, 2, 3, \ldots$ is called the order of diffraction and θ is known as the glancing angle. The above equation is known as Bragg's law and gives the angular positions of the reinforced diffracted beams.

PROBLEMS

17.1 A plane wave ($\lambda = 5000$ Å) falls normally on a long narrow slit of width 0.5 mm. Calculate the angles of diffraction corresponding to the first three minima. Repeat the calculations corresponding to a slit width of 0.1 mm. Interpret physically the change in the diffraction pattern.

[**Ans:** 0.057°, 0.115°, 0.17°; 0.29°, 0.57°, 0.86°]

17.2 A convex lens of focal length 20 cm is placed after a slit of width 0.6 mm. If a plane wave of wavelength 6000 Å falls normally on the slit, calculate the separation between the second minima on either side of the central maximum.

[**Ans:** $\simeq$ 0.08 cm]

17.3 In Problem 17.2 calculate the ratio of the intensity of the principal maximum to the first maximum on either side of the principal maximum. [**Ans:** ~21]

17.4 Consider a laser beam of circular crosssection of diameter 3 cm and of wavelength 5×10^{-5} cm. Calculate the order of the beam diameter after it has traversed a distance of 3 km. [**Ans:** ~14 cm. This shows the extremely high directionality of laser beams.]

17.5 A circular aperture of radius 0.01 cm is placed in front of a convex lens of focal length 25 cm and illuminated by a parallel beam of light of wavelength 5×10^{-5} cm. Calculate the radii of the first three dark rings.

[**Ans:** 0.76, 1.4, 2.02 mm]

17.6 Consider a plane wave incident on a convex lens of diameter 5 cm and of focal length 10 cm. If the wavelength of the incident light is 6000 Å, calculate the radius of the first dark ring on the focal plane of the lens. Repeat the calculations for a lens of same focal length but diameter 15 cm. Interpret the results physically.

[**Ans:** 1.46×10^{-4} cm, 4.88×10^{-5} cm]

17.7 Consider a set of two slits each of width $b = 5 \times 10^{-2}$ cm and separated by a distance $d = 0.1$ cm, illuminated by a monochromatic light of wavelength 6.328×10^{-5} cm. If a convex lens of focal length 10 cm is placed beyond the double slit arrangement, calculate the positions of the minima inside the first diffraction minimum.

[**Ans:** 0.0316 mm, 0.094 mm]

17.8 Show that when $b = d$, the resulting diffraction pattern corresponds to a slit of width $2b$.

17.9 Show that the first order and second order spectra will never overlap when the grating is used for studying a light beam containing wavelength components from 4000 Å to 7000 Å.

17.10 Consider a diffraction grating of width 5 cm with slits of width 0.0001 cm separated by a distance of 0.0002 cm. What is the corresponding grating element? How many order would be observable at $\lambda = 5.5 \times 10^{-5}$ cm? Calculate the width of the principal maximum. Would there be any missing orders?

17.11 For the diffraction grating of Problem 17.10, calculate the dispersion in the different orders. What will be the resolving power in each order?

17.12 A grating (with 15000 lines per inch) is illuminated by white light. Assuming that white light consists of wavelengths lying between 4000 and 7000 Å, calculate the angular widths of the first and the second order spectra. [*Hint:* You should not use Eq. (17.65); why?]

17.13 A grating (with 15,000 lines per inch) is illuminated by sodium light. The grating spectrum is observed on the focal plane of a convex lens of focal length 10 cm. Calculate the separation between the D_1 and D_2 lines of sodium. (The wavelengths of the D_1 and D_2 lines are 5890 and 5896 Å, respectively.) [*Hint:* You may use Eq. (17.65).]

17.14 Calculate the resolving power in the second order spectrum of a 1 inch grating having 15,000 lines.

17.15 Consider a wire grating of width 1 cm having 1,000 wires. Calculate the angular width of the second order principal maxima and compare the value with the one corresponding to a grating having 5000 lines in 1 cm. Assume $\lambda = 5 \times 10^{-5}$ cm.

17.16 In the minimum deviation position of a diffraction grating the first order spectrum corresponds to an angular deviation of 30°. If $\lambda = 6 \times 10^{-5}$ cm, calculate the grating element.

17.17 Calculate the diameter of a telescope lens if a resolution of 0.1 seconds of arc is required at $\lambda = 6 \times 10^{-5}$ cm.

17.18 Assuming that the resolving power of the eye is determined by diffraction effects only, calculate the maximum distance at which two objects separated by a distance of 2 m can be resolved by the eye. (Assume pupil diameter to be 2 mm and $\lambda = 6000$ Å.)

17.19 **(a)** A pinhole camera is essentially a rectangular box with a tiny pinhole in front. An inverted image of the object is formed on the rear of the box. Consider a parallel beam of light incident normally on the pinhole. If we neglect diffraction effects then the diameter of the image will increase linearly with the diameter of the pinhole. On the other hand, if we assume Fraunhofer diffraction, then the diameter of the first dark ring will go on increasing as we reduce the diameter of the pinhole. Find the pinhole diameter for which the diameter of the geometrical image is approximately equal to the diameter of the first dark ring in the Airy pattern. Assume $\lambda = 6000$ Å and a separation of 15 cm between the pinhole and the rear of the box.

(b) Figure 17.52 shows the quality of the image formed for various values of the diameter of the pinhole. Discuss qualitatively the fact that the image will get blurred if the diameter of the pinhole is too big or too small.

[**Ans:** (a) 0.47 mm]

17.20 Copper is an FCC structure with lattice constant 3.615 Å. An X-ray powder photograph of copper is taken. The X-ray beam consists of wavelengths 1.540 Å and 1.544 Å. Show that diffraction maxima will be observed at θ = (21.64°, 21.70°), (25.21°, 25.28°), (37.05°, 37.16°), (44.94°, 45.09°), (47.55°, 47.71°), (58.43°, 58.67°), (68.20°, 68.58°), (72.29°, 72.76°).

17.21 Tungsten is a BCC structure with lattice constant 3.1648 Å. Show that in the powder photograph of tungsten (corresponding to an X-ray wavelength of 1.542 Å) one would observe diffraction maxima at θ = 20.15°, 29.17°, 36.64°, 43.56°, 50.39°, 57.55°, 65.74° and 77.03°.

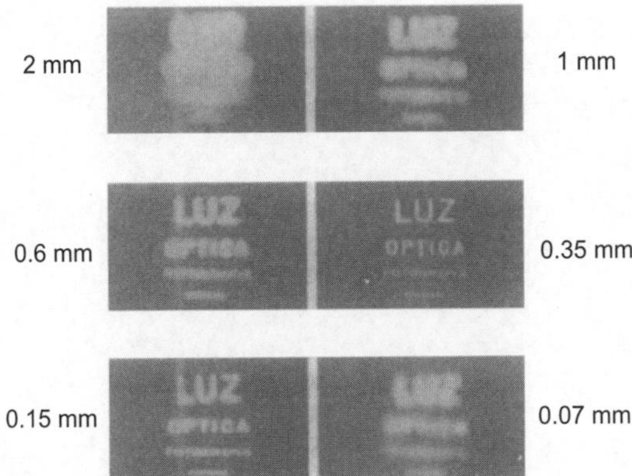

Figure 17.52

The image formed in a pinhole camera for different diameters of the pinhole. [*Photograph downloaded from the internet by Professor K Thyagarajan; Ref: http://www. cs.berkeley.edu/~daf/book/chapter-4.pdf*].

17.22 **(a)** In the simple cubic structure if we alternately place Na and Cl atoms we would obtain the NaCl structure. Show that the Na atoms (and the Cl atoms) independently form FCC structures. The lattice constant associated with each fcc structure is 5.6402 Å. Corresponding to the X-ray wavelength 1.542 Å, show that diffraction maxima will be observed at θ = 13.69°, 15.86°, 22.75°, 26.95°, 28.27°, 33.15°, 36.57°, 37.69°, 42.05° 45.26°, 50.66°, 53.98°, 55.10°, 59.84°, 63.69°, 65.06°, 71.27°, 77.45° and 80.66°.

(b) Show that if we treat NaCl as a simple cubic structure with lattice parameter 2.82 Å then the maxima at θ = 13.69°, 26.95°, 36.57°, 45.26°, 53.98°, 63.69° and 77.45° will not be observed. Indeed in the X-ray diffraction pattern of NaCl, the maxima corresponding to these angles will be very weak.

17.23 Show that the *m*th order reflection from the planes characterized by (*hkl*) can be considered as the same as the first order reflection from the planes characterized by (*mh mk ml*).

17.24 Calculate the Fraunhofer diffraction pattern produced by a double-slit arrangement with slits of widths b and $3b$, with their centres separated by a distance $6b$.

17.25 Consider the propagation of a 1 kW laser beam (λ = 6943 Å, beam diameter $\simeq$ 1 cm) in CS_2. Calculate f_d and f_{nl} and discuss the defocusing (or focusing) of the beam. Repeat the calculations corresponding to a 1000 kW beam and discuss any qualitative differences that exist between the two cases. The data for n_0 and n_2 are given in Sec. 17.10.

17.26 The values of n_0 and n_2 for benzene are 1.5 and 0.6×10^{-10} cgs. units, respectively. Obtain an approximate expression for the critical power.

CHAPTER

18

Fourier analysis is a ubiquitous tool that has found application to diverse areas of physics and engineering.

—Joseph Goodman in the Preface to *Introduction to Fourier Optics*

Fraunhofer Diffraction II and Fourier Optics

LEARNING OBJECTIVES

After reading this chapter, the reader should be able to:

LO 1: *derive the Fresnel diffraction integral.*

LO 2: *understand conditions for Fraunhofer diffraction.*

LO 3: *describe the Fraunhofer diffraction by a long narrow slit, and by rectangular and circular apertures.*

LO 4: *discuss Fraunhofer diffraction by an array of identical apertures.*

LO 5: *explain spatial frequency filtering.*

LO 6: *derive the Fourier transforming property of a thin lens.*

Above Image: Close-up view of a red laser on a cutting machine in a college physics laboratory. Photograph courtesy McGraw Hill Digital Access Library.

18.1 Introduction

In this chapter, we will present a more general analysis of the far-field diffraction of a plane wave by different types of aperture; this is known as **Fraunhofer diffraction**. We will first derive the formula for what is known as **Fresnel diffraction**, which will be used in the next chapter. We will then make the far-field approximation, which will give us the Fraunhofer diffraction pattern; this will be shown to be the Fourier transform of the aperture function. We will also derive the Fourier transforming property of a thin lens that forms the basis of Fourier optics and of spatial frequency filtering.

18.2 The Fresnel Diffraction Integral

LO1

We consider a plane wave (of amplitude A) incident normally on an aperture as shown in Fig. 18.1. The plane of the aperture is assumed to be $z = 0$. We wish to calculate the intensity distribution on the plane $z = d$. Now, for an electromagnetic wave propagating in a homogeneous medium of dielectric constant ε, the transverse components of the electric field (E_x or E_y) would satisfy the scalar wave equation

$$\nabla^2 E = \varepsilon\mu_0 \frac{\partial^2 E}{\partial t^2} \tag{18.1}$$

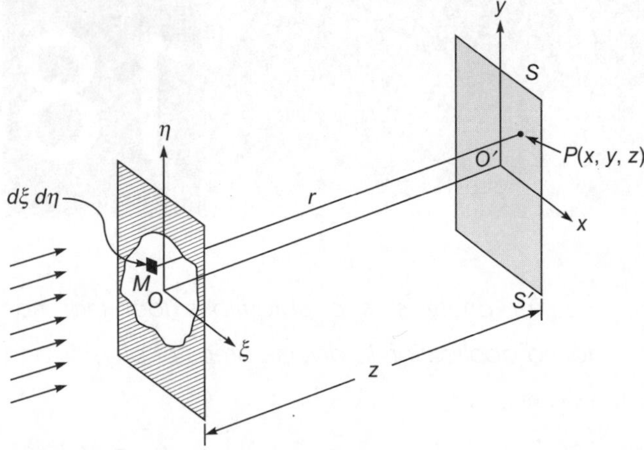

Figure 18.1
A plane wave incident normally on an aperture. The diffraction pattern is observed on the screen SS′.

If we assume the time dependence of the form $e^{-j\omega t}$ and write

$$E(x, y, z, t) = u(x, y, z)e^{-i\omega t} \tag{18.2}$$

we would obtain

$$\nabla^2 u + k^2 u = 0 \tag{18.3}$$

where $k = \omega\sqrt{\varepsilon\mu_0} = \dfrac{\omega}{v}$

u represents one of the Cartesian components of the electric field and v represents the velocity of the electromagnetic wave. In Example 9.6 we had shown that the solution of Eq. (18.3) is given by

$$e^{i(k_x x+k_y y+k_z z)} \quad \text{with} \quad k_x^2 + k_y^2 + k_z^2 = k^2 = \frac{\omega^2}{v^2}$$

For a given frequency of a propagating electromagnetic wave, the value of k is fixed and therefore the general solution of Eq. (18.3) can be written as

$$u(x, y, z) = \int_{-\infty}^{+\infty}\int_{-\infty}^{+\infty} F(k_x, k_y)e^{i(k_x x+k_y y+k_z z)}dk_x dk_y \tag{18.4}$$

where $k_z = \pm\sqrt{k^2 - k_x^2 - k_y^2}$

For waves making small angles with the z-axis we may write

$$k_z = \sqrt{k^2 - k_x^2 - k_y^2} \approx k\left[1 - \frac{k_x^2 + k_y^2}{2k^2}\right]$$

Substituting in Eq. (18.4) we obtain

$$u(x, y, z) = e^{ikz}\iint F(k_x, k_y)\exp\left[i\left(k_x x + k_y y - \frac{k_x^2 + k_y^2}{2k}z\right)\right]dk_x dk_y \tag{18.5}$$

Thus the field distribution on the plane $z = 0$ will be given by

$$u(x, y, z = 0) = \iint F(k_x, k_y)e^{i(k_x x+k_y y)}dk_x dk_y \tag{18.6}$$

The above equation tells us that $u(x, y, z = 0)$ is the Fourier transform of $F(k_x, k_y)$. The (2-dimensional) inverse transform will give us (see Sec. 8.6)

$$F(k_x, k_y) = \frac{1}{(2\pi)^2}\iint A(\xi, \eta)e^{-i(k_x\xi+k_y\eta)}d\xi d\eta$$

where $A(x, y) \equiv u(x, y, z = 0)$ is the field distribution on the plane $z = 0$. Substituting the above expression for $F(k_x, k_y)$ in Eq. (18.5), we get

$$u(x, y, z) = \frac{e^{ikz}}{4\pi^2}\iint A(\xi, \eta)I_1 I_2\, d\xi d\eta \tag{18.7}$$

where
$$I_1 = \int_{-\infty}^{+\infty}\exp[ik_x(x-\xi)]\exp\left[-\frac{ik_x^2}{2k}z\right]dk_x$$

$$= \sqrt{\frac{4\pi^2}{i\lambda z}}\exp\left[\frac{ik(x-\xi)^2}{2z}\right]$$

and we have used the following integral (see Appendix A):

$$\int_{-\infty}^{+\infty} e^{-\alpha x^2+\beta x}dx = \sqrt{\frac{\pi}{\alpha}}\exp\left[\frac{\beta^2}{4\alpha}\right] \tag{18.8}$$

Similarly

$$I_2 = \int_{-\infty}^{+\infty}\exp[ik_y(\eta - y)]\exp\left[\frac{ik_y^2}{2k^2}\right]dk_y$$

$$= \sqrt{\frac{4\pi^2}{i\lambda z}}\exp\left[\frac{ik(y-\eta)^2}{2z}\right]$$

Thus

$$u(x, y, z) = \frac{1}{i\lambda z}e^{ikz}\iint A(\xi, \eta) \times \exp\left[\frac{ik}{2z}\{(x-\xi)^2 + (y-\eta)^2\}\right]d\xi d\eta$$

Fresnel Diffraction Integral (18.9)

where the integral is over the area of the aperture on the plane $z = 0$. The above equation can be written in the form

$$u(x, y, z) \approx \frac{1}{i\lambda z}e^{ikz}\exp\left\{\frac{ik}{2z}(x^2 + y^2)\right\}\iint A(\xi, \eta) \times \exp\left\{\frac{ik}{2z}(\xi^2 + \eta^2)\right\}e^{-i(u\xi+v\eta)}d\xi d\eta \tag{18.10}$$

where $u = \dfrac{2\pi x}{\lambda z}$ and $v = \dfrac{2\pi y}{\lambda z}$ (18.11) are known as spatial frequencies. Both Eqs. (18.9) and (18.10) are usually referred to as the **Fresnel diffraction integral**. In the next chapter, we will use the above integrals to calculate the Fresnel diffraction pattern. We must mention here that in the Fresnel approximation, we have neglected the terms proportional to α^2; this will be justified if it leads to maximum phase change which is much less than π. Thus, the Fresnel approximation will be valid when

$$\frac{1}{8}kz\alpha^2 << \pi \Rightarrow \frac{1}{8}\frac{2\pi}{\lambda}\frac{\left[(x-\xi)^2+(y-\eta)^2\right]^2}{z^3} << \pi \quad (18.12)$$

Thus, we must have

$$z >> \left(\frac{1}{4\lambda}\left[(x-\xi)^2+(y-\eta)^2\right]^2_{\max}\right)^{\frac{1}{3}}$$

Condition for Fresnel approximation to be valid (18.13)

As an example, we consider a circular aperture of radius a; if we observe in a region of dimensions much greater than a, then we may neglect the terms involving ξ and η on the right hand side to obtain:

$$z >> \left(\frac{1}{4\lambda}(x^2+y^2)^2\right)^{\frac{1}{3}} \quad (18.14)$$

Thus for a circular aperture of radius 0.1 cm, if we observe in a radius of about 1 cm the maximum value of $(x^2 + y^2)$ will be about 1 cm²; if we assume $\lambda \approx 5 \times 10^{-5}$ cm, Eq. (18.14) would imply $z >> 17$ cm.

18.3 Uniform Amplitude and Phase Distribution

We first consider the absence of any aperture. Thus, at $z = 0$

$$A(\xi, \eta) = A \quad \text{for all values of } \xi \text{ and } \eta$$

and Eq. (18.9) can be written as

$$u(x, y, z) = \frac{A}{i\lambda z}e^{ikz}\int_{-\infty}^{+\infty} e^{\frac{ik}{2z}X^2}dX\int_{-\infty}^{+\infty} e^{\frac{ik}{2z}Y^2}dY$$

where $X = x - \xi$ and $Y = y - \eta$. If we now use the integral given by Eq. (18.8), we would get

$$u(x, y, z) = \frac{A}{i\lambda z}e^{ikz}\left[\sqrt{\frac{\pi 2z}{-ik}}\right]\left[\sqrt{\frac{\pi 2z}{-ik}}\right] \quad (18.15)$$

or $\quad u(x, y, z) = A\,e^{ikz} \quad$ (18.16)

as it indeed should for a uniform plane wave. This shows that in spite of all the approximations that we have made, we have ended up getting the correct result!

18.4 The Fraunhofer Approximation

LO2

In the Fraunhofer approximation, we assume z to be so large that inside the integral in Eq. (18.10), the function

$$\exp\left\{\frac{ik}{2z}(\xi^2+\eta^2)\right\}$$

can be replaced by unity or, the maximum phase change should be much less than π. Thus, **in addition** to the condition given by Eq. (18.13), we must have

$$z >> \frac{[\xi^2+\eta^2]_{\max}}{\lambda}$$

Condition for Fraunhofer approximation to be valid (18.17)

In this approximation, Eq. (18.10) takes the form

$$u(x, y, z) \approx \frac{1}{i\lambda z}e^{ikz}\exp\left\{\frac{ik}{2z}(x^2+y^2)\right\} \times$$

$$\iint A(\xi, \eta)\, e^{-i(u\xi+v\eta)}d\xi\, d\eta$$

Fraunhofer Diffraction Integral (18.18)

which represents the Fraunhofer diffraction pattern. The integral on the right-hand side is the two-dimensional Fourier transform of the function $A(\xi, \eta)$ (see Sec. 8.6). Thus Eq. (18.18) gives the very important result that the

Fraunhofer diffraction pattern is the Fourier transform of the aperture function.

For a circular aperture of radius a, Eq. (18.17) would become

$$z >> \frac{a^2}{\lambda} \quad (18.19)$$

We introduce the Fresnel number

$$N_F = \frac{a^2}{\lambda z} \quad (18.20)$$

Thus for the Fraunhofer approximation to be valid, we must have

$$N_F << 1 \quad (18.21)$$

18.5 Fraunhofer Diffraction by a Long Narrow Slit

LO3

We first consider Fraunhofer diffraction of a plane wave incident normally on a long narrow slit of width b (along the ξ-axis) placed on the aperture plane. Figure 18.2 corresponds to a rectangular slit – if the slit is very long along the η-axis, then we will have a long narrow slit. For such a case, we will have

$$\left.\begin{aligned} A(\xi,\eta) &= A \quad |\xi| < \frac{b}{2} \\ &= 0 \quad |\xi| > \frac{b}{2} \end{aligned}\right\} \tag{18.22}$$

for all values of η. Substituting Eq. (18.22) in Eq. (18.18), we obtain

$$u(x, y, z) = \frac{A}{i\lambda z} e^{ikz} \exp\left\{\frac{ik}{2z}(x^2 + y^2)\right\} \times \int_{-b/2}^{+b/2} e^{-iu\xi}\, d\xi \int_{-\infty}^{+\infty} e^{-iv\eta}\, d\eta \tag{18.23}$$

Now, in Sec. 8.3, we have shown

$$\delta(v) = \frac{1}{2\pi}\int_{-\infty}^{+\infty} e^{-iv\eta}\, d\eta \tag{18.24}$$

and

$$\int_{-b/2}^{+b/2} e^{-iu\xi}\, d\xi = \frac{1}{-iu} e^{-iu\xi}\Big|_{-b/2}^{+b/2}$$

$$= \frac{2}{u}\frac{e^{iub/2} - e^{-iub/2}}{2i} = b\frac{\sin\beta}{\beta}$$

where
$$\beta = \frac{ub}{2} = \frac{\pi b x}{\lambda z} \approx \frac{\pi b \sin\theta}{\lambda} \tag{18.25}$$

and $\sin\theta \approx \dfrac{x}{z}$; θ representing the angle of diffraction along the x-direction. Thus,

$$u(x, y, z) = \frac{Ab}{i\lambda z} e^{ikz} \exp\left\{\frac{ik}{2z}(x^2 + y^2)\right\}\left(\frac{\sin\beta}{\beta}\right) 2\pi\delta(v) \tag{18.26}$$

Because of the δ function, the intensity is zero except on the x-axis; thus the intensity distribution along the x-axis will be

$$I = I_0\left(\frac{\sin^2\beta}{\beta^2}\right) \tag{18.27}$$

We thus obtain the single slit diffraction pattern as discussed in Sec. 17.3. Actually for a long narrow slit, Eq. (18.17) is not valid and we must use the analysis given in Sec. 19.7. However, on the focal plane of a lens we will observe the pattern given by Eq. (18.27) – see Fig. 17.3.

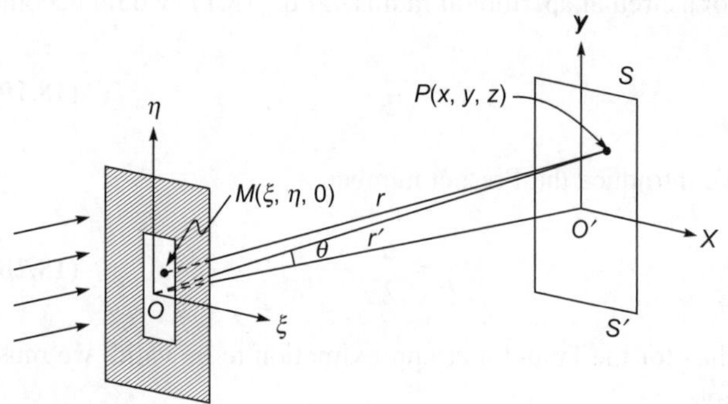

Figure 18.2
Diffraction of a plane wave incident normally on a rectangular aperture.

18.6 Fraunhofer Diffraction by a Rectangular Aperture

LO3

We next consider a rectangular aperture (of dimension $a \times b$) [see Fig. 18.2]. The Fraunhofer diffraction of a plane wave incident normally on such a rectangular aperture will be given by

$$u(x, y, z) = \frac{A}{i\lambda z} e^{ikz} \exp\left\{\frac{ik}{2z}(x^2 + y^2)\right\} \times \int_{-b/2}^{+b/2} e^{-iu\xi}\, d\xi \int_{-a/2}^{+a/2} e^{-iv\eta}\, d\eta \tag{18.28}$$

where we have chosen the origin to be at the center of the rectangular aperture [see Fig. 18.2]. Carrying out the integration as in the previous section, we obtain

$$u(x, y, z) = \frac{Aba}{i\lambda z} e^{ikz} \exp\left\{\frac{ik}{2z}(x^2 + y^2)\right\}\left(\frac{\sin\beta}{\beta}\right)\left(\frac{\sin\gamma}{\gamma}\right) \tag{18.29}$$

where β is given by Eq. (18.25),

$$\gamma = \frac{va}{2} = \frac{\pi a y}{\lambda z} \approx \frac{\pi a \sin\phi}{\lambda} \tag{18.30}$$

and $\sin\phi \approx \dfrac{y}{z}$; ϕ representing the angle of diffraction along the y-direction. Thus, we may write for the intensity distribution

$$I(P) = I_0 \frac{\sin^2\gamma}{\gamma^2}\frac{\sin^2\beta}{\beta^2} \tag{18.31}$$

The above equation represents the Fraunhofer diffraction pattern by a rectangular aperture. We must remember that Eqs. (18.29) and (18.31) are valid when both Eqs. (18.13) and (18.17) are satisfied. The intensity distribution due to a square aperture ($a = b$) is shown in Fig. 18.3; the figure corresponds to $a = b = 0.01$ cm, $z = 100$ cm and we have assumed $\lambda = 5 \times 10^{-5}$ cm. Now, if we observe in a region of radius

0.5 cm [i.e., $(x^2 + y^2) < 0.25$ cm^2] then Eq. (18.13) would give us

$$z >> \left(\frac{1}{4 \times 5 \times 10^{-5}} (0.25)^2 \right)^{\frac{1}{3}} \approx 7 \text{ cm}$$

Further Eq. (18.17) would give us

$$z >> \left(\frac{1}{5 \times 10^{-5}} 2 \times (0.01)^2 \right) \approx 4 \text{ cm}$$

We have chosen $z = 100$ cm and we get the diffraction pattern as shown in Fig. 18.3. Although in the above, we have assumed that we are observing a region of radius 0.5 cm, we have plotted the diffraction pattern for -2 cm $< x, y < +2$ cm. We may note that along the x-axis, the intensity will be zero when

$$\beta = \left(\frac{\pi b x}{\lambda z} \right) = m\pi; \quad m = 0, 1, 2, 3 \ldots \quad \textbf{(18.32)}$$

or

$$x = \frac{m\lambda}{b} z = m\ 0.5 \text{ cm}$$

$$= 0.5 \text{ cm}, 1.0 \text{ cm}, 1.5 \text{ cm}, 2.0 \text{ cm}, \ldots$$

corresponding to $m = 1, 2, 3, 4, \ldots$ respectively; this is consistent with the positions of the minima in Fig. 18.3.

For the case of a long narrow slit (i.e., for $a \to \infty$), the function

$$\frac{a \sin \gamma}{\gamma} = \frac{\sin \left[a \dfrac{\pi \sin \phi}{\lambda} \right]}{\left[\dfrac{\pi \sin \phi}{\lambda} \right]}$$

becomes very sharply peaked around $\phi = 0$. Since $\phi = 0$ implies $y = 0$, there is no diffraction along the y-axis (see Sec. 18.4). The diffraction of a plane wave incident on a long narrow slit and the transition to the Fraunhofer region is discussed in Sec. 19.7.

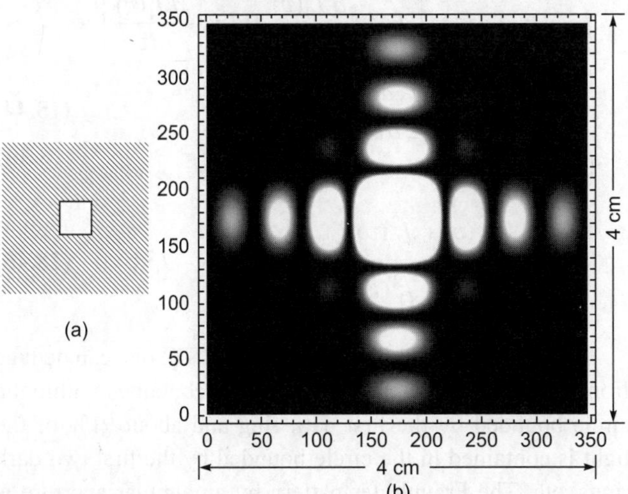

Figure 18.3

(a) A square aperture of side 0.01 cm. (b) The corresponding (computer generated) Fraunhofer diffraction pattern on a screen at a distance of 100 cm from the aperture; $\lambda = 5 \times 10^{-5}$ cm.

18.7 Fraunhofer Diffraction by a Circular Aperture

LO3

We consider a plane wave incident normally on a circular aperture as shown in Fig. 18.4. On the plane of the circular aperture we choose cylindrical coordinates [see Fig. 18.5]

$$\xi = \rho \cos \phi \quad \text{and} \quad \eta = \rho \sin \phi \quad \textbf{(18.33)}$$

Further, because of the circular symmetry of the system, the diffraction pattern will be of the form of concentric circular rings with their centers at the point O'. Consequently, we may calculate the intensity distribution only along the x-axis

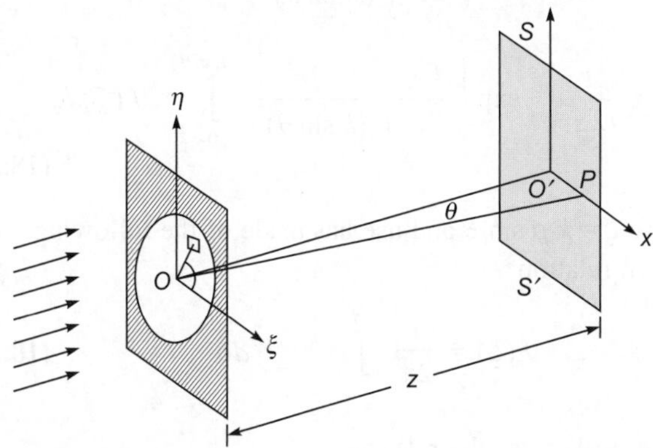

Figure 18.4

Diffraction of a plane wave incident on a circular aperture of radius a.

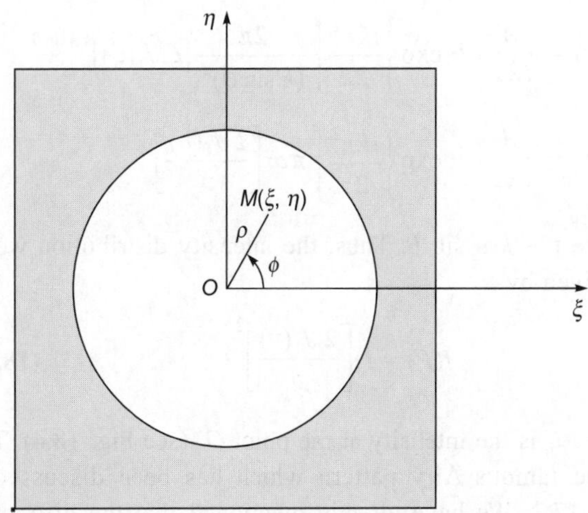

Figure 18.5

Cylindrical coordinates (ρ, ϕ) on the plane of the circular aperture.

(i.e., at points for which $y = 0$) and in the final result replace x by $\sqrt{x^2 + y^2}$. Now, when $y = 0$

$$v = 0 \quad \text{and} \quad \sin\theta \approx \frac{x}{z} \tag{18.34}$$

where θ is the angle that OP makes with the z-axis. Thus,

$$u = \frac{2\pi x}{\lambda z} = k \sin\theta$$

and Eq. (18.18) becomes

$$u(P) = \frac{A}{i\lambda z} e^{ikz} \exp\left\{\frac{ikr^2}{2z}\right\} \int_0^a \int_0^{2\pi} e^{-ik\rho\sin\theta\cos\phi} \rho\, d\rho\, d\phi \tag{18.35}$$

Thus,

$$u(P) = \frac{A}{i\lambda z} e^{ikz} \exp\left\{\frac{ikr^2}{2z}\right\} \frac{1}{(k\sin\theta)^2} \int_0^{k a \sin\theta} \zeta\, d\zeta \int e^{-i\zeta\cos\phi}\, d\phi$$

$$= \frac{A}{i\lambda z} e^{ikz} \exp\left\{\frac{ikr^2}{2z}\right\} \frac{2\pi}{(k\sin\theta)^2} \int_0^{k a \sin\theta} \zeta J_0(\zeta) d\zeta \tag{18.36}$$

where $\zeta = k\rho\sin\theta$ and use has made of the following well-known relation*

$$J_0(\zeta) = \frac{1}{2\pi} \int_0^{2\pi} e^{\pm i\zeta\cos\phi}\, d\phi \tag{18.37}$$

If we further use the relation

$$\frac{d}{d\zeta}[\zeta J_1(\zeta)] = \zeta J_0(\zeta) \tag{18.38}$$

then Eq. (18.36) becomes

$$u(P) = \frac{A}{i\lambda z} e^{ikz} \exp\left\{\frac{ikr^2}{2z}\right\} \frac{2\pi}{(k\sin\theta)^2} \left[\zeta J_1(\zeta)\right]_0^{k a \sin\theta}$$

$$= \frac{A}{i\lambda z} e^{ikz} \exp\left\{\frac{ikr^2}{2z}\right\} \pi a^2 \left[\frac{2J_1(v)}{v}\right]$$

where $v = k\,a\sin\theta$. Thus, the intensity distribution would be given by

$$I(P) = I_0 \left[\frac{2J_1(v)}{v}\right]^2 \tag{18.39}$$

where I_0 is the intensity at the point O' (see Fig. 18.4). This is the famous Airy pattern which has been discussed in Sec. 17.3. We have already mentioned that the diffraction pattern (in the plane SS') will consist of concentric rings with their centers at the point O'. If $F(r)$ represents the fractional energy contained in a circle of radius r, then

$$F(r) = \frac{\int_0^r I(\sigma) 2\pi\sigma\, d\sigma}{\int_0^\infty I(\sigma) 2\pi\sigma\, d\sigma} \tag{18.40}$$

where $I(\sigma)\, 2\pi\sigma\, d\sigma$ would be proportional to the energy contained in the annular region whose radii lie between σ and $\sigma + d\sigma$. Clearly,

$$\sin\theta \approx \frac{\sigma}{z} \tag{18.41}$$

Since $v = ka\sin\theta$, we obtain

$$\sigma = \frac{z}{ka} v \tag{18.42}$$

and Eq. (18.40) becomes

$$F(r) = \frac{\int_0^v \left[\frac{2J_1(v)}{v}\right]^2 v\, dv}{\int_0^\infty \left[\frac{2J_1(v)}{v}\right]^2 v\, dv} \tag{18.43}$$

where we have used Eq. (18.39) for the intensity distribution. Now,

$$\frac{J_1^2(v)}{v} = J_1(v)\left[J_0(v) - \frac{dJ_1(v)}{dv}\right]$$

$$= -\left[J_0(v)\frac{dJ_0(v)}{dv} + J_1(v)\frac{dJ_1(v)}{dv}\right]$$

$$= -\frac{1}{2}\frac{d}{dv}[J_0^2(v) + J_1^2(v)] \tag{18.44}$$

Thus,

$$F(r) = \frac{J_0^2(v) + J_1^2(v)\big|_0^v}{J_0^2(v) + J_1^2(v)\big|_0^\infty} = 1 - J_0^2(v) - J_1^2(v) \tag{18.45}$$

The above function is plotted in Fig. 18.6; one can deduce from the curve that about 84% of light is contained within the circle bounded by the first dark ring and about 91% of the light is contained in the circle bounded by the first two dark rings, etc. The Fraunhofer pattern by an annular aperture is discussed in Problem 18.5.

* The identities associated with Bessel functions can be found in most books on mathematical physics; see, e.g., Ref. 18.5–18.7.

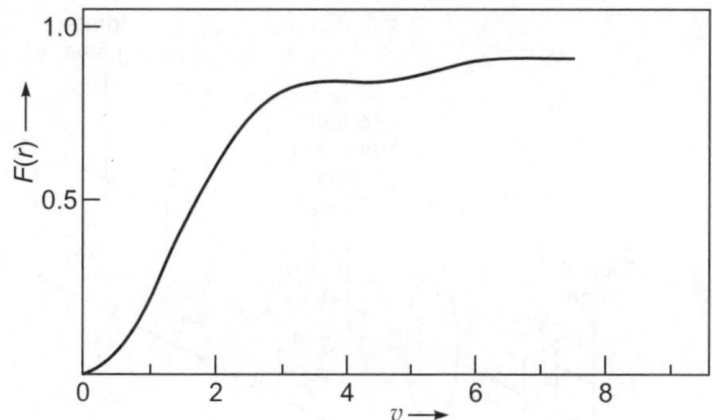

Figure 18.6
The fractional energy contained in a circle of radius r.

18.8 Array of Identical Apertures

LO4

We next consider an array of N identical apertures as shown in Fig. 18.7. The Fraunhofer diffraction pattern will be the sum of the fields produced by the individual apertures and will be given by [see Eq. (18.18)]:

$$u = C\left[\iint_{S_1} + \iint_{S_2} + \ldots\right] \exp\left[-i(u\xi + v\eta)\right] d\xi\, d\eta \tag{18.46}$$

where each integral represents the contribution from a particular aperture. Let $O_1, O_2, O_3, \ldots$ represent points that are identically situated inside the apertures. For example, if the apertures are rectangular in nature, then $O_1, O_2, O_3, \ldots$ could represent the centers of the (rectangular) aperture. Let (ξ_1, η_1), (ξ_2, η_2), (ξ_3, η_3), … represent the coordinates of the points $O_1, O_2, O_3, \ldots$ respectively; then

$$u = C\sum_{n=1}^{N}\iint \exp[-i\{u(\xi_n + \xi') + v(\eta_n + \eta')\}]\, d\xi'\, d\eta' \tag{18.47}$$

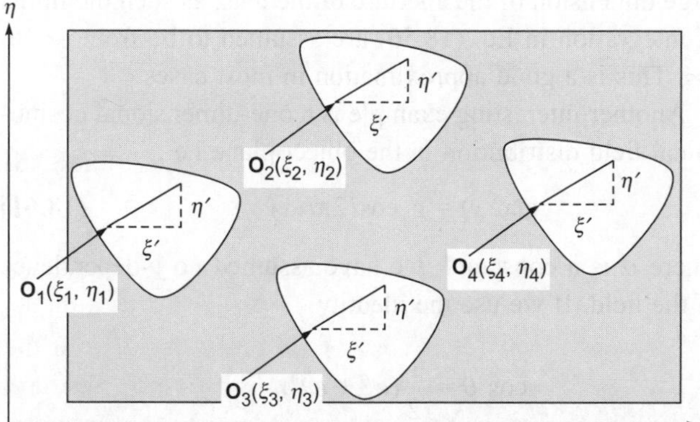

Figure 18.7
Diffraction of a plane wave incident normally on an array of N identical apertures.

where (ξ', η') represent the coordinates of an arbitrary point in a given aperture with respect to the point (ξ_n, η_n) as shown in Fig. 18.7. Thus,

$$u = u_s \sum_{n=1}^{N} \exp[-i(u\xi_n + v\eta_n)] \tag{18.48}$$

where

$$u_s = C\iint \exp[-i(u\xi' + v\eta')d\xi'\, d\eta' \tag{18.49}$$

is the field produced by a single aperture. Thus, the resultant intensity distribution would be given by

$$I = I_s I_1 \tag{18.50}$$

where I_s represent the intensity produced by a single aperture and

$$I_1 = \left|\sum_{n=1}^{N} \exp[-i(u\xi_n + v\eta_n)]\right|^2 \tag{18.51}$$

represents the intensity distribution produced by N point sources.

As an example, we consider N equally spaced identical apertures as shown in Fig. 18.8. Without loss of generality, we may assume

$$\xi_n = (n-1)d \quad \text{and} \quad \eta_n = 0; \quad n = 1, 2, 3 \ldots N$$

Thus,

$$\sum_{n=1,2,3}^{N} e^{-iu(n-1)d} = 1 + e^{-iud} + \ldots + e^{-i(N-1)ud} = \frac{1-e^{-iNud}}{1-e^{-iud}}$$

$$= \exp\left[-\frac{1}{2}i(N-1)ud\right]\frac{\sin N\gamma}{\sin\gamma} \tag{18.52}$$

where $\gamma = \dfrac{ud}{2} = \dfrac{\pi d \sin\theta}{\gamma}$ (18.53)

and $\sin\theta = \dfrac{x}{z}$ (18.54)

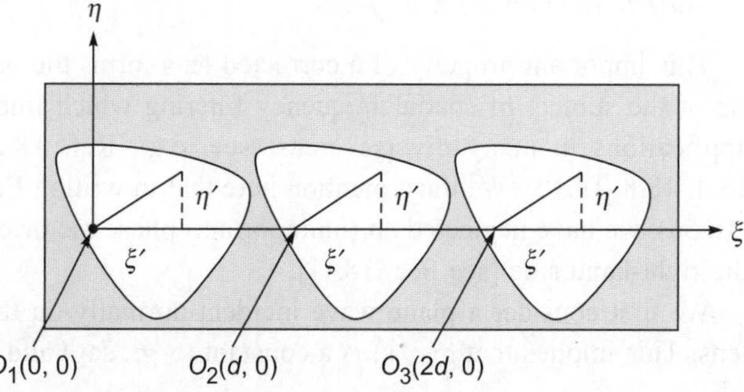

Figure 18.8
Diffraction of a plane wave incident normally on an array of N identical equally spaced apertures.

We therefore obtain

$$I_1 = \left| \sum_{n=1,2,3...}^{N} \exp[-iu(n-1)d] \right|^2 = \frac{\sin^2 N\gamma}{\sin^2 \gamma} \quad \textbf{(18.55)}$$

which is the interference pattern produced by N identically placed point sources; this is the same result as derived in Sec. 17.7. When $N = 2$, we obtain the interference pattern produced by 2 point sources.

If each aperture is a long narrow slit, we obtain the diffraction pattern produced by a grating [see Eq. (17.50)]. On the other hand, if each aperture is circular we obtain the product of the Airy pattern and the interference pattern produced by two point sources [see Figs. 16.4 and 16.5].

18.9 Spatial Frequency Filtering

LO5

In the next section, we will show that if $g(x, y)$ represents the field distribution on the front focal plane of a corrected lens (i.e., on the plane P_1 in Fig. 18.9) then on the back focal plane P_2 of the lens, one obtains the Fourier transform of $g(x, y)$, the z-axis represents the optical axis of the lens. Thus if $G(x, y)$ represents the field distribution on the back focal plane P_2 then it is related to $g(x, y)$ through the following relation:

$$G(u, v) = \frac{1}{\lambda f} \iint g(x', y') \exp[-i(ux' + vy')]dx'dy' \quad \textbf{(18.56)}$$

where $$u \equiv \frac{2\pi x}{\lambda f} \quad \text{and} \quad v \equiv \frac{2\pi y}{\lambda f} \quad \textbf{(18.57)}$$

represent the spatial frequencies. Further, λ represents the wavelength of light and f is the focal length of the lens. If we compare Eq. (18.56) with Eq. (8.39), we find that

the field distribution on the back focal plane of a corrected lens is the Fourier transform of the field distribution on the front plane.

This important property of a corrected lens forms the basis of the subject of spatial frequency filtering which finds applications in many diverse areas (see, e.g., Ref. 18.2, 18.4, 18.8–18.10). We must mention here that in writing Eq. (18.56), we have neglected an (unimportant) phase factor on the right-hand side [see Sec. 18.11].

We first consider a plane wave incident normally on the lens. This implies that $g(x, y)$ is a constant ($= g_0$, say) and

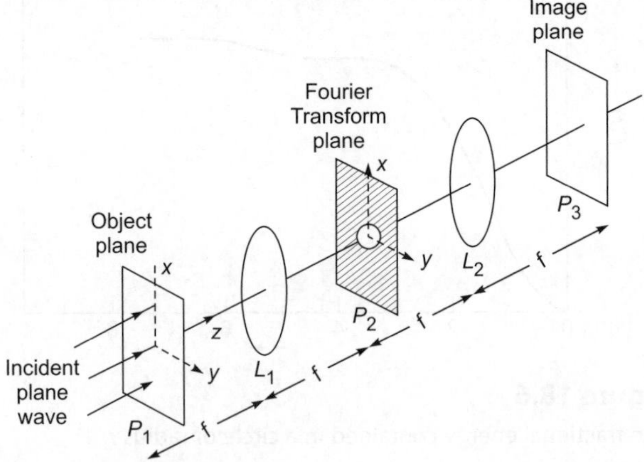

Figure 18.9
The plane P_2 is the Fourier transform plane where the spatial frequency components of the object (placed in the plane P_1) are displayed. In the above figure, a small hole is placed on the axis (in the plane P_2) which filters out the high-frequency components.

$$G(u, v) = \frac{g_0}{\lambda f} \iint \exp[-i(ux' + vy')]dx'dy' \quad \textbf{(18.58)}$$

Now, if we use

$$\int_{-\infty}^{+\infty} e^{-iux}\, dx = 2\pi\,\delta(u) \quad \textbf{(18.59)}$$

[see Eq. (8.9)], we would obtain

$$G(u, v) = \frac{g_0}{\lambda f} 4\pi^2\, \delta(u)\, \delta(v) \quad \textbf{(18.60)}$$

where $\delta(u)$ and $\delta(v)$ represent the Dirac delta functions. Since $\delta(u) = 0$ for $u \neq 0$, one can infer from Eq. (18.60) that the intensity is zero at all points excepting at the point $x = 0$, $y = 0$. This is to be expected because a plane wave gets focused to a point by a corrected lens; we are assuming a very large dimension of the aperture of the lens; as such the limits of integration in Eq. (18.56) are assumed to be from $-\infty$ to $+\infty$. This is a good approximation in most cases.

Another interesting example is a one-dimensional cosinusoidal field distribution in the object plane i.e.,

$$g(x, y) = g_0 \cos(2\pi\alpha x) \quad \textbf{(18.61)}$$

where α is a constant*; we have assumed no y-dependence of the field. If we use the identity

$$\cos\theta = \frac{1}{2}(e^{i\theta} + e^{-i\theta})$$

* On the plane P_1 (see Fig. 18.9), if we place the negative of the photograph shown in Fig. 13.11(b) with the y-axis along the length of a fringe and assume a plane wave to be incident normally on the film, then the field distribution would be proportional to $\cos^2(2\pi\alpha x)$ which is equal to $\frac{1}{2}[1 + \cos(2\pi\alpha x)]$.

we would obtain

$$G(u, v) = \frac{g_0}{\lambda f} \int \frac{1}{2} [e^{i2\pi\alpha x'} + e^{-i2\pi\alpha x'}] e^{-iux'} dx' \times \int e^{ivy'} dy' \quad \textbf{(18.62)}$$

If we now use Eq. (18.59), we get

$$G(u, v) = \frac{g_0}{\lambda f} 2\pi^2 [\delta(u - 2\pi\alpha) + \delta(u + 2\pi\alpha)]\delta(v) \quad \textbf{(18.63)}$$

Thus, we will obtain two spots in the plane P_2. These two spots will be lying on the x-axis (where $v = 0$) at $u = \pm 2\pi\alpha$ (i.e., at $x = \pm\lambda f\alpha$). Physically this can be understood from the following consideration: When a plane wave is incident normally on the plane P_1 (see Fig. 18.9), the time dependence is of the form $\cos \omega t$. If in the plane P_1, we have an object whose transmittance is proportional to $\cos (2\pi\alpha\, x)$, then the field to the right of the plane P_1 would be proportional to

$$\cos \omega t \cos (2\pi\alpha\, x)$$

$$= \frac{1}{2}[\cos (\omega t + 2\pi\alpha\, x) + \cos (\omega t - 2\pi\alpha\, x)] \quad \textbf{(18.64)}$$

We know that for a plane wave with $k_y = 0$, the field variation is of the form (see Example 9.6):

$$\cos (\omega t - k_x x - k_z z) \quad \textbf{(18.65)}$$

where $k_x = k \sin \theta$, $k_z = k \cos \theta$, $k = \frac{2\pi}{\lambda}$ and θ is the angle that the propagation vector **k** makes with the z-axis. At $z = 0$, the field becomes

$$\cos(\omega t - k_x x) \quad \textbf{(18.66)}$$

Comparing the above equation with Eq. (18.64), we find that the two terms on the RHS of Eq. (18.64) represent two plane waves propagating along directions making angles $-\theta$ and $+\theta$ with the z-axis, where

$$\sin \theta = \frac{k_x}{k} = \frac{2\pi\alpha}{2\pi/\lambda} = \alpha\lambda \quad \textbf{(18.67)}$$

These plane waves will obviously focus to two points at $x = -\lambda f\alpha$ and $x = +\lambda f\alpha$ on the x-axis in the plane P_2. Since α represents the spatial frequency associated with the object, one essentially obtains, on the back focal plane, the spatial frequency spectrum of the object.

We are familiar with the fact that a general time varying signal can be expressed as a superposition of pure sinusoidal signals [see Eq. (8.29)]. In a similar manner, the field variation across an arbitrary object (placed on the plane P_1), can be expressed as a superposition of sinusoidal variations and one would get the corresponding (spatial) frequency components on the plane P_2. For this reason, the plane P_2 is often termed as the Fourier transform plane.

As another example, if the amplitude variation of the object is of the form

$$g(x, y) = A \cos 2\pi\alpha x + B \cos 2\pi\beta x \quad \textbf{(18.68)}$$

then one would obtain four spots on the plane P_2 (all lying on the x-axis); these spots will appear at $x = \pm\lambda f\alpha, \pm\lambda f\beta$. Since the Fourier transform of the Fourier transform is the original function itself [see Chapter 8], if we place the plane P_2 on the front focal plane of lens L_2, then on its back focal plane (i.e., in the plane P_3 in Fig. 18.9) we will obtain the amplitude distribution associated with the object. [There will however be an inversion; i.e., $f(x, y)$ will become $f(-x, -y)$ on the plane P_3. This can also be seen by simple ray tracing.] If we now put stops at the points ($x = +\lambda f\alpha, y = 0$) and ($x = -\lambda f\alpha, y = 0$) on the plane P_2, then the field distribution on the plane P_3 would be proportional to $\cos 2\pi\beta x$. Thus, we have been able to filter out the spatial frequency α. This is the basic principle behind spatial frequency filtering.

For an arbitrary object, if we put a small hole on the plane P_2, then it will filter out the high frequency components [see Fig. 18.10(a)]; if we put a small stop on the axis, we filter out the low frequency components [see Fig. 18.10(b)]. On the other hand, an annular aperture on plane P_2 will act as a band pass filter as shown in Fig. 18.10(c).

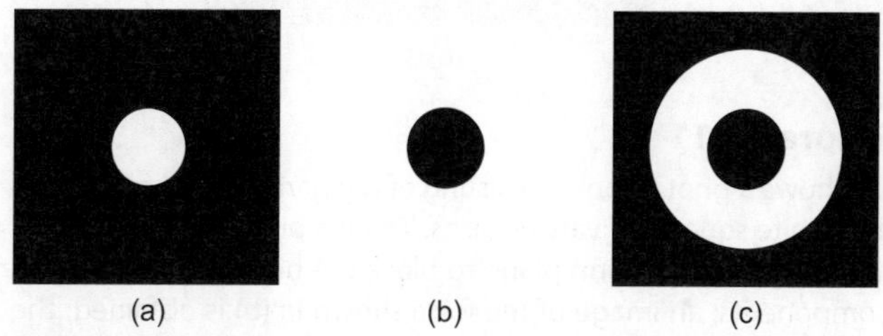

Figure 18.10

(a) Low pass filter, (b) high pass filter and (c) band pass filter; the filters are to be put on the plane P_2.

As a simple application, we consider a half-tone photograph (like that in a newspaper), which consists of a large number of spots of varying shades that produce the image pattern. Since the spots are closely spaced, it represents a high frequency noise and the overall image has much smaller frequencies associated with it. Thus, if we put a transparency similar to that shown in Fig. 18.11(a) and allow only the low frequency components to pass through (as shown in Fig. 18.9), we will obtain, on the plane P_3, an image which does not contain the unwanted high-frequency noise (see Fig 18.11(c)).

The subject of spatial frequency filtering finds applications in many other areas like contrast improvement, character recognition, etc. (see, e.g., Refs. 18.2, 18.4 and 18.9).

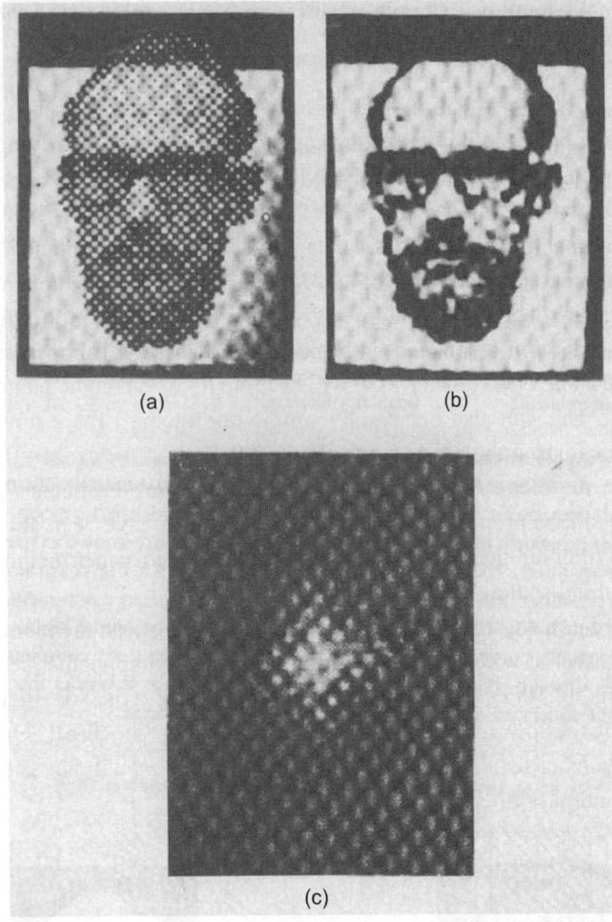

Figure 18.11

(a) Shows a photograph consisting of regularly spaced black and white squares of varying sizes. When a pinhole is placed in the Fourier transform plane to block the high-frequency components, an image of the form shown in (b) is obtained; the frequency spectrum is shown in (c). Notice that in (b) shades of gray appear as well details such as the missing part of the eye glass frame. [After R. A. Phillips, *Spatial Filtering Experiments for Undergraduate Laboratories, American Journal of Physics*, 37, 536 (1969); used with permission.]

18.9.1 The 4f Correlator

The 4f correlator is based on the convolution theorem discussed in Sec. 8.7. A plane wave is assumed to be incident on a transparency containing one two-dimensional function $g(x, y)$ which is placed on the front focal plane of the first lens as shown in Fig. 18.12. The Fourier transform of $g(x, y)$ [$= G(u, v)$] is formed on the back focal plane of the lens. A transmission mask containing the Fourier transform of the second function, $h(x, y)$ [$= H(u, v)$], is placed on this plane. Thus, the product $G(u, v)\, H(u, v)$ lies on the front focal plane of the second lens and therefore on its back focal plane, we will obtain the Fourier transform of $G(u, v)\, H(u, v)$ which is nothing but the convolution of $g(x, y)$ and $h(x, y)$. This concept is of considerable use in many applications (see, e.g., Ref. 18.2, 18.4, 18.8–18.10).

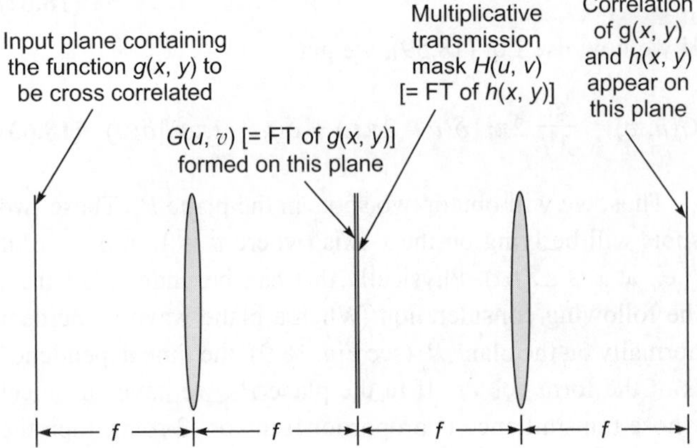

Figure 18.12

The 4f correlator. [*Figure adapted from Ref. 18.11*].

18.10 The Fourier Transforming Property of a Thin Lens

LO6

In this section, we will derive the Fourier transforming property of a thin lens [see Eq. (18.56)]. We will first show that the effect of a thin lens of focal length f is to multiply the incident field distribution by a factor p_L given by

$$p_L = \exp\left[-\frac{ik}{2f}(x^2 + y^2)\right] \tag{18.69}$$

Consider an object point O at a distance d_1 from an aberrationless thin lens of focal length f (see Fig. 18.13). If the image point I is at a distance d_2 from the lens, then d_2 is given by [see Sec. 3.4]:

$$\frac{1}{d_1} + \frac{1}{d_2} = \frac{1}{f} \tag{18.70}$$

where d_1 and d_2 represent the magnitude of the distances of the object and image points from the lens. The phase factor corresponding to the disturbance emanating from the point O is simply $\exp(+ikr)$, where r is the distance measured from the point O. Now

$$r = (x^2 + y^2 + d_1^2)^{1/2} = d_1\left[1 + \frac{x^2 + y^2}{d_1^2}\right]^{1/2}$$

$$\approx d_1 + \frac{x^2 + y^2}{2d_1}$$

where in writing the last expression, we have assumed x, $y << d_1$, i.e., we have confined ourselves to a region close to the axis of the lens; this is known as the **paraxial approximation**. Thus, the phase distribution on the transverse plane P_2 at a distance d_1 from the point O (i.e., immediately in front of the lens; see Fig. 18.13) is given by

$$\exp(+ikr) \approx \exp\left[ik\left(d_1 + \frac{x^2+y^2}{2d_1}\right)\right]$$

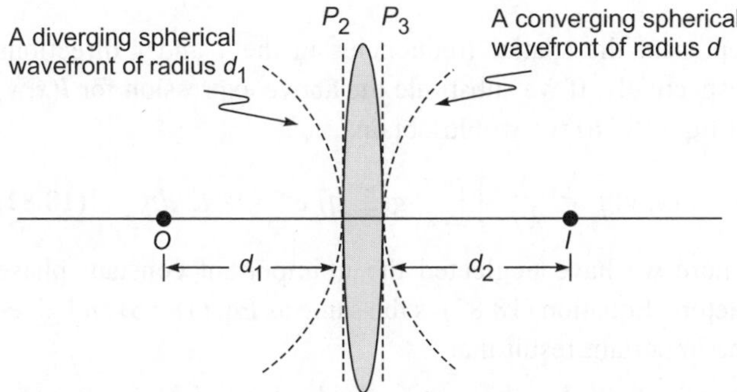

Figure 18.13
Spherical waves emanating from an object point O, after refraction through a convex lens, emerge as spherical waves converging to the image point I.

Since the image is formed at I, the incident spherical wave emerges as another spherical wave of radius d_2, which under the paraxial approximation is

$$\exp\left[-ik\left(d_2 + \frac{x^2+y^2}{2d_2}\right)\right]$$

The negative sign in the exponent refers to the fact that we now have a converging spherical wave. Thus, if p_L represents the factor that when multiplied to the incident phase distribution gives the phase distribution of the emergent wave, then

$$\exp\left[-ik\left(d_2 + \frac{x^2+y^2}{2d_2}\right)\right] = \exp\left[+ik\left(d_1 + \frac{x^2+y^2}{2d_1}\right)\right] p_L$$

or

$$p_L = \exp[-ik(d_1 + d_2)] \exp\left[-\frac{ik}{2}\left(\left(\frac{1}{d_1}+\frac{1}{d_2}\right)(x^2+y^2)\right)\right], \quad (18.71)$$

the subscript L on p corresponds to the fact that we are referring to a lens. If we use Eq. (18.70) and neglect the first factor in the above equation, because it is independent of x and y, we obtain Eq. (18.69). Thus the effect of a thin lens on an incident field is to multiply the incident phase distribution by a factor that is given by Eq. (18.69). For a plane wave incident along the axis, the emerging disturbance will simply be p_L, which can be seen to be the paraxial approximation of a converging spherical wave front of radius f.

Now, let $g(x, y)$ represent the field distribution on the plane P_1 (see Fig. 18.14). We would first like to determine the field distribution on the plane P_2 i.e., at a distance f from the plane P_1 (see Fig. 18.14). Obviously the field will undergo Fresnel diffraction and on plane P_2 it will be given by [using Eq. (18.9)]

$$u(x, y)|_{P_2} = \frac{1}{i\lambda f}\exp(ikf) \times$$

$$\iint g(\xi, \eta) \times \exp\left\{\frac{ik}{2f}[(x-\xi)^2 + (y-\eta)^2\right\} d\xi d\eta \quad (18.72)$$

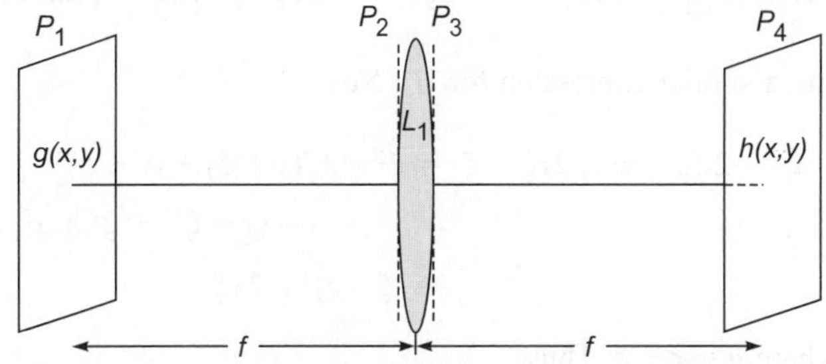

Figure 18.14
A field distribution $g(x, y)$ placed at the front focal plane of a lens produces a field distribution $h(x, y)$ in the plane P_4 at the back focal plane of the lens. The field $g(x, y)$ first undergoes Fresnel diffraction from plane P_1 to P_2, then it gets multiplied by a phase factor due to the presence of the lens, and the resultant field again undergoes Fresnel diffraction from plane P_3 to P_4 to produce the field distribution $h(x, y)$.

Now, as shown earlier in this section, the effect of a thin lens of focal length f is to multiply the incident field distribution by the factor p_L given by Eq. (18.69), thus on the plane P_3, the field distribution will be given by

$$u(x, y)|_{P_3} = \frac{1}{i\lambda f} e^{ikf} \exp[-i\alpha(x^2 + y^2)] \times$$

$$\iint g(\xi, \eta) \times \exp\{i\alpha[(x-\xi)^2 + (y-\eta)^2]\} d\xi d\eta \quad (18.73)$$

where $$\alpha = \frac{k}{2f} = \frac{\pi}{\lambda f} \quad (18.74)$$

From plane P_3 the field will again undergo Fresnel diffraction and therefore on plane P_4, it will be given by [using Eq. (18.9)]

$$u(x, y)|_{P_4} = \frac{1}{i\lambda f} e^{ikf} \iint u(\zeta, \tau)|_{P_3} \times$$

$$\exp\{i\alpha[(x-\zeta)^2 + (y-\tau)^2]\} d\zeta d\tau \quad (18.75)$$

Substituting for $u|_{P_3}$ from Eq. (18.73) we get

$$u(x, y)|_{P_4} = \left[\frac{1}{i\lambda f}e^{ikf}\right]^2 I(x, y) \quad \textbf{(18.76)}$$

where $I(x, y) = \iint_{-\infty}^{+\infty} g(\xi, \eta) H(x, y, \xi, \eta) d\xi d\eta$ **(18.77)**

$$\begin{aligned} H(x, y, \xi, \eta) &= \iint_{-\infty}^{+\infty} \exp\{-i\alpha(\zeta^2 + \tau^2)\} \\ &\times \exp\{i\alpha[(\zeta - \xi)^2 + (\tau - \eta)^2]\} \\ &\times \exp\{i\alpha[(x - \zeta)^2 + (y - \tau)^2]\} d\zeta\, d\tau \\ &= H_\xi(x) H_\eta(y) \end{aligned} \quad \textbf{(18.78)}$$

$$H_\xi(x) = \int_{-\infty}^{+\infty} \exp\{i\alpha[\xi^2 - 2\xi\zeta + x^2 - 2x\zeta + \zeta^2]\} d\zeta \quad \textbf{(18.79)}$$

and a similar expression for H_η. Now,

$$\begin{aligned} \xi^2 - 2\xi\zeta + x^2 - 2x\zeta + \zeta^2 &= \zeta^2 - 2\zeta(x + \xi) + (x + \xi)^2 \\ &\quad - (x + \xi)^2 + \xi^2 + x^2 \\ &= (\zeta - g)^2 - 2x\xi \end{aligned}$$

where $g = x + \xi$. Thus,

$$H_\xi = \exp[-2i\alpha x\xi] \int_{-\infty}^{+\infty} \exp[i\alpha(\zeta - g)^2] d\zeta$$

or $$H_\xi(x) = e^{-2i\alpha x\xi} \sqrt{\frac{\pi}{-i\alpha}} \quad \textbf{(18.80)}$$

and a similar expression for $H_\eta(y)$. Thus,

$$\begin{aligned} I(x, y) &= \iint_{-\infty}^{+\infty} g(\xi, \eta) H_\xi(x) H_\eta(y) d\xi\, d\eta \\ &= \frac{\pi}{-i\alpha} \iint_{-\infty}^{+\infty} g(\xi, \eta)\, e^{-2i\alpha(x\xi + y\eta)} d\xi\, d\eta \\ &= i\lambda f \iint_{-\infty}^{+\infty} g(\xi, \eta)\, e^{-i(u\xi + v\eta)} d\xi\, d\eta \end{aligned}$$

where we have used Eq. (18.74) and

$$u = 2\alpha x = \frac{2\pi x}{\lambda f} \quad \text{and} \quad v = 2\alpha y = \frac{2\pi y}{\lambda f} \quad \textbf{(18.81)}$$

represent the spatial frequencies in the x and y directions respectively. If we substitute the above expression for $I(x, y)$ in Eq. (18.76) we would obtain

$$u(x, y)|_{P_4} = \frac{1}{\lambda f} \iint_{-\infty}^{+\infty} g(\xi, \eta)\, e^{-i(u\xi + v\eta)} d\xi\, d\eta \quad \textbf{(18.82)}$$

where we have neglected the unimportant constant phase factors. Equation (18.82) is the same as Eq. (18.56) and gives the important result that

the field distribution on the back focal plane of a corrected lens is the Fourier transform of the field distribution on the front plane.

We should mention here that in writing the limits in the integral from $-\infty$ to $+\infty$, we have assumed the lens to be of infinite extent; the error involved is usually very small because in almost all practical cases

$$a/\lambda >>> 1$$

where a represents the aperture of the lens.

SUMMARY

- If the amplitude and phase distribution on the plane $z = 0$ is given by $A(\xi, \eta)$ then the Fresnel diffraction pattern is given by

$$u(x, y, z) \approx \frac{1}{i\lambda z} e^{ikz} \iint A(\xi, \eta) \times \exp\left\{\frac{ik}{2z}[(x - \xi)^2 + (y - \eta)^2\right\} d\xi d\eta$$

where $k = 2\pi/\lambda$.

- The Fraunhofer diffraction pattern is the Fourier transform of the aperture function and is given by

$$u(x, y, z) \approx \frac{1}{i\lambda z} e^{ikz} \exp\left\{\frac{ik}{2z}(x^2 + y^2)\right\} \times \iint A(\xi, \eta) e^{-i(u\xi + v\eta)} d\xi d\eta$$

- For a plane wave incident normally on a circular aperture of radius a, the Fraunhofer diffraction pattern is given by

$$I(P) = I_0 \left[\frac{2J_1(v)}{v}\right]^2$$

where $v = k\, a \sin\theta$

- If $g(x, y)$ and $G(x, y)$ represent the filed distributions on the front focal plane and on the back focal plane of a corrected lens then

$$G(u, v) = \frac{1}{\lambda f} \iint g(x', y') \exp[-i(ux' + vy')] dx' dy'$$

where, $u \equiv \frac{2\pi x}{\lambda f}$ and $v \equiv \frac{2\pi y}{\lambda f}$ represent the spatial frequencies. Thus on the back focal plane of the lens one obtains the Fourier transform of $g(x, y)$, the z-axis represents the optical axis of the lens. This important property of a corrected lens forms the basis of the subject of spatial frequency filtering.

PROBLEMS

18.1 Consider a rectangular aperture of dimensions 0.2 mm × 0.3 mm with a screen placed at a distance of 100 cm from the aperture. Assume a plane wave with $\lambda = 5 \times 10^{-5}$ cm incident normally on the aperture. Calculate the positions of maxima and minima in a region 0.2 cm × 0.2 cm of the screen. Show that both Fresnel and Fraunhofer approximations are satisfied.

18.2 In the above problem, assume a convex lens (of focal length 20 cm) placed immediately after the aperture. Calculate the positions of the first three maxima and minima on the x-axis (implying $\phi = 0$) and also on the y-axis (implying $\theta = 0$).

18.3 The Fraunhofer diffraction pattern of a circular aperture (of radius 0.5 mm) is observed on the focal plane of a convex lens of focal length 20 cm. Calculate the radii of the first and the second dark rings. Assume $\lambda = 5.5 \times 10^{-5}$ cm.

[**Ans:** 0.13 mm, 0.18 mm]

18.4 In the above problem, calculate the area of the patch (on focal plane) which will contain 95% of the total energy.

18.5 Obtain the diffraction pattern of an annular aperture bounded by circles of radii a_1 and $a_2(> a_1)$. [**Hint:** The integration limits of ρ in Eq. (103) must be a_1 and a_2]

18.6 Consider a rectangular aperture of dimensions 0.2 mm × 0.3 mm. Obtain the positions of the first few maxima and minima in the Fraunhofer diffraction pattern along directions parallel to the length and breadth of the rectangle. Assume $\lambda = 5 \times 10^{-5}$ cm and that the diffraction pattern is produced at the focal plane of a lens of focal length 20 cm.

[**Ans:** Along the x-axis, minima will occur at $x \approx 0.05$, 0.10, 0.15, … cm; along the y-axis, minima will occur at $y \approx 0.033$, 0.067, 0.1, … cm]

18.7 The Fraunhofer diffraction pattern of a circular aperture (of radius 0.5 mm) is observed on the focal plane of a convex lens of focal length 20 cm. Calculate the radii of the first and the second dark rings. Assume $\lambda = 5.5 \times 10^{-5}$ cm.

[**Ans:** 0.13 mm, 0.25 mm]

18.8 In Problem 18.7, calculate the area of the patch (on focal plane) which will contain 95% of the total energy.

[**Ans:** $\approx 5.55 \times 10^{-3}$ cm^2]

CHAPTER

19

Fresnel Diffraction

One of your commissioners, M. Poisson, had deduced from the integrals reported by the author [Fresnel] the singular result that the centre of the shadow of an opaque circular screen must, when the rays penetrate there at incidences which are only a little oblique, be just as illuminated as if the screen did not exist. The consequence have been submitted to the test of a direct experiment, and observation has perfectly confirmed the calculation.

—Dominique Arago to the French Academy of Sciences (1818)*

LEARNING OBJECTIVES

After reading this chapter, the reader should be able to:

LO 1: *analyze Fresnel half-period zones and its applications.*

LO 2: *describe a more rigorous approach to Fresnel diffraction.*

LO 3: *describe propagation of Gaussian beams.*

LO 4: *study diffraction by a straight edge.*

LO 5: *evaluate the diffraction of a plane wave by a long narrow slit and study its transition to the Fraunhofer region.*

Important Milestones

1816: Augustin Fresnel developed the theory of diffraction using the wave theory of light.

1817: Using Fresnel's theory, Poisson predicted a bright spot at the center of the shadow of an opaque disc—this is usually referred to as the 'Poisson spot'.

1818: Fresnel and Arago carried out the experiment to demonstrate the existence of the Poisson spot validating the wave theory.

1874: Marie Cornu developed a graphical approach to study Fresnel diffraction—this came to be known as the Cornu's spiral.

Above Image: Close-up view of a red laser on a cutting machine in a college physics laboratory. Photograph courtesy McGraw Hill Digital Access Library.

19.1 Introduction

In Chapter 17, we had mentioned that the phenomenon of diffraction can be broadly classified under two categories: under the first category comes the Fresnel class of diffraction in which either the source or the screen (or both) are at a finite distance from the diffracting aperture. In the second category comes the Fraunhofer class of diffraction (discussed in the last two chapters) in which the wave incident on the aperture is a plane wave and the diffraction pattern is observed on the focal plane of a convex lens, so that the screen is effectively at an infinite distance from the aperture. In the present chapter, we will discuss the Fresnel class of diffraction and also study the transition to the Fraunhofer region. The underlying principle in the entire analysis is the Huygens–Fresnel principle according to which:

Each point on a wavefront is a source of secondary disturbance and the secondary wavelets emanating from different points mutually interfere.

In order to appreciate the implications of this principle we consider the incidence of a plane wave on a circular hole of radius a as shown in Fig. 19.1. In Sec. 17.3, we had shown that the beam will undergo diffraction divergence and the angular spreading will be given by

$$\Delta\theta \sim \frac{\lambda}{2a}$$

Thus, when $a >>> \lambda$ the intensity at a point R (which is deep inside the geometrical shadow) will be negligible; on the other hand, if $a \sim \lambda$ there will be almost uniform spreading out of the beam resulting in an (almost) uniform illumination of the screen. This phenomenon is a manifestation of the fact that when $a >>> \lambda$, the secondary wavelets emanating from different points on the circular aperture so beautifully interfere to produce (almost) zero intensity in the geometrical shadow and a large intensity inside the circular region (see Fig. 19.1). However, if $a \sim \lambda$ then the aperture almost acts as a point source resulting in a uniform illumination of the screen (see Fig. 17.12).

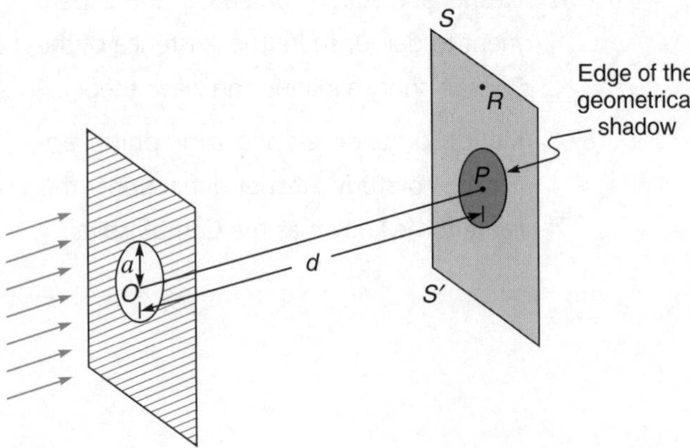

Figure 19.1
Diffraction of a plane wave incident normally on a circular aperture of radius a.

We will first introduce the concept of Fresnel half-period zones to have a qualitative understanding of the Fresnel diffraction pattern; this will be followed by a more rigorous analysis of the Fresnel class of diffraction and its transition to the Fraunhofer region.

19.2 Fresnel Half-Period Zones LO1

Let us consider a plane wavefront WW' propagating in the z-direction as shown in Fig. 19.2. In order to determine the field at an arbitrary point P due to the disturbances reaching from different portions of the wavefront, we make the following construction: from the point P we drop a perpendicular PO on the wavefront. If $PO = d$, then with point P as centre we draw spheres of radii $d + \lambda/2$, $d + 2\lambda/2$, $d + 3\lambda/2, \ldots$; these spheres will intersect WW' in circles as shown in Fig. 19.2. The radius of the nth circle will obviously be given by

$$r_n = \left[\left(d + n\frac{\lambda}{2}\right)^2 - d^2\right]^{1/2}$$

$$= \sqrt{n\lambda d}\left[1 + \frac{n\lambda}{4d}\right]^{1/2}$$

or $$r_n \approx \sqrt{n\lambda d} \qquad (19.1)$$

where we have assumed $d >>> \lambda$, this is indeed justified for practical systems using visible light; of course, we are assuming that n is not a very large number. The annular region between the nth circle and $(n-1)^{th}$ circle is known as the nth **half-period zone**; the area of the nth half-period zone is given by

$$A_n = \pi r_n^2 - \pi r_{n-1}^2$$

$$\approx \pi[n\lambda d - (n-1)\lambda d] = \pi\lambda d \qquad (19.2)$$

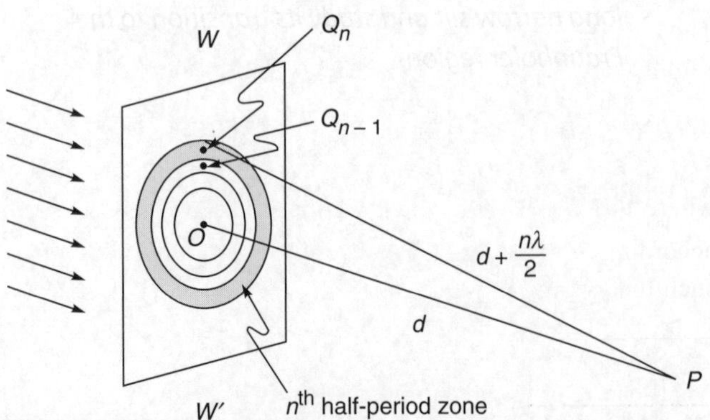

Figure 19.2
Construction of Fresnel half-period zones.

Thus the areas of all the half-period zones are approximately equal. Now the resultant disturbance produced by the nth zone will be π out-of-phase with the disturbance produced by the $(n-1)^{\text{th}}$ [or the $(n+1)^{\text{th}}$] zone. This can easily be seen from the following consideration: For infinitesimal area surrounding a point Q_n in the nth half-period zone, there is a corresponding infinitesimal area surrounding the point Q_{n-1} in the $(n-1)^{\text{th}}$ half-period zone such that

$$Q_nP - Q_{n-1}P = \frac{\lambda}{2}$$

which corresponds to a phase difference of π. Since the areas of the zones are approximately equal, one can have a one-to-one correspondence between points in various zones. Thus, the resultant amplitude at the point P can be written as

$$u(P) = u_1 - u_2 + u_3 - u_4 + \ldots + (-1)^{m+1} u_m + \ldots \quad \textbf{(19.3)}$$

where u_n represents the net amplitude produced by the secondary wavelets emanating from the nth zone; the alternate negative and positive signs represent the fact that the resultant disturbances produced by two consecutive zones are π out-of-phase with respect to each other. The amplitude produced by a particular zone is proportional to the area of the zone and inversely proportional to the distance of the zone from the point P; further, it also depends on an obliquity factor which is proportional to $\frac{1}{2}(1 + \cos\chi)$ where χ is the angle that the normal to the zone makes with the line QP; this obliquity factor comes out automatically from rigorous diffraction theory.* Thus, we may write

$$u_n = \text{constant}\ \frac{A_n}{Q_nP}\frac{(1+\cos\chi)}{2} \quad \textbf{(19.4)}$$

where A_n represents the area of the nth zone. It can be shown that if we use the exact expression for r_n, the area of the zones increases with n; however, this slight increase in the area is exactly compensated by the increased distance of the zone from the point P. In spite of this, the amplitudes u_1, u_2, u_3... decrease monotonically because of increased obliquity. Thus, we may write

$$u_1 > u_2 > u_3 \ldots \quad \textbf{(19.5)}$$

The series expressed by Eq. (19.3) can be approximately summed due to a method by Schuster. We rewrite Eq. (19.3) as

$$u(P) = \frac{u_1}{2} + \left(\frac{u_1}{2} - u_2 + \frac{u_3}{2}\right) + \left(\frac{u_3}{2} - u_4 + \frac{u_5}{2}\right) + \ldots \quad \textbf{(19.6)}$$

where the last term would be either $\frac{1}{2}u_m$ or $\left(\frac{1}{2}u_{m-1} - u_m\right)$ according to m being odd or even. If the obliquity factor is such that

$$u_n > \frac{1}{2}(u_{n-1} + u_{n+1}) \quad \textbf{(19.7)}$$

then the quantities inside the brackets in Eq. (19.6) will be negative; consequently,

$$\left.\begin{aligned} &u(P) < \frac{1}{2}u_1 + \frac{1}{2}u_m\ ;\ (m \text{ odd}) \\ \text{and}\quad &u(P) < \frac{1}{2}u_1 + \frac{1}{2}u_{m-1} - u_m \approx \frac{u_1}{2} - \frac{u_m}{2}\ ;\ (m \text{ even}) \end{aligned}\right\} \quad \textbf{(19.8)}$$

where we have assumed that the amplitude of the fields produced by consecutive zones differ only slightly. In order to obtain the upper limits, we rewrite Eq. (19.3) in the form

$$u(P) = u_1 - \frac{u_2}{2} - \left(\frac{u_2}{2} - u_3 + \frac{u_4}{2}\right) - \left(\frac{u_4}{2} - u_5 + \frac{u_6}{2}\right) \quad \textbf{(19.9)}$$

where the last term would now be $\left(-\frac{1}{2}u_{m-1} + u_m\right)$ when m is odd and $-\frac{1}{2}u_m$ when m is even. Since the quantities inside the brackets are negative, we obtain

$$\left.\begin{aligned} &u(P) > u_1 - \frac{u_2}{2} - \frac{u_{m-1}}{2} + u_m \approx \frac{u_1}{2} + \frac{u_m}{2} \\ &\qquad\qquad (\text{when } m \text{ is odd}) \\ \text{and}\quad &u(P) > u_1 - \frac{u_2}{2} - \frac{u_m}{2} \approx \frac{u_1}{2} - \frac{u_m}{2} \\ &\qquad\qquad (\text{when } m \text{ is even}) \end{aligned}\right\} \quad \textbf{(19.10)}$$

Using Eqs. (19.8) and (19.10) we may approximately write

$$\left.\begin{aligned} &u(P) \approx \frac{u_1}{2} + \frac{u_m}{2}\ (\text{when } m \text{ is odd}) \\ \text{and}\quad &u(P) \approx \frac{u_1}{2} - \frac{u_m}{2}\ (\text{when } m \text{ is even}) \end{aligned}\right\} \quad \textbf{(19.11)}$$

If we can neglect u_m in comparison to u_1 then the Eq. (19.11)** gives the remarkable result that

$$u(P) \approx \frac{u_1}{2} \quad \textbf{(19.12)}$$

implying that *the resultant amplitude produced by the entire wavefront is only one half of the amplitude produced by the first half-period zone.*

19.2.1 Diffraction by a Circular Aperture

We may use the above analysis to study the diffraction of a plane wave by a circular aperture. Let the point P be at a distance d from the circular aperture (see Fig. 19.1). We assume that the radius of the circular aperture, a, can be increased from zero onwards. As a increases, the intensity

*See, e.g., Ref. 19.3.

**If one assumes a form of the obliquity factor as given by Eq. (19.4) then it decreases from 1 to 1/2 as m increases from 1 to ∞; this implies that $|u_m|$ can never be smaller than $\frac{u_1}{2}$. However, when m is large, a slight shift of the point P on the axis will change the amplitude from $\frac{u_1}{2} + \frac{u_m}{2}$ to $\frac{u_1}{2} - \frac{u_m}{2}$, the changes will occur with such great rapidity that one can only observe the average value which will be $\frac{u_1}{2}$.

at the point P would also increase till the circular aperture contains the first half-period zone; this would happen when $a = \sqrt{\lambda d}$. The resultant amplitude at the point P would be u_1 which is twice the value of the amplitude for the unobstructed wavefront [see Eq. (19.12)]. The intensity would therefore be $4I_0$, where I_0 represents the intensity at the point P due to the unobstructed wavefront. If we further increase a then $u(P)$ would start decreasing and when the circular aperture contains the first two half-period zones (which would happen when $a = \sqrt{2\lambda d}$) the resultant amplitude ($= u_1 - u_2$) would be almost zero. *Thus, by increasing the hole diameter, the intensity at the point P decreases almost to zero.* This interesting result is once again due to the validity of the Huygens–Fresnel principle and hence would be valid for sound waves also. We may generalize the above result by noting that if

$$a = \sqrt{(2n+1)\lambda d}\ ;\ n = 0, 1, 2, \ldots \text{ [maxima]}$$

the aperture will contain an odd number of half-period zones and the intensity will be maximum; on the other hand, if

$$a = \sqrt{2n\lambda d}\ ;\ n = 1, 2, \ldots \text{ [minima]}$$

the aperture will contain an even number of half-period zones and the intensity will be minimum. In order to have a numerical appreciation, we note that for $d = 50$ cm and $\lambda = 5 \times 10^{-5}$ cm, the radii of the first, second and third zones would be 0.500 mm, 0.707 mm and 0.866 mm, respectively. As a corollary of the above analysis we can consider a circular aperture of a fixed radius a and study the intensity variation along the axis. Whenever the distance

$$d = \frac{a^2}{(2n+1)\lambda}\ ;\ n = 0, 1, 2, \ldots \text{ (maxima)}$$

the point P (see Fig. 19.1) will correspond to a maximum. Similarly, when

$$d = \frac{a^2}{2n\lambda}\ ;\ n = 1, 2, \ldots \text{ (minima)}$$

the point P will correspond to a minimum. The intensity distribution on a screen SS' at off-axis points can be approximately calculated by using the half-period zones, but such a calculation is fairly cumbersome. However, from the symmetry of the problem, one can deduce that the diffraction pattern has to be in the form of concentric circular rings with their centres at the point P.

19.2.2 Diffraction by an Opaque Disc–The Poisson Spot

If instead of the circular aperture we have a circular disc [see Fig. 19.3(a)] and if the disc obstructs the first p half-period zones then the field at the point P would be

$$u(P) = u_{p+1} - u_{p+2} + \ldots \approx \frac{u_{p+1}}{2} \tag{19.13}$$

Thus, we should always obtain a bright spot on the axis behind a circular disc; (the more rigorous theory also predicts the same result — see Sec. 19.4.2). This is called the '**Poisson spot**'. We may mention here that it was in 1816 that the French physicist Augustin Fresnel developed the mathematical theory of diffraction using the wave theory of light. Simeon Poisson, the famous mathematician, used Fresnel's theory to predict a bright spot at the center of the shadow of an opaque disc. Poisson was a great supporter of the corpuscular theory of light and he said that since the bright spot is against common sense, the wave theory must be wrong. Shortly afterwards, Fresnel and Arago carried out the experiment to demonstrate the existence of the Poisson spot [see Fig. 19.3(b)], validating the wave theory.

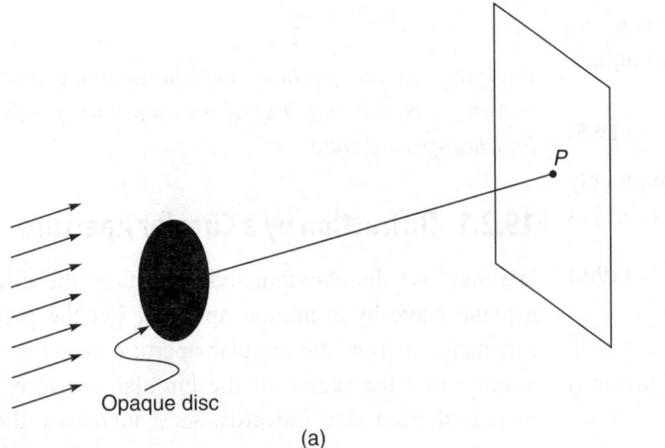

(a)

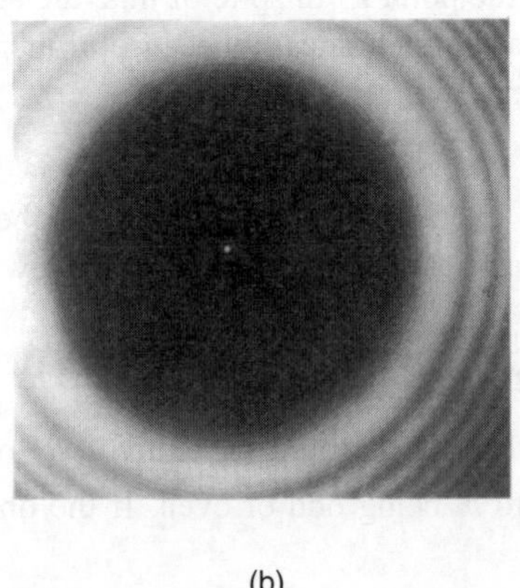

(b)

Figure 19.3

(a) When a plane wave is incident normally on an opaque disc, a bright spot is always formed on an axial point. This spot is known as the Poisson spot. (b) The Poisson spot at the center of the shadow of a one cent coin; the screen is 20 m from the coin and the source of light is also 20 m from the coin. [Photograph reprinted with permission from P.M. Rinard, *Large scale diffraction patterns from circular objects*, American Journal of Physics, Vol. 44, 70, 1976; Copyright (1976), American Association of Physics Teachers used with Permission].

19.3 The Zone-Plate

LO1

A beautiful application of the concept of Fresnel half-period zones lies in the construction of the zone-plate which consists of a large number of concentric circles whose radii are proportional to the square root of natural numbers and the alternate annular regions of which are blackened (see Fig. 19.4). Let the radii of the circles be $\sqrt{1}\,K$, $\sqrt{2}\,K$, $\sqrt{3}\,K$, $\sqrt{4}\,K$, … where K is a constant and has the dimension of length. We consider a point P_1 which is at a distance K^2/λ from the zone plate; for this point the blackened rings correspond to the 2nd, 4th, 6th, … half-period zones. Thus, the even zones are obstructed and the resultant amplitude at P_1 [see Fig. 19.5(a)] will be

$$u_1 + u_3 + u_5 + \dots \tag{19.14}$$

producing an intense maximum. For the point P_3 (which is at a distance $K^2/3\lambda$) the first blackened ring contains the 4th, 5th, 6th zones, the second blackened ring contains the 10th, 11th and 12th zones, etc.; thus the resultant amplitude would be

$$(u_1 - u_2 + u_3) + (u_7 - u_8 + u_9) + \dots \tag{19.15}$$

which would again correspond to a maximum, but it would not be as intense as the point P_1. Between the points P_1 and P_3 there will be a point P_2 (at a distance $K^2/2\lambda$) where the resultant amplitude would be

$$(u_1 - u_2) + (u_5 - u_6) + \dots \tag{19.16}$$

implying that corresponding to P_2 the first blackened ring contains the 3rd and 4th half-period zones, etc. Obviously, the point P_2 will correspond to a minimum. Thus, if a plane wave is incident normally on a zone-plate, then the corresponding focal points are at distances

$$\frac{K^2}{\lambda}, \frac{K^2}{3\lambda}, \frac{K^2}{5\lambda}, \dots \tag{19.17}$$

Figure 19.4
The zone plate.

from the zone-plate. Elementary calculations will show that the zone-plate suffers from considerable chromatic aberrations [see Problem 19.5].

EXAMPLE 19.1 Assume a plane wave ($\lambda = 5 \times 10^{-5}$ cm) to be incident on a circular aperture of radius 0.5 mm. We will calculate the positions of the brightest and darkest points on the axis. For the brightest point, the aperture should contain only the first zone and thus we must have (see Fig. 19.1)

$$(0.05)^2 = OP(5 \times 10^{-5})$$

Thus $OP = 50$ cm. Similarly, the darkest point would be at a distance

$$\frac{(0.05)^2}{2 \times 5 \times 10^{-5}} = 25 \text{ cm}$$

EXAMPLE 19.2 Consider a zone-plate with radii

$$r_n = 0.1\sqrt{n} \text{ cm}$$

For $\lambda = 5 \times 10^{-5}$ cm, we will calculate the positions of various foci. The most intense focal point will be at a distance

$$\frac{r_1^2}{\lambda} = \frac{0.01}{5 \times 10^{-5}} = 200 \text{ cm}$$

The other focal points will be at distances of 200/3, 200/5, 200/7 cm, etc. Between any two consecutive foci there will be dark points on the axis corresponding to which the first circle will contain an even number of half-period zones.

The zone-plate can also be used for imaging points on the axis, e.g., if we have a point source at S then a bright image will be formed at P, where the point P should be such that (see Fig. 19.5(b)):

$$SL + LP - SP = \frac{\lambda}{2} \tag{19.18}$$

the point L being on the periphery of the first circle of the zone plate [see Fig. 19.5(b)]. If the radius of the first circle is r_1, then

$$\begin{aligned} SL + LP - SP &= \sqrt{a^2 + r_1^2} + \sqrt{b^2 + r_1^2} - (a+b) \\ &\approx a\left[1 + \frac{r_1^2}{2a^2}\right] + b\left[1 + \frac{r_1^2}{2b^2}\right] - (a+b) \\ &\approx \frac{r_1^2}{2}\left(\frac{1}{a} + \frac{1}{b}\right) \end{aligned} \tag{19.19}$$

Thus Eq. (19.18) becomes

$$\frac{1}{a} + \frac{1}{b} = \frac{1}{f} \tag{19.20}$$

where $f = r_1^2/\lambda$ represents the focal length. Equation (19.20) resembles the lens law. A very interesting demonstration experiment of the zone-plate can be carried out by using microwave sources ($\lambda \sim 1$ cm) and, instead of the dark rings, having aluminum rings on a perspex sheet of dimension ~40 cm × 40 cm.

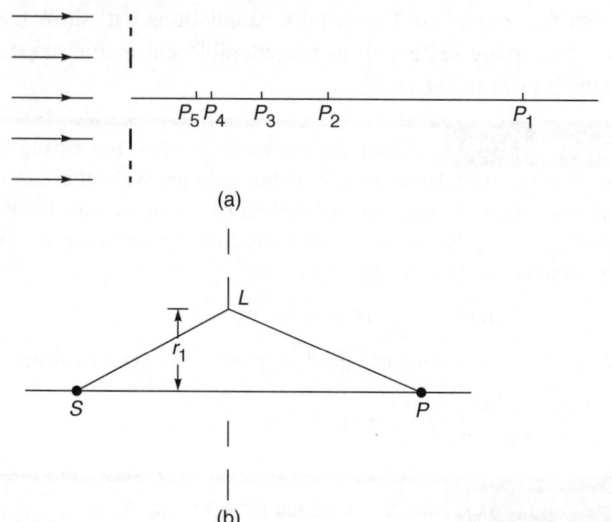

Figure 19.5
(a) For a plane wave incident on a zone-plate, the maximum intensity occurs at the points P_1, P_3 etc.; the minima occur at P_2, P_4, ... (b) Imaging of a point object by a zone-plate.

19.4 Fresnel Diffraction: A More Rigorous Approach

LO2

We consider a plane wave (of amplitude A) incident normally on an aperture as shown in Fig. 19.6. Now, for a spherical wave *diverging* from a point, the field distribution is proportional to e^{ikr}/r (see Example 9.7). Thus, if we consider an infinitesimal area $d\xi d\eta$ (around the point M – see Fig. 19.6) on the plane containing the aperture; the field at the point P due to waves emanating from this infinitesimal area will be proportional to

$$\frac{A\,e^{ikr}}{r}\,d\xi d\eta$$

where $r = MP$. To calculate the total field (at point P), we will have to sum over all the infinitesimal areas (in the aperture) to obtain

$$u(P) = C\iint \frac{A\,e^{ikr}}{r}\,d\xi d\eta$$

where C is a constant. If the amplitude and phase distribution on the plane $z = 0$ is given by $A(\xi, \eta)$ then the above integral will be modified to

$$u(P) = C\iint \frac{A(\xi,\eta)\,e^{ikr}}{r}\,d\xi d\eta \quad \textbf{(19.21)}$$

Now, in the Fresnel approximation,

$$r = [z^2 + (x-\xi)^2 + (y-\eta)^2]^{1/2} \approx z + \frac{(x-\xi)^2}{2z} + \frac{(y-\eta)^2}{2z} \quad \textbf{(19.22)}$$

In the exponent of the integrand in Eq. (19.21), if we replace r by the above expression (and in the denominator we replace r by z), we would obtain an expression for $u(P)$ which is the same as Eq, (18.9) provided we assume $C = (1/i\lambda)$. Thus we obtain

$$u(x, y, z) = \frac{1}{i\lambda z}e^{ikz}\iint A(\xi,\eta)\exp\left[\frac{ik}{2z}\left\{(x-\xi)^2 + (y-\eta)^2\right\}\right]d\xi d\eta \quad \textbf{(19.23)}$$

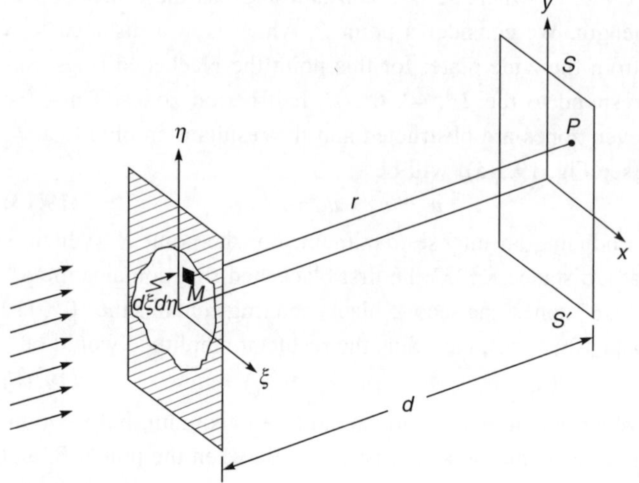

Figure 19.6
A plane wave incident normally on an aperture.

19.4.1 Diffraction of a Plane Wave Incident Normally on a Circular Aperture

We assume a plane wave incident normally on a circular aperture of radius a as shown in Fig. 19.7. The z-axis is normal to the plane of the aperture and the screen SS' is assumed to be normal to the z-axis. It is obvious from the

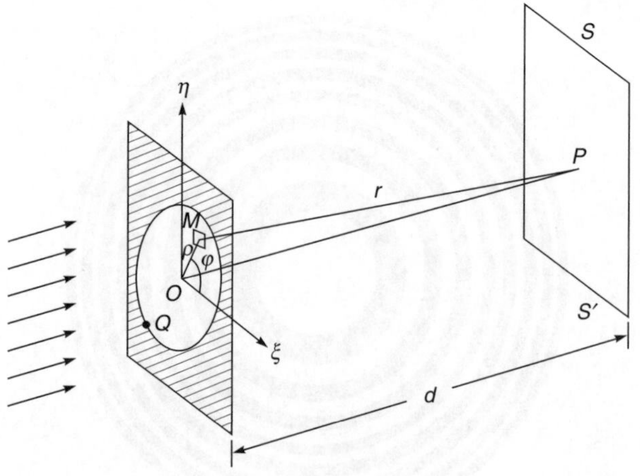

Figure 19.7
Diffraction of a plane wave incident normally on a circular aperture of radius a; Q is an arbitrary point on the periphery of the aperture.

symmetry of the problem that we will obtain circular fringes on the screen SS'; however, it is very difficult to calculate the actual intensity variation on the screen. Therefore, for the sake of mathematical simplicity, we will calculate the variation of intensity only along the z-axis. Obviously, it will be more convenient to use the circular system of coordinates. In this system, the coordinates of an arbitrary point M on the aperture will be (ρ, ϕ) where ρ is the distance of the point M from the center O and ϕ is the angle that OM makes with the ξ-axis [see Fig. 19.7] and a small element area dS surrounding the point M will be $\rho\, d\rho\, d\phi$. Thus, if we use Eq. (19.21), with $C = -i/\lambda$, we would get

$$u(P) \approx -\frac{i A}{\lambda} \int_0^{2\pi} \int_0^{a} \frac{e^{ikr}}{r} \rho \, d\rho \, d\phi \qquad \textbf{(19.24)}$$

Now, $\rho^2 + d^2 = r^2 \;\Rightarrow\; \rho\, d\rho = r\, dr$

and Eq. (19.24) becomes

$$u(P) \approx -\frac{i A}{\lambda} \int_0^{2\pi} \int_d^{\sqrt{a^2+d^2}} e^{ikr} \, dr \, d\phi \qquad \textbf{(19.25)}$$

The integration is very simple and since $k = 2\pi/\lambda$, we readily obtain

$$u(P) \approx A\, e^{ikd} (1 - e^{ip\pi}) \qquad \textbf{(19.26)}$$

where we have defined p by the following equation

$$k \left[\sqrt{a^2 + d^2} - d \right] = p\pi$$

The above equation implies

$$QP - OP = \frac{p\lambda}{2}$$

where Q is a point on the periphery of the circular aperture (see Fig. 19.7). From Eq. (19.26) we readily get

$$I(P) = 4 I_0 \sin^2 \frac{p\pi}{2} \qquad \textbf{(19.27)}$$

where I_0 is the intensity associated with the incident plane wave. Equation (19.27) tells us that the intensity is zero or maximum when p is an even or odd integer, i.e., when $QP - OP$ is an even or odd multiple of $\lambda/2$. This can be understood physically by using the concept of Fresnel half-period zones discussed in Sec. 19.2. Thus, if the aperture contains an even number of half-period zones, the intensity at the point P will be negligibly small and conversely, if the circular aperture contains an odd number of zones, the intensity at the point P will be maximum. Now, when $d << a$ (as is usually the case)

$$p \approx \frac{k}{\pi} \left[d \left(1 + \frac{a^2}{2d^2} \right) - d \right]$$

or

$$p \approx \frac{a^2}{\lambda d} \qquad \textbf{(19.28)}$$

which is known as the **Fresnel number** of the aperture. In Fig. 19.8, we have plotted the corresponding intensity variation as a function of the dimensionless parameter

$$\frac{\lambda d}{a^2}$$

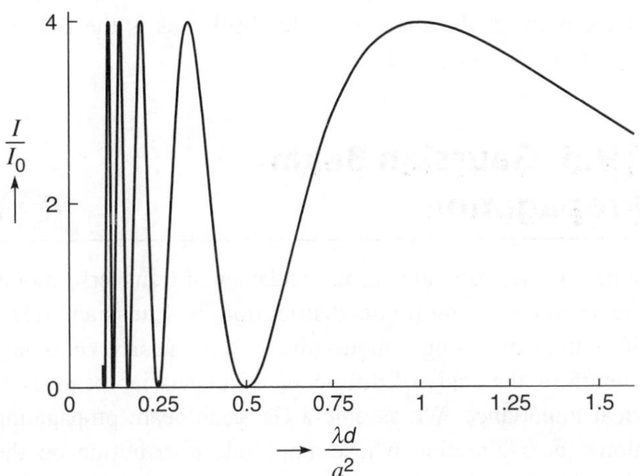

Figure 19.8
The intensity variation on an axial point corresponding to a plane wave incident on a circular aperture of radius a.

The figure shows that when the (circular) aperture contains an even number of half-period zones, the intensity at the point P will be zero and when the aperture contains an odd number of zones, the intensity at the point P will be maximum.

19.4.2 Diffraction by a Circular Disc

We next consider the diffraction pattern produced by an opaque disc of radius a (see Fig. 19.3). Once again we will assume that the observation point lies on the axis of the disc. Equation (19.21) tells us that in order to calculate the field we have to carry out an integration over the open region of the aperture. Obviously, if $u_1(P)$ and $u_2(P)$ respectively represent the fields at the point P due to a circular aperture and an opaque disc (of the same radius), then

$$u_1(P) + u_2(P) = u_0(P) \qquad \textbf{(19.29)}$$

where $u_0(P)$ represents the field in the absence of any aperture; Eq. (19.29) is known as the **Babinet's principle**.

Thus,

$$u_2(P) = u_0(P) - u_1(P)$$
$$= u_0(P) - u_0(P)[1 - e^{ip\pi}]$$

or
$$u_2(P) = u_0(P) e^{ip\pi} \qquad (19.30)$$

where, for $u_1(P)$ we have used Eq. (19.26). Thus the intensity at the point P on the axis of a circular disc would be

$$I_2(P) = |u_2(P)|^2 = I_0(P) \qquad (19.31)$$

which gives us the remarkable result that the intensity at a point on the axis of an opaque disc is equal to the intensity at the point in the absence of the disc! This is the Poisson spot discussed in Sec. 19.2.2.

19.5 Gaussian Beam Propagation

LO3

When a laser oscillates in its fundamental transverse mode, the transverse amplitude distribution is Gaussian. Also, the output of a single mode fiber is very nearly Gaussian. Therefore, the study of diffraction of a Gaussian beam is of great importance. We assume a Gaussian beam propagating along the z-direction whose amplitude distribution on the plane $z = 0$ is given by

$$A(\xi, \eta) = a \exp\left[-\frac{\xi^2 + \eta^2}{w_0^2}\right] \qquad (19.32)$$

implying that the phase front is plane at $z = 0$. From Eq. (19.32), it follows that at a distance w_0 from the z-axis, the amplitude falls by a factor $1/e$ (i.e., the intensity reduces by a factor $1/e^2$). This quantity w_0 is called the *spot size* of the beam. Substituting Eq. (19.32) in Eq. (19.23) and carrying out the integration, we obtain [see Appendix B]

$$u(x, y, z) \approx \frac{a}{\left(1 + \dfrac{iz}{\sqrt{\alpha}}\right)} \exp\left[-\frac{x^2 + y^2}{w^2(z)}\right] e^{i\Phi} \qquad (19.33)$$

where

$$\alpha = \frac{\pi^2 w_0^4}{\lambda^2} \qquad (19.34)$$

$$w(z) = w_0 \sqrt{1 + \frac{z^2}{\alpha}} \qquad (19.35)$$

$$\Phi = kz + \frac{k}{2R(z)}(x^2 + y^2) \qquad (19.36)$$

$$R(z) = z\left[1 + \frac{\pi^2 w_0^4}{\lambda^2 z^2}\right] = z + \frac{\alpha}{z} \qquad (19.37)$$

Thus, the intensity distribution is given by

$$I(x, y, z) = \frac{I_0}{\left(1 + \dfrac{z^2}{\alpha}\right)} \exp\left[-\frac{2(x^2 + y^2)}{w^2(z)}\right] \qquad (19.38)$$

which show that the transverse intensity distribution remains Gaussian with the beam-width increasing with z which essentially implies diffraction divergence. In Sec. 17.4, we had shown that

(i) For a given value of λ, the diffraction divergence increases as we decrease the value of the initial spot size (see Fig. 17.13).

(ii) For a given value of w_0, the diffraction divergence decreases with decrease in the value of λ (see Fig. 17.14).

Now, for a spherical wave *diverging* from the origin, the field distribution is given by (see Example 9.7)

$$u \sim \frac{1}{r} e^{ikr} \qquad (19.39)$$

On the plane $z = R$ (see Fig. 19.9)

$$r = \sqrt{x^2 + y^2 + R^2} = R\sqrt{1 + \frac{x^2 + y^2}{R^2}}$$
$$\approx R + \frac{x^2 + y^2}{2R}$$

where we have assumed $|x|, |y| << R$. Thus on the plane $z = R$, the phase distribution (corresponding to a spherical wave of radius R) would be given by

$$e^{ikr} \approx e^{ikR}\, e^{\frac{ik}{2R}(x^2 + y^2)} \qquad (19.40)$$

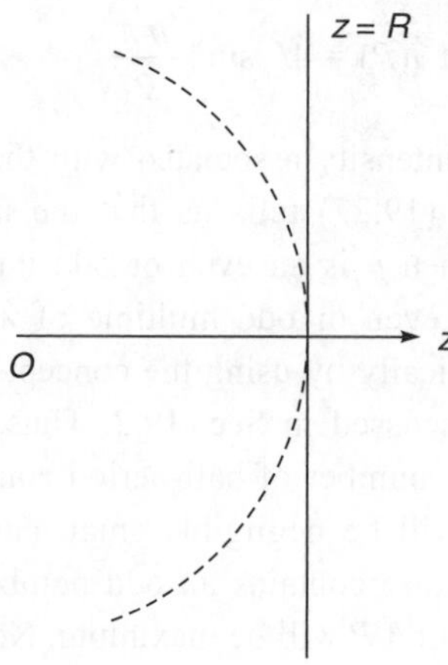

Figure 19.9
A spherical wave diverging from the point O. The dashed curve represents a section of the spherical wavefront at a distance R from the source.

From the above equation it follows that a phase variation of the type

$$\exp\left[i\frac{k}{2R}(x^2+y^2)\right]$$

(on the x-y plane) represents a *diverging* spherical wave of radius R. If we now compare the above expression with Eqs. (19.36) and (19.37) we can say that the radius of curvature of the phase front of the propagating Gaussian beam is given by Eq. (19.37). Thus as the beam propagates, the phase front which was plane at $z = 0$ becomes curved. In Sec. 27.5, we will use the above analysis to determine conditions for a Gaussian beam to resonate between two spherical mirrors. Here, as a simple application, we will consider a resonator configuration consisting of a plane mirror and a spherical mirror separated by a distance d (see Fig. 19.10); indeed such a configuration is used to produce a single transverse mode oscillation in a ruby laser. On the plane $z = 0$, the phase front is plane and for the beam to resonate, the phase front must have a radius of curvature equal to the radius of curvature of the mirror:

$$R = d\left[1+\frac{\pi^2 w_0^4}{\lambda^2 d^2}\right] \Rightarrow w_0^2 = \frac{\lambda d}{\pi}\sqrt{\left(\frac{R}{d}-1\right)} \tag{19.41}$$

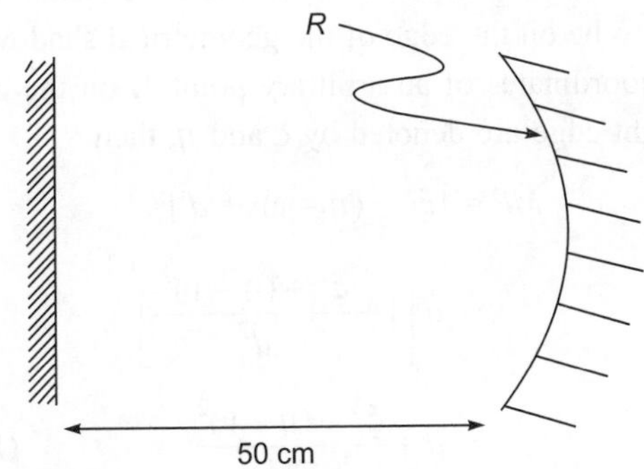

Figure 19.10
A simple resonator consisting of a plane mirror and a concave mirror of radius R.

EXAMPLE 19.3 We assume $\lambda \approx 0.6328$ µm, $d \approx 50$ cm and $R \approx 100$ cm; which are typical parameters for a He-Ne laser. Simple calculations will show that $w_0 \approx 0.32$ mm. If we increase R to 200 cm, we will get $w_0 \approx 0.38$ mm. Obviously R should be greater than d.

In Sec. 27.5, we will consider the more general case of a Gaussian beam resonating between two mirrors of radii of curvatures R_1 and R_2 as shown in Fig. 27.26.

19.6 Diffraction at a Straight Edge

LO4

Before we discuss the straight edge diffraction pattern, we introduce the Fresnel integrals.

Fresnel Integrals: Fresnel integrals are defined by the following equations:

$$C(\tau) = \int_0^{\tau} \cos\left(\frac{1}{2}\pi u^2\right) du \tag{19.42}$$

and

$$S(\tau) = \int_0^{\tau} \sin\left(\frac{1}{2}\pi u^2\right) du \tag{19.43}$$

Since the integrands are even functions of τ, the Fresnel integrals $C(\tau)$ and $S(\tau)$ are odd functions of τ:

$$C(-\tau) = -C(\tau) \quad \text{and} \quad S(-\tau) = -S(\tau) \tag{19.44}$$

Further, since

$$\int_{-\infty}^{\infty} e^{-\alpha x^2} dx = \sqrt{\frac{\pi}{\alpha}} \tag{19.45}$$

we have

$$\int_{-\infty}^{\infty} e^{i\pi u^2/2} du = \sqrt{\frac{\pi}{-i\pi/2}} = \sqrt{2}\, e^{i\pi/4} = (1+i) \tag{19.46}$$

Now,

$$\int_{-\infty}^{+\infty} \exp\left[i\frac{\pi u^2}{2}\right] du$$

$$= 2\left[\int_0^{\infty} \cos\left(\frac{1}{2}\pi u^2\right) du + i\int_0^{\infty} \sin\left(\frac{1}{2}\pi u^2\right) du\right]$$

$$= 2[C(\infty) + iS(\infty)]$$

Thus, using Eq. (19.46), we get $C(\infty) = \dfrac{1}{2} = S(\infty)$.

To summarize, the Fresnel integrals have the following important properties:

$$C(\infty) = S(\infty) = \frac{1}{2};\ C(0) = S(0) = 0 \tag{19.47}$$

$$C(-\tau) = -C(\tau) \quad \text{and} \quad S(-\tau) = -S(\tau) \tag{19.48}$$

The values of the Fresnel integrals for typical values of τ are tabulated in Table 19.1.

TABLE 19.1 **Table of Fresnel Integrals***

$$C(\tau)=\int_0^{\tau}\cos\left(\frac{\pi}{2}v^2\right)dv;\ S(\tau)=\int_0^{\tau}\sin\left(\frac{\pi}{2}v^2\right)dv$$

τ	$C(\tau)$	$S(\tau)$	τ	$C(\tau)$	$S(\tau)$
0.0	0.00000	0.00000	2.6	0.38894	0.54999
0.2	0.19992	0.00419	2.8	0.46749	0.39153
0.4	0.39748	0.03336	3.0	0.60572	0.49631
0.6	0.58110	0.11054	3.2	0.46632	0.59335
0.8	0.72284	0.24934	3.4	0.43849	0.42965
1.0	0.77989	0.43826	3.6	0.58795	0.49231
1.2	0.71544	0.62340	3.8	0.44809	0.56562
1.4	0.54310	0.71353	4.0	0.49843	0.42052
1.6	0.36546	0.63889	4.2	0.54172	0.56320
1.8	0.33363	0.45094	4.4	0.43833	0.46227
2.0	0.48825	0.34342	4.6	0.56724	0.51619
2.2	0.63629	0.45570	4.8	0.43380	0.49675
2.4	0.55496	0.61969	5.0	0.56363	0.49919
			∞	0.5	0.5

Figure 19.11 gives a parametric representation of the Fresnel integrals and is known as the **Cornu's spiral**. The horizontal and the vertical axes represent $C(\tau)$ and $S(\tau)$, respectively and the numbers written on the spiral are the values of τ. For example, as can be seen from the figure, for $\tau = 1.0$, $C(\tau) \approx 0.77989$ and $S(\tau) \approx 0.43826$.

We will now use Eq. (19.23) to calculate the diffraction pattern of a plane wave incident normally on a straight edge

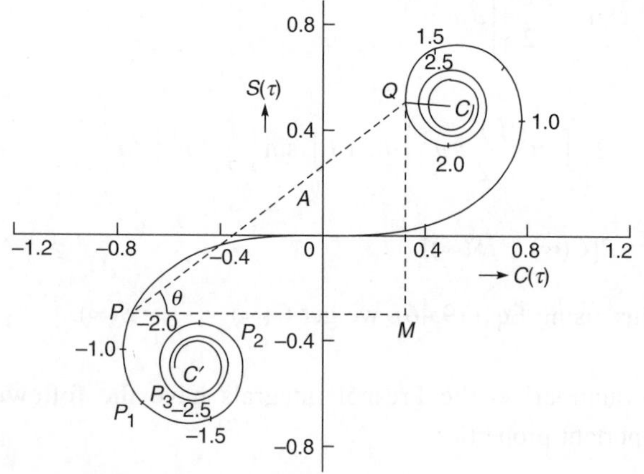

Figure 19.11

The Cornu's spiral which is a parametric plot of $C(\tau)$ and $S(\tau)$.

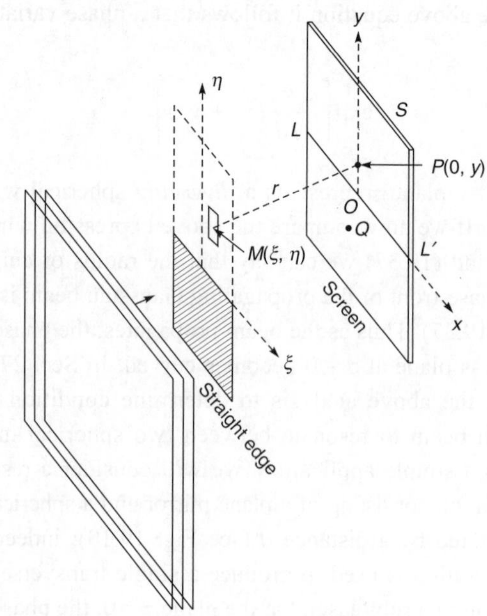

Figure 19.12

Diffraction of a plane wave incident normally on a straight edge.

(see Fig. 19.12). Obviously, there will be no variation of intensity along the x-axis and, therefore, without any loss of generality, we may assume the coordinates of an arbitrary point P (on the screen) to be $(0, y)$, where the origin has been assumed to be on the edge of the geometrical shadow. If the x and y coordinates of an arbitrary point M on the plane of the straight edge are denoted by ξ and η, then

$$r = MP = [\xi^2 + (\eta - y)^2 + d^2]^{1/2}$$

$$= d\left[1+\frac{\xi^2+(\eta-y)^2}{d^2}\right]^{1/2}$$

$$\approx d+\frac{\xi^2+(\eta-y)^2}{2d} \tag{19.49}$$

where d is the distance between the straight edge and the screen. On substituting the expression for r from Eq. (19.49) in Eq. (19.21), we obtain

$$u(P)\approx -\frac{i}{\lambda}\frac{A}{d}\int_{-\infty}^{\infty}d\xi\int_{0}^{\infty}d\eta\exp\left[ik\left\{d+\frac{\xi^2+(\eta-y)^2}{2d}\right\}\right] \tag{19.50}$$

where, in the denominator of the integrand, we have replaced r by its minimum value**, d. In order to express the above

* Table adapted from Ref. 19.5; a more detailed table (with greater accuracy) has been given there.

** This is justified because in carrying out the integration, only a small region around the point $r = d$ contributes; the contribution due to far-off points is small because of the rapid oscillations of the exponential term in the integrand (see also footnote in Sec. 18.2).

expression in terms of the Fresnel integrals, we introduce two dimensionless variables u and v such that

$$\left.\begin{aligned}\frac{1}{2}\pi u^2 &= \frac{k}{2d}\xi^2 = \frac{\pi}{\lambda d}\xi^2 \\ \text{and} \qquad \frac{1}{2}\pi v^2 &= \frac{k}{2d}(\eta - y)^2 = \frac{\pi}{\lambda d}(\eta - y)^2\end{aligned}\right\}$$

Thus we may assume u and v to be *defined* by the following equations:

$$\text{and} \qquad u = \sqrt{\frac{2}{\lambda d}}\,\xi \quad \text{and} \quad v = \sqrt{\frac{2}{\lambda d}}\,(\eta - y) \tag{19.51}$$

With these substitutions, Eq. (19.51) becomes

$$u(P) = -\frac{i}{2}u_0 \int_{-\infty}^{+\infty} \exp\left(\frac{i\pi u^2}{2}\right) du \int_{v_0}^{\infty} \exp\left(\frac{i\pi v^2}{2}\right) dv \tag{19.52}$$

$$\text{where} \qquad v_0 = -\sqrt{\frac{2}{\lambda d}}\, y \tag{19.53}$$

$$\text{and} \qquad u_0 = A\, e^{ikd}$$

represents the field at the point P in the absence of the straight edge. In order to calculate the intensity distribution we use the Fresnel integrals; thus,

$$\int_{-\infty}^{+\infty} \exp\left[i\frac{\pi u^2}{2}\right] du = 2[C(\infty) + S(\infty)] = (1 + i) \tag{19.54}$$

Further,

$$\int_{v_0}^{\infty} \exp\left(\frac{i\pi v^2}{2}\right) dv = \left[\int_0^{\infty} \cos\left(\frac{\pi}{2}v^2\right) dv - \int_0^{v_0} \cos\left(\frac{\pi}{2}v^2\right) dv\right] + i\left[\int_0^{\infty} \sin\left(\frac{\pi}{2}v^2\right) dv - \int_0^{v_0} \sin\left(\frac{\pi}{2}v^2\right) dv\right]$$

$$= \left[\frac{1}{2} - C(v_0)\right] + i\left[\frac{1}{2} - S(v_0)\right] \tag{19.55}$$

Substituting in Eq. (19.52), we obtain

$$u(P) = -\frac{i}{2}u_0(1+i)\left[\left\{\frac{1}{2} - C(v_0)\right\} + i\left\{\frac{1}{2} - S(v_0)\right\}\right]$$

$$= \frac{1-i}{2}u_0\left[\left\{\frac{1}{2} - C(v_0)\right\} + i\left\{\frac{1}{2} - S(v_0)\right\}\right] \tag{19.56}$$

It is of interest to note that a large value of y corresponds to a point which is very far above the edge of the geometrical shadow. For such a point v_0 would tend to $-\infty$ [see Eq. (19.53)] and we would obtain

$$u(P) = \frac{1-i}{2}u_0\left[\left(\frac{1}{2} + \frac{1}{2}\right) + i\left(\frac{1}{2} + \frac{1}{2}\right)\right] = u_0 \tag{19.57}$$

Thus, as expected, the amplitude at such a point is the same as that in the absence of the edge. This also justifies the value of the constant in Eq. (19.21). On the other hand, when the point P is deep inside the geometrical shadow (i.e., when $y \to -\infty$ and hence $v_0 \to \infty$), we obtain

$$C(v_0) = S(v_0) \to \tfrac{1}{2}$$

$$\text{giving} \qquad u(P) \to 0$$

as it should indeed be. The intensity distribution corresponding to Eq. (19.56) would be given by

$$I(P) = \frac{1}{2}I_0\left[\left\{\frac{1}{2} - C(v_0)\right\}^2 + \left\{\frac{1}{2} - S(v_0)\right\}^2\right] \tag{19.58}$$

If the point P is such that it lies on the edge of the geometrical shadow (i.e., on the line LL' (see Fig. 19.12) then $y = 0$ and hence $v_0 = 0$; thus

$$I(P) = \frac{1}{2}I_0\left[\frac{1}{4} + \frac{1}{4}\right] = \frac{1}{4}I_0 \tag{19.59}$$

where we have used the fact that $C(0) = S(0) = 0$. Thus the intensity on the edge of the geometrical shadow is 1/4th of the intensity that would have been in the absence of the edge. In order to determine the field at an arbitrary point P, we may use Table 19.1 to calculate the RHS of Eq. (19.58). The intensity variation is plotted in Fig. 19.16 from which one can make the following observations:

(i) Figure 19.13 represents a universal curve, i.e., for given values of λ and d, one simply has to calculate v_0 as the observation point moves along the y-axis. For example, the first three maxima occur at

$$\left.\begin{aligned} v_0 &\approx -1.22 \text{ with } I \approx 1.37\, I_0 \\ v_0 &\approx -2.34 \text{ with } I \approx 1.20\, I_0 \\ \text{and} \quad v_0 &\approx -3.08 \text{ with } I \approx 1.15\, I_0 \end{aligned}\right\} \text{maxima}$$

Similarly, the first three minima occur at

$$\left.\begin{aligned} v_0 &\approx -1.87 \text{ with } I \approx 0.778\, I_0 \\ v_0 &\approx -2.74 \text{ with } I \approx 0.843\, I_0 \\ \text{and} \quad v_0 &\approx -3.39 \text{ with } I \approx 0.872\, I_0 \end{aligned}\right\} \text{minima}$$

Thus, as we go inside the geometrical shadow, the intensity modulation decreases (see Fig. 19.13).

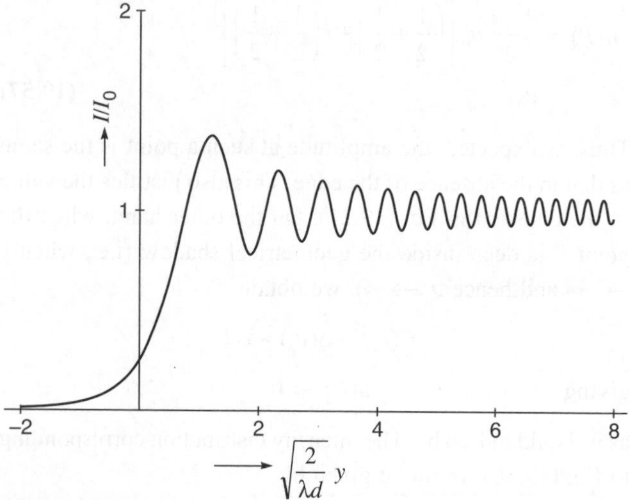

Figure 19.13
The intensity variation corresponding to the straight edge diffraction pattern.

(ii) For a given experimental set-up, the determination of the positions of maxima and minima is quite straightforward. For example, for $\lambda = 6 \times 10^{-5}$ cm and $d = 120$ cm

$$y = -\sqrt{\frac{\lambda d}{2}}\, v_0 = -0.06\, v_0 \text{ cm}$$

Thus, the first three maxima will occur at

$$y \approx 0.732,\ 1.404 \quad \text{and} \quad 1.848 \text{ mm}$$

respectively. Similarly, the first three minima will occur at

$$y \approx 1.122,\ 1.644 \text{ and } 2.034 \text{ mm}$$

respectively.

(iii) As we go inside the geometrical shadow the intensity monotonically decreases to zero.

(iv) One could have also studied the intensity variation directly from the Cornu's spiral (see Fig. 19.11). This is due to the fact that associated with the Cornu's spiral, we have the following interesting property: let us write

$$[C(\tau_2) - C(\tau_1)] + i[S(\tau_2) - S(\tau_1)] \equiv A\, e^{i\theta} \tag{19.60}$$

Thus, $\quad [C(\tau_2) - C(\tau_1)] = A \cos\theta$

and $\quad [S(\tau_2) - S(\tau_1)] = A \sin\theta$

Let the points P and Q on the Cornu's spiral (see Fig. 19.11) correspond to $\tau = \tau_1$ and $\tau = \tau_2$ respectively. It is obvious that

$$PM = [C(\tau_2) - C(\tau_1)] = A \cos\theta$$

and $\quad QM = [S(\tau_2) - S(\tau_1)] = A \sin\theta$

Thus the length of the line joining the points P and Q will be A and the angle that the line makes with the abscissa will be θ. In order to use the Cornu's spiral we rewrite Eq. (19.56):

$$u = \frac{1-i}{2} u_0 \left[\left\{\frac{1}{2} - C(v_0)\right\} + i\left\{\frac{1}{2} - S(v_0)\right\}\right]$$

Let us first consider a point of observation Q in the geometrical shadow region. Consequently v_0 will be positive. Let the point Q on the spiral (see Fig. 19.11) correspond to $\tau = v_0$. Since the point C in the curve corresponds to $\tau = \infty$, we have

$$\left\{\frac{1}{2} - C(v_0)\right\} + i\left\{\frac{1}{2} - S(v_0)\right\} = (QC)\, e^{i\psi}$$

where ψ is the angle that QC makes with the abscissa [see Eq. (19.60)]. Thus,

$$u(Q) = \frac{1-i}{2} (QC)\, e^{i\psi}\, u_0$$

or

$$I(Q) = \frac{1}{2} (QC)^2\, I_0 \tag{19.61}$$

We can easily see that as the point of observation moves into the shadow region, the value of v_0 increases. Thus the point Q keeps on moving on the spiral towards the point C and the length QC decreases uniformly. Hence in the shadow region the intensity uniformly decreases to zero (see Figs. 19.13 and 19.14).

As we move away from the edge of the geometrical shadow to the illuminated region, the value of v_0 becomes negative and the corresponding point P (on the Cornu's spiral) lies in the third quadrant as shown in Fig. 19.11. The intensity is again given by

$$I(P) = \frac{1}{2} (PC)^2\, I_0$$

As the value of v_0 becomes more and more negative, the length PC keeps on increasing till the point P reaches P_1 which corresponds to $v_0 \approx -1.22$. The intensity at this point is maximum and the length $P_1C \approx 1.66$. Thus, the corresponding intensity is

$$I(P_1) \approx \frac{1}{2} (1.66)^2\, I_0 \approx 1.37\, I_0 \tag{19.62}$$

As the value of v_0 becomes further negative the length PC starts decreasing till it reaches the point P_2. Thus, the intensity keeps on oscillating with decreasing amplitude about I_0 as we move more and more into the illuminated region (see Figs. 19.13 and 19.14).

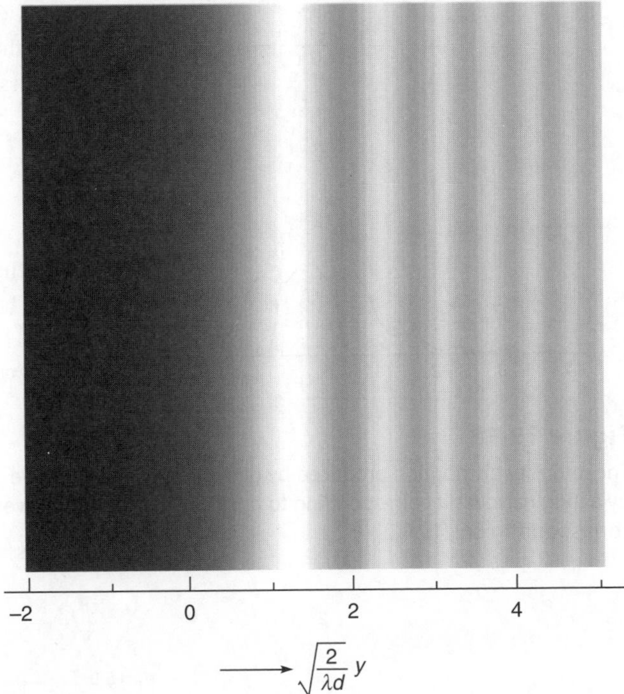

Figure 19.14
Computer generated intensity distribution corresponding to the straight edge diffraction pattern

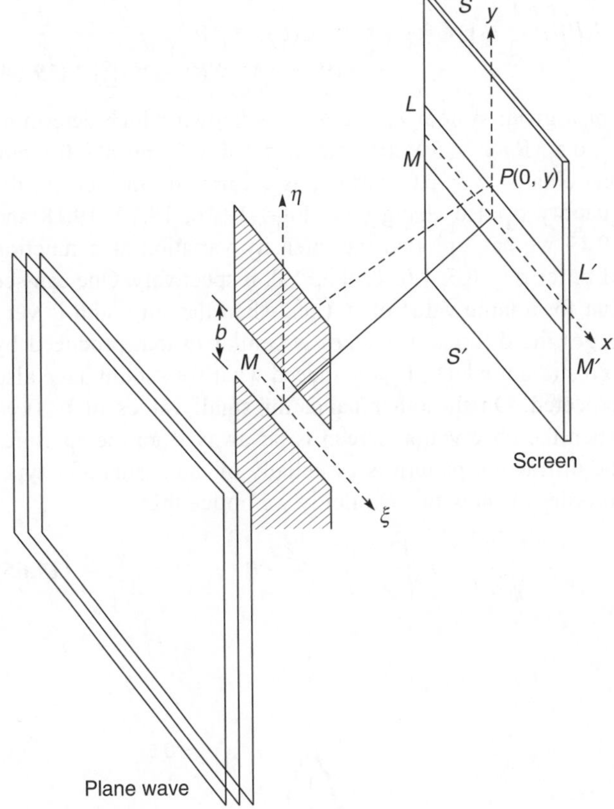

Figure 19.15
Diffraction of a plane wave incident normally on a long narrow slit.

19.7 Diffraction of a Plane Wave by a Long Narrow Slit and Transition to the Fraunhofer Region

LO5

We next consider a plane wave incident normally on a long narrow slit (of width b) as shown in Fig. 19.15. We wish to calculate the intensity distribution at an arbitrary point P on the screen SS'. The lines LL' and MM' represent the edges of the geometrical shadow. Once again, there will be no variation of the intensity along the x-axis and we may (without any loss of generality) assume the coordinates of the point P to be (0, y). The field at the point P will again be given by Eq. (19.50) except that the limits of the η-integral will be $-b/2$ and $+b/2$ (we are assuming the origin to be at the centre of the slit)

$$u(P) = -\frac{iA}{\lambda d}\int_{-\infty}^{\infty} d\xi \int_{-b/2}^{+b/2} d\eta \exp\left(ik\left\{d + \frac{\xi^2 + (\eta - y)^2}{2d}\right\}\right)$$

Carrying out manipulations similar to that in the previous section, we obtain

$$u(P) = -\frac{i}{2}u_0 \int_{-\infty}^{\infty} \exp\left(\frac{i\pi u^2}{2}\right) du \int_{-(v_2+v_1)}^{-(v_2-v_1)} \exp\left(\frac{i\pi v^2}{2}\right) dv$$

where $\quad u = \sqrt{\frac{2}{\lambda d}}\,\xi, \quad v = \sqrt{\frac{2}{\lambda d}}\,(\eta - y)$

and $\quad v_1 = \sqrt{\frac{2}{\lambda d}}\,\frac{b}{2}, \quad v_2 = \sqrt{\frac{2}{\lambda d}}\,y$

Using Eq. (19.46) we obtain

$$u(P) = -\frac{i}{2}u_0(1+i) \times \left\{\int_0^{-(v_2-v_1)}\left[\cos\left(\frac{\pi}{2}v^2\right) + i\sin\left(\frac{\pi}{2}v^2\right)\right]dv - \int_0^{-(v_2+v_1)}\left[\cos\left(\frac{\pi}{2}v^2\right) + i\sin\left(\frac{\pi}{2}v^2\right)\right]dv\right\}$$

or

$$u(P) = \frac{(1-i)}{2}u_0\left[\{C(v_2+v_1) - C(v_2-v_1)\} + i\{S(v_2+v_1) - S(v_2-v_1)\}\right] \quad \textbf{(19.63)}$$

where we have used Eq. (19.44). Thus, the intensity distribution would be

$$I(P) = \frac{1}{2} I_0 [\{C(v_2 + v_1) - C(v_2 - v_1)\}^2 + \{S(v_2 + v_1) - S(v_2 - v_1)\}^2] \quad \textbf{(19.64)}$$

For a given system λ, d and b are known which determine v_1; e.g., for $\lambda = 5 \times 10^{-5}$ cm, $d = 100$ cm and $b = 0.1$ cm, one obtains $v_1 = 2.0$; further, as y varies on the screen, the quantity v_2 also changes. In Figs. 19.16, 19.17, 19.18 and 19.19 we have plotted the intensity variation as a function of v_2 for $v_1 = 0.5$, 1.0, 1.5 and 5.0, respectively. One can see that for a large value of v_1 (i.e., when the slit width is very large) the diffraction pattern is similar to that produced by two straight edges. This is indeed what we should have also expected. On the other hand, for small values of v_1 (i.e., when the observation screen is far away from the aperture) the diffraction pattern is essentially of the Fraunhofer type. In order to show this explicitly we notice that

$$v_2 = \sqrt{\frac{2}{\lambda d}}\, y = \sqrt{\frac{2d}{\lambda}}\frac{y}{d} \approx \sqrt{\frac{2d}{\lambda}}\, \theta \quad \textbf{(19.65)}$$

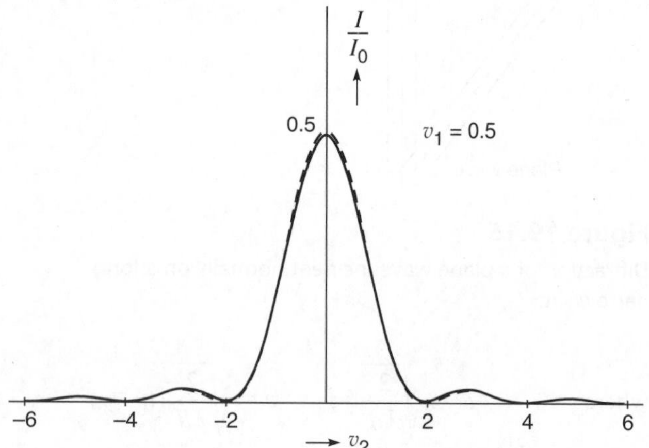

Figure 19.16
The intensity distribution produced by diffraction of a plane wave by a long narrow slit corresponding to $v_1 = 0.5$. The dashed curves correspond to Eq. (19.66).

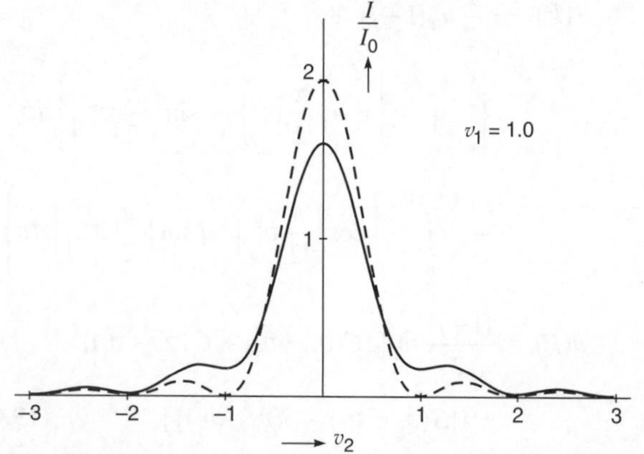

Figure 19.17
The intensity distribution produced by diffraction of a plane wave by a long narrow slit corresponding to $v_1 = 1.0$. The dashed curves correspond to Eq. (19.66).

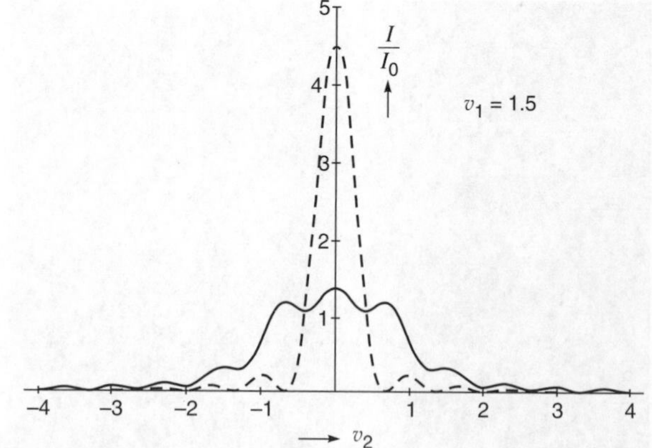

Figure 19.18
The intensity distribution produced by diffraction of a plane wave by a long narrow slit corresponding to $v_1 = 1.5$. The dashed curves correspond to Eq. (19.66).

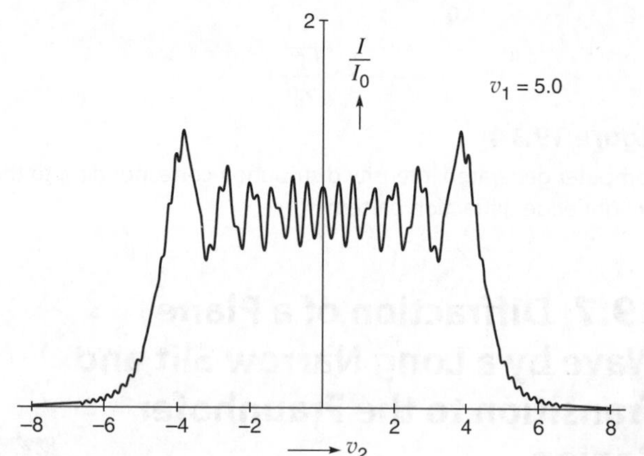

Figure 19.19
The intensity distribution produced by diffraction of a plane wave by a long narrow slit corresponding to $v_1 = 5.0$.

where θ represents the angle of diffraction (see Fig. 19.20). Clearly, in the Fraunhofer region since d is very large, the value of v_2 will also be very large and thus we must look for expressions of the Fresnel integrals in the limit of $v \rightarrow \infty$. Now, we may write

$$C(v) = \int_0^v \cos\frac{\pi}{2}v^2\, dv$$

$$= \int_0^\infty \cos\frac{\pi}{2}v^2\, dv - \int_v^\infty \cos\frac{\pi}{2}v^2\, dv$$

$$= \frac{1}{2} - \int_v^\infty \frac{1}{\pi v}\cos\left(\frac{\pi}{2}v^2\right)\pi v\, dv$$

$$= \frac{1}{2} - \frac{1}{\pi v}\sin\left(\frac{\pi}{2}v^2\right)\Big|_v^\infty + \int_v^\infty \frac{1}{\pi v^2}\sin\left(\frac{\pi}{2}v^2\right) dv$$

$$\cong \frac{1}{2} + \frac{1}{\pi v}\sin\left(\frac{\pi}{2}v^2\right)$$

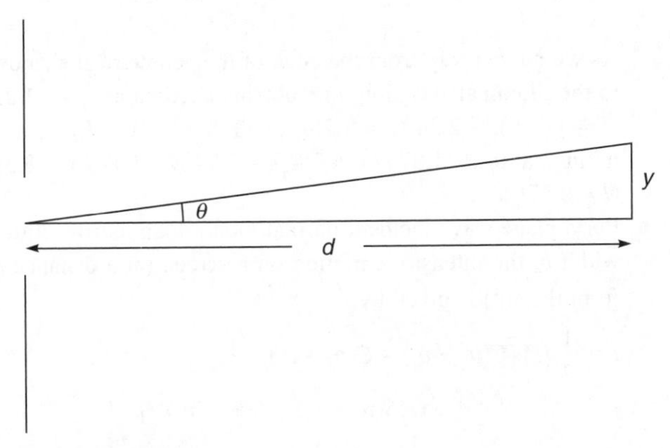

Figure 19.20
In the Fraunhofer region, *d* is very large.

where we have neglected terms which would be of order $1/v^3$. Similarly,

$$S(v) = \frac{1}{2} - \frac{1}{\pi v}\cos\left(\frac{\pi}{2}v^2\right)$$

Since v_2 is large and v_1 is small, we have

$$C(v_2 + v_1) - C(v_2 - v_1) \approx \left[\frac{1}{2} + \frac{1}{\pi v_2}\sin\frac{\pi}{2}(v_2 + v_1)^2\right] - \left[\frac{1}{2} + \frac{1}{\pi v_2}\sin\frac{\pi}{2}(v_2 - v_1)^2\right]$$

$$\cong \frac{2}{\pi v_2}\cos\frac{\pi}{2}(v_2^2 + v_1^2)\sin\pi v_1 v_2$$

Similarly,

$$S(v_2 + v_1) - S(v_2 - v_1) \approx \frac{2}{\pi v_2}\sin\frac{\pi}{2}(v_2^2 + v_1^2)\sin(\pi v_1 v_2)$$

Thus, in the Fraunhofer limit, Eq. (19.64) becomes

$$I(P) = \frac{1}{2}I_0\left[\frac{4}{\pi^2 v_2^2}\sin^2(\pi v_1 v_2)\right]$$

$$= I_{00}\frac{\sin^2\beta}{\beta^2} \qquad (19.66)$$

where $I_{00} = 2I_0 v_1^2$

and $$\beta = \pi v_1 v_2 = \frac{\pi}{\lambda d}b\,y \approx \frac{\pi b}{\lambda}\theta \qquad (19.67)$$

and $$\theta \approx \frac{y}{d} \qquad (19.68)$$

represents the diffraction angle. Equation (19.66) shows that the intensity distribution is indeed of the Fraunhofer type (see Sec. 17.2). In Figs. 19.16–19.19 the dashed curves correspond to Eq. (19.66) and one can see that the intensity distribution is almost of the Fraunhofer type for $v_1 \le 0.5$.

SUMMARY

- The underlying principle in the theory of diffraction is the Huygens–Fresnel principle according to which: *Each point on a wavefront is a source of secondary disturbance and the secondary wavelets emanating from different points mutually interfere.*
- For a plane wave incident normally on a circular aperture of radius *a*, the intensity variation on an axial point *P* is given by

$$I = I_0\sin^2\frac{p\pi}{2}$$

where $$p \approx \frac{a^2}{\lambda d}$$

λ is the wave length and *d* is the distance of the point *P* from the center of the circular aperture. The quantity *p* is known as the Fresnel number of the aperture. When $p = 1, 3, 5, 7, \ldots$ we have maximum intensity and the circular aperture will contain (with respect to the point *P*) odd number of Fresnel half period zones and when $p = 2, 4, 6, 8 \ldots$ we have minimum intensity and the circular aperture will contain even number of half-period zones.
- If instead of the circular aperture we have opaque disc, then we would always obtain a bright spot on the axis behind the disc; this is called the 'Poisson spot'.
- For a Gaussian beam (whose phase front is plane at $z = 0$), the variation of the spot size is given by

$$w(z) \approx w_0\left[1 + \frac{\lambda^2 z^2}{\pi^2 w_0^4}\right]^{1/2}$$

where w_0 is the spot size at $z = 0$. For large values of *z*:

$$w(z) \approx \frac{\lambda z}{\pi w_0}$$

which shows that the width increases linearly with *z*. We define the diffraction angle as

$$\tan\theta = \frac{w(z)}{z} \approx \frac{\lambda}{\pi w_0}$$

showing that the rate of increase in width is proportional to the wavelength and inversely proportional to the initial width of the beam; this is characteristic of diffraction. The corresponding radius of curvature of the wavefront is given by

$$R(z) \approx z\left[1 + \frac{\pi^2 w_0^4}{\lambda^2 z^2}\right]$$

- For a plane wave incident normally on a straight edge, the intensity variation on a screen (at a distance d from the straight edge) is given by

$$I = \frac{1}{2} I_0 \left[\left\{ \frac{1}{2} - C(v_0) \right\}^2 + \left\{ \frac{1}{2} - S(v_0) \right\}^2 \right]$$

where I_0 is the intensity in the absence of the straight edge,

$$v_0 = -\sqrt{\frac{2}{\lambda d}}\, y$$

y being the distance from the edge of the geometrical shadow and

$$C(x) = \int_0^x \cos\left(\tfrac{1}{2}\pi u^2\right) du$$

and

$$S(x) = \int_0^x \sin\left(\tfrac{1}{2}\pi u^2\right) du$$

are known as Fresnel integrals. The intensity monotonically goes to zero as we go deep inside the geometrical shadow.

As we move away from the edge of the geometrical shadow to the illuminated region, one obtains maxima at $v_0 \approx -1.22$ ($I \approx 1.37 I_0$), -2.34 ($I \approx 1.20 I_0$), -3.08 ($I \approx 1.15 I_0$) ... and minima at $v_0 \approx -1.87$ ($I \approx 0.78 I_0$), -2.74 ($I \approx 0.84 I_0$), -3.39 ($I \approx 0.87 I_0$), ...

- For a plane wave incident normally on a long narrow slit of width b, the intensity variation on a screen (at a distance d from the slit) is given by

$$I = \frac{1}{2} I_0 \left[\{C(v_2 + v_1) - C(v_2 - v_1)\}^2 + \{S(v_2 + v_1) - S(v_2 - v_1)\}^2 \right]$$

where

$$v_1 = \sqrt{\frac{2}{\lambda d}}\,\frac{b}{2};\quad v_2 = \sqrt{\frac{2}{\lambda d}}\, y$$

and y is the distance from the midpoint of the edges of the geometrical shadow. As v_1 becomes large, we obtain the intensity distribution corresponding to two straight edges and for $v_1 \to 0$ we get the Fraunhofer diffraction pattern.

PROBLEMS

19.1 Consider a plane wave of wavelength 6×10^{-5} cm incident normally on a circular aperture of radius 0.01 cm. Calculate the positions of the brightest and the darkest points on the axis. [**Ans:** $d \approx 1.67$ cm, 0.56 cm, 0.33 cm, ... (Maxima); $d \approx 0.83$ cm, 0.42 cm, ... (Minima)]

19.2 What would happen if the circular aperture in Problem 19.1 is replaced by a circular disc of the same radius?

19.3 **(a)** A plane wave ($\lambda = 6 \times 10^{-5}$ cm) is incident normally on a circular aperture of radius a.

(i) Assume $a = 1$ mm. Calculate the values of z (on the axis) for which maximum intensity will occur. Plot the intensity as a function of z and interpret physically.

(ii) Assume $z = 50$ cm. Calculate the values of a for which minimum intensity will occur on the axial point. Plot the intensity variation as a function of a and interpret physically.

(b) Repeat the calculations for $\lambda = 5 \times 10^{-5}$ cm and discuss chromatic aberration of a zone plate.

[**Ans:** (i) (a) $z \approx 166.7$ cm, 55.6 cm, 33.3 cm, ... (maxima); (b) Minimum intensity will occur when $a \approx 0.0775$ cm, 0.110 cm, 0.134 cm, ...]

19.4 Consider a circular aperture of diameter 2 mm illuminated by a plane wave. The most intense point on the axis is at a distance of 200 cm from the aperture. Calculate the wavelength. [**Ans.** 5×10^{-5} cm]

19.5 If a zone-plate has to have a principle focal length of 50 cm corresponding to $\lambda = 6 \times 10^{-5}$ cm, obtain an expression for the radii of different zones. What would be its principle focal length for $\lambda = 5 \times 10^{-5}$ cm?

[$(\sqrt{0.3n})$ mm, 60 cm]

19.6 In a zone-plate, the second, fourth, sixth ... zones are blackened; what would happen if instead the 1st, 3rd, 5th, etc., zones were blackened?

19.7 **(a)** A plane wave is incident normally on a straight edge (see Fig. 19.21). Show that the field at an arbitrary point P is given by

$$u(P) = \frac{1-i}{2} u_0 \left[\left\{ \frac{1}{2} - C(v_0) \right\} + i \left\{ \frac{1}{2} - S(v_0) \right\} \right]$$

where $v_0 = -\sqrt{\frac{2}{\lambda d}}\, y$.

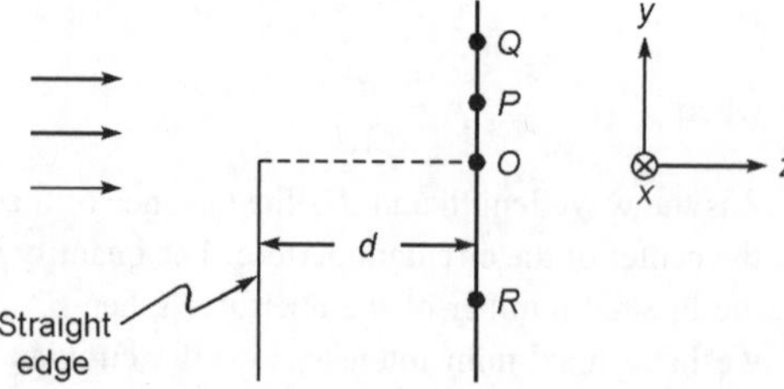

Figure 19.21

(b) Assume $\lambda_0 = 5000$ Å and $d = 100$ cm. Using Table 19.1, write approximately the values of I/I_0 at the points O, P ($y = 0.5$ mm), Q ($y = 1$ mm) and R ($y = -1$ mm) where O is at the edge of the geometrical shadow.

[**Ans:** (b) $I/I_0 \approx 1.26$, 0.24, 0.01]

19.8 Consider a straight edge being illuminated by a parallel beam of light with $\lambda = 6 \times 10^{-5}$ cm. Calculate the positions of the first two maxima and minima on a screen at a distance of 50 cm from the edge.

[**Ans:** The first two maxima occur at $y \approx 0.0473$ cm and 0.0906 cm. The first two minima occur at $y \approx 0.0724$ cm and 0.1061 cm.]

19.9 In a straight edge diffraction pattern, one observes that the most intense maximum occurs at a distance of 1 mm from the edge of the geometrical shadow. Calculate the wavelength of light, if the distance between the screen and the straight edge is 300 cm. [**Ans.** ≈ 4480 Å]

19.10 In a straight edge diffraction pattern, if the wavelength of the light used is 6000 Å and if the distance between the screen and the straight edge is 100 cm, calculate the distance between the most intense maximum and the next maximum. Find approximately the distance in centimeters inside the geometrical shadow where $I/I_0 = 0.1$. [**Ans:** $y \approx 0.027$ cm]

19.11 Consider a plane wave falling normally on a narrow slit of width 0.5 mm. If the wavelength of light is 6×10^{-5} cm, calculate the distance between the slit and the screen so that the value of v_1 would be 0.5, 1.0, 1.5 and 5.0 (see Figs. 19.16–19.19). Discuss the transition to the Fraunhofer region.

19.12 Consider the Fresnel diffraction pattern produced by a plane wave incident normally on a slit of width b. Assume $\lambda = 5 \times 10^{-5}$ cm, $d = 100$ cm. Using Table 19.1, approximately calculate the intensity values (for $b = 0.1$ cm) at $y = 0, \pm 0.05$ cm, ± 0.1 cm. Repeat the analysis for $b = 5$ cm.

[**Ans:** At $y = 0$, $I/I_0 \approx 1.60$; at $y = \pm 0.05$ cm, $I/I_0 \approx 0.356$; at $y = \pm 0.01$ cm, $I/I_0 \approx 0.01685$]

19.13 **(a)** The output of a He–Ne laser ($\lambda = 6328$ Å) can be assumed to be Gaussian with plane phase front. For $w_0 = 1$ mm and $w_0 = 0.2$ mm, calculate the beam diameter at $z = 20$ m.

(b) Repeat the calculation for $\lambda = 5000$ Å and interpret the results physically.

[**Ans:** (a) 0.83 cm and (b) 4.0 cm]

19.14 A Gaussian beam is coming out of a laser. Assume $\lambda = 6000$ Å and that at $z = 0$, the beam width is 1 mm and the phase front is plane. After traversing 10 m through vacuum what will be **(a)** the beam width, and **(b)** the radius of curvature of the phase front.

[**Ans:** $2w \approx 0.77$ cm; $R(z) \approx 1017$ cm]

19.15 A plane wave of intensity I_0 is incident normally on a circular aperture as shown in Fig. 19.22. What will be the intensity on the axial point P? [**Ans:** $3I_0$]

[**Hint:** You may use Eq. (19.27)]

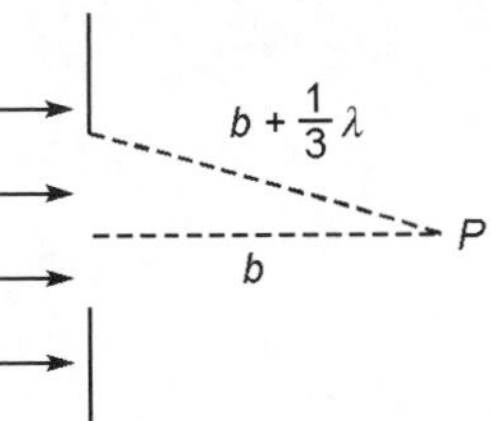

Figure 19.22

19.16 Show that a phase variation of the type

$$\exp\left[ikz + \frac{ik(x^2 + y^2)}{2R(z)}\right]$$

represents a diverging spherical wave of radius R.

19.17 The output of a semiconductor laser can be approximately described by a Gaussian function with two different widths along the transverse (w_T) and lateral (w_L) directions as

$$\psi(x, y) = A\exp\left(-\frac{x^2}{w_L^2} - \frac{y^2}{w_T^2}\right)$$

where x and y represent axes parallel and perpendicular to the junction plane. Typically $w_T \approx 0.5$ μm and $w_L = 2$ μm. Discuss the far field of this beam (see Fig. 19.23).

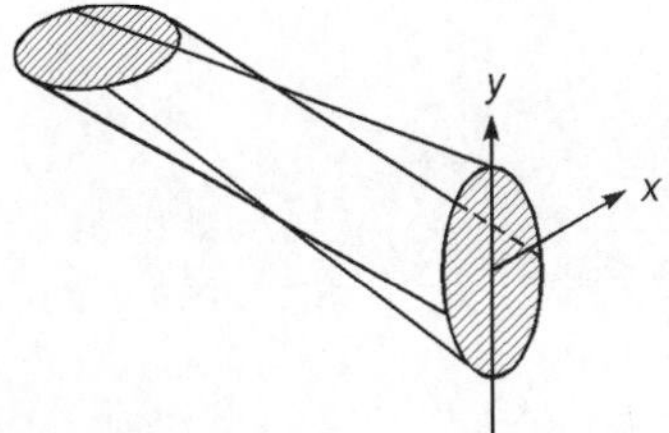

Figure 19.23

CHAPTER 20

Holography*

The electron microscope was to produce the interference figure between the object beam and the coherent background, that is to say the non-diffracted part of the illuminating beam. This interference pattern I called a hologram, from the Greek word holos – the whole, because it contained the whole information. The hologram was then reconstructed with light, in an optical system which corrected the aberrations of the electron optics.

—Dennis Gabor in his Nobel lecture**
December 11, 1971

LEARNING OBJECTIVES

After reading this chapter, the reader should be able to:

LO 1: *explain the phenomenon of holography.*

LO 2: *describe the requirements needed for making a hologram.*

LO 3: *apply holography in diverse fields.*

Important Milestones

1948: Dennis Gabor discovered the principle of holography.

1960: The first successful operation of a laser device by Theodore Maiman.

1962: Off-axis technique of holography by Leith and Upatnieks.

1962: Denisyuk suggested the idea of three-dimensional holograms based on thick photoemulsion layers. His holograms can be reconstructed in ordinary sun light. These holograms are called Lippmann – Bragg holograms.

1964: Leith and Upatnieks pointed out that a multi-color image can be produced by a

Above Image: Close-up view of a red laser on a cutting machine in a college physics laboratory. Photograph courtesy McGraw Hill Digital Access Library.

* A portion of this chapter is based on the unpublished lecture notes of Professor K. Thyagarajan.

** Dennis Gabor received the 1971 Nobel Prize in Physics for discovering the *principles of holography*; the original paper of Gabor appeared in 1948 [see Ref. 20.1]. Gabor's Nobel lecture entitled *Holography, 1948–1971* is non-mathematical and full of beautiful illustrations; it is reprinted in Ref. 20.2

hologram recorded with three suitably chosen wavelengths.

1969: Benton invented 'Rainbow Holography' for display of holograms in white light. This was a vital step to make holography suitable for display applications.

20.1 Introduction

A photograph represents a two-dimensional recording of a three-dimensional scene. What is recorded is the intensity distribution that prevailed at the plane of the photograph when it was exposed. The light sensitive medium is sensitive only to the intensity variations and hence while recording a photograph, the phase distribution which prevailed at the plane of the photograph is lost. Since only the intensity pattern has been recorded, the three-dimensional character (e.g., parallax) of the object scene is lost. Thus, one cannot change the perspective of the image in the photograph by viewing it from a different angle or one cannot refocus any unfocussed part of the image in the photograph. Holography is a method invented by Dennis Gabor in 1947, in which one not only records the amplitude but also the phase of the light wave; this is done by using interferometric techniques. Because of this, the image produced by the technique of holography has a true three-dimensional form. Thus, as with the object, one can change one's position and view a different perspective of the image or one can focus at different distances. The capability to produce images as true as the object itself is what is responsible for the wide popularity gained by holography.

The basic technique in holography is the following: In the recording of the hologram, one superimposes on the object wave another wave called the reference wave and the photographic plate is made to record the resulting interference pattern (see Fig. 20.1). The reference wave is usually a plane wave. This recorded interference pattern forms the hologram and (as will be shown) contains information not only about the amplitude but also about the phase of the object wave. Unlike a photograph, a hologram has little resemblance with the object; in fact, information about the object is coded into the hologram. To view the image, we again illuminate the hologram with another wave, called the **reconstruction wave** (which in most cases is identical to the reference wave used during the formation of the hologram); this process is termed as **reconstruction** (see Fig. 20.2). The reconstruction process leads, in general, to a virtual and a real image of the object scene. The virtual image has all the characteristics of the object like parallax, etc. Thus, one can move the position of the eye and look behind the objects or one can focus at different distances. The real image can be photographed without the aid of lenses just by placing a light sensitive medium at the position where the real image is formed. Figures 20.3(a), (b) and (c) represent the object, its hologram and the reconstructed image, respectively.

20.2 Basic Theory

LO1

If the object is a point scatterer, then the object wave would just be $\frac{A}{r}\cos(kr - \omega t + \phi)$ where r represents the distance of the point of observation from the point scatterer and A represents a constant; $k = 2\pi/\lambda$. Any general object can be thought of as being made up of a large number of points and the composite wave reflected by the object would be vectorial sum of these. The fundamental problem in holography is the recording of this object wave, in particular, the phase distribution associated with it.

Let us consider the recording process. Let

$$O(x, y) = a(x, y)\cos[\phi(x, y) - \omega t] \quad \textbf{(20.1)}$$

represents the object wave (which, as mentioned earlier, is due to the superposition of waves from point scatterers on the object) in the plane of the photographic plate which is assumed to be $z = 0$ (see Fig. 20.1). We consider a plane reference wave and assume, for simplicity, that it is propagating in the x–z-plane inclined at an angle θ with the

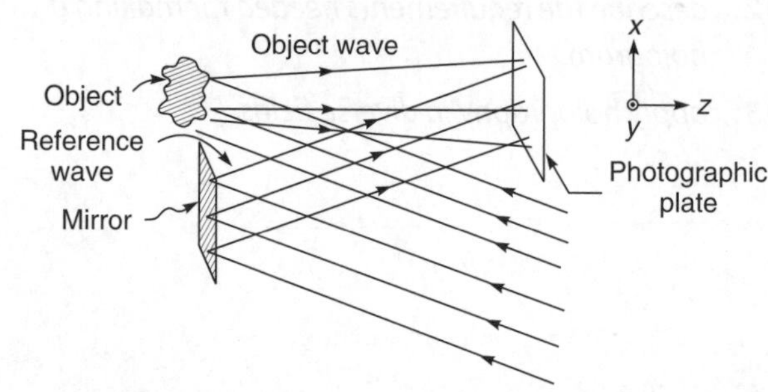

Figure 20.1
Recording of a hologram.

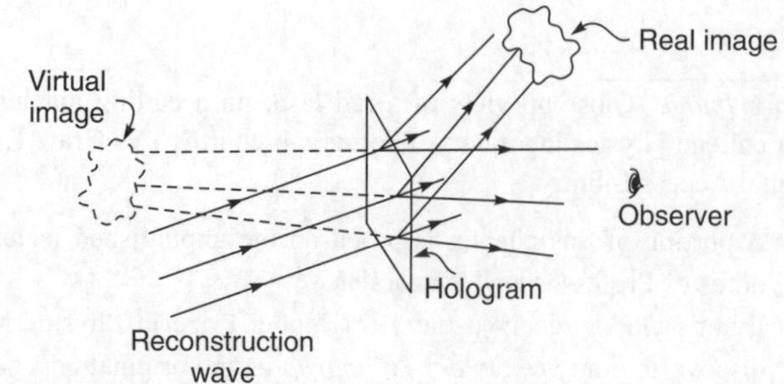

Figure 20.2
Reconstruction process.

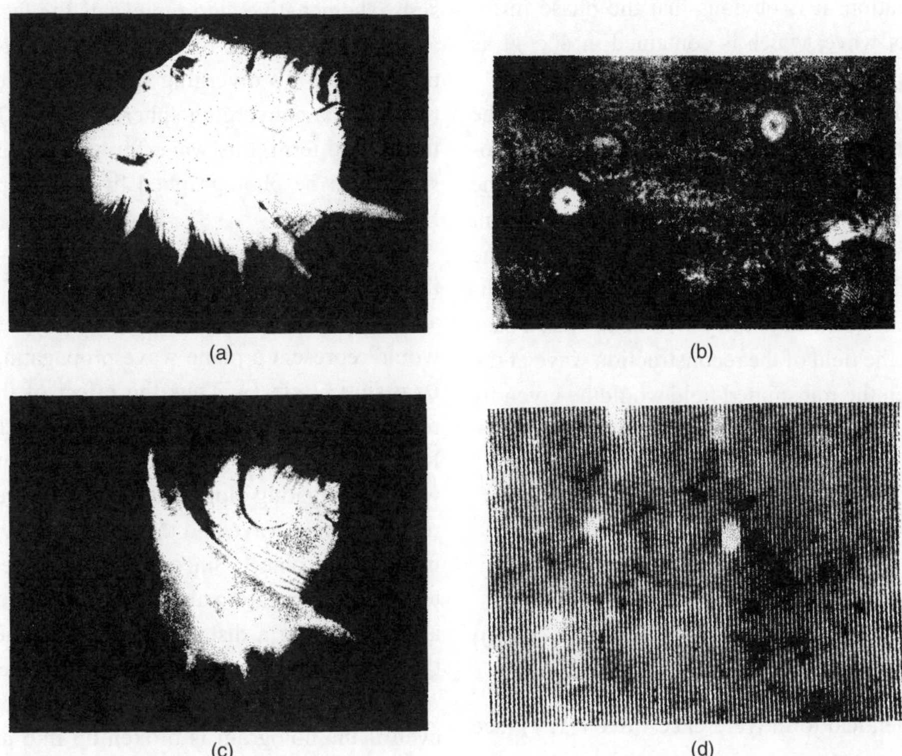

Figure 20.3

(a) An ordinary photograph of an object. (b). The hologram of the object produced by a method similar to the one as shown in Fig. 20.1, (c) The reconstructed image as seen by an observer, (d) A magnified view of a small portion of the hologram shown in (b). [*Photographs courtesy: Professor R. S. Sirohi*].

z-direction (see Fig. 20.1). Thus, the field associated with this plane wave would be given by

$$\begin{aligned} r(x, y, z) &= A \cos [\mathbf{k} \cdot \mathbf{r} - \omega t] \\ &= A \cos (kx \sin \theta + kz \cos \theta - \omega t) \end{aligned} \quad \textbf{(20.2)}$$

If $r(x, y)$ represents the field at the plane $z = 0$ due to this reference wave, then one can see that

$$\begin{aligned} r(x, y) &= A \cos [kx \sin \theta - \omega t] \\ &= A \cos [2\pi\alpha x - \omega t] \end{aligned} \quad \textbf{(20.3)}$$

where $\alpha = \sin \theta/\lambda$ is the spatial frequency (see Sec. 18.9). The above equation represents the field due to a plane wave inclined at an angle θ with the z-axis and as can be seen the phase varies linearly with x. Notice that there is no y-dependence because the plane wave has been assumed to have its propagation vector in the x–z-plane. Thus, the total field at the photographic plate (which is coincident with the plane $z = 0$) would be given by

$$u(x, y, t) = a(x, y) \cos [\phi(x, y) - \omega t] + A \cos [2\pi\alpha x - \omega t] \quad \textbf{(20.4)}$$

The photographic plate responds only to the intensity which would be proportional to the time average of $[u(x, y, t)]^2$. Thus, the intensity pattern recorded by the photographic plate would be

$$\begin{aligned} I(x, y) &= \langle u^2(x, y, t)\rangle \\ &= \langle [a(x, y) \cos \{\phi(x, y) - \omega t\} \\ &\quad + A \cos(2\pi\alpha x - \omega t)]^2\rangle \end{aligned} \quad \textbf{(20.5)}$$

where the angular brackets denote time averaging (see Sec. 16.5). Thus,

$$\begin{aligned} I(x, y) = {} & a^2(x, y) \langle\cos^2 \{\phi(x, y) - \omega t\}\rangle \\ & + A^2\langle\cos^2 (2\pi\alpha x - \omega t)\rangle \\ & + 2a(x, y) A \langle\cos \{\phi(x, y) - \omega t\} \cos (2\pi\alpha x - \omega t)\rangle \end{aligned} \quad \textbf{(20.6)}$$

Since

$$\langle\cos^2 [\phi(x, y) - \omega t]\rangle = \frac{1}{2} = \langle\cos^2 (2\pi\alpha x - \omega t)\rangle \quad \textbf{(20.7)}$$

and

$$\begin{aligned} &\langle\cos [\phi(x, y) - \omega t] \cos (2\pi\alpha x - \omega t)\rangle \\ &= \frac{1}{2}\langle\cos [\phi(x, y) + 2\pi\alpha x - 2\omega t]\rangle + \frac{1}{2}\langle\cos [\phi(x, y) - 2\pi\alpha x]\rangle \\ &= \frac{1}{2}\cos [\phi(x, y) - 2\pi\alpha x] \end{aligned} \quad \textbf{(20.8)}$$

Eq. (20.6) becomes

$$I(x, y) = \frac{1}{2} a^2(x, y) + \frac{1}{2} A^2 + A a(x, y) \cos [\phi(x, y) - 2\pi\alpha x] \quad \textbf{(20.9)}$$

From the above relation, it is obvious that the phase information of the object wave, which is contained in $\phi(x, y)$, is recorded in the intensity pattern.

When the photographic plate (which has recorded the above intensity pattern) is developed, one obtains a hologram [see Figs. 20.3(b) and (d)]. The transmittance of the hologram, i.e., the ratio of the transmitted field to the incident field, depends on $I(x, y)$. By a suitable developing process one can obtain a condition under which the amplitude transmittance would be linearly related to $I(x, y)$. Thus, in such a case if $R(x, y)$ represents the field of the reconstruction wave at the hologram plane, then the transmitted field would be given by

$$\begin{aligned} v(x, y) &= KR(x, y)\, I(x, y) \\ &= K\left[\frac{1}{2}a^2(x, y) + \frac{1}{2}A^2\right] R(x, y) \\ &\quad + KA\, a(x, y)\, R(x, y) \cos\left[\phi(x, y) - 2\pi\alpha x\right] \end{aligned} \tag{20.10}$$

where K is a constant. We consider the case when the reconstruction wave is identical to the reference wave $r(x, y)$ (see Fig. 20.2). In such a case we would obtain (omitting the constant K)

$$\begin{aligned} v(x, y) &= \left[\frac{1}{2}a^2(x, y) + \frac{1}{2}A^2\right] A\cos(2\pi\alpha x - \omega t) \\ &\quad + A^2 a(x, y)\cos\left[2\pi\alpha x - \omega t\right]\cos\left[\phi(x, y) - 2\pi\alpha x\right] \\ &= \left[\frac{1}{2}a^2(x, y) + \frac{1}{2}A^2\right] A\cos(2\pi\alpha x - \omega t) \\ &\quad + \frac{1}{2}A^2\, a(x, y)\cos\left[\phi(x, y) - \omega t\right] \\ &\quad + \frac{1}{2}A^2\, a(x, y)\cos\left[4\pi\alpha x - \phi(x, y) - \omega t\right] \end{aligned} \tag{20.11}$$

Equation (20.11) gives the transmitted field in the plane $z = 0$. We consider each of the three terms separately. The first term is nothing but the reconstruction wave itself whose amplitude is modulated due to the presence of the term $a^2(x, y)$. This part of the total field is traveling in the direction of the reconstructed wave. The second term is identical (within a constant term) to the RHS of Eq. (20.1) and hence represents the original object wave; this gives rise to a virtual image. Thus, the effect of viewing this wave is the same as viewing the object itself. The reconstructed object wave is traveling in the same direction as the original object wave.

To study the last term we first observe that in addition to the term $4\pi\alpha x$, the phase term $\phi(x, y)$ carries a negative sign. The negative sign represents the fact that the wave has a curvature opposite to that of the object wave. Thus, if the object wave is a diverging spherical wave then the last term represents a converging spherical wave. Thus, in contrast to the second term, this wave forms a real image of the object which can be photographed by simply placing a film (see Fig. 20.2).

To determine the effect of the term $4\pi\alpha x$, we consider the case when the object wave is also a plane wave traveling along the z-axis. For such a wave $\phi(x, y) = 0$ and the last term would represent a plane wave propagating along a direction $\theta' = \sin^{-1}(2\sin\theta)$. Thus the effect of the term $4\pi\alpha x$ is to rotate the direction of the wave. Hence the last term on the RHS of Eq. (20.11) represents the conjugate of the object wave propagating along a direction different from that of the reconstruction wave and the object wave, which forms a real image of the object. Since the waves represented by the three terms are propagating along different directions they separate after traversing a distance and enable the observer to view the virtual image without any disturbance.

A very interesting property possessed by holograms is that even if the hologram is broken up into different fragments, each separate fragment is capable of producing a complete virtual image of the object. This property of a hologram exists only when the object is a diffuse scatterer such that the wave from each scattering point of the object reaches all parts of the hologram plate. There are cases where this does not hold good; for example, when a hologram of a transparency is to be recorded. This property can be understood from the fact that for a diffusely reflecting object, each point of the object illuminates the complete hologram and consequently each point in the hologram receives waves from the complete object. But the resolution in the image decreases as the size of the fragment decreases. For non-diffusely reflecting objects or for transparencies, one makes use of an additional diffusing screen through which the object is illuminated.

EXAMPLE 20.1 As an explicit example of the formation and reconstruction of a hologram, we consider the simple case when both the object wave and the reference wave are plane waves [see Fig. 20.4(a)]—a plane object wave corresponds to a single object point lying far away from the hologram. (a) Show that for such a case, the hologram consists of a series of Young's interference fringes having an intensity distribution of the $\cos^2$ type. [see also Fig. 13.11(b)]. If we reconstruct the hologram with another plane wave [see Fig. 20.4(b)], then show that the transmitted light consists of a zero-order plane wave and two first-order plane waves; the two first-order waves correspond to the primary and conjugate waves.

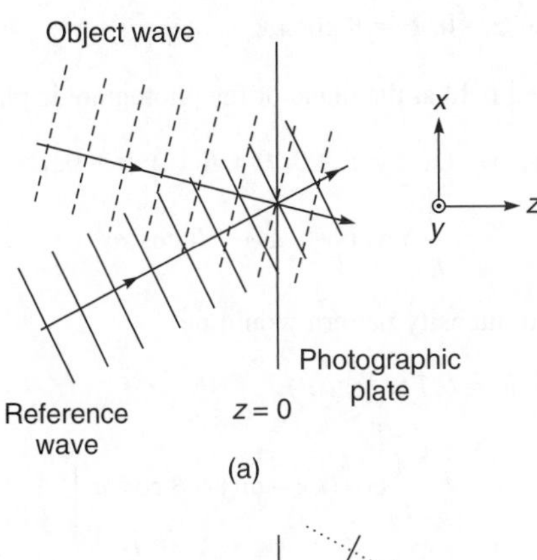

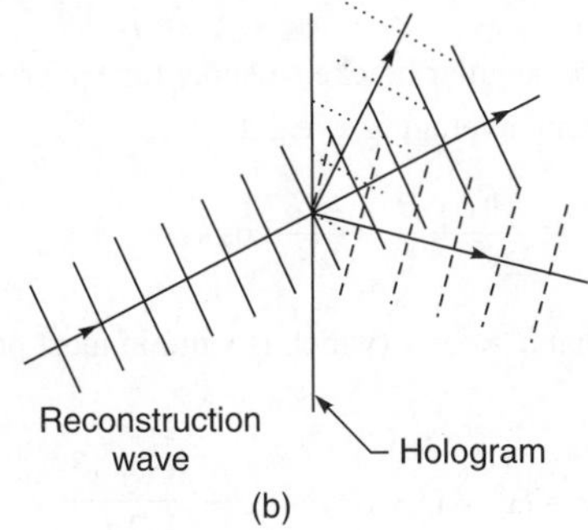

Figure 20.4

(a) Formation of a hologram, when both the object wave and the reference wave are plane waves. (b) Reconstruction of the hologram with another plane wave.

Solution: (a) Consider a plane wave with its propagation vector lying in the x–z-plane and making an angle θ_1 with the z-axis. For such a wave, the field is of the form

$$A_1 \cos\ [kx \sin\theta_1 + kz \cos\theta_1 - \omega t]$$

If the photographic film is assumed to coincide with the plane $z = 0$, then the field distribution on this plane would be given by

$$A_1 \cos\ [kx \sin\theta_1 - \omega t]$$

Similarly, the field (on the plane of the film) due to a plane wave making an angle θ_2 with the z-axis, will be given by

$$A_2 \cos\ [kx \sin\theta_2 - \omega t]$$

The resultant intensity distribution would be proportional to $\langle [A_1 \cos\{kx \sin\theta_1 - \omega t\} + A_2 \cos\{kx \sin\theta_2 - \omega t\}]^2 \rangle$

$$= \frac{1}{2}A_1^2 + \frac{1}{2}A_2^2 + A_1 A_2 \cos\ [kx\ (\sin\theta_1 - \sin\theta_2)]$$

$$= \frac{1}{2}(A_1 - A_2)^2 + 2A_1 A_2 \cos^2\left[\frac{kx}{2}(\sin\theta_1 - \sin\theta_2)\right]$$

For $A_1 = A_2$, the above expression simplifies to

$$2A^2 \cos^2\left[\frac{kx}{2}(\sin\theta_1 - \sin\theta_2)\right]$$

showing that the intensity remains constant along lines parallel to the y-axis with fringe spacing depending on the values of θ_1 and θ_2. Further, the intensity distribution is of the cos² type (cf. Fig. 13.11).

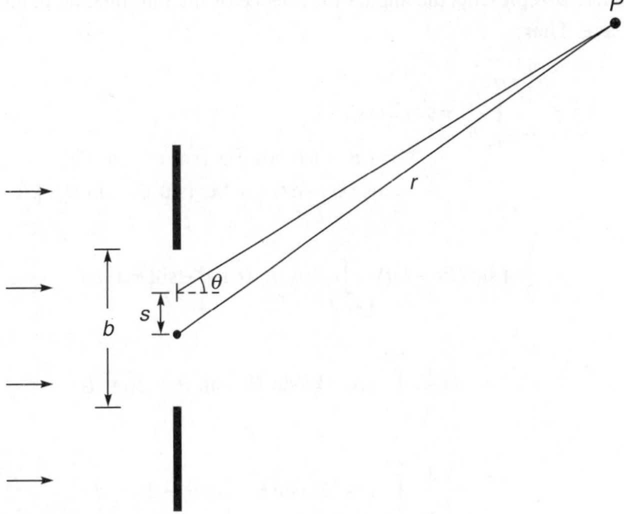

Figure 20.5

A plane wave incident on a narrow slit of width b.

(b) Before we calculate the transmitted field of the hologram, we first consider a narrow slit of width b being illuminated by a plane wave (see Fig. 20.5). Consider an element ds at a distance s from the center of the slit. Then the amplitude at a far away point P due to this element would be proportional to $\sin\ [k(r - s\sin\theta) - \omega t]ds$; here $k = 2\pi/\lambda$ and θ is defined in Fig. 20.5. Thus the total field in the direction θ would be given by

$$E \approx A \int_{-b/2}^{+b/2} \sin\ [k(r - s\sin\theta) - \omega t]\, ds \tag{20.12}$$

where A is a constant. The above integral can also be written as

$$E = A \int_{-b/2}^{+b/2} [\sin\ (kr - \omega t)\cos\ (ks\sin\theta) - \cos\ (kr - \omega t)\sin\ (ks\sin\theta)]ds$$

$$= 2A \sin\ (kr - \omega t)\ \frac{\sin\left(\frac{kb}{2}\sin\theta\right)}{k\sin\theta}$$

where the second integral is zero because the integrand is an odd function of s. Thus,

$$E = Ab \sin\ (kr - \omega t)\ \frac{\sin\beta}{\beta} \tag{20.13}$$

where

$$\beta = \frac{1}{2}kb\sin\theta = \frac{\pi b\sin\theta}{\lambda}$$

which is of the same form as obtained in Sec. 17.2. In the present case, the hologram has a $\cos^2\alpha s$ type of variation in transmittance and hence the transmitted field will be of the form

$$E = A \int_{-b/2}^{+b/2} \cos^2 \alpha s\ \sin\ [kr - ks(\sin\theta - \sin\theta_i) - \omega t]ds \tag{20.14}$$

where θ_i represents the angle of incidence of the illuminating plane wave. Thus,

$$E = \frac{1}{2}\int_{-b/2}^{+b/2} (1+\cos 2\alpha s) \times [\sin(kr-\omega t)\cos\{ks(\sin\theta-\sin\theta_i)\} - \cos(kr-\omega t)\sin\{ks(\sin\theta-\sin\theta_i)\}]ds$$

$$= \frac{1}{2}A\sin(kr-\omega t)\left[\int_{-b/2}^{+b/2}\cos\{ks(\sin\theta-\sin\theta_i)\}\,ds + \frac{1}{2}\int_{-b/2}^{+b/2}\cos\{ks(\sin\theta-\sin\theta_i+2\alpha)\}ds + \frac{1}{2}\int_{-b/2}^{+b/2}\cos\{ks(\sin\theta-\sin\theta_i-2\alpha)\}\,ds\right] \quad (20.15)$$

The above integrations can easily be carried out. Thus, for example,

$$\int_{-b/2}^{+b/2}\cos\{ks(\sin\theta-\sin\theta_i+2\alpha)\}\,ds = \frac{\sin\left[b\frac{k}{2}(\sin\theta-\sin\theta_i+2\alpha)\right]}{\frac{k}{2}(\sin\theta-\sin\theta_i+2\alpha)} \quad (20.16)$$

which becomes more and more sharply peaked around $\sin\theta = \sin\theta_i - 2\alpha$ as $b \to \infty$, i.e., as the size of the hologram becomes larger. Thus, the three integrals in Eq. (20.15) in the limit of a large value of b give rise to three plane waves propagating along $\sin\theta = \sin\theta_i$, $\sin\theta = \sin\theta_i - 2\alpha$ and $\sin\theta = \sin\theta_i + 2\alpha$, which represent the zero-order and two first order waves.

EXAMPLE 20.2 Consider the formation of a hologram with a point object and a plane reference wave [(see Fig. 13.13(a))]. Choose the z-axis to be along the normal from the point source to the plane of the photograph, assumed to be coincident with the plane $z = 0$. For simplicity, assume the reference wave to fall normally on the photographic plate. Obtain the interference pattern recorded by the hologram.

Solution: Let the point source be situated at a distance d from the photographic plate. The field at any point $P(x, y, 0)$ on the photographic plate, due to waves emanating from the point object would be given by

$$O(x, y, z = 0, t) = \frac{A}{r}\cos(kr - \omega t) \quad (20.17)$$

where $r = (x^2 + y^2 + d^2)^{1/2}$ and A represents a constant. A plane wave traveling along a direction parallel to the z-axis would be given by

$$R(x, y, z, t) = B\cos(kz - \omega t) \quad (20.18)$$

Hence, the field due to the reference wave at the plane of the photographic plate ($z = 0$) would be

$$R(x, y, z = 0, t) = B\cos\omega t \quad (20.19)$$

Thus, the total field at the plane of the photographic plate would be

$$T(x, y, t) = O(x, y, z = 0, t) + R(x, y, z = 0, t) = \frac{A}{r}\cos(kr - \omega t) + B\cos\omega t \quad (20.20)$$

The recorded intensity pattern would be

$$I(x, y) = \langle |T(x, y, t)|^2\rangle = \left\langle\left|\frac{A}{r}\cos(kr-\omega t) + B\cos\omega t\right|^2\right\rangle \quad (20.21)$$

where, as before, angular brackets denote time averaging. Carrying out the above time averaging, we get

$$I(x, y) = \frac{A^2}{2r^2} + \frac{B^2}{2} + \frac{AB}{r}\cos kr \quad (20.22)$$

If we assume that $d >> x, y$ (which is valid in most practical cases), we can write

$$r = (x^2 + y^2 + d^2)^{1/2} \approx d + \frac{x^2+y^2}{2d} \quad (20.23)$$

Thus,

$$I(x, y) = \frac{A^2}{2d^2} + \frac{B^2}{2} + \frac{AB}{r}\cos\left[kd + \frac{k}{2d}(x^2+y^2)\right] \quad (20.24)$$

The resultant fringe pattern is circular and centered at the origin (see Example 13.7). The hologram thus formed is essentially a zone plate with the transmittance varying sinusoidally in contrast to the Fresnel zone plate [see Fig. 13.13(b) and Sec. 19.3].

20.3 Requirements

LO2

Since holography is essentially an interference phenomenon, certain coherence requirements have to be met with. In Chapter 16, we had introduced the notion of coherence length. Thus, if stable interference fringes are to be formed (so that they are recordable), the maximum path difference between the object wave and the reference wave should not exceed the coherence length. Further, the spatial coherence is important so that the waves scattered from different regions of the object could interfere with the reference beam.

During reconstruction, the reconstructed image depends both on the wavelength and the position of the reconstructing source. Hence if the resolution in the reconstructed image has to be good, the source must not be broad and must be emitting a narrow band of wavelengths. It may be worthwhile mentioning here that the reconstruction process has associated with it aberrations similar to that in the images formed by lenses. If the reconstruction source is of the same wavelength and is situated at the same relative position with respect to the hologram as the reference source, then the reconstructed image does not suffer from any aberrations.

Another critical requirement in making holograms is stability of the recording arrangement. Thus, the film, the object and any mirrors used in producing the reference beam must be motionless with respect to one another during exposure. One more requirement which is not so obvious (but is a necessity) is the resolution of the film. Two plane waves making angles $+\theta$ and $-\theta$ with the axis, produce an interference pattern with spacing $d = \frac{\lambda}{2\sin\theta}$. Assuming $\theta = 15°$ and $\lambda = 6328$ Å (He–Ne laser), one obtains $d = 1.222 \times 10^{-3}$ mm; thus the spatial frequency is 818 limes/mm. Thus the photographic plate should be able to record fringes as close as 0.1222×10^{-4} mm apart. This requires special kinds of material which tend to be exceedingly slow, thus taking the stability requirements even further. Some of the holographic materials are 649F Kodak or 10E 75 or 8E 75 Agfa–Gaevert films and plates.

20.4 Some Applications of Holography

LO3

The principle of holography finds applications in many diverse fields.* The ability to record information about the depth finds application in studying transient microscopic events. Thus, if one has to study some transient phenomenon which occurs in a certain volume, then using ordinary microscopic techniques it becomes difficult to first locate the position and make observation. If a hologram is recorded of the scene, then the event gets frozen into the hologram and hence one can focus through the depth of the reconstructed image and study the phenomenon at leisure.

One of the most promising applications of holography lies in the field of interferometry. The ability of the holographic process to release the object wave when reconstructed with a reconstruction wave allows us to perform interference between different waves which exist at different times. Thus, in the technique called **double exposure holographic interferometry**, the photographic plate is first partially exposed to the object wave and the reference wave. Then, the object is stressed and the photographic plate is again exposed along with the same reference wave. The photographic plate after development forms the hologram. When this hologram is illuminated with a reconstruction wave, then two object waves emerge from the hologram; one of them corresponds to the unstressed object and the other to the stressed object. Since the object waves themselves have been reconstructed, they interfere and produce interference fringes. These interference fringes are characteristic of the strain suffered by the body. A quantitative study of the fringe pattern produced in the body gives the distribution of strain in the object.

To understand the formation of the fringe pattern, we assume that the deformation of the object has been such as to alter only the phase distribution. Thus, if

$$O(x, y, t) = A(x, y) \cos [\phi(x, y) - \omega t] \quad (20.25)$$

represents the object wave (in the hologram plane) when the object is unstressed [see Fig. 20.6(a)] and if $O'(x, y, t)$ represents the object wave when the object is stressed [see Fig. 20.6(b)] then we may write

$$O'(x, y, t) = A(x, y) \cos [\phi'(x, y) - \omega t] \quad (20.26)$$

where the phase distribution has been assumed to change from $\phi(x, y)$ to $\phi'(x, y)$. On reconstruction, each of the above two object waves emerge from the hologram and what would be observed will be the intensity pattern due to interference of the two waves which would be given by**

$$\begin{aligned} I(x, y) &= \langle [A(x, y) \cos\{\phi(x, y) - \omega t\} \\ &\quad + A(x, y) \cos\{\phi'(x, y) - \omega t\}]^2 \rangle \\ &= A^2(x, y) + A^2(x, y) \cos [\phi'(x, y) - \phi(x, y)] \end{aligned} \quad (20.27)$$

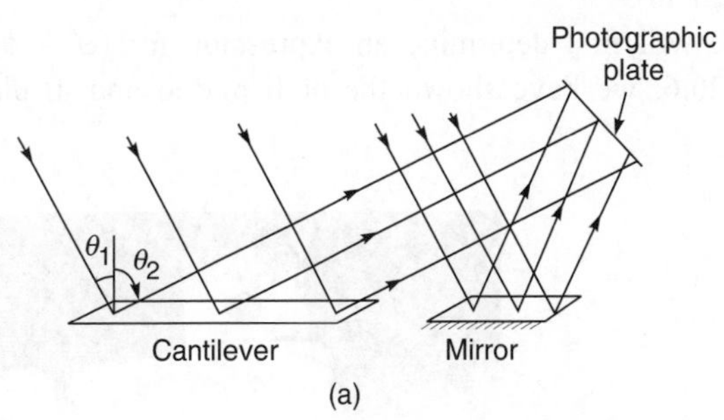

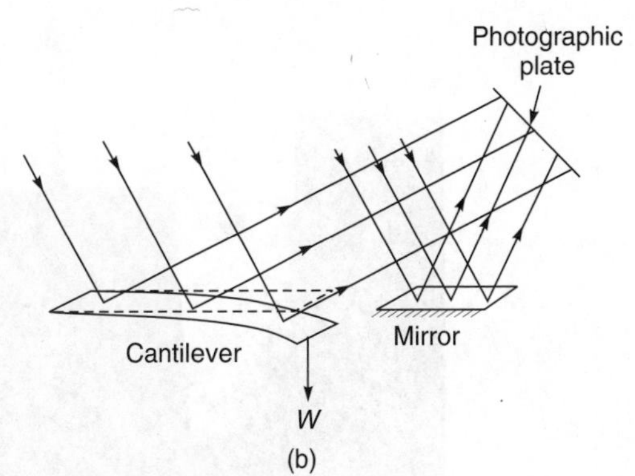

Figure 20.6
(a) Recording of the unstressed object wave. (b) Recording of the stressed object wave on the same emulsion to produce the doubly exposed hologram.

* See, e.g., Refs. 20.3–20.12.

** The reconstruction process produces other wave components also but as was observed earlier, these components travel along different directions. Here we are concerned only with the object waves.

Thus, whenever

$$\phi'(x, y) - \phi(x, y) = 2m\pi, m = 0, 1, 2, \ldots \qquad \textbf{(20.28)}$$

the two waves would interfere constructively and whenever,

$$\phi'(x, y) - f(x, y) = (2m + 1)\frac{\pi}{2}; m = 0, 1, 2, \ldots \qquad \textbf{(20.29)}$$

the two waves interfere destructively. Thus, depending on $[\phi'(x, y) - \phi(x, y)]$, one obtains, on reconstruction, the object superimposed with bright and dark fringes (see Fig. 20.7).

We will consider here a simple application of the above technique in the determination of the Young's modulus of a material. If we have a bar fixed at one end and loaded at the other and if it results in a displacement δ of the end of the bar, then one can show that*

$$\delta = \frac{W L^3}{3Y I} \qquad \textbf{(20.30)}$$

where W is the load, L is the length of the bar, I is the moment of inertia of cross section which for a rectangular bar of width a and thickness b, is given by $I = ab^3/12$; Y represents the Young's modulus of the material of the rod. Thus if we could determine δ for a given load, then Y can be determined from Eq. (20.30).

We will first determine an expression for $(\phi' - \phi)$. In Fig. 20.6, we have shown the undisplaced and displaced positions of the cantilever illuminated by a laser light along a direction making an angle θ_1 with the z-axis. We observe the cantilever along a direction making an angle θ_2 with the z-axis. The phase change when the cantilever undergoes a displacement δ as shown in Fig. 20.6(b) would be

$$\phi' - \phi = \frac{2\pi}{\lambda}(\delta\cos\theta_1 + \delta\cos\theta_2)$$

$$= \frac{2\pi}{\lambda}\delta(\cos\theta_1 + \cos\theta_2) \qquad \textbf{(20.31)}$$

If there are N fringes over the length L of the cantilever, then since a phase difference of 2π corresponds to one fringe [see Eq. (20.28)] we can write

$$\frac{2\pi}{\lambda}\delta(\cos\theta_1 + \cos\theta_2) = N \cdot 2\pi$$

or

$$\delta = \frac{N\lambda}{(\cos\theta_1 + \cos\theta_2)}$$

Thus by measuring N, θ_1 and θ_2 and knowing λ, δ can be determined. Figure 20.7 shows the reconstruction of a double exposed hologram of an aluminum strip of width 4 cm, thickness 0.2 cm and of length 12 cm. From the number of fringes formed, one can calculate the Young's modulus (see Problem 20.3).

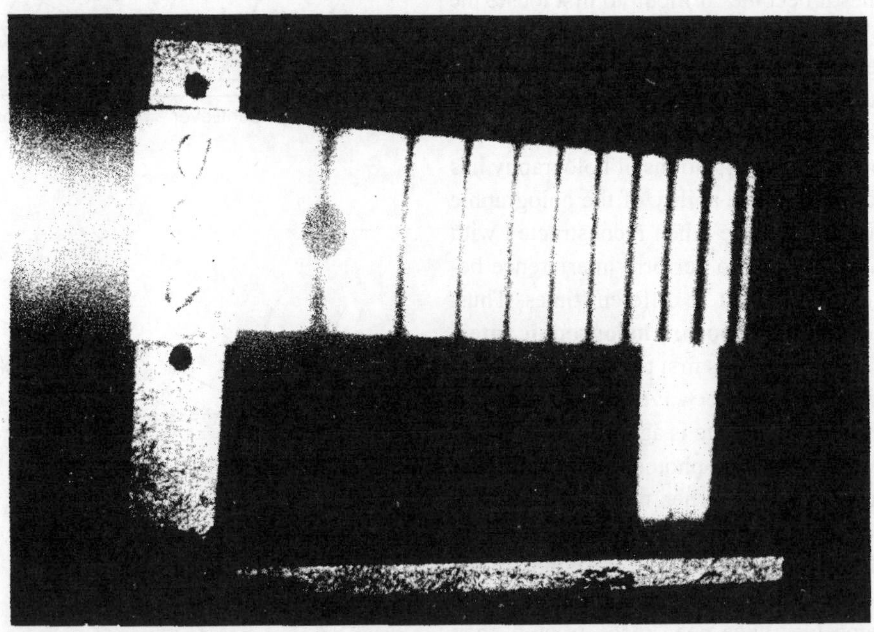

Figure 20.7
Interference fringes produced in the measurement of Young's modulus using double exposure interferometry. [*Photograph courtesy: Professor R. S. Sirohi*].

* See, e.g., Ref. 20.13, p. 75.

SUMMARY

- The basic technique in holography is the following: In the recording of the hologram, one superimposes on the object wave another wave called the reference wave and the photographic plate is made to record the resulting interference pattern. The reference wave is usually a plane wave. This recorded interference pattern forms the hologram and contains information not only about the amplitude but also about the phase of the object wave. To view the image, we again illuminate the hologram with another wave, called the reconstruction wave. The reconstruction process leads, in general, to a virtual and a real image of the object scene. The virtual image has all the characteristics of the object like parallax, etc.
- If the object wave and the reference wave are plane waves, the hologram consists of a series of Young's interference fringes.
- An important property possessed by hologram is that even if the hologram is broken up into different fragments, each separate fragment is capable of producing a complete virtual image of the object.
- The resolution in the reconstructed image has to be good, the source must not be broad and must be emitting a narrow band of wavelengths.
- Holography is commonly applied in studying transient microscopic events and in the field of interferometry. It also helps to determine Young's modulus of a material.
- For a point object and a plane reference wave, the hologram is very similar to a zone plate with the transmittance varying sinusoidally in contrast to the Fresnel zone plate.

PROBLEMS

20.1 Consider the reconstruction of the hologram as formed in the configuration of Example 20.2, by a plane wave traveling along a direction parallel to the *z*-axis. Show the formation of a virtual and a real image.

20.2 In continuation of Example 20.2, calculate the interference pattern when the incident plane wave makes an angle θ with the *z*-axis [see Fig. 13.13]. Assume $B \approx A/d$.

$$\left[\textbf{Ans. } 4B^2 \cos^2\left\{kd - kx\sin\theta + \frac{k}{2d}(x^2+y^2)\right\}\right]$$

20.3 Figure 20.7 corresponds to the reconstruction of a doubly exposed hologram, the objects corresponding to the unstrained and strained positions of an aluminum bar of width 4 cm, thickness 0.2 cm and length 12 cm. If the strained position corresponds to a load of 1 gm force applied at the end of the bar, calculate the Young's modulus of aluminum. Assume $\theta_1 \approx \theta_2 \approx 0$; assume $\lambda = 6328$ Å.

[**Hint:** *N* represents the number of fringes produced over the length of the cantilever.]

[**Ans.** 0.7×10^{11} N/m^2]

CHAPTER

21

... As to the other emanation which should produce the irregular refraction, I wished to try what Elliptical waves, or rather spheroidal waves, would do; and these I suppose would spread differently both in the ethereal matter diffused throughout the crystal and in the particles of which it is composed ...

Christiaan Huygens

Polarization and Double Refraction

Important Milestones

1669: Erasmus Bartholinus discovered double refraction in calcite.

1678: In the wave theory of light communicated to the Academie des Science in Paris, Christiaan Huygens gave the theory of double refraction in calcite discovered by Bartholinus.

1815: David Brewster showed polarization of light by reflection.

1828: William Nicol invented the prism which produced polarized light – this prism came to be known as the Nicol Prism.

1929: Edwin Land, an American scientist and inventor, patented Polaroid which is the name of a type of synthetic plastic sheet which is used to polarize light.

LEARNING OBJECTIVES

After reading this chapter, the reader should be able to:

LO 1: *know how to produce various forms of polarized light waves.*

LO 2: *discuss superposition of two disturbances and their mathematical analysis.*

LO 3: *describe the phenomenon of double refraction.*

LO 4: *know about the interference of polarized light.*

LO 5: *analyze polarized light.*

LO 6: *discuss optical activity.*

LO 7: *discuss change in state of polarization (SOP) of light beam propagating through an elliptic core single-mode optical fiber.*

LO 8: *discuss the working of Wollaston and Rochon prisms for producing linearly polarized waves.*

LO 9: *discuss the propagation of electromagnetic waves in anisotropic media.*

LO 10: *derive an expression for the velocity of the extra-ordinary ray in uniaxial crystals.*

LO 11: *use Jones calculus to study the propagation of polarized waves through various plates.*

LO 12: *discuss Faraday rotation and its applications.*

LO 13: *understand the theory of optical activity.*

LO 14: *understand theory of Faraday rotation.*

Above Image: View from a polarized lens. Photograph courtesy Darksoul72/Shutterstock

21.1 Introduction

LO1

If we oscillate one end of a string up and down then a transverse wave is generated [see Fig. 21.1(a)]. Each point of the string executes a sinusoidal oscillation in a straight line (along the x-axis) and the wave is, therefore, known as a **linearly polarized wave**. It is also known as a **plane polarized wave** because the string is always confined to the x-z plane. The displacement for such a wave can be written in the form

$$\left.\begin{array}{l} x(z,t) = a\cos(kz - \omega t + \phi_1) \\ \text{and} \quad y(z,t) = 0 \end{array}\right\} \tag{21.1}$$

where a represents the amplitude of the wave and ϕ_1 is the phase constant to be determined from the instant we choose as $t = 0$; the y-coordinate of the displacement is always zero. At any instant the displacement will be a cosine curve as shown in Fig. 21.1(a). Further, an arbitrary point $z = z_0$ will execute a simple harmonic motion of amplitude a. The string can also be made to vibrate in the y-z plane [see Fig. 21.1(b)] for which the displacement would be given by

$$\left.\begin{array}{l} x(z,t) = 0 \\ \text{and} \quad y(z,t) = a\cos(kz - \omega t + \phi_2) \end{array}\right\} \tag{21.2}$$

In general, the string can be made to vibrate in any plane containing the z-axis. If one rotates the end of the string on the circumference of a circle then each point of the string will move in a circular path as shown in Fig. 21.2; such a wave is known as a circularly polarized wave and the corresponding displacement would be given by

$$\left.\begin{array}{l} x(z,t) = a\cos(kz - \omega t + \phi) \\ \text{and} \quad y(z,t) = -a\sin(kz - \omega t + \phi) \end{array}\right\} \tag{21.3}$$

so that $x^2 + y^2$ is a constant ($= a^2$). As we will see later, Eq. (21.3) represents a right circularly polarized wave.

We next consider a long narrow slit placed in the path of the string as shown in Fig. 21.3(a). If the length of the slit is along the direction of the displacement then the entire amplitude will be transmitted as shown in Fig. 21.3(a). On the other hand, if the slit is at right angle to the direction of the displacement, then almost nothing will be transmitted to the other side of the slit [see Fig. 21.3(b)]. This is because of the fact that the slit allows only the component of the displacement, which is along the length of the slit, to pass through; as such, if a longitudinal wave was propagating through the string then the amplitude of the transmitted wave would have been the same for all orientations of the slit. Thus, the change in the amplitude of the transmitted wave with the orientation of the slit is due to the transverse character of the wave. Indeed, an experiment which is, in principle, very similar to the experiment discussed above proves the transverse character of light waves. However, before we discuss the experiment with light waves we must define an unpolarized wave.

We once again consider transverse waves generated at one end of a string. If the plane of vibration is changed in a random manner in very short intervals of time, then such a wave is known as an unpolarized wave*. If an unpolarized wave falls on a slit S_1 (see Fig. 21.4) then the displacement associated with the transmitted wave will be along the length of the slit and a rotation of the slit will not affect the amplitude of the transmitted wave although the plane of polarization of

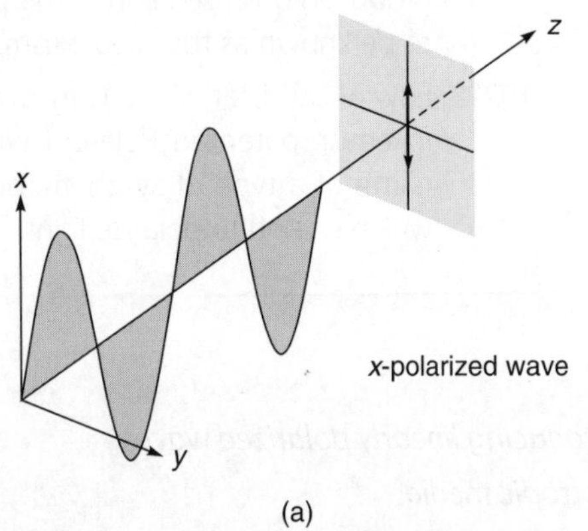

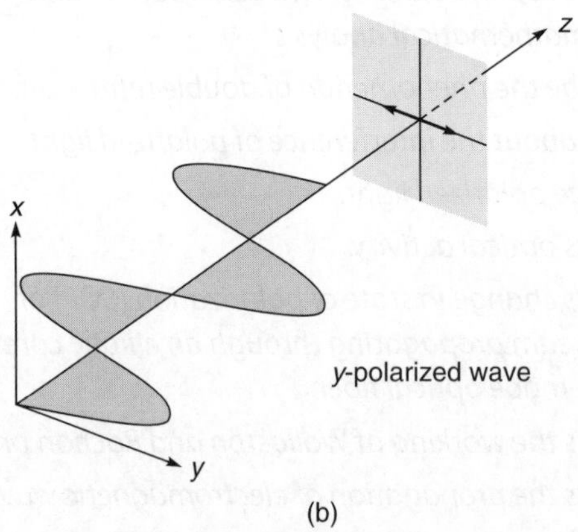

Figure 21.1
(a) A linearly polarized wave on a string with the displacement confined to the x-z plane; (b) A linearly polarized wave on a string with the displacement confined to the y-z plane.

* By a short interval, we imply times which are short compared to the detection time, however, for the wave to be characterized with a certain frequency ν, this time has to be much greater than $1/\nu$, so that in the short interval it executes a large number of oscillations (see also Sec. 16.1).

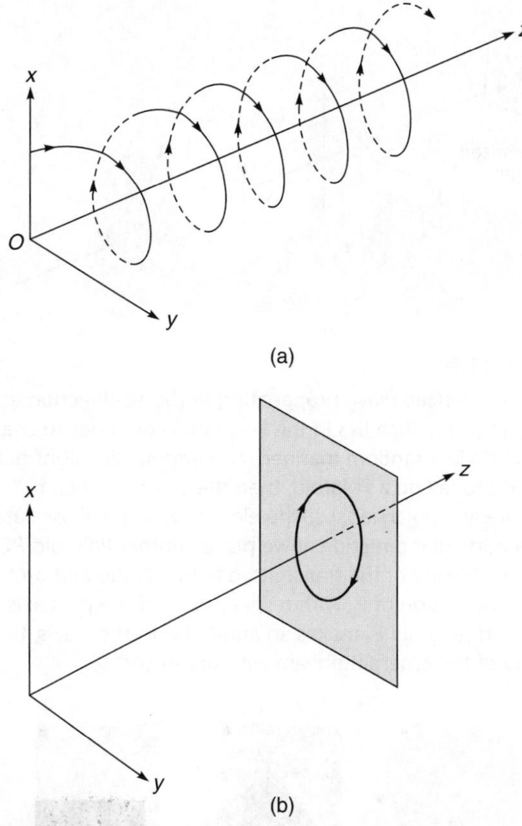

Figure 21.2

(a) The displacement corresponding to a circularly polarized wave – all points on the string are at the same distance from the z-axis. (b) Each point on the string rotates on the circumference of the circle.

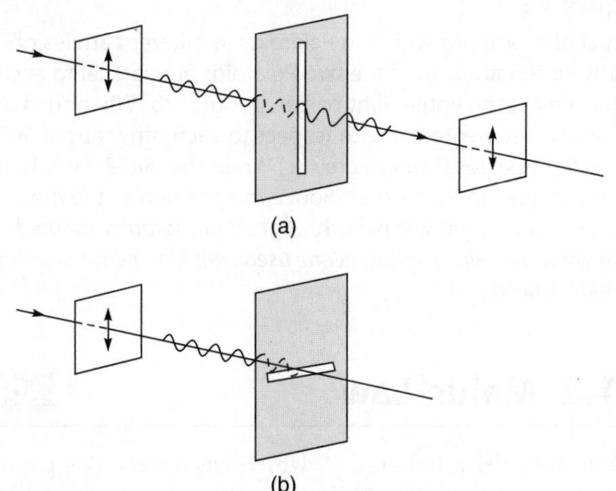

Figure 21.3

If a linearly polarized transverse wave (propagating on a string) is incident on a long narrow slit, then the slit will allow only the component of the displacement, which is along the length of the slit, to pass through.

transmitted wave depend on the orientation of the slit (see Fig. 21.4). Thus, the transmitted wave will be linearly polarized and the slit S_1 is said to act as a polarizer. If this polarized beam falls on another slit S_2 (see Fig. 21.4), then by rotating the slit S_2, we obtain a variation of the transmitted amplitude as discussed earlier; the second slit is said to act as an analyzer.

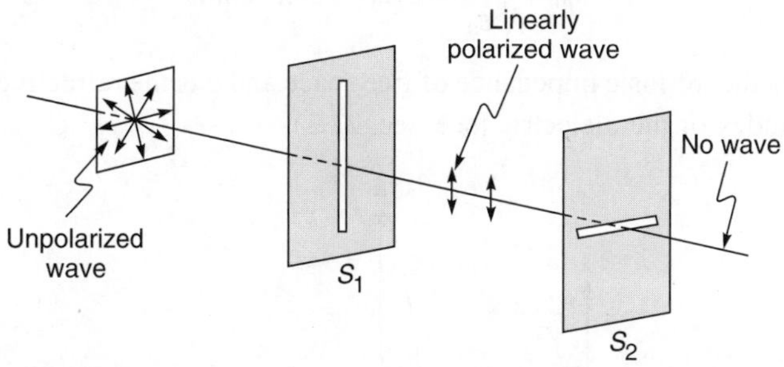

Figure 21.4

If an unpolarized wave propagating on a string is incident on a long narrow slit S_1, then the transmitted beam will be linearly polarized and its amplitude will not depend on the orientation of S_1. If this polarized wave is allowed to pass through another slit S_2, then the intensity of the emerging wave will depend on the relative orientation of S_2 with respect to S_1.

The transverse character of light waves was known in the early years of the nineteenth century; however, the nature of the displacement associated with a light wave was known only after Maxwell had put forward his famous electromagnetic theory. We will discuss the basic electromagnetic theory in the next chapter where we will show that associated with a plane electromagnetic wave there is an electric field **E** and a magnetic field **H** which are at right angles to each other. For a linearly polarized wave propagating in the z direction (in a dielectric) the electric and magnetic fields can be written in the form [see Fig. 21.5]

$$E_x = E_0 \cos(kz - \omega t),\ E_y = 0,\ E_z = 0 \tag{21.4}$$

and
$$H_x = 0,\ H_y = H_0 \cos(kz - \omega t),\ H_z = 0 \tag{21.5}$$

where
$$k = \frac{\omega}{v} = \omega\sqrt{\varepsilon\mu} \tag{21.6}$$

and
$$v = \frac{1}{\sqrt{\varepsilon\mu}} \tag{21.7}$$

represents the velocity of the waves, ε and μ are the dielectric permittivity and the magnetic permeability of the medium. Since $E_z = 0$ and $H_z = 0$, the wave is transverse. Equations (21.4) and (21.5) also show that **E** and **H** are at right angles to each other and both the vectors are at right angles to the direction of propagation (which is along the z-axis). In fact, the direction of propagation is along the vector (**E** × **H**). Electromagnetic theory also tells us that for a dielectric [see Sec. 22.3]:

$$H_0 = \frac{k}{\omega\mu} E_0 = \frac{1}{\eta_0/n} E_0 \tag{21.8}$$

where

$$\eta_0 = \sqrt{\frac{\mu_0}{\varepsilon_0}} = c\,\mu_0 \approx 120\pi \text{ ohms}$$

is the intrinsic impedance of free space and n is the refractive index of the dielectric (see Sec. 22.3).

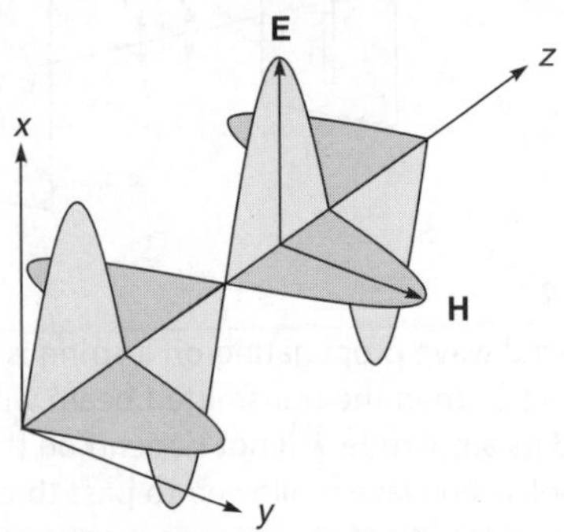

Figure 21.5
An x-polarized electromagnetic wave propagating in the z-direction.

We consider an ordinary light beam falling on a Polaroid P_1 as shown in Fig. 21.6; a Polaroid is a plastic-like material used for producing polarized light—it will be discussed in detail in Sec. 21.3.1. In general, an ordinary light beam (like the one coming from a sodium lamp or from the sun) is unpolarized, i.e., the electric vector (in a plane transverse to the direction of propagation) keeps changing its direction in a random manner (see Fig. 21.6). When such a beam is incident on a Polaroid the emergent light is linearly polarized with its electric vector oscillating in a particular direction as shown in Fig. 21.6. The direction of the electric vector of the emergent beam will depend on the orientation of the Polaroid. As will be shown in Sec. 21.3.1 the component of **E** along a particular direction gets absorbed by the Polaroid and the component at right angles to it passes through. The direction of the electric vector of the emergent wave is usually called the pass axis of the Polaroid. If the Polaroid P_2 is absent and if the Polaroid P_1 is rotated about the z-axis, there will be no variation of intensity. However, if we place another Polaroid P_2, then by rotating the Polaroid P_2 (about the z-axis) one will observe variation of intensity and at two positions there will be almost complete darkness (see Fig. 21.7). A similar phenomenon will also be observed if instead of rotating the Polaroid P_2 we rotate P_1. On the basis of our earlier discussions, this phenomenon proves the transverse character of light; i.e., the displacement associated with a light wave is at right angles to the direction of propagation of the wave. The Polaroid P_1 acts as a polarizer and the transmitted beam is linearly polarized. The second Polaroid acts as an analyzer.

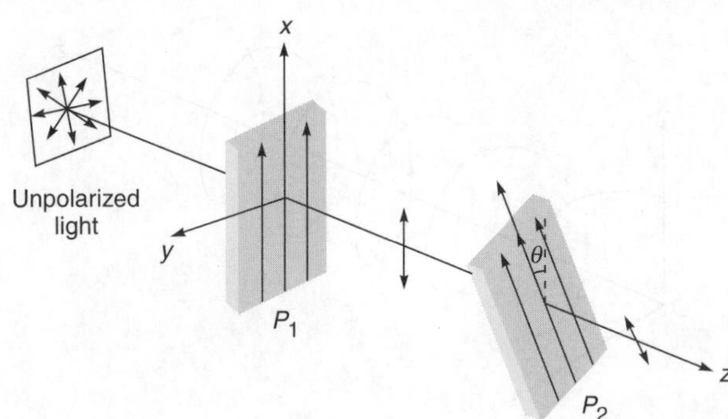

Figure 21.6
For an unpolarized wave propagating in the +z-direction, the electric vector (which lies in the x-y plane) continues to change its direction in a random manner. If an unpolarized light beam is allowed to fall on a Polaroid, then the emerging beam will be linearly polarized; i.e., the electric vector will oscillate along a particular direction. If we place another Polaroid P_2, then the intensity of the transmitted light will depend on the relative orientation of P_2 with respect to P_1.; if the pass axis of the second polaroid P_2 makes an angle θ with the x-axis, the intensity of the emerging beam will vary as $\cos^2\theta$.

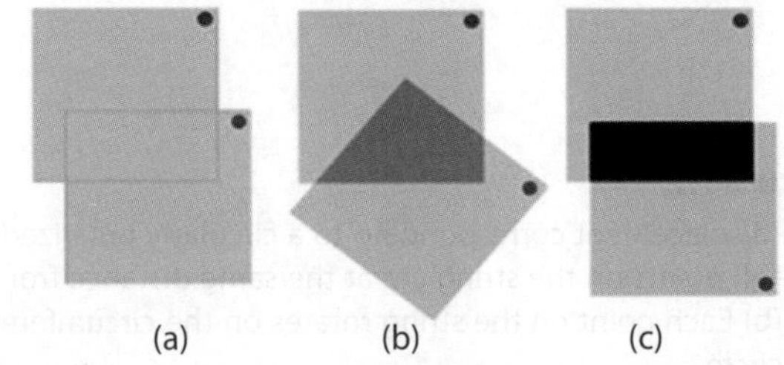

Figure 21.7
Actual photographs with two Polaroids at different angles of relative orientation. (a) If the two Polaroids are parallel to each other, almost the entire light passes through. (b) When the two Polaroids are oriented at with respect to each other about 50% of the light passes through grey. (c) When the two Polaroids are at right angles to each other (notice the position of the grey dot) almost no light will pass through. [*Photographs adapted from www.a-levelphysicstutor.com; used with kind permission from Dr. Alan J. Reed.*]

21.2 Malus' Law

LO1

Let us consider a Polaroid P_1 which has a pass-axis parallel to the x-axis (see Fig. 21.6); i.e., if an unpolarized beam propagating in the z direction is incident on the Polaroid, then the electric vector associated with the emergent wave will oscillate along the x-axis. We next consider the incidence of the x-polarized beam on the Polaroid P_2 whose pass axis makes an angle θ with the x-axis (see Fig. 21.6). If the amplitude of the incident electric field is E_0, then the amplitude of the wave emerging from the polaroid P_2 will be $E_0 \cos\theta$ and thus the intensity of the emerging beam will be given by

$$I = I_0 \cos^2\theta \tag{21.9}$$

where I_0 represents the intensity of the emergent beam when the pass axis of P_2 is also along the x-axis (i.e., when $\theta = 0$). Equation (21.9) represents Malus' Law. Thus, if a linearly polarized beam is incident on a Polaroid and if the Polaroid is rotated about the z-axis, then the intensity of the emergent wave will vary according to the above law. For example, if the Polaroid P_2 shown in Fig. 21.6 is rotated in the clockwise direction, then the intensity will increase till the pass-axis is parallel to the x-axis; a further rotation will result in a decrease in intensity till the pass-axis is parallel to the y-axis, where the intensity will be almost zero. If we further rotate it, it will pass through a maximum and again a minimum before it reaches its original position.

Figure 21.7 shows actual photographs of two Polaroids at different relative orientations. In Fig. 21.7(a) the two are parallel to each other and therefore almost the entire light passes through. In Fig. 21.7(b) the two Polaroids are oriented at 45° with respect to each other and about 50% of the light passes through; because according to Malus' law $I = I_0 \cos^2 45 = \frac{1}{2} I_0$. Finally, in Fig. 21.7(c) the two Polaroids are at right angles to each other (notice the position of the blue dot) and almost no light passes through because $I = I_0 \cos^2 90° = 0$.

21.3 Production of Polarized Light

LO1

In this section we will discuss various methods for producing linearly polarized light waves.

21.3.1 The Wire Grid Polarizer and the Polaroid

The physics behind the working of the wire grid polarizer is probably the easiest to understand. It essentially consists of a large number of thin copper wires placed parallel to each other as shown in Fig. 21.8. When an unpolarized electromagnetic wave is incident on it, then the component of the electric vector along the length of the wire is absorbed.

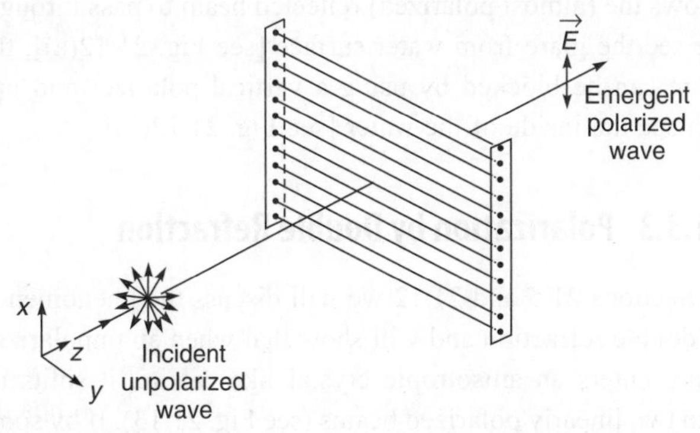

Figure 21.8
The wire-grid polarizer.

This is due to the fact that the electric field does work on the electrons inside the thin wires and the energy associated with the electric field is lost in the Joule heating of the wires. On the other hand, (since the wires are assumed to be very thin) the component of the electric vector along the x-axis passes through without much attenuation. Thus, the emergent wave is linearly polarized with the electric vector along the x-axis. However, for the system to be effective (i.e., for the E_y component to be almost completely attenuated) the spacing between the wires should be less than λ. Clearly, the fabrication of such a polarizer for a 3 cm microwave is relatively easy because the spacing has to be less than 3 cm. On the other hand, since the light waves are associated with a very small wavelength (~0.5 μm), the fabrication of a polarizer in which the wires are placed at distances less than 0.5 μm is extremely difficult. Nevertheless, Bird and Parrish did succeed in putting about 30,000 wires in about one inch; for further details see Refs. 21.1 and 21.2. The details of the procedure for making this wire grating are also discussed in Ref. 21.1. The original work of Bird and Parrish was published in 1950 (see Ref. 21.2).

As already pointed out, it is extremely difficult to fabricate a wire grid polarizer which would be effective for visible light. However, instead of long thin wires, one may employ long chain polymer molecules that contain atoms (like iodine) which provide high conductivity along the length of the chain. These long chain molecules are aligned so that they are almost parallel to each other. Because of the high conductivity provided by the iodine atoms, the electric field parallel to the molecules get absorbed. A sheet containing such long chain polymer molecules (which are aligned parallel to each other) is known as a **Polaroid**. When a light beam is incident on such a Polaroid, the molecules (aligned parallel to each other) absorb the component of electric field which is parallel to the direction of alignment because of the high conductivity provided by the iodine atoms; the component perpendicular to it passes through. Thus, the aligned conducting molecules act similar to the wires in the wire grid polarizer and since the spacing between two adjacent long chain molecules is small compared to the optical wavelength, the Polaroid is usually very effective in producing linearly polarized light. The aligning of the long chain conducting molecules is not very difficult and the experimental details of producing the polarizer are given in Ref. 21.1.

21.3.2 Polarization by Reflection

We consider the incidence of a plane wave on a dielectric; we assume that the electric vector associated with the incident wave lies in the plane of incidence as shown in Fig. 21.9(a). It will be shown in Sec. 23.5 that if the angle of incidence θ is such that

$$\theta = \theta_p = \tan^{-1}\left(\frac{n_2}{n_1}\right) \tag{21.10}$$

then the reflection coefficient is zero. Thus, if an unpolarized beam is incident at this angle, then the reflected beam will be linearly polarized with its electric vector perpendicular to the plane of incidence [see Fig. 21.9(b)]. Equation (21.10) is referred to as the *Brewster's law* and at this angle of incidence, the reflected and the transmitted rays are at right angles to each other; the angle θ_p is known as the polarizing angle or the Brewster angle.

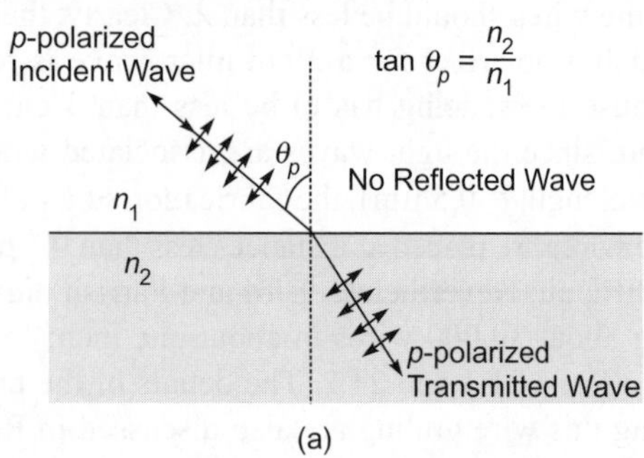

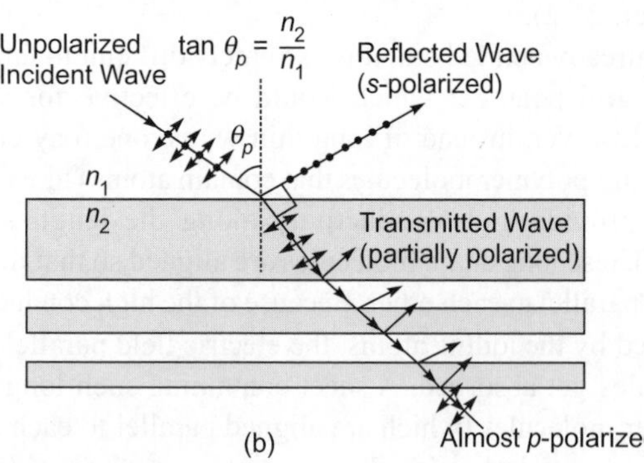

Figure 21.9

(a) If a *p*-polarized wave (**E** in the plane of incidence) is incident on the interface of two dielectrics with the angle of incidence equal to q_p (= $\tan^{-1} n_2/n_1$) then the reflection coefficient is zero. (b) If an unpolarized beam is incident at Brewster's angle, the reflected beam is plane polarized whose electric vector is perpendicular to the plane of incidence. The transmitted beam is partially polarized and if this beam is made to undergo several reflections, then the emergent beam is almost plane polarized with its electric vector in the plane of incidence.

A (commercially available) polarized sunglass blocks the horizontal component and allows only the vertical component to pass through [see Fig. 21.10(a)]. For the air-water interface, $n_1 \approx 1$ and $n_2 \approx 1.33$ and the polarizing angle $\theta_p \approx 53°$. Thus, if the sunlight is incident on the sea at an angle close to the polarizing angle, then the reflected light will be almost linearly polarized [see Fig. 21.10(b)] and if we now wear polarized sunglasses, the glare, i.e., the light reflected from the water surface, will not be seen. This is the reason why polarized sunglasses are often used by fishermen to remove the glare on the surface and see the fish inside water. Figure 21.11(a) shows a photograph on the road with

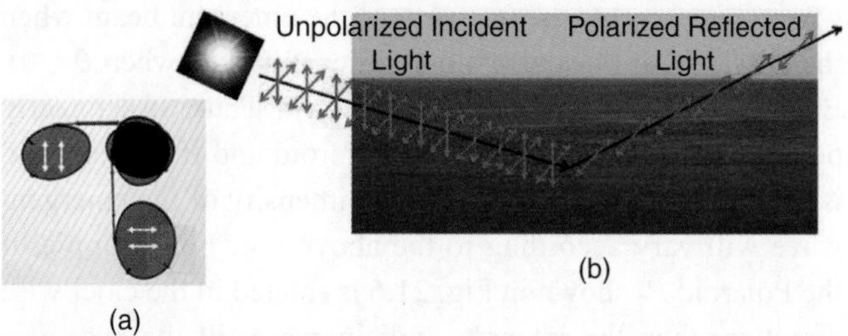

Figure 21.10

(a) A (commercially available) polarized sunglass blocks the horizontal component and allows only the vertical component to pass through. (b) If the sunlight is incident on the water surface at an angle close to the Brewster angle, then the reflected light will be almost polarized and if we now wear polarized sunglasses, the glare, i.e., the light reflected from the water surface will not be seen. Polarized sunglasses are often used by fishermen to remove the glare on the surface and see the fish inside water.

Figure 21.11

(a) A photograph on the road with ordinary glasses. (b) If we use polarized lenses, the glare can be considerably reduced. [*Photographs adapted from www.esaver.com.my/index.php?option=com_content&view=article&id=95& Itemid=220*]

ordinary glasses; if we use polarized lenses, the glare can be considerably reduced as shown in Fig. 21.11(b); see 27 and 28 in the prelim pages. Figure 21.12 shows sunlight incident on a water surface at an angle close to the polarizing angle so that the reflected light is almost polarized. If the Polaroid allows the (almost polarized) reflected beam to pass through, we see the glare from water surface [see Fig. 21.12(a)]; the glare can be blocked by using a vertical polarizer and one can see the inside of the water [see Fig. 21.12(b)].

21.3.3 Polarization by Double Refraction

In Sections 21.5 and 21.12 we will discuss the phenomenon of double refraction and will show that when an unpolarized beam enters an anisotropic crystal like calcite, it splits up into two linearly polarized beams (see Fig. 21.13). If by some method, we could eliminate one of the beams, then we would obtain a linearly polarized beam.

Figure 21.12
If the sunlight is incident on the water surface at an angle close to the Brewster angle, then the reflected light will be almost polarized. (a) If the polaroid allows the (almost polarized) reflected beam to pass through, we see the glare from water surface. (b) The glare can be blocked by using a vertical polarizer and one can see the inside of the water. [*Figure adapted from the http://polarization.com/water/water.html. Photographs were taken by Dr J. Alcoz; used with permission from Dr. Alcoz*].

Figure 21.13
When an unpolarized light beam is incident normally on a calcite crystal, it usually splits up into two linearly polarized beams. [*Photograph courtesy: Professor Vasudevan Lakshminarayanan* and adapted from *The sunstone and polarised skylight: ancient Viking navigational tools* by G. Ropars, A. Le Flocha and V. Lakshminarayanan, Contemporary Physics, 2014].

A simple method for eliminating one of the beams is through selective absorption; this property of selective absorption is known as dichroism. A crystal like tourmaline has different coefficients of absorption for the two linearly polarized beams into which the incident beam splits up. Consequently, one of the beams gets absorbed quickly and the other component passes through without much attenuation. Thus, if an unpolarized beam is passed through a tourmaline crystal, the emergent beam will be almost linearly polarized (see Fig. 21.14).

Another method for eliminating one of the polarized beams is through total internal reflection. We will show in Sections 21.5 and 21.10 that the refractive indices corresponding to the two beams are different. If one can sandwich a layer of a material whose refractive index lies between the two, then for one of the beams, the incidence will be at a rarer medium and for the other it will be at a denser medium. This principle is used in a Nicol prism which consists of a calcite crystal cut in such

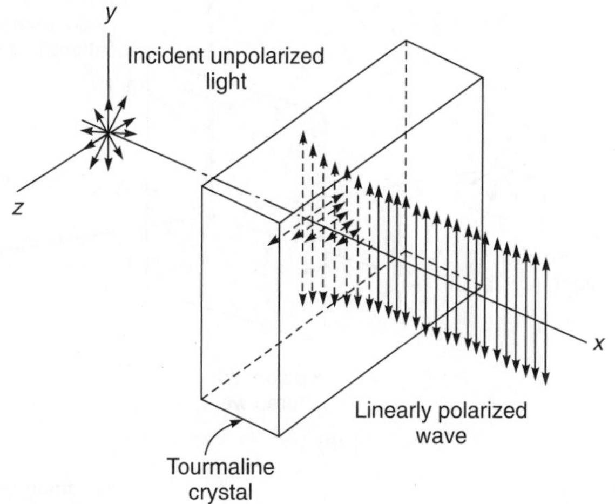

Figure 21.14
When an unpolarized beam enters a dichroic crystal like tourmaline, it splits up into two linearly polarized components. One of the components gets absorbed quickly and the other component passes through without much attenuation. [Adapted from Ref. 21.3; used with permission.]

a way that for the beam, for which the sandwiched material is a rarer medium, the angle of incidence is greater than the critical angle. Thus, this particular beam will be eliminated by total internal reflection. Figure 21.15 shows a properly cut calcite crystal in which a layer of Canada Balsam has been introduced so that the ordinary ray undergoes total internal reflection. The extraordinary component passes through and the beam emerging from the crystal is linearly polarized.

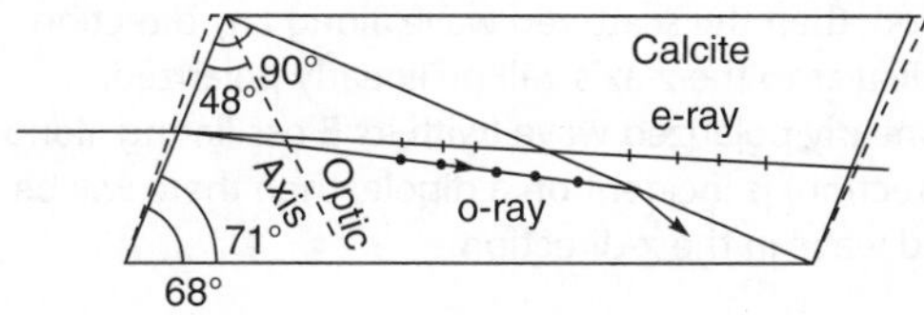

Figure 21.15
The Nicol prism. The dashed outline corresponds to the natural crystal which is cut in such a way that the ordinary ray undergoes total internal reflection at the Canada Balsam layer.

21.3.4 Polarization by Scattering

If an unpolarized beam is allowed to fall on a gas, then the beam scattered at 90° to the incident beam is linearly polarized. This follows from the fact that the waves propagating in the y direction are produced by the x-component of the dipole oscillations (see Fig. 21.16). The y component of the dipole oscillations will produce no field in the y direction (see Sec. 22.5.1). Indeed, it was through scattering experiments that Barkla could establish the transverse character of X-rays. Clearly, if the incident beam is linearly polarized with its electric vector along the x direction, then there will be no scattered light along the x-axis. As such, one can carry out

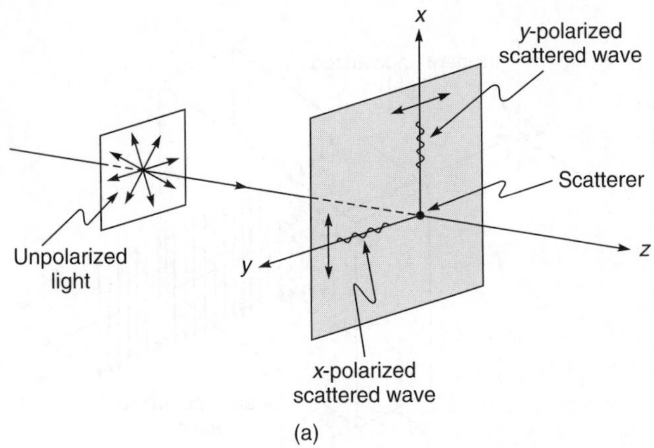

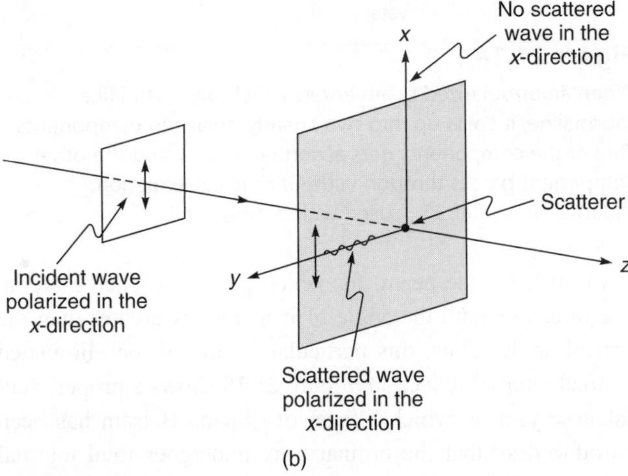

Figure 21.16
(a) If the electromagnetic wave is propagating along the z-direction, then the scattered wave along any direction perpendicular to the z-axis will be linearly polarized.
(b) If a linearly polarized wave (with its **E** oscillating along the x-direction) is incident on a dipole, then there will be no scattered wave in the x-direction.

an analysis of a scattered wave by allowing it to undergo a further scattering [see Fig. 21.16(b)].

As discussed in Sec. 6.6, the blue color of the sky is due to Rayleigh scattering of sunlight by molecules in our atmosphere. When the sun is about to set, if we look vertically upwards, light will have a high degree of polarization; this is because the angle of scattering will be very close to 90°. If we view the blue sky (which is vertically above us) with a rotating Polaroid, we will observe considerable variation of intensity.

21.4 Superposition of Two Disturbances

LO2

Let us consider the propagation of two linearly polarized electromagnetic waves (both propagating along the z-axis) with their electric vectors oscillating along the x-axis. The electric fields associated with the waves can be written in the form

$$\mathbf{E}_1 = \hat{\mathbf{x}}\, a_1 \cos(kz - \omega t + \theta_1) \tag{21.11}$$

$$\mathbf{E}_2 = \hat{\mathbf{x}}\, a_2 \cos(kz - \omega t + \theta_2) \tag{21.12}$$

where a_1 and a_2 represent the amplitudes of the waves; $\hat{\mathbf{x}}$ represents the unit vector along the x-axis and θ_1 and θ_2 are phase constants. The resultant of these two waves would be given by

$$\mathbf{E} = \mathbf{E}_1 + \mathbf{E}_2 \tag{21.13}$$

which can always be written in the form

$$\mathbf{E} = \hat{\mathbf{x}}\, a \cos(kz - \omega t + \theta) \tag{21.14}$$

where $$a = \left[a_1^2 + a_2^2 + 2a_1 a_2 \cos(\theta_1 - \theta_2)\right]^{1/2} \tag{21.15}$$

represents the amplitude of the resultant wave. Equation (21.14) tells us that the resultant is also a linearly polarized wave with its electric vector oscillating along the same axis.

We next consider the superposition of two linearly polarized electromagnetic waves (both propagating along the z-axis) but with their electric vectors oscillating along two mutually perpendicular directions. Thus, we may have

$$\mathbf{E}_1 = \hat{\mathbf{x}}\, a \cos(kz - \omega t) \tag{21.16}$$

$$\mathbf{E}_2 = \hat{\mathbf{y}}\, b \cos(kz - \omega t + \theta) \tag{21.17}$$

For $\theta = m\pi (m = 0, \pm 1, \pm 2, \ldots)$, the resultant will also be a linearly polarized wave with its electric vector oscillating along a direction making a certain angle with the y-axis; this angle will depend on the relative values of a and b.

In order to find the state of polarization of the resultant field, we consider the time variation of the resultant electric field at an arbitrary plane perpendicular to the z-axis which we may, without any loss of generality, assume to be $z = 0$. If E_x and E_y represent the x- and y-components of the resultant field $\mathbf{E}(= \mathbf{E}_1 + \mathbf{E}_2)$, then

$$E_x = a \cos \omega t \tag{21.18}$$

and $$E_y = b \cos(\omega t - \theta) \tag{21.19}$$

where we have used Eqs. (21.16) and (21.17) with $z = 0$. For $\theta = m\pi$, the above equations simplify to

$$E_x = a \cos \omega t \quad \text{and} \quad E_y = (-1)^m\, b \cos \omega t \tag{21.20}$$

from which one obtains

$$\frac{E_x}{E_y} = \pm\frac{a}{b} \quad \text{(independent of } t\text{)} \tag{21.21}$$

where the upper and lower signs correspond to m even and m odd respectively. In the $E_x - E_y$ plane, Eq. (21.21) represents a straight line; the angle θ that this line makes with the E_y axis will be given by

$$\phi = \tan^{-1}\left(\pm\frac{a}{b}\right) \tag{21.22}$$

The condition $\theta = m\pi$ implies that the two vibrations are either in phase (m = 0, ±2, ±4, ...) or out of phase (m = ±1, ±3, ...). Thus, the superposition of two linearly polarized electromagnetic waves with their electric fields at right angles to each other and oscillating in phase (or π out of phase), is again a linearly polarized wave with its electric vector, in general, oscillating in a direction which is different from the fields of either of the two waves. Figure 21.17 is a plot of the resultant field corresponding to Eq. (21.20) for various values of a/b. The tip of the electric vector oscillates (with angular frequency ω) along the thick lines shown in the figure. The equation of the straight line is given by Eq. (21.21).

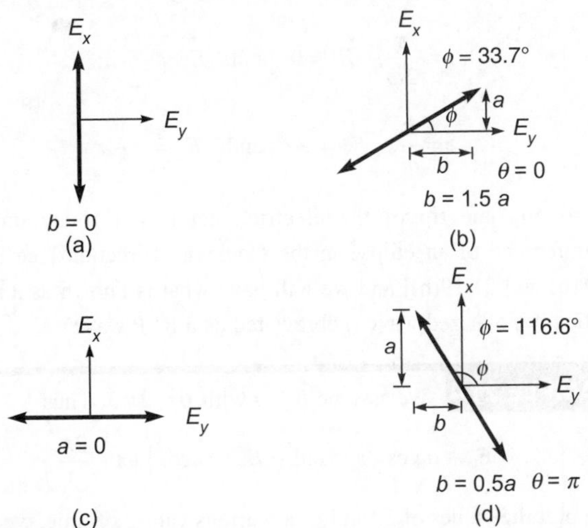

Figure 21.17
The superposition of two linearly polarized waves with their electric fields oscillating in phase along the x-axis and the y-axis. The resultant is a linearly polarized wave

For $\theta \neq m\pi$, the resultant electric vector does not, in general, oscillate along a straight line as we will illustrate through a few examples.

EXAMPLE 21.1 We first consider the simple case corresponding to $\theta = \pi/2$ with $b = a$. Thus,

$$E_x = a \cos \omega t \tag{21.23}$$

and

$$E_y = a \sin \omega t \tag{21.24}$$

Now at $t = 0,\ E_x = a$ and $E_y = 0$;

$$t = \frac{\pi}{2\omega},\ E_x = 0 \text{ and } E_y = a$$

$$t = \frac{\pi}{\omega},\ E_x = -a \text{ and } E_y = 0;$$

$$t = \frac{3\pi}{2\omega},\ E_x = 0 \text{ and } E_y = -a$$

and at $t = \frac{2\pi}{\omega}, \frac{4\pi}{\omega}, \frac{6\pi}{\omega}...;\ E_x = a$ and $E_y = 0$

Thus, if we plot the time variation of the resultant electric vector whose x- and y-components are given by Eqs. (21.23) and (21.24), one would find that the tip of the electric vector rotates on the circumference of a circle (of radius a) in the clockwise direction [see Figs. 21.18(a) and 21.19(c)]; the propagation is in the $+z$ direction which is going into the page. Such a wave is known as a right circularly polarized wave (usually abbreviated as a RCP wave); our

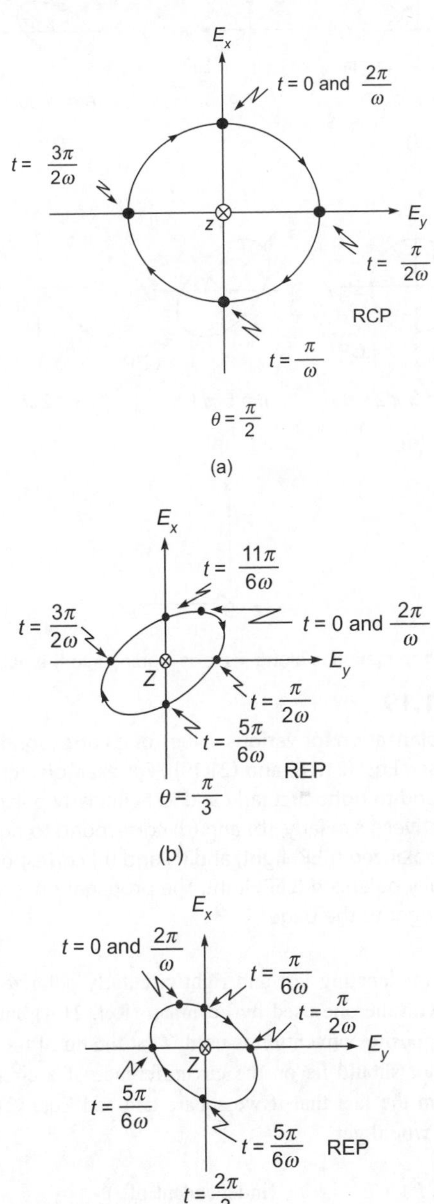

Figure 21.18
The position of the tip of the electric vector at various times corresponding to

(a) $\theta = \frac{\pi}{2}$, (b) $\theta = \frac{\pi}{3}$ and (c) $\theta = \frac{2\pi}{3}$.

The propagation is along the +z direction.

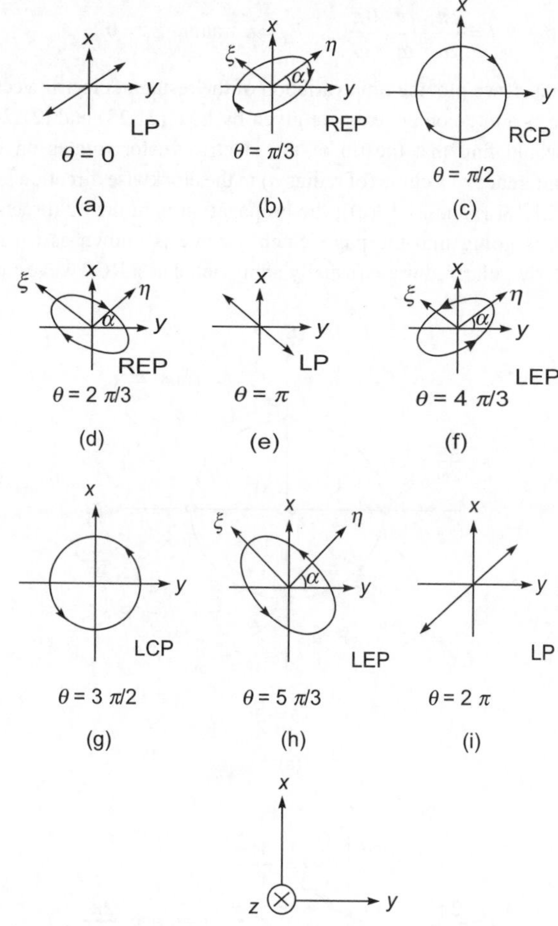

Figure 21.19

States of polarization for various values of q corresponding to $a_1 = a_2$ [see Eqs. (21.18) and (21.19)]. For example, (c) and (g) correspond to right circularly and left circularly polarized light respectively; similarly, (b) and (d) correspond to right elliptically polarized (REP) light, and (f) and (h) correspond to left elliptically polarized (LEP) light. The propagation is along + z-axis-going into the page.

convention for labeling left and right circularly polarized light is consistent with the one used by Feynman (Ref. 21.4) but in some books the opposite convention is used. That the tip of the resultant electric vector should lie on the circumference of a circle is also obvious from the fact that if we square and add Eqs. (21.23) and (21.24), we would get

$$E_x^2 + E_y^2 = a^2 \quad \text{(independent of } t\text{)}$$

which represents the equation of a circle.

EXAMPLE 21.2 We assume $b = a$ with $\theta = 3\pi/2$. Thus

$$E_x = a \cos \omega t \quad \text{and} \quad E_y = -a \sin \omega t$$

As in Example 21.1, we evaluate E_x and E_y at various values of time. We will find that we will again have a circularly polarized wave; however, the electric vector will now rotate in the anti-clockwise direction [see Fig. 21.19(g)]. Such a wave is known as a left circularly polarized wave (usually abbreviated as a LCP wave).

For $\theta \neq m\pi/2$ ($m = 0, 1, 2, \ldots$), the tip of the electric vector rotates on the circumference of an ellipse. In Fig. 21.19, we have shown the rotation of the electric vector for various values of θ; we have assumed $b = a$. As can be seen from the figure, this ellipse would degenerate into a straight line or a circle when θ becomes an even or an odd multiple of $\pi/2$.

EXAMPLE 21.3 We assume $b = a$ with $\theta = \pi/3$. Thus

$$E_x = a \cos \omega t \quad \text{and} \quad E_y = a \cos\left(\omega t - \frac{\pi}{3}\right)$$

Now at
$$t = 0, \quad E_x = a \quad \text{and} \quad E_y = \frac{1}{2}a;$$
$$t = \frac{\pi}{3\omega}, \quad E_x = \frac{1}{2}a \quad \text{and} \quad E_y = a$$
$$t = \frac{\pi}{2\omega}, \quad E_x = 0 \quad \text{and} \quad E_y = \frac{\sqrt{3}}{2}a;$$
$$t = \frac{\pi}{\omega}, \quad E_x = -a \quad \text{and} \quad E_y = -\frac{1}{2}a$$

and so on. The tip of the electric vector will rotate on the circumference of an ellipse in the clockwise direction [see Figs. 21.18(b) and 21.19(b)] and we will have what is known as a right elliptically polarized wave (abbreviated as a REP wave).

EXAMPLE 21.4 We assume $b = a$ with $\theta = 2\pi/3$. Thus

$$E_x = a \cos \omega t \quad \text{and} \quad E_y = a \cos\left(\omega t - \frac{2\pi}{3}\right).$$

If we plot the values of E_x and E_y at various values of time, we will find that the tip of the electric vector will rotate on the circumference of an ellipse in the clockwise direction [see Figs. 21.18(c) and 21.19(d)] and we will again have a right elliptically polarized wave.

In Examples 21.3 and 21.4, the major (or minor) axis would make an angle of 45 with the y-axis; this is because of the fact that $b = a$ [see Eq. (21.35)]. In general, when $b \neq a$, one obtains an elliptically polarized wave whose axes will make a different angle with the y-axis [see Eq. (21.35)]; this ellipse will degenerate into a straight line for $\theta = 0, \pi, 2\pi, 3\pi, \ldots$. We will show this mathematically in Sec. 21.4.1.

Now, as discussed in Sec. 21.1, if we move a stretched string up and down, we will generate a linearly polarized wave with its displacement confined to the vertical plane. Similarly, we may generate a linearly polarized wave with its displacement confined to the horizontal plane. Further, we may rotate the end of the string on the circumference of a circle (or an ellipse) to produce a circularly polarized (or an elliptically polarized) wave [see Fig. 21.2(b)]. For such a wave, the particles of the string actually move on the circumference of a circle (or an ellipse). On the other hand, for an elliptically polarized electromagnetic wave, it is the electric (or the magnetic field) which changes its magnitude and direction at a particular point; the presence of these fields can be felt by their interaction with a charged particle. In particular, for a circularly polarized wave, the magnitude of the field remains the same; the direction changes with an angular frequency ω. On the other hand, for a linearly polarized wave, the direction of the field does not change; it is the magnitude which keeps on oscillating about the zero value with angular frequency ω of the wave.

21.4.1 The Mathematical Analysis

In this section, we will show that Eqs. (21.18) and (21.19) represent an elliptically polarized wave. We rewrite Eqs. (21.18) and (21.19)

$$E_x = a \cos(\omega t)$$
$$E_y = b \cos(\omega t - \theta)$$

We assume that the major axis of the ellipse to be along the ξ or the η axis and that the η axis makes an angle α with the y-axis [see Fig. 21.19(b)]; i.e.,

$$E_\xi = E_1 \cos(\omega t - \phi) \tag{21.25}$$
$$E_\eta = E_2 \sin(\omega t - \phi) \tag{21.26}$$

Obviously,
$$\left(\frac{E_\xi}{E_1}\right)^2 + \left(\frac{E_\eta}{E_2}\right)^2 = 1 \tag{21.27}$$

which represents the equation of an ellipse. Now, for the rotated coordinates

$$E_\xi = E_x \cos\alpha - E_y \sin\alpha \tag{21.28}$$
$$E_\eta = E_x \sin\alpha + E_y \cos\alpha \tag{21.29}$$

Substituting Eqs. (21.18), (21.19), (21.25) and (21.26) in Eqs. (21.28) and (21.29), we get

$$E_1 \cos(\omega t - \phi) = a \cos\omega t \cos\alpha - b\cos(\omega t - \theta)\sin\alpha$$
$$E_2 \sin(\omega t - \phi) = a \cos\omega t \sin\alpha + b\cos(\omega t - \theta)\cos\alpha$$

These equations have to be valid at all times; thus, we equate the coefficients of $\cos\omega t$ and $\sin\omega t$ on both sides of the equation to obtain

$$E_1 \cos\phi = a\cos\alpha - b\cos\theta\sin\alpha \tag{21.30}$$
$$E_1 \sin\phi = -b\sin\theta\sin\alpha \tag{21.31}$$

and

$$-E_2 \sin\phi = a\sin\alpha + b\cos\theta\cos\alpha \tag{21.32}$$
$$E_2 \cos\phi = +b\sin\theta\cos\alpha \tag{21.33}$$

If we square the four equations above and add, we would get

$$E_1^2 + E_2^2 = a^2 + b^2$$

which is to be expected because the total intensity of both the beams should be equal. Further, if we divide Eq. (21.30) by Eq. (21.33) and Eq. (21.31) by Eq. (21.32), we would obtain

$$\frac{E_1}{E_2} = \frac{a\cos\alpha - b\cos\theta\sin\alpha}{b\sin\theta\cos\alpha} = \frac{b\sin\theta\sin\alpha}{a\sin\alpha + b\cos\theta\cos\alpha} \tag{21.34}$$

Thus,

$$a^2\sin\alpha\cos\alpha - b^2\cos^2\theta\sin\alpha\cos\alpha + ab\cos\theta[\cos^2\alpha - \sin^2\alpha]$$
$$= b^2\sin^2\theta\sin\alpha\cos\alpha$$

Simple manipulations would give

$$\tan 2\alpha = \frac{2ab\cos\theta}{b^2 - a^2} \tag{21.35}$$

EXAMPLE 21.5 We assume $b = a$ so that $2\alpha = \pi/2 \Rightarrow \alpha = \pi/4$ implying that the major (or minor) axis of the ellipse makes 45° with the y-axis [see Fig. 21.19(b)]. Further,

$$\frac{E_1}{E_2} = \frac{1 - \cos\theta}{\sin\theta} = \tan\frac{\theta}{2}$$

Thus, for $b = a$, and for

$$\theta = \frac{\pi}{3}, \frac{\pi}{2}, \frac{2\pi}{3}, \frac{4\pi}{3}, \frac{3\pi}{2} \text{ and } \frac{5\pi}{3}$$

we will respectively have

$$\frac{E_1}{E_2} = +0.577,\ 1,\ 1.732,\ -1.732,\ -1 \text{ and } -0.577$$

which correspond to REP, RCP, REP, LEP, LCP and LEP respectively as shown in Fig. 21.19. For example, for $\theta = \pi/3$ we will have

$$E_x = \alpha\cos(\omega t) \text{ and } E_y = a\cos(\omega t - \pi/3)$$

(see also Example 21.20). As discussed in Example 21.1, we will have a right elliptically polarized wave as shown in Figs. 21.18(b) and 21.19 (b). From Eqs. (21.30) and (21.31) [or from Eqs. (21.32) and (21.33)] we will have

$$\tan\phi = -\frac{1 + \cos\theta}{\sin\theta} = -\cot\frac{\theta}{2} \Rightarrow \phi = -\frac{\pi}{2} + \frac{\theta}{2}$$

where we have used the fact that $\cos\phi$ is positive and $\sin\phi$ is negative [see Eqs. (21.30)–(21.31)]. Therefore, in the rotated coordinates

$$E_\xi = -E_1\sin\left(\omega t - \frac{\pi}{6}\right) \text{ and } E_\eta = 1.733\, E_1\cos\left(\omega t - \frac{\pi}{6}\right).$$

21.5 The Phenomenon of Double Refraction LO3

If an unpolarized light beam is incident normally on a calcite crystal [see Fig. 21.13 and 21.20(a)], it will split up into two linearly polarized beams. The beam which travels undeviated is known as the ordinary ray (usually abbreviated as the

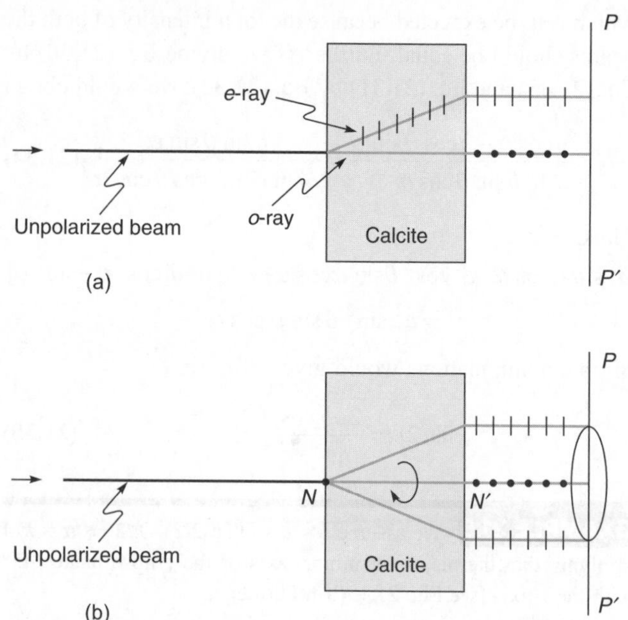

Figure 21.20

(a) When an unpolarized light beam is incident on a calcite crystal, it usually splits up into two linearly polarized beams. (b) If we rotate the crystal about *NN′* then the *e*-ray will rotate about *NN′*.

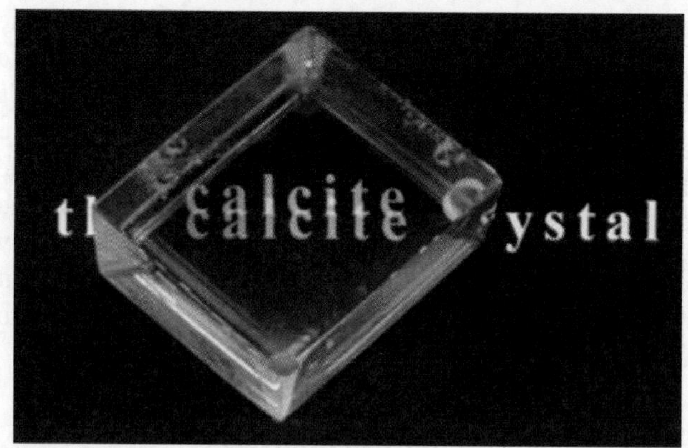

Figure 21.21

Typical double image of a sentence in a printed text. The ordinary image is fixed, while the upper extraordinary image is shifted and can rotate. [Photograph courtesy: Professor Vasudevan Lakshminarayanan and adapted from *The sunstone and polarised skylight: ancient Viking navigational tools* by G. Ropars, A. Le Flocha and V. Lakshminarayanan, Contemporary Physics, 2014].

o-ray) and obeys Snell's laws of refraction. On the other hand, the second beam, which in general does not obey Snell's laws, is known as the extra-ordinary ray (usually abbreviated as the *e*-ray). The appearance of two beams is due to the phenomenon of double refraction and a crystal like calcite is usually referred to as a "double refracting" crystal. If we put a polaroid *PP′* behind the calcite crystal and rotate the polaroid (about *NN′*) then for two positions of the polaroid (when the pass-axis is perpendicular to the plane of the paper) the *e*-ray will be completely blocked and only the *o*-ray will pass through. On the other hand, when the pass-axis of the polaroid is in the plane of the paper (i.e., along the line *PP′*) then the *o*-ray will be completely blocked and only the *e*-ray will pass through. Further, if we rotate the crystal about *NN′* then the *e*-ray will rotate about the axis [see Fig. 21.20(b)]. Figure 21.21 shows a typical double image as viewed through a doubly refracting crystal like calcite. If we rotate the crystal about the vertical axis, one of the images will be fixed, while the other image will rotate.

In Sec. 21.13 we will show that whereas the velocity of the ordinary ray is the same in all directions, the velocity of the extraordinary ray is different in different directions; a medium (like calcite, quartz), which exhibits different properties in different directions, is called an anisotropic medium. Along a particular direction (fixed in the crystal), the two velocities are equal; this direction is known as the optic axis of the crystal. In a crystal like calcite, the two rays have the same speed only along one direction (which is the optic axis); such crystals are known as uniaxial crystals*. The velocities of the ordinary and the extraordinary rays are given by the following equations [see Eqs. (21.120) and (21.123)]:

$$v_{ro} = \frac{c}{n_o} \qquad \text{(ordinary ray)} \qquad \textbf{(21.36)}$$

$$\frac{1}{v_{re}^{\,2}} = \frac{\sin^2\theta}{(c/n_e)^2} + \frac{\cos^2\theta}{(c/n_o)^2} \qquad \text{(extraordinary ray)} \qquad \textbf{(21.37)}$$

where n_o and n_e are constants of the crystal and θ is the angle that the ray makes with the optic axis; we have assumed the optic axis to be parallel to the *z*-axis. Thus, c/n_o and c/n_e are the velocities of the extraordinary ray when it propagates parallel and perpendicular to the optic axis. Now, the equation of an ellipse (in the *z*-*x* plane) is given by

$$\frac{z^2}{a^2} + \frac{x^2}{b^2} = 1 \qquad \textbf{(21.38)}$$

If (ρ, θ) represent the polar coordinates, then $z = \rho\cos\theta$ and $x = \rho\sin\theta$ and the equation of the ellipse can be written in the form

$$\frac{1}{\rho^2} = \frac{\cos^2\theta}{a^2} + \frac{\sin^2\theta}{b^2} \qquad \textbf{(21.39)}$$

In three dimensions, the above equation will represent an ellipsoid of revolution with the optic axis as the axis of

* In general, there may be two directions along which the two rays have the same speed; such crystals are known as biaxial crystals. The analysis of biaxial crystals is quite difficult; interested readers may look up References 21.5 and 21.6.

revolution. (If we rotate a circle about one of its diameters, we will obtain a sphere, and if we rotate an ellipse about its major (or minor) axis, we will obtain an ellipsoid of revolution). Thus, if we plot v_{re} as a function of θ, we will obtain an ellipsoid of revolution; on the other hand, since v_{ro} is independent of θ, if we plot v_{ro} (as a function of θ), we will obtain a sphere. Along the optic axis, $\theta = 0$ and

$$v_{ro} = v_{re} = \frac{c}{n_o}$$

We next consider the value of v_{re} perpendicular to the optic axis (i.e., for $\theta = \pi/2$). For a negative crystal $n_e < n_o$ and

$$v_{re}\left(\theta = \frac{\pi}{2}\right) = \frac{c}{n_e} > v_{ro} \quad \textbf{(21.40)}$$

Thus, the minor axis will be along the optic axis and the ellipsoid of revolution will lie outside the sphere [see Fig. 21.22(a)]. On the other hand, for a positive crystal $n_e > n_o$ and

$$v_{re}\left(\theta = \frac{\pi}{2}\right) = \frac{c}{n_e} < v_{ro} \quad \textbf{(21.41)}$$

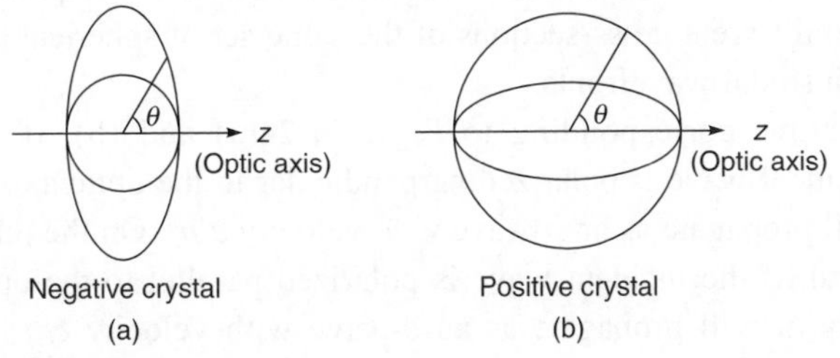

Figure 21.22

(a) In a negative crystal, the ellipsoid of revolution (which corresponds to the extraordinary ray) lies outside the sphere; the sphere corresponds to the ordinary ray. (b) In a positive crystal, the ellipsoid of revolution (which corresponds to the extraordinary ray) lies inside the sphere.

The major axis will now be along the optic axis and the ellipsoid of revolution will lie inside the sphere [see Fig. 21.22(b)]. The ellipsoid of revolution and the sphere are known as the ray velocity surfaces.

We next consider an unpolarized plane wave incident on a calcite crystal. The plane wave will split up into 2 plane waves. One is referred to as the ordinary wave (usually abbreviated as the *o*-wave) and the other is referred to as the extraordinary wave (usually abbreviated as the *e*-wave). For both waves, the space and time dependence of the vectors **E**, **D**, **B** and **H** can be assumed to be of the form

$$e^{i(\mathbf{k}.\mathbf{r} - \omega t)}$$

where **k** denotes the propagation vector and represents the direction normal to the phase fronts. In general, the **k** vector for the *o*- and *e*-waves will be different. In Sec. 21.12 we will show that

1. Both ordinary and extraordinary waves are linearly polarized.
2. $\mathbf{D}.\mathbf{k} = 0$ for both *o*- and *e*-waves **(21.42)**
   Thus, **D** is always at right angles to **k** and for this reason the direction of **D** is chosen as the direction of "vibrations".
3. If we assume the *z*-axis to be parallel to the optic axis then,
   $\mathbf{D}.\hat{\mathbf{z}} = 0$ (and $\mathbf{D} \,.\, \mathbf{k} = 0$) for the *o*-wave **(21.43)**
   Thus, for the *o*-wave, the **D** vector is at right angles to the optic axis as well as to **k**.
4. On the other hand, for the *e*-wave,
   D lies in the plane containing **k** and the optic axis (and of course, $\mathbf{D} \,.\, \mathbf{k} = 0$) **(21.44)**

Using the recipe given above, we will consider the refraction of a plane electromagnetic wave incident on a negative crystal like calcite; a similar analysis can be carried out for positive crystals.

21.5.1 Normal Incidence

We first assume a plane wave incident normally on a uniaxial crystal as shown in Fig. 21.23. Without loss of generality, we can always choose the optic axis to lie on the plane of the paper. The direction of the optic axis is shown as a dashed line in Fig. 21.23. In order to determine the ordinary ray, with the point B as the center, we draw a sphere of radius c/n_o. Similarly, we draw another sphere (of the same radius) from the point D. The common tangent plane to these spheres is shown as OO′, which represents the wavefront corresponding to the ordinary refracted ray. It may be noted that the dots show the direction of "vibrations" (i.e., direction of **D**) which are perpendicular to **k** and to the optic axis [see Eq. 21.43].

In order to determine the extraordinary ray, we draw an ellipse (centered at the point B) with its minor axis ($= c/n_o$) along the optic axis and with major axis equal to c/n_e. The ellipsoid of revolution is obtained by rotating the ellipse about the optic axis. Similarly, we draw another ellipsoid of revolution from the point D. The common tangent plane to these ellipsoids (which will be perpendicular to **k**) is shown as EE′ in Fig. 21.23. If we join the point B to the point of contact O, then corresponding to the incident ray AB, the direction of the ordinary ray will be along BO. Similarly, if we join the point B to the point of contact E (between the ellipsoid of revolution and the tangent plane EE′), then corresponding to the incident ray AB, the direction of the extraordinary ray will be along BE.

It is to be noted that the direction of **k** is the *same* for both *o*- and *e*-waves i.e., both are along BO. However, if we have a narrow beam incident as AB, then while the ordinary ray will propagate along BO, the extraordinary ray will propagate in a

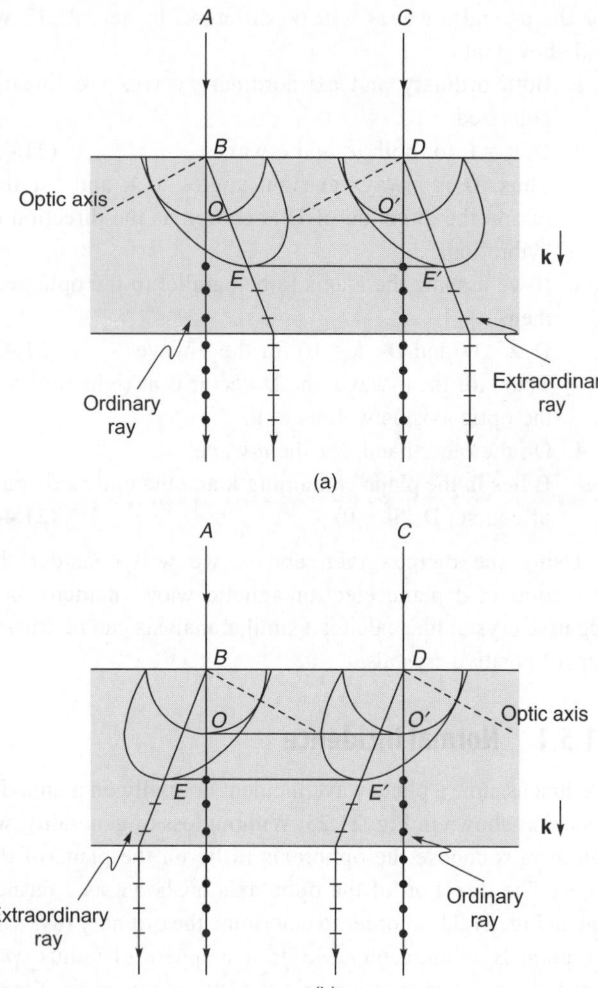

Figure 21.23
The refraction of a plane wave incident on a negative crystal whose optic axis is along the dashed line. The 'dots' and 'dashes' represent the direction of **D** associated with the *o*-wave and *e*-wave respectively.

different direction BE, as shown in Fig. 21.23(a). Obviously, if we have a different direction of the optic axis [see Fig. 21.23(b)], then, although the direction of the ordinary ray will remain the same, the extraordinary ray will propagate in a different direction. Thus, if a ray is incident normally on a calcite crystal, and if the crystal is rotated about the normal, then the optic axis and the extraordinary ray will also rotate (about the normal) on the periphery of a cone; each time the ray will lie in the plane containing the normal and the optic axis [see Fig. 21.20(b)].

The ray refractive index corresponding to the extraordinary ray (n_{re}) will be given by

$$n_{re} = \frac{c}{v_{re}} = \sqrt{n_o^2 \cos^2\theta + n_e^2 \sin^2\theta} \tag{21.45}$$

If one starts with the above equation and uses Fermat's principle to obtain the refracted ray, the results will be consistent with the ones obtained in this section (see Sec. 2.5).

Now, as mentioned earlier, the direction of vibrations for the ordinary ray is normal to the optic axis and the vector **k**; as such, the directions of these vibrations in this case, will be normal to the plane of the paper and have been shown as dots in Fig. 21.23. Similarly, since the direction of vibrations for the extraordinary ray is perpendicular to **k** and lies in the plane containing the extraordinary ray and the optic axis, they are along the small straight lines drawn on the extraordinary ray in Fig. 21.23. Thus, an incident ray will split up into two rays propagating in different directions and when they leave the crystal, we will obtain two linearly polarized beams.

In the above case, we have assumed the optic axis to make an arbitrary angle α with the normal to the surface. In the special cases of $\alpha = 0$ and $\alpha = \pi/2$, the ordinary and the extraordinary rays travel along the same directions as shown in Figs. 21.24(a), (b) and (c). Figure 21.24(b) corresponds to the case when the optic axis is normal to the plane of the paper; and as such, the section of the extraordinary wavefront in the plane of the paper will be a circle. Once again, both the ordinary and the extraordinary rays travel along the same direction. It may be mentioned that Figs. 21.24(a) and (b) correspond to the same configuration; in both cases the optic axis is parallel to the surface. The figures represent two different cross-sections of the same set of spherical and ellipsoidal wavefronts.

Now, corresponding to Figs. 21.24(a) and (b), if the incident wave is polarized perpendicular to the optic axis, it will propagate as an *o*-wave with velocity c/n_o. On the other hand, if the incident wave is polarized parallel to the optic axis, it will propagate as an *e*-wave with velocity c/n_e. In Fig. 21.24(c) the optic axis is normal to the surface and both waves will travel with the same velocity.

Notice that in the configuration shown in Figs. 21.24(a) and (b), although both the waves travel in the same direction, they propagate with different velocities. This phenomenon is used in the fabrication of quarter and half wave plates (see Sec. 21.6). On the other hand, in the configuration shown in Fig. 21.24(c), both the waves not only travel in the same direction but they also propagate with the same velocity.

21.5.2 Oblique Incidence

We next consider the case of a plane wave incident obliquely on a negative uniaxial crystal [see Fig. 21.25(a)]. Once again we use Huygens' principle to determine the shape of the refracted wavefronts. Let BD represent the incident wavefront. If the time taken for the disturbance to reach the point F from D is t, then with B as center we draw a sphere of radius $(c/n_o)t$ and an ellipsoid of revolution of semi-minor and semi-major axes $(c/n_o)t$ and $(c/n_e)t$ respectively; the semi-minor axis is along the optic axis. From the point F we draw tangent planes FO and FE to the sphere and the ellipsoid of revolution respectively. These planes would represent

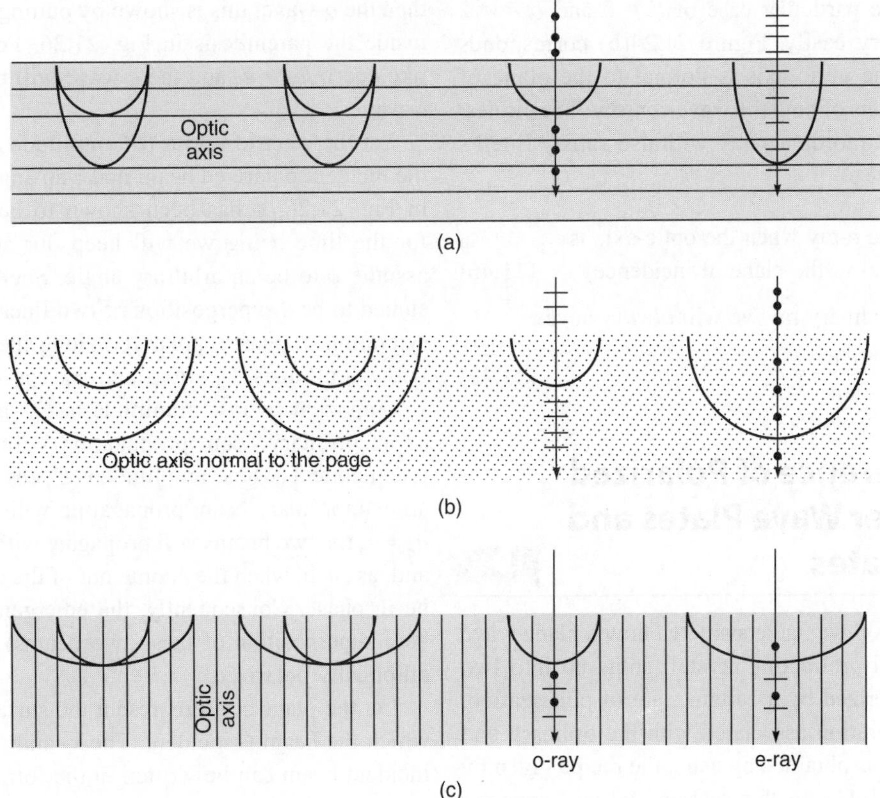

Figure 21.24

Propagation of a plane wave incident normally on a negative uniaxial crystal. In (a) and (c) the optic axis is shown as parallel straight lines and in (b) the optic axis is perpendicular to the plane of the figure and is shown in dots. In each case, the extraordinary and the ordinary rays travel in the same direction.

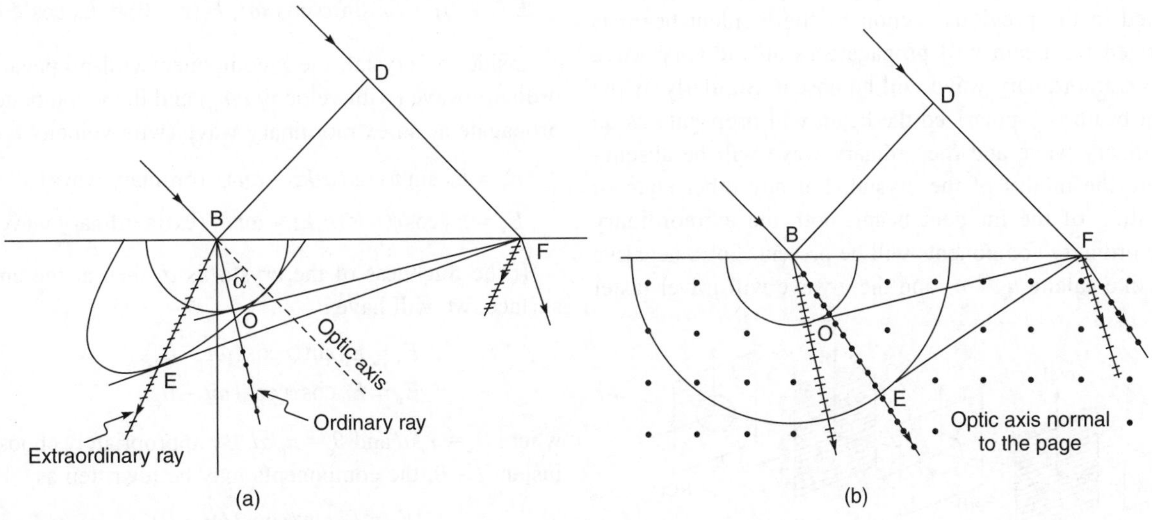

Figure 21.25

Refraction of a plane wave incident obliquely on a negative uniaxial crystal. In (a), the direction of the optic axis is along the dashed line. In (b), the optic axis is perpendicular to the plane of the paper.

the refracted wavefronts corresponding to the ordinary and the extraordinary rays respectively. If the points of contact are O and E, then the ordinary and extraordinary refracted rays will propagate along BO and BE respectively; this can also be shown using Fermat's principle (see Sec. 2.5). The directions of vibration of these rays are shown by dots and small lines respectively and are obtained by using the general rules discussed earlier. The shape of the refracted wavefronts corresponding to the particular case of $\alpha = 0$ and $\alpha = \pi/2$ can be obtained very easily. Figure 21.24(b) corresponds to the case when the optic axis is normal to the plane of incidence. The sections of both the wavefronts will be circles; consequently, the extraordinary ray will also satisfy Snell's law and we will have

$$\frac{\sin i}{\sin r} = n_e \quad \text{(for the } e\text{-ray when the optic-axis is normal to the plane of incidence)} \tag{21.46}$$

Of course, for the ordinary ray we will *always* have

$$\frac{\sin i}{\sin r} = n_o \tag{21.47}$$

21.6 Interference of Polarized Light: Quarter Wave Plates and Half Wave Plates

LO4

In the previous section we had considered how a plane wave (incident on a doubly refracting crystal) splits up into two waves each characterized by a certain state of polarization. The direction of vibration associated with the ordinary and extraordinary waves is obtained by using the recipe given by Eqs. (21.42) and (21.43). In this section, we will consider the normal incidence of a plane-polarized beam on a calcite crystal whose optic axis is parallel to the surface of the crystal as shown in Fig. 21.26. We will study the state of polarization of the beam emerging from the crystal. We will assume the y-axis to be along the optic axis. Now, as discussed in the previous section, if the incident beam is x-polarized the beam will propagate as an ordinary wave and the extraordinary wave will be absent. Similarly, if the incident beam is y-polarized the beam will propagate as an extraordinary wave and the ordinary wave will be absent–these are the modes of the crystal. For any other state of polarization of the incident beam, both the extraordinary and the ordinary components will be present. For a negative crystal like calcite $n_e < n_o$ and the e-wave will travel faster

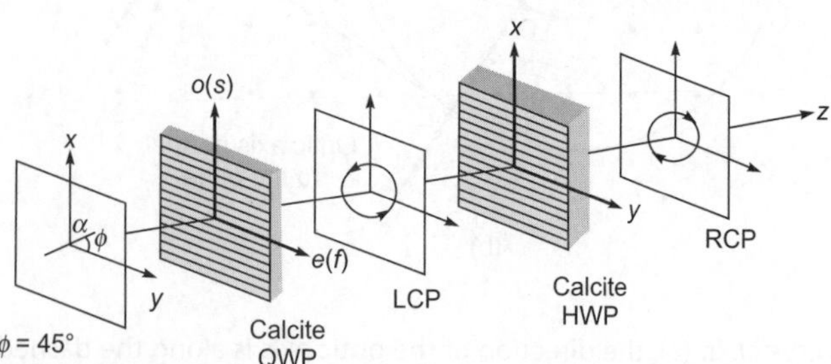

Figure 21.26

A linearly polarized beam making an angle 45° with the y-axis gets converted to a LCP after propagating through a calcite QWP; further, an LCP gets converted to a RCP after propagating through a calcite HWP. The optic axis in the QWP and HWP is along the y-direction as shown by lines parallel to the y-axis.

than the o-wave; this is shown by putting s (slow) and f (fast) inside the parenthesis in Fig. 21.26. For a positive crystal like quartz $n_e > n_o$ and the e-wave will travel faster than the o-wave.

Let the electric vector (of amplitude E_0) associated with the incident polarized beam make an angle ϕ with the y-axis; in Fig. 21.26, ϕ has been shown to be equal to 45°—but for the time being we will keep our analysis general and assume ϕ to be an arbitrary angle. Such a beam can be assumed to be a superposition of two linearly polarized beams (vibrating in phase), polarized along the x- and y-directions with amplitudes $E_0 \sin \phi$ and $E_0 \cos \phi$ respectively. The x-component (whose amplitude is $E_0 \sin \phi$) passes through as an ordinary beam propagating with velocity c/n_o. The y-component (whose amplitude is $E_0 \cos \phi$) passes through as an extraordinary beam propagating with velocity c/n_e. Since $n_e \neq n_o$ the two beams will propagate with different velocities and, as such, when they come out of the crystal, they will not be in phase. Consequently, the emergent beam (which will be a superposition of these two beams) will be, in general, elliptically polarized.

Let the plane $z = 0$ represent the surface of the crystal on which the beam is incident. The x- and y-components of the incident beam can be written in the form

$$\begin{aligned} E_x &= E_0 \sin\phi \cos(kz - \omega t) \\ E_y &= E_0 \cos\phi \cos(kz - \omega t) \end{aligned} \tag{21.48}$$

where $k = (\omega/c)$ represents the free-space wave number. Thus, at $z = 0$, we will have

$$E_x(z = 0) = E_0 \sin \phi \cos \omega t; \; E_y(z = 0) = E_0 \cos \phi \cos \omega t$$

Inside the crystal, the x-component will propagate as an ordinary wave (with velocity c/n_o) and the y-component will propagate as an extraordinary wave (with velocity c/n_e)

$$E_x = E_0 \sin\phi \cos(n_o kz - \omega t) \quad \text{(ordinary wave)}$$

$$E_y = E_0 \cos\phi \cos(n_e kz - \omega t) \quad \text{(extraordinary wave)}$$

If the thickness of the crystal is d, then at the emerging surface, we will have

$$E_x = E_0 \sin\phi \cos(\omega t - \theta_o)$$

$$E_y = E_0 \cos\phi \cos(\omega t - \theta_e)$$

where $\theta_o = n_o kd$ and $\theta_e = n_e kd$. By appropriately choosing the instant $t = 0$, the components may be rewritten as

$$\begin{aligned} E_x &= E_0 \sin\phi \cos(\omega t - \theta) \\ E_y &= E_0 \cos\phi \cos \omega t \end{aligned} \tag{21.49}$$

$$\text{where} \quad \theta = \theta_o - \theta_e = k\,d\,(n_o - n_e) = \frac{\omega}{c}(n_o - n_e)d \tag{21.50}$$

represents the phase difference between the ordinary and the extraordinary beams. Clearly, if the thickness of the crystal is such that $\theta = 2\pi, 4\pi, 6\pi, \ldots$, the emergent beam will have the same state of polarization as the incident beam. Now, if the thickness d of the crystal is such that $\theta = \pi/2$, the crystal is said to be a quarter wave plate (usually abbreviated as QWP)—a phase difference of $\pi/2$ implies a path difference of a quarter of a wavelength. On the other hand, if the thickness of the crystal is such that $\theta = \pi$, the crystal is said to be a half wave plate (usually abbreviated as HWP).

EXAMPLE 21.6 As an example, let us consider the case when $\phi = \pi/4$ and $\theta = \pi/2$, i.e., the x- and y-components of the incident wave have equal amplitudes and the crystal introduces a phase difference of $\pi/2$ (see Fig. 21.24). Thus, for the emergent beam we have

$$E_x = \frac{E_0}{\sqrt{2}} \sin \omega t; \; E_y = \frac{E_0}{\sqrt{2}} \cos \omega t \tag{21.51}$$

If we use a method similar to that described in Example 21.1, we will find that a wave described by the above equation represents a left circularly polarized wave. In order to introduce a phase difference of $\pi/2$, the thickness of the crystal should have a value given by the following equation:

$$d = \frac{c}{\omega(n_o - n_e)} \frac{\pi}{2} = \frac{1}{4} \frac{\lambda_0}{(n_o - n_e)} \tag{21.52}$$

where λ_0 is the free-space wavelength. For calcite, for $\lambda_0 = 5893$ Å and at 18 C, $n_o = 1.65836$ and $n_e = 1.48641$. Substituting these values, we obtain

$$d = \frac{5.893 \times 10^{-7}}{4 \times 0.17195} \text{ m} \approx 0.000857 \text{ mm}$$

Thus a calcite QWP (at $\lambda_0 = 5893$ Å = 0.5893 μm) will have a thickness of 0.000857 mm and will have its optic axis parallel to the surface; such a QWP will introduce a phase difference of $\pi/2$ between the ordinary and the extraordinary components at $\lambda_0 = 5893$ Å. It should be pointed out that if the thickness is an odd multiple of the above quantity, i.e., if

$$d = (2m + 1) \frac{\lambda_0}{4(n_o - n_e)} \; ; \; m = 0, 1, 2, \ldots \tag{21.53}$$

then in the example considered above (i.e., when $\phi = \pi/4$), it can easily be shown that the emergent beam will be left circularly polarized for $m = 0, 2, 4, \ldots$ and right circularly polarized for $m = 1, 3, 4, \ldots$

We next consider the case when the linearly polarized beam (with $\phi = \pi/4$) is incident on a HWP so that $\theta = \pi$, i.e., the x- and y-components of the incident wave have equal amplitudes and the crystal introduces a phase difference of π (see Fig. 21.27). Thus, for the emergent beam we have

$$E_x = -\frac{E_0}{\sqrt{2}} \cos \omega t \; ; \; E_y = \frac{E_0}{\sqrt{2}} \cos \omega t$$

which represents a linearly polarized wave with the direction of polarization making an angle of 135° with the y-axis (see Fig. 21.27). If we now pass this beam through a calcite QWP, the emergent beam will be right circularly polarized as shown in Fig. 21.27. On the other hand, if a left circularly polarized is incident normally on a calcite HWP, the emergent beam will be right circularly polarized as shown in Fig. 21.26.

Thus, for a HWP the thickness (for a negative crystal) would be given by

$$d = (2m + 1) \frac{\lambda_0}{2(n_o - n_e)}$$

We may mention that if the crystal thickness is such that if $\theta \neq \pi/2, \pi, 3\pi/2, 2\pi, \ldots$ the emergent beam will be elliptically polarized. For a positive crystal (like quartz), $n_e > n_o$ and Eq. (21.49) should be written in the form

$$\begin{aligned} E_y &= E_0 \sin \phi \cos(\omega t + \theta') \\ E_z &= E_0 \cos \phi \cos \omega t \end{aligned} \tag{21.54}$$

where

$$\theta' = \frac{\omega}{c} d(n_e - n_o)$$

For a quarter wave plate,

$$d = (2m + 1) \frac{\lambda_0}{4(n_e - n_o)}; \; m = 0, 1, 2, \ldots$$

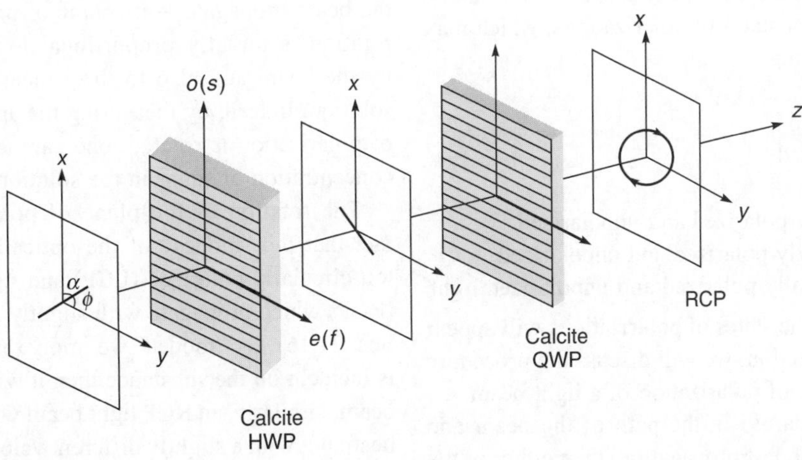

Figure 21.27
If the linearly polarized beam making an angle 45° with the y-axis is incident on a HWP, the plane of polarization gets rotated by 90°; this beam gets converted to a RCP after propagating through a calcite QWP. The optic axis in the QWP and HWP is along the y-direction as shown by lines parallel to the z-axis.

Thus, if in Fig. 21.26, the calcite QWP is replaced by a quartz QWP, the beam emerging from the QWP will be right circularly polarized.

EXAMPLE 21.7 We consider a left circularly polarized beam (λ_0 = 5893 Å = 0.5893 μm) incident normally on a calcite crystal (with its optic axis cut parallel to the surface) of thickness 0.005141 mm. The electric field for the incident left circularly polarized beam at $z = 0$ can be written as

$$E_x = E_1 \sin \omega t;\ E_y = E_1 \cos \omega t \tag{21.55}$$

Now

$$\theta = \frac{(n_o - n_e) d \times 2\pi}{\lambda_0} = \frac{0.17195 \times 5.141 \times 10^{-6} \times 2\pi}{5.893 \times 10^{-7}} \approx 3\pi$$

Thus the emergent wave will be [cf. Eq. (21.49)]

$$E_x = E_1 \sin (\omega t - 3\pi) = -E_1 \sin \omega t;\ E_y = E_1 \cos \omega t$$

which represents a right circularly polarized beam.

EXAMPLE 21.8 We next consider a left circularly polarized beam (λ_0 = 0.5890 μm) incident on a quartz crystal (with its optic axis cut parallel to the surface) of thickness 25 μm. We assume n_o and n_e to be 1.54424 and 1.55335 (see Table 21.1) respectively. The electric field for the incident left circularly polarized beam at $z = 0$ would be given by Eq. (21.55). Further,

$$\theta' = (n_e - n_o) \frac{2\pi}{\lambda_0} d = 0.00911 \times \frac{2\pi}{0.589} \times 25 = 0.77\pi$$

Thus the emergent beam will be

$$E_x = E_1 \sin (\omega t + 0.77\pi)\ ;\quad E_y = E_1 \cos \omega t$$

which will represent a right elliptically polarized light. (Calculate and plot E_x and E_y at $\omega t = 0, \pi/4, \pi/2, 3\pi/4, \ldots$).

21.7 Analysis of Polarized Light

LO5

In the earlier sections we have seen that a plane wave can be characterized by different states of polarizations, which may be anyone of the following:

(a) linearly polarized
(b) circularly polarized
(c) elliptically polarized
(d) unpolarized
(e) mixture of linearly polarized and unpolarized
(f) mixture of circularly polarized and unpolarized
(g) mixture of elliptically polarized and unpolarized light

To the naked eye all the states of polarizations will appear to be the same. In this section, we will discuss the procedure for determining the state of polarization of a light beam.

If we introduce a polaroid in the path of the beam and rotate it about the direction of propagation, then either of the following three possibilities can occur:

(i) If there is complete extinction at two positions of the polarizer, then the beam is linearly polarized.

(ii) If there is no variation of intensity, then the beam is either unpolarized or circularly polarized or a mixture of unpolarized and circularly polarized light. We now put a quarter wave plate on the path of the beam followed by the rotating polaroid. If there is no variation of intensity then the incident beam is unpolarized. If there is complete extinction at two positions, then the beam is circularly polarized (this is due to the fact that a quarter wave plate will transform a circularly polarized light into a linearly polarized light). If there is a variation of intensity (without complete extinction) then the beam is a mixture of unpolarized and circularly polarized light.

(iii) If there is a variation of intensity (without complete extinction) then the beam is either elliptically polarized or a mixture of linearly polarized and unpolarized or a mixture of elliptically polarized and unpolarized light. We now put a quarter wave plate in front of the polaroid with its optic axis parallel to the pass-axis of the polaroid at the position of maximum intensity. The elliptically polarized light will transform to a linearly polarized light. Thus, if one obtains two positions of the polaroid where complete extinction occurs, then the original beam is elliptically polarized. If complete extinction does not occur, and the position of maximum intensity occurs at the same orientation as before, the beam is a mixture of unpolarized and linearly polarized light. Finally, if the position of maximum intensity occurs at a different orientation of the polaroid, the beam is a mixture of elliptically polarized and unpolarized light.

21.8 Optical Activity

LO6

When a linearly polarized light beam propagates through an "optically active" medium like sugar solution then—as the beam propagates—its plane of polarization rotates. This rotation is directly proportional to the distance traversed by the beam and also to the concentration of sugar in the solution. Indeed, by measuring the angle by which the plane of polarization is rotated, one can accurately determine the concentration of sugar in the solution.

The rotation of the plane of polarization is due to the fact that the "modes" of the optically active substance are left circularly polarized (LCP) and right circularly polarized (RCP) which propagate with slightly different velocities (see Sec. 21.16). By "modes" we imply that if an LCP light beam is incident on the substance then it will propagate as an LCP beam; similarly, an RCP light beam will propagate as an RCP beam but with a slightly different velocity. On the other hand, if a linearly polarized light beam is incident, then we must express the linear polarization as a superposition of an RCP and an LCP beam and then consider the independent propagation of the two beams. We illustrate through an example.

We consider an RCP beam propagating in the +z direction

$$\left.\begin{aligned} E_x^R &= E_0 \cos(k_R z - \omega t) \\ E_y^R &= -E_0 \sin(k_R z - \omega t) \end{aligned}\right\} \quad (21.56)$$

where $k_R = \frac{\omega}{c} n_R$ and the superscript (and the subscript) R signify that we are considering an RCP beam. Similarly, an LCP beam (of the same amplitude) propagating in the +z direction can be described by the following equations:

$$\left.\begin{aligned} E_x^L &= E_0 \cos(k_L z - \omega t) \\ E_y^L &= E_0 \sin(k_L z - \omega t) \end{aligned}\right\} \quad (21.57)$$

where $k_L = \frac{\omega}{c} n_L$; n_R and n_L are the refractive indices corresponding to the RCP and LCP beams respectively. If we assume the simultaneous propagation of the two beams then the x and y components of the resultant fields would be given by the following equations:

$$E_x = E_0 [\cos(k_R z - \omega t) + \cos(k_L z - \omega t)]$$

or $$E_x = 2E_0 \cos\left[\frac{1}{2}(k_L - k_R) z\right] \cos[\omega t - \theta(z)]$$

Similarly

$$E_y = 2E_0 \sin\left[\frac{1}{2}(k_L - k_R) z\right] \cos[\omega t - \theta(z)]$$

where $\theta(z) = \frac{1}{2}(k_L + k_R) z$

Thus the resultant wave is *always* linearly polarized with the plane of polarization rotating with z. If the direction of the oscillating electric vector makes an angle ϕ with the x-axis then [see Fig. 21.28]:

$$\phi(z) = \frac{1}{2}(k_L - k_R) z = \frac{\pi}{\lambda}(n_L - n_R) z = \frac{\omega}{2c}(n_L - n_R) z \quad (21.58)$$

where λ is the free space wavelength. Now, if

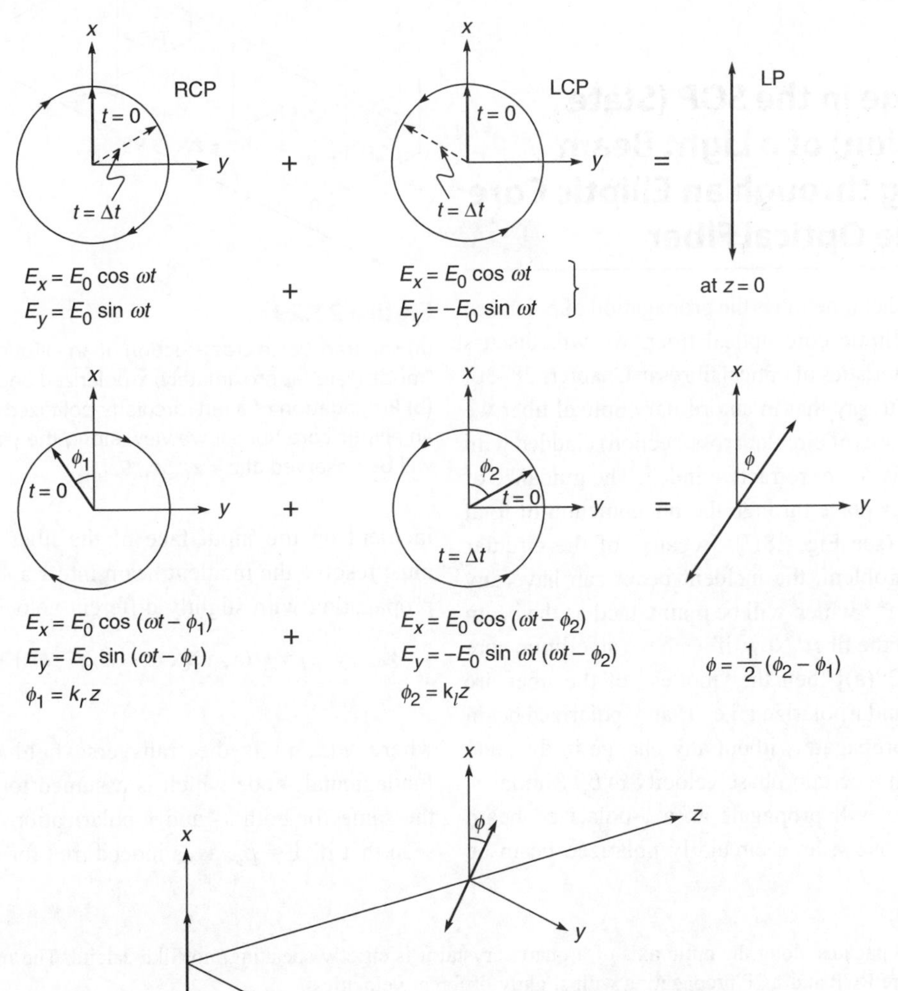

Figure 21.28
The "clockwise" rotation of a linearly polarized wave as it propagates through a "right-handed" optically active medium.

$n_L > n_R \Leftrightarrow$ the optically active substance is said to be right-handed or dextro-rotatory

$n_L < n_R \Leftrightarrow$ the optically active substance is said to be left-handed or laevo-rotatory

For example, for turpentine, $\phi = +37$ for $z = 10$ cm.

As mentioned earlier, we observe optical activity even in a sugar solution, and this is due to the helical structure of sugar molecules. The method of determining the concentration of sugar solutions by measuring the rotation of the plane of polarization is a widely used method in industry. It may be noted that if $n_L = n_R$ (as is indeed the case in an isotropic substance) then $\phi(z) = 0$ and a linearly polarized beam remains linearly polarized along the same direction. Optical activity is also exhibited in crystals. For example, for a linearly polarized light propagating along the optic axis of a quartz crystal*, the plane of polarization gets rotated. Indeed

$$|n_L - n_R| \approx 7 \times 10^{-5} \quad \Rightarrow \quad \phi \approx \frac{7}{60}\pi = 21^\circ \text{ for } z = 0.1 \text{ cm};$$

$$\lambda_0 = 0.6\ \mu\text{m} = 6000\ \text{Å}$$

21.9 Change in the SOP (State of Polarization) of a Light Beam Propagating through an Elliptic Core Single-Mode Optical Fiber

LO7

A very interesting phenomenon is the propagation of polarized light through an elliptic core optical fiber. We will discuss propagation characteristics of optical fibres in Chapters 28–30; it will suffice here to say that in an ordinary optical fiber we have a cylindrical core (of circular cross-section) cladded with a medium of slightly lower refractive index. The guidance of the light beam takes place through the phenomenon of total internal reflection (see Fig. 28.7). Because of the circular symmetry of the problem, the incident beam can have any state of polarization** which will be maintained as the beam propagates through the fiber. Now, if we have an elliptic core fiber [see Fig. 21.29(a)] then the "modes" of the fiber are (approximately) x and y polarized; i.e., if an x-polarized beam is incident it will propagate without any change in the state of polarization with a certain phase velocity ω/β_x. Similarly, a y-polarized beam will propagate as a y-polarized beam with velocity ω/β_y. Now, let a circularly polarized beam be

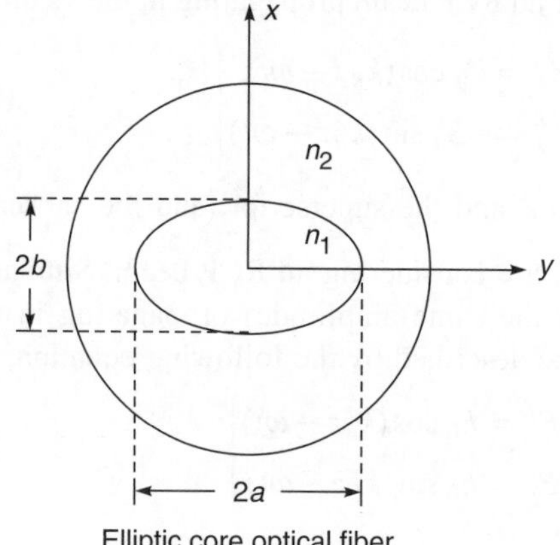

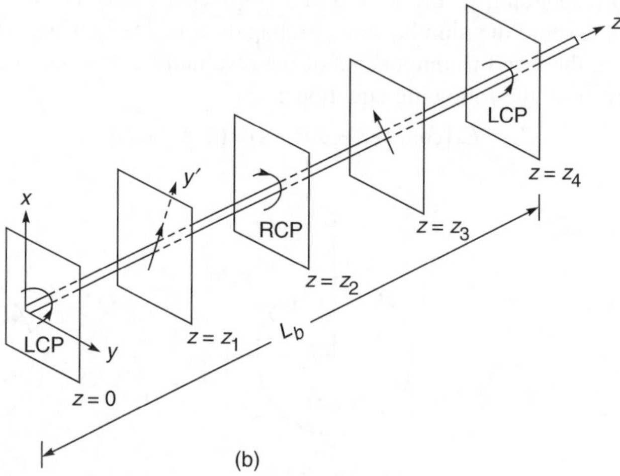

Figure 21.29

(a) The transverse cross-section of an elliptic core fiber; the "modes" are (approximately) x-polarized and y-polarized.
(b) Propagation of a left-circularly polarized beam incident on an elliptic core fiber. If we view along the y-axis then dark spots will be observed at $z = z_1, 5z_1, 9z_1, \ldots$

incident on the input face of the fiber at $z = 0$. Then we must resolve the incident beam into x and y polarized beams propagating with slightly different velocities. Thus

$$\mathbf{E}(x, y, z) = \psi(x, y)[\hat{\mathbf{x}} \cos(\beta_x z - \omega t) + \hat{\mathbf{y}} \sin(\beta_y z - \omega t)] \qquad \textbf{(21.59)}$$

where $\psi(x, y)$ is the transverse field distribution of the fundamental mode which is assumed to be (approximately) the same for both x- and y-polarizations. It may be readily seen that if $\beta_x = \beta_y$, as is indeed true for circular core fibers,

* When a wave propagates along the optic axis of a quartz crystal it is strictly speaking, not like calcite. The modes are *not* linearly polarized; they are RCP and LCP propagating with slightly different velocities.

** We are considering here a single mode fiber so that no matter what the incident transverse field distribution is, it soon "settles down" to the transverse field distribution of the fundamental mode which propagates with the velocity ω/β_0. This velocity is independent of the SOP of the incident beam.

the beam will remain circularly polarized for all values of z. Now, at $z = 0$,

$$\begin{aligned} E_x &= \psi(x, y)\cos\omega t \\ E_y &= -\psi(x, y)\sin\omega t \end{aligned} \quad (21.60)$$

which represents a left-circularly polarized wave [see Fig. 21.29(b)]. For

$$z = z_1 = \frac{\pi}{2(\beta_y - \beta_x)} \quad (21.61)$$

i.e., for $\beta_y z_1 = \beta_x z_1 + \pi/2$,

$$E_x = \psi(x, y)\cos(\phi_1 - \omega t) = +\psi(x, y)\cos(\omega t - \phi_1)$$

$$E_y = \psi(x, y)\sin\left(\phi_1 + \frac{\pi}{2} - \omega t\right) = +\psi(x, y)\cos(\omega t - \phi_1)$$

where

$$\phi_1 = \beta_x z_1$$

which represents a linearly polarized wave [see Fig. 21.29(b)]; we assume the direction of the **E**-vector to be along the y' axis. Similarly, at

$$z = z_2 = \frac{\pi}{(\beta_y - \beta_x)} = 2z_1$$

$$\begin{aligned} E_x &= \psi(x, y)\cos(\phi_2 - \omega t) = \psi(x, y)\cos(\omega t - \phi_2) \\ E_y &= \psi(x, y)\sin(\phi_2 + \pi - \omega t) = \psi(x, y)\sin(\omega t - \phi_2) \end{aligned} \quad (21.62)$$

where $\phi_2 = \beta_x z_2$, and the wave will be right-circularly polarized [see Fig. 21.29(b)]. At

$$z = z_3 = \frac{3\pi}{2(\beta_x - \beta_y)} = 3z_1$$

we will have

$$E_x = \psi(x, y)\cos(\phi_3 - \omega t) = \psi(x, y)\cos(\omega t - \phi_3)$$

$$E_y = \psi(x, y)\sin\left(\phi_3 + \frac{3\pi}{2} - \omega t\right) = -\psi(x, y)\cos(\omega t - \phi_3)$$

where $\phi_3 = \beta_x z_3$. Thus the wave would again be linearly polarized but now the direction of the oscillating electric field will be at right angles to the field at $z = z_1$. In a similar manner, we can easily continue to determine the SOP of the propagating beam. Thus at $z = 5z_1, 9z_1, 13z_1, \ldots$ the SOP will be the same as at $z = z_1$ and at $z = 7z_1, 11z_1, 15z_1 \ldots$ the SOP will be the same as at $z = 3z_1$. Similarly at $z = 4z_1, 8z_1, 12z_1 \ldots$ the beam will be LCP and at $z = 2z_1, 6z_1, 10z_1 \ldots$ the beam will be RCP.

Now, let the fiber be rotated in such a way that the y' axis is along the vertical line (the x' and the z-axes are assumed to lie in the horizontal plane). Thus if we put our eyes vertically above the fiber and view vertically down then the regions $z = z_1, 5z_1, 9z_1 \ldots$ will appear dark (see Fig. 21.30). This is because of the fact that in these regions the electric field is oscillating in the y' direction (which is the vertical direction) and we know that if the dipole oscillates along the y' direction, there is no radiation emitted in that particular direction (Sec. 22.5.1 and Fig. 21.16(b)). Thus by measuring the distance

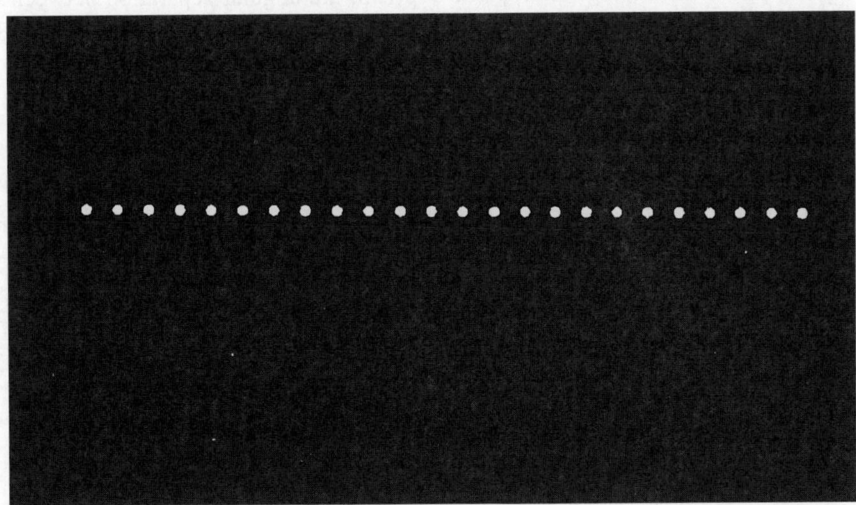

Figure 21.30

Schematic of the intensity variation as seen from the top (or side) of an elliptic core fiber when a circularly polarized beam is incident on it. The actual photograph from an experiment by Andrew Corporation is given in Ref. 21.13.

between two consecutive black spots $(=4z_1)$ one can calculate z_1 and hence $\beta_y - \beta_x$. Furthermore, by moving the eyes to the horizontal plane, i.e., viewing along the x' axis we will see the regions $z = z_1, 5z_1, 9z_1, \ldots$ appear bright and the regions $z = 3z_1, 7z_1, 11z_1, \ldots$ appear dark. Thus the experiment not only allows one to understand the changing SOP of a beam propagating through a birefringent fiber, but also helps us understand the radiation pattern of an oscillating dipole.

EXAMPLE 21.9 As a numerical example, we consider an elliptical core fiber for which

$$2a = 2.14\ \mu\text{m}, \quad 2b = 8.85\ \mu\text{m}$$
$$n_1 = 1.535, \quad n_2 = 1.47$$

[see Fig. 21.29(a)]. For such a fiber operating at $\lambda_0 = 6328$ Å ($k_0 \approx 9.929 \times 10^4$ cm^{-1}),

$$\frac{\beta_x}{k_0} \approx 1.506845 \quad \text{and} \quad \frac{\beta_y}{k_0} \approx 1.507716$$

The quantity

$$L_b = \frac{2\pi}{\Delta\beta} = \frac{2\pi}{\beta_y - \beta_x} \approx 0.727 \text{ mm}$$

is known as the coupling length.

21.10 Wollaston Prism

LO8

A Wollaston prism is used to produce two linearly polarized beams. It consists of two similar prisms (of say calcite) with the optic axis of the first prism parallel to the surface and the optic axis of the second prism parallel to the edge of the prism as shown in Fig. 21.31. Let us first consider the incidence of a y-polarized beam as shown in Fig. 21.31(a). The beam will propagate as an o-ray in the first prism (because the vibrations are perpendicular to the optic axis) and will see the refractive index n_o. When this beam enters the second prism it will become an e-ray and will see the refractive index n_e. For calcite $n_o > n_e$ and therefore the ray will bend away from the normal. Since the optic axis is normal to the plane of incidence, the refracted ray will obey Snell's laws [see Fig. 21.25(b)] and the angle of refraction will be given by

$$n_o \sin 20° = n_e \sin r_1$$

where we have assumed the angle of the prism to be 20° (see Fig. 21.31). Assuming $n_o \approx 1.658$ and $n_e \approx 1.486$, we readily get

$$r_1 \approx 22.43°$$

Thus the angle of incidence at the second surface will be $i_1 = 22.43° - 20° = 2.43°$. The output angle θ_1 will be given by $n_e \sin 2.43° = \sin \theta_1 \Rightarrow \theta_1 \approx 3.61°$.

We next consider the incidence of a x-polarized beam as shown in Fig. 21.31(b). The beam will propagate as an e-ray in the first prism and as an o-ray in the second prism. The angle of refraction will now be given by

$$n_e \sin 20° = n_o \sin r_2 \Rightarrow r_2 \approx 17.85°$$

Thus the angle of incidence at the second interface will be

$$i_2 = 20° - 17.85° = 2.15°$$

The output angle θ_2 will be given by

$$n_o \sin 2.15° = \sin \theta_2 \quad \Rightarrow \quad \theta_2 \approx 3.57°$$

Thus, if an unpolarized beam is incident on the Wollaston prism, the angular separation between the two orthogonally polarized beams will be $\theta = \theta_1 + \theta_2 \approx 7.18°$; see also Fig. 21.32.

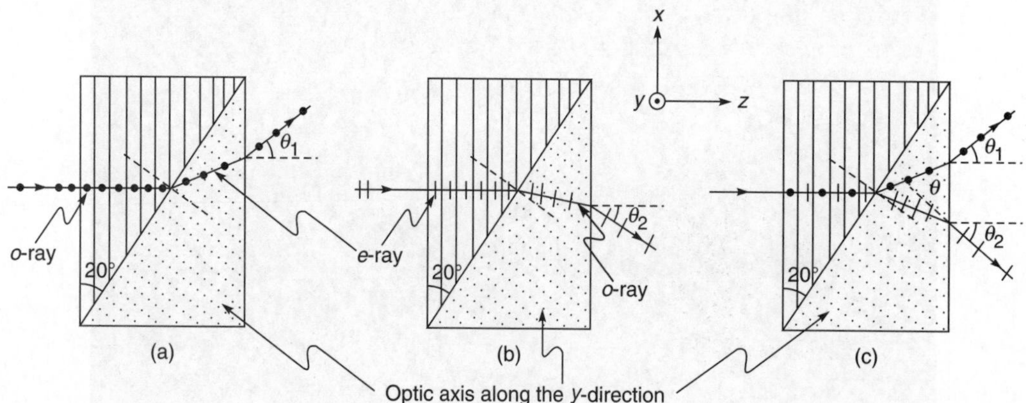

Figure 21.31
A Wollaston prism. The optic axis of the first prism is along the x-axis and the optic axis of the second prism is along the y-axis. (a) If the incident beam is y-polarized, it will propagate as an o-wave in the first prism and an e-wave in the second prism. (b) If the incident beam is x-polarized, it will propagate as an e-wave in the first prism and an o-wave in the second prism. (c) For an unpolarized beam incident normally, there will be 2 linearly polarized beams propagating in different directions. The ray paths correspond to prisms being of calcite.

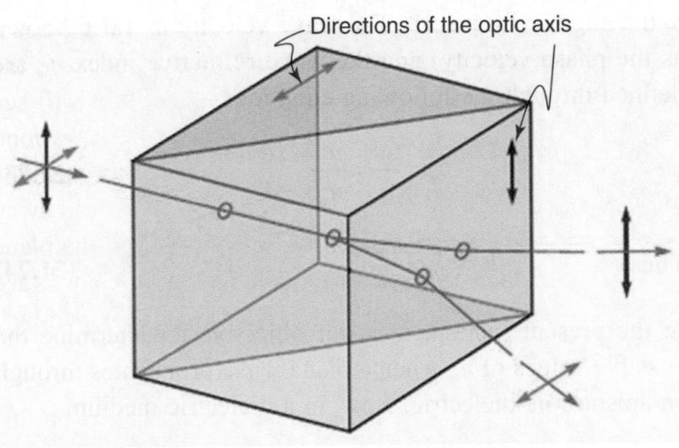

Figure 21.32

Schematic of an actual Wollaston prism. The prism separates an unpolarized light beam into two linearly polarized beams. It typically consists of two properly oriented calcite prisms (so that the optic axes are perpendicular to each other), cemented together typically with Canada balsam. A commercially available Wollaston prism would have divergence angles from 15° to about 45°.

21.11 Rochon Prism LO8

We next consider the Rochon prism which consists of two similar prisms of (say) calcite; the optic axis of the first prism is normal to the face of the prism while the optic axis of the second prism is parallel to the edge as shown in Fig. 21.33. Now, in the first prism both the beams will *see* the same refractive index n_o; this follows from the fact that the ordinary and extraordinary waves travel with the same velocity ($= c/n_o$) along the optic axis of the crystal [see Fig. 21.24(c)].

When the beam enters the second crystal, the ordinary ray (whose **D** is normal to the optic axis) will *see* the same refractive index and go undeviated as shown in Fig. 18.26. On the other hand, the extraordinary ray (whose **D** is along the optic axis) will *see* the refractive index n_e and will bend away from the normal. The angle of refraction will be determined from the following equation

$$n_o \sin 25° = n_e \sin r$$

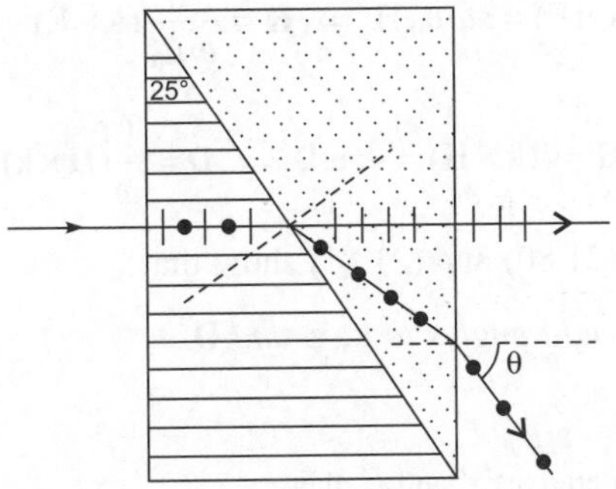

Figure 21.33

Production of two orthogonally polarized beams by a Rochon prism.

Thus,

$$\sin r = \frac{n_o}{n_e} \sin 25° = \frac{1.658}{1.486} \times 0.423 \approx 0.472$$

$$\Rightarrow \qquad r = 28.2°$$

Therefore the angle of incidence at the second surface will be 28.2 – 25° = 3.2°. The emerging angle will be given by

$$\sin \theta = n_e \sin (3.2°) \approx 0.083 \quad \Rightarrow \quad \theta \approx 4.8°$$

21.12 Plane Wave Propagation in Anisotropic Media LO9

In this section, we will discuss the plane wave solutions of Maxwell's equations in an anisotropic medium and prove the various assumptions made in Sec. 21.5. The difference between an isotropic and an anisotropic medium is in the relationship between the displacement vector **D** and the electric vector **E**; the displacement vector **D** is defined in Sec. 22.11. In an isotropic medium, **D** is in the same direction as **E** and one can write

$$\mathbf{D} = \varepsilon \mathbf{E} \tag{21.63}$$

where ε is the dielectric permittivity of the medium. On the other hand, in an anisotropic medium **D** is not, in general, in the direction of **E** and the relation between **D** and **E** can be written in the form

$$\left.\begin{aligned} D_x &= \varepsilon_{xx} E_x + \varepsilon_{xy} E_y + \varepsilon_{xz} E_z \\ D_y &= \varepsilon_{yx} E_x + \varepsilon_{yy} E_y + \varepsilon_{yz} E_z \\ D_z &= \varepsilon_{zx} E_x + \varepsilon_{zy} E_y + \varepsilon_{zz} E_z \end{aligned}\right\} \tag{21.64}$$

where ε_{xx}, ε_{xy}, ... are constants. One can show that [see, for example, Ref. 21.5]

$$\varepsilon_{xy} = \varepsilon_{yx} \,;\, \varepsilon_{yz} = \varepsilon_{zy} \quad \text{and} \quad \varepsilon_{zx} = \varepsilon_{xz} \tag{21.65}$$

Further, one can always choose a coordinate system (i.e., one can always choose appropriately the directions of x, y and z axes inside the crystal) such that

$$D_x = \varepsilon_x E_x;\; D_y = \varepsilon_y E_y \quad \text{and} \quad D_z = \varepsilon_z E_z \tag{21.66}$$

This coordinate system is known as the principal axis system and the quantities ε_x, ε_y and ε_z are known as the principle dielectric permittivities of the medium. If

$$\varepsilon_x \neq \varepsilon_y \neq \varepsilon_z \quad \text{(biaxial)} \tag{21.67}$$

we have what is known as a biaxial medium and the quantities

$$n_x = \sqrt{\frac{\varepsilon_x}{\varepsilon_0}},\, n_y = \sqrt{\frac{\varepsilon_y}{\varepsilon_0}},\, n_z = \sqrt{\frac{\varepsilon_z}{\varepsilon_0}} \tag{21.68}$$

are said to be the principal refractive indices of the medium; in the above equation $\varepsilon_0 (= 8.8542 \times 10^{-12}\ \text{C}^2\ \text{N}^{-1}\ \text{m}^{-2})$ represents the dielectric permittivity of free space. If

$$\varepsilon_x = \varepsilon_y \neq \varepsilon_z \quad \text{(uniaxial)} \tag{21.69}$$

we have what is known as a uniaxial medium with the z-axis representing the optic axis of the medium. The quantities

$$n_o = \sqrt{\frac{\varepsilon_x}{\varepsilon_0}} = \sqrt{\frac{\varepsilon_y}{\varepsilon_0}} \quad \text{and} \quad n_e = n_z = \sqrt{\frac{\varepsilon_z}{\varepsilon_0}} \tag{21.70}$$

are known as ordinary and extraordinary refractive indices; typical values for some uniaxial crystals are given in Table 21.1. For a uniaxial medium, since $\varepsilon_x = \varepsilon_y$ the x- and y-directions can be arbitrarily chosen as long as they are perpendicular to the optic axis, i.e., *any* two mutually perpendicular axes (which are also perpendicular to the z-axis) can be taken as the principal axes of the medium*. On the other hand, if

$$\varepsilon_x = \varepsilon_y = \varepsilon_z \quad \text{(isotropic)} \tag{21.71}$$

we have an isotropic medium, and can choose any three mutually perpendicular axes as the principal axis system. We will assume the anisotropic medium to be non-magnetic so that

$$\mathbf{B} = \mu_0 \mathbf{H}$$

where μ_0 is the free space magnetic permeability. Let us consider the propagation of a plane electromagnetic wave; for such a wave the vectors **E**, **H**, **D** and **B** would be proportional to exp $[i(\mathbf{k}.\mathbf{r} - \omega t)]$. Thus

$$\left.\begin{aligned} \mathbf{E} = \mathbf{E}_0\, e^{i(\mathbf{k}.\mathbf{r}-\omega t)}, \quad \mathbf{H} = \mathbf{H}_0\, e^{i(\mathbf{k}.\mathbf{r}-\omega t)} \\ \mathbf{D} = \mathbf{D}_0\, e^{i(\mathbf{k}.\mathbf{r}-\omega t)}, \quad \mathbf{B} = \mathbf{B}_0\, e^{i(\mathbf{k}.\mathbf{r}-\omega t)} \end{aligned}\right\} \tag{21.72}$$

TABLE 21.1 Ordinary and Extraordinary Refractive Indices for some Uniaxial Crystals (Table adapted from Ref. 21.7).

Name of the crystal	*Wavelength*	n_o	n_e
Calcite	4046 Å	1.68134	1.49694
	5890 Å	1.65836	1.48640
	7065 Å	1.65207	1.48359
Quartz	5890 Å	1.54424	1.55335
Lithium niobate	6000 Å	2.2967	2.2082
KDP	6328 Å	1.50737	1.46685
ADP	6328 Å	1.52166	1.47685

where the vectors $\mathbf{E}_0$, $\mathbf{H}_0$, $\mathbf{D}_0$ and $\mathbf{B}_0$ are independent of space and time; **k** represents the propagation vector of the wave and ω the angular frequency. The wave velocity v_w (also known as the phase velocity) and the wave refractive index n_w are defined through the following equations:

$$v_w = \frac{\omega}{k} = \frac{c}{n_w} \tag{21.73}$$

Thus

$$|\mathbf{k}| = k = \frac{\omega}{c} n_w \tag{21.74}$$

In the present section, it is our objective to determine the possible values of n_w when a plane wave propagates through an anisotropic dielectric. Now, in a dielectric medium

$$\text{div}\ \mathbf{D} = 0 \ \Rightarrow \ \frac{\partial D_x}{\partial x} + \frac{\partial D_y}{\partial y} + \frac{\partial D_z}{\partial z} = 0 \tag{21.75}$$

For a plane wave given by Eq. (21.72) the above equation becomes

$$i(k_x D_x + k_y D_y + k_z D_z) = 0 \ \Rightarrow \ \mathbf{D}.\mathbf{k} = 0 \tag{21.76}$$

implying that **D** is always at right angles to **k**. Similarly since in a non-magnetic medium

$$\text{div}\ \mathbf{H} = 0 \Rightarrow \mathbf{H} \textit{ will always be right angles to } \mathbf{k}. \tag{21.77}$$

Now, in the absence of any currents (i.e, **J** = 0) Maxwell's curl equations [see Eqs. (22.9) and (22.10) become

$$\nabla \times \mathbf{E} = -\frac{\partial \mathbf{B}}{\partial t} = i\,\omega \mathbf{B} = i\,\omega \mu_0\, \mathbf{H} \tag{21.78}$$

and

$$\nabla \times \mathbf{H} = \frac{\partial \mathbf{D}}{\partial t} = -i\,\omega \mathbf{D} \tag{21.79}$$

where we have assumed the medium to be non-magnetic (i.e., $\mathbf{B} = \mu_0 \mathbf{H}$). Now, if

$$\mathbf{E} = \mathbf{E}_0\, e^{i(\mathbf{k}.\mathbf{r}-\omega t)}$$

then

$$(\nabla \times \mathbf{E})_x = \frac{\partial E_z}{\partial y} - \frac{\partial E_y}{\partial z} = (i k_y\, E_{0z} - i k_z\, E_{0y})\, e^{i(\mathbf{k}.\mathbf{r}-\omega t)}$$
$$= i(k_y\, E_z - k_z\, E_y) = i(\mathbf{k} \times \mathbf{E})_x$$

Thus

$$\nabla \times \mathbf{E} = i(\mathbf{k} \times \mathbf{E}) = i\,\omega \mu_0\, \mathbf{H} \ \Rightarrow \ \mathbf{H} = \frac{1}{\omega \mu_0}(\mathbf{k} \times \mathbf{E}) \tag{21.80}$$

and

$$\nabla \times \mathbf{H} = i(\mathbf{k} \times \mathbf{H}) = -i\,\omega \mathbf{D} \ \Rightarrow \ \mathbf{D} = \frac{1}{\omega}(\mathbf{H} \times \mathbf{k}) \tag{21.81}$$

Equations (21.80) and (21.81) show that

$$\mathbf{H} \textit{ is at right angles to } \mathbf{k}, \mathbf{E} \textit{ and } \mathbf{D} \tag{21.82}$$

---

* This follows from the fact that for a uniaxial medium $D_x = \varepsilon_x E_x$ and $D_y = \varepsilon_y E_y = \varepsilon_x E_y$.
Now, if we rotate the x-y axes (about the z-axis) by an angle θ and call the rotated axes x' and y', then

$$D_{x'} = D_x \cos\theta + D_y \sin\theta = \varepsilon_x (E_x \cos\theta + E_y \sin\theta) = \varepsilon_x E_{x'}$$

Similarly, $D_{y'} = \varepsilon_x E_{y'}$ implying that x'-y' can also be chosen as principal axes.

implying **k**, **E** *and* **D** *will always be in the same plane*. Further [see Eq. (21.76)]

$$\mathbf{D} \text{ is at right angles to } \mathbf{k} \tag{21.83}$$

Substituting for **H** in Eq. (21.81), we get

$$\mathbf{D} = \frac{1}{\omega^2 \mu_0}[(\mathbf{k}\times\mathbf{E})\times\mathbf{k}] = \frac{1}{\omega^2 \mu_0}[(\mathbf{k}.\mathbf{k})\mathbf{E} - (\mathbf{k}.\mathbf{E})\mathbf{k}] \tag{21.84}$$

where we have used the vector identity

$$(\mathbf{A} \times \mathbf{B}) \times \mathbf{C} = (\mathbf{A} \,.\, \mathbf{C})\, \mathbf{B} - (\mathbf{B} \,.\, \mathbf{C})\, \mathbf{A}$$

Thus

$$\mathbf{D} = \frac{k^2}{\omega^2 \mu_0}[\mathbf{E} - (\hat{\boldsymbol{\kappa}}.\mathbf{E})\hat{\boldsymbol{\kappa}}] = \frac{n_w^{\,2}}{c^2 \mu_0}[\mathbf{E} - (\hat{\boldsymbol{\kappa}}.\mathbf{E})\hat{\boldsymbol{\kappa}}] \tag{21.85}$$

where $$\hat{\boldsymbol{\kappa}} = \frac{\mathbf{k}}{k} \tag{21.86}$$

represents the unit vector along **k** (see Fig. 21.34). Since

$$D_x = \varepsilon_x E_x = \varepsilon_0 n_x^{\,2} E_x$$

we have for the x-component of Eq. (21.85)

$$\frac{\varepsilon_0 \mu_0 c^2 n_x^{\,2}}{n_w^{\,2}} E_x = E_x - \kappa_x \left(\kappa_x E_x + \kappa_y E_y + \kappa_z E_z\right)$$

Since $c^2 = 1/(\varepsilon_0\mu_0)$, we have

$$\left(\frac{n_x^{\,2}}{n_w^{\,2}} - \kappa_y^{\,2} - \kappa_z^{\,2}\right) E_x + \kappa_x \kappa_y E_y + \kappa_x \kappa_z E_z = 0 \tag{21.87}$$

where we have used the relation $\kappa_x^{\,2} + \kappa_y^{\,2} + \kappa_z^{\,2} = 1$ (since $\hat{\boldsymbol{\kappa}}$ is a unit vector). Similarly,

$$\kappa_x \kappa_y E_x + \left(\frac{n_y^{\,2}}{n_w^{\,2}} - \kappa_x^{\,2} - \kappa_z^{\,2}\right) E_y + \kappa_y \kappa_z E_z = 0 \tag{21.88}$$

$$\kappa_x \kappa_z E_x + \kappa_y \kappa_z E_y + \left(\frac{n_z^{\,2}}{n_w^{\,2}} - \kappa_x^{\,2} - \kappa_y^{\,2}\right) E_z = 0 \tag{21.89}$$

Since the above equations form a set of three homogenous equations, for non-trivial solutions, we must have

$$\begin{vmatrix} \dfrac{n_x^{\,2}}{n_w^{\,2}} - \kappa_y^{\,2} - \kappa_z^{\,2} & \kappa_x \kappa_y & \kappa_x \kappa_z \\ \kappa_x \kappa_y & \dfrac{n_y^{\,2}}{n_w^{\,2}} - \kappa_x^{\,2} - \kappa_z^{\,2} & \kappa_y \kappa_z \\ \kappa_x \kappa_z & \kappa_y \kappa_z & \dfrac{n_z^{\,2}}{n_w^{\,2}} - \kappa_x^{\,2} - \kappa_y^{\,2} \end{vmatrix} = 0 \tag{21.90}$$

We should remember that we still do not know the possible values of n_w. Indeed, for a given direction of propagation (i.e., for given values of κ_x, κ_y and κ_z) the solutions of the above equation gives us the two allowed values of n_w. It may be mentioned that from Eq. (21.90) it appears as if for a given direction of propagation, we will have a cubic equation in n_w^2 which would give us three roots of n_w^2; however, the coefficient of n_w^6 will always be zero and hence, there will be *always* two roots. We illustrate the general procedure by considering propagation through a uniaxial medium.

21.12.1 Propagation in Uniaxial Crystals

In this section, we will restrict ourselves to uniaxial crystals for which

$$n_x = n_y = n_o \quad \text{and} \quad n_z = n_e \tag{21.91}$$

As discussed earlier, for a uniaxial crystal, the x and y directions can be arbitrarily chosen as long as they are perpendicular to the optic axis. Now, for a wave propagating along *any* direction **k**, we choose our y-axis in such a way that it is at right angles to **k**, i.e., the y-axis is normal to the plane defined by **k** and the z-axis; obviously, the x-axis will lie in the same plane (see Fig. 21.34). Thus we may write

$$\kappa_x = \sin\psi,\ \kappa_y = 0 \quad \text{and} \quad \kappa_z = \cos\psi$$

where ψ is the angle that the **k** vector makes with the optic axis (see Fig. 21.34). Equations (21.87)–(21.89) therefore become

$$\left(\frac{n_o^{\,2}}{n_w^{\,2}} - \cos^2\psi\right) E_x + \sin\psi\cos\psi\, E_z = 0 \tag{21.92}$$

$$\left(\frac{n_o^{\,2}}{n_w^{\,2}} - 1\right) E_y = 0 \tag{21.93}$$

and $$\sin\psi\cos\psi\, E_x + \left(\frac{n_e^{\,2}}{n_w^{\,2}} - \sin^2\psi\right) E_z = 0 \tag{21.94}$$

Once again we have a set of three homogenous equations and for non-trivial solutions, the determinant must be zero. However, since two equations involve only E_x and E_z and

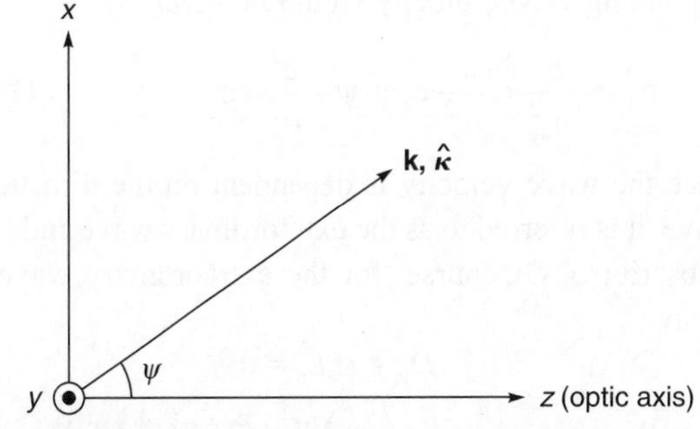

Figure 21.34
In uniaxial crystals, we can always choose the y axis in such a way that $\kappa_y = 0$; the optic axis is assumed to be in the z-direction. If ψ is the angle that k makes with the optic axis then $\kappa_x = \kappa \sin\psi$ and $\kappa_z = \kappa \cos\psi$.

one equation involves only E_y we have the following two independent solutions:

First Solution: We assume $E_y \neq 0$ then $E_x = 0 = E_z$. From Eq. (21.93) one obtains the solution

$$n_w = n_{wo} = n_o \text{ (ordinary wave)} \qquad \textbf{(21.95)}$$

The corresponding wave velocity is

$$v_w = v_{wo} = \frac{c}{n_o} \text{ (y-polarized o-wave)} \qquad \textbf{(21.96)}$$

Since the wave velocity is independent of the direction of the wave, it is referred to as the ordinary wave (usually abbreviated as the *o*-wave) and hence the subscript '*o*' on n_w and v_w. Further, for the *o*-wave, the **D** vector (and the **E** vector) is *y*-polarized. Thus,

*for the o-wave, the **D** vector (and the **E** vector) are perpendicular to the plane containing the **k** vector and the optic axis.*

[see Fig. 21.35]. This was the recipe that was given in Eqs. (21.42)–(21.44).

Second Solution: The second solution of Eqs. (21.92)–(21.94) will correspond to

$$E_y = 0 \text{ with } E_x, E_z \neq 0 \qquad \textbf{(21.97)}$$

We use Eqs. (21.92) and (21.94) to obtain

$$\frac{E_z}{E_x} = -\frac{\dfrac{n_o^2}{n_w^2} - \cos^2\psi}{\sin\psi\cos\psi} = -\frac{\sin\psi\cos\psi}{\dfrac{n_e^2}{n_w^2} - \sin^2\psi}$$

Simple manipulations would give us

$$\frac{1}{n_w^2} = \frac{1}{n_{we}^2} = \frac{\cos^2\psi}{n_o^2} + \frac{\sin^2\psi}{n_e^2} \qquad \textbf{(21.98)}$$

where the subscript *e* refers to the fact that the wave refractive index corresponds to the extraordinary wave. The corresponding wave velocity would be given by

$$v_{we}^2 = \frac{c^2}{n_{we}^2} = \frac{c^2}{n_o^2}\cos^2\psi + \frac{c^2}{n_e^2}\sin^2\psi \qquad \textbf{(21.99)}$$

Since the wave velocity is dependent on the direction of the wave, it is referred to as the extraordinary wave and hence the subscript *e*. Of course, for the extraordinary wave, we must have

$$D_y = \varepsilon_y E_y = 0$$

From the above equation and Eq. (21.81), it follows that the displacement vector **D** of the wave is normal to the *y*-axis and also to **k** implying that

*the displacement vector **D** associated with the extraordinary wave lies in the plane containing the propagation vector **k** and the optic axis and is normal to **k**.*

[see Fig. 21.36]. This was the recipe given through Eq. (21.44). Figure 21.36 also shows the Poynting vector **S** (= **E** × **H**) which represents the direction of energy propagation (i.e., the direction of the *e*-ray). The small dashes on the extraordinary ray in Figs. 21.23(a) and (b) represent the directions of the **D** vector. For the extraordinary wave, let ϕ and θ represent the angles that the **S** vector makes with the **k** vector and the optic axis respectively (see Fig. 21.36). In order to determine the angle ϕ we note that

$$\frac{\varepsilon_z E_z}{\varepsilon_x E_x} = \frac{D_z}{D_x} = -\tan\psi$$

and since

$$\frac{E_z}{E_x} = -\tan(\phi + \psi)$$

we get

$$\frac{n_e^2}{n_o^2}\tan(\phi+\psi) = \tan\psi \;\Rightarrow\; \phi = \tan^{-1}\left[\frac{n_o^2}{n_e^2}\tan\psi\right] - \psi \qquad \textbf{(21.100)}$$

Obviously, for negative crystals $n_o > n_e$ and ϕ will be positive implying that ray direction is further away from the optic axis as shown in Fig. 21.36. Conversely, for positive crystals $n_o < n_e$ and ϕ will be negative implying that the ray direction will be towards the optic axis.

EXAMPLE 21.4 We consider calcite for which (at λ = 5893 Å and 18° C)

$$n_o = 1.65836,\ n_e = 1.48641$$

If we consider **k** making an angle of 30° to the optic axis, then ψ = 30° and elementary calculations give us ϕ = 5.7°.

21.13 Ray Velocity and Ray Refractive Index

LO10

The direction of energy propagation (or the ray propagation) is along the Poynting vector **S** which is given by

$$\mathbf{S} = \mathbf{E} \times \mathbf{H} \qquad \textbf{(21.101)}$$

Thus, since the plane containing the vectors **k**, **E** and **D** is normal to **H**, the Poynting vector **S** will also lie in the plane containing the vectors **k**, **E** and **D** (see Figs. 21.35 and 21.36). For the extraordinary wave, the direction of the propagation of the wave ($\hat{\mathbf{k}}$) is not along the direction of energy propagation ($\hat{\mathbf{s}}$), where $\hat{\mathbf{s}}$ is the unit vector along **S**. The ray velocity (or the energy transmission velocity) v_r is defined as

$$v_r = \frac{S}{u} \qquad \textbf{(21.102)}$$

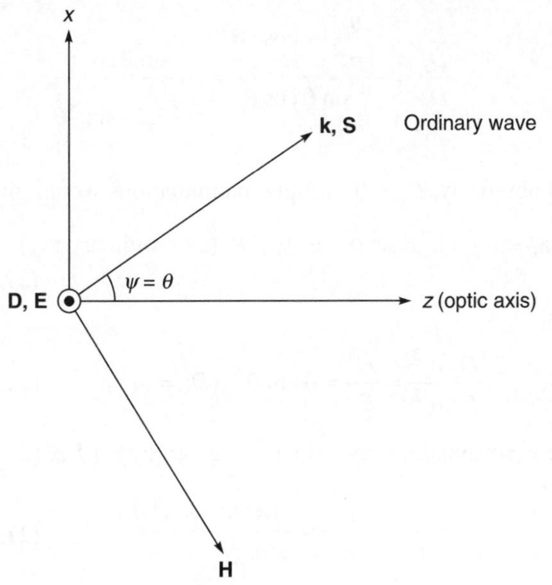

Figure 21.35
For the ordinary wave (in uniaxial crystals), **D** and **E** vectors are in the *y*-direction; **k** and **S** are in the same direction in the *x-z* plane and **H** also lies in the *x-z* plane.

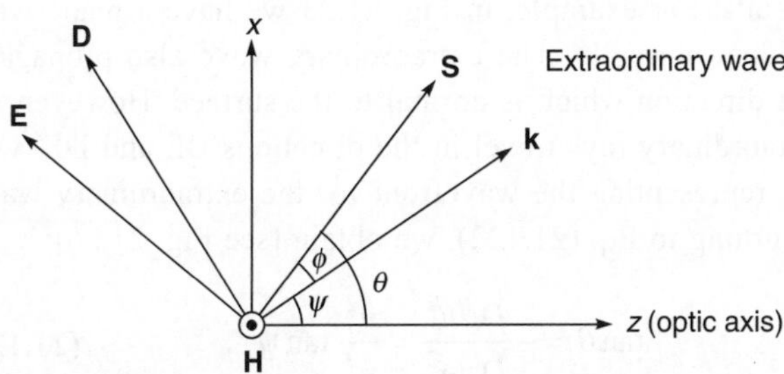

Figure 21.36
For the extraordinary wave (in uniaxial crystals), **E, D, S** and **k** vectors would lie in the *x-z* plane and **H** will be in the *y*-direction. **S** is at right angles to **E** and **H**; **D** is at right angles to **k** and **H**.

where u is the energy density. Now,

$$u = \frac{1}{2}(\mathbf{D}.\mathbf{E} + \mathbf{B}.\mathbf{H}) = \frac{1}{2}(\mathbf{D}.\mathbf{E} + \mu_0\,\mathbf{H}.\mathbf{H}) \qquad \textbf{(21.103)}$$

[see Sec. 22.5]. Substituting for **H** and **D** from Eqs. (21.80) and (21.81), we obtain

$$u = \frac{1}{2\omega}[(\mathbf{H}\times\mathbf{k}).\mathbf{E} + (\mathbf{k}\times\mathbf{E}).\mathbf{H}]$$

$$= \frac{1}{2\omega}[\mathbf{k}.(\mathbf{E}\times\mathbf{H}) + \mathbf{k}.(\mathbf{E}\times\mathbf{H})]$$

$$= \frac{1}{\omega}\mathbf{k}.\mathbf{S} \qquad \textbf{(21.104)}$$

Thus Eq. (21.102) becomes

$$v_r = \frac{\omega S}{\mathbf{k}.\mathbf{S}} = \frac{\omega}{k\cos\phi} = \frac{v_w}{\cos\phi} \qquad \textbf{(21.105)}$$

where ϕ is the angle between $\hat{\boldsymbol{\kappa}}$ and $\hat{\mathbf{s}}$ (see Fig. 21.36). The ray refractive index, n_r is defined as

$$n_r = \frac{c}{v_r} = \frac{c}{v_w}\cos\phi = n_w\cos\phi \qquad \textbf{(21.106)}$$

In order to express **E** in terms of **D**, we refer to Fig. 21.36 and write

$$\mathbf{D} = (\mathbf{D}.\hat{\mathbf{e}})\hat{\mathbf{e}} + (\mathbf{D}.\hat{\mathbf{s}})\hat{\mathbf{s}}$$

where $\hat{\mathbf{e}}$ is a unit vector along the direction of the electric field **E**. Thus

$$\mathbf{D} - (\mathbf{D}.\hat{\mathbf{s}})\hat{\mathbf{s}} = (\mathbf{D}.\hat{\mathbf{e}})\hat{\mathbf{e}} = (D\cos\phi)\frac{\mathbf{E}}{E} \qquad \textbf{(21.107)}$$

Similarly,

$$\mathbf{E} = (\mathbf{E}.\hat{\mathbf{d}})\hat{\mathbf{d}} + (\mathbf{E}.\hat{\kappa})\hat{\kappa} \qquad \textbf{(21.108)}$$

where $\hat{\mathbf{d}}$ represents a unit vector along the displacement vector **D**. If we now substitute for $\mathbf{E} - (\mathbf{E}.\hat{\kappa})\hat{\kappa}$ in Eq. (21.85), we would get

$$\mathbf{D} = \frac{n_w^2}{\mu_0 c^2}(\mathbf{E}.\hat{\mathbf{d}})\hat{\mathbf{d}} \;\Rightarrow\; D = \frac{n_w^2}{\mu_0 c^2}E\cos\phi \qquad \textbf{(21.109)}$$

Substituting in Eq. (21.107), we get

$$\mathbf{D} - (\mathbf{D}.\hat{\mathbf{s}})\hat{\mathbf{s}} = \frac{n_w^2}{\mu_0 c^2}\cos^2\phi\,\mathbf{E} = \frac{n_r^2}{\mu_0 c^2}\mathbf{E}$$

where, in the last step, we have used Eq. (21.106). Taking the x component of the above equation (where x represents the direction of one of the principal axes), we obtain

$$D_x - (D_x s_x + D_y s_y + D_z s_z)\,s_x = \frac{n_r^2}{\mu_0 c^2}E_x = \frac{n_r^2}{\mu_0 c^2\,\varepsilon_x}D_x$$

If we use the relations

$$n_x^2 = \frac{\varepsilon_x}{\varepsilon_0},\; c^2 = \frac{1}{\varepsilon_0\,\mu_0} \text{ and } s_x^2 + s_y^2 + s_z^2 = 1$$

we would get

$$\left(\frac{n_r^2}{n_x^2} - s_y^2 - s_z^2\right)D_x + s_x s_y D_y + s_x s_z D_z = 0 \qquad \textbf{(21.110)}$$

Similarly

$$s_x s_y D_x + \left(\frac{n_r^2}{n_y^2} - s_x^2 - s_z^2\right)D_y + s_z s_y D_z = 0 \qquad \textbf{(21.111)}$$

$$s_x s_z D_x + s_z s_y D_y + \left(\frac{n_r^2}{n_z^2} - s_x^2 - s_y^2\right)D_z = 0 \qquad \textbf{(21.112)}$$

As in the previous section, the above set of equations form a set of three homogenous equations. For non-trivial solutions, we must have

$$\begin{vmatrix} \frac{n_r^2}{n_x^2} - s_y^2 - s_z^2 & s_x s_y & s_x s_z \\ s_x s_y & \frac{n_r^2}{n_y^2} - s_x^2 - s_z^2 & s_z s_y \\ s_x s_z & s_z s_y & \frac{n_r^2}{n_z^2} - s_x^2 - s_y^2 \end{vmatrix} = 0 \quad \textbf{(21.113)}$$

We still do not know the possible values of n_r. Indeed for a given ray direction (i.e., for given values of s_x, s_y and s_z) the solution of the above equation gives us the two allowed values of n_r and hence two possible values of the ray velocities. We illustrate this by considering propagation through uniaxial media.

21.13.1 Ray Propagation in Uniaxial Crystals

We next consider a uniaxial crystal with its optic axis along the z direction. Thus

$$n_x = n_y = n_o \text{ and } n_z = n_e \quad \textbf{(21.114)}$$

As discussed in the previous section, x and y directions can be arbitrarily chosen as long as they are perpendicular to the z-axis. We choose the y-axis in such a way that the ray propagates in the x-z plane making an angle θ with the z-axis (see Figs. 21.35 and 21.36); thus

$$s_x = \sin\theta,\ s_y = 0 \text{ and } s_z = \cos\theta \quad \textbf{(21.115)}$$

and Eqs. (21.110)–(21.112) become

$$\left(\frac{n_r^2}{n_o^2} - \cos^2\theta\right) D_x + \sin\theta\cos\theta\, D_z = 0 \quad \textbf{(21.116)}$$

$$\left(\frac{n_r^2}{n_o^2} - 1\right) D_y = 0 \quad \textbf{(21.117)}$$

$$\sin\theta\cos\theta\, D_x + \left(\frac{n_r^2}{n_e^2} - \sin^2\theta\right) D_z = 0 \quad \textbf{(21.118)}$$

Obviously, one of the roots is given by

$$n_r = n_{ro} = n_o \text{ with } D_x = 0 = D_z \text{ } (y\text{-polarized}) \quad \textbf{(21.119)}$$

The corresponding ray velocity is given by

$$v_r = v_{ro} = \frac{c}{n_{ro}} = \frac{c}{n_o} \text{ (ordinary ray)} \quad \textbf{(21.120)}$$

Since the ray velocity is independent of the direction of the ray, it is referred to as the ordinary ray and hence the subscript 'o' on v_r and n_r. In order to obtain the other solution we use Eqs. (21.116) and (21.118) to obtain

$$\frac{D_z}{D_x} = -\frac{\dfrac{n_r^2}{n_o^2} - \cos^2\theta}{\sin\theta\cos\theta} = -\frac{\sin\theta\cos\theta}{\dfrac{n_r^2}{n_e^2} - \sin^2\theta}$$

and obviously, $D_y = 0$. Simple manipulations would give us

$$n_r^2 = n_{re}^2 = n_o^2\cos^2\theta + n_e^2\sin^2\theta \text{ (extraordinary ray)} \quad \textbf{(21.121)}$$

with

$$\frac{D_z/n_e^2}{D_x/n_o^2} = \frac{E_z}{E_x} = -\tan\theta, \quad (D_y = 0) \quad \textbf{(21.122)}$$

The corresponding ray velocity is given by [cf Eq. (21.37)]

$$\frac{1}{v_r^2} = \frac{1}{v_{re}^2} = \frac{n_{re}^2}{c^2} = \frac{\cos^2\theta}{c^2/n_o^2} + \frac{\sin^2\theta}{c^2/n_e^2} \quad \textbf{(21.123)}$$

which corresponds to the extraordinary ray and hence the subscript 'e' on v_r and n_r. As discussed in Sec. 21.5, the above equation represents an ellipse and if we rotate it around the z-axis (i.e., the optic axis) we will get an ellipsoid of revolution. These *ray velocity* surfaces are used in constructing Huygens' secondary wavelets while discussing propagation in uniaxial crystals. For example, in Fig. 21.23 we have a plane wave incident normally. The extraordinary wave also propagates in a direction which is normal to the surface. However, the extraordinary rays travel in the directions BE and DE′ with EE′ representing the wavefront for the extraordinary wave. Returning to Eq. (21.122), we obtain [see Fig. 21.36]:

$$\tan\theta = -\frac{D_z/n_e^2}{D_x/n_o^2} = \frac{n_o^2}{n_e^2}\tan\psi \quad \textbf{(21.124)}$$

Thus when the wave propagates along a direction which makes an angle ψ with the optic axis, then the ray will propagate along the direction

$$\theta = \tan^{-1}\left[\frac{n_o^2}{n_e^2}\tan\psi\right] \quad \textbf{(21.125)}$$

EXAMPLE 21.11 As an example, for calcite

$$n_o = 1.65836,\ n_e = 1.48641 \text{ with } \psi = 30°$$

we obtain $\theta \approx 35.7°$. Thus the ray direction is further away from the optic axis, consistent with what is shown in Fig. 21.36.

21.14 Jones Calculus

LO11

Through Jones calculus, it becomes quite straightforward to determine the polarization state of the beam emerging from a polarizer or a phase retarder (like a QWP or a HWP); it was introduced by R C Jones in 1941. We will illustrate this through some simple examples. We use the exponential notation—for example, an x-polarized beam (propagating in the $+z$ direction) is described by

$$E_x(z, t) = E_0 e^{i(kz - \omega t)} \text{ and } E_y(z, t) = 0 \quad \textbf{(21.126)}$$

As discussed earlier, in the exponential notation, the actual field is the real part of the right hand sides of Eq. (21.126). We will represent such a wave by the vector

$$|\mathbf{E}\rangle = E_0 |x\rangle \quad \textbf{(21.127)}$$

where
$$|x\rangle = \begin{pmatrix} 1 \\ 0 \end{pmatrix} \quad \textbf{(21.128)}$$

is the normalized Jones vector representing the x-polarized wave; the symbol $|x\rangle$ is read as "ket x" and represents an x-polarized wave. Similarly, a y- polarized beam (propagating in the $+z$ direction) is described by

$$E_x(z, t) = 0 \text{ and } E_y(z, t) = E_0 e^{i(kz - \omega t)} \quad \textbf{(21.129)}$$

and would be represented by the vector

$$|\mathbf{E}\rangle = E_0 |y\rangle \quad \textbf{(21.130)}$$

where
$$|y\rangle = \begin{pmatrix} 0 \\ 1 \end{pmatrix} \quad \textbf{(21.131)}$$

is the normalized Jones vector representing the y-polarized wave. In writing $|\mathbf{E} >$ [see Eqs. (21.127) and (21.130)], the phase factor $e^{i(kz - \omega t)}$ is suppressed. Now, for an RCP wave propagating in the z direction [see Eqs. (21.23), (21.24) and Fig. 21.16(a)], we may write

$$E_x(z, t) = E_0 e^{i(kz - \omega t)}$$

and
$$E_y(z,t) = E_0\, e^{i\left(kz - \omega t + \frac{\pi}{2}\right)} = iE_0\, e^{i(kz - \omega t)} \quad \textbf{(21.132)}$$

Thus, neglecting the common phase factor, the normalized Jones vector representing the RCP wave will be

$$|\mathrm{RCP}\rangle = \frac{1}{\sqrt{2}}\begin{pmatrix} 1 \\ i \end{pmatrix} \quad \textbf{(21.133)}$$

where the factor $1/\sqrt{2}$ normalizes the vector; a normalized vector will be given by

$$\frac{1}{\sqrt{|a|^2 + |b|^2}}\begin{pmatrix} a \\ b \end{pmatrix}$$

Similarly, the normalized Jones vector representing the LCP wave, will be

$$|\mathrm{LCP} > = \frac{1}{\sqrt{2}}\begin{pmatrix} 1 \\ -i \end{pmatrix} \quad \textbf{(21.134)}$$

We can express $|\mathrm{RCP}\rangle$ and $|\mathrm{LCP}\rangle$ as superposition of x- and y-polarized waves with a phase difference; thus

$$|\mathrm{RCP}\rangle = \frac{1}{\sqrt{2}}\begin{pmatrix} 1 \\ i \end{pmatrix} = \frac{1}{\sqrt{2}}\left[|x\rangle + i|y\rangle\right] \quad \textbf{(21.135)}$$

and
$$|\mathrm{LCP}\rangle = \frac{1}{\sqrt{2}}\begin{pmatrix} 1 \\ -i \end{pmatrix} = \frac{1}{\sqrt{2}}\left[|x\rangle - i|y\rangle\right] \quad \textbf{(21.136)}$$

Also
$$|x\rangle = \begin{pmatrix} 1 \\ 0 \end{pmatrix} = \frac{1}{\sqrt{2}}\left[|\mathrm{RCP}\rangle + |\mathrm{LCP}\rangle\right] \quad \textbf{(21.137)}$$

and
$$|y\rangle = \begin{pmatrix} 0 \\ 1 \end{pmatrix} = \frac{1}{i\sqrt{2}}\left[|\mathrm{RCP}\rangle - |\mathrm{LCP}\rangle\right] \quad \textbf{(21.138)}$$

A linearly polarized light oriented at α with respect to the x-axis [see Fig. 21.26] will be given by (from now on, we will be measuring the angle with respect to the vertical axis)

$$|\mathrm{LP}\ \alpha\rangle = \cos\alpha |x\rangle + \sin\alpha |y\rangle = \begin{pmatrix} \cos\alpha \\ \sin\alpha \end{pmatrix} \quad \textbf{(21.139)}$$

We next consider a calcite (or a quartz) phase retarder like a QWP or a HWP; we assume its optic axis to be along the y-axis (see Fig. 21.26). The "modes" of such a device are linearly polarized along the x and y directions; the x-polarized wave will be the ordinary wave and the y-polarized wave will be the extraordinary wave. Thus if E_x $(z = d)$ and E_y $(z = d)$ are the x and y components of the electric field after propagating through the retardation plates (of thickness d) then

$$E_x(z = d) = e^{ik_o d}\ E_x(z = 0)$$

and
$$E_y(z = d) = e^{ik_e d}\ E_y(z = 0)$$

where
$$k_o = \frac{2\pi}{\lambda_0} n_o \text{ and } k_e = \frac{2\pi}{\lambda_0} n_e \quad \textbf{(21.140)}$$

Since, only the relative phase difference is of relevance, we may write

$$\begin{pmatrix} E_x(z = d) \\ E_y(z = d) \end{pmatrix} = \begin{pmatrix} e^{i\Phi} & 0 \\ 0 & 1 \end{pmatrix}\begin{pmatrix} E_x(z = 0) \\ E_y(z = 0) \end{pmatrix} = T_{PR}\begin{pmatrix} E_x(z = 0) \\ E_y(z = 0) \end{pmatrix}$$

where

$$\Phi = (k_o - k_e)\, d = \frac{2\pi}{\lambda_0}(n_o - n_e) d \quad \textbf{(21.141)}$$

is the phase difference introduced by the phase retarder and T_{PR} is Jones matrix for the phase retarder and is given by

$$T_{PR} = \begin{pmatrix} e^{i\Phi} & 0 \\ 0 & 1 \end{pmatrix} \quad \textbf{(21.142)}$$

For a negative crystal like calcite, $n_o > n_e$, and Φ will be positive; the y-polarized extraordinary wave will travel faster than the x-polarized ordinary wave. Thus for a calcite QWP (with its optic axis along the y direction), $\Phi = +\frac{\pi}{2}$ and

$$(T_{QWP})_{\text{fy}} = \begin{pmatrix} i & 0 \\ 0 & 1 \end{pmatrix} \text{(fast axis along the } y \text{ direction)} \quad \textbf{(21.143)}$$

where the subscript 'fy' denotes the fact that the fast axis is along the y direction. For a quartz QWP, $n_o < n_e$ and with its optic axis along the y direction, $\Phi = -\frac{\pi}{2}$ and

$$(T_{QWP})_{\text{sy}} = \begin{pmatrix} -i & 0 \\ 0 & 1 \end{pmatrix} \text{(slow axis along the } y \text{ direction)} \quad \textbf{(21.144)}$$

where the subscript 'sy' denotes the fact that the slow axis is along the y direction.

EXAMPLE 21.12 Consider a x-polarized wave incident normally on a QWP with its fast axis along the y direction then the output SOP will be

$$(T_{QWP})_{\text{fy}} |x\rangle = \begin{pmatrix} i & 0 \\ 0 & 1 \end{pmatrix} \begin{pmatrix} 1 \\ 0 \end{pmatrix} = i \begin{pmatrix} 1 \\ 0 \end{pmatrix} \quad \textbf{(21.145)}$$

Thus a x-polarized wave remains a x-polarized wave; similarly, a y-polarized wave will remain y-polarized–these are the "modes" of the QWP. We next consider a linearly polarized wave oriented with $\alpha = \frac{\pi}{4}$ (see Fig. 21.26) incident normally on the same QWP; the output SOP will be

$$(T_{QWP})_{\text{fy}} |\text{LP } 45^\circ\rangle = \begin{pmatrix} i & 0 \\ 0 & 1 \end{pmatrix} \frac{1}{\sqrt{2}} \begin{pmatrix} 1 \\ 1 \end{pmatrix} = \frac{i}{\sqrt{2}} \begin{pmatrix} 1 \\ -i \end{pmatrix} = |\text{LCP}\rangle \quad \textbf{(21.146)}$$

which is a left circularly polarized wave (see Fig. 21.26). If the same linearly polarized wave was incident normally on a QWP with its slow axis along the y direction then the output SOP will be

$$(T_{QWP})_{\text{sy}} |\text{LP } 45^\circ\rangle = \begin{pmatrix} -i & 0 \\ 0 & 1 \end{pmatrix} \frac{1}{\sqrt{2}} \begin{pmatrix} 1 \\ 1 \end{pmatrix} = \frac{-i}{\sqrt{2}} \begin{pmatrix} 1 \\ i \end{pmatrix} = |\text{RCP}\rangle$$

which represents a right circularly polarized wave. On the other hand, if $\alpha = \pi/6$, the output SOP will be

$$(T_{QWP})_{\text{fy}} |\text{LP } 60^\circ\rangle = \begin{pmatrix} i & 0 \\ 0 & 1 \end{pmatrix} \frac{1}{2} \begin{pmatrix} \sqrt{3} \\ 1 \end{pmatrix} = \frac{i}{2} \begin{pmatrix} \sqrt{3} \\ -i \end{pmatrix} = \frac{i}{2} \begin{bmatrix} \sqrt{3} \\ -i \end{bmatrix} = |\text{LEP}\rangle$$

which is a left elliptically polarized wave.

For a HWP, $\Phi = +\pi$ for calcite and $\Phi = -\pi$ for quartz. Thus for both cases

$$T_{HWP} = \begin{pmatrix} -1 & 0 \\ 0 & 1 \end{pmatrix} \quad \textbf{(21.147)}$$

One could have also used the fact that

$$(T_{HWP})_{\text{fy}} = (T_{QWP})_{\text{fy}} (T_{QWP})_{\text{fy}}$$

EXAMPLE 21.13 Consider a linearly polarized wave (making an angle of 45° with the x-axis) incident normally on a HWP with its fast axis along the y direction then the output SOP will be

$$(T_{HWP})_{\text{fy}} |\text{LP } 45^\circ\rangle = \begin{pmatrix} -1 & 0 \\ 0 & 1 \end{pmatrix} \frac{1}{\sqrt{2}} \begin{pmatrix} 1 \\ 1 \end{pmatrix} = \frac{1}{\sqrt{2}} \begin{pmatrix} -1 \\ 1 \end{pmatrix} \quad \textbf{(21.148)}$$

Thus the polarization state gets rotated by 90° (see Fig. 21.27). What would happen if the incident linearly polarized wave makes an angle of α with the x-axis?

EXAMPLE 21.14 In this example, we will calculate the Jones matrix for a phase retarder whose fast axis makes an angle θ with respect to the x-axis (see Fig. 21.37); we write the Jones matrix for the phase retarder as

$$(T_{PR})_{\text{f}\theta} = \begin{pmatrix} a & b \\ c & d \end{pmatrix} \text{ (fast axis making } \theta \text{ with the } x\text{-axis)}$$

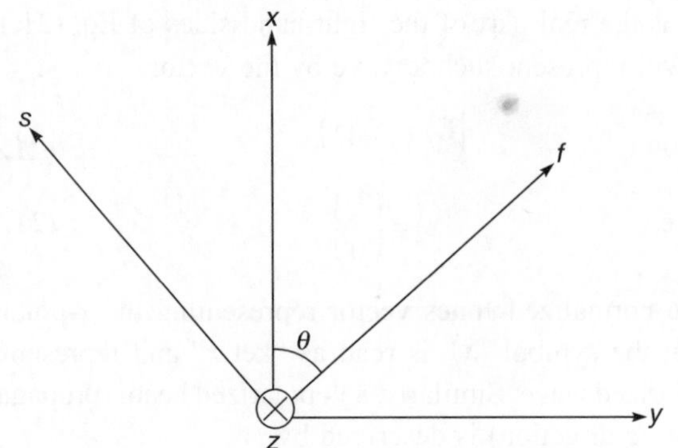

Figure 21.37
The fast axis of the phase retarder makes an angle θ with the x-axis. The propagation of the wave is in the $+z$ direction, which is going into the page.

For a x-polarized wave incident on such a phase retarder, the output will be given by

$$|\text{output}\rangle = (T_{PR})_{\text{f}\theta} |x\rangle = \begin{pmatrix} a & b \\ c & d \end{pmatrix} \begin{pmatrix} 1 \\ 0 \end{pmatrix} = \begin{pmatrix} a \\ c \end{pmatrix} \quad \textbf{(21.149)}$$

Now
$$|x\rangle = \begin{pmatrix} 1 \\ 0 \end{pmatrix} = \cos\theta |f\rangle + \sin\theta |s\rangle \quad \textbf{(21.150)}$$

where
$$|f\rangle = \begin{pmatrix} \cos\theta \\ \sin\theta \end{pmatrix} \text{ and } |s\rangle = \begin{pmatrix} \sin\theta \\ -\cos\theta \end{pmatrix} \quad \textbf{(21.151)}$$

represent the Jones vectors for linearly polarized waves along the fast and slow axes respectively. Now, for an x-polarized wave incident on a phase retarder, the output will be

$$|\text{output}\rangle = \cos\theta |f\rangle e^{ik_f d} + \sin\theta |s\rangle e^{ik_s d}$$
$$= e^{ik_f d} \left[\cos\theta \begin{pmatrix} \cos\theta \\ \sin\theta \end{pmatrix} + \sin\theta \begin{pmatrix} \sin\theta \\ -\cos\theta \end{pmatrix} e^{i\Phi} \right] \quad \textbf{(21.152)}$$

where

$$\Phi = (k_s - k_f)d = \frac{2\pi}{\lambda_0}(n_s - n_f)d \quad \textbf{(21.153)}$$

is the phase shift introduced by the phase retarder. Neglecting the unimportant phase factor $e^{ik_f d}$ and comparing with Eq. (21.149), we get

$$a = \cos^2\theta + \sin^2\theta\, e^{i\Phi} \quad \text{and} \quad c = \cos\theta \sin\theta (1 - e^{i\Phi})$$

Similarly, for a y-polarized wave incident on the phase retarder, the output will be given by

$$|\text{output}\rangle = (T_{PR})_{\text{f}\theta} |y\rangle = \begin{pmatrix} a & b \\ c & d \end{pmatrix} \begin{pmatrix} 0 \\ 1 \end{pmatrix} = \begin{pmatrix} b \\ d \end{pmatrix} \quad \textbf{(21.154)}$$

Since $$|y\rangle = \begin{pmatrix} 0 \\ 1 \end{pmatrix} = \sin\theta|f\rangle - \cos\theta|s\rangle \tag{21.155}$$

the output for a y-polarized wave incident on the phase retarder will be

$$|\text{output}\rangle = \sin\theta|f\rangle e^{ik_f d} - \cos\theta|s\rangle e^{ik_s d}$$

$$= e^{ik_f d}\left[\sin\theta\begin{pmatrix}\cos\theta \\ \sin\theta\end{pmatrix} - \cos\theta\begin{pmatrix}\sin\theta \\ -\cos\theta\end{pmatrix}e^{i\Phi}\right] \tag{21.156}$$

Once again, neglecting the unimportant phase factor $e^{ik_f d}$ and comparing with Eq. (21.154), we get

$$b = \cos\theta\sin\theta(1 - e^{i\Phi}) \text{ and } d = \sin^2\theta + \cos^2\theta e^{i\Phi}$$

Thus

$$(T_{PR})_{f\theta} = \begin{pmatrix} \cos^2\theta + \sin^2\theta e^{i\Phi} & \cos\theta\sin\theta\left(1 - e^{i\Phi}\right) \\ \cos\theta\sin\theta\left(1 - e^{i\Phi}\right) & \sin^2\theta + \cos^2\theta e^{i\Phi} \end{pmatrix}$$

(fast axis making θ with the x-axis) **(21.157)**

For a QWP, $\Phi = \pi/2$, and we obtain

$$(T_{QWP})_{f\theta} = \begin{pmatrix} \cos^2\theta + i\sin^2\theta & (1-i)\cos\theta\sin\theta \\ (1-i)\cos\theta\sin\theta & \sin^2\theta + i\cos^2\theta \end{pmatrix}$$

(fast axis making θ with the x-axis) **(21.158)**

For a HWP $\Phi = \pi$, and we obtain

$$(T_{HWP})_{f\theta} = \begin{pmatrix} \cos 2\theta & \sin 2\theta \\ \sin 2\theta & -\cos 2\theta \end{pmatrix}$$

(fast axis making θ with the x-axis) **(21.159)**

When the fast axis is along the y direction, $\theta = \pi/2$ and we obtain Eqs. (21.143) and (21.147) respectively. We may note that $(T_{HWP})_{f\theta}$ can also be obtained by using the following relation

$$(T_{HWP})_{f\theta} = (T_{QWP})_{f\theta}(T_{QWP})_{f\theta} \tag{21.160}$$

Using a similar method, the Jones matrix for a linear polarizer making an angle α with the vertical axis (x-axis) can easily be calculated; it is given by

$$T_{LP}(\alpha) = \begin{pmatrix} \cos^2\alpha & \sin\alpha\cos\alpha \\ \sin\alpha\cos\alpha & \sin^2\alpha \end{pmatrix} \tag{21.161}$$

EXAMPLE 21.15 Consider a RCP beam incident on a linear polarizer making an angle α with the x-axis; the polarization state of the output beam will be

$$T_{LP}(\alpha)|\text{RCP}\rangle = \begin{pmatrix} \cos^2\alpha & \sin\alpha\cos\alpha \\ \sin\alpha\cos\alpha & \sin^2\alpha \end{pmatrix}\frac{1}{\sqrt{2}}\begin{pmatrix}1 \\ i\end{pmatrix} = e^{i\alpha}\frac{1}{\sqrt{2}}\begin{pmatrix}\cos\alpha \\ \sin\alpha\end{pmatrix}$$

which represents a linearly polarized wave with its electric vector making an angle α with the vertical (i.e., x-axis) but with intensity half of the incident intensity. This can be easily understood by the fact that the RCP can be written as a superposition of two linearly polarized waves one with its electric vector making an angle α with the x-axis and the other at right angles to this direction; this component gets absorbed by the linear polarizer.

EXAMPLE 21.16 Consider a x-polarized wave incident on a linear polarizer making an angle α with the x-axis; the polarization state of the output beam will be

$$T_{LP}(\alpha)|x\rangle = \begin{pmatrix} \cos^2\alpha & \sin\alpha\cos\alpha \\ \sin\alpha\cos\alpha & \sin^2\alpha \end{pmatrix}\begin{pmatrix}1 \\ 0\end{pmatrix} = \cos\alpha\begin{pmatrix}\cos\alpha \\ \sin\alpha\end{pmatrix}$$

which represents a linearly polarized wave with its electric vector making an angle α with the x-axis but with intensity $\cos^2\alpha$ of the incident intensity; this is obvious from Malus' law. Similarly, if a y-polarized wave was incident on the linear polarizer, the output will again be a linearly polarized wave with its electric vector making an angle α with the x-axis but now with intensity $\sin^2\alpha$ of the incident intensity.

EXAMPLE 21.17 The Jones matrix for a linear polarizer making an angle 45° with the x-axis (see Fig. 21.26) followed by a QWP with its fast axis along the y direction will be

$$(T_{QWP})_{fy}(T_{LP})_{\pi/4} = \begin{pmatrix} i & 0 \\ 0 & 1 \end{pmatrix}\frac{1}{2}\begin{pmatrix} 1 & 1 \\ 1 & 1 \end{pmatrix} = \frac{1}{2}\begin{pmatrix} i & i \\ 1 & 1 \end{pmatrix}$$

One can easily show that any state of polarization incident on such a system will produce a LCP. For example, if we have a linearly polarized wave (making an angle 30° with the x-axis) incident on the system, then the output will be

$$|\text{output}\rangle = (T_{QWP})_{fy}(T_{LP})_{\pi/4}|\text{LP } 30^\circ\rangle$$

$$= \frac{1}{2}\begin{pmatrix} i & i \\ 1 & 1 \end{pmatrix}\frac{1}{2}\begin{pmatrix}\sqrt{3} \\ 1\end{pmatrix} = \frac{i\left(1+\sqrt{3}\right)}{2\sqrt{2}}\frac{1}{\sqrt{2}}\begin{pmatrix}1 \\ -i\end{pmatrix}$$

which is an LCP with intensity $(2+\sqrt{3})/4$ of the incident intensity; this number is nothing but $\cos^2 15°$ which follows from the law of Malus.

The Jones matrix for a **Right Polarization Rotator** (like an optically active medium or a Faraday rotator) is given by

$$T_{RPR} = \begin{pmatrix} \cos\alpha & -\sin\alpha \\ \sin\alpha & \cos\alpha \end{pmatrix} \tag{21.162}$$

EXAMPLE 21.18 Consider a RCP beam incident on a Right Polarization Rotator; the polarization state of the output beam will be

$$T_{RPR}|\text{RCP}\rangle$$

$$= \begin{pmatrix} \cos\alpha & -\sin\alpha \\ \sin\alpha & \cos\alpha \end{pmatrix}\frac{1}{\sqrt{2}}\begin{pmatrix}1 \\ i\end{pmatrix} = e^{-i\alpha}\left[\frac{1}{\sqrt{2}}\begin{pmatrix}1 \\ i\end{pmatrix}\right] = e^{-i\alpha}|\text{RCP}\rangle$$

Thus a RCP beam will come out as a RCP beam. Similarly, a LCP beam will come out as a LCP beam

EXAMPLE 21.19 Consider a linearly polarized beam with the electric field along a direction making an angle θ with the x-axis incident on a Right Polarization Rotator (see Fig. 21.28), thus

$$T_{RPR}|\text{LP } \theta\rangle$$

$$= \begin{pmatrix} \cos\alpha & -\sin\alpha \\ \sin\alpha & \cos\alpha \end{pmatrix}\begin{pmatrix}\cos\theta \\ \sin\theta\end{pmatrix} = \begin{pmatrix}\cos(\theta+\alpha) \\ \sin(\theta+\alpha)\end{pmatrix} \tag{21.163}$$

showing that the linear polarization will rotate the state of linear polarization by an angle α in the clockwise direction.

Similarly, the Jones matrix for a **left polarization rotator** is given by

$$T_{LPR} = \begin{pmatrix} \cos\alpha & \sin\alpha \\ -\sin\alpha & \cos\alpha \end{pmatrix} \quad \textbf{(21.164)}$$

When a RCP (or a LCP) wave propagates through a right (or left) polarization rotator, the state of polarization does not change. On the other hand when a linearly polarized wave propagates through a right (or left) polarization rotator, the state of polarization remains linear but gets rotated in the clockwise direction for a right polarization rotator and in the anti-clockwise direction for a left polarization rotator.

An elliptically polarized wave [described by Eqs. (21.18) and (21.19)] will be given by

$$E_x = a\, e^{i(kz-\omega t)} \text{ and } E_y = b\, e^{i(kz-\omega t+\theta)} \quad \textbf{(21.165)}$$

where a and b are assumed to be real and positive. The corresponding normalized Jones vector will be

$$|\text{EP}\rangle = \frac{1}{\sqrt{a^2+b^2}} \begin{pmatrix} a \\ b e^{i\theta} \end{pmatrix} \quad \textbf{(21.166)}$$

If $\theta = +\frac{\pi}{2}$, we will have a right elliptically polarized wave with its axes along the x and y directions:

$$|\text{REP}\rangle = \frac{1}{\sqrt{a^2+b^2}} \begin{pmatrix} a \\ b e^{+i\pi/2} \end{pmatrix} = \begin{pmatrix} \cos\varepsilon \\ i\sin\varepsilon \end{pmatrix}$$

$$\varepsilon = \tan^{-1}\left(\frac{b}{a}\right) \text{ with } 0 \le \varepsilon \le \frac{\pi}{2} \quad \textbf{(21.167)}$$

On the other hand, if $\theta = -\frac{\pi}{2}$, we will have a left elliptically polarized wave with its axes along the x and y directions:

$$|\text{LEP}\rangle = \frac{1}{\sqrt{a^2+b^2}} \begin{pmatrix} a \\ b e^{-i\pi/2} \end{pmatrix} = \begin{pmatrix} \cos\varepsilon \\ -i\sin\varepsilon \end{pmatrix};$$

$$\varepsilon = \tan^{-1}\left(\frac{b}{a}\right) \text{ with } 0 \le \varepsilon \le \frac{\pi}{2} \quad \textbf{(21.168)}$$

EXAMPLE 21.20 In Examples 21.1–21.4, we had assumed $b = a$; the corresponding Jones vector will be

$$|\text{EP}\rangle = \begin{pmatrix} E_x \\ E_y \end{pmatrix} = a \begin{pmatrix} 1 \\ e^{i\theta} \end{pmatrix} \quad \textbf{(21.169)}$$

where a is assumed to be positive. We now rotate the coordinates by angle α (see Sec. 21.4.1) to obtain

$$\begin{pmatrix} E_\xi \\ E_\eta \end{pmatrix} = \begin{pmatrix} \cos\alpha & -\sin\alpha \\ \sin\alpha & \cos\alpha \end{pmatrix} \begin{pmatrix} E_x \\ E_y \end{pmatrix}$$

$$= \frac{a}{\sqrt{2}} \begin{pmatrix} 1 & -1 \\ 1 & 1 \end{pmatrix} \begin{pmatrix} 1 \\ e^{i\theta} \end{pmatrix} = -i\sqrt{2}\, a e^{i\theta/2} \begin{pmatrix} \sin\frac{\theta}{2} \\ i\cos\frac{\theta}{2} \end{pmatrix} \quad \textbf{(21.170)}$$

where we have used the fact that for $b = a$, $\alpha = \pi/4$. Thus, neglecting the common phase factors, we get

$$E_\xi = \sqrt{2}\, a \sin\frac{\theta}{2} \cos\omega t \text{ and } E_\eta = \sqrt{2}\, a \cos\frac{\theta}{2} \sin\omega t$$

which represents the equation of an ellipse [see Eq. (21.27)] with its axes along the ξ and η axes; the ratio of the major to minor axis is $\tan\frac{\theta}{2}$ (see Example 21.5). As can be easily seen for $\theta = \pi/2$ we will have a RCP wave and for $\theta = 3\pi/2$ we will have a LCP wave; in general for, $0 < \theta < \pi$ we will have a REP wave and for $\pi < \theta < 2\pi$ we will have a LEP wave (see Fig. 21.17)—the ellipse becoming a straight line for $\theta = 0, \pi, 2\pi$.

The use of Jones matrices makes it very straightforward to consider more complicated cases like two QWP with their axes at an angle.

21.15 Faraday Rotation

LO12

An electromagnetic wave is propagating through a dielectric. If we apply a static magnetic field along the direction of propagation of the wave, the modes are now Right Circularly Polarized (RCP) and Left Circularly Polarized (LCP). Thus a RCP wave will propagate as a RCP wave with a particular velocity, and a LCP wave will also propagate as a LCP wave but with a slightly different velocity (see Fig. 21.38 and Sec. 21.16.2). Thus the situation is somewhat similar to the phenomenon of optical activity discussed in Sec. 21.8. Consider now a linearly polarized light propagating through such a medium. The linearly polarized light can be expressed

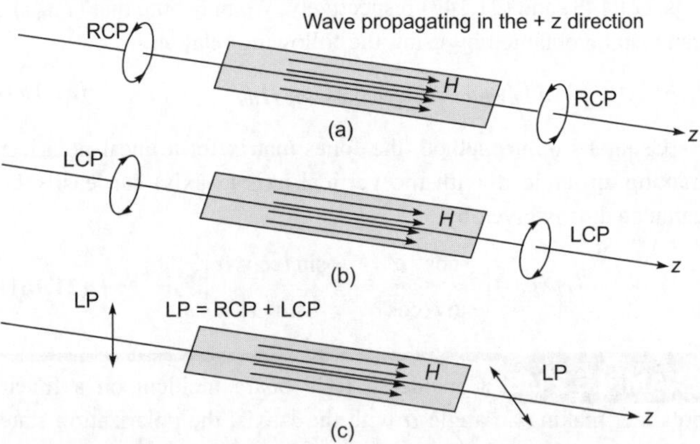

Figure 21.38
An electromagnetic wave is propagating through a dielectric. If we apply a static magnet field along the direction of propagation of the wave, the modes are now Right Circularly Polarized (RCP) and Left Circularly Polarized (LCP). (a) Thus a right circularly polarized wave will propagate as a right circularly polarized wave with a particular velocity, and (b) a left circularly polarized wave will also propagate as a left circularly polarized wave but with a slightly different velocity.(c) If a linearly polarized wave is incident, the direction of the electric vector will get rotated.

as a superposition of an RCP wave and a LCP wave and since they propagate with different velocities, the direction of the electric vector will get rotated—this rotation is usually referred to as Faraday rotation after the famous physicist Michael Faraday who discovered this phenomenon in 1845. The angle θ by which the plane of polarization rotates is given by the empirical formula

$$\theta = VHl \tag{21.171}$$

where H is the magnetic field l is the length of the medium and V is called the Verdet constant. For silica $V \approx 2.64 \times 10^{-4}$ degrees/ampere $\approx 4.6 \times 10^{-6}$ radians/ampere.

21.15.1 The Faraday Isolator

One of the very important applications of Faraday rotation is in the construction of the device known as the Faraday isolator [see Fig. 21.39(a) and (b)]. Faraday isolators allow light to pass through only in one direction and are extensively used to avoid optical feedback. In Fig. 21.39, P_1 and P_2 are two linear polarizers with pass axes at 45° to each other.

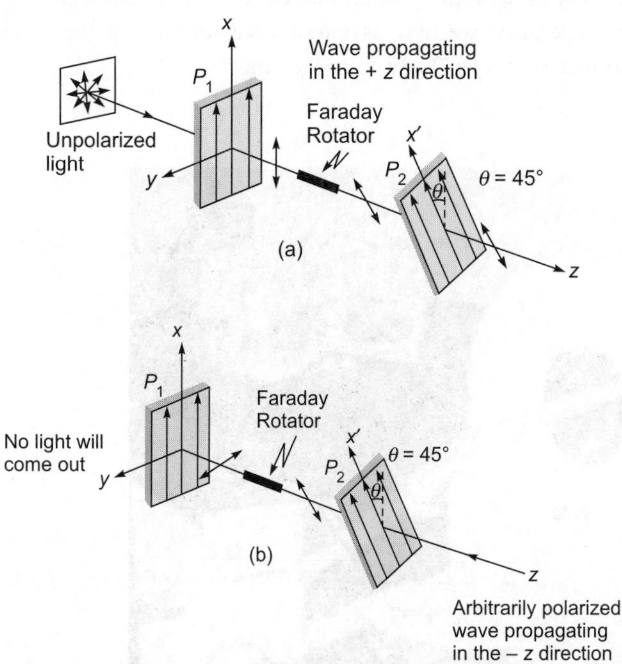

Figure 21.39

P_1 and P_2 are two linear polarizers with pass axes at 45° to each other. (a) The light beam incident from the left gets polarized along the x direction. The x-polarized light passes through the Faraday rotator which rotates the state of polarization by 45°, which is along the pass axis of the second polarizer P_2; thus the light passes through. (b) An arbitrarily polarized light beam (incident from the right), will get polarized along the x' direction. The x'-polarized light passes through the Faraday rotator which will further rotate the state of polarization by 45°. Thus the beam coming out of the Faraday rotator will be polarized along the y direction and is perpendicular to the pass axis of the second polarizer P_1–thus no light will pass through P_1.

The Faraday rotator is chosen to give a 45° degree rotation. The light beam incident from the left gets polarized along the x-direction. The x-polarized light passes through the Faraday rotator which rotates the state of polarization by 45°. Thus the beam coming out of the Faraday rotator is polarized along the x' direction and is along the pass axis of the second polarizer P_2 [see Fig. 21.39(a)]. Thus the light passes through and for a good isolator the transmission can be very high. Now if a light beam is incident from the right, it will get polarized along the x'-direction. The x' polarized light passes through the Faraday rotator which will further rotate the state of polarization by 45°. Thus the beam coming out of the Faraday rotator is polarized along the y direction and is perpendicular to the pass axis of the second polarizer P_1-thus no light will pass through P_1 [see Fig. 21.39 (b)]. We must note that if the magnetic field is along the $+z$ direction, then for the wave propagating along the $+z$ direction [see Fig. 21.39(a)] the rotation will be in the clockwise direction. On the other hand, for the wave propagating along the $-z$ direction [see Fig. 21.39(b)], the magnetic field is opposite to the direction of propagation and the Faraday rotation will be in the anti-clockwise direction.

In the wavelength region 0.7 to 1.1 μm one often uses terbium-doped borosilicate glass. Faraday isolators are extensively used in many fiber optic devices and in the wavelength range 1.3 to 1.55 μm (which is the wavelength range of interest in fiber-optic communication systems) one often uses YIG (Yttrium Iron Garnet) crystals.

21.15.2 Large Current Measurement using Faraday Rotation

The Faraday rotation has a very important application in measuring large currents using single-mode optical fibers. We consider a large length of a single mode fiber wound in many turns in the form of a loop around a current-carrying conductor (see Figs. 21.40 and 21.41). If a current I is passing through the conductor then by Ampere's law

$$\int \mathbf{H}.d\mathbf{l} = NI \tag{21.172}$$

where N represents the number of loops of the fiber around the conductor. Thus if a linearly polarized light is incident on the fiber, then its plane of polarization will get rotated by the angle

$$\theta = VNI \tag{21.173}$$

The rotation θ does not depend on the shape of the loop. As an example, for I = 200 amperes and N = 50, $\theta \approx 0.26$ degrees. The light from the fiber is allowed to fall on a Wollaston prism, which splits the incident beam into two orthogonally polarized components (see Fig. 21.31) whose intensities change when the plane of polraization (of the incident beam) rotates.

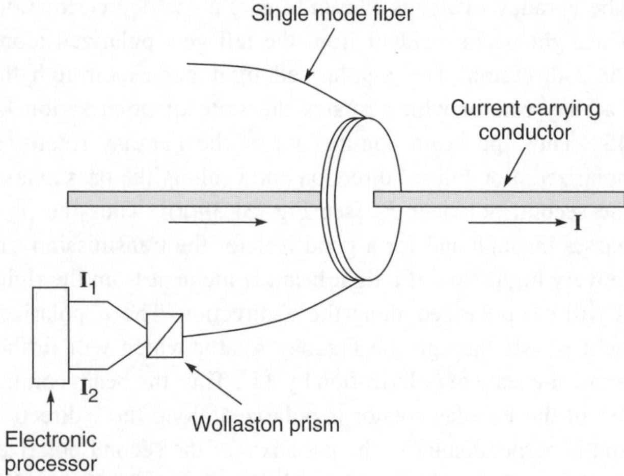

Figure 21.40

A single-mode fiber wound helically around a current carrying conductor. The rotation of the plane of polarization is detected by passing the light through a Wollaston prism and then an electronic processor.

Figure 21.41 shows an actual set up can be used to measure very high currents (~ 10000 amperes) by measuring Faraday rotation.

21.16 Theory of Optical Activity

LO13

As mentioned earlier, in an isotropic dielectric, the **D** vector is in the same direction as **E** and we have

$$\mathbf{D} = \varepsilon \mathbf{E} = \varepsilon_0 n^2 \mathbf{E} \qquad (21.174)$$

where ε_0 (= 8.854 × 10^{-12} MKS units) is the permittivity of free space and $n\,(=\sqrt{\varepsilon/\varepsilon_0})$ is the refractive index of the medium. Now, if we dissolve cane sugar in water, the medium is still isotropic; however, because of the spiral like structure of sugar molecules, the relation between **D** and **E** is given by the following relation

$$\mathbf{D} = \varepsilon_0 n^2 \mathbf{E} + ig\,\hat{\kappa} \times \mathbf{E}$$

$$= \varepsilon_0 n^2\,[\mathbf{E} + i\alpha\,\hat{\kappa} \times \mathbf{E}] \qquad (21.175)$$

where $\alpha = \dfrac{g}{\varepsilon_0 n^2}$ (21.176)

and $\hat{\kappa}$ is the unit vector along the direction of propagation of the wave. The parameter α can be positive or negative but it is usually an extremely small number (<< 1). Without any loss of generality, we may assume propagation along the *z*-axis so that $\kappa_x = \kappa_y = 0$ and $\kappa_z = 1$ giving

Figure 21.41

The experimental setup at IIT Delhi to measure large currents by measuring Faraday rotation. [*Slide courtesy: Professor Chandra Sakher and Professor K. Thyagarajan, IIT Delhi*]

$$\hat{\kappa} \times \mathbf{E} = \begin{pmatrix} \hat{\mathbf{x}} & \hat{\mathbf{y}} & \hat{\mathbf{z}} \\ 0 & 0 & 1 \\ E_x & E_y & E_z \end{pmatrix} = -\hat{\mathbf{x}} E_y + \hat{\mathbf{y}} E_x$$

Thus,

$$\begin{pmatrix} D_x \\ D_y \\ D_z \end{pmatrix} = \begin{pmatrix} \varepsilon_0 n^2 & -ig & 0 \\ ig & \varepsilon_0 n^2 & 0 \\ 0 & 0 & \varepsilon_0 n^2 \end{pmatrix} \begin{pmatrix} E_x \\ E_y \\ E_z \end{pmatrix} \quad \textbf{(21.177)}$$

The ε matrix is still Hermitian but there is a "small" off diagonal imaginary element. The presence of these off diagonal terms give rise to optical activity. We rewrite Eq. (21.85)

$$\frac{n_w^2}{c^2 \mu_0} [\mathbf{E} - (\hat{\kappa} . \mathbf{E})\hat{\kappa}] = \mathbf{D}$$

We write the x and y components of the above equation and since $\kappa_x = 0 = \kappa_y$ and $\kappa_z = 1$, we get

$$\frac{n_w^2}{c^2 \mu_0} E_x = D_x = \varepsilon_0 n^2 E_x - igE_y$$

and
$$\frac{n_w^2}{c^2 \mu_0} E_y = D_y = igE_x + \varepsilon_0 n^2 E_y$$

Thus,
$$\left(\frac{n_w^2}{n^2} - 1\right) E_x = -i\alpha E_y$$

and
$$\left(\frac{n_w^2}{n^2} - 1\right) E_y = i\alpha E_x$$

where we have used the fact that $c = 1/\sqrt{\varepsilon_0 \mu_0}$. For non-trival solutions

$$\left(\frac{n_w^2}{n^2} - 1\right)^2 = \alpha^2$$

giving
$$n_w = n\sqrt{1 \pm \alpha} \quad \textbf{(21.178)}$$

and
$$E_y = \pm iE_x \quad \textbf{(21.179)}$$

We write the two solutions as $n_R (= n\sqrt{1+\alpha})$ and $n_L (= n\sqrt{1-\alpha})$; the corresponding propagation constants will be given by

$$k = k_R = \frac{\omega}{c} n_R = \frac{\omega}{c} n\sqrt{1+\alpha} \quad \textbf{(21.180)}$$

and
$$k = k_L = \frac{\omega}{c} n_L = \frac{\omega}{c} n\sqrt{1-\alpha} \quad \textbf{(21.181)}$$

For $n_w = n_R$, if

$$E_x = E_0 e^{i(k_R z - \omega t)}$$

then
$$E_y = +iE_x = E_0 e^{i\left(k_R z - \omega t + \frac{\pi}{2}\right)}$$

which would represent an RCP (Right Circularly Polarized) wave and hence the subscript R. Similarly, For $n_w = n_L$, if

$$E_x = E_0 e^{i(k_L z - \omega t)}$$

then
$$E_y = -iE_x = E_0 e^{i\left(k_L z - \omega t - \frac{\pi}{2}\right)}$$

which would represent an LCP (Left Circularly Polarized) wave and hence the subscript L. The RCP and LCP waves are the two "modes" of the "optically active" substance and for an arbitrary incident state of polarization, we must write it as a superposition of the two modes and study the independent propagation of the two modes. Now,

$$n_R - n_L = n\left[\sqrt{1+\alpha} - \sqrt{1-\alpha}\right] \approx n\alpha \quad \textbf{(21.182)}$$

If d grams of pure cane sugar is dissolved in 100 gm of water solution, then for $\lambda = 5893$ Å (sodium light)

$$n_R - n_L \approx 2.2 \times 10^{-6}\, d$$

Thus, if $d = 5$ gm then $n_R - n_L \approx 1.1 \times 10^{-5}$ and $\alpha \approx 0.83 \times 10^{-5}$ where we have assumed $n \approx 1.33$. Further, the angle of rotation is given by [see Eq. (21.58)]

$$\Phi = \frac{\pi}{\lambda_0}(n_L - n_R)z \quad \textbf{(21.183)}$$

The specific rotation ρ is defined as the angle through which the plane of polarization rotates in traversing through a distance of 1 cm; thus

$$\rho = \frac{\pi}{\lambda_0}(n_l - n_r) \quad \textbf{(21.184)}$$

where λ_0 is measured in centimeters. For the sugar solution mentioned above (5 gm dissolved in 100 gm of water solution)

$$\rho \approx -0.59 \text{ radians/cm}$$

the negative sign indicating that the direction of polarization is in the anticlockwise direction.

21.16.1 Optical Activity in Quartz

One observes optical activity for a plane polarized wave propagating along the optic axis of a quartz crystal. The general theory of propagation of electromagnetic wave in such crystals is quite difficult; however, if the propagation is not along the optic axis the "modes" are very nearly linearly polarized and one may use the analysis discussed in Sec. (21.16). If the propagation is along the z-axis then we may write [cf. Eq. (21.177)]

$$\begin{pmatrix} D_x \\ D_y \\ D_z \end{pmatrix} = \begin{pmatrix} \varepsilon_0 n_o^2 & -ig & 0 \\ ig & \varepsilon_0 n_o^2 & 0 \\ 0 & 0 & \varepsilon_0 n_e^2 \end{pmatrix} \begin{pmatrix} E_x \\ E_y \\ E_z \end{pmatrix} \quad \textbf{(21.185)}$$

where n_o and n_e are constants of the crystal. Carrying out an identical analysis, we could get

$$n_R \approx n_o\left[1+\frac{1}{2}\alpha\right]$$

and $$n_L \approx n_o\left[1-\frac{1}{2}\alpha\right]$$

giving $$n_R - n_L \approx n_o\alpha$$

and $$\rho = \frac{\pi}{\lambda_0}(n_L - n_R) \approx -\frac{\pi n_o \alpha}{\lambda_0}$$

where λ_0 is measured in centimeters. For quartz,

$$\rho \approx \pm 8.54 \text{ radians/cm} \quad \text{at } \lambda_0 = 4046.56 \text{ Å}$$

$$\approx \pm 3.79 \text{ radians/cm} \quad \text{at } \lambda_0 = 5892.90 \text{ Å}$$

$$\approx \pm 2.43 \text{ radians/cm} \quad \text{at } \lambda_0 = 7281.35 \text{ Å}$$

[data adapted from Ref. 21.7]. In quartz, we can have $n_R > n_L$ or $n_R < n_L$. For λ_0 = 4046.56 Å, we readily get

$$|n_L - n_R| \approx 1.1 \times 10^{-4}$$

At higher wavelengths, the value of $|n_L - n_R|$ is much less. We may compare the above value with the value of $n_e - n_o \approx 0.9 \times 10^{-2}$.

21.17 Theory of Faraday Rotation

LO13

As discussed in Sec. 6.5, the equation of motion for the electron, in the presence of an external electric field **E** is given by [see Eq. (6.62)]:

$$\frac{d^2\mathbf{r}}{dt^2} + \omega_0^2\mathbf{r} = -\frac{q}{m}\mathbf{E} \quad \textbf{(21.186)}$$

In the presence of a static magnetic field **B**, we would have an additional (**v** × **B**) term:

$$\frac{d^2\mathbf{r}}{dt^2} + \omega_0^2\mathbf{r} = -\frac{q}{m}\mathbf{E} - \frac{q}{m}\dot{\mathbf{r}} \times \mathbf{B} \quad \textbf{(21.187)}$$

where $\mathbf{r} = x\hat{\mathbf{x}} + y\hat{\mathbf{y}} + z\hat{\mathbf{z}}$ represents the position vector of the electron; $\hat{\mathbf{x}}$, $\hat{\mathbf{y}}$ and $\hat{\mathbf{z}}$ are the unit vectors and $q\,(=+1.6\times10^{-19}\text{ C})$ is the magnitude of the electronic charge. We assume the magnetic field to be in the z-direction

$$B_x = 0 = B_y \quad \text{and} \quad B_z = B_0 \quad \textbf{(21.188)}$$

Thus,

$$\dot{\mathbf{r}} \times \mathbf{B} = \begin{vmatrix} \hat{\mathbf{x}} & \hat{\mathbf{y}} & \hat{\mathbf{z}} \\ \frac{dx}{dt} & \frac{dy}{dt} & \frac{dz}{dt} \\ 0 & 0 & B_0 \end{vmatrix} = \left[\hat{\mathbf{x}}\frac{dy}{dt} - \hat{\mathbf{y}}\frac{dx}{dt}\right]B_0 \quad \textbf{(21.189)}$$

Now, for a circular polarized light wave propagating along the z-direction

$$\mathbf{E}_\pm = (\hat{\mathbf{x}} \pm i\hat{\mathbf{y}})\,E_0\, e^{i(kz-\omega t)} \quad \textbf{(21.190)}$$

where the upper and lower signs correspond to RCP and LCP respectively. If we now write the x and y components of Eq. (21.187), we would get

$$\frac{d^2x}{dt^2} + \omega_0^2 x + \frac{qB_0}{m}\frac{dy}{dt} = -\frac{q}{m}E_0 e^{i(kz-\omega t)} \quad \textbf{(21.191)}$$

and

$$\frac{d^2y}{dt^2} + \omega_0^2 x - \frac{qB_0}{m}\frac{dx}{dt} = \mp i\frac{q}{m}E_0 e^{i(kz-\omega t)} \quad \textbf{(21.192)}$$

where the upper and lower signs correspond to RCP and LCP respectively. Writing

$$x = x_0 e^{i(kz-\omega t)} \quad \text{and} \quad y = y_0 e^{i(kz-\omega t)}$$

we get

$$\left.\left(\omega^2 - \omega_0^2\right)x_0 + i\omega_c\omega\, y_0 = +\frac{q}{m}E_0\right\} \times \left(\omega^2 - \omega_0^2\right) \quad \textbf{(21.193)}$$

$$\left.\left(\omega^2 - \omega_0^2\right)y_0 - i\omega_c\omega\, x_0 = \pm i\frac{q}{m}E_0\right\} \times -i\omega_c\omega \quad \textbf{(21.194)}$$

where $$\omega_c = \frac{qB_0}{m} \quad \textbf{(21.195)}$$

is the electron cyclotron frequency. If we multiply Eq. (21.191) by $(\omega^2 - \omega_0^2)$ and Eq. (21.192) by $-i\omega_c\,\omega$ and add the two equations, we would get

$$\left[\left(\omega^2 - \omega_0^2\right)^2 - \omega_c^2\omega^2\right]x_0 = \frac{q}{m}E_0\left[\left(\omega^2 - \omega_0^2\right) \pm \omega_c\omega\right]$$

giving $$x_0 = \frac{qE_0}{m\left[\left(\omega^2 - \omega_0^2\right) \mp \omega_c\omega\right]}$$

Similarly,

$$y_0 = \pm i\frac{qE_0}{m\left[\left(\omega^2 - \omega_0^2\right) \mp \omega_c\omega\right]} = \pm i x_0$$

Thus, the polarization is given by

$$\mathbf{P} = -Nq\mathbf{r} = -Nq \cdot \frac{qE_0\,(\hat{\mathbf{x}} \pm i\hat{\mathbf{y}})}{m\left[\left(\omega^2 - \omega_0^2\right) \mp \omega_c\omega\right]} e^{i(kz-\omega t)}$$

$$= \chi\,\mathbf{E}_\pm$$

where the susceptibility χ is given by

$$\chi = \frac{Nq^2}{m} \cdot \frac{1}{\left[\left(\omega_0^2 - \omega^2\right) \pm \omega_c \omega\right]} \quad \textbf{(21.196)}$$

Thus the modes are circularly polarized and the corresponding refractive indices are given by [cf. Eq. (6.84)]

$$n_{\pm}^2 = 1 + \frac{Nq^2}{m\varepsilon_0} \cdot \frac{1}{\left[\left(\omega_0^2 - \omega^2\right) \pm \omega_c \omega\right]} \quad \textbf{(21.197)}$$

where the upper and lower signs correspond to RCP and LCP respectively.

21.18 Poincare Sphere Representation of Polarized Light*

The Poincare sphere representation was conceived by the French physicist H. Poincare in 1892. It is a simple and extremely useful geometrical representation of various polarization states and their evolution through a birefringent medium. This representation makes the explanation of a difficult problem very easy due to the graphical picture of actions of polarizers and birefringent media involved.

According to this representation, one represents various polarization states, polarizers/analyzers and birefringent media by specific points on the surface of a sphere (of unit radius) in terms of the longitude and latitude as discussed below.

21.18.1 Various Polarization States

The most general polarization state is an elliptically polarized state, which is described by the following three parameters,

(i) The orientation θ of the major axis of the polarization ellipse with respect to some fixed direction. Let us select this direction as the horizontal direction (x-axis) in the (x-y) plane, transverse to the direction of propagation taken as z-axis (see Fig. 21.42).

(ii) The ellipticity of the ellipse representing the SOP which is measured in terms of an angle $\varepsilon = \tan^{-1}(b/a)$, where b and a represents the semi-minor and semi-major axis respectively; obviously a and b are both positive quantities and $a \geq b$ thus $0 \leq \varepsilon \leq \pi/4$.

(iii) The sense of rotation of the electric field with time is specified by assigning a 'plus' or 'minus' sign to ε; 'plus' sign is for right rotations and the 'minus' sign for left rotations. Here the right/left rotations are the clockwise/anticlockwise rotations as seen by an observer looking into the source of the light.

[Till now we have been considering light beams moving away from the observer (see Figs. 21.26 and 21.27). To be consistent with literature, in this section, we will assume the light beam to propagate towards the observer; thus, right circular rotations will correspond to LCP (Left Circular Polarization) and left circular rotations will correspond to RCP (Right Circular Polarization). I hope this will not cause any confusion].

(iv) Thus a general SOP can be uniquely defined in terms of two angles namely θ and $\chi = \pm\varepsilon$, called azimuth and ellipticity angle respectively. All possible SOPs are covered by the following range of θ and χ:

$$0 \leq \theta \leq \pi \text{ and } -\frac{\pi}{4} \leq \chi \leq +\frac{\pi}{4} \quad \textbf{(21.198)}$$

(v) Figure 21.42 shows the polarization ellipse for a right and left elliptic polarization state **with** orientation $\theta = \pi/6$ and ellipticity $b/a = 1/\sqrt{3}$ implying $\varepsilon = \pi/6$.

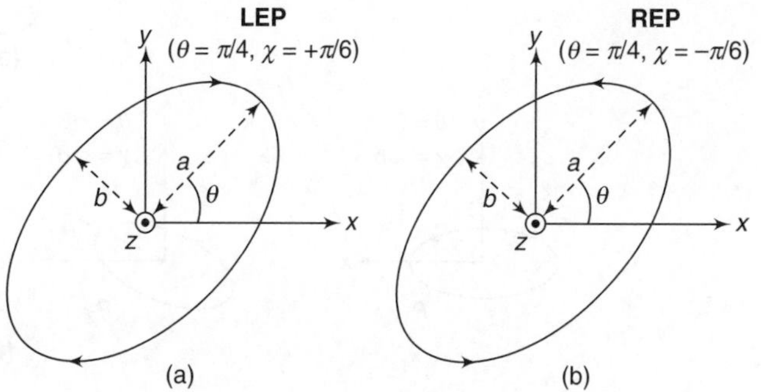

Figure 21.42

Polarization ellipse of (a) left and (b) right elliptic SOP with $\theta = \pi/4$. The propagation is along $+z$-direction, out of the page. We have assumed $a = \sqrt{3}b$.

21.18.2 Poincare Sphere Representation

A given SOP can be uniquely represented by a point on the surface of a sphere of unit radius, whose longitude and latitude have the values 2θ and 2χ respectively (see Fig. 21.43). This representation is called the Poincare Sphere representation and the sphere is called the Poincare Sphere (PS).

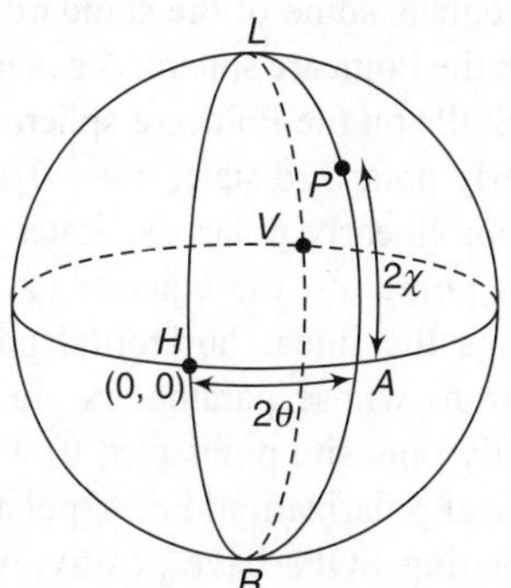

Figure 21.43

Poincare sphere representation of a general SOP

* A major portion of this section has been written by Professor Arun Kumar.

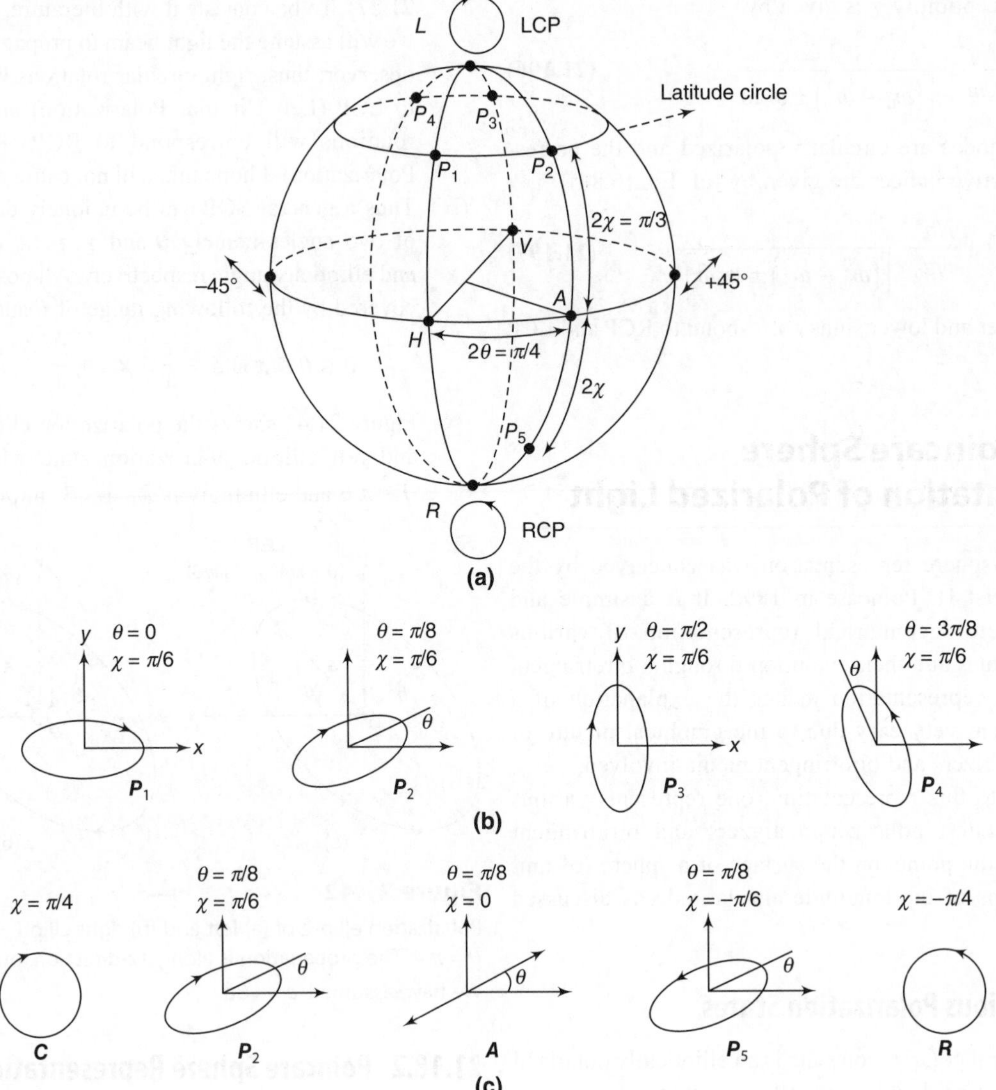

Figure 21.44

(a) Various Polarization states on the Poincare Sphere (b) Polarization states represented by points P_1, P_2, P_3, and P_4 on the latitude circle as shown in (a). (c) Polarization states represented by points R, P_2, A, P_5, and L on the meridian RAL as shown in (a).

Figure 21.44 enlists some of the standard SOPs and their representation on the Poincare sphere. A general rule of representing various SOPs on the Poincare sphere is given below:

(i) For a linearly polarized state, $b/a = 0$ and hence $\chi = 0$. Thus various linearly polarized states are represented by various points on the equator ($\chi = 0$). Let point H represents the linear horizontal polarization (i.e., x-polarization) whose parameters are (0, 0) then the diametrically opposite point $V(\pi, 0)$ will represent the linear vertical polarization; i.e., y-polarization.

(ii) All left rotating SOPs have positive values of χ and hence will lie on the upper hemisphere and all right rotating ones on the lower hemisphere.

(iii) For a circularly polarized light, $b/a = 1$ and hence $\varepsilon = \pi/4$. Thus

$$2\chi = +\frac{\pi}{2} \quad \textbf{LCP} \quad \text{and} \quad 2\chi = -\frac{\pi}{2} \quad \textbf{RCP}$$

On the Poincare sphere, north and south poles corresponds to $2\chi = +\frac{\pi}{2}$ and $2\chi = -\frac{\pi}{2}$ and will represent LCP and RCP respectively. Obviously, orientation θ has no meaning for a circularly polarized light.

(iv) Points on a circle parallel to the equator, i.e. a latitude circle have same values of χ and hence will represent various elliptic SOPs with same ellipticity but different orientations.

(v) Points on a meridian RAL corresponds to a constant value of θ and hence, will represent different elliptic SOPs with same orientation θ but different ellipticities.

21.18.3 Some Applications of PS Representation

Using the PS representation, it is extremely simple to predict the effect of a polarizer/analyzer or a birefringent medium on a given SOP, which can be obtained using the following two basic properties of the PS representation.

Property 1-*Effect of a polarizer/analyzer:* If a SOP represented by a point P on PS is passed through an analyzer represented by A, then the fractional intensity transmitted by the analyzer is given by

$$I = \cos^2 \frac{\widehat{PA}}{2} \tag{21.199}$$

where $\widehat{PA}$ is the arc length along the great circle connecting the two points on the Poincare sphere (see Fig. 21.43). We verify this rule through the following simple example.

EXAMPLE 21.21 Obtain the fractional output intensity if a right (or left) circularly polarized beam is passed through a linear analyzer.

Solution: A right (or left) circularly polarized state will be represented by the south (or north) pole on the PS while the linear analyzer will be represented by some point A on the equator. It is obvious that in this case $\widehat{PA} = \pi/2$, which means $I = \cos^2(\pi/4) = 1/2$, i.e. 50%.

EXAMPLE 21.22 Obtain the fractional output intensity if a x-polarized beam is passed through a linear analyzer whose pass axis makes $\pi/8$ with the horizontal.

Solution: The x-polarized state will be represented by the point H on the equator while the linear analyzer will be represented by the point A on the equator [see Fig. 21.44(a)]. It is obvious that in this case $\widehat{HA} = \pi/4$, which means $I = \cos^2(\pi/8)$.

Property 2 *Effect of a birefringent medium:* If a SOP given by $P_i(\theta_i, \chi_i)$ is passed through a birefringent medium, then the output SOP, $P_o(\theta_o, \chi_o)$, can be obtained from the input state by rotating it on the sphere about the line FS representing the medium, clockwise while looking from F to S by an angle δ, where δ represents the phase difference introduced between the fast and the slow polarization states.

In the following, we take a simple example to demonstrate the usage of the above property of the PS. More examples can be found in Ref. 21.14.

EXAMPLE 21.23 Consider a linearly polarized wave making an angle of 45° with the x-axis. Obtain the output SOP if it is passed through a $\lambda/4$ wave plate (QWP) with its fast axis parallel to the x-axis.

Solution: On PS, the given SOP will be represented by a point P and the $\lambda/4$ wave plate by the diameter HV, with H representing the fast axis as shown in Fig 21.45 and $\widehat{HP} = \pi/2$. To obtain the output SOP we should rotate the point P on the sphere around FS clockwise by an angle $\pi/2$, which will shift P to R. Thus the output SOP will be right circularly polarized.

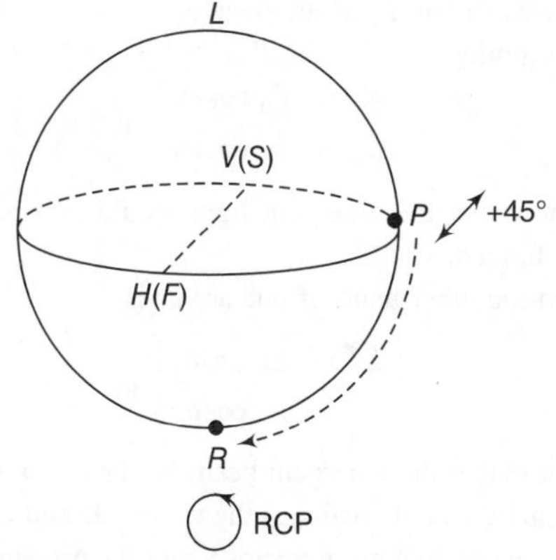

Figure 21.45

A QWP having fast axis along horizontal direction will convert a linear +45° state to a RCP.

PROBLEMS

21.1 Discuss the state of polarization when the x and y components of the electric field are given by the following equations:

(a) $$\left.\begin{aligned} E_x &= E_0 \cos(\omega t + kz) \\ E_y &= \frac{1}{\sqrt{2}} E_0 \cos(\omega t + kz + \pi) \end{aligned}\right\}$$

(b) $$\left.\begin{aligned} E_x &= E_0 \sin(\omega t + kz) \\ E_y &= E_0 \cos(\omega t + kz) \end{aligned}\right\}$$

(c) $$\left.\begin{aligned} E_x &= E_0 \sin\left(kz - \omega t + \frac{\pi}{3}\right) \\ E_y &= E_0 \sin\left(kz - \omega t - \frac{\pi}{6}\right) \end{aligned}\right\}$$

(d) $$\left.\begin{aligned} E_x &= E_0 \cos\left(kz - \omega t + \frac{\pi}{4}\right) \\ E_y &= \frac{1}{\sqrt{2}} E_0 \sin(kz - \omega t) \end{aligned}\right\}$$

In each case, plot the rotation of the tip of the electric vector on the plane $z = 0$.

[**Ans:** (a) Linearly polarized, (b) Right-circularly polarized, (c) Left-circularly polarized, and (d) Left-elliptically polarized.]

21.2 The electric field components of a plane electromagnetic wave are

$$E_x = 2E_0 \cos(\omega t - kz + \phi); \; E_y = E_0 \sin(\omega t - kz)$$

Draw the diagram showing the state of polarization (i.e., circular, plane, elliptical or unpolarized) when

(a) $\phi = 0$
(b) $\phi = \pi/2$
(c) $\phi = \pi/4$

21.3 Using the data given in Table 21.1, calculate the thickness of quartz half-wave plate for $\lambda_0 = 5890$ Å.

[**Ans:** 32.34 μm]

21.4 A right-circularly polarized beam is incident on a calcite half-wave plate. Show that the emergent beam will be left-circularly polarized.

21.5 What will be the Brewster angle for a glass slab ($n = 1.5$) immersed in water ($n = 4/3$)?

[**Ans:** 48.4°]

21.6 Consider the normal incidence of a plane wave on a quartz quarter wave plate whose optic axis is parallel to the surface (see Fig. 21.26). Thus the optic axis is along the y-axis and the propagation is along the z-axis. Show that E_x propagates as an o-wave and E_y as an e-wave.

(a) Assuming

$$\left.\begin{aligned} E_x &= E_0 \cos \omega t \\ E_y &= E_0 \cos \omega t \end{aligned}\right\} \text{ at } z = 0$$

show that the emergent light would be right circularly polarized.

(b) On the other hand, if one assumes

$$\left.\begin{aligned} E_x &= E_0 \sin \omega t \\ E_y &= E_0 \cos \omega t \end{aligned}\right\} \text{ at } z = 0$$

show that the emergent beam is linearly polarized.

21.7 Show that the angle between the vectors **D** and **E** is the same as between the poynting vector **S** and the propagation vector **k**.

21.8 Consider the propagation of an extraordinary wave through a KDP crystal. If the wave vector is at an angle of 45° to the optic axis, calculate the angle between **S** and **k**. Repeat the calculation for $LiNbO_3$. The values of n_o and n_e for KDP and $LiNbO_3$ are given in Table 21.1.

[**Ans:** 1.56° and 2.25°]

21.9 Prove that when the angle of incidence corresponds to the Brewster angle, the reflected and refracted rays are at right angles to each other.

21.10 (a) Consider two crossed polaroids placed in the path of an unpolarized beam of intensity I_o [see Fig. 21.7(c)]. If we place a third polaroid in between the two then, in general, some light will be transmitted through. Explain this phenomenon.

(b) Assuming the pass axis of the third polaroid to be at 45° to the pass axis of either of the polaroids, calculate the intensity of the transmitted beam. Assume that all the polaroids are perfect.

[**Ans:** $1/8 I_o$]

21.11 A quarter-wave plate is rotated between two crossed polaroids. If an unpolarized beam is incident on the first polaroid, discuss the variation of intensity of the emergent beam as the quarter-wave plate is rotated. What will happen if we have a half-wave instead of a quarter-wave plate?

21.12 In the above problem, if the optic axis of the quarter-wave plate makes an angle of 45° with the pass axis of either polaroid, show that only a quarter of the incident intensity will be transmitted. If the quarter-wave plate is replaced by a half-wave plate, show that half of the incident intensity will be transmitted through.

21.13 For calcite the values of n_o and n_e for $\lambda_0 = 4046$ Å are 1.68134 and 1.49694 respectively; corresponding to $\lambda_0 = 7065$ Å the values are 1.65207 and 1.48359 respectively. We have a calcite quarter-wave plate corresponding to $\lambda_0 = 4046$ Å. A left-circularly polarized beam of $\lambda_0 = 7065$ Å is incident on this plate. Obtain the state of polarization of the emergent beam.

[**Ans:** LEP]

21.14 A HWP (half wave plate) is introduced between two crossed polaroids P_1 and P_2. The optic axis makes an angle 15° with the pass axis of P_1 as shown in Fig. 21.46(a) and (b). If an unpolarized beam of intensity I_0 is normally incident on P_1 and if I_1, I_2, and I_3 are the intensities after P_1, after HWP and after P_2 respectively then calculate I_1/I_0, I_2/I_0 and I_3/I_0.

[**Ans:** ½, ½, 1/8]

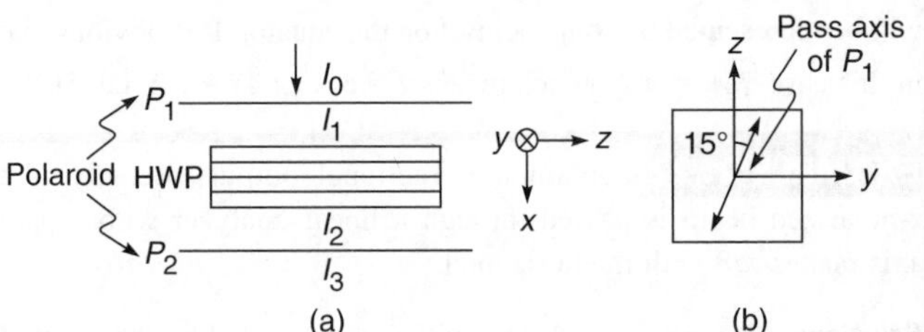

Figure 21.46

21.15 Two prisms of calcite ($n_0 > n_e$) are cemented together as shown in Fig. 21.47, so as to form a cube. Lines and dots show the direction of the optic axis. A beam of unpolarized light is incident normally from region I. Assume the angle of the prism to be 12°. Determine the path of rays in regions II, III and IV indicating the direction of vibrations (i.e., the direction of **D**).

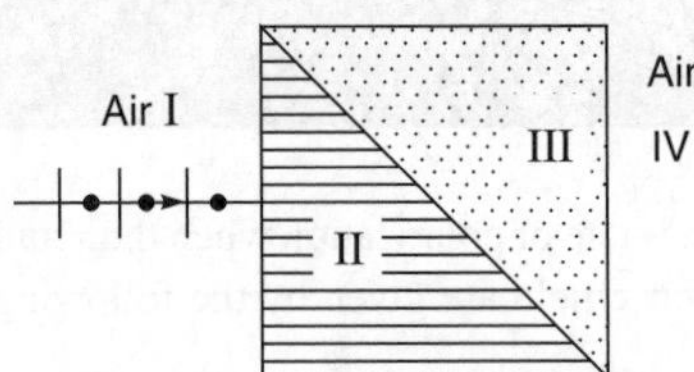

Figure 21.47

21.16 Consider a calcite QWP whose optic axis is along the y-axis (see Fig. 21.26). By using Jones matrices, obtain the output state of polarization when the incident beam is

(a) x polarized
(b) y polarized
(c) Left Circularly Polarized (LCP)
(d) Linearly Polarized with its E making an angle of 45° with the x-axis
(e) Linearly Polarized with its E making an angle of 60° with the x-axis

(f) Left Elliptically Polarized (LEP) with its E given by

$$E_x = \frac{\sqrt{3}}{2} E_0 \cos(kz - \omega t)$$
$$E_y = \frac{1}{2} E_0 \sin(kz - \omega t) \quad \textbf{(21.200)}$$

21.17 Consider a calcite HWP whose optic axis is along the y-axis (see Fig. 21.26). By using Jones matrices, obtain the output state of polarization when the incident beam is
(a) x-polarized
(b) y polarized
(c) Left Circularly Polarized (LCP)
(d) Linearly Polarized with its E making an angle of 45° with the x-axis
(e) Linearly Polarized with its E making an angle of 60° with the x-axis
(f) Left Elliptically Polarized (LEP) with its E given by Eq. (21.200).

21.18 A $\lambda/6$ plate is introduced in between the two crossed polarizers in such a way that the optic axis of the $\lambda/6$ plate makes an angle of 45° with the pass axis of the first polarizer (see Fig. 21.48). Consider an unpolarized beam of intensity I_0 to be incident normally on the polarizer. Assume the optic axis to be along the x-axis and the propagation along the z-axis. Write the x and y components of the electric fields (and the corresponding total intensities) after passing through (i) P_1 (ii) $\lambda/6$ plate and (iii) P_2.

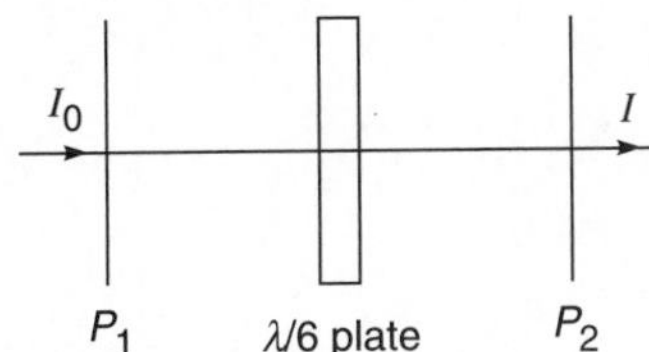

Figure 21.48

21.19 A beam of light is passed through a polarizer. If the polarizer is rotated with the beam as an axis, the intensity I of the emergent beam does not vary. What are the possible states of polarization of the incident beam? How to ascertain its state of polarization with the help of the given polarizer and a QWP?

21.20 Consider a Wollaston prism consisting of two similar prisms of calcite (n_o = 1.66 and n_e = 1.49) as shown in Fig. 21.31, with angle of prism now equal to 20°. Calculate the angular divergence of the two emerging beams.

21.21 (a) Consider a plane wave incident normally on a calcite crystal with its optic axis making an angle of 20° with the normal [see Fig. 21.23(a)]. Thus ψ = 20°. Calculate the angle that the Poynting Vector will make with the normal to the surface. Assume $n_o \approx 1.66$ and $n_e \approx 1.49$.
(b) In the above problem assume the crystal to be quartz with $n_o \approx 1.544$ and $n_e \approx 1.553$.

[Ans: (a) 4.31°]

21.22 Write the Jones matrix for a linear polarizer whose pass axis makes an angle of +45° with respect to the x-axis; the x-axis is assumed to be along the vertical direction (see Fig. 21.6). Use Jones matrices to write the output state of polarization when
(a) the incident beam is linearly polarized along the x-axis
(b) the incident beam is linearly polarized along a direction which makes an angle of +45° with respect to the x-axis
(c) the incident beam is linearly polarized along a direction which makes an angle of –45° with respect to the x-axis, and when
(d) the incident beam is right circularly polarized

21.23 Write the Jones matrix for a QWP whose fast axis is along the y direction and also for a linear polarizer whose pass axis makes an angle of – 45° with respect to the x-axis.
(a) An x-polarized beam is incident first on the QWP and then on the linear polarizer. Use Jones matrices to write the output state of polarization.
(b) We now reverse the ordering of the elements. The x-polarized beam is incident first on the linear polarizer and then on the QWP. Use Jones matrices to write the output state of polarization.

21.24 The Jones matrix for a QWP, with its fast axis making an angle θ with respect to the x-axis, is given by

$$(T_{QWP})_{f\theta} = \begin{pmatrix} \cos^2\theta + i\sin^2\theta & (1-i)\cos\theta\sin\theta \\ (1-i)\cos\theta\sin\theta & \sin^2\theta + i\cos^2\theta \end{pmatrix} \quad \textbf{(21.201)}$$

Show that the Jones matrix for a HWP, with its fast axis making an angle θ with respect to the x-axis, is given by

$$(T_{HWP})_{f\theta} = (T_{QWP})_{f\theta}(T_{QWP})_{f\theta} = \begin{pmatrix} \cos 2\theta & \sin 2\theta \\ \sin 2\theta & -\cos 2\theta \end{pmatrix} \quad \textbf{(21.202)}$$

21.25 A linearly polarized light oriented at an angle ϕ with respect to x-axis [see Eq. (21.139)] is incident on a HWP, with its fast axis making an angle θ with respect to the x-axis. Show that the output remains linearly polarized with the state of polarization rotated by an angle 2θ.

21.26 For calcite, the values of n_o and n_e for λ_0 = 4046 Å are 1.68134 and 1.49694 respectively; corresponding to λ_0 = 7065 Å the values are 1.65207 and 1.48359 respectively. At λ_0 = 4046 Å the calcite plate is a QWP. Determine the thickness d. Show that the Jones matrix for the calcite plate for λ_0 = 4046 Å and for λ_0 = 7065 Å would be:

$$T\left(\lambda_0 = 4046\,\text{Å}\right) = \begin{pmatrix} i & 0 \\ 0 & 1 \end{pmatrix}$$

and

$$T\left(\lambda_0 = 7065\,\text{Å}\right) = \begin{pmatrix} e^{i\pi/3.82} & 0 \\ 0 & 1 \end{pmatrix}$$

[Ans: $d \approx 5.49 \times 10^{-5}$ cm]

21.27 Consider the incidence of the following REP beam on a sugar solution at z = 0:

$$E_x = 5 \cos \omega t \; ; \; E_y = 5 \sin \omega t$$

with $\lambda = 6328$ Å. Assume

$$n_l - n_r = 10^{-5} \text{ and } n_l = \frac{4}{3}$$

study the evolution of the SOP of the beam.

21.28 Consider the incidence of the above REP beam on an elliptic core fiber with

$$\frac{\beta_x}{k_0} \approx 1.506845 \text{ and } \frac{\beta_x}{k_0} \approx 1.507716$$

Calculate the SOP at $z = 0.25\ L_b$, $0.5\ L_b$, $0.75\ L_b$ and L_b.

21.29 When the optic axis lies on the surface of the crystal and in the plane of incidence, show (by geometrical considerations) that the angles of refraction of the ordinary and the extraordinary rays (which we denote by r_o and r_e respectively) are related through the following equation:

$$\frac{\tan r_o}{\tan r_e} = \frac{n_o}{n_e}$$

21.30 In order to convert an x-polarized light to a y-polarized light, we make the x-polarized light fall on a Polaroid whose pass axis makes an angle 45° with the x-axis followed by another Polaroid whose pass axis is along the y-axis. Assuming the Polaroids to be lossless, show that the intensity of the y-polarized light will be $0.25\ I_0$ where I_0 is the intensity of the incident light.

21.31 (a) In continuation of the previous problem, if we want to increase the output intensity, we make the x-polarized light fall on a Polaroid whose pass axis makes an angle 30° with the x-axis followed by a second Polaroid whose pass axis makes an angle 60° with the x-axis; the emerging light is made to pass through another Polaroid whose pass axis is along the y-axis. Assuming the Polaroids to be lossless, show that the intensity of the y-polarized light will be about $0.42\ I_0$ where I_0 is the intensity of the incident light. (b) We next assume that the x-polarized light falls on a set of 5 Polaroids whose pass axes make an angle 15°, 30°, 45°, 60°, 75° with the x-axis followed by a 6th Polaroid whose pass axis is along the y-axis. Assuming the Polaroids to be lossless, show that the intensity of the y-polarized light will be about $0.66\ I_0$ where I_0 is the intensity of the incident light. Thus by using a large number of Polaroids, the output intensity will increase; of course, each Polaroid will have additional absorption losses.

CHAPTER

22

Electromagnetic Waves

Maxwell could say, when he was finished with his discovery, 'Let there be electricity and magnetism, and there is light'

....Richard Feynman*

Important Milestones

1785: Charles Coulomb had put forward the inverse square law.

1820: Hans Christian Oersted discovered that a conductor carrying current produces a magnetic field. Shortly after this discovery, Biot and Savart found that a current carrying conductor exerts a force on a magnet. Based on Oersted's discovery, Ampere gave the theory of electromagnetism. In 1855 Maxwell wrote the equation what we now call as Amperes circuital law.

1831: Michael Faraday discovered electromagnetic induction in which a changing magnetic field induces a current; Joseph Henry also discovered this independently in 1832. Around 1861, Maxwell put the law in the form of a vector equation.

1861-1862: James Clerk Maxwell introduced the concept of displacement current and wrote down the equations which are now known as Maxwell's equations. He predicted the existence of electromagnetic waves and also propounded that light is an electromagnetic wave.

1862: James Clerk Maxwell showed that the electromagnetic wave carries momentum and exerts pressure on a surface on which the electromagnetic radiation is incident; this was experimentally verified by Lebedev in the year 1900 and also by Nichols and Hull in 1901. It is believed that in 1619 Johannes Kepler had also put forward the concept of radiation pressure.

LEARNING OBJECTIVES

After reading this chapter, the reader should be able to:

LO 1: *discuss Maxwell's equations.*

LO 2: *show that plane wave solutions in a dielectric satisfy Maxwell's equations.*

LO 3: *derive three-dimensional plane wave equation in a dielectric.*

LO 4: *define the Poynting vector.*

LO 5: *discuss energy density and intensity of an electromagnetic wave.*

LO 6: *describe wave propagation in an absorbing medium.*

LO 7: *describe wave propagation in a conducting medium.*

LO 8: *derive an expression for radiation pressure due to a plane wave incident on a perfect absorber and on a perfect reflector.*

LO 9: *derive the continuity conditions for electric and magnetic fields at the interface of two media.*

LO 10: *discuss the physical significance of Maxwell's equations.*

---

* Ref. 22.6

Above Image: View from a polarized lens. Photograph courtesy Darksoul72/Shutterstock

22.1 Introduction

In this chapter we will show that in a **dielectric**, the following expressions of the electric and magnetic fields

$$\mathbf{E} = \hat{\mathbf{x}} E_0 e^{i(kz-\omega t)} \quad (22.1)$$

$$\mathbf{H} = \hat{\mathbf{y}} H_0 e^{i(kz-\omega t)}; \; H_0 = \frac{E_0}{\eta} \; \& \; \eta = \frac{120\pi}{n} \text{ ohms} \quad (22.2)$$

are solutions of Maxwell's equations. In the above equations, we have used the MKS system of units, n is the refractive index and η the "intrinsic impedance" of the medium—these will be defined in Sec. 22.3. These equations describe a plane electromagnetic wave (in this case, propagating in the z-direction); the actual fields are real part of the above equations. As can be seen, the electric and magnetic fields are in phase and always at right angles to each other and also to the direction of propagation of the wave. The plane electromagnetic wave described by Eqs. (22.1) and (22.2) is referred to as an x-polarized wave because the electric field is oscillating along the x-direction. Further, the speed of propagation of the electromagnetic wave is given by

$$v = \frac{\omega}{k} = \frac{c}{n} \quad (22.3)$$

where $$c = 2.99792458 \times 10^8 \text{ m/s} \quad (22.4)$$

is the velocity of the electromagnetic wave in vacuum; all frequencies travel with an identical velocity in vacuum. The energy flow is in the z-direction (which represents the direction of propagation of the wave) and, on an average, $\frac{E_0^2}{2\eta}$ amount of energy crosses a unit area (perpendicular to the z-axis) per unit time. The corresponding average energy density (associated with the electromagnetic wave) is given by

$$\langle u \rangle = \frac{1}{2} \varepsilon E_0^2 \qquad \left[\text{J/m}^3\right] \quad (22.5)$$

and the intensity is given by

$$I = \frac{1}{2} \varepsilon v E_0^2 = \frac{1}{2} \varepsilon_0 c n E_0^2 \qquad \left[\text{W/m}^2\right] \quad (22.6)$$

ε_0 and ε represent the dielectric permittivity of free space and of the medium, respectively.

We will also discuss propagation of electromagnetic waves in metals and derive expressions for the complex refractive index. Such solutions are of great importance in many diverse areas like solid state physics, plasma physics, electrical engineering, etc.

22.2 Maxwell's Equations LO1

All electromagnetic phenomena can be said to follow from Maxwell's equations. These equations are based on experimental observations and are given by the following equations:

$$\nabla \cdot \mathbf{D} = \rho \quad (22.7)$$

$$\nabla \cdot \mathbf{B} = 0 \quad (22.8)$$

$$\nabla \times \mathbf{E} = -\frac{\partial \mathbf{B}}{\partial t} \quad (22.9)$$

and

$$\nabla \times \mathbf{H} = \frac{\partial \mathbf{D}}{\partial t} + \mathbf{J} \quad (22.10)$$

where ρ represents the free charge density and **J** the current density; **E**, **D**, **B** and **H** represent the electric field, electric displacement, magnetic induction and magnetic field, respectively. Further,

$$\nabla \cdot \mathbf{D} \equiv \text{div } \mathbf{D} \quad \text{and} \quad \nabla \times \mathbf{D} \equiv \text{curl } \mathbf{D}$$

The famous physicist, Richard Feynman, in his very famous book (Ref. 22.6) has written:

> *... From a long view of the history of mankind – seen from, say ten thousand years from now – there can be little doubt that the most significant event of the 19th century will be judged as Maxwell's discovery of the laws of electrodynamics. The American Civil war will pale into provincial insignificance in comparison with this important scientific event of the same decade.*

In the same book, Feynman further writes

> *... untold numbers of experiments have confirmed Maxwell's equations. If we take away the scaffolding he used to build it, we find that Maxwell's beautiful edifice stands on its own. He brought together all of the laws of electricity and magnetism and made one complete and beautiful theory.*

Equations (22.7)–(22.10) can be solved only if the 'constitutive relations' are known which relate **D** to **E**, **B** to **H** and **J** to **E**; the 'constitutive relations' depend on the properties of the medium, field strengths, etc. For example, for an anisotropic medium ε is a tensor of second tank (see Sec. 21.12); for high field strengths ε may itself depend on **E**. For a linear, isotropic and homogeneous medium the 'constitutive relations' are given by the following equations

$$\mathbf{D} = \varepsilon \mathbf{E} \quad (22.11)$$

$$\mathbf{B} = \mu \mathbf{H} \quad (22.12)$$

and

$$\mathbf{J} = \sigma \mathbf{E} \quad (22.13)$$

where ε, μ and σ denote the dielectric permittivity, magnetic permeability and conductivity of the medium, respectively. For a charge free dielectric, we may write

$$\rho = 0 \tag{22.14}$$

and

$$\mathbf{J} = 0 \tag{22.15}$$

Further, in most dielectrics, we may assume

$$\mu \approx \mu_0 = 4\pi \times 10^{-7}\ \text{Ns}^2/\text{C}^2 \tag{22.16}$$

represents the magnetic permeability of vacuum. In many problems of interest, the propagation is in a dielectric medium and the above 'constitutive relations' are valid. If we use the above relations, Maxwell's equations simplify to

$$\nabla \cdot \mathbf{E} = 0 \tag{22.17}$$

$$\nabla \cdot \mathbf{H} = 0 \tag{22.18}$$

$$\nabla \times \mathbf{E} = -\mu_0 \frac{\partial \mathbf{H}}{\partial t} \tag{22.19}$$

and

$$\nabla \times \mathbf{H} = \varepsilon \frac{\partial \mathbf{E}}{\partial t} \tag{22.20}$$

22.3 Plane Waves in a Dielctric LO2

In the next section, we will (using the above equations) derive the wave equation; however, in this section we will show that plane wave solutions satisfy Maxwell's equations and study the properties of plane waves. For plane waves propagating in the direction of **k**, the electric and magnetic fields can be written in the form:

$$\mathbf{E} = \mathbf{E}_0 \exp\left[i(\mathbf{k}\cdot\mathbf{r} - \omega t)\right] \tag{22.21}$$

and

$$\mathbf{H} = \mathbf{H}_0 \exp\left[i(\mathbf{k}\cdot\mathbf{r} - \omega t)\right] \tag{22.22}$$

where $\mathbf{E}_0$ and $\mathbf{H}_0$ are space and time independent vectors; but may, in general, be complex. Now

$$\nabla \cdot \mathbf{E} = \frac{\partial E_x}{\partial x} + \frac{\partial E_y}{\partial y} + \frac{\partial E_z}{\partial z} \tag{22.23}$$

and since, $E_x = E_{0x} \exp\left[i(\mathbf{k}\cdot\mathbf{r} - \omega t)\right]$

$$= E_{0x} \exp\left[i(k_x x + k_y y + k_z z - \omega t)\right]$$

we get $\dfrac{\partial E_x}{\partial x} = ik_x E_{0x} \exp\left[i(k_x x + k_y y + k_z z - \omega t)\right]$

Thus the equation $\nabla \cdot \mathbf{E} = 0$ would give us

$$i(k_x E_{0x} + k_y E_{0y} + k_z E_{0z}) \exp\left[i(\mathbf{k}\cdot\mathbf{r} - \omega t)\right] = 0$$

implying

$$\mathbf{k}\cdot\mathbf{E} = 0 \tag{22.24}$$

Similarly the equation $\nabla \cdot \mathbf{H} = 0$ would give us

$$\mathbf{k}\cdot\mathbf{H} = 0 \tag{22.25}$$

The above two equations tell us that **E** and **H** are at right angles to **k**, thus the waves are transverse in nature. Now, using Eq. (22.19)

$$(\nabla \times \mathbf{E})_x = \left(\frac{\partial E_z}{\partial y} - \frac{\partial E_y}{\partial z}\right)$$

$$= i(k_y E_{0z} - k_z E_{0y}) \exp\left[i(\mathbf{k}\cdot\mathbf{r} - \omega t)\right] = i(\mathbf{k}\times\mathbf{E})_x$$

Thus the x-component of Eq. (22.19) will give us

$$i(\mathbf{k}\times\mathbf{E})_x = i\omega\mu_0 H_x \Rightarrow H_x = \frac{(\mathbf{k}\times\mathbf{E})_x}{\omega} \tag{22.26}$$

Similarly we can write for the y and z components of Eq. (22.19) and obtain the vector equation

$$\mathbf{H} = \frac{\mathbf{k}\times\mathbf{E}}{\omega\mu} \tag{22.27}$$

Similarly, Eq. (22.20) would give us

$$\mathbf{E} = \frac{\mathbf{H}\times\mathbf{k}}{\omega\varepsilon} \tag{22.28}$$

showing that **k**, **E** and **H** are at right angles to each other (see Fig. 22.1). From the above two equations one readily gets

$$H_0 = \frac{k}{\omega\mu} E_0 \tag{22.29}$$

and

$$E_0 = \frac{k}{\omega\varepsilon} H_0 \tag{22.30}$$

If we multiply the above two equations, we would get

$$\frac{k^2}{\omega^2 \varepsilon\mu} = 1 \Rightarrow k = \omega\sqrt{\varepsilon\mu} \tag{22.31}$$

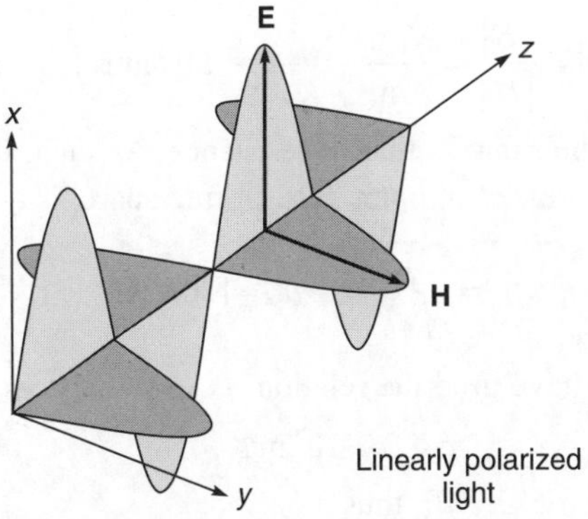

Figure 22.1

The arrows represent the direction and magnitude of the **E** and **H** vectors (at a particular instant of time) for a plane polarized wave. The electric vectors always lie in the *x-z* plane and the magnetic vectors lie in the *y-z* plane.

Thus the speed of propagation of the electromagnetic wave is given by

$$v = \frac{\omega}{k} = \frac{1}{\sqrt{\varepsilon\mu}} \tag{22.32}$$

In free-space

$$\varepsilon = \varepsilon_0 = 8.8542... \times 10^{-12}\ \text{C}^2\ \text{N}^{-1}\ \text{m}^{-2} \tag{22.33}$$

and $\quad v = c = \dfrac{1}{\sqrt{\varepsilon_0\mu_0}}$

$$= \frac{1}{\sqrt{8.8542...\times 10^{-12} \times 4\pi \times 10^{-7}}} = 2.99792458 \times 10^8\ \text{m/s} \tag{22.34}$$

is the velocity of the electromagnetic wave in vacuum. We must mention that the speed of light in vacuum, usually denoted by c, is an universal physical constant and its value is exactly 299792458 meters per second; thus

$$\varepsilon_0 = \frac{1}{\mu_0 c^2} = 8.8542... \times 10^{-12}\ \text{C}^2\ \text{N}^{-1}\ \text{m}^{-2} \tag{22.35}$$

Thus the plane wave solutions given by Eqs. (22.21) and (22.22) do indeed satisfy Maxwell's equations with **k**, **E** and **H** are at right angles to each other and related through Eqs. (22.27)–(22.29). We rewrite Eq. (22.27) as

$$\mathbf{H} = \frac{\mathbf{k} \times \mathbf{E}}{\omega\mu} = \frac{1}{\eta}\left(\hat{\mathbf{k}} \times \mathbf{E}\right) \tag{22.36}$$

where $\hat{\mathbf{k}}$ is the unit vector along the direction of **k**, and

$$\eta = \frac{\omega\mu}{k} = \frac{\omega\mu}{\omega\sqrt{\varepsilon\mu}}$$

Thus, $\quad \eta = \sqrt{\dfrac{\mu}{\varepsilon}} \qquad (22.37)$

is known as the "intrinsic impedance" of the medium. The dimension of η will be given by

$$[\eta] = \frac{[E]}{[H]} = \frac{\text{V/m}}{\text{A/m}} = \text{V/A} = \ \Omega(\text{ohms}) \tag{22.38}$$

which is the same as that of resistance. As such, it is almost always expressed in ohms (Ω). In free space

$$\eta = \eta_0 = \sqrt{\frac{\mu_0}{\varepsilon_0}} = c\,\mu_0 \approx 120\pi\ \Omega \tag{22.39}$$

where we have used the relation

$$c \approx 3 \times 10^8\ \text{m/s} \tag{22.40}$$

In a dielectric $\mu \approx \mu_0$; thus

$$\frac{\eta}{\eta_0} = \sqrt{\frac{\varepsilon_0}{\varepsilon}} = \frac{1}{n} \quad \Rightarrow \eta = \frac{\eta_0}{n} = \frac{120\pi}{n}\ \Omega \tag{22.41}$$

where $\quad n = \sqrt{\dfrac{\varepsilon}{\varepsilon_0}} \qquad (22.42)$

is the refractive index of the dielectric. Thus if we write

$$\mathbf{H} = \mathbf{H}_0 \exp\left[i(\mathbf{k}.\mathbf{r}\text{-}\omega t)\right] \tag{22.43}$$

then $\quad H_0 = \dfrac{1}{\eta}E_0 \qquad (22.44)$

If we assume propagation along the z-axis and the electric vector to be along the x-axis, then the magnetic vector will be along the y-axis so that we may write

$$\mathbf{E} = \hat{\mathbf{x}}\,E_0 e^{i(kz-\omega t)} \tag{22.45}$$

$$\mathbf{H} = \hat{\mathbf{y}}\,H_0 e^{i(kz-\omega t)} \tag{22.46}$$

The actual electric fields are the real part of the exponentials appearing on the RHS of Eqs. (22.45) and (22.46):

$$\mathbf{E} = \hat{\mathbf{x}}\,E_0 \cos(kz - \omega t) \tag{22.47}$$

$$\mathbf{H} = \hat{\mathbf{y}}\,H_0 \cos(kz - \omega t) \tag{22.48}$$

with H_0 related to E_0 through Eq. (22.44); we have assumed E_0 and H_0 to be real. The plane wave as represented by Eq. (22.45) [or by Eq. (22.47)] is said to be linearly polarized (or, x-polarized) because the electric vector oscillates along the x-axis and, the magnetic vector oscillates along the y-axis [see Fig. 22.1]. Similarly, for a y-polarized wave, the electric vector will oscillate along the y-axis and the magnetic vector will oscillate along the x-axis. We may also have superposition of two independent plane waves [we are considering the real part of the exponentials appearing on the RHS of Eqs. (22.45) and (22.46)]:

$$\mathbf{E}_1 = \hat{\mathbf{x}}\,E_0 \cos(kz - \omega t) \tag{22.49}$$

$$\mathbf{H}_1 = \hat{\mathbf{y}}\,H_0 \cos(kz - \omega t) \tag{22.50}$$

and

$$\mathbf{E}_2 = \hat{\mathbf{y}}\,E_0 \cos\left(kz - \omega t + \frac{\pi}{2}\right) = -\hat{\mathbf{y}}\,E_0 \sin(kz - \omega t) \tag{22.51}$$

$$\mathbf{H}_2 = -\hat{\mathbf{x}}\,\mathbf{H}_0 \cos\left(kz - \omega t + \frac{\pi}{2}\right) = +\hat{\mathbf{x}}\,H_0 \sin(kz - \omega t) \tag{22.52}$$

The first wave is x-polarized and the second wave is y-polarized and there is a phase difference of $\pi/2$. The superposition of these two waves will give us the resultant

$$\mathbf{E} = \mathbf{E}_1 + \mathbf{E}_2 = E_0\left[\hat{\mathbf{x}}\cos(kz - \omega t) - \hat{\mathbf{y}}\,E_0 \sin(kz - \omega t)\right] \tag{22.53}$$

and

$$\mathbf{H} = \mathbf{H}_1 + \mathbf{H}_2 = H_0\left[\hat{\mathbf{y}}\cos(kz - \omega t) + \hat{\mathbf{x}}\sin(kz - \omega t)\right] \tag{22.54}$$

Now, at $z = 0$

$$E_x = E_0 \cos\omega t \quad \text{and} \quad E_y = E_0 \sin\omega t \tag{22.55}$$

and the tip of the electric vector will rotate (on the circumference of a circle) in the clockwise direction as shown

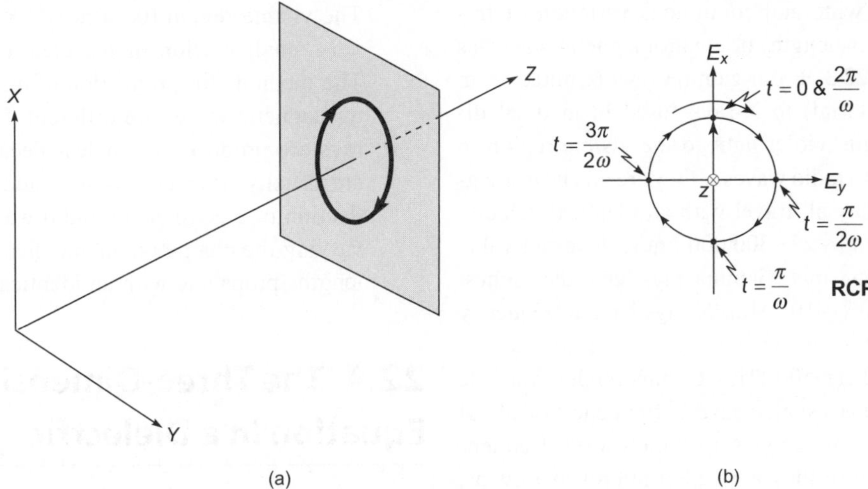

Figure 22.2
For a right circularly polarized wave (usually abbreviated as RCP), if we look in the direction of the propagation of the wave, the electric vector rotates in a clockwise direction on the circumference of a circle.

in Fig. 22.2; this will represent a right-circularly polarized (usually abbreviated as RCP) wave—see also Sec. 21.4. Also, at $z = 0$

$$H_x = -H_0 \sin \omega t \quad \text{and} \quad H_y = +H_0 \cos \omega t$$

and the tip of the **H** vector will also rotate (on the circumference of a circle) in the clockwise direction and at all times the **E** vector will be at right angle to the **H** vector.

From the above equations we may draw the following inferences for plane waves propagating in a dielectric:

(i) The vectors **E** and **H** are at right angles to each other and also to the direction of propagation implying that the waves are transverse. Thus, if the direction of propagation is along the z-axis and if **E** is assumed to point in the x-direction then **H** will point in the y-direction. The plane wave as represented by Eq. (22.45) is said to be x-polarized because the electric vector is always along the x-axis.

(ii) In a charge-free dielectric, η is a real number, and the electric and magnetic vectors are in phase; thus if at any instant, **E** is zero then **H** is also zero, similarly when **E** attains its maximum value, **H** also attains its maximum value, etc.

(iii) For a RCP wave, both the electric (and the magnetic) vectors rotate on the circumference of a circle (in the clockwise direction) and at each instant, they are orthogonal to each other—similarly, for a LCP wave.

(iv) The refractive index (n) of a dielectric (characterized by dielectric permittivity ε and magnetic permeability (μ_0) would be given by

$$n = \frac{c}{v} = \sqrt{\frac{\varepsilon\mu_0}{\varepsilon_0\mu_0}} = \sqrt{\frac{\varepsilon}{\varepsilon_0}} = \sqrt{\kappa} \tag{22.56}$$

where $\kappa(=\varepsilon/\varepsilon_0)$ is known as the **dielectric constant** of the medium.

(v) The electric and magnetic waves are interdependent; neither can exist without the other. Physically, an electric field varying in time produces a magnetic field varying in space and time; this changing magnetic field produces an electric field varying in space and time, and so on. This mutual generation of electric and magnetic fields results in the propagation of the electromagnetic wave.

(vi) As mentioned in Sec. 1.5,

the displacement associated with the propagating light wave is the electric field which oscillates in time with a certain frequency.

We could have equally well chosen the magnetic field as the displacement associated with the propagating electromagnetic wave because associated with a time varying electric field there is always a time varying magnetic field.

(vii) Since Maxwell's equations are linear in **E** and **H**, so, if ($\mathbf{E}_1$, $\mathbf{H}_1$) and ($\mathbf{E}_2$, $\mathbf{H}_2$) are two independent solutions of the Maxwell's equations, then ($\mathbf{E}_1 + \mathbf{E}_2$, $\mathbf{H}_1 + \mathbf{H}_2$) will also be a solution of the Maxwell's equations. This is the superposition principle according to which the resultant displacement produced by two independent disturbances is the vector sum of the displacements produced by the disturbances independently*.

* Thus the superposition principle is a consequence of the linearity of the Maxwell's equations. If, for example, the field associated with the electromagnetic wave is so high that the dielectric permittivity ε depends on **E** itself, then Maxwell's equations will become nonlinear and superposition principle will not remain valid. Indeed, when we discuss any nonlinear phenomenon, the superposition principle does not hold true.

(viii) There exists a wide and continuous variation of frequency (and wavelength) of electromagnetic waves as shown in Fig. 22.3. From gamma rays (emitted from radioactive material) to X-rays (used in medical diagnostics), to ultraviolet light to the visible region to infrared beams to radio waves—they are all electromagnetic waves. They all travel with an identical velocity in vacuum given by $c \approx 300{,}000$ km/s; the exact value is $c = 299792458$ m/s. Gamma rays have the highest frequency ($\approx 10^{20} - 10^{24}$ Hz), X-rays have a frequency of about 10^{18} Hz and visible light has frequency of about 5×10^{14} Hz (= 500 THz). Commercially available microwave ovens usually have a frequency of about 2.45 GHz – it corresponds to "microwave frequencies" and therefore they are called microwave ovens. Electromagnetic radiation at these frequencies quickly heat up water, fat and other food substances. The frequency band allocated for cell phones can be from 1 to 2 GHz. The radio waves correspond to wavelengths in the range 10–1000 m whereas the wavelengths of X-rays are in the region of Angstroms (1 Å = 10^{-10} m).

The visible region (0.4 μm < λ < 0.7 μm) occupies a very small portion of the electromagnetic spectrum. The methods for production of different kinds of electromagnetic waves are different. For example, gamma rays are produced in nuclear decay processes; X-rays are usually produced by the sudden stopping and deflection of electrons and radio waves are produced by varying the charge on an antenna. However, all wavelengths propagate with an identical speed in vacuum.

22.4 The Three-Dimensional Wave Equation in a Dielectric

LO3

In Sec. 22.2 we had shown that plane wave solutions indeed satisfy the above equations. In this section we will show that the wave equation can be derived from the above equations.

If we take the curl of Eq. (22.19), we would obtain

$$\text{curl curl } \mathbf{E} = -\mu \frac{\partial}{\partial t} \text{curl} \mathbf{H} = -\varepsilon\mu \frac{\partial^2 \mathbf{E}}{\partial t^2} \tag{22.57}$$

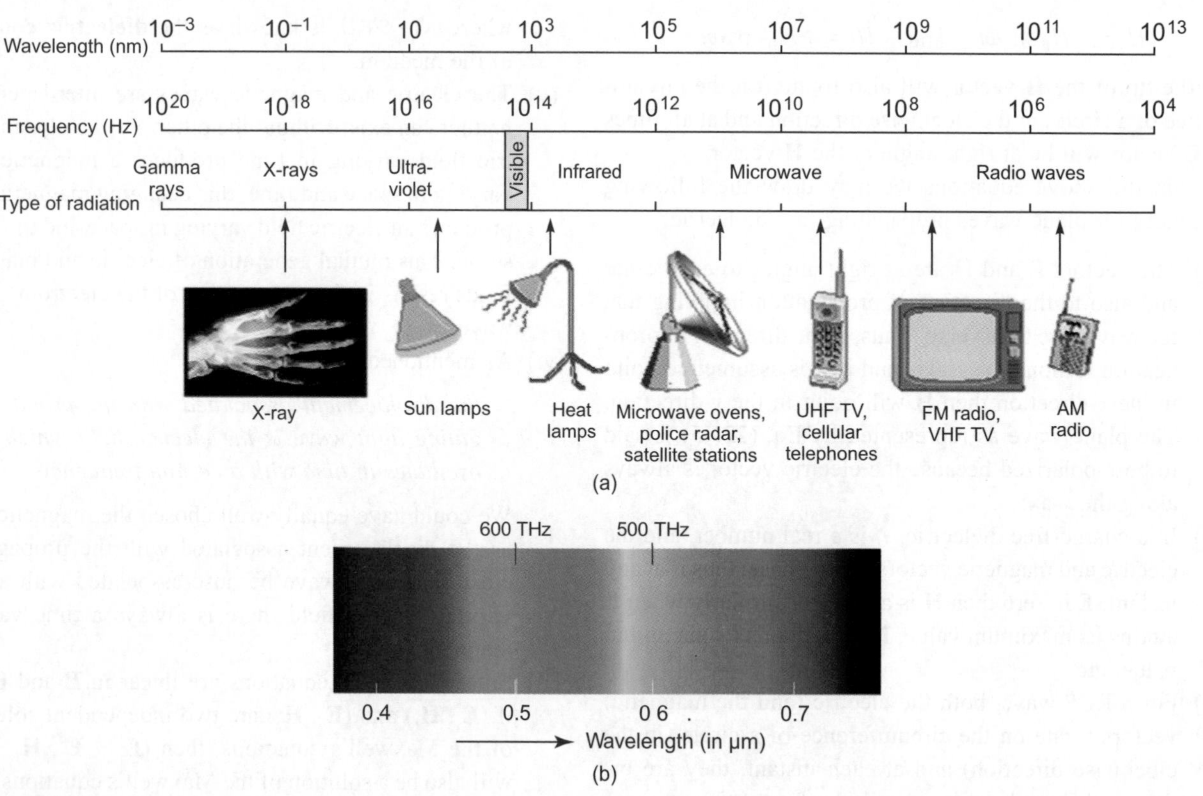

Figure 22.3

(a) The electromagnetic spectrum; gamma rays have the highest frequency (and the shortest wavelength) and radio waves have the lowest frequency (and the longest wavelength). All wavelengths travel with an identical velocity in vacuum. *Photograph courtesy: McGraw Hill Digital Access Library.* **(b)** Wavelengths associated with the visible portion of the electromagnetic spectrum (which is sensitive to the retina of our eye) ranges from about 0.4 μm (blue region of the spectrum) to about 0.7 μm (red region of the spectrum), the corresponding frequencies are about 750 THz and 420 THz; 1 THz = 10^{12} Hz. A wavelength of 0.5 μm corresponding to the bluish green region of the spectrum has a frequency of 600 THz and a wavelength of 0.6 μm (corresponding to the reddish yellow green region of the spectrum) has a frequency of 500 THz.

where we have used Eq. (22.20). Now, the operator $\nabla^2\mathbf{E}$ is *defined* by the following equation;

$$\nabla^2\mathbf{E} \equiv \text{grad}\,\text{div}\,\mathbf{E} - \text{curl}\,\text{curl}\,\mathbf{E} \qquad \textbf{(22.58)}$$

Using Cartesian coordinates, one can easily show that

$$(\nabla^2\mathbf{E})_x = \text{div grad}\,E_x = \frac{\partial^2 E_x}{\partial x^2} + \frac{\partial^2 E_x}{\partial y^2} + \frac{\partial^2 E_x}{\partial z^2}$$

that is, a Cartesian component of $\nabla^2\mathbf{E}$ is the div grad of the Cartesian component*. Thus, using

$$\text{curl}\,\text{curl}\,\mathbf{E} = \text{grad}\,\text{div}\,\mathbf{E} - \nabla^2\mathbf{E}$$

we obtain

$$\text{grad}\,\text{div}\,\mathbf{E} - \nabla^2\mathbf{E} = -\varepsilon\mu\frac{\partial^2\mathbf{E}}{\partial t^2} \qquad \textbf{(22.59)}$$

or

$$\nabla^2\mathbf{E} = \varepsilon\mu\frac{\partial^2\mathbf{E}}{\partial t^2} \qquad \textbf{(22.60)}$$

where we have used the equation div $\mathbf{E} = 0$ [see Eq. (22.17)]. Equation (22.60) is known as the **three-dimensional wave** equation and each Cartesian component of **E** satisfies the scalar wave equation [see Sec. 9.9]:

$$\nabla^2\psi = \varepsilon\mu\frac{\partial^2\psi}{\partial t^2} \qquad \textbf{(22.61)}$$

The velocity of propagation (v) of the wave is simply given by

$$v = \frac{1}{\sqrt{\varepsilon\mu}} \qquad \textbf{(22.62)}$$

In a similar manner, one can derive the wave equation satisfied by **H**

$$\nabla^2\mathbf{H} = \varepsilon\mu\frac{\partial^2\mathbf{H}}{\partial t^2} \qquad \textbf{(22.63)}$$

It can be easily seen that the solutions expressed by Eqs. (22.45) and (22.46) [or, Eqs. (22.47) and (22.48)] indeed satisfy Eqs. (22.60) and (22.63) provided

$$\frac{\omega}{k} = \frac{1}{\sqrt{\varepsilon\mu}} \qquad \textbf{(22.64)}$$

which is the speed of propagation of the electromagnetic wave. Around 1860, Maxwell derived the wave equation, *predicted* the existence of electromagnetic waves and calculated their speed to be about 3.1074×10^8 m/s; this he found to be very close to the velocity of light which was, at that time, known to be 3.14858×10^8 m/s (as measured by Fizeau in 1849). Just based on the closeness of these two numbers and with *'faith in the rationality of nature'*, he propounded the electromagnetic theory of light and predicted that light must be an electromagnetic wave. In the words of Maxwell himself, the speed of electromagnetic waves

> "... calculated from the electromagnetic measurements of Kohlrausch and Weber, agrees so exactly with the velocity of light calculated from the experiments of M. Fizeau, that we can scarcely avoid the inference that *light consists in the transverse undulations of the same medium which is the cause of electric and magnetic phenomena.*"

We should also mention here that the physical laws described by Eqs. (22.7), (22.8) and (22.9) were known before Maxwell; he had only introduced the term $\frac{\partial \mathbf{D}}{\partial t}$ (which is the concept of displacement current) in Eq. (22.10) and it is the presence of this term which leads to the prediction of electromagnetic waves.

It was only in 1888, that Heinrich Hertz carried out experiments which could produce and detect electromagnetic waves of frequencies smaller than those of light. Hertz showed that the velocity of electromagnetic waves that he generated were the same as that of light (see Sections 1.4 and 12.2). In 1931 (during the birth centenary celebration of Maxwell), Max Planck had said

> "(Maxwell's equations) ... *remain for all time one of the greatest triumphs of human intellectual endeavor*".

Albert Einstein had said "(The work of Maxwell was) ... *the most profound and the most fruitful that physics has experienced since the time of Newton*".

22.5 The Poynting Vector

LO4

We rewrite Eqs. (22.9) and (22.10)

$$\text{curl}\,\mathbf{E} = -\frac{\partial \mathbf{B}}{\partial t} \qquad \textbf{(22.65)}$$

and

$$\text{curl}\,\mathbf{H} = \frac{\partial \mathbf{D}}{\partial t} + \mathbf{J} \qquad \textbf{(22.66)}$$

Now,

$$\text{div}(\mathbf{E}\times\mathbf{H}) = \mathbf{H}\cdot\text{curl}\,\mathbf{E} - \mathbf{E}\cdot\text{curl}\,\mathbf{H} \qquad \textbf{(22.67)}$$

Thus,

$$\text{div}(\mathbf{E}\times\mathbf{H}) = -\mathbf{H}\cdot\frac{\partial \mathbf{B}}{\partial t} - \mathbf{J}\cdot\mathbf{E} - \mathbf{E}\cdot\frac{\partial \mathbf{D}}{\partial t} \qquad \textbf{(22.68)}$$

* However, $(\nabla^2\mathbf{E})_r \neq \text{div}\,(\text{grad}\,E_r)$

For a linear material,

$$\mathbf{H}\cdot\frac{\partial \mathbf{B}}{\partial t}+\mathbf{E}\cdot\frac{\partial \mathbf{D}}{\partial t}=\mu\mathbf{H}\cdot\frac{\partial \mathbf{H}}{\partial t}+\varepsilon\mathbf{E}\cdot\frac{\partial \mathbf{E}}{\partial t}$$

$$=\frac{1}{2}\mu\frac{\partial}{\partial t}(\mathbf{H}\cdot\mathbf{H})+\frac{1}{2}\varepsilon\frac{\partial}{\partial t}(\mathbf{E}\cdot\mathbf{E})=\frac{1}{2}\frac{\partial}{\partial t}(\mathbf{B}\cdot\mathbf{H}+\mathbf{D}\cdot\mathbf{E})$$

Thus, Eq. (22.68) can be rewritten in the form

$$\text{div}\,\mathbf{S}+\frac{\partial u}{\partial t}=-\mathbf{J}\cdot\mathbf{E} \tag{22.69}$$

where

$$\mathbf{S}\equiv\mathbf{E}\times\mathbf{H} \tag{22.70}$$

is known as the Poynting vector and*

$$u=\frac{1}{2}\mathbf{B}\cdot\mathbf{H}+\frac{1}{2}\mathbf{D}\cdot\mathbf{E} \tag{22.71}$$

Equation (22.69) resembles the equation of continuity and for a physical interpretation we note that if a charge q (moving with velocity $\mathbf{v}$) is acted on by an electromagnetic field then the work done by the field in moving it through a distance $d\mathbf{s}$ would be $\mathbf{F}\cdot d\mathbf{s}$; thus the work done per unit time would be

$$\mathbf{F}\cdot\frac{d\mathbf{s}}{dt}=\mathbf{F}\cdot\mathbf{v}=[q\mathbf{E}+q\mathbf{v}\times\mathbf{B}]\cdot\mathbf{v}=q\mathbf{E}\cdot\mathbf{v} \tag{22.72}$$

If there are N charged particles per unit volume, each carrying a charge q, then the work done per unit volume per unit time would be

$$Nq\mathbf{v}\cdot\mathbf{E}=\mathbf{J}\cdot\mathbf{E} \tag{22.73}$$

where $\mathbf{J}$ represents the current density. The energy appears in the form of kinetic (or heat) energy of the charged particles. Thus the term $\mathbf{J}\cdot\mathbf{E}$ represents the familiar Joule loss and, therefore, the quantity $\mathbf{J}\cdot\mathbf{E}$ appearing on the R.H.S. of Eq. (22.69) would represent the rate at which energy is produced per unit volume per unit time. Consequently, we may interpret Eq. (22.69) as an equation of continuity** for energy with u representing the energy per unit volume. The quantities $\frac{1}{2}\mathbf{D}\cdot\mathbf{E}$ and $\frac{1}{2}\mathbf{B}\cdot\mathbf{H}$ represent the electrical and magnetic energies per unit volume respectively. Further, we may interpret $\mathbf{S}\cdot d\mathbf{a}$ as the electromagnetic energy crossing the area $d\mathbf{a}$ per unit time. For plane waves in a dielectric, we may write

$$\left.\begin{aligned}&\mathbf{E}=\hat{\mathbf{x}}E_0\cos(kz-\omega t)\\ \text{and}\quad&\mathbf{H}=\hat{\mathbf{y}}H_0\cos(kz-\omega t)=\hat{\mathbf{y}}\frac{E_0}{\eta}\cos(kz-\omega t)\end{aligned}\right\} \tag{22.74}$$

Thus, $\mathbf{S}=\mathbf{E}\times\mathbf{H}$

$$=\hat{\mathbf{z}}\frac{E_0^2}{\eta}\cos^2(kz-\omega t) \tag{22.75}$$

which implies that the energy flow is in the z-direction (which represents the direction of propagation of the wave) and that an amount of energy

$$\frac{E_0^2}{\eta}\cos^2(kz-\omega t)$$

crosses a unit area (perpendicular to the z-axis) per unit time. For optical beams $\omega\approx 10^{15}\ \text{s}^{-1}$ and $\cos^2$ term fluctuates with extreme rapidity, and any detector would record only an average value (see Section 13.6) to obtain

$$\langle\mathbf{S}\rangle=\hat{\mathbf{z}}\frac{1}{2\eta}E_0^2 \tag{22.76}$$

We must hasten to point out that $\mathbf{S}\cdot d\mathbf{a}$ does not *always* represent the rate of energy flow through the area $d\mathbf{a}$; for example, we may have static electric and magnetic fields where $\mathbf{E}\times\mathbf{H}$ is finite but we know that there is no energy flow. However, the integral

$$\oint\mathbf{S}\cdot d\mathbf{a} \tag{22.77}$$

over a closed surface rigorously represents the net energy flowing out of the surface. This follows immediately if we carry out a volume integral of Eq. (22.69) to give

$$\int\text{div}\,\mathbf{S}\,dV+\frac{\partial}{\partial t}\int u\,dV=-\int\mathbf{J}\cdot\mathbf{E}\,dV \tag{22.78}$$

or

$$-\frac{\partial}{\partial t}\int u\,dV=\oint\mathbf{S}\cdot d\mathbf{a}+\int\mathbf{J}\cdot\mathbf{E}\,dV \tag{22.79}$$

* Equation (22.71) is valid even for anisotropic media because in the principal axis system [see Sec. 22.12]

$$\mathbf{E}\cdot\frac{\partial\mathbf{D}}{\partial t}=\frac{1}{2}\varepsilon_x\frac{\partial E_x^2}{\partial t}+\frac{1}{2}\varepsilon_y\frac{\partial E_y^2}{\partial t}+\frac{1}{2}\varepsilon_z\frac{\partial E_z^2}{\partial t}$$

$$=\frac{1}{2}\frac{\partial}{\partial t}[D_xE_x+D_yE_y+D_zE_z]$$

** The equation of continuity is always written in the form

$$\text{div}\,\mathbf{J}+\frac{\partial\rho}{\partial t}=0$$

where ρ represents the charge density and $\mathbf{J}$ the current density, i.e. $\mathbf{J}\cdot d\mathbf{a}$ represents the amount of charge crossing the area $d\mathbf{a}$ per unit time.

where we have used the divergence theorem. The quantity on the LHS represents the rate of decrease of the total energy, this must be equal to the Joule loss plus the net flow out of the surface enclosing the volume.

22.5.1 The Oscillating Dipole

Consider an oscillating dipole in the z-direction:

$$\mathbf{p} = p_0 e^{-i\omega t}\hat{\mathbf{z}} \tag{22.80}$$

At large distances from such a dipole, the fields are of the form (see, for example, Ref. 22.5)

$$\mathbf{E} = -\left(\frac{\omega^2 p_0 \mu_0}{4\pi}\right)\sin\theta \frac{e^{i(kr-\omega t)}}{r}\hat{\boldsymbol{\theta}} \tag{22.81}$$

$$\mathbf{H} = -\left(\frac{1}{\eta_0}\frac{\omega^2 p_0 \mu_0}{4\pi}\right)\sin\theta \frac{e^{i(kr-\omega t)}}{r}\hat{\boldsymbol{\phi}} \tag{22.82}$$

(see Fig 22.4). In the above equations, $k = \omega\sqrt{\varepsilon_0 \mu_0}$ and other symbols have their usual meaning. Notice that the fields fall off as $1/r$ and that they are in phase. Because of the $\sin\theta$ factor in Eqs. (22.81) and (22.82), the dipole does not produce any field along the direction of oscillation [see also Sec. 21.2.4 and 21.8]. Thus*

$$\mathbf{S} = \mathbf{E} \times \mathbf{H}$$

$$= \frac{\omega^4 p_0^2 \mu_0}{16\pi^2 c}\sin^2\theta \frac{\cos^2(kr - \omega t)}{r^2}\hat{\mathbf{r}} \tag{22.83}$$

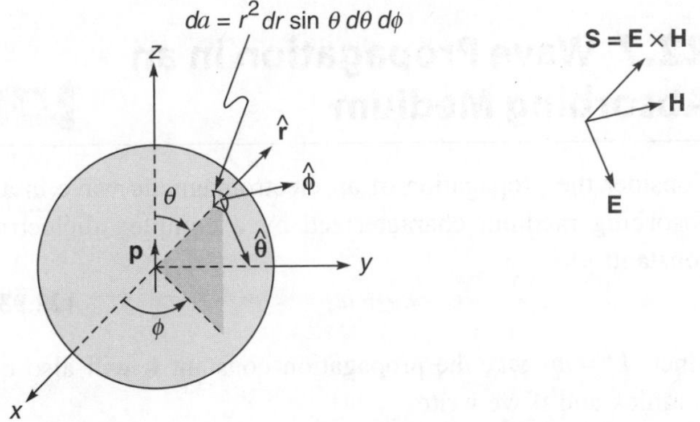

Figure 22.4
The direction of the electric and magnetic fields and of the Poynting vector from an oscillating dipole. In order to calculate the total energy radiated per unit time, we must integrate the Poynting vector over the surface of a sphere.

where we have used Eq. (22.39). Equation (22.83) shows that $\mathbf{S}$ falls off as $1/r^2$ as it indeed should be for a spherical wave (this is the inverse square law). If we integrate over a sphere of radius r, we would obtain

$$P = \oint \mathbf{S}\cdot d\mathbf{a} = r^2 \iint \mathbf{S}\cdot\hat{\mathbf{r}}\,\sin\theta\, d\theta\, d\phi$$

$$= \frac{\omega^4 p_0^2 \mu_0}{16\pi^2 c}\cos^2(kr - \omega t)\int_0^{\pi}\sin^2\theta \sin\theta\, d\theta \int_0^{2\pi} d\phi$$

$$= \frac{\omega^4 p_0^2 \mu_0}{6\pi c}\cos^2(kr - \omega t) \tag{22.84}$$

where P represents the instantaneous radiated power. Since the $\cos^2$ term fluctuates very rapidly, the average radiated power would be given by

$$\overline{P} = \frac{\omega^4 p_0^2 \mu_0}{12\pi c} \tag{22.85}$$

22.6 Energy Density and Intensity of an Electromagnetic Wave

LO5

In Sec. 22.4 we have shown that the energy/unit volume associated with a plane wave is given by

$$u = \frac{1}{2}\mathbf{D}\cdot\mathbf{E} + \frac{1}{2}\mathbf{B}\cdot\mathbf{H} = \frac{1}{2}\varepsilon E^2 + \frac{1}{2}\mu H^2 \tag{22.86}$$

For a linearly polarized plane wave, we may write

$$E_x = E_0\cos(kz - \omega t), E_y = 0, E_z = 0 \tag{22.87}$$

$$B_x = 0, H_y = H_0\cos(kz - \omega t), B_z = 0 \tag{22.88}$$

Thus

$$u = \frac{1}{2}\varepsilon E_0^2\cos^2(kz - \omega t) + \frac{1}{2}\mu H_0^2\cos^2(kz - \omega t)$$

Since

$$H_0 = \frac{E_0}{\eta} = \sqrt{\frac{\varepsilon}{\mu}}\, E_0, \text{ we get } \frac{1}{2}\mu H_0^2 = \frac{1}{2}\varepsilon E_0^2;$$

thus the energy associated with the electric field is equal to the energy associated with the magnetic field. If we take the time average of the $\cos^2$ terms, we would get

$$\langle u \rangle = \frac{1}{2}\varepsilon E_0^2 \tag{22.89}$$

Further, in order to obtain the intensity of the beam we must multiply $\langle u \rangle$ by the speed of propagation which will give us the energy crossing a unit area in unit time. Thus, the

* In order to calculate the Poynting vector we must take the products of the real parts of **E** and **H**. We may note that in the complex representation, if $\mathbf{E} = \mathbf{E}_1 + \mathbf{E}_2$ then

$$\text{Re}(\mathbf{E}) = \text{Re}(\mathbf{E}_1) + \text{Re}(\mathbf{E}_2)$$

However,

$$(\text{Re}\mathbf{E}_1) \times (\text{Re}\mathbf{E}_2) \neq \text{Re}(\mathbf{E}_1 \times \mathbf{E}_2)$$

Here Re(**E**) denotes the real part of **E**.

intensity is given by

$$I = \frac{1}{2}\varepsilon v E_0^2 = \frac{1}{2}\sqrt{\frac{\varepsilon}{\mu}}\, E_0^2 = \frac{1}{2\eta}\, E_0^2 \tag{22.90}$$

which is consistent with Eq. (22.76). In free space

$$I = \frac{1}{2\eta_0}\, E_0^2 = \frac{1}{240\pi}\, E_0^2$$

$$= \left(1.33\times 10^{-3}\ \text{W/V}^2\right) E_0^2$$

EXAMPLE 22.1 We consider a RCP (Right Circularly Polarized) wave propagating along the $+z$ direction in a dielectric; i.e., $\mathbf{k} = \hat{\mathbf{z}}k$

$$\mathbf{E} = \hat{\mathbf{x}}\, E_0 \cos(\mathbf{k.r} - \omega t) - \hat{\mathbf{y}}\, E_0 \sin(\mathbf{k.r} - \omega t) \tag{22.91}$$

Thus

$$\mathbf{H} = \frac{\mathbf{k}\times\mathbf{E}}{\omega\mu} = \frac{k}{\omega\mu}\hat{\mathbf{z}}\times\left[\hat{\mathbf{x}}\, E_0 \cos(\mathbf{k.r} - \omega t) - \hat{\mathbf{y}}\, E_0 \sin(\mathbf{k.r} - \omega t)\right]$$

$$= \frac{1}{\eta} E_0 \left[\hat{\mathbf{y}} \cos(kz - \omega t) + \hat{\mathbf{x}} \sin(kz - \omega t)\right]$$

Thus

$$\left.\begin{aligned} E_x &= E_0 \cos(kz - \omega t) \quad \text{and} \quad E_y = -E_0 \sin(kz - \omega t) \\ H_x &= \frac{1}{\eta} E_0 \sin(kz - \omega t) \text{ and } H_y = \frac{1}{\eta} E_0 \cos(kz - \omega t) \end{aligned}\right\} \tag{22.92}$$

If at $z = 0$ we plot the time variation of the electric or the magnetic field, we will find that the tip of the electric (or the magnetic) vector will rotate on the circumference of a circle in the clockwise direction. The Poynting vector will be given by

$$\mathbf{S} = \mathbf{E}\times\mathbf{H} = \frac{E_0^2}{\eta}\left[\hat{\mathbf{x}} \cos(kz - \omega t) - \hat{\mathbf{y}} \sin(kz - \omega t)\right]$$

$$\times\left[\hat{\mathbf{y}} \cos(kz - \omega t) + \hat{\mathbf{x}} \sin(kz - \omega t)\right]$$

$$= \frac{E_0^2}{\eta}\left[\cos^2(kz - \omega t) + \sin^2(kz - \omega t)\right]\hat{\mathbf{z}}$$

or,

$$\langle\mathbf{S}\rangle = \langle\mathbf{E}\times\mathbf{H}\rangle = \frac{E_0^2}{\eta}\hat{\mathbf{z}}$$

EXAMPLE 22.2 Consider an x-polarized plane electromagnetic wave propagating (in free space) along the z-direction. The corresponding electric field is assumed to be given by

$$\mathbf{E} = \hat{\mathbf{x}}\, 10\cos\left(2\times 10^7 z - \omega t\right)\ \text{V/m}$$

Thus $k = \frac{2\pi}{\lambda} = 2\times 10^7\ \text{m}^{-1} \Rightarrow \lambda \approx 3.14\times 10^{-7}\text{m}$

$$\omega = ck = 3\times 10^8 \times 2\times 10^7\ \text{rad/s}$$

$$= 6\times 10^{15}\ \text{rad/s},\ \nu = \frac{\omega}{2\pi} = 9.54\times 10^{14}\ \text{Hz}$$

$$\eta = \eta_0 = 120\pi\ \text{ohms}$$

$$\mathbf{H} = \frac{1}{\eta} E_0 \cos(kz - \omega t)\,\hat{\mathbf{y}}$$

$$\approx 2.65\times 10^{-2} \cos\left(2\times 10^7 z - 6\times 10^{15} t\right)\hat{\mathbf{y}}\ \ \text{A/m}$$

$$\langle\mathbf{S}\rangle = \frac{1}{2\eta} E_0^2\,\hat{\mathbf{z}} \approx 0.13\,\hat{\mathbf{z}}\ \ \text{W/m}^2$$

EXAMPLE 22.3 For a 100 W lamp, the intensity at a distance of 10 m would be

$$I = \frac{100}{4\pi(10)^2} \approx 7.96\times 10^{-2}\ \text{W/m}^2$$

where we have assumed light to spread out uniformly in all directions. Thus

$$E_0 = \left[\frac{7.96\times 10^{-2}}{1.33\times 10^{-3}}\right]^{1/2} \approx 7.74\ \text{V/m}$$

EXAMPLE 22.4 Since a laser beam is almost perfectly parallel, it can be focused by a lens to a cross–sectional area of about 10^{-10} m^2 (see Sec. 17.4.1). Thus for a 10^5 watt laser beam, the intensity at the focal plane would be

$$I = \frac{10^5}{10^{-10}} = 10^{15}\ \ \text{W/m}^2$$

Thus

$$E_0 = \left[\frac{10^{15}}{1.33\times 10^{-3}}\right]^{1/2} \approx 0.87\times 10^9\ \ \text{V/m}$$

Such high electric fields can cause extreme high temperatures which may result in the burning of a target.

22.7 Wave Propagation in an Absorbing Medium

LO6

Consider the propagation of an electromagnetic wave in an absorbing medium characterized by a complex dielectric constant:

$$\varepsilon = \varepsilon_r + i\varepsilon_i \tag{22.93}$$

Since $k^2 = \omega^2\, \varepsilon\mu$, the propagation constant **k** will also be complex and if we write

$$k = \beta + i\gamma \tag{22.94}$$

we would obtain

$$\beta^2 - \gamma^2 = \omega^2 \varepsilon_r \mu \tag{22.95}$$

$$2\beta\gamma = \omega^2 \varepsilon_i \mu \tag{22.96}$$

Substituting for γ from Eq. (22.96) in Eq. (22.95) we get

$$\beta^4 - \omega^2 \varepsilon_r \mu\, \beta^2 - \frac{1}{4}\omega^4 \mu^2\, \varepsilon_i^2 = 0 \tag{22.97}$$

Simple manipulations will give

$$\beta = \omega\sqrt{\frac{\mu\varepsilon_r}{2}}\left[\sqrt{1+g^2}+1\right]^{1/2} \tag{22.98}$$

where $$g = \frac{\varepsilon_i}{\varepsilon_r} \tag{22.99}$$

and we have used the fact that β by definition is real. Further,

$$\gamma = \frac{\omega^2\varepsilon_i\mu}{2\beta} = \omega\sqrt{\frac{\mu\varepsilon_r}{2}}\left[\sqrt{1+g^2}-1\right]^{1/2} \tag{22.100}$$

For an x-polarized electromagnetic wave propagating in the z-direction, we may write:

$$\mathbf{E} = E_0\, e^{i(kz-\omega t)}\,\hat{\mathbf{x}} = E_0\, e^{-\gamma z}\, e^{i(\beta z-\omega t)}\,\hat{\mathbf{x}}$$

The corresponding magnetic field can be obtained from the equation

$$\nabla\times\mathbf{E} = -\frac{\partial\mathbf{B}}{\partial t} = +\,i\omega\mu\,\mathbf{H} \tag{22.101}$$

Thus

$$\mathbf{H} = \frac{1}{\eta}E_0\, e^{i(kz-\omega t)}\,\hat{\mathbf{y}} = \frac{1}{\eta}E_0\, e^{-\gamma z}\, e^{i(\beta z-\omega t)}\,\hat{\mathbf{y}} \tag{22.102}$$

Now $$\eta = \sqrt{\frac{\mu}{\varepsilon}} = \sqrt{\frac{\mu}{\varepsilon_r + i\varepsilon_i}} = \sqrt{\frac{\mu}{\varepsilon_r(1+ig)}}$$

We write $\eta = |\eta|e^{-i\theta} \Rightarrow |\eta|^2 e^{-2i\theta} = \dfrac{\mu}{\varepsilon_r\left(1+g^2\right)}(1-ig)$

Thus $$|\eta| = \sqrt{\frac{\mu}{\varepsilon_r}}\left(1+g^2\right)^{-1/4} \tag{22.103}$$

and $$\tan 2\theta = g = \frac{\varepsilon_i}{\varepsilon_r};\ 0<\theta<\frac{\pi}{4} \tag{22.104}$$

In order to calculate the Poynting vector, we must calculate the actual fields which will be given by

$$\mathbf{E} = E_0\, e^{-\gamma z}\cos(\beta z-\omega t)\,\hat{\mathbf{x}} \tag{22.105}$$

and $$\mathbf{H} = \frac{E_0}{|\eta|}\, e^{-\gamma z}\cos(\beta z-\omega t+\theta)\,\hat{\mathbf{y}} \tag{22.106}$$

Thus $\langle\mathbf{S}\rangle = \langle\mathbf{E}\times\mathbf{H}\rangle$

$$= \frac{E_0^2}{2|\eta|}\, e^{-2\gamma z}\left\langle 2\cos(\beta z-\omega t)\cos(\beta z-\omega t+\theta)\right\rangle\hat{\mathbf{z}}$$

$$= \frac{E_0^2}{2|\eta|}\, e^{-2\gamma z}\cos\theta\,\hat{\mathbf{z}} \tag{22.107}$$

where we have used the fact that

$$\left\langle\cos(2\beta z-2\omega t+\theta)\right\rangle = 0$$

22.8 Propagation in a Conducting Medium

LO7

In Sec. 22.3 we had assumed $\mathbf{J} = 0$. For a conducting medium

$$\mathbf{J} = \sigma\mathbf{E} \tag{22.108}$$

where σ represents the conductivity of the medium. Thus, Maxwell's equations become

$$\text{div }\mathbf{E} = 0 \tag{22.109}$$

$$\text{div }\mathbf{H} = 0 \tag{22.110}$$

$$\text{curl }\mathbf{E} = -\mu\frac{\partial\mathbf{H}}{\partial t} \tag{22.111}$$

$$\text{curl }\mathbf{H} = \sigma\mathbf{E} + \varepsilon\frac{\partial\mathbf{E}}{\partial t} \tag{22.112}$$

Taking the curl of Eq. (22.111), we get

$$\text{curl curl }\mathbf{E} = -\mu\frac{\partial}{\partial t}\text{curl }\mathbf{H}$$

or

$$\text{grad div }\mathbf{E} - \nabla^2\mathbf{E} = -\mu\sigma\frac{\partial\mathbf{E}}{\partial t} - \mu\varepsilon\frac{\partial^2\mathbf{E}}{\partial t^2}$$

Using Eq. (22.109), we get

$$\nabla^2\mathbf{E} - \mu\sigma\frac{\partial\mathbf{E}}{\partial t} - \mu\varepsilon\frac{\partial^2\mathbf{E}}{\partial t^2} = 0 \tag{22.113}$$

which is the wave equation for a conducting medium. For a plane wave of the type

$$\mathbf{E} = \mathbf{E}_0\exp\left[i(kz-\omega t)\right] \tag{22.114}$$

we obtain

$$k^2 = \omega^2\varepsilon\mu + i\omega\mu\sigma = \omega^2\mu\varepsilon(1+ig) \tag{22.115}$$

where

$$g = \frac{\sigma}{\omega\varepsilon} \tag{22.116}$$

Thus the entire analysis in Sec. 22.7 will be valid with ε_r replaced by ε with the value g given by Eq. (22.116) to obtain:

$$\beta = \omega\sqrt{\frac{\mu\varepsilon}{2}}\left[\sqrt{1+\left(\frac{\sigma}{\omega\varepsilon}\right)^2}+1\right]^{1/2} \tag{22.117}$$

and $$\gamma = \omega\sqrt{\frac{\mu\varepsilon}{2}}\left[\sqrt{1+\left(\frac{\sigma}{\omega\varepsilon}\right)^2}-1\right]^{1/2} \tag{22.118}$$

Once again,

$$\mathbf{E} = E_0\, e^{-\gamma z}\cos(\beta z-\omega t)\,\hat{\mathbf{x}} \tag{22.119}$$

which represents an attenuated wave. The attenuation is due to the Joule-loss. For a good conductor

$$g = \frac{\sigma}{\omega\varepsilon} >> 1 \tag{22.120}$$

and one obtains

$$\beta \approx \gamma \approx \omega\sqrt{\frac{\mu\varepsilon g}{2}} = \left(\frac{\omega\mu\sigma}{2}\right)^{1/2} \quad \textbf{(22.121)}$$

The corresponding expressions for an insulator are given in Problem 22.12. Indeed if $\frac{\sigma}{\omega\varepsilon} << 1$ (say $\lesssim 0.01$), the medium can be classified as a dielectric and if $\frac{\sigma}{\omega\varepsilon} >> 1$ (say $\gtrsim 100$), the medium can be classified as a conductor. For

$$0.01 \lesssim \frac{\sigma}{\omega\varepsilon} \lesssim 100$$

the medium is said to be a quasi-conductor. Thus, depending on the frequency, a particular material can behave as a dielectric or as a conductor. From Eq. (22.119), it can be easily seen that the field decreases by a factor e in traversing a distance

$$\delta = \frac{1}{\gamma} \quad \textbf{(22.122)}$$

which is known as the penetration depth, or skin depth.

Example 22.5

For fresh water, there is considerable variation in the measured values of the conductivity and dielectric constant. At low frequencies, we assume

$$\frac{\varepsilon}{\varepsilon_0} \approx 80;\ \mu \approx \mu_0 \text{ and } \sigma \approx 10^{-3} \text{ mhos/m}$$

$$\Rightarrow \frac{\sigma}{\omega\varepsilon} = \frac{10^{-3}}{\omega \times 80 \times 8.854 \times 10^{-12}} \approx \frac{1.4 \times 10^6}{\omega}$$

Thus at 10 Hz ($\omega = 2\pi \times 10\ \text{s}^{-1}$)

$$\frac{\sigma}{\omega\varepsilon} \approx \frac{1.4\times 10^6}{20\pi} \approx 2\times 10^4 \gg 1$$

At 10 GHz $\left(\omega = 2\pi \times 10^{10}\ \text{s}^{-1}\right)$, $\frac{\sigma}{\omega\varepsilon} \approx 2\times 10^{-5} << 1$

(Both ε and σ can be assumed to be constants at low frequencies). Thus, fresh water behaves as a good conductor for $\nu \lesssim 10^3$ sec^{-1} and as a dielectric for $\nu \gtrsim 10^7$ s^{-1}.

EXAMPLE 22.6

For copper one may assume $\varepsilon = \varepsilon_0$ and $\sigma \approx 5.8 \times 10^7$ mhos/m. At $\nu = 100$ Hz

$$\frac{\sigma}{\omega\varepsilon} = \frac{5.8\times 10^7}{2\pi \times 100 \times 8.854 \times 10^{-12}} \approx 10^{16}$$

and at $\nu = 10^8$ Hz

$$\frac{\sigma}{\omega\varepsilon} = \frac{5.8 \times 10^7}{2\pi \times 10^8 \times 8.854 \times 10^{-12}} \approx 10^{10}$$

Thus at both frequencies copper behaves like a very good conductor. We, therefore, have

$$\delta = \frac{1}{\gamma} \approx \sqrt{\frac{2}{\omega\mu\sigma}} \approx \sqrt{\frac{2}{2\pi\nu \times 4\pi \times 10^{-7} \times 5.8 \times 10^7}}$$

$$\approx \frac{0.066}{\sqrt{\nu}} \text{ m}$$

$$\approx 6.6 \text{ mm} \quad \text{at } \nu = 100 \text{ Hz}$$

$$\approx 6.6\ \mu\text{m} \quad \text{at } \nu = 100 \text{ MHz}$$

showing that the penetration decreases with increase in frequency.

22.9 Radiation Pressure

LO8

(We follow Sec. 34.9 of Ref. 22.6; a rigorous analysis has been given in Chapter 11 of Ref. 22.5). Let us consider a linearly polarized electromagnetic wave propagating in the +z-direction; we assume the electric field to be along the x-direction and the magnetic field along the y-direction (see Fig. 22.1). The electromagnetic wave is assumed to interact with a charge q; the electric field makes the charge move up and down along the x-axis. Thus the charge acquires a certain velocity in the x-direction and since the magnetic field is along the y-axis, a force

$$\mathbf{F} = q\ \mathbf{v} \times \mathbf{B} \quad \textbf{(22.123)}$$

acts on the charge q. This force acts along the z-axis* is (i.e. along the direction of propagation of the wave) and constitutes what is known as 'radiation pressure'. Thus,

$$\mathbf{F} = qvB\ \hat{\mathbf{z}} \quad \textbf{(22.124)}$$

---

* Using the analysis of Sections 6.4 and 6.5, we can show that in the presence of a field $\mathbf{E} = \hat{\mathbf{x}} E_0 \cos(kz - \omega t)$, the displacement is given by

$$\mathbf{x} = \hat{\mathbf{x}} qE_0 A \cos(kz - \omega t + \phi)$$

where we have explicitly shown that the amplitude is proportional to q and E_0. Thus

$$\mathbf{v} = \frac{d\mathbf{x}}{dt} = +\hat{\mathbf{x}} qE_0 A\omega \sin(kz - \omega t + \phi)$$

Now $$\mathbf{B} = \hat{\mathbf{y}} B_0 \cos(kz - \omega t) = \hat{\mathbf{y}} \frac{E_0}{c} \cos(kz - \omega t)$$

Thus $$\mathbf{F} = q\,\mathbf{v} \times \mathbf{B} = +\hat{\mathbf{z}} q^2 \frac{E_0^2\omega}{c} A\left[\cos(kz - \omega t)\right]\left[\sin(kz - \omega t)\cos\phi + \cos(kz - \omega t)\sin\phi\right]$$

If we carry out a time averaging, then

$$\langle \mathbf{F} \rangle = \hat{\mathbf{z}} \frac{q^2 E_0^2 \omega}{2c} A \sin\phi = \hat{\mathbf{z}} \frac{1}{c} \langle q\mathbf{E} \cdot \mathbf{v} \rangle$$

Since $\sin\phi$ is always positive (see Sec. 6.4) and the force is always in the z-direction.

But $$B = \mu_0 H = \frac{\mu_0}{\eta_0} E = \mu_0 \sqrt{\frac{\varepsilon_0}{\mu_0}}\, E$$

$$= \sqrt{\varepsilon_0 \mu_0}\, E = \frac{1}{c} E \tag{22.125}$$

Thus $$\mathbf{F} = \frac{qEv}{c}\hat{\mathbf{z}} \tag{22.126}$$

Now qEv represents the work done by the field on the charge per unit time (see Sec. 22.4); thus, if we consider a unit volume, then

$$\mathbf{F} = \frac{1}{c}\frac{du}{dt}\hat{\mathbf{z}} \tag{22.127}$$

But the force is equal to the change in momentum per unit time. Consequently, the momentum per unit volume associated with the plane wave would be given by

$$\mathbf{p} = \frac{u}{c}\hat{\mathbf{z}} \tag{22.128}$$

In Chapter 24, we will show that light essentially consists of corpuscles called photons. Each photon carries an energy equal to $h\nu$; the photon momentum would, therefore, be given by

$$p = \frac{h\nu}{c} \tag{22.129}$$

Let us consider a plane wave incident normally on a perfect absorber. If we consider an area dS on the absorbing surface then the momentum transferred to area dS in time dt would be

$$p\, dS\, cdt$$

which represents the momentum contained in a cylindrical volume $dS\, cdt$ (see Fig. 22.5). Thus the force acting on the area dS would be

$$pc\, dS$$

Hence $$P_{\text{rad}} = cp = u \tag{22.130}$$

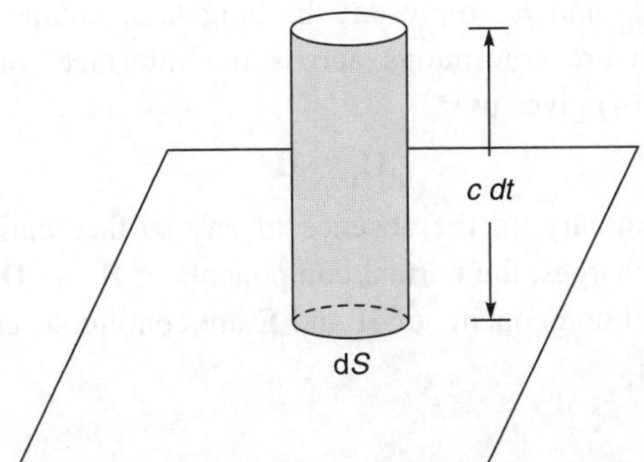

Figure 22.5
A cylindrical volume to calculate radiation pressure.

where P_{rad} represents the radiation pressure due to a plane wave incident on a perfect absorber. On the other hand, for a perfect reflector, the momentum of the reflected wave is equal and opposite of the momentum associated with the incident wave. Thus the momentum transferred would be twice of the above value and hence

$$P_{\text{rad}} = 2cp = 2u \tag{22.131}$$

EXAMPLE 22.7 We consider a light beam of intensity $I = 3000$ W/m² falling on a perfectly reflecting mirror. Since $I = cu$, we have

$$u = \frac{3000 \text{ W/m}^2}{3\times 10^8 \text{ m/sec}} = 10^{-5}\,\text{J/m}^3$$

The radiation pressure would be $2\times 10^{-5}\,\text{N/m}^2$ which may be compared with the atmospheric pressure $\left(\approx 10^{+5}\,\text{N/m}^2\right)$.

It has been possible to measure the radiation pressure by allowing a light beam to fall on a highly polished mirror M (see Fig. 22.6), the radiation pressure caused a twist in the suspension which was measured. The experiment was first carried out by Lebedev in Russia in 1899; experimental arrangement shown in Fig. 22.6 is of Nichols and Hull who performed the experiment in 1901 and confirmed the prediction of radiation pressure. The intensity of the beam can be determined by allowing it to fall on an absorber (like a blackened disc) and measuring the temperature rise. In a particular run, the radiation pressure was found to be about 7.01×10^{-6} N/m² which was in good agreement with the predicted value of 7.05×10^{-6} N/m².

For oblique incidence on a perfect reflector, the change in momentum per unit volume would be $2p\cos\theta$ and the radiation pressure would be

$$P_{\text{rad}} = 2cp\cos^2\theta = 2u\cos^2\theta \tag{22.132}$$

where θ represents the angle of incidence.

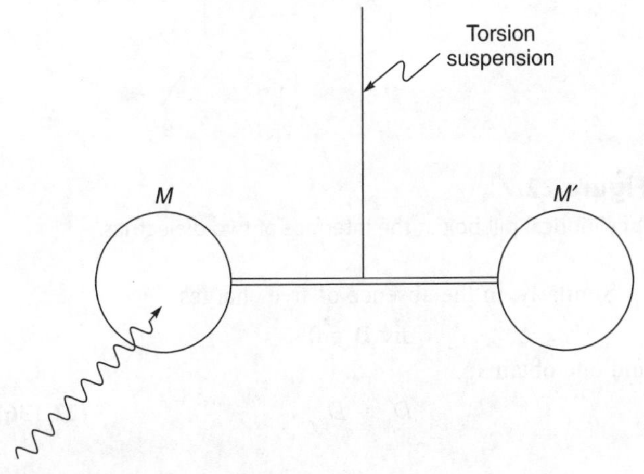

Figure 22.6
An experimental arrangement to measure radiation pressure.

22.10 Continuity Conditions

LO9

In this section we will derive the continuity conditions for electric and magnetic fields at the interface of two media. Let us first consider the equation

$$\text{div } \mathbf{B} = 0 \qquad \textbf{(22.133)}$$

At the interface of two media, we consider a pill box which encloses an area ΔS of the interface (see Fig 22.7). Let the height of the pill box be l. Now, if we integrate div **B** over the cylindrical volume then, using Gauss' theorem, we obtain

$$0 = \int \text{div } \mathbf{B}\, dV = \oint_{S_1} \mathbf{B} \cdot d\mathbf{a} + \oint_{S_2} \mathbf{B} \cdot d\mathbf{a} + \oint_{S_3} \mathbf{B} \cdot d\mathbf{a}$$

where S_1 and S_2 represent the flat faces of the cylinder and S_3 represents the curved surface of the cylinder. If we let $l \to 0$, then the third integral vanishes and we obtain

$$\oint_{S_1} \mathbf{B} \cdot d\mathbf{a} = -\oint_{S_2} \mathbf{B} \cdot d\mathbf{a}$$

or
$$\mathbf{B}_1 \cdot \hat{\mathbf{n}}_1 \Delta S = -\mathbf{B}_2 \cdot \hat{\mathbf{n}}_2 \Delta S \qquad \textbf{(22.134)}$$

or
$$B_{1n} = B_{2n} \qquad \textbf{(22.135)}$$

where the directions of $\hat{\mathbf{n}}_1$ and $\hat{\mathbf{n}}_2$ are shown in Fig. 22.7. Thus the normal component of **B** is continuous across the interface.

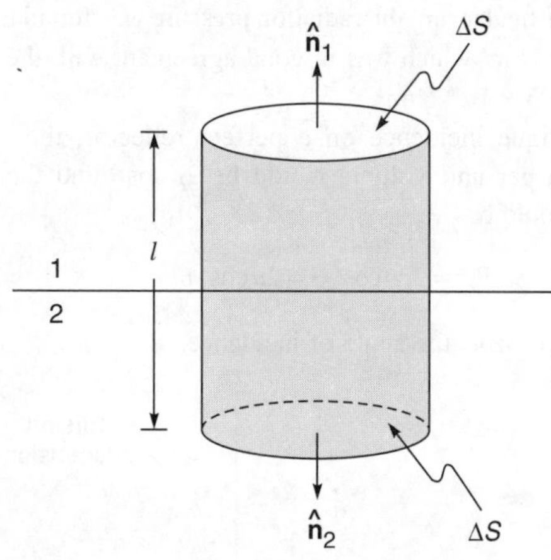

Figure 22.7
A cylindrical pill box at the interface of two dielectrics.

Similarly, in the absence of free charges

$$\text{div } \mathbf{D} = 0$$

and one obtains*

$$D_{1n} = D_{2n} \qquad \textbf{(22.136)}$$

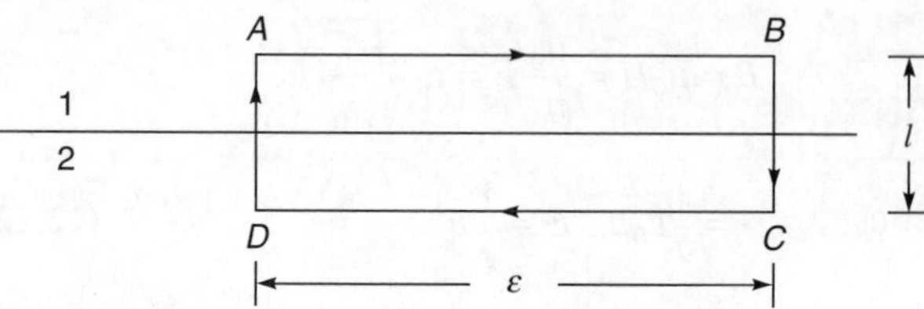

Figure 22.8
A rectangular loop at the interface of two dielectrics.

showing that the normal component of **D** is also continuous across the interface.

We next consider the equation

$$\text{curl } \mathbf{E} + \frac{\partial \mathbf{B}}{\partial t} = 0$$

We consider a rectangular loop *ABCD* as shown in Fig. 22.8. Now

$$0 = \oint_S \text{curl } \mathbf{E} \cdot d\mathbf{a} + \oint_S \frac{\partial \mathbf{B}}{\partial t} \cdot d\mathbf{a} \qquad \textbf{(22.137)}$$

where the surface integral is over any surface bounding the loop *ABCD*. Using Stokes' theorem, we get

$$\oint \mathbf{E} \cdot d\mathbf{l} = -\int_S \frac{\partial \mathbf{B}}{\partial t} \cdot d\mathbf{a} \qquad \textbf{(22.138)}$$

or
$$\left(\int_{AB} + \int_{BC} + \int_{CD} + \int_{DA} \right) \mathbf{E} \cdot d\mathbf{l} = -\int \frac{\partial \mathbf{B}}{\partial t} \cdot d\mathbf{a}$$

If we let $l \to 0$ then the integrals along *BC* and *DA* tend to zero and since the area of the loop also tends to zero the RHS also vanishes. Thus we obtain

$$\int_{AB} \mathbf{E} \cdot d\mathbf{l} + \int_{CD} \mathbf{E} \cdot d\mathbf{l} = 0$$

or
$$(\mathbf{E}_1 \cdot \hat{\mathbf{t}})\varepsilon + [\mathbf{E}_1 \cdot (-\hat{\mathbf{t}})]\varepsilon = 0$$

or
$$\mathbf{E}_{1t} = \mathbf{E}_{2t}$$

where $\mathbf{E}_{1t}$ and $\mathbf{E}_{2t}$ represent the tangential components of **E** which are continuous across the interface. Similarly, Eq. (22.14) gives us**

$$\mathbf{H}_{1t} = \mathbf{H}_{2t}$$

In summary, in the absence of any surface current and surface charges, the normal components of **B** and **D** and the tangential components of **H** and **E** are continuous across an interface.

* Rigorously $D_{1n} = D_{2n} = \sigma$, where σ represents the surface charge density

** More rigorously $\mathbf{H}_{1t} - \mathbf{H}_{2t}$ is equal to the normal component of the surface current density. However, if there are no surface currents, which is indeed true for most cases, $\mathbf{H}_{1t} = \mathbf{H}_{2t}$.

22.11 Physical Significance of Maxwell's Equations

LO10

Let us first consider the equation

$$\text{div } \mathbf{D} = \rho \tag{22.139}$$

In free space $\mathbf{D} = \varepsilon_0 \mathbf{E}$ **(22.140)**

and Eq. (22.139) becomes

$$\text{div } \mathbf{E} = \frac{\rho}{\varepsilon_0} \tag{22.141}$$

If we integrate the above equation over a volume V, we would obtain

$$\int_V \text{div } \mathbf{E}\, d\tau = \frac{1}{\varepsilon_0}\int_V \rho\, d\tau = \frac{1}{\varepsilon_0} Q$$

where Q is the total charge inside the volume V. Applying the divergence theorem, we get

$$\int_V \text{div } \mathbf{E}\, d\tau = \oint \mathbf{E}\cdot d\mathbf{S} = \frac{1}{\varepsilon_0} Q \tag{22.142}$$

which is simply the Gauss' law, i.e. the electric flux through a closed surface is the total charge inside the volume divided by ε_0.

EXAMPLE 22.8 As a simple application of Gauss' law, we consider a point charge Q; at the origin O; the field produced by this point charge will be given by

$$\mathbf{E} = \frac{Q}{4\pi\varepsilon_0}\frac{1}{r^2}\hat{\mathbf{r}} \tag{22.143}$$

If we integrate over a spherical surface S (of radius R), we would obtain

$$\oint_S \mathbf{E}.d\mathbf{S} = \frac{Q}{4\pi\varepsilon_0}\int_{\phi=0}^{2\pi}\int_{\theta=0}^{\pi}\frac{1}{R^2}R^2 \sin\theta\, d\theta\, d\phi = \frac{Q}{4\pi\varepsilon_0}\iint \frac{1}{R^2}R^2 d\Omega = \frac{Q}{\varepsilon_0}$$

which is the same as Eq. (22.142).

EXAMPLE 22.9 In this example we will show that

$$\nabla^2\left(\frac{1}{r}\right) = -4\pi\delta(\mathbf{r}) \tag{22.144}$$

where

$$\delta(\mathbf{r}) = \delta(x)\delta(y)\delta(z) \tag{22.145}$$

is the 3-dimensional Dirac delta function and has the units of m^{-3}. In spherical polar coordinates, for a function depending only on r we have

$$\nabla^2\psi(r) = \frac{1}{r^2}\frac{d}{dr}\left(r^2\frac{d\psi}{dr}\right) \tag{22.146}$$

Elementary differentiation shows that

$$\frac{d}{dr}\left(r^2\frac{d}{dr}\left(\frac{1}{r}\right)\right) = 0 \quad \text{for all } r \tag{22.147}$$

Thus

$$\nabla^2\left(\frac{1}{r}\right) = 0 \quad \text{for } r > 0 \tag{22.148}$$

At $r = 0$, we cannot say that $\nabla^2(1/r) = 0$ because of the factor $(1/r^2)$ in Eq. (22.146). Now

$$\nabla^2\left(\frac{1}{r}\right) = \text{div grad}\left(\frac{1}{r}\right) = \text{div } \mathbf{F}$$

where

$$\mathbf{F} \equiv \text{grad}\left(\frac{1}{r}\right) = -\frac{1}{r^2}\hat{\mathbf{r}} \tag{22.149}$$

Thus integrating over a spherical volume of radius R, we get

$$\int_V \nabla^2\left(\frac{1}{r}\right)d\tau = \int_V \text{div } \mathbf{F}\, d\tau = \oiint \mathbf{F}\cdot d\mathbf{S}$$

where we have used the divergence theorem and the last integral is over a spherical surface of radius R. Now, on the spherical surface, the magnitude of $\mathbf{F}$ has a constant value and therefore

$$\mathbf{F} = -\frac{1}{R^2}\hat{\mathbf{r}}$$

Thus

$$\oiint \mathbf{F}\cdot d\mathbf{S} = \int_{\theta=0}^{\pi}\int_{\phi=0}^{2\pi}\left(-\frac{1}{R^2}\right)(\hat{\mathbf{r}}\cdot\hat{\mathbf{r}})R^2 \sin\theta\, d\theta\, d\phi = 4\pi$$

$$\Rightarrow \quad \int_V \nabla^2\left(\frac{1}{r}\right)d\tau = -4\pi \tag{22.150}$$

where, because of Eq. (22.148), V is now an arbitrary volume surrounding the origin. Since

$$\delta(\mathbf{r}) = 0 \text{ for } r > 0 \quad \text{and} \quad \int_V \delta(\mathbf{r})d\tau = 1 \tag{22.151}$$

This Eqs. (22.148) and (22.150) would imply

$$\nabla^2\left(\frac{1}{r}\right) = -4\pi\,\delta(\mathbf{r}) \tag{22.152}$$

EXAMPLE 22.10 In all electrostatics problems $\partial\mathbf{B}/\partial t = 0$ and therefore Eq. (22.9) gives us $\nabla \times \mathbf{E} = 0$; thus we may write $\mathbf{E} = -\nabla V$ where V is known as the electrostatic potential. Thus Eq. (22.141) becomes

$$\nabla^2 V = -\frac{\rho}{\varepsilon_0} \tag{22.153}$$

Now, for a point charge sitting at the origin, the charge density is given by

$$\rho = Q\delta(\mathbf{r}) \;\Rightarrow\; \nabla^2 V = -\frac{Q}{\varepsilon_0}\delta(\mathbf{r}) \tag{22.154}$$

Notice that since the unit of $\delta(\mathbf{r})$ is m^{-3}, the unit of $\rho(\mathbf{r})$ will be Cm^{-3}. Comparing Eqs. (22.152) and (22.154), we get

$$V(r) = \frac{Q}{4\pi\varepsilon_0}\frac{1}{r} \;\Rightarrow\; \mathbf{E} = -\nabla V = -\frac{\partial V}{\partial r}\hat{\mathbf{r}} = \frac{Q}{4\pi\varepsilon_0}\frac{1}{r^2}\hat{\mathbf{r}} \tag{22.155}$$

which is the inverse square law.

We may mention here that for a dielectric we would get

$$\oint \mathbf{D}\cdot d\mathbf{S} = Q \tag{22.156}$$

where

$$\mathbf{D} = \varepsilon_0\mathbf{E} + \mathbf{P} \tag{22.157}$$

P being the dipole moment per unit volume. For a linear homogenous medium,

$$\mathbf{P} = \chi \mathbf{E} \tag{22.158}$$

where χ is known as the susceptibility. Thus $\mathbf{D} = \varepsilon \mathbf{E}$ where

$$\varepsilon \equiv \varepsilon_0 + \chi \tag{22.159}$$

is known as the dielectric permittivity of the medium.

Now, for the equation div **B** = 0, if we use the divergence theorem, we would get

$$\int \text{div}\,\mathbf{B}\,dV = \oint \mathbf{B}\cdot d\mathbf{S} = 0 \tag{22.160}$$

i.e. the magnetic flux through a closed surface is always zero; this implies the absence of magnetic monopoles.

We next consider the equation

$$\text{curl}\,\mathbf{E} = -\frac{\partial \mathbf{B}}{\partial t} \tag{22.161}$$

which associates a space and time–dependent electric field with a changing magnetic field. Now, Stokes' theorem tells us that

$$\oint_\Gamma \mathbf{E}\cdot d\mathbf{l} = \int_S \text{curl}\,\mathbf{E}\cdot d\mathbf{S} \tag{22.162}$$

where the LHS represents a line integral over a closed path Γ and the RHS represents a surface integral over any surface bounding the path Γ. Thus

$$\oint_\Gamma \mathbf{E}\cdot d\mathbf{l} = \int_S \text{curl}\,\mathbf{E}\cdot d\mathbf{S} = -\int_S \frac{\partial \mathbf{B}}{\partial t}\cdot d\mathbf{S} \tag{22.163}$$

or

$$\oint_\Gamma \mathbf{E}\cdot d\mathbf{l} = -\frac{\partial}{\partial t}\int_S \mathbf{B}\cdot d\mathbf{S} \tag{22.164}$$

where in the last step we have used the fact that the surface S is fixed. (The above equation is not valid for a moving system; see, for example, Ref. 21.7, p. 526). The LHS of the above equation represents the induced emf in a closed circuit which is equal to the negative of the rate of change of the magnetic flux through the circuit. This is the famous Faraday's law of induction. The above law was discovered by Faraday, it was put in the differential form [see Eq. (22.161) by Maxwell.

We now come to the last of the Maxwell's equations

$$\text{curl}\,\mathbf{H} = \mathbf{J} + \frac{\partial \mathbf{D}}{\partial t} \tag{22.165}$$

For static fields $\frac{\partial \mathbf{D}}{\partial t} = 0$ and one obtains Ampere's law:

$$\text{curl}\,\mathbf{H} = \mathbf{J} \tag{22.166}$$

which implies that a magnetic field is produced only by currents.

EXAMPLE 22.11 A long wire carrying a current I (see Fig. 22.9), produces a magnetic field **H** given by.

$$\int_S \text{curl}\,\mathbf{H}\cdot d\mathbf{S} = \int_S \mathbf{J}\cdot d\mathbf{S} = I \;\Rightarrow\; \oint_\Gamma \mathbf{H}\cdot d\mathbf{l} = I \tag{22.167}$$

where in the last step we have used Stokes' theorem. We assume the line integral to be over a circle of radius r as shown in Fig. 22.9. On the circumference of the circle, $d\mathbf{l} = (r\,d\phi)\hat{\boldsymbol{\phi}}$ where r is the cylindrical coordinate and $\hat{\boldsymbol{\phi}}$ is the unit vector shown in Fig. 22.9. From the symmetry of the problem, the magnitude of **H** will be the same on the circumference of the circle; thus

$$H_\phi(2\pi r) = I \tag{22.168}$$

Indeed

$$\mathbf{H} = \frac{I}{2\pi r}\hat{\phi} \tag{22.169}$$

one obtains the same expression for **H** by using Biot–Savart law.

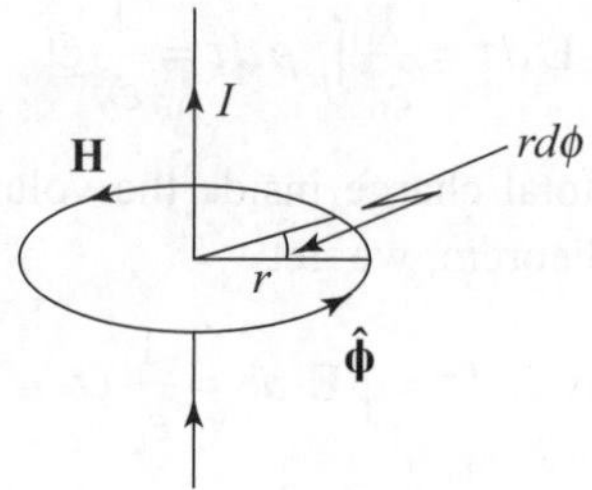

Figure 22.9
Magnetic field produced by a long wire carrying current I.

Ampere's law was known before Maxwell; Maxwell had put it in the form of a vector equation. Since the divergence of the curl of any vector is zero, one obtains

$$\text{div}\,\mathbf{J} = 0 \tag{22.170}$$

which may be compared with the equation of continuity

$$\text{div}\,\mathbf{J} + \frac{\partial \rho}{\partial t} = 0 \tag{22.171}$$

Thus Eq. (22.166) is valid only when $\frac{\partial \rho}{\partial t} = 0$. Thus, for the Ampere's law to be consistent with the equation of continuity, Maxwell argued that there must be an additional term $\frac{\partial \mathbf{D}}{\partial t}$ on the RHS of Eq. (22.166) so that:

$$\text{div curl}\,\mathbf{H} = 0 = \text{div}\,\mathbf{J} + \frac{\partial}{\partial t}\text{div}\,\mathbf{D} \;\Rightarrow\; \text{div}\,\mathbf{J} + \frac{\partial \rho}{\partial t} = 0 \tag{22.172}$$

which is the equation of continuity. The introduction of term $\partial \mathbf{D}/\partial t$ (which is known as the displacement current) revolutionized physics. Physically it implies that not only a current produces a magnetic field but a changing electric field also produces a magnetic field (as it indeed happens during the charging and discharging of a condenser). For static fields $\frac{\partial D}{\partial t} = 0$ and one obtains Ampere's law. It may be mentioned that it is the presence of the term $\partial \mathbf{D}/\partial t$ which leads to the wave equation (see Sec. 22.3) and, therefore, the prediction of electromagnetic waves. One can thus argue on physical grounds that a changing electric field produces a magnetic field which varies in space and time and this changing magnetic field produces an electric field varying in space and time, and so on. This mutual generation of electric and magnetic fields results in the propagation of electromagnetic waves.

SUMMARY

- In a homogeneous charge free dielectric (with dielectric permittivity ε), the x-polarized wave defined by the equations

$$\mathbf{E} = \hat{\mathbf{x}} E_0 e^{i(kz-\omega t)} \qquad (22.173)$$

$$\mathbf{H} = \hat{\mathbf{y}} H_0 e^{i(kz-\omega t)};\ H_0 = \frac{E_0}{\eta} \ \ \&\ \ \eta = \sqrt{\frac{\mu_0}{\varepsilon}}$$

are solutions of Maxwell's equations; here we have assumed the medium to be non-magnetic so that $\mu \approx \mu_0 = 4\pi \times 10^{-7}$ N–s²/C². The speed of propagation of the electromagnetic wave is given by

$$v = \frac{\omega}{k} = \frac{1}{\sqrt{\varepsilon\mu_0}} = \frac{c}{n} \qquad (22.174)$$

where

$$c = \frac{1}{\sqrt{\varepsilon_0\mu_0}} = \frac{1}{\sqrt{8.8542...\times 10^{-12} \times 4\pi \times 10^{-7}}}$$

$$= 2.99792458 \times 10^8 \text{ m/s} \qquad (22.175)$$

is the velocity of the electromagnetic wave in free space. Thus

$$\eta = \sqrt{\frac{\mu_0}{\varepsilon_0}}\sqrt{\frac{\varepsilon_0}{\varepsilon}} = \frac{\eta_0}{n};\ \eta_0 = \sqrt{\frac{\mu_0}{\varepsilon_0}} = 120\,\pi\,\Omega$$

The corresponding time averaged Poynting vector is given by

$$\langle \mathbf{S} \rangle = \langle \mathbf{E} \times \mathbf{H} \rangle = \hat{\mathbf{z}} \frac{E_0^2}{\eta} \langle \cos^2(kz-\omega t) \rangle = \hat{\mathbf{z}} \frac{E_0^2}{2\eta} \qquad (22.176)$$

which implies that the energy flow is in the z-direction (which represents the direction of propagation of the wave) and that, on an average,

$$\frac{E_0^2}{2\eta}$$

amount of energy crosses a unit area (perpendicular to the z-axis) per unit time. The corresponding average energy density is given by

$$\langle u \rangle = \frac{1}{2}\varepsilon E_0^2 \qquad [\text{J/m}^3]$$

and the intensity is given by

$$I = \frac{1}{2}\varepsilon v E_0^2 = \frac{1}{2}\varepsilon_0 c n E_0^2 \qquad [\text{W/m}^3]$$

- In a conductor, the field decays exponentially

$$\mathbf{E} = E_0 e^{-\gamma z} \cos(\beta z - \omega t)\,\hat{\mathbf{x}}$$

with $\gamma = \omega\sqrt{\dfrac{\mu\varepsilon}{2}}\left[\sqrt{1+\left(\dfrac{\sigma}{\omega\varepsilon}\right)^2} - 1\right]^{1/2}$

- The momentum associated with a plane wave is given by

$$\mathbf{p} = \frac{u}{c}\hat{\mathbf{z}}$$

PROBLEMS

22.1 A y-polarized electromagnetic wave propagating in vacuum is described by the following equation

$$\mathbf{E} = \hat{\mathbf{y}} E_0 \exp[i(300x - 400z - \omega t)]$$

(a) Calculate the wavelength and frequency of the wave.

(b) Calculate the unit vector along $\hat{\mathbf{k}}$.

(c) Calculate the corresponding **H**.

[**Ans:** $\lambda \approx 1.26 \times 10^{-2}$ m ; $\nu \approx 23.9$ GHz ; $\hat{\mathbf{k}} = 0.6\,\hat{\mathbf{x}} - 0.8\hat{\mathbf{z}}$]

22.2 The magnetic field for a plane wave propagating (in a dielectric of refractive index 1.5) along the x direction is given by

$$\mathbf{H} = \hat{\mathbf{y}}\ 0.04 \sin(kx - 10^{15} t) \text{ A/m}$$

Calculate the free space wavelength and the time averaged Poynting vector.

[**Ans:** $\lambda_0 \approx 1.886 \times 10^{-6}$ m ; $\langle \mathbf{S} \rangle \approx 0.20\,\hat{\mathbf{x}}$ W/m²]

22.3 On the surface of the earth we receive about 1.33 kW of energy per square meter from the sun. Calculate the electric field associated with the sunlight (on the surface of the earth) assuming that it is essentially monochromatic with $\lambda = 6000$ Å.

[**Ans:** ~1000 V/m]

22.4 A 100 W sodium lamp ($\lambda \approx 5890$ Å) is assumed to emit waves uniformly in all directions. What is the momentum associated with each photon? Calculate the radiation pressure on a plane mirror at distance of 10 m from the bulb?

[**Ans:** $\approx 5.3\times10^{-10}$ N/m^2]

22.5 On the surface of the earth we receive about 1.33 kW of energy per square metre from the sun. Calculate the corresponding radiation pressure.

[**Ans:** ~ 4.6 μPa; 1Pa $\approx 10^{-5}$ N/m^2]

22.6 A 1 kW transmitter is emitting electromagnetic waves of (of wavelength 40 m) uniformly in all directions. Calculate the electric field at a distance of 1 km from the transmitter.

[**Ans:** ~0.25 V/m]

22.7 For fresh water, there is considerable variation in the measured values of the conductivity and dielectric constant. If we assume

$$\frac{\varepsilon}{\varepsilon_0} \approx 80;\ \mu \approx \mu_0 \text{ and } \sigma \approx 10^{-3} \text{ mhos/m}$$

Show that it behaves as a good conductor for $\nu \approx 10$ Hz and as a poor conductor for $\nu \approx 10$ GHz.

22.8 Ocean water can be assumed to be a non-magnetic dielectric with $\kappa = \left(\frac{\varepsilon}{\varepsilon_0}\right) = 80$ and $\sigma = 4.3$ mhos/m. (a) Calculate the frequency at which the penetration depth will be 10 cm. (b) Show that for frequencies less than 10^8 sec^{-1}, it can be considered as a good conductor.

[**Ans:** (a) ~6×10^6 s^{-1}]

22.9 For silver, one may assume $\mu \approx \mu_0$ and $\sigma \approx 3 \times 10^7$ mhos/m. Calculate the skin depth at 10^8 s^{-1}.

[**Ans:** $\approx 9 \times 10^{-4}$ cm]

22.10 Show that for frequencies $\lesssim 10^9$s^{-1}, a sample of silicon will act like a good conductor. For silicon one may assume $\frac{\varepsilon}{\varepsilon_0} \approx 12$ and $\sigma \approx 2$ mhos/cm. Also calculate the penetration depth for this sample at $\nu = 10^6$ s^{-1}.

22.11 In a conducting medium show that **H** also satisfies an equation similar to Eq. (22.113).

22.12 Using the analysis given in Sec. 20.7 and assuming $\sigma/\omega\varepsilon \ll 1$ (which is valid for an insulator) show that

$$\beta \approx \omega\sqrt{\varepsilon\mu}\left[1+\tfrac{1}{8}\left(\frac{\sigma}{\omega\varepsilon}\right)^2\right] = \frac{2\pi}{\lambda_0} n\left[1+\tfrac{1}{8}\left(\frac{\sigma}{\omega\varepsilon}\right)^2\right]$$

and

$$\beta \approx \omega\sqrt{\varepsilon\mu}\left[\tfrac{1}{2}\left(\frac{\sigma}{\omega\varepsilon}\right)\right] = \frac{2\pi}{\lambda_0} n\left[\tfrac{1}{2}\left(\frac{\sigma}{\omega\varepsilon}\right)\right]$$

where

$$n = \sqrt{\varepsilon/\varepsilon_0}.$$

22.13 For the glass used in typical optical fibre at $\lambda_0 \approx 8500$Å, $n = (\varepsilon/\varepsilon_0)^{1/2} = 1.46$, $\sigma = 3.4\times10^{-6}$ mhos/m. Calculate $\frac{\sigma}{\omega\varepsilon}$ and show that we can use the formulae given in the previous problem. Calculate β and loss in dB/km.

[**Hint:** The power would decrease as exp $(-2\beta z)$; loss in dB/km is defined in Sec. 27.8]

[**Ans:** $\sigma/\omega\varepsilon \approx 8\times10^{-11}$; $\beta \approx 4.3\times10^{-4}$ m^{-1}; loss ≈ 3.7 dB/km.]

CHAPTER

23

Reflection and Refraction of Electromagnetic Waves

All of electromagnetism is contained in Maxwell's equations… Untold number of experiments have confirmed Maxwell's equations. If we take away the scaffolding he used to build it, we find that Maxwell's beautiful edifice stands on its own.

—Richard Feynman

LEARNING OBJECTIVES

After reading this chapter, the reader should be able to:

LO 1: *explain reflection and refraction at an interface of two media.*

LO 2: *calculate reflection and transmission coefficients when a plane electromagnetic wave is incident normally at the interface of two media.*

LO 3: *calculate reflection and transmission coefficients when a plane electromagnetic wave (with its **E** is the plane of incidence) is incident obliquely at the interface of two media.*

LO 4: *illustrate polarization by reflection through Brewster's law.*

LO 5: *understand the phenomenon of total internal reflection and existence of evanescent waves.*

LO 6: *calculate reflection and transmission coefficients when a plane electromagnetic wave (with its **E** perpendicular to the plane of incidence) is incident obliquely at the interface of two media.*

LO 7: *calculate Poynting vector for the evanescent wave.*

LO 8: *calculate reflectivity of a dielectric film for a normally incident plane wave.*

Above Image: View from a polarized lens. Photograph courtesy Darksoul72/Shutterstock

23.1 Introduction

In the previous chapter we had shown the existence of electromagnetic waves. Using the continuity conditions of electric and magnetic fields, we will, in this chapter, study the reflection and refraction of plane waves at an interface of two dielectrics and also at an interface of a dielectric and a metal. We will show that by reflection from a dielectric surface we can produce linearly polarized light. We will discuss the phenomenon of total internal reflection and study the explicit nature of the evanescent wave created in the rarer medium. In Sec. 23.4 we will consider reflectivity (and transmittivity) of a dielectric film.

23.2 Reflection and Refraction at an Interface of Two Media

LO1

Let us consider the incidence of a plane polarized electromagnetic wave on an interface of two media; we assume the plane $x = 0$ to represent the interface (see Fig. 23.1). Let η_1 and η_2 represent the intrinsic impedance of the media below and above the plane $x = 0$; the intrinsic impedance of a medium is defined in Sec. 22.4. Let $\mathbf{E}_1$, $\mathbf{E}_2$ and $\mathbf{E}_3$ denote the electric fields associated with the incident wave, refracted wave and reflected wave, respectively. For an incident plane wave, these fields will be of the form

$$\left.\begin{aligned} \mathbf{E}_1 &= \mathbf{E}_{10} \exp\left[i\left(\mathbf{k}_1.\mathbf{r} - \omega t\right)\right] \\ \mathbf{E}_2 &= \mathbf{E}_{20} \exp\left[i\left(\mathbf{k}_2.\mathbf{r} - \omega_2 t\right)\right] \\ \mathbf{E}_3 &= \mathbf{E}_{30} \exp\left[i\left(\mathbf{k}_3.\mathbf{r} - \omega_3 t\right)\right] \end{aligned}\right\} \quad \textbf{(23.1a)}$$

where $\mathbf{E}_{10}$, $\mathbf{E}_{20}$ and $\mathbf{E}_{30}$ are independent of space and time but may, in general, be complex. The vectors $\mathbf{k}_1$, $\mathbf{k}_2$ and $\mathbf{k}_3$ represent the propagation vectors associated with the incident, refracted and reflected waves, respectively. At the interface, the continuity conditions are as follows:

Case I: If both media are non-conducting ($\sigma_1 = \sigma_2 = 0$): Tangential components of **E** and **H** are continuous at the interface of two media. Further, normal components of **D** and **B** are also continuous at the interface.

Case II: If the second medium is perfectly conducting ($\sigma_2 = \infty$): The tangential components of **E** are continuous and are zero at the interface.

Case III: For arbitrary values of σ_1 and σ_2, tangential components of **E** and normal components of **B** are continuous.

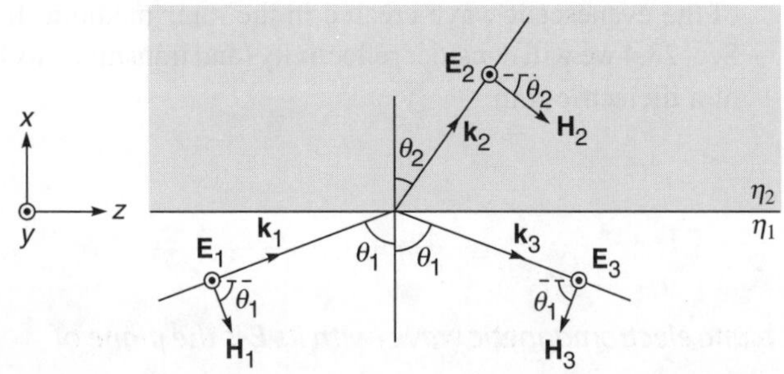

Figure 23.1

The reflection and refraction of a plane wave with the electric vector lying perpendicular to the plane of incidence (along the *y*-axis) and with the **H** vector in the plane of incidence.

Further, (at the end of Sec. 23.7) we will show that **if the electric vector associated with the incident wave lies in the plane of incidence, then the electric vectors associated with the reflected and transmitted waves will also lie in the plane of incidence. Similarly, if the electric vector associated with the incident wave is normal to the plane of incidence, then the electric vectors associated with the reflected and transmitted waves will also lie normal to the plane of incidence.** (see also Example 23.11)

As mentioned above, the fields have to satisfy certain boundary conditions at the interface (which corresponds to $x = 0$) where Eq. (23.1a) takes the form

$$\left.\begin{aligned} \mathbf{E}_1 &= \mathbf{E}_{10} \exp\left[i\left(k_{1y}\, y + k_{1z}\, z - \omega t\right)\right] \\ \mathbf{E}_2 &= \mathbf{E}_{20} \exp\left[i\left(k_{2y}\, y + k_{2z}\, z - \omega_2 t\right)\right] \\ \mathbf{E}_3 &= \mathbf{E}_{30} \exp\left[i\left(k_{3y}\, y + k_{3z}\, z - \omega_3 t\right)\right] \end{aligned}\right\} \quad \textbf{(23.1b)}$$

where k_{1x}, k_{1y} and k_{1z} represent the *x*, *y* and *z*-components of $\mathbf{k}_1$; similarly for $\mathbf{k}_2$ and $\mathbf{k}_3$. Now, for example, the *z*-component of the electric field (which is a tangential component) must be continuous at $x = 0$ for all values of *y*, *z* and *t*. Consequently, the coefficients of *y*, *z* and *t* in the exponents appearing in the above equation must be equal*. Thus

$$\omega = \omega_2 = \omega_3$$

showing that all the waves have the same frequency. Further, we must have

$$k_{1y} = k_{2y} = k_{3y}$$

and

$$k_{1z} = k_{2z} = k_{3z} \quad \textbf{(23.2)}$$

Without any loss of generality we may choose the *y*-axis such that

$$k_{1y} = 0$$

(i.e., k_1 is assumed to lie in the *x*-*z* plane—see Fig. 23.1). Consequently,

$$k_{2y} = k_{3y} = 0 \quad \textbf{(23.3)}$$

Equation (23.2) implies that the vectors $\mathbf{k}_1$, $\mathbf{k}_2$ and $\mathbf{k}_3$ will lie in the same plane. Further, from Eq. 23.2 we get

$$k_1 \sin\theta_1 = k_2 \sin\theta_2 = k_3 \sin\theta_3 \quad \textbf{(23.4)}$$

Since $k_1 = k_3$ (because k_1 and k_3 represent the magnitude of the propagation vector in the same medium), we must have $\theta_1 = \theta_3$, i.e. the angle of incidence is equal to angle of reflection. Further,

$$\frac{\sin\theta_1}{\sin\theta_2} = \frac{k_2}{k_1} \quad \textbf{(23.5)}$$

* We may mention here that the exponent of the magnetic field will also be the same; thus, even the continuity of any component of the magnetic field would have led to the same equations.

If the two media are **dielectrics** and if (ε_1, μ_1) and (ε_2, μ_2) represent the dielectric permittivity and magnetic permeability of the media below and above the plane $x = 0$, then (see Sec. 22.3)

$$k_1^2 = \omega^2\, \varepsilon_1 \mu_1 \tag{23.6}$$

and

$$k_2^2 = \omega^2\, \varepsilon_2 \mu_2 \tag{23.7}$$

Thus, Eq. (23.5) would imply

$$\frac{\sin\theta_1}{\sin\theta_2} = \sqrt{\frac{\varepsilon_2\mu_2}{\varepsilon_1\mu_1}} \tag{23.8}$$

If $$v_1 = \frac{1}{\sqrt{\varepsilon_1\mu_1}} \text{ and } v_2 = \frac{1}{\sqrt{\varepsilon_2\mu_2}} \tag{23.9}$$

represent speeds of propagation of the waves in media 1 and 2, respectively, then

$$\frac{\sin\theta_1}{\sin\theta_2} = \frac{v_1}{v_2} = \frac{c/n_1}{c/n_2} = \frac{n_2}{n_1}$$

where

$$n_1 = \frac{c}{v_1} \text{ and } n_2 = \frac{c}{v_2} \tag{23.10}$$

represent the refractive indices of the two media. Thus, we have

$$n_1 \sin\theta_1 = n_2 \sin\theta_2 \tag{23.11}$$

which is Snell's law.

23.3 Normal Incidence on a Medium

LO2

When a linearly polarized electromagnetic wave is incident normally at the interface of two media, we can always assume the wave to be y-polarized. Let the two media be characterized by intrinsic impedances η_1 and η_2 (see Fig. 23.2). The electric fields associated with the incident, transmitted and reflected waves can be written as

$$\mathbf{E}_1 = \hat{\mathbf{y}}\, E_{10}\, e^{i(k_1 x - \omega t)} \quad \text{(Incident Wave)} \tag{23.12}$$

$$\mathbf{E}_2 = \hat{\mathbf{y}}\, E_{20}\, e^{i(k_2 x - \omega t)} \quad \text{(Transmitted Wave)} \tag{23.13}$$

$$\mathbf{E}_3 = \hat{\mathbf{y}}\, E_{30}\, e^{-i(k_1 x + \omega t)} \quad \text{(Reflected Wave)} \tag{23.14}$$

The $\mathbf{k}$ vector associated with the incident, transmitted and reflected beams are given by (see Fig. 23.2)

$$\mathbf{k}_1 = k_1\,\hat{\mathbf{x}}, \quad \mathbf{k}_2 = k_2\,\hat{\mathbf{x}} \quad \text{and} \quad \mathbf{k}_3 = -k_1\hat{\mathbf{x}} \tag{23.15}$$

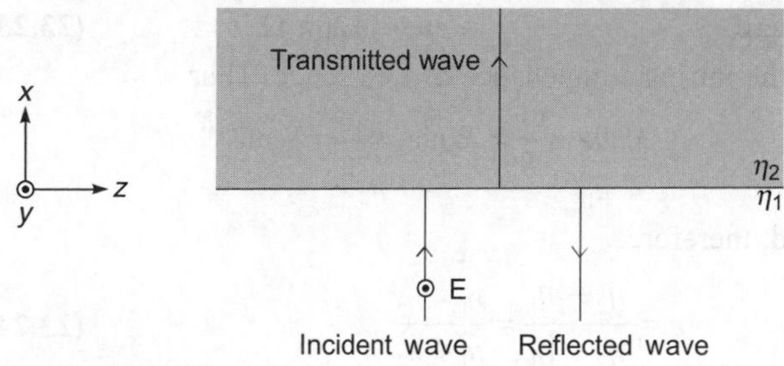

Figure 23.2

The reflection and refraction of a plane wave incident normally at the interface of two media.

Since $\hat{\mathbf{x}} \times \hat{\mathbf{y}} = \hat{\mathbf{z}}$, the corresponding magnetic fields will be given by

$$\left.\begin{aligned} \mathbf{H}_1 &= \frac{\mathbf{k}_1 \times \mathbf{E}_1}{\omega\mu_1} = \hat{\mathbf{z}}\, H_{10}\, e^{i(k_1 x - \omega t)} \\ \mathbf{H}_2 &= \frac{\mathbf{k}_2 \times \mathbf{E}_2}{\omega\mu_2} = \hat{\mathbf{z}}\, H_{10}\, e^{i(k_2 x - \omega t)} \\ \mathbf{H}_3 &= \frac{\mathbf{k}_3 \times \mathbf{E}_3}{\omega\mu_1} = -\hat{\mathbf{z}}\, H_{30}\, e^{-i(k_1 x + \omega t)} \end{aligned}\right\} \tag{23.16}$$

$$\text{where} \quad H_{10} = \frac{E_{10}}{\eta_1}, \quad H_{20} = \frac{E_{20}}{\eta_2} \quad \text{and} \quad H_{30} = \frac{E_{30}}{\eta_1} \tag{23.17}$$

$$\text{where} \quad \eta_1 = \frac{\omega\mu_1}{k_1} \quad \text{and} \quad \eta_2 = \frac{\omega\mu_2}{k_2} \tag{23.18}$$

Since the electric and magnetic fields are tangential to the surface, they must be continuous (at $x = 0$) to obtain

$$E_{10} + E_{30} = E_{20}$$

and $$\frac{E_{10}}{\eta_1} - \frac{E_{30}}{\eta_1} = \frac{E_{20}}{\eta_2}$$

$$\text{Thus,} \quad E_{10} - E_{30} = \frac{\eta_1}{\eta_2} E_{20} \tag{23.19}$$

Using the above equations, we get

$$2E_{10} = \left(1 + \frac{\eta_1}{\eta_2}\right) E_{20} \Rightarrow \quad t = \frac{E_{20}}{E_{10}} = \frac{2\eta_2}{\eta_1 + \eta_2} \tag{23.20}$$

$$\text{Futher,} \quad E_{30} = E_{20} - E_{10} = \left(\frac{2\eta_2}{\eta_1 + \eta_2} - 1\right) E_{10}$$

$$\text{implying } r = \frac{E_{30}}{E_{10}} = \frac{\eta_2 - \eta_1}{\eta_2 + \eta_1} \tag{23.21}$$

23.3.1 Lossless Dielectrics

We next derive complete expressions for **E, H** and **S** for a y-polarized electromagnetic wave incident normally at the interface of two lossless dielectrics characterized by refractive indices n_1 and n_2. Now, in a lossless dielectric (see Sec. 22.3)

$$\eta = \frac{c\mu_0}{n} = \frac{\eta_0}{n} \tag{23.22}$$

where $$\eta_0 = c\mu_0 = 120\pi\ \Omega \quad \textbf{(23.23)}$$
is the intrinsic impedance of free space. Thus,

$$\eta_1 = \frac{\eta_0}{n_1} \quad \text{and} \quad \eta_2 = \frac{\eta_0}{n_2}$$

and, therefore,

$$r = \frac{\eta_2 - \eta_1}{\eta_2 + \eta_1} = \frac{n_1 - n_2}{n_1 + n_2} \quad \textbf{(23.24)}$$

and $$t = \frac{2\eta_2}{\eta_1 + \eta_2} = \frac{2n_1}{n_1 + n_2} \quad \textbf{(23.25)}$$

Thus, when $n_2 > n_1$ there is a phase change on reflection. In order to obtain the actual fields, we take the real parts of **E** and **H** to obtain

$$\mathbf{E}_1 = \hat{\mathbf{y}}\, E_{10} \cos(k_1 x - \omega t)$$
$$\mathbf{H}_1 = \hat{\mathbf{z}}\, \frac{E_{10}}{\eta_1} \cos(k_1 x - \omega t)$$
$$\mathbf{E}_2 = \hat{\mathbf{y}}\, E_{20} \cos(k_2 x - \omega t)$$
$$\mathbf{H}_2 = \hat{\mathbf{z}}\, \frac{E_{20}}{\eta_2} \cos(k_2 x - \omega t)$$
$$\mathbf{E}_3 = \hat{\mathbf{y}}\, E_{30} \cos(k_1 x + \omega t)$$
$$\mathbf{H}_3 = -\hat{\mathbf{z}}\, \frac{E_{30}}{\eta_1} \cos(k_1 x + \omega t)$$

The corresponding time averaged Poynting vectors will be

$$\langle \mathbf{S}_1 \rangle = \langle \mathbf{E}_1 \times \mathbf{H}_1 \rangle = \hat{\mathbf{x}}\, \frac{E_{10}^2}{2\eta_1}$$

$$\langle \mathbf{S}_2 \rangle = \langle \mathbf{E}_2 \times \mathbf{H}_2 \rangle = \hat{\mathbf{x}}\, \frac{E_{20}^2}{2\eta_2}$$

$$\langle \mathbf{S}_3 \rangle = \langle \mathbf{E}_3 \times \mathbf{H}_3 \rangle = -\hat{\mathbf{x}}\, \frac{E_{30}^2}{2\eta_1}$$

Thus, the reflectivity and transmitivity will be given by:

$$R = \frac{|\langle \mathbf{S}_3 \rangle|}{|\langle \mathbf{S}_1 \rangle|} = \frac{|\langle \mathbf{E}_3 \times \mathbf{H}_3 \rangle|}{|\langle \mathbf{E}_1 \times \mathbf{H}_1 \rangle|} = \left| \frac{E_{30}}{E_{10}} \right|^2 = \left(\frac{n_1 - n_2}{n_1 + n_2} \right)^2 \quad \textbf{(23.26)}$$

$$T = \frac{|\langle \mathbf{S}_2 \rangle|}{|\langle \mathbf{S}_1 \rangle|} = \frac{|\langle \mathbf{E}_2 \times \mathbf{H}_2 \rangle|}{|\langle \mathbf{E}_1 \times \mathbf{H}_1 \rangle|} = \frac{n_2}{n_1} \left| \frac{E_{20}}{E_{10}} \right|^2$$

$$= \frac{n_2}{n_1} \left(\frac{2n_1}{n_1 + n_2} \right)^2 = \frac{4 n_1 n_2}{(n_1 + n_2)^2} \quad \textbf{(23.27)}$$

Obviously, $R + T = 1$.

For oblique incidence one has to be careful – see Sec. 23.8.

EXAMPLE 23.1 We consider the air-glass interface, for which $n_1 = 1.0$ and $n_2 = 1.5$ we readily obtain

$$R = 0.04 \quad \text{and} \quad T = 0.96$$

showing 4% reflection at the air-glass interface. Further, since, we have reflection by a denser medium, $\frac{E_{30}}{E_{10}}$ is negative showing a phase of charge of π on reflection.

EXAMPLE 23.2 In this example, we will consider a *y*-polarized electromagnetic wave with E_{10} = 10 V/m (traveling in air with n_1 = 1) incident normally on a dielectric for which n_2 = 2.5. Assuming the free space wavelength to be 6000 Å (= 6 × 10^{-7} m), we will calculate the amplitudes of the reflected and transmitted fields and also the corresponding magnetic fields and the Poynting vectors.

$$r = \frac{n_1 - n_2}{n_1 + n_2} = -0.429$$

and $$t = \frac{2n_1}{n_1 + n_2} = +0.571$$

Thus, $$E_{20} = tE_{10} = 5.71 \text{ V/m}$$

and $$E_{30} = rE_{10} = -4.29 \text{ V/m}$$

Further, $$\eta_1 = \eta_0 = 120\pi = 377\ \Omega$$

and $$\eta_2 = \frac{\eta_0}{n_2} = 150.8\ \Omega$$

Therefore,

$$H_{10} = \frac{E_{10}}{\eta_1} = 2.66 \times 10^{-2} \text{ A/m}$$

$$H_{20} = \frac{E_{20}}{\eta_2} = 3.80 \times 10^{-2} \text{ A/m}$$

and $$H_{30} = -\frac{E_{30}}{\eta_1} = +1.14 \times 10^{-2} \text{ A/m}$$

The complete fields are therefore given by incident wave:

$$\mathbf{E}_1 = \hat{\mathbf{y}}\, 10 \cos(k_1 x - \omega t) \text{ V/m}$$
$$\mathbf{H}_1 = \hat{\mathbf{z}}\, (2.66 \times 10^{-2}) \cos(k_1 x - \omega t) \text{ A/m}$$

Transmitted wave $\mathbf{E}_2 = \hat{\mathbf{y}}\, 5.71 \cos(k_2 x - \omega t)$ V/m
$$\mathbf{H}_2 = \hat{\mathbf{z}}\, (3.80 \times 10^{-2}) \cos(k_2 x - \omega t) \text{ A/m}$$

Reflected wave $\mathbf{E}_3 = -\hat{\mathbf{y}}\, 4.29 \cos(k_1 x + \omega t)$ V/m
$$\mathbf{H}_3 = \hat{\mathbf{z}}\, (1.14 \times 10^{-2}) \cos(k_1 x + \omega t) \text{ A/m}$$

where $$k_1 = \frac{\omega}{c} n_1 = \frac{2\pi}{\lambda_0} = 1.047 \times 10^7 \text{ m}^{-1}$$

and $$k_2 = \frac{\omega}{c} n_2 = \frac{2\pi}{\lambda_0} n_2 = 2.618 \times 10^7 \text{ m}^{-1}$$

The corresponding pointing vectors are given by

$$\langle \mathbf{S}_1 \rangle = \langle \mathbf{E}_1 \times \mathbf{H}_1 \rangle = 0.133\ \hat{\mathbf{x}} \text{ J/m}^2$$
$$\langle \mathbf{S}_2 \rangle = \langle \mathbf{E}_2 \times \mathbf{H}_2 \rangle = 0.1085\ \hat{\mathbf{x}} \text{ J/m}^2$$
$$\langle \mathbf{S}_3 \rangle = \langle \mathbf{E}_3 \times \mathbf{H}_3 \rangle = -0.0244\ \hat{\mathbf{x}} \text{ J/m}^2$$

Thus,

$$R = \frac{|\langle \mathbf{S}_3 \rangle|}{|\langle \mathbf{S}_1 \rangle|} \approx 0.183 \quad \text{and} \quad T = \frac{|\langle \mathbf{S}_2 \rangle|}{|\langle \mathbf{S}_1 \rangle|} \approx 0.816$$

Also,

$$R=\left(\frac{n_1-n_2}{n_1+n_2}\right)^2=\left(\frac{1.5}{3.5}\right)^2=0.1836$$

$$T=\frac{4n_1 n_2}{(n_1+n_2)^2}=\frac{4\times1\times2.5}{3.5\times3.5}=0.8163$$

23.3.2 Normal Incidence on a Perfect Conductor

We next consider a y-polarized electromagnetic wave incident normally on a perfect conductor for which $\sigma_2=\infty$. Thus,

$$g_2=\frac{\sigma_2}{\omega\varepsilon_2}=\infty \Rightarrow |\eta_2|=0$$

(see Sec. 22.8 and also Sec. 23.33). Thus, $t=\frac{2\eta_2}{\eta_1+\eta_2}=0$, and therefore, there is no transmitted wave. Further,

$$r=\frac{\eta_2-\eta_1}{\eta_2+\eta_1}=-1 \Rightarrow E_{30}=-E_{10} \tag{23.28}$$

Thus, the actual electric fields associated with the incident and reflected waves would be given by:

$$\mathbf{E}_1=\hat{\mathbf{y}}\,\mathbf{E}_{10}\cos(k_1x-\omega t)$$

$$\mathbf{E}_3=-\hat{\mathbf{y}}\,\mathbf{E}_{10}\cos(k_1x+\omega t)$$

The incident and reflected waves superpose to give a standing wave (see Sec. 12.2):

$$\mathbf{E}_1+\mathbf{E}_3=\hat{\mathbf{y}}\,(2E_{10})\sin k_1x\sin\omega t$$

23.3.3 Reflectivity of a Good Conductor

We next consider the reflection of an electromagnetic wave incident normally on the interface of a dielectric (characterized by ε_1 and μ_1) and a good conductor (characterized by σ_2, ε_2 and μ_2). By a good conductor we imply (see Sec. 22.8)

$$g_2=\frac{\sigma_2}{\omega\varepsilon_2}\gg1 \tag{23.29}$$

Now, for the conductor

$$k_2^2=\omega^2\varepsilon_2\mu_2+i\,\omega\mu_2\sigma_2 \tag{23.30}$$

Thus $\quad k_2=\beta_2+i\gamma_2=\omega\sqrt{\varepsilon_2\mu_2}\,[1+ig_2]^{1/2}$ (23.31)

where g_2 is defined above. Therefore

$$\eta_2=\frac{\omega\mu_2}{k_2}=\sqrt{\frac{\mu_2}{\varepsilon_2}}\,(1+ig_2)^{-1/2} \tag{23.32}$$

where we have assumed ε_2 to be real and $g_2=\frac{\sigma_2}{\omega\varepsilon_2}$; β_2 and γ_2 are defined in Sec. 22.8. The amplitude reflection coefficient is given by

$$r=\frac{E_{30}}{E_{10}}=\frac{\eta_2-\eta_1}{\eta_2+\eta_1}=-\frac{1-\frac{\eta_2}{\eta_1}}{1+\frac{\eta_2}{\eta_1}} \tag{23.33}$$

Now,

$$\eta_1=\sqrt{\frac{\mu_1}{\varepsilon_1}} \quad\text{and}\quad \eta_2=|\eta_2|e^{-i\theta_2} \tag{23.34}$$

with $\quad |\eta_2|=\sqrt{\frac{\mu_2}{\varepsilon_2}}\cdot\left[1+g_2^2\right]^{-1/4}$ (23.35)

where, $\quad \tan2\theta_2=g_2=\frac{\sigma_2}{\omega\varepsilon_2};\ 0<\theta_2<\frac{\pi}{4}$ (23.36)

Since, $\quad g_2\gg1,\ |\eta_2|\approx\sqrt{\frac{\mu_2}{\varepsilon_2}}\cdot\frac{1}{\sqrt{g_2}}=\sqrt{\frac{\omega\mu_2}{\sigma_2}}$ and $\theta_2\approx\frac{\pi}{4}$.

Thus, $\quad \frac{\eta_2}{\eta_1}\approx\sqrt{\frac{\omega\mu_2\,\varepsilon_1}{\sigma_2\mu_1}}\,e^{-i\pi/4}=(1-i)\,h$ (23.37)

where, $\quad h=\sqrt{\frac{\omega\mu_2\,\varepsilon_1}{2\sigma_2\mu_1}}$ (23.38)

Thus, $\quad r=-\frac{[1-(1-i)h]}{[1+(1-i)h]}$

Since $h\ll1$, we may write

$$r\approx-[1-(1-i)h][1-(1-i)h]\approx-[1-2(1-i)h] \tag{23.39}$$

Thus,

$$R=|r|^2\approx(1-2h)^2+4h^2\approx1-4h$$

or, the reflectivity is approximately given by

$$R\approx1-2\sqrt{\frac{2\omega\mu_2\,\varepsilon_1}{\sigma_2\,\mu_1}} \tag{23.40}$$

Further, the transmitted field is given by

$$\mathbf{E}_2=tE_{10}\,\hat{\mathbf{y}}\,e^{i(k_2x-\omega t)} \tag{23.41}$$

where,

$$t=\frac{2\eta_2}{\eta_1+\eta_2}=\frac{2\frac{\eta_2}{\eta_1}}{1+\frac{\eta_2}{\eta_1}}\approx\frac{2(1-i)h}{1+(1-i)h}\approx\sqrt{2}\,h\,e^{-i\pi/4}$$

where we have used Eq. (23.37). Thus,

$$\mathbf{E}_2=\sqrt{2}\,h\,E_{10}\,\hat{\mathbf{y}}\;e^{-\gamma_2x}e^{i(\beta_2x-\omega t-\pi/4)} \tag{23.42}$$

Thus, there is exponentially decaying electromagnetic wave in the conductor; this will result in Joule heating and absorption.

EXAMPLE 23.3 We consider a linearly polarized electromagnetic wave (with frequency 10 GHz and E_{10} = 15 V/m) propagating in air and incident normally on copper for which

σ_2 = 5.6 × 10^7 mhos/m. Assuming
$\mu_2 = \mu_1 = \mu_0 = 4\pi \times 10^{-7}$ Ns²C⁻²
and $\varepsilon_2 = \varepsilon_1 = \varepsilon_0 = 8.854 \times 10^{-12}$ C²N⁻¹m⁻², we get

$$g_2 = \frac{\sigma_2}{\omega\varepsilon_2} = \frac{5.6\times10^7}{(2\pi\times10^{10})\times8.854\times10^{-12}} \approx 1.0\times10^8$$

Thus, g_2 >>> 1 and therefore, at 10 GHz, copper behaves like a very good conductor. Further,

$$R \approx 1 - 2\sqrt{\frac{2\omega\mu_2\varepsilon_1}{\sigma_2\mu_1}} = 1 - 2\sqrt{\frac{2\times2\pi\times10^{10}\times\mu_0\times8.854\times10^{-12}}{5.6\times10^7\times\mu_0}}$$

$$\approx 0.9997$$

showing extremely high reflectivity. Further,

$$h = \sqrt{\frac{\omega\mu_2\varepsilon_1}{2\sigma_2\mu_1}} \approx \sqrt{\frac{2\pi\times10^{10}\times\mu_0\times8.854\times10^{-12}}{2\times5.6\times10^7\times\mu_0}} \approx 7.05\times10^{-5}$$

Now, $k_2 = \beta_2 + i\gamma_2$, where (for large values of g_2 – see Sec. 22.8):

$$\beta_2 \approx \gamma_2 \approx \omega\sqrt{\frac{\varepsilon_2\mu_2 g_2}{2}} = \sqrt{\frac{\omega\mu_0\sigma_2}{2}}$$

$$\approx \sqrt{\frac{2\pi\times10^{10}\times4\pi\times10^{-7}\times5.6\times10^7}{2}}$$

$$\approx 1.49\times10^6 \text{ m}^{-1}$$

Thus, the complete expression for the transmitted field will be

$$\mathbf{E}_2 = \hat{\mathbf{y}}(1.50\times10^{-3})e^{-1.49\times10^6 x}\cos\left(1.49\times10^6 x - \omega t - \frac{\pi}{4}\right) \text{ V/m}$$

where, x and t are measured in meters and seconds, respectively. The intensity will decrease as

$$I = I_0\, e^{-2\gamma x}$$

If x_0 is the distance in which the intensity will decrease by a factor of 2, then

$$\tfrac{1}{2} = e^{-2\gamma x_0}$$

$$\Rightarrow\ x_0 = \frac{\ln 2}{2\gamma} \approx 2.5\times10^{-7}\,\text{m} = 0.25\,\mu\text{m}$$

The transmitted wave will result in the Joule heating of the conductor.

23.4 Oblique Incidence: E Parallel to the Plane of Incidence

LO3

In this section, we will calculate the amplitude reflection coefficient and the amplitude transmission coefficient for an electromagnetic wave incident (at an angle θ_1) on the interface of two media characterized by intrinsic impedances η_1 and η_2; the interface corresponds to the plane $x = 0$ (see Fig. 23.3). We assume the electric field of the incident wave to be in the plane of incidence so that we may write (for the incident wave)

$$\mathbf{E}_1 = \hat{\mathbf{e}}_1 E_{10}\, e^{i(\mathbf{k}_1\cdot\mathbf{r}-\omega t)} \tag{23.43}$$

$$\mathbf{k}_1 = \hat{\mathbf{k}}_1 k_1$$

where $\hat{\mathbf{e}}_1 = \hat{\mathbf{x}}\sin\theta_1 - \hat{\mathbf{z}}\cos\theta_1$

and $\hat{\mathbf{k}}_1 = \hat{\mathbf{x}}\cos\theta_1 + \hat{\mathbf{z}}\sin\theta_1$

are the unit vector along $\mathbf{E}_1$ and $\mathbf{k}_1$ respectively (see Fig. 23.3). Obviously $\hat{\mathbf{e}}_1\cdot\hat{\mathbf{k}}_1 = 0$ implying $\mathbf{E}_1\cdot\mathbf{k}_1 = 0$. Since, $\hat{\mathbf{k}}_1\times\hat{\mathbf{e}}_1 = \hat{\mathbf{y}}$, we get

$$\mathbf{H}_1 = \frac{\mathbf{k}_1\times\mathbf{E}_1}{\omega\mu_1} = \hat{\mathbf{y}}\,\frac{\mathbf{E}_{10}}{\eta_1}\,e^{i(\mathbf{k}_1\cdot\mathbf{r}-\omega t)} \tag{23.44}$$

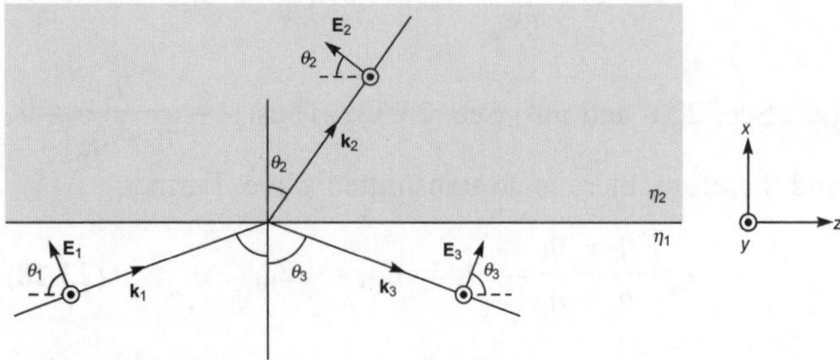

Figure 23.3
The reflection and refraction of a plane wave with its **H** vector lying perpendicular to the plane of incidence (along the *y*-axis) and with the electric vector in the plane of incidence.

It can be readily seen that $\mathbf{H}_1\cdot\mathbf{k}_1 = 0$. The refracted wave will be along

$$\hat{\mathbf{k}}_2 = \hat{\mathbf{x}}\cos\theta_2 + \hat{\mathbf{z}}\sin\theta_2$$

Thus,

$$\hat{\mathbf{e}}_2 = \hat{\mathbf{x}}\sin\theta_2 - \hat{\mathbf{z}}\cos\theta_2$$

$$\mathbf{E}_2 = \hat{\mathbf{e}}_2 E_{20}\, e^{i(\mathbf{k}_2\cdot\mathbf{r}-\omega t)}$$

$$\mathbf{H}_2 = \hat{\mathbf{y}}\,\frac{E_{20}}{\eta_2}\,e^{i(\mathbf{k}_2\cdot\mathbf{r}-\omega t)}$$

The reflected wave will be along

$$\hat{\mathbf{k}}_3 = -\hat{\mathbf{x}}\cos\theta_1 + \hat{\mathbf{z}}\sin\theta_1$$

Thus,

$$\mathbf{E}_3 = \hat{\mathbf{e}}_3 E_{30}\, e^{i(\mathbf{k}_3\cdot\mathbf{r}-\omega t)}$$

$$\hat{\mathbf{e}}_3 = \hat{\mathbf{x}}\sin\theta_1 + \hat{\mathbf{z}}\cos\theta_1$$

and

$$\mathbf{H}_3 = \hat{\mathbf{y}}\,\frac{E_{30}}{\eta_1}\,e^{i(\mathbf{k}_3\cdot\mathbf{r}-\omega t)}$$

As can be easily seen $\mathbf{E}_2\cdot\mathbf{k}_2 = 0 = \mathbf{E}_3\cdot\mathbf{k}_3$

and $\mathbf{H}_2\cdot\mathbf{k}_2 = 0 = \mathbf{H}_3\cdot\mathbf{k}_3$

Now (see Fig. 23.3)

$$E_{1z} = -E_{10}\cos\theta_1\, e^{i(\mathbf{k}_1\cdot\mathbf{r}-\omega t)}$$

$$E_{2z} = -E_{20}\cos\theta_2\, e^{i(\mathbf{k}_2\cdot\mathbf{r}-\omega t)}$$

$$E_{3z} = E_{30}\cos\theta_1\, e^{i(\mathbf{k}_3\cdot\mathbf{r}-\omega t)}$$

Since, E_z and H_y are tangential components, and therefore, they must be continuous at $x = 0$ giving

$$-E_{10} \cos \theta_1 + E_{30} \cos \theta_1 = -E_{20} \cos \theta_2$$

$$\Rightarrow \qquad E_{20} = \frac{\cos \theta_1}{\cos \theta_2}(E_{10} - E_{30}) \tag{23.45}$$

Continuity of H_y would give

$$\frac{E_{10}}{\eta_1} + \frac{E_{30}}{\eta_1} = \frac{E_{20}}{\eta_2}$$

$$\Rightarrow \qquad \frac{\eta_2}{\eta_1}(E_{10} + E_{30}) = E_{20} = \frac{\cos \theta_1}{\cos \theta_2}(E_{10} - E_{30})$$

where we have used Eq. (23.45). Thus,

$$\left(\frac{\eta_2}{\eta_1} + \frac{\cos \theta_1}{\cos \theta_2}\right) E_{30} = \left(\frac{\cos \theta_1}{\cos \theta_2} - \frac{\eta_2}{\eta_1}\right) E_{10}$$

$$r_{\|} = r_p = \frac{E_{30}}{E_{10}} = \frac{\eta_1 \cos \theta_1 - \eta_2 \cos \theta_2}{\eta_1 \cos \theta_1 + \eta_2 \cos \theta_2} \tag{23.46}$$

where $r_{\|}$ denotes the amplitude reflection coefficient by (often also represented by r_p); the subscripts $\|$ and p refer to the fact that we are considering polarization parallel to the plane of incidence. The amplitude transmission coefficient represented by $t_{\|}$ (often also represented by t_p) is given by

$$t_{\|} = t_p = \frac{E_{20}}{E_{10}} = \frac{\eta_2}{\eta_1}\left(1 + \frac{E_{30}}{E_{10}}\right) = \frac{2\eta_2 \cos \theta_1}{\eta_1 \cos \theta_1 + \eta_2 \cos \theta_2} \tag{23.47}$$

For normal incidence $\theta_1 = 0 = \theta_2$ and we get the same expressions as derived in Sec. 23.2. If the two media are lossless dielectrics characterized by refractive indices n_1 and n_2, then

$$\eta_1 = \frac{c}{n_1} \quad \text{and} \quad \eta_2 = \frac{c}{n_2} \tag{23.48}$$

Thus,

$$r_{\|} = r_p = \frac{n_2 \cos \theta_1 - n_1 \cos \theta_2}{n_2 \cos \theta_1 + n_1 \cos \theta_2} \tag{23.49}$$

and

$$t_{\|} = t_p = \frac{2n_1 \cos \theta_1}{n_2 \cos \theta_1 + n_1 \cos \theta_2} \tag{23.50}$$

From the above equations we may deduce the following:

(a) ***No reflection when*** $n_2 = n_1$**:** When $n_2 = n_1$, $\theta_2 = \theta_1$ and we get

$$r_{\|} = 0 \quad \text{and} \quad t_{\|} = 1$$

Thus, there is no reflection when the second medium has the same refractive index as the first medium (obviously!). Thus, if we have a transparent solid immersed in a liquid of the same refractive index, the solid would not be seen!

(b) ***Phase Change on Reflection:*** When light is incident on a denser medium, $\theta_2 < \theta_1$ and for $(\theta_1 + \theta_2) > \pi/2$ (i.e., for $\theta_1 > \theta_p$), $r_{\|}$ is negative implying a phase change of π; θ_p is the Brewster angle defined in Sec. 23.5. However, no such phase change occurs when $\theta_1 < \theta_p$. We will discuss this point in detail later.

(c) ***Stokes' Relations*****:** Figure 23.4 shows that if the media are interchanged, the angles of incidence and refraction are reversed. If $r'_{\|}$ and $t'_{\|}$ denote the amplitude reflection and transmission coefficients corresponding to Fig. 23.4(b), then one can show that (see Problem 23.4)

$$1 + r_{\|} r'_{\|} = t_{\|} t'_{\|} \tag{23.51}$$

This is one of the Stokes' relations—see also Sec. 13.12.

(d) ***Reflection at Grazing Incidence*****:** For grazing incidence $\left(\theta_1 \approx \frac{\pi}{2}\right)$, Eq. (23.49) can be written in the form

$$r_{\|} = \frac{n \sin \alpha_1 - \sin \alpha_2}{n \sin \alpha_1 + \sin \alpha_2} \tag{23.52}$$

(where $n = n_2/n_1$, $\alpha_1 = \frac{\pi}{2} - \theta_1$ and $\alpha_2 = \frac{\pi}{2} - \theta_2$ and at grazing incidence both these angles will be small. Now,

$$n = \frac{\sin \theta_1}{\sin \theta_2} = \frac{\cos \alpha_1}{\cos \alpha_2}$$

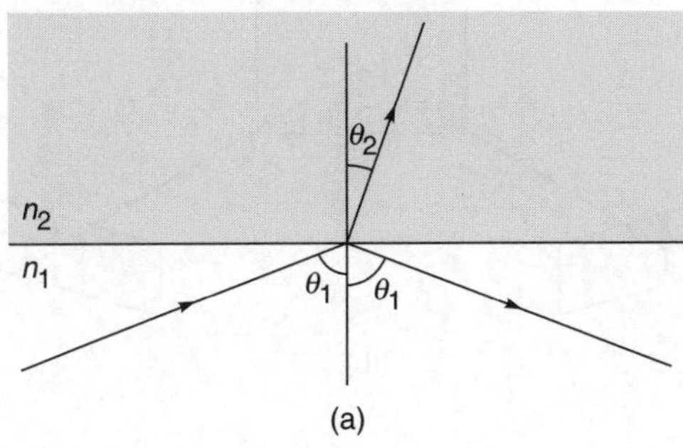

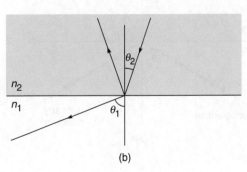

Figure 23.4
The angles of incidence and refraction are reversed if the media are interchanged.

or,

$$\sin\alpha_2 = \left[1-\cos^2\alpha_2\right]^{1/2} = \left[1-\frac{\cos^2\alpha_1}{n^2}\right]^{1/2}$$

Thus,

$$r_{\parallel} = \frac{n\sin\alpha_1 - \left[1-\frac{\cos^2\alpha_1}{n^2}\right]^{1/2}}{n\sin\alpha_1 + \left[1-\frac{\cos^2\alpha_1}{n^2}\right]^{1/2}} \approx \frac{n\,\alpha_1 - \left[1-\frac{1}{n^2}\right]^{1/2}}{n\,\alpha_1 + \left[1-\frac{1}{n^2}\right]^{1/2}} \quad \textbf{(23.53)}$$

where we have replaced sin α_1 by α_1 and cos α_1 by 1 (thus we have retained terms proportional to α_1 but neglected terms of higher order—this will be justified when α_1 is small). Thus,

$$r_{\parallel} \approx -\left[1-\frac{n\alpha_1}{\sqrt{(n^2-1)/n^2}}\right]\left[1+\frac{n\alpha_1}{\sqrt{(n^2-1)/n^2}}\right]^{-1}$$

$$\approx -\left[1-\frac{2n^2\alpha_1}{\sqrt{n^2-1}}\right] \to -1 \text{ as } \alpha_1 \to 0 \quad \textbf{(23.54)}$$

which shows that the reflection is complete at grazing incidence. Thus, if we hold a glass plate horizontally at the level of the eye (see Fig. 23.5) the angle of incidence will be close to $\pi/2$ and the plate will act as a mirror.

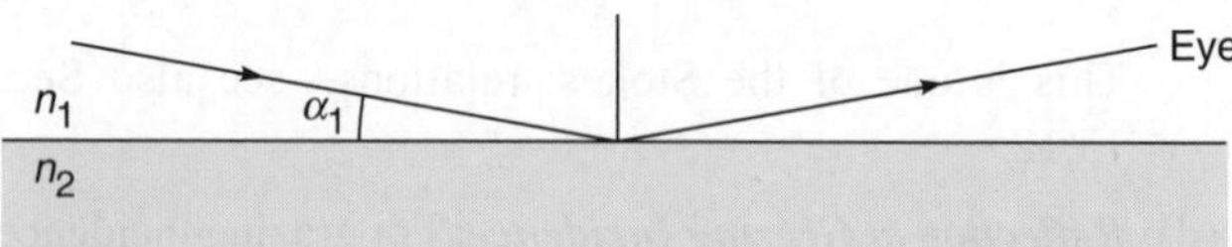

Figure 23.5
When light is incident at grazing angle (i.e., $\alpha_1 \approx 0$) the reflection is almost complete.

23.5 Polarization by Reflection: Brewster's Law

LO4

Now, $r_{\parallel} = 0$ when $n_2 \cos\theta_1 = n_1 \cos\theta_2$ implying

$$\frac{\cos\theta_1}{\cos\theta_2} = \frac{n_1}{n_2} = \frac{\sin\theta_2}{\sin\theta_1}$$

where we have used Snell's law, $n_1 \sin\theta_1 = n_2 \sin\theta_2$. Thus, $\sin 2\theta_1 = \sin 2\theta_2$, giving

$$2\theta_1 = \pi - 2\theta_2 \;\Rightarrow\; \theta_1 + \theta_2 = \frac{\pi}{2} \quad \textbf{(23.55)}$$

(we have neglected the solution $\theta_1 = \theta_2$ which will happen when $n_2 = n_1$, implying that there is no discontinuity!). Thus,

$$n_1 \sin\theta_1 = n_2 \sin\theta_2 = n_2 \sin\left(\frac{\pi}{2}-\theta_1\right) = n_2\cos\theta_1$$

$$\Rightarrow \quad \tan\theta_1 = \frac{n_2}{n_1} \quad \textbf{(23.56)}$$

This is the Brewster angle θ_p

$$\theta_1 = \theta_p = \tan^{-1}\frac{n_2}{n_1} \quad \text{(Brewster's Angle)} \quad \textbf{(23.57)}$$

Thus, when a beam is incident at the Brewster's angle, $r_{\parallel} = 0$ and the reflected light is linearly polarized with its electric vector normal to the plane of incidence (see Fig. 23.6). This is one of the methods for producing linearly polarized light—see Sec. 21.2.2.

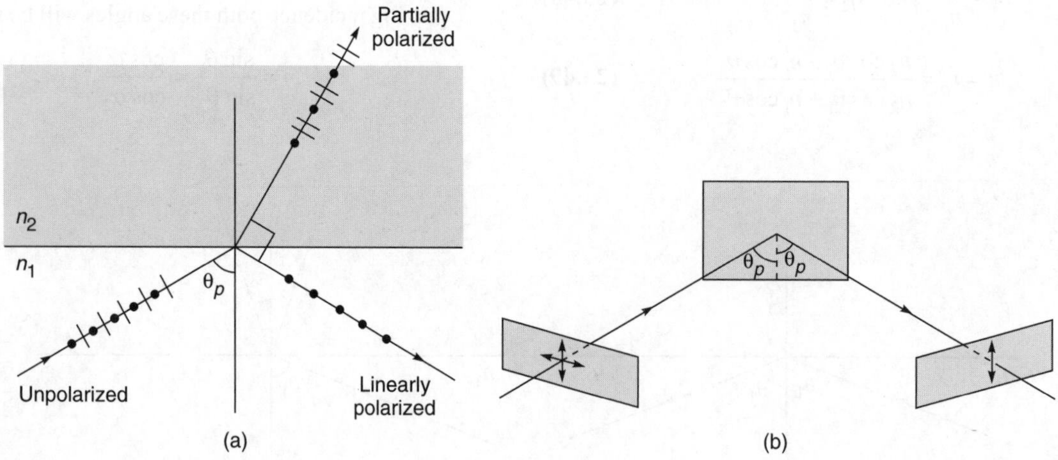

Figure 23.6
When an unpolarized beam of light is incident on a dielectric at the polarizing angle [i.e., the angle of incidence is equal to $\tan^{-1}(n_2/n_1)$] then the reflected beam is plane-polarized with its **E**-vector perpendicular to the plane of incidence. The transmitted beam is partially polarized. The dashed line in (b) is normal to the reflecting surface.

23.6 Total Internal Reflection and the Evanescent Wave

LO5

Consider the incidence of a plane wave (with the electric field in the plane of incidence) at the interface ($x = 0$) of two dielectrics with $n_2 < n_1$. Since $n_1 \sin\theta_1 = n_2 \sin\theta_2$, the angle of refraction $\theta_2 = \dfrac{\pi}{2}$, when

$$\theta_1 = \theta_c \equiv \sin^{-1}\left(\frac{n_2}{n_1}\right) \tag{23.58}$$

The angle of incidence θ_c is referred to as the critical angle and hence the subscript c. For $\theta_1 > \theta_c$, $\sin\theta_2 > 1$ and $\cos\theta_2 \left(= \sqrt{1-\sin^2\theta_2}\right)$ will become imaginary. Now, the electric field associated with the transmitted wave (in the second medium) is given by

$$\mathbf{E}_2 = \mathbf{E}_{20} \exp\left[i(\mathbf{k}_2 \cdot \mathbf{r} - \omega t)\right]$$

$$= \mathbf{E}_{20} \exp\left[i(k_{2x}x + k_{2z}z - \omega t)\right]$$

where, as before, we have chosen our y-axis at right angles to the plane of incidence (thus, $k_{2y} = 0$). Thus,

$$\mathbf{E}_2 = \mathbf{E}_{20} \exp\left[i(k_2 \cos\theta_2\, x + k_2 \sin\theta_2\, z - \omega t)\right] \tag{23.59}$$

Now, $$\cos^2\theta_2 = 1 - \sin^2\theta_2 = 1 - \frac{n_1^2 \sin^2\theta_1}{n_2^2}$$

$$= -\frac{n_1^2}{n_2^2}(\sin^2\theta_1 - \sin^2\theta_c)$$

or, $$\cos\theta_2 = +i\frac{n_1}{n_2}\sqrt{\sin^2\theta_1 - \sin^2\theta_c} \tag{23.60}$$

where we have chosen the + sign so that we have an exponentially attenuating wave:

$$e^{i k_{2x} x} = e^{i k_2 \cos\theta_2 x} = e^{-\alpha x}$$

where, $$\alpha = \frac{\omega}{c} n_1 \sqrt{\sin^2\theta_1 - \sin^2\theta_c}$$

$$= \frac{\omega}{c}\sqrt{n_1^2 \sin^2\theta_1 - n_2^2} \tag{23.61}$$

(We reject the solution $\cos\theta_2 = -i\dfrac{n_1}{n_2}\sqrt{\sin^2\theta_1 - \sin^2\theta_c}$ as it will lead to an exponentially amplifying solution in the region $x > 0$). Thus,

$$\mathbf{E}_2 = \mathbf{E}_{20}\, e^{-\alpha x}\, e^{i(k_{2z}z - \omega t)} \tag{23.62}$$

where, $$k_{2z} = k_2 \sin\theta_2 = \frac{\omega}{c} n_2 \sin\theta_2 = \frac{\omega}{c} n_1 \sin\theta_1$$

Thus, for $\theta_1 > \theta_c \left[= \sin^{-1}\left(\dfrac{n_2}{n_1}\right)\right]$, we have, in the second medium, a wave which decays exponentially in the x-direction and propagates along the z-direction; such a wave is known as an evanescent wave (see Fig. 23.7). The above analysis is valid both when the **E** vector is in the plane of incidence as well as when **E** vector is perpendicular to the plane of incidence.

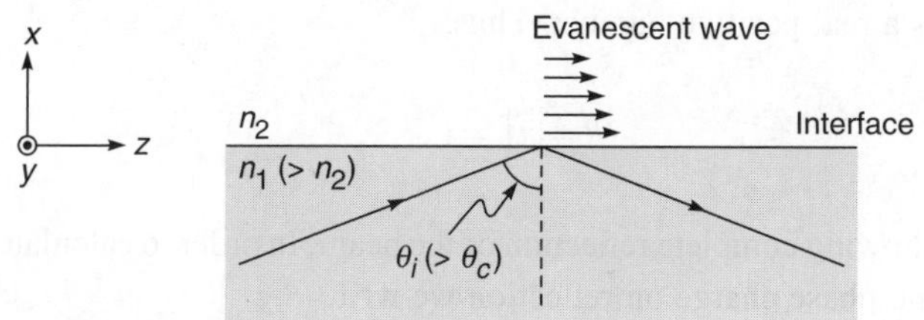

Figure 23.7
An evanescent wave is generated in the rarer medium when a beam undergoes total internal reflection. The evanescent wave propagates along the z-axis and the amplitude decreases along the x-axis.

EXAMPLE 23.4 For the glass-air interface $n_1 = 1.5$, $n_2 = 1.0$, the critical angle is given by

$$\theta_c = \sin^{-1}\left(\frac{n_2}{n_1}\right) = \sin^{-1}\left(\frac{1}{1.5}\right) \approx 41.8°$$

We assume, $\lambda_0 = 6 \times 10^{-7}$ m and the angle of incidence to be 60°, so that

$$\alpha = \frac{\omega}{c} n_1 \sin\theta_1 = \frac{2\pi}{6\times10^{-7}} \times 1.5 \times \sin 60 = 1.36 \times 10^7\ \text{m}^{-1}$$

The evanescent field decreases as $e^{-\alpha x}$; thus, if x_0 is the distance (in the rarer medium) in which the field reduces by a factor of 2, then

$$e^{-\alpha x_0} = \frac{1}{2} \Rightarrow x_0 = \frac{\ln 2}{\alpha}$$

Thus, $$x_0 = \frac{\ln 2}{\alpha} \approx 5.1 \times 10^{-8}\ \text{m} = 51\ \text{nm}$$

which implies that the field associated with the evanescent wave falls of very rapidly.

23.6.1 Reflectivity and Phase Change on Total Internal Reflection

As shown above, when $\theta_1 > \theta_c \left[= \sin^{-1}\left(\frac{n_2}{n_1}\right)\right]$, the beam undergoes total internal reflection and cos θ_2 becomes imaginary [see Eq. (23.60)]; thus, we may write

$$r_{\parallel} = \frac{n_2 \cos\theta_1 - n_1 \cos\theta_2}{n_2 \cos\theta_1 + n_1 \cos\theta_2} = \frac{\cos\theta_1 - iu}{\cos\theta_1 + iu}$$

where, $$u = -i\frac{n_1}{n_2}\cos\theta_2 = \left(\frac{n_1}{n_2}\right)^2 \sqrt{\sin^2\theta_1 - \sin^2\theta_c} \quad (23.63)$$

is a real positive number. Thus,

$$R = |r_{\parallel}|^2 = 1$$

showing complete reflection of the beam. In order to calculate the phase charge on reflection we write

$$r_{\parallel} = \frac{Ae^{-i\phi}}{Ae^{i\phi}} = e^{-2i\phi} \quad (23.64)$$

where, $$A = \sqrt{\cos^2\theta_1 + u^2} \quad (23.65)$$

$$\cos\phi = \frac{\cos\theta_1}{A}; \quad \sin\phi = \frac{u}{A}$$

$$\Rightarrow \quad \phi = \tan^{-1}\left(\frac{u}{\cos\theta_1}\right); \quad 0 < \phi < \frac{\pi}{2}$$

and $$E_{30} = E_{10}\, e^{-2i\phi}$$

Thus, the total phase change on reflection will be given by

$$2\phi = 2\tan^{-1}\left[\left(\frac{n_1}{n_2}\right)^2 \frac{\sqrt{\sin^2\theta_1 - \sin^2\theta_c}}{\cos\theta_1}\right]; \quad 0 < \phi < \frac{\pi}{2} \quad (23.66)$$

The actual electric field will be

$$\mathbf{E}_{30} = E_{10}\, \hat{\mathbf{e}}_3 \cos(\mathbf{k}_3 \cdot \mathbf{r} - \omega t - 2\phi) \quad (23.67)$$

showing the phase shift that would occur when the beam undergoes total internal reflection.

EXAMPLE 23.5 As an example, we will calculate the phase shift for reflection at the glass-air interface ($n_1 = 1.5$ and $n_2 = 1.0$) when the angle of incidence θ_1 is 60°.

Thus, $u = \frac{n_1^2}{n_2^2}\sqrt{\sin^2\theta_1 - \sin^2\theta_c} = 1.5^2\sqrt{\frac{3}{4} - \left(\frac{1}{1.5}\right)^2} = 1.244$

$$\Rightarrow \quad 2\phi = 2\tan^{-1}\left(\frac{u}{\cos\theta_1}\right) \approx \frac{\pi}{1.32}$$

23.7 Oblique Incidence: E Perpendicular to the Plane of Incidence

LO6

We next consider a plane electromagnetic wave, with its electric field perpendicular to the plane of incidence, incident at an angle θ_1 on the interface of two media of intrinsic impedances η_1 and η_2; the interface being at $x = 0$ (see Fig. 23.1). Since the electric field is along the y direction we may write for the incident wave

$$\mathbf{E}_1 = \hat{\mathbf{e}}_1 E_{10} \exp[i(\mathbf{k}_1 \cdot \mathbf{r} - \omega t)]$$

$$\mathbf{H}_1 = (\hat{\mathbf{k}}_1 \times \hat{\mathbf{e}}_1)\frac{E_{10}}{\eta_1} \exp[i(\mathbf{k}_1 \cdot \mathbf{r} - \omega t)]$$

where $\hat{\mathbf{e}}_1 = \hat{\mathbf{y}}$ and $\hat{\mathbf{k}}_1 = \hat{\mathbf{x}}\cos\theta_1 + \hat{\mathbf{z}}\sin\theta_1$ are the unit vectors along the directions of $\mathbf{E}_1$ and $\mathbf{k}_1$. Similarly, for the transmitted wave we have (see Fig. 23.1)

$$\mathbf{E}_2 = \hat{\mathbf{e}}_2 E_{20} \exp[i(\mathbf{k}_2 \cdot \mathbf{r} - \omega t)]$$

$$\mathbf{H}_2 = (\hat{\mathbf{k}}_2 \times \hat{\mathbf{e}}_2)\frac{E_{20}}{\eta_2} \exp[i(\mathbf{k}_2 \cdot \mathbf{r} - \omega t)]$$

$$\mathbf{E}_3 = \hat{\mathbf{e}}_3 E_{30} \exp[i(\mathbf{k}_3 \cdot \mathbf{r} - \omega t)]$$

$$\mathbf{H}_3 = (\hat{\mathbf{k}}_3 \times \hat{\mathbf{e}}_3)\frac{E_{30}}{\eta_3} \exp[i(\mathbf{k}_3 \cdot \mathbf{r} - \omega t)]$$

where

$$\hat{\mathbf{e}}_2 = \hat{\mathbf{e}}_3 = \hat{\mathbf{e}}_1 = \hat{\mathbf{y}}; \quad \hat{\mathbf{k}}_2 = \hat{\mathbf{x}}\cos\theta_2 + \hat{\mathbf{z}}\sin\theta_2$$

$$\hat{\mathbf{k}}_3 = -\hat{\mathbf{x}}\cos\theta_1 + \hat{\mathbf{z}}\sin\theta_1$$

are the unit vectors associated with the transmitted and reflected waves. Both E_y and H_z are components tangential to the interface $x = 0$, their continuity would give us

$$E_{10} + E_{30} = E_{20}$$

and $\frac{E_{10}}{\eta_1}\cos\theta_1 - \frac{E_{30}}{\eta_1}\cos\theta_1 = \frac{E_{20}}{\eta_2}\cos\theta_2 = \frac{E_{10}+E_{30}}{\eta_2}\cos\theta_2$

Thus, $\left(\frac{\cos\theta_1}{\eta_1} - \frac{\cos\theta_2}{\eta_2}\right)E_{10} = \left(\frac{\cos\theta_1}{\eta_1} + \frac{\cos\theta_2}{\eta_2}\right)E_{30}$

Let $r_\perp$ and $t_\perp$ denote the amplitude reflection coefficient and the amplitude transmission coefficient; the subscript $\perp$ refers to the fact that we are considering "perpendicular" polarization; one often uses the subscript *s*; the letter *s* stands for the German word *senkrecht* which means perpendicular. The parallel polarization (or the *p* polarization) is also called the Transverse Magnetic (or the TM) polarization as the magnetic field is perpendicular to the plane of incidence. On the other hand, perpendicular polarization (or the *s* polarization) is also called the Transverse Electric (or the TE) polarization as the electric field is perpendicular to the plane of incidence. Using the above equations we get

$$r_s = r_\perp = \frac{E_{30}}{E_{10}} = \frac{\eta_2\cos\theta_1 - \eta_1\cos\theta_2}{\eta_2\cos\theta_1 + \eta_1\cos\theta_2} \quad \textbf{(23.68)}$$

Further,

$$t_s = t_\perp = \frac{E_{20}}{E_{10}} = 1 + \frac{E_{30}}{E_{10}} = \frac{2\eta_2\cos\theta_1}{\eta_2\cos\theta_1 + \eta_1\cos\theta_2} \quad \textbf{(23.69)}$$

23.7.1 Lossless Dielectrics

We consider the incidence of a plane electromagnetic wave (with its electric field perpendicular to the plane of incidence) at the interface of two dielectrics characterized by refractive indices n_1 and n_2, so that $\eta_1 = \frac{c}{n_1}$ and $\eta_2 = \frac{c}{n_2}$ and we obtain

$$r_s = r_\perp = \frac{n_1\cos\theta_1 - n_2\cos\theta_2}{n_1\cos\theta_1 + n_2\cos\theta_2} \quad \textbf{(23.70)}$$

and $$t_s = t_\perp = \frac{2n_1\cos\theta_1}{n_1\cos\theta_1 + n_2\cos\theta_2} \quad \textbf{(23.71)}$$

For given values of n_1 and n_2, if we wish to study the variations of $|r_{||}|$ and $|r_\perp|$ as a function of θ_1, we must use Snell's law $n_1 \sin\theta_1 = n_2 \sin\theta_2$ to write

$$n_2\cos\theta_2 = \sqrt{n_2^2 - n_1^2\sin^2\theta_1}\ .$$

Thus, $$r_\perp = \frac{n_1\cos\theta_1 - \sqrt{n_2^2 - n_1^2\sin^2\theta_1}}{n_1\cos\theta_1 + \sqrt{n_2^2 - n_1^2\sin^2\theta_1}} \quad \textbf{(23.72)}$$

Similarly, using Eq. (23.49)

$$r_{||} = \frac{n_2^2\cos\theta_1 - n_1\sqrt{n_2^2 - n_1^2\sin^2\theta_1}}{n_2^2\cos\theta_1 + n_1\sqrt{n_2^2 - n_1^2\sin^2\theta_1}} \quad \textbf{(23.73)}$$

Similar expressions for $t_\perp$ and $t_{||}$ can be derived. The variations of $|r_{||}|$ and $|r_\perp|$ (for $n_1 = 1.0$ and $n_2 = 1.5$) are plotted in Fig. 23.8. When

$$\theta_1 = \theta_p = \tan^{-1}\left(\frac{n_2}{n_1}\right) \approx 56.3°$$

(i.e., when the angle of incidence is equal to the Brewster angle $r_{||} = 0$. Further, at this angle $r_\perp \approx -0.385$. Equations (23.68) – (23.73) are known as Fresnel equations. We write

$$r = |r|e^{i\phi} \quad \textbf{(23.74)}$$

The variations of $|r_{||}|$, $|r_\perp|$, $\phi_{||}$ and $\phi_\perp$ are plotted in Figs. 23.8 and 23.9 for $n_2/n_1 = 1.5$. The directions of the **E**-vector in the reflected components are shown in Fig. 23.10. Referring to Fig. 23.8 we note that when

$$\theta_1 = \theta_p = \tan^{-1}\left(\frac{n_2}{n_1}\right) \approx 56°, |r_{||}| = 0$$

This is the Brewster's angle. At grazing incidence (i.e. as $\theta_1 \to 90°$), both $|r_{||}|$ and $|r_\perp|$ tend to 1 implying complete reflection. At normal incidence (i.e. $\theta_1 = 0$), both parallel

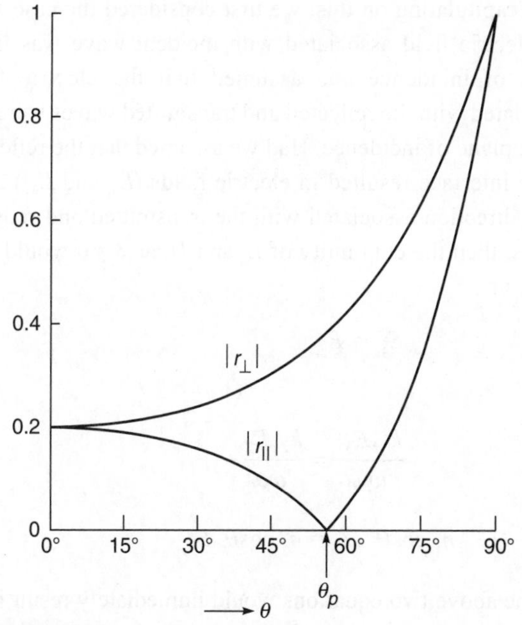

Figure 23.8
Variation of $|r_{||}|$ and $|r_\perp|$ with the angle of incidence when $n_2 = 1.5$ and $n_1 = 1.0$.

polarization as well as perpendicular polarization should give the same result; this is due to the fact that at normal incidence the direction of propagation is coincident with the normal to the reflecting surface and *any* plane containing the normal could be thought of us plane of incidence. Figure 23.8 shows that both $|r_{||}|$ and $|r_{\perp}|$ have the same value at $\theta_1 = 0$; however, Fig. 23.9 shows that while the perpendicular component predicts a phase change of π, there is no phase change associated with the parallel component. There is, however, no inconsistency, if we study the direction of the electric vector associated with the reflected components [see (b) and (d) of Fig. 23.10].

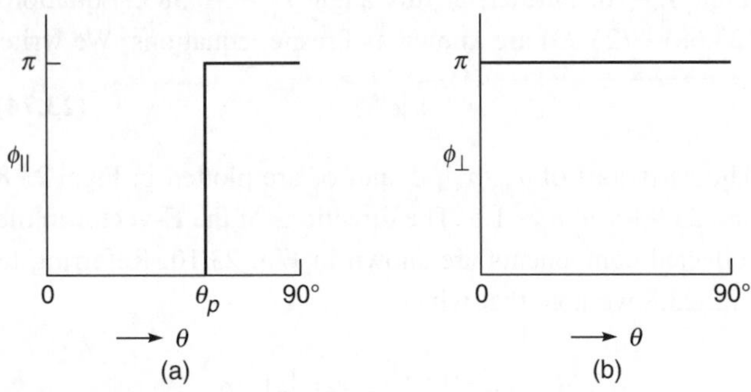

Figure 23.9

The phase change on reflection (a) for the parallel component and (b) for the perpendicular component for $n_2 = 1.5$ and $n_1 = 1.0$; $\phi_{\perp} = \pi$ for all values of θ.

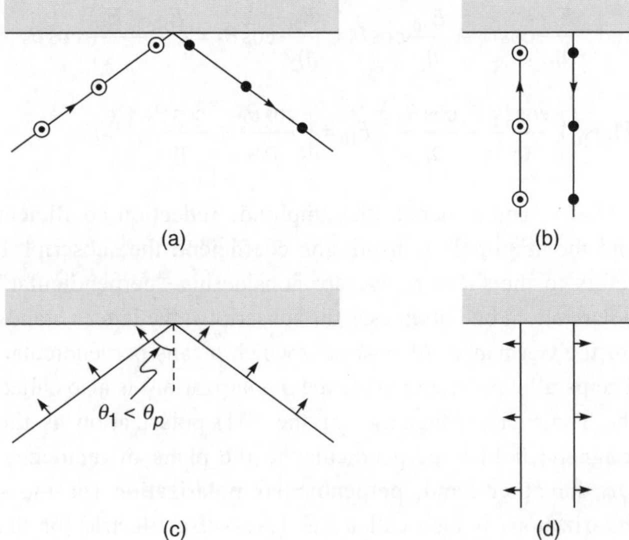

Figure 23.10

For the perpendicular component, there is a phase change of π at all angles [(a) and (b)]. For the parallel component there is no phase change for $\theta_1 < \theta_p$ [see (c) and (d)]. Notice that at normal incidence, the electric field changes direction in both the cases.

Recapitulating on this, we first considered the case when the electric field associated with incident wave was in the plane of incidence and assumed that the electric fields associated with the reflected and transmitted waves were also in the plane of incidence. Had we assumed that the reflection at the interface resulted in electric fields (E_{2y} and E_{3y}) along the y direction associated with the transmitted and reflected waves, then the continuity of E_y and H_z at $x = 0$ would have given us

$$E_{3y} = E_{2y}$$

and

$$\frac{k_{3x}E_{3y}}{\omega\mu_0} = \frac{k_{2x}E_{2y}}{\omega\mu_0}$$

$$\Rightarrow \quad -n_1 \cos\theta_1 E_{3y} = n_2 \cos\theta_2 E_{2y}$$

The above two equations would immediately result in the solutions $E_{3y} = E_{2y} = 0$. Thus, we may conclude that if the incident electric field lies in the plane of incidence then the electric fields associated with the reflected and transmitted waves must also lie in that plane. Similarly, if the incident electric field is perpendicular to the plane of incidence, then the electric field associated with the reflected and transmitted waves will also lie perpendicular to the same plane. In general, for an arbitrary state of polarization of the incident wave, we must resolve the incident electric field in components which are parallel and perpendicular to the plane of incidence and consider the reflection (and transmission) of each of the components and then superpose to find the resultant state of polarization (see Example 23.9). Indeed by studying the polarization characteristics of the reflected wave, one can determine the (complex) refractive index of the material. This is known as the field of "ellipsometry" – a subject of great importance (see, e.g., Ref. 23.11).

23.8 Expressions for Reflectivity and Transmittivity

LO6

In order to calculate the reflection coefficient we must determine the ratio of the x-components of the Poynting vectors associated with the reflected and transmitted waves. The reason why we should take the ratio of the x-component, can easily be understood by referring to Fig. 23.11. If S_1 denotes the magnitude of the Poynting vector associated with the incident wave then the energy incident on the area dA (on the surface $x = 0$) per unit time would be $S_{1x} dA = S_1 dA \cos\theta_1$. Similarly, the energy transmitted through the area dA would be

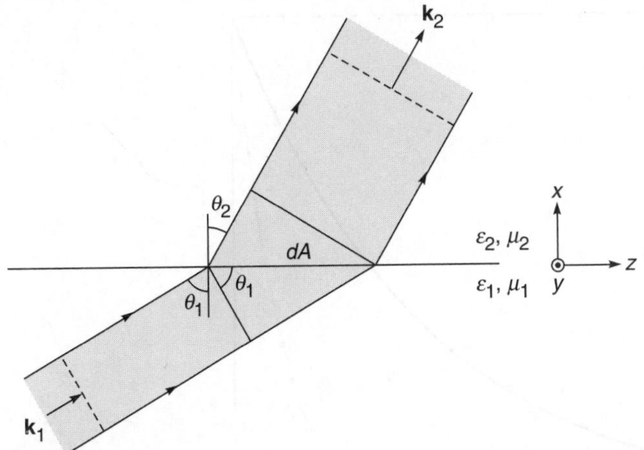

Figure 23.11

If the cross-sectional area of the incident beam is $dA \cos \theta_1$ then the cross-sectional area of the transmitted beam is $dA \cos \theta_2$ where θ_1 and θ_2 represent the angles of incidence and refraction, respectively.

$$S_{2x} dA = S_2 \cos \theta_2 \, dA$$

and the energy reflected from the area dA would be

$$S_{3x} dA = S_3 \cos \theta_1 \, dA$$

Thus, if R and T denote the reflection and transmission coefficients, then

$$R = \frac{S_{3x}}{S_{1x}} = \frac{S_3 \cos \theta_1}{S_1 \cos \theta_1} = \frac{S_3}{S_1} \tag{23.75}$$

and

$$T = \frac{S_{2x}}{S_{1x}} = \frac{S_2 \cos \theta_2}{S_1 \cos \theta_1} \tag{23.76}$$

We must remember that in order to calculate the Poynting vector, we must use the real parts of **E** and **H**; (see Sec. 22.3). We assume that a plane electromagnetic wave, with its electric field perpendicular to the plane of incidence, is incident at an angle θ_1 on the interface of two dielectrics with refractive indices n_1 and n_2; thus,

$$R_s = R_\perp = \frac{S_{3x}}{S_{1x}} = \frac{S_3 \cos \theta_1}{S_1 \cos \theta_1}$$

$$= \frac{|\langle \mathbf{E}_3 \times \mathbf{H}_3 \rangle|}{|\langle \mathbf{E}_1 \times \mathbf{H}_1 \rangle|} = \frac{\frac{1}{\eta_1} |\mathbf{E}_{30}|^2}{\frac{1}{\eta_1} |\mathbf{E}_{10}|^2}$$

$$\Rightarrow \quad R_s = R_\perp = |r_\perp|^2 = \left(\frac{n_1 \cos \theta_1 - n_2 \cos \theta_2}{n_1 \cos \theta_1 + n_2 \cos \theta_2} \right)^2 \tag{23.77}$$

Further,

$$T_s = T_\perp = \frac{S_{2x}}{S_{1x}} = \frac{S_2 \cos \theta_2}{S_1 \cos \theta_1}$$

$$= \frac{|\langle \mathbf{E}_2 \times \mathbf{H}_2 \rangle| \cos \theta_2}{|\langle \mathbf{E}_1 \times \mathbf{H}_1 \rangle| \cos \theta_1} = \frac{\frac{1}{\eta_2} |\mathbf{E}_{20}|^2 \cos \theta_2}{\frac{1}{\eta_1} |\mathbf{E}_{10}|^2 \cos \theta_1}$$

$$\Rightarrow \; T_s = T_\perp = \frac{n_2 \cos \theta_2}{n_1 \cos \theta_1} |t_\perp|^2 = \frac{4 n_1 n_2 \cos \theta_1 \cos \theta_2}{(n_1 \cos \theta_1 + n_2 \cos \theta_2)^2} \tag{23.78}$$

Thus, as expected $R_\perp + T_\perp = 1$. In a similar manner, we can consider the case of a plane electromagnetic wave with its electric field parallel to the plane of incidence to obtain

$$R_p = R_\parallel = \frac{S_{3x}}{S_{1x}} = \frac{S_3}{S_1} = |r_\parallel|^2 = \left(\frac{n_2 \cos \theta_1 - n_1 \cos \theta_2}{n_2 \cos \theta_1 + n_1 \cos \theta_2} \right)^2 \tag{23.79}$$

$$T_p = T_\parallel = \frac{S_{2x}}{S_{1x}} = \frac{S_2 \cos \theta_2}{S_1 \cos \theta_1}$$

$$T_p = T_\parallel = \frac{n_2 \cos \theta_2}{n_1 \cos \theta_1} |t_\parallel|^2 = \frac{4 n_1 n_2 \cos \theta_1 \cos \theta_2}{(n_2 \cos \theta_1 + n_1 \cos \theta_2)^2} \tag{23.80}$$

Once again $R_\parallel + T_\parallel = 1$.

In Fig. 23.12 we have plotted the reflection coefficients for the parallel (p) and the perpendicular (s) components when light is incident from air on a denser medium of refractive index 2.0; notice that $R_p = 0$ at the Brewster's angle (or the polarizing angle) showing that, at this angle of incidence, the reflected light will always be s-polarized. On the other hand, in Fig. 23.13 we have plotted the reflection coefficients for the parallel (p) and the perpendicular (s) components when light is incident from a denser medium of refractive index 2.0 on air; notice that both $R_s = R_p = 1$ at all angles of incidence greater than the critical angle. Further, at the Brewester's angle $R_p = 0$ showing that, at the angle of incidence, the reflected light will again be s-polarized.

EXAMPLE 23.6 In Fig. 23.12 we have plotted the reflection coefficients $R_\parallel$ and $R_\perp$ as a function of the angle of incidence for $n_1 = 1.0$ and $n_2 = 2.0$. The Brewster angle is 63.43° where $R_\perp$ is zero and the reflected wave is linearly polarized. In Fig. 23.13, we have plotted the reflection coefficients $R_\parallel$ and $R_\perp$ as a function of the angle of incidence for $n_1 = 2.0$ and $n_2 = 1.0$. The Brewster angle is 26.56° where $R_\perp$ is zero and the reflected wave is linearly polarized. The critical angle is 30° beyond which the reflectivity is unity for both parallel and perpendicular polarizations.

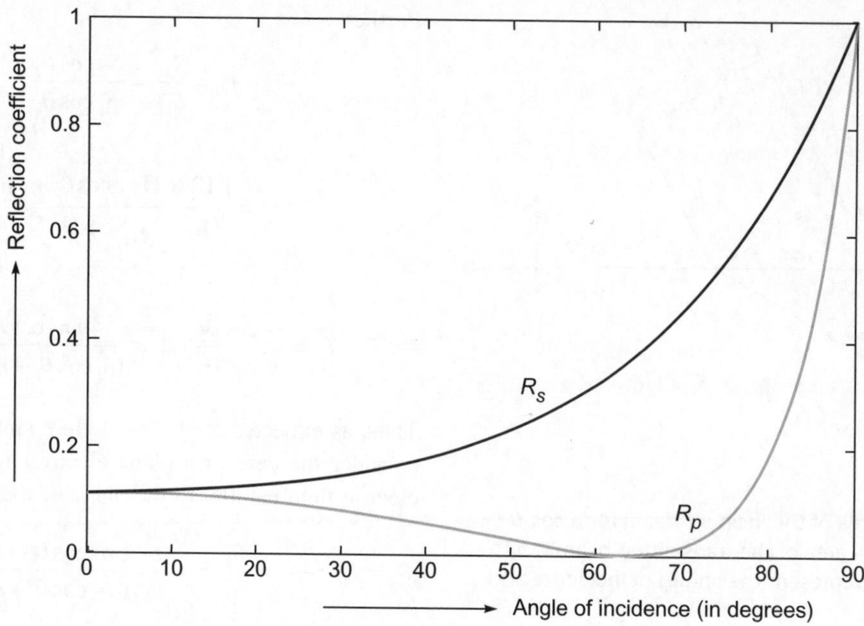

Figure 23.12

The reflection coefficients for the *p* (parallel) and *s* (perpendicular) components when a light beam is incident from a rarer medium (of refractive index 1.0) on a denser medium of refractive index 2.0. The Brewster angle is 63.43° where R_p is zero and the reflected wave is *s* polarized.

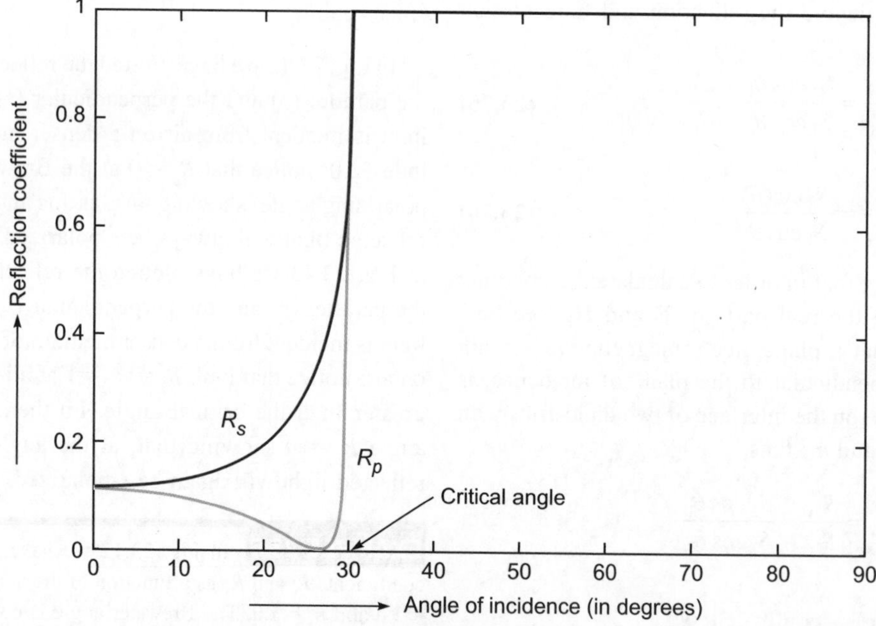

Figure 23.13

The reflection coefficients for the *p* (parallel) and *s* (perpendicular) components when a light beam is incident from a denser medium (of refractive index 2.0) on a rarer medium of refractive index 1.0. The Brewster angle is 26.56° where R_p is zero and the reflected wave is *s* polarized. The critical angle is 30° beyond which the reflection coefficient is unity.

23.9 Poynting Vector Calculation for the Evanescent Wave LO7

Consider the incidence of a plane electromagnetic wave (with its electric field perpendicular to the plane of incidence) at the interface of two dielectrics with $n_2 < n_1$. Assume the angle of incidence θ_1 to be greater than the critical angle θ_c. In this section we will calculate $\langle S_{2x}\rangle$ and $\langle S_{2z}\rangle$ (where $\mathbf{S}_2$ is the Poynting vector associated with the transmitted wave) and interpret the results physically. Now, the electric and magnetic fields associated with the incident wave are

$$\mathbf{E}_1 = \hat{\mathbf{y}}\, E_{10}\, e^{i(k_{1x}x + k_{1z}z - \omega t)}$$

$$\mathbf{H}_1 = (-\hat{\mathbf{x}}\cos\theta_1 + \hat{\mathbf{z}}\sin\theta_1)\frac{E_{10}}{\eta_1}\, e^{i(k_{1x}x + k_{1z}z - \omega t)}$$

where $\eta_1 = \dfrac{c}{n_1}$, $k_{1x} = \dfrac{\omega}{c} n_1 \cos\theta_1$, $k_{1z} = \dfrac{\omega}{c} n_1 \sin\theta_1$

Thus,

$$\langle S_{1x}\rangle = \frac{E_{10}^2}{\eta_1}\sin\theta_1 \langle \cos^2(k_{1x}x + k_{1z}z - \omega t)\rangle = \frac{E_{10}^2}{2\eta_1}\sin\theta_1$$

Similarly $\langle S_{1z}\rangle = \dfrac{E_{10}^2}{2\eta_1}\cos\theta_1$

$$\text{Now } t_\perp = \frac{2n_1\cos\theta_1}{n_1\cos\theta_1 + n_2\cos\theta_2} = \frac{2\cos\theta_1}{\cos\theta_1 + i\sqrt{\sin^2\theta_1 - \sin^2\theta_c}}$$

$$= |t_\perp| e^{-i\phi_\perp}$$

where,

$$|t_\perp| = \frac{2\cos\theta_1}{\cos\theta_c};\ \cos\phi_\perp = \frac{\cos\theta_1}{\cos\theta_c};\ \sin\phi_\perp = \frac{\sqrt{\sin^2\theta_1 - \sin^2\theta_c}}{\cos\theta_c}$$

Thus, for the transmitted wave

$$\mathbf{E}_2 = \hat{\mathbf{y}}\, E_{10}\, |t_\perp| e^{-\alpha x}\, e^{i(k_{2z}z - \omega t - \phi_\perp)} \tag{23.81}$$

where (see Sec. 23.6)

$$\alpha = \frac{\omega}{c} n_1 \sqrt{\sin^2\theta_1 - \sin^2\theta_c}$$

and
$$k_{2z} = \frac{\omega}{c} n_2 \sin\theta_2 = \frac{\omega}{c} n_1 \sin\theta_1 \tag{23.82}$$

Since, k_{2x} $(= +i\alpha)$ is imaginary, we have to be little careful in calculating the magnetic field. We start with writing the actual electric field

$$\mathbf{E}_2 = \hat{\mathbf{y}}\, E_{10}\, |t_\perp| e^{-\alpha x}\cos(k_{2z}z - \omega t - \phi_\perp)$$

Since,

$$\nabla \times \mathbf{E} = -\frac{\partial \mathbf{B}}{\partial t} = -\mu\frac{\partial \mathbf{H}}{\partial t}$$

we get,

$$-\mu_2 \frac{\partial \mathbf{H}_2}{\partial t} = -\hat{\mathbf{x}}\frac{\partial E_{2y}}{\partial z} + \hat{\mathbf{z}}\frac{\partial E_{2y}}{\partial x}$$

$$= \hat{\mathbf{x}}\, k_{2z}\, E_{10} |t_\perp| e^{-\alpha x}\sin(k_{2z}z - \omega t - \phi_\perp)$$

$$- \hat{\mathbf{z}}\, \alpha\, E_{10} |t_\perp| e^{-\alpha x}\cos(k_{2z}z - \omega t - \phi_\perp)$$

$$\Rightarrow \quad \mathbf{H}_2 = -\hat{\mathbf{x}}\frac{k_{2z}}{\omega\mu_2} E_{10} |t_\perp| e^{-\alpha x}\cos(k_{2z}z - \omega t - \phi_\perp)$$

$$- \hat{\mathbf{z}}\frac{\alpha}{\omega\mu_2} E_{10} |t_\perp| e^{-\alpha x}\sin(k_{2z}z - \omega t - \phi_\perp)$$

Thus, H_{2z} is $\dfrac{\pi}{2}$ out of phase with E_{2y} and, therefore,

$$\langle S_{2x}\rangle = \langle E_{2y} H_{2z}\rangle = 0$$

which shows that there is no power flow along the x direction and, therefore, the transmission coefficient is zero and the reflection is complete. Further,

$$\langle S_{2z}\rangle = \langle E_{2y} H_{2x}\rangle = \frac{k_{2z}}{2\omega\mu_2}|t_\perp E_{10}|^2 e^{-2\alpha x}$$

showing that there is power flow along the z-axis. Indeed, when a spatially bounded beam is incident at an interface making an angle greater than the critical angle, then the beam undergoes a lateral shift which can be interpreted as the beam entering the rarer medium and reemerging (from the rarer medium) after reflection—see Fig. 23.14. This is known as the Goos–Hanchen shift.

EXAMPLE 23.7 We consider the incidence of a plane electromagnetic wave on an air-glass interface (see Fig. 23.1). Thus, $n_1 = 1.0$ and $n_2 = 1.5$ giving

$$\theta_p = \tan^{-1}(1.5) \approx 56.31°$$

For $\theta_1 = 30°$; $\theta_2 = 19.47°$ we get

$r_\parallel \approx 0.1589$; $t_\parallel \approx 0.7725$
$r_\perp \approx -0.2404$; $t_\perp \approx 0.7596$

On the other hand, for $\theta_1 = 89°$ (grazing incidence), $\theta_2 = 41.80°$ and

$r_\parallel \approx -0.9321$ (~87% reflection); $t_\parallel \approx 0.0452$
$r_\perp \approx -0.9693$; and $t_\perp \approx 0.0307$

EXAMPLE 23.8 We next consider the incidence of a plane electromagnetic wave on a rarer medium like a glass air interface. Thus, $n_1 = 1.5$ and $n_2 = 1.0$ giving

$$\theta_p = \tan^{-1}\left(\frac{1}{1.5}\right) \approx 33.69° \text{ and } \theta_c = \sin^{-1}\left[\frac{1}{1.5}\right] \approx 41.81°$$

(i) For $\theta_1 = 30°$, and $\theta_2 = 48.59°$ and

$r_\parallel \approx -0.06788$; $t_\parallel \approx +1.3982$
$r_\perp \approx +0.3252$; $t_\perp \approx +1.3252$

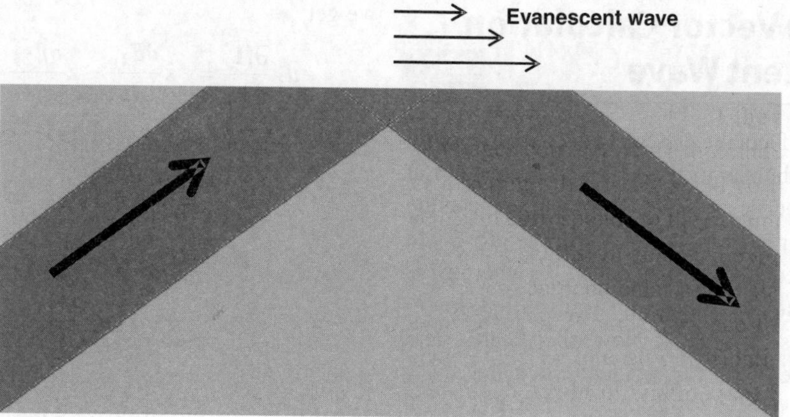

Figure 23.14
The lateral shift (referred to as the Goos-Hanchen shift) of a beam undergoing total internal reflection by a rarer medium; the lateral shift has been exaggerated.

(ii) For $\theta_1 = 60°$, $\cos\theta_2 = i\alpha$, with $\alpha = 0.82916$

$$r_{\|} = \frac{n_2\cos\theta_1 - n_1\cos\theta_2}{n_2\cos\theta_1 + n_1\cos\theta_2}$$

$$= \frac{0.5 - i1.5\alpha}{0.5 + i1.5\alpha} \approx -0.7217 - i0.6922$$

$$\approx e^{-0.7567\pi i}$$

[Use of Eq. (23.65) would give the same result]

$$t_{\|} = \frac{2n_2\cos\theta_1}{n_2\cos\theta_1 + n_1\cos\theta_2}$$

$$\approx \frac{1.5}{0.5 + i1.5\alpha} \approx 0.41739 - i1.0382$$

$$\approx 1.1190e^{-0.3783\pi i}$$

$$r_{\perp} = \frac{n_1\cos\theta_1 - n_2\cos\theta_2}{n_1\cos\theta_1 + n_2\cos\theta_2} \approx \frac{0.75 - i\alpha}{0.75 + i\alpha}$$

$$\approx -0.1 - i0.9950 \approx e^{0.532\pi i}$$

(Notice $|r_{\|}| = |r_{\perp}| = 1$). Further,

$$t_{\perp} = \frac{2n_1\cos\theta_1}{n_1\cos\theta_1 + n_2\cos\theta_2} \approx 0.9 - i0.995$$

$$\approx 1.3416e^{-0.266\pi i}$$

EXAMPLE 23.9 Consider a linearly polarized electromagnetic wave (with its electric vector along the y-direction of magnitude 5 V/m) propagating in vacuum. It is incident on a dielectric interface at $x = 0$ at an angle of incidence of 30°. The frequency associated with the wave is 6×10^{14} Hz. The refractive index of the dielectric is 1.5. We will calculate complete expressions for the electric and magnetic fields associated with the incident, reflected and transmitted waves.

The wave vector associated with the incident wave is given by

$$\mathbf{k}_1 = (k_0\cos 30)\hat{\mathbf{x}} + (k_0\sin 30)\hat{\mathbf{z}} = \frac{\sqrt{3}}{2}k_0\,\hat{\mathbf{x}} + \frac{1}{2}k_0\,\hat{\mathbf{z}}$$

Thus, $$\mathbf{E}_1 = \hat{\mathbf{y}}\,5\exp\left[i\left(\frac{\sqrt{3}}{2}k_0\,x + \frac{1}{2}k_0\,z - \omega t\right)\right] \text{V/m}$$

where, $$\omega = 12\pi\times 10^{14}\text{ Hz};\ k_0 = \frac{\omega}{c} = 4\pi\times 10^6\text{ m}^{-1}$$

Now, $$\sin\theta_2 = \frac{n_1\sin\theta_1}{n_2} = \frac{1}{3} \Rightarrow \cos\theta_2 = \frac{\sqrt{8}}{3}$$

Thus, $$r_{\perp} = \frac{n_2\cos\theta_1 - n_2\cos\theta_2}{n_2\cos\theta_1 + n_2\cos\theta_2} = -0.2404$$

$\Rightarrow$ $$R_s = R_{\perp} = 0.057796$$

and $$t_{\perp} = \frac{2\cos\theta_1\sin\theta_2}{\sin(\theta_1+\theta_2)} = 0.7596$$

implying $$T_s = T_{\perp} = \frac{n_2\cos\theta_2}{n_1\cos\theta_1}|t_{\perp}|^2 = 0.942204$$

showing that $R_{\perp} + T_{\perp} = 1$. Now,

$$\mathbf{k}_2 = \hat{\mathbf{x}}(n_2k_0\cos\theta_2) + \hat{\mathbf{z}}(n_2k_0\sin\theta_2) = \hat{\mathbf{x}}\left(\sqrt{2}k_0\right) + \hat{\mathbf{z}}\left(\frac{1}{2}k_0\right)$$

and $$\mathbf{k}_3 = -\hat{\mathbf{x}}\,k_0\cos\theta_1 + \hat{\mathbf{z}}(k_0\sin\theta_1)$$

$$= -\hat{\mathbf{x}}\left(\frac{\sqrt{3}}{2}k_0\right) + \hat{\mathbf{z}}\left(\frac{1}{2}k_0\right)$$

Thus, the electric fields associated with the transmitted and reflected waves would be given by

$$\mathbf{E}_2 = 3.8\hat{\mathbf{y}}\exp\left[i\left(\sqrt{2}k_0x + \frac{1}{2}k_0z - \omega t\right)\right] \text{V/m}$$

and $$\mathbf{E}_3 = -1.2\hat{\mathbf{y}}\exp\left[i\left(-\frac{\sqrt{3}}{2}k_0x + \frac{1}{2}k_0z - \omega t\right)\right] \text{V/m}$$

respectively. Notice that the values of k_z in $\mathbf{E}_1$, $\mathbf{E}_2$ and $\mathbf{E}_3$ are the same [see Eq. (23.2)].

Now, $\eta_1 = \eta_0 = \sqrt{\dfrac{\mu_0}{\varepsilon_0}} = 120\pi\,\Omega$ and $\eta_2 = \dfrac{\eta_0}{n_2} = 80\pi\,\Omega$. The corresponding magnetic fields would be

$$\mathbf{H}_1 = 0.0133(-\hat{\mathbf{x}}\sin\theta_1 + \hat{\mathbf{z}}\cos\theta_1)$$

$$\times \exp\left[i\left(\frac{\sqrt{3}}{2}k_0 x + \frac{1}{2}k_0 z - \omega t\right)\right] \text{A/m}$$

$$\mathbf{H}_2 = 0.0151(-\hat{\mathbf{x}}\sin\theta_2 + \hat{\mathbf{z}}\cos\theta_2)$$

$$\times \exp\left[i\left(\sqrt{2}k_0 x + \frac{1}{2}k_0 z - \omega t\right)\right] \text{A/m}$$

and

$$\mathbf{H}_3 = -0.00318(-\hat{\mathbf{x}}\sin\theta_1 - \hat{\mathbf{z}}\cos\theta_1)$$

$$\times \exp\left[i\left(-\frac{\sqrt{3}}{2}k_0 x + \frac{1}{2}k_0 z - \omega t\right)\right] \text{A/m}$$

EXAMPLE 23.10 Consider once again the situation described in Example 23.9 except that the magnetic vector is now along the y-direction. We will calculate the expressions for the electric fields associated with the incident, reflected and transmitted waves. Referring to Fig. 23.3, we have

$$\mathbf{E}_1 = 5\left(\frac{1}{2}\hat{\mathbf{x}} - \frac{\sqrt{3}}{2}\hat{\mathbf{z}}\right) \times \exp\left[i\left(\frac{\sqrt{3}}{2}k_0 x + \frac{1}{2}k_0 z - \omega t\right)\right] \text{V/m}$$

Now

$$r_{\|} = \frac{n_2\cos\theta_1 - n_1\cos\theta_2}{n_2\cos\theta_1 + n_1\cos\theta_2} = 0.1589$$

$$\Rightarrow \qquad R_{\|} = 0.02525$$

and

$$t_{\|} = \frac{2n_1\cos\theta_1}{n_2\cos\theta_1 + n_1\cos\theta_2} = 0.7726$$

implying

$$T_{\|} = \frac{n_2\cos\theta_2}{n_1\cos\theta_1}\left|t_{\|}\right|^2 = 0.97475$$

showing that $R_{\|} + T_{\|} = 1$. Furthermore,

$$\mathbf{E}_2 = 3.863\left(\frac{1}{3}\hat{\mathbf{x}} - \frac{\sqrt{8}}{3}\hat{\mathbf{z}}\right).\exp\left[i\left(\sqrt{2}\,k_0 x + \frac{1}{2}k_0 z - \omega t\right)\right] \text{V/m}$$

$$\mathbf{E}_3 = 0.7945\left(\frac{1}{2}\hat{\mathbf{x}} + \frac{\sqrt{3}}{2}\hat{\mathbf{z}}\right).\exp\left[i\left(-\frac{\sqrt{3}}{2}k_0 x + \frac{1}{2}k_0 z - \omega t\right)\right] \text{V/m}$$

EXAMPLE 23.11 For the situation described in Example 23.9, we consider a right-circularly polarized wave incident at the air-glass interface at $\theta_1 = 30°$. We will determine the state of polarization of the reflected and transmitted fields.

We refer to Fig. 23.15. We must resolve the electric field in components parallel and perpendicular to the plane of incidence. We write for the y-component of the incident field

$$E_{\perp} = E_y = E_0 \cos(k_1 \cos\theta_1\, x + k_1 \sin\theta_1\, z - \omega t)$$

then for the beam to be right-circularly polarized, the parallel component must be given by

$$E_{\|} = E_0 \cos\left(k_1\cos\theta_1\, x + k_1\sin\theta_1\, z - \omega t - \frac{\pi}{2}\right)$$

Neglecting the space-dependent parts (or, assuming $x = 0$, $z = 0$), we will have

$$E_{\perp} = E_y = E_0 \cos\omega t \quad \text{and} \quad E_{\|} = -E_0 \sin\omega t$$

The direction of the 'parallel axis', is as shown in Fig. 23.15(b), is consistent with Fig. 23.3. Thus,

$$E_x = E_{\|} \sin\theta_1 = -E_0 \sin\theta_1 \sin\omega t$$

and
$$E_z = -E_{\|} \cos\theta_1 = +E_0 \cos\theta_1 \sin\omega t$$

In the reflected field, the 'parallel component' will be along the direction shown in Fig. 23.15(c)-consistent with Fig. 23.3. Now, $r_{\perp} \approx -0.24$ (see Example 23.9) and $r_{\|} \approx +0.16$ (see Example 23.10); thus, associated with the reflected wave

$$E_y = E_{\perp} = r_{\perp} E_0 \cos\omega t \approx -0.24\, E_0 \cos\omega t$$

and
$$E_{\|} = -r_{\|} E_0 \sin\omega t \approx -0.16\, E_0 \sin\omega t$$

If we now refer to Fig. 23.15(c), the electric vector will rotate in the clockwise direction and since the propagation is 'out of the page' the reflected wave is left-elliptically polarized. We can carry out a similar analysis for the transmitted wave to show that it is right-elliptically polarized.

23.10 Reflectivity of a Dielectric Film

LO8

In this section we will calculate the reflectivity of a dielectric film for a plane wave incident normally on it. We will determine the thickness of the film for which the film will become anti-reflecting and compare our results with those obtained in Sec. 14.4. In Problem 23.13, we will apply our results to a Fabry-Perot interferometer [cf. Sec. 15.2].

We consider a plane wave incident normally on a dielectric film of thickness d (see Fig. 23.16). Without any loss of generally, we assume the electric field to be along the y-axis. Thus, the electric fields in media 1, 2 and 3 is given by

$$\mathbf{E}_1 = \hat{\mathbf{y}}\, E_{10}^{+}\, e^{i(k_1 x - \omega t)} + \hat{\mathbf{y}}\, E_{10}^{-}\, e^{-i(k_1 x + \omega t)}$$

$$\mathbf{E}_2 = \hat{\mathbf{y}}\, E_{20}^{+}\, e^{i(k_2 x - \omega t)} + \hat{\mathbf{y}}\, E_{20}^{-}\, e^{-i(k_2 x + \omega t)} \qquad \textbf{(23.83)}$$

$$\mathbf{E}_3 = \hat{\mathbf{y}}\, E_{30}^{+}\, e^{i[k_3(x-d) - \omega t]}$$

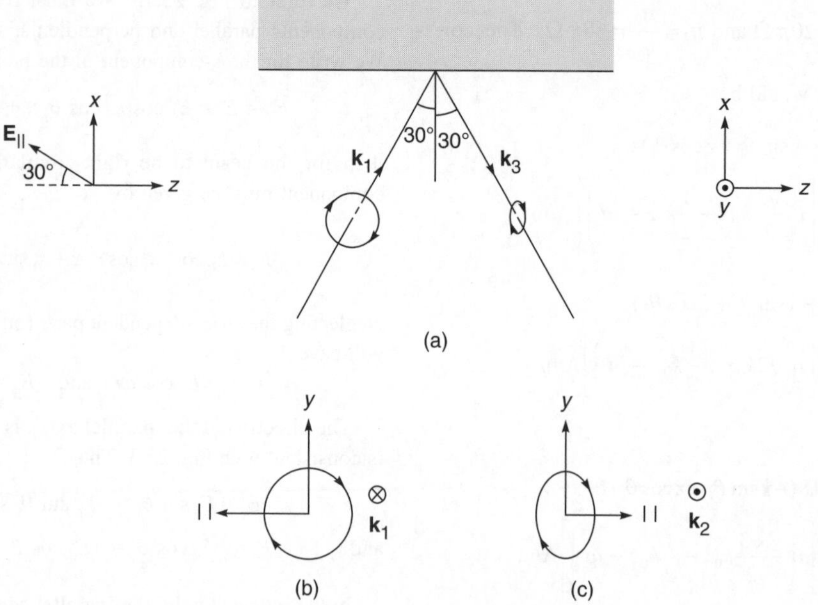

Figure 23.15

(a) A right–circularly polarized beam is incident on an air-glass interface at 30°. The reflected beam is left-elliptically polarized; (b) shows the direction of rotation of the **E**-vector for the incident wave. The direction of propagation (shown as ⊗) is into the page; (c) shows the direction of rotation of the **E**-vector for the reflected wave. The direction of propagation (shown as ⊙) is coming out of the page.

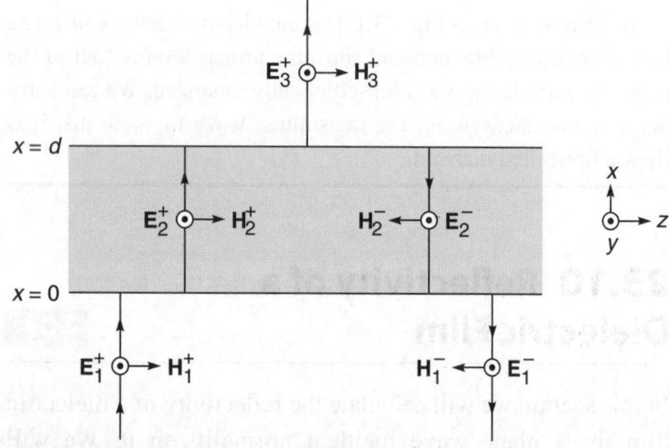

Figure 23.16

Reflection of a plane wave incident normally on a dielectric slab of thickness *d*.

where E_{10}^+ and E_{10}^- represent the amplitude of the forward and backward propagating waves in region 1; similarly for other fields. Since, the 3rd medium extends to infinity, there is no backward propagating wave in region 3. For $\mathbf{E}_3$, we have for the sake of convenience, introduced a phase factor of exp $[-ik_3d]$; this term makes the analysis more straightforward. The corresponding magnetic field is given by (see Sec. 22.2):

$$\mathbf{H} = \frac{1}{\eta}(\hat{\mathbf{k}} \times \mathbf{E}) \tag{23.84}$$

where $\hat{\mathbf{k}} = \hat{\mathbf{x}}$ for waves propagating in the $+x$ direction, and $= -\hat{\mathbf{x}}$ for waves propagating in the $-x$ direction

Thus,

$$\mathbf{H}_1 = \hat{\mathbf{z}}\frac{1}{\eta_1}\left[E_{10}^+ e^{i(k_1x-\omega t)} - E_{10}^- e^{-i(k_1x+\omega t)}\right]$$

$$\mathbf{H}_2 = \hat{\mathbf{z}}\frac{1}{\eta_2}\left[E_{20}^+ e^{i(k_2x-\omega t)} - E_{20}^- e^{-i(k_2x+\omega t)}\right]$$

$$\mathbf{H}_3 = \hat{\mathbf{z}}\frac{1}{\eta_3} E_{30}^+ e^{i[k_3(x-d)-\omega t]} \tag{23.85}$$

Both E_y and H_z represent tangential components, and should therefore be continuous at interfaces $x = 0$ and $x = d$. The continuity conditions at $x = 0$ give us

$$E_{10}^+ + E_{10}^- = E_{20}^+ + E_{20}^-$$

and

$$\frac{1}{\eta_1}(E_{10}^+ - E_{10}^-) = \frac{1}{\eta_2}(E_{20}^+ - E_{20}^-)$$

or

$$E_{10}^+ - E_{10}^- = \frac{n_2}{n_1}(E_{20}^+ - E_{20}^-)$$

where we have used the relations

$$\eta_1 = \frac{\eta_0}{n_1} \quad \text{and} \quad \eta_2 = \frac{\eta_0}{n_2}$$

Simple manipulations give us

$$\begin{pmatrix} E_{10}^+ \\ E_{10}^- \end{pmatrix} = \begin{pmatrix} \dfrac{n_1+n_2}{2n_1} & \dfrac{n_1-n_2}{2n_1} \\ \dfrac{n_1-n_2}{2n_1} & \dfrac{n_1+n_2}{2n_1} \end{pmatrix} \begin{pmatrix} E_{20}^+ \\ E_{20}^- \end{pmatrix} \quad (23.86)$$

Similarly, the continuity of E_y and H_z at $x = d$ gives us

$$E_{20}^+ e^{i\delta} + E_{20}^- e^{-i\delta} = E_{30}^+$$

$$E_{20}^+ e^{i\delta} - E_{20}^- e^{-i\delta} = \frac{n_3}{n_2} E_{30}^+$$

where $\delta = k_2 d$. Elementary manipulations give us

$$\begin{pmatrix} E_{20}^+ \\ E_{20}^- \end{pmatrix} = \begin{pmatrix} \dfrac{n_2+n_3}{2n_2} e^{-i\delta} \\ \dfrac{n_2-n_3}{2n_2} e^{i\delta} \end{pmatrix} E_{30}^+ \quad (23.87)$$

Combining Eqs. (23.86) and (23.87), we get

$$E_{10}^+ = \left[\left(\frac{n_1+n_2}{2n_1} \right) \left(\frac{n_2+n_3}{2n_2} e^{-i\delta} \right) + \left(\frac{n_1-n_2}{2n_1} \right) \left(\frac{n_2-n_3}{2n_2} e^{i\delta} \right) \right] E_{30}^+ \quad (23.88)$$

and

$$E_{10}^- = \left[\left(\frac{n_1-n_2}{2n_1} \right) \left(\frac{n_2+n_3}{2n_2} e^{-i\delta} \right) + \left(\frac{n_1+n_2}{2n_1} \right) \left(\frac{n_2-n_3}{2n_2} e^{i\delta} \right) \right] E_{30}^+ \quad (23.89)$$

Dividing Eq. (23.88) by Eq. (23.89), we get the amplitude reflection coefficient

$$r = \frac{E_{10}^-}{E_{10}^+} = \frac{r_1 e^{-i\delta} + r_2 e^{i\delta}}{e^{-i\delta} + r_1 r_2 e^{i\delta}} \quad (23.90)$$

where
$$r_1 = \frac{n_1 - n_2}{n_1 + n_2} \quad (23.91)$$

and
$$r_2 = \frac{n_2 - n_3}{n_2 + n_3} \quad (23.92)$$

represent the amplitude reflection coefficients at the first and second interface respectively. The reflectivity would therefore be given by

$$R = |r|^2 = \frac{r_1^2 + r_2^2 + 2 r_1 r_2 \cos 2\delta}{1 + r_1^2 r_2^2 + 2 r_1 r_2 \cos 2\delta} \quad (23.93)$$

In Sections 15.2–15.4, we had discussed the above equation in detail with $r_2 = -r_1$; however, the definition of δ here differs by a factor of 2 from the definition of δ in Chapter 15 (see Problem 23.13). We should mention here that a more general analysis shows that the above equation remains valid even for oblique incidence with δ now equal to $k_2 d \cos\theta_2$, θ_2 being the angle of refraction in the second medium and r_1 and r_2 representing the appropriate Fresnel reflection coefficients corresponding to the particular angle of incidence and state of polarization.

SUMMARY

- Consider the incidence of a linearly polarized electromagnetic wave on an interface of two dielectrics (which we assume to be $x = 0$); the x–y plane is assumed to be the plane of incidence. Let $n_1 \left(= \sqrt{\dfrac{\varepsilon_1}{\varepsilon_0}} \right)$ and $n_2 \left(= \sqrt{\dfrac{\varepsilon_2}{\varepsilon_0}} \right)$ be the refractive indices of the two media. The incident wave, refracted wave and reflected waves can be written as

$$\mathbf{E}_1 = \mathbf{E}_{10} \exp[i(\mathbf{k}_1 \cdot \mathbf{r} - \omega t)] \quad \text{incident wave}$$

$$\mathbf{E}_2 = \mathbf{E}_{20} \exp[i(\mathbf{k}_2 \cdot \mathbf{r} - \omega t)] \quad \text{refracted wave}$$

$$\mathbf{E}_3 = \mathbf{E}_{30} \exp[i(\mathbf{k}_3 \cdot \mathbf{r} - \omega t)] \quad \text{reflected wave}$$

where $\mathbf{E}_{10}$, $\mathbf{E}_{20}$ and $\mathbf{E}_{30}$ are independent of space and time and

$$k_1 = \frac{\omega}{c} n_1 = k_3; \quad k_2 = \frac{\omega}{c} n_2$$

$$k_1 \sin\theta_1 = k_2 \sin\theta_2 = k_3 \sin\theta_3$$

where θ_1, θ_2 and θ_3 are the angle of incidence, angle of refraction and angle of reflection respectively. The above equations readily give $n_1 \sin\theta_1 = n_2 \sin\theta_2$ (Snell's law).

- For $\mathbf{E}_1$ lying in the x–z plane (which is the plane of incidence)

$$\mathbf{E}_{10} = E_{10} (\hat{\mathbf{x}} \sin\theta_1 - \hat{\mathbf{z}} \cos\theta_1)$$

$$\mathbf{E}_{20} = t_\parallel E_{10} (\hat{\mathbf{x}} \sin\theta_2 - \hat{\mathbf{z}} \cos\theta_2)$$

$$\mathbf{E}_{30} = r_\parallel E_{10} (\hat{\mathbf{x}} \sin\theta_1 + \hat{\mathbf{z}} \cos\theta_1)$$

$$r_\parallel = \frac{n_2 \cos\theta_1 - n_1 \cos\theta_2}{n_2 \cos\theta_1 + n_1 \cos\theta_2} = \frac{\tan(\theta_1 - \theta_2)}{\tan(\theta_1 + \theta_2)}$$

$$t_\parallel = \frac{2 n_1 \cos\theta_1}{n_2 \cos\theta_1 + n_1 \cos\theta_2} = \frac{2 \cos\theta_1 \sin\theta_2}{\sin(\theta_1 + \theta_2) \cos(\theta_1 - \theta_2)}$$

Notice that $r_\parallel = 0$ when $\theta_1 + \theta_2 = \dfrac{\pi}{2}$, which implies

$$\theta_1 = \theta_p = \tan^{-1}(n_2/n_1).$$

This is the Brewster's angle.

- For $\mathbf{E}_1$ perpendicular to the plane of incidence (i.e., along $\hat{\mathbf{y}}$),

$$\mathbf{E}_{10} = E_{10}\hat{\mathbf{y}};\ \ \mathbf{E}_{20} = t_\perp E_{10}\hat{\mathbf{y}} \text{ and } \mathbf{E}_{30} = r_\perp E_{10}\hat{\mathbf{y}}$$

we have

$$r_\perp = \frac{n_1\cos\theta_1 - n_2\cos\theta_2}{n_1\cos\theta_1 + n_2\cos\theta_2} = -\frac{\sin(\theta_1-\theta_2)}{\sin(\theta_1+\theta_2)}$$

and

$$t_\perp = \frac{2n_1\cos\theta_1}{n_1\cos\theta_1 + n_2\cos\theta_2} = \frac{2\sin\theta_2\cos\theta_1}{\sin(\theta_1+\theta_2)}$$

- In both cases, if $n_2 < n_1$ and $\theta_1 < \theta_c = \sin^{-1}\left(\frac{n_2}{n_1}\right)$ we have total internal reflection. We can still use the above expressions for $r_\parallel$, $t_\parallel$, $r_\perp$ and $t_\perp$ but we must remember that $\sin\theta_2 = \frac{n_1}{n_2}\sin\theta_1$ will be greater than 1

and $$\cos\theta_2 = \sqrt{1-\sin^2\theta_2} = i\alpha$$

will be pure imaginary. Thus $r_\parallel$, $t_\parallel$, $r_\perp$ and $t_\perp$ will be complex quantities with $|r_\parallel| = 1 = |r_\perp|$ showing that the entire energy is reflected; however, there will be an evanescent wave in the second medium whose field will decay along the x-axis and propagate along the z-axis.

PROBLEMS

23.1 (a) Consider reflection at the interface of two dielectrics. Starting with the expression $r_\parallel = \frac{n_2\cos\theta_1 - n_1\cos\theta_2}{n_2\cos\theta_1 + n_1\cos\theta_2}$ and use Snell's law $n_1 \sin\theta_1 = n_2 \sin\theta_2$ to show that

$$r_\parallel = \frac{\tan(\theta_1-\theta_2)}{\tan(\theta_1+\theta_2)} \quad \textbf{(23.94)}$$

(b) Using the above expression for $r_\parallel$, derive Brewster's Law.

23.2 Consider reflection at the interface of two dielectrics. Show that the expressions for r_s, t_p and t_s can be written in the form

$$r_s = r_\perp = \frac{n_1\cos\theta_1 - n_2\cos\theta_2}{n_1\cos\theta_1 + n_2\cos\theta_2} = -\frac{\sin(\theta_1-\theta_2)}{\sin(\theta_1+\theta_2)} \quad \textbf{(23.95)}$$

$$t_p = t_\parallel = \frac{2n_1\cos\theta_1}{n_2\cos\theta_1 + n_1\cos\theta_2} = \frac{2\cos\theta_1\sin\theta_2}{\sin\theta_1\cos\theta_1 + \sin\theta_2\cos\theta_2} \quad \textbf{(23.96)}$$

$$t_s = t_\perp = \frac{2n_1\cos\theta_1}{n_1\cos\theta_1 + n_2\cos\theta_2} = \frac{2\cos\theta_1\sin\theta_2}{\sin(\theta_1+\theta_2)} \quad \textbf{(23.97)}$$

Equations (23.94)–(23.97) are known as Fresnel equations.

23.3 Consider the incidence of a plane electromagnetic wave (with its electric field in the plane of incidence) at the interface of two dielectrics characterized by refractive indices n_1 and n_2. Derive the reflection and transmission coefficients by assuming the continuity of tangential components of **E** and normal components of **D** and show that the results are the same as obtained in Sec. 23.4.

23.4 Consider the incidence of a plane wave (with the electric field in the plane of incidence) at the interface ($x = 0$) of two dielectrics with $n_2 < n_1$. Figure 23.4 shows that if the media are interchanged the angles of incidence and refraction are reversed. If $r'_\parallel$ and $r'_\parallel$ denote the amplitude reflection and transmission coefficients corresponding to Fig. 23.5(b), then show that

$$1 + r_\parallel r'_\parallel = t_\parallel t'_\parallel$$

23.5 Show that in the limit of $\theta_1 \to 0$ (i.e., at normal incidence) the reflection coefficient is the same for parallel and perpendicular polarizations.

23.6 Consider a magnetic dielectric with a permeability such that $\mu/\mu_0 = \varepsilon/\varepsilon_0$. Show that for such a material, the reflection coefficient for normal incidence is identically equal to zero. This realization is equivalent to the situation where the impedance is matched at the junction of two transmission lines.

23.7 In Sec. 23.8 we had calculated the Poynting vector for the evanescent wave. Show that, if we use the formula

$$\mathbf{H}_2 = \frac{\mathbf{k}_2 \times \mathbf{E}_2}{\omega\mu}$$

we get the some expressions for H_x and H_z although the vector $\mathbf{k}_2$ is now complex.

23.8 A right-circularly polarized beam is incident on a perfect conductor at 45°. Show that the reflected beam is left-circularly polarized.

23.9 Assume $n_1 = 1.5$ and $n_2 = 1.0$ (see Example 23.7)

(a) For $\theta_1 = 45°$ show that

$$r_\parallel = +0.28 - i0.96;\ t_\parallel = 1.92 - i1.44$$

Similarly calculate $r_\perp$ and $t_\perp$.

(b) On the other hand, for $\theta_1 = 33.69°$ show that

$$r_\parallel = 0,\ t_\parallel = 1.5$$

$$r_\perp = +0.3846,\ t_\perp = 1.3846$$

23.10 Consider a right-circularly polarized beam incident on a medium of refractive index 1.6 at an angle 60°. Calculate $r_\parallel$ and $r_\perp$ and show that the reflected beam is right elliptically polarized with its major axis much longer than its minor axis. What will happen at 58°?

[Ans: $r_\parallel = -0.0249$, $r_\perp = -0.4581$**]**

23.11 Consider a y-polarized wave incident on a glass-air interface ($n_1 = 1.5$, $n_2 = 1.0$) at $\theta_1 = 45°$ and at $\theta_1 = 80°$. Wave the complete expressions for the transmitted field and show that in the latter case it is an evanescent wave with depth of penetration (= $1/\beta$) equal 0 about 8.8×10^{-8} m; assume $\lambda = 6000$ Å.

23.12 For gold, at $\lambda_0 = 6530$ Å the complex refractive index given by $n_2 = 0.166 + 3.15i$. Calculate k_2 and show that the reflectivity at normal incidence is approximately 94%. On the other hand, at $\lambda_0 = 4000$ Å, $n_2 = 1.658 + 1.956i$; show that the reflectivity is only 39%.

23.13 Show that for $\delta = 0$, Eq. (23.93) takes the form

$$R = \left(\frac{n_1 - n_3}{n_1 + n_3}\right)^2 \quad \textbf{(23.98)}$$

as it indeed should be. Using the various equations in Sec. 23.9, calculate the transitivity and show that

$$T = \frac{\frac{1}{2} n_3 \left|E_3^+\right|^2}{\frac{1}{2} n_1 \left|E_1^+\right|^2} = 1 - R$$

Assume the third medium in Fig. 23.16 to be identical to the first medium, i.e., $n_3 = n_1$. Thus,

$$r_2 = -r_1 = \frac{n_1 - n_2}{n_1 + n_2}$$

Using Eq. (23.92), show that

$$R = \frac{F \sin^2 \delta}{1 + F \sin^2 \delta} \quad \textbf{(23.99)}$$

where $$F = \frac{4r_1^2}{\left(1 - r_1^2\right)^2} \quad \textbf{(23.100)}$$

is called the coefficient of finese. Equations (23.99) and (23.100) are the same as Eqs. (16.3) and (16.4) except that, in this chapter $\delta = k_2 d = \frac{2\pi}{\lambda_0} n_2 d$ and in Chapter 15, $\delta = \frac{4\pi}{\lambda_0} n_2 h \cos \theta_2$ [see Eq. (15.1)].

PART 3

QUANTUM THEORY

This part consists of three chapters. The first one is on the particle model of radiation. The photoelectric effect (discovered by Hertz in 1888) had certain peculiarities which cannot be explained on the basis of wave theory. In 1905, Einstein provided a simple explanation of the peculiarities by assuming that light consisted of quanta of energy $h\nu$ (where ν is the frequency) and that the emission of a photoelectron was the result of the interaction of a single quantum (i.e., of the photon) with an electron. Chapter 24 also discusses the Compton effect (for which Professor Compton received the 1927 Nobel Prize in Physics) which established that the photon has a momentum equal to h/λ. In Chapter 25 we discuss the Bohr model for the hydrogen atom and in Chapter 26 we will discuss important concepts in quantum theory: the indeterminateness in measurements, the superposition of states and the collapse of the wave function. The concept of entanglement will also be discussed.

CHAPTER

24

Particle Nature of Radiation: The Photon

Are not the rays of light very small bodies emitted from shining substances.

—Isaac Newton in OPTICKS*

It is undeniable that there is an extensive group of data concerning radiation which shows that light has certain fundamental properties that can be understood much more readily from the standpoint of the Newton emission (particle) theory than from the standpoint of the wave theory. It is my opinion, therefore, that the next phase of the development of theoretical physics will bring us a theory of light that can be interpreted as a kind of fusion of the wave and emission theories.

—Albert Einstein (1909)**

LEARNING OBJECTIVES

After reading this chapter, the reader should be able to:

LO 1: *know about photoelectric effect and Einstein's photoelectric equation.*

LO 2: *explain Compton effect quantitatively and demonstrate kinematics of Compton scattering.*

LO 3: *derive angular momentum of a photon.*

LO 4: *discuss optical tweezers and their research applications.*

Important Milestones

1887: Heinrich Hertz while receiving the electromagnetic waves in a coil with a spark gap, found that the maximum spark length was reduced when the apparatus was put in a black box.

1897: J.J. Thomson discovered the electron.

1899: J.J. Thomson showed that electrons are emitted when light falls on a metal surface; these are known as photoelectrons.

1900: In order to derive the blackbody radiation formula, Planck made a drastic assumption that the oscillators can only assume discrete energies.

1902: Philip Lenard observed that maximum kinetic energy of the emitted photoelectrons

* Query 29; p. 371 in Ref. 24.1.

** The author found this quotation in Ref. 24.2.

Above Image: Extremely important spectroscopic data are obtained during total solar eclipse shown above. Diagram courtesy: McGraw Hill Digital Access Library.

was independent of the intensity of the incident light and that the energy of the emitted electron increased when the frequency of the incident light was increased.

1905: In a paper entitled, ***On a heuristic point of view about the creation and conversion of light***, Einstein introduced the light quanta. In this paper he wrote that when a light ray starting from a point is propagated, the energy is not continuously distributed over an ever increasing volume, but it consists of a finite number of energy quanta, localized in space, which move without being divided and which can be absorbed or emitted only as a whole. Using his 'quanta of energy', Einstein put forward his famous photoelectric equation, which was experimentally verified to a tremendous degree of accuracy by Millikan (around 1914). Einstein received the 1921 Nobel Prize in Physics, 'for his services to Theoretical Physics, and especially for his explanation of the photoelectric effect'.

1923: Compton reported his studies on the scattering of X-rays by solid materials (mainly graphite) and showed that the shift of the wavelength of the scattered photon could be explained by assuming the photon having momentum equal to $h\nu/c$. Compton received the 1927 Nobel Prize in Physics 'for his discovery of the effect named after him'.

1926: Gilbert Lewis, an American chemist, coined the word 'photon' to describe Einstein's localized energy quanta.

24.1 Introduction

In earlier chapters, we have discussed interference, diffraction and polarization of light. All these phenomena can be explained satisfactorily on the basis of wave theory of light. We have also discussed the electromagnetic character of light waves (see Chapters 21, 22 and 23) and have shown that electromagnetic theory can be successfully used to explain reflection and refraction of waves from dielectric and metal surfaces, the phenomenon of double refraction and many other experimental results.

In spite of the tremendous success of Maxwell's electromagnetic wave theory, Einstein, in his year of miracles (1905) published a paper (Ref. 24.3), in which he proposed that light can be emitted or absorbed only in discrete amounts, called *quanta*; the energy of which is given by

$$E = h\nu \tag{24.1}$$

where ν is the frequency and $h\left(\approx 6.626 \times 10^{-34}\ \text{Js}\right)$ is the Planck's constant. Einstein interpreted the photoelectric effect experiment by stating that the emission of a photoelectron was the result of the interaction of a single quantum (i.e., of the photon) with an electron. It was only in 1926 that Gilbert Lewis, an American chemist, coined the word 'photon' to describe Einstein's 'localized energy quanta'. Now, according to Maxwell's electromagnetic wave theory, the momentum per unit volume associated with a plane electromagnetic wave (propagating in the $+z$–direction) is given by (see Sec. 22.9)

$$\mathbf{p} = \frac{u}{c}\hat{\mathbf{z}} \tag{24.2}$$

where u is the energy (per unit volume) associated with the propagating electromagnetic wave, $c(\approx 3 \times 10^8\ \text{m/s})$ is the speed of light in free space and $\hat{\mathbf{z}}$ is the unit vector along the z-direction. In a later paper, Einstein said that the momentum of the photon would be given by

$$p = \frac{h\nu}{c} = \frac{h}{\lambda} \tag{24.3}$$

Also from Einstein's mass-energy relation (see Sec. 31.4),

$$E^2 = m^2c^4 = m_0^2c^4 + p^2c^2 \tag{24.4}$$

where m_0 is the rest mass of the particle. For the photon, $m_0 = 0$ and

$$p^2 = \frac{E^2}{c^2} \quad \Rightarrow p = \frac{E}{c} = \frac{h\nu}{c} = \frac{h}{\lambda} \tag{24.5}$$

Around 1924, Arthur Compton carried out scattering of high energy photons by electrons. He showed that scattering experiments could only be explained if the energy and momentum of the photon are assumed to be given by the above equations (see Sec. 24.3). In the early part of 20th century, Maxwell's wave theory was so well established that no one really believed in Einstein's 'localized energy quanta'; it was only after the analysis of Compton's experiment that people started believing in Einstein's 'localized energy quanta' which eventually led to wave-particle duality and quantum theory.

In this chapter we will discuss famous experiments on photoelectric effect and Compton effect which established the particle nature of light; a wave model is inadequate to explain these effects. In Chapter 1, we had briefly discussed how one can reconcile to the dual nature of radiation (i.e., the wave and the particle aspects) on the basis of quantum theory. In Chapter 26, we will have more discussions on quantum theory.

24.2 The Photoelectric Effect LO1

In 1887, while receiving the electromagnetic waves in a coil with a spark gap, Hertz found that the maximum spark length was reduced when the apparatus was put in a black box; this is due to what is now known as the **photoelectric effect** and the box absorbed the ultraviolet radiation which helped the electrons in jumping across the gap. Hertz reported the observations but did not pursue further and also did not make any attempt to explain them. In 1897, J J Thomson discovered the electron and in 1899 he showed that electrons are emitted when light falls on a metal surface; these are now known as photoelectrons. In 1902, Philip Lenard observed that

(a) the kinetic energy of the emitted electrons was independent of the intensity of the incident light, and
(b) that the energy of the emitted electron increased when the frequency of the incident light was increased.

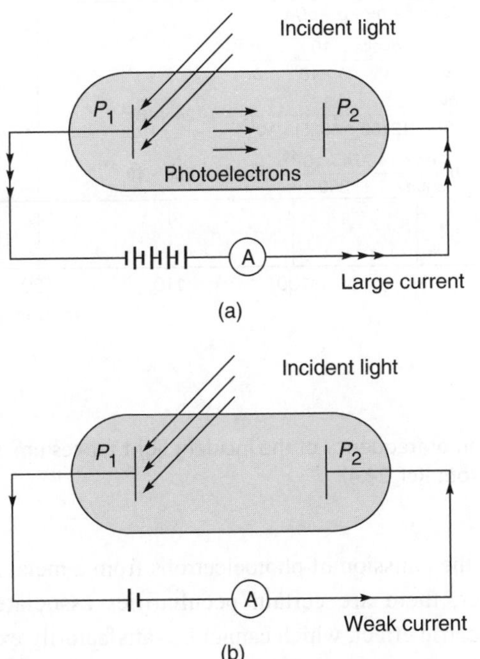

Figure 24.1
If light (of certain frequency) is allowed to fall on a metal like sodium, electrons are emitted which can be collected by the plate P_2. (a) and (b) correspond to positive and negative voltage applied to the plate P_2. Even when the plate is kept at a low negative voltage, one can detect a small current.

Later Millikan carried out very careful experiments (see References 24.4 and 24.5) on the photoelectric effect and the apparatus that he used was similar to the one shown in Fig. 24.1; these photoelectrons constitute a current between the plates P_1 and P_2 and can be collected by a metal plate P_2 which can be detected by means of an ammeter A. When the voltage across the plates is varied, the current also varies; typical variations of the current with voltage are shown in Fig. 24.2. The figure corresponds to monochromatic light of a particular frequency and different curves correspond to different intensities of the beam. From the figure one can draw the following conclusions:

(a) At zero voltage there is a finite value of the current implying that some of the emitted photoelectrons reach the metal surface P_2.
(b) As the voltage is increased, the current increases till it reaches a saturation value; this will happen when the plate P_2 collects all the emitted photoelectrons.
(c) If the plate P_2 is kept at a slightly negative potential, there is a weak current implying that some of the photoelectrons do manage to reach the plate P_2. However, beyond a certain voltage (which is shown as $-V_c$ in the figure) the current is zero; V_c is known as the cut-off voltage and the quantity $|q|V_c$ will represent the maximum kinetic energy of the photoelectrons (q represents the charge of the electron). For example, for sodium $V_c \approx 2.3$ Volts and for copper $V_c \approx 4.7$ Volts.

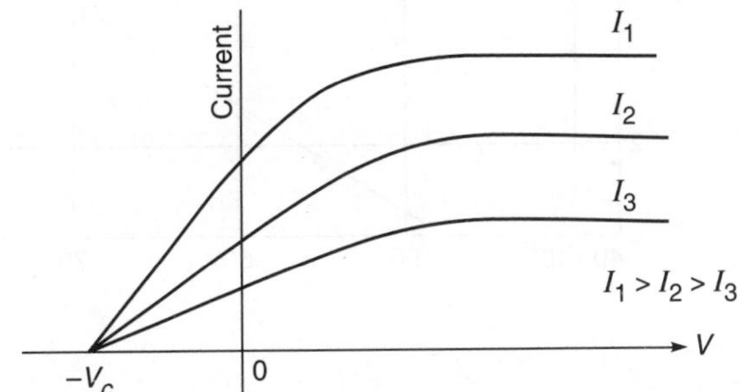

Figure 24.2
Typical variation of the photocurrent with voltage. The curves correspond to light (of the same frequency) having different intensities.

(d) If we do not change the frequency of the incident radiation but make it more intense, the magnitude of the current will become larger as shown in Fig. 24.2 implying a greater emission of photoelectrons. Notice that the value of the cut-off potential remains the same; this important result implies that the **maximum kinetic energy of the emitted photoelectron does not depend on the intensity of the incident radiation**.
(e) If the frequency of the incident radiation is increased then the cut-off potential and hence the maximum

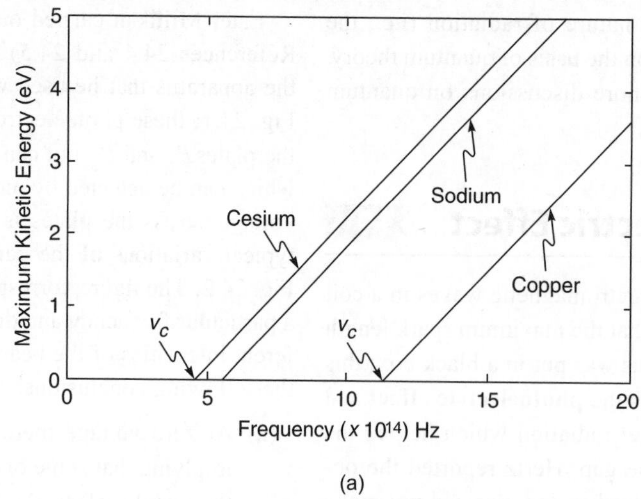

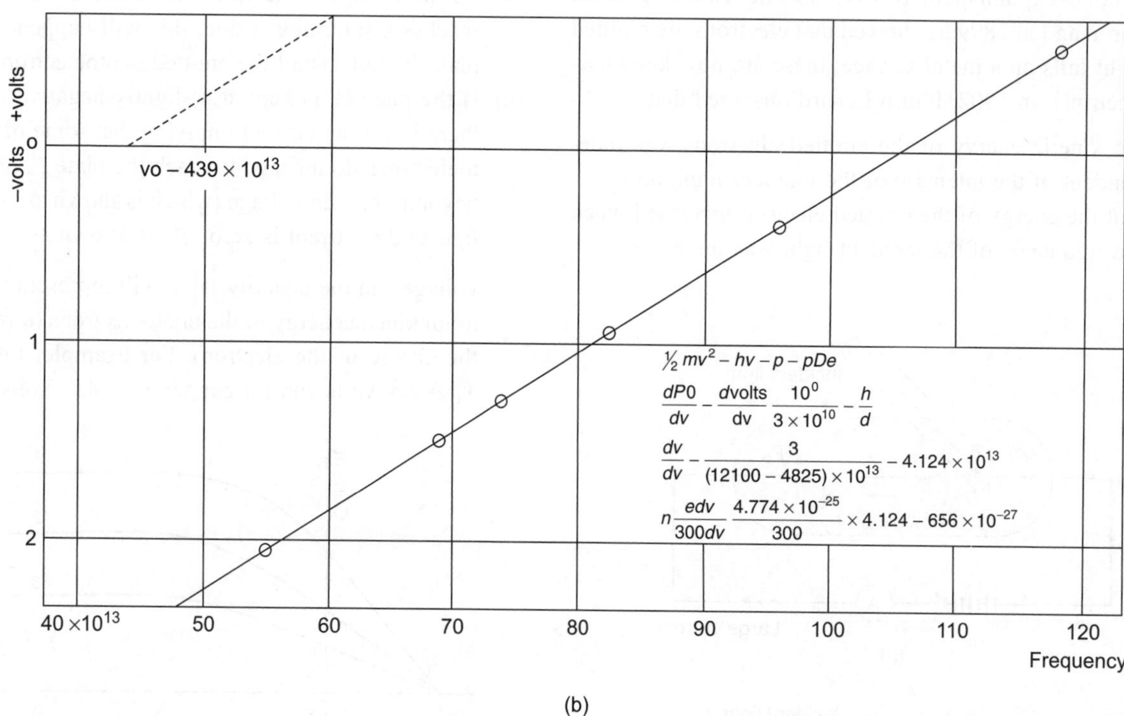

Figure 24.3

(a) The variation of the maximum kinetic energy of the electrons as a function of frequency of the incident light for cesium, sodium and copper. (b) The original experimental data of Robert Millikan (adapted from Ref. 24.4).

kinetic energy of the electron $\left(=|q|V_c\right)$ varies linearly with the frequency as shown in Fig. 24.3. Further, for frequencies less than a critical value (shown as v_c in Fig. 24.3), there is no emission of photoelectrons no matter what the intensity of the incident radiation may be.

At first sight, it appears that since electromagnetic waves carry energy, the wave model for light should be able to explain the emission of photoelectrons from a metal surface. However, there are certain peculiarities associated with photoelectric effect, which cannot be satisfactorily explained by means of a wave model:

1. The first peculiarity is the fact that the maximum kinetic energy of the electrons does not depend on the intensity of the incident radiation, it only depends on its frequency; further, a greater intensity leads to a

larger number of electrons constituting a larger current. **Thus, a faint violet light would eject electrons of greater kinetic energy than an intense yellow light although the latter would produce a large number of electrons**. A wave model would, however, predict that a large intensity of the incident radiation would result in a greater kinetic energy of the emitted electrons.

2. The second peculiarity is the fact that there is almost no time lag between the times of incidence of the radiation and the ejection of the photoelectron. For weak intensities of the incident beam, the wave theory predicts considerable time lag for the electrons to absorb enough energy to leave the metal surface. This can be illustrated by considering a specific example. One can observe a detectable photocurrent if the surface of sodium metal is illuminated by violet light of intensity as low as $10^{-10}\ \text{W/cm}^2$. Now, 10 layers of sodium will contain about

$$\frac{6\times10^{23}\times10\times10^{-8}}{23}\approx2\times10^{15}\ \text{atoms/cm}^3$$

where we have assumed the density of sodium to be $\approx 1\text{g/cm}^3$. Assuming that the energy is uniformly absorbed by the upper 10 layers of sodium, each atom would receive energy at the rate of

$$\frac{10^{-10}}{2\times10^{15}}\approx5\times10^{-26}\ \text{J/s}\approx3\times10^{-7}\ \text{eV/s}$$

Assuming that an electron should acquire an energy $\sim 1\ \text{eV}$ to escape from the metal, we should expect a time lag of order 10^7 s to ~few months. However, experiments showed that there is no detectable time lag between the incidence of the radiation and the emission of the photoelectrons. Indeed, in 1928, Lawrence and Beams had devised an experiment to find out whether the time lag was $\leq 3\times10^{-9}$ sec; the experiment gave a negative result.

In 1905, Einstein provided a simple explanation of the above mentioned peculiarities. He argued that light consisted of quanta of energy $h\nu$ (where ν is the frequency) and that the emission of a photoelectron was the result of the interaction of a single quantum (i.e., of the photon) with an electron. In his 1905 paper [Ref. 24.3], Einstein wrote:

> *Monochromatic radiation behaves as if it consists of mutually independent energy quanta of magnitude [hν]...... the production of cathode rays [electrons] by light can be conceived in the following way: The body's surface layer is penetrated by energy quanta whose energy is converted at least partially into kinetic energy of the electrons. The simplest conception is that a light quantum transfers its entire energy to a single electron; we will assume that this can occur.*

Thus the observed maximum kinetic energy of the photoelectrons is linearly related to the frequency of the incident radiation and one may write (see Fig. 24.3)

$$T_{\max}=-B+h\nu=h\left(\nu-\nu_c\right) \qquad \textbf{(24.6)}$$

where $B(=h\nu_c)$ is a constant and h is the Planck's constant $\left(=6.627\times10^{-34}\ \text{Js}\right)$. The frequency ν_c represents the cut-off frequency and is a characteristic of the metal. Einstein's theory gives a very satisfactory explanation of the photoelectric effect*. According to this theory, a light beam (of frequency ν) essentially consists of individual corpuscles called photons. Each photon carries an energy equal to $h\nu$. This corpuscular model can explain all the observations discussed above. Thus, for all frequencies below the cut-off ν_c, each photon will carry energy less than $h\nu_c$ which will not be sufficient to eject the electron from the metal. For $\nu > \nu_c$, a major fraction of the excess energy [$= h(\nu - \nu_c)$] appears as kinetic energy of the emitted electron. Further, the non-measurable time lag

* We must mention that Einstein, in his 1905 paper (Ref. 24.3), had shown that the change in entropy of radiation when the volume changes from V_0 to V (while keeping the total energy fixed) is given by

$$S-S_0=k\ln\left(\frac{V}{V_0}\right)^{E/h\nu}$$

Einstein then compared this with the corresponding expression for a gas of N molecules of an ideal gas:

$$S-S_0=k\ln\left(\frac{V}{V_0}\right)^{N}$$

Comparing the two expressions, Einstein concluded that radiation behaves as if it consisted of a gas of independent 'light quanta' and that $E/h\nu$ must represent the total number of light quanta, each having energy $h\nu$.

between the incidence of the radiation and the ejection of the electron follows immediately from the corpuscular nature of the radiation. Equation (24.6) is often referred to as Einstein's photoelectric equation; it was verified to a tremendous degree of accuracy in a series of beautiful experiments by Millikan who also made the first direct determination of Planck's constant h. In his Nobel lecture, Millikan [Ref. 24.4] said

> *After ten years of testing and changing and learning and sometimes blundering, all efforts being directed from the first toward the accurate experimental measurement of the energies of emission of photoelectrons, now as a function of temperature, now of wavelength, now of material (contact e.m.f. relation), this work resulted, contrary to my own expectation, in the first direct experimental proof in 1914 of the exact validity, within narrow limits of experimental error, of the Einstein equation* [Eq. (24.6)], *and the first direct photoelectric determination of Planck's constant h.*

Millikan further wrote:

> *Einstein's equation is one of exact validity (always within the present small limits of experimental error) and of very general applicability, is perhaps the most conspicuous achievement of Experimental Physics during the past decade.*

For example,

for cesium $B \approx 1.9$ eV $\Rightarrow$ $\nu_c \approx 4.6 \times 10^{14}$ Hz

for sodium $B \approx 2.3$ eV $\Rightarrow$ $\nu_c \approx 5.6 \times 10^{14}$ Hz

for copper $B \approx 4.7$ eV $\Rightarrow$ $\nu_c \approx 11.4 \times 10^{14}$ Hz

In Fig. 24.3, ν_c is the intercept on the horizontal axis. In making this transition from Planck's quantized oscillators to quanta of radiation, Einstein had made a very important conceptual transition, and introduced the idea of corpuscular behaviour of radiation. Although Newton had described light as a stream of particles, this view had been completely superseded by the wave picture of light, a picture that culminated in the electromagnetic theory of Maxwell. The revival of the particle picture now posed a severe conceptual problem, one of reconciling wave and particle like behaviour of radiation. It also soon became apparent that matter also exhibited wave-particle duality. For example, an electron with an accurately measured value of mass and charge could undergo diffraction in a manner similar to that of light waves—this led to the development of the uncertainty principle and quantum theory.

After Millikan's experiments, Duane and his associates found unambiguous proof of a relation, which is just the inverse of Einstein's. They bombarded a metal target with electrons of known and constant energy and found that the maximum frequency of the emitted X-rays was given, with great accuracy, by the following equation

$$\frac{1}{2}mv^2 = h\nu \tag{24.7}$$

In the following section we will discuss a very important experiment carried out by Arthur Compton; this experiment could be satisfactorily explained by assuming that the energy and momentum of the photon are given by $E = h\nu$ and $p = h\nu/c$, respectively.

24.3 The Compton Scattering LO2

We have seen that Einstein's explanation for the photoelectric effect implies that quanta of light (photons) carry a definite amount of energy. In 1923, Compton investigated the scattering of X-rays by a block of paraffin (see References 24.7–24.10); he found that the wavelength of the radiation scattered at an angle of 90° is greater than the wavelength of the incident radiation. In other words, the frequency ν' of the scattered wave is smaller than the frequency of the incident wave (see Fig. 24.4). Compton was able to explain the result* quantitatively as that of an elastic collision between a photon (of energy $E = h\nu$ and momentum $h\nu/c$) and an electron. The light quantum imparts some of its energy to the electron and emerges with less energy. Thus the scattered radiation has a lower frequency. The kinematics of this collision process can be worked out on elementary application of the laws

* According to the classical explanation of Compton scattering, the electron undergoes oscillatory motion because of the electric field associated with the incident electromagnetic radiation. The accelerated electron emits electromagnetic waves and because of Doppler shifts due to the motion of the electron, the emitted wavelength differs from the wavelength of the incident radiation; however, the classical theory predicts that for a given angle of scattering a continuous range in the value of the scattered wavelength should be formed, which is contrary to experimental findings. The details of this analysis are given in Sec. 2.9 of Ref. 24.6.

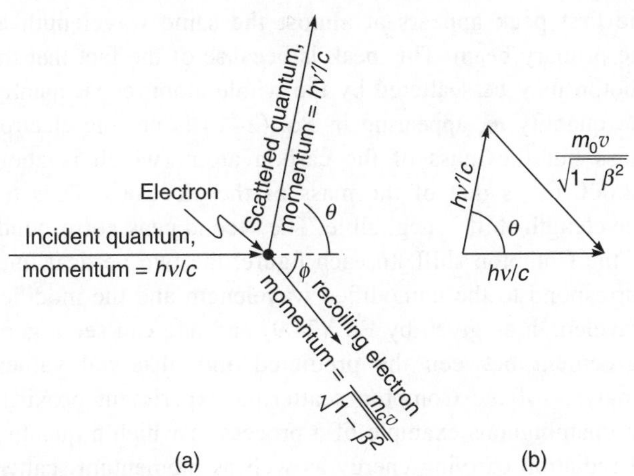

Figure 24.4

Compton scattering of a photon: the figure shows the incidence of a photon (of frequency ν) on an electron; the scattered photon (having a reduced frequency ν') propagating along the direction which makes an angle θ with the original direction; the electron also acquires a momentum. Figure adapted from the original paper of Compton (Ref. 24.8).

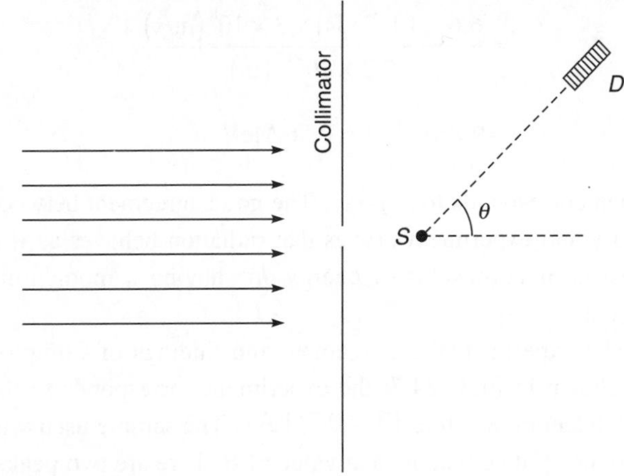

Figure 24.5

Outline of the experimental arrangement for the measurement of the Compton shift. A collimated beam of monochromatic X-rays is scattered by the scatterer *S*; the wavelength of the scattered photon is measured by the detector *D*.

of conservation of energy and momentum (see Sec. 24.3.1); these calculations give the following expression for the shift in the wavelength

$$\Delta\lambda = \frac{2h}{m_0 c}\sin^2\frac{\theta}{2} \tag{24.8}$$

where θ is the angle of scattering of the light quantum (see Fig. 24.4) and m_0 represents the rest mass of the electron. Now,

$$\frac{2h}{m_0 c} = \frac{2\times 6.6261\times 10^{-34}\ (\text{Js})}{9.1094\times 10^{-31}(\text{kg})\times 2.998\times 10^{8}\ (\text{m/s})}$$

$$\approx 4.85\times 10^{-12}\ \text{m} = 0.0485\ \text{Å}$$

Thus, $$\Delta\lambda = \lambda' - \lambda = 0.0485\sin^2\frac{\theta}{2} \tag{24.9}$$

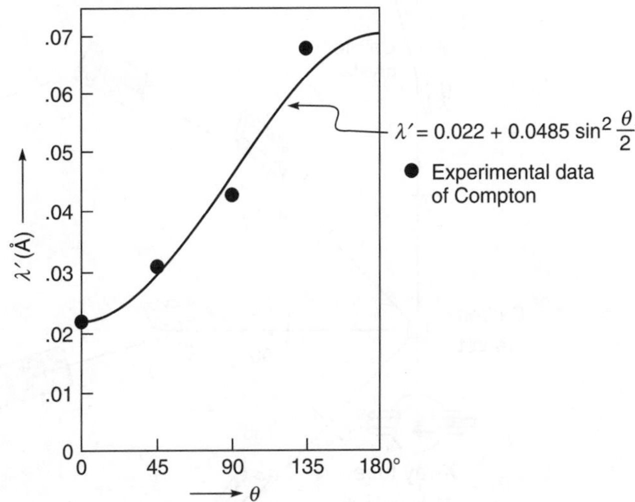

Figure 24.6

The variation of wavelength of the scattered photon with the angle of scattering. The solid curve corresponds to Eq. (24.9) with $\lambda = 0.022$ Å. The dots represent the experimental points obtained by Compton. The figure has been adapted from the original paper of Compton on (Ref. 24.7).

where λ is measured in Angstroms. Equation (24.9) shows that the maximum change in the wavelength is about 0.05 Å, and as such for a measurable shift one must use radiation of smaller wavelength. In Fig. 24.5, we have given the schematic of the experimental arrangement for the measurement of the Compton shift. A monochromatic beam of X-rays (or γ-rays) is allowed to fall on a sample scatterer and the scattered photons were detected by means of a crystal spectrometer. The crystal spectrometer allows one to find the intensity distribution (as a function of λ) for a given value of θ. In Fig. 24.6, we have shown the wavelength of the scattered photon at different angles with respect to the primary beam as obtained by Compton in his original experiments carried out in 1923; see References 24.7–24.10. The solid curve in Fig. 24.6 corresponds to Eq. (24.9) with $\lambda = 0.022$ Å; the corresponding photon energy is

$$\approx \frac{6.6\times10^{-34}\,(\text{Js})\times3\times10^{8}\,(\text{m/s})}{2.2\times10^{-12}\,(\text{m})}$$

$$\approx 9\times10^{-14}\ \text{J}\simeq 0.56\ \text{MeV}$$

which corresponds to a γ-ray. The good agreement between theory and experiment proves that radiation behaves as if it consists of corpuscles of energy $h\nu$ having a momentum $h\nu/c$.

The experimental arrangement and findings of Compton are shown in Figs. 24.7; the experiment corresponds to the molybdenum K_α line $(\lambda = 0.711\ \text{Å})$. The sample used was graphite. Notice that at each value of θ, there are two peaks; the first peak appears at almost the same wavelength as the primary beam. This peak is because of the fact that the photon may be scattered by the whole atom; consequently, the quantity m_0 appearing in Eq. (24.8) is not the electron mass but the mass of the carbon atom (which is about 22,000 times that of the mass of the electron). Thus the wavelength shift is negligible. The second peak corresponds to the Compton shift. In each figure, the two vertical lines correspond to the unmodified wavelength and the modified wavelength as given by Eq. (24.9) and one can see a good agreement between the predicted and observed values. Analysis of the Compton scattering experiment provided an unambiguous example of a process in which a quantum of radiation carrying energy as well as momentum scatters

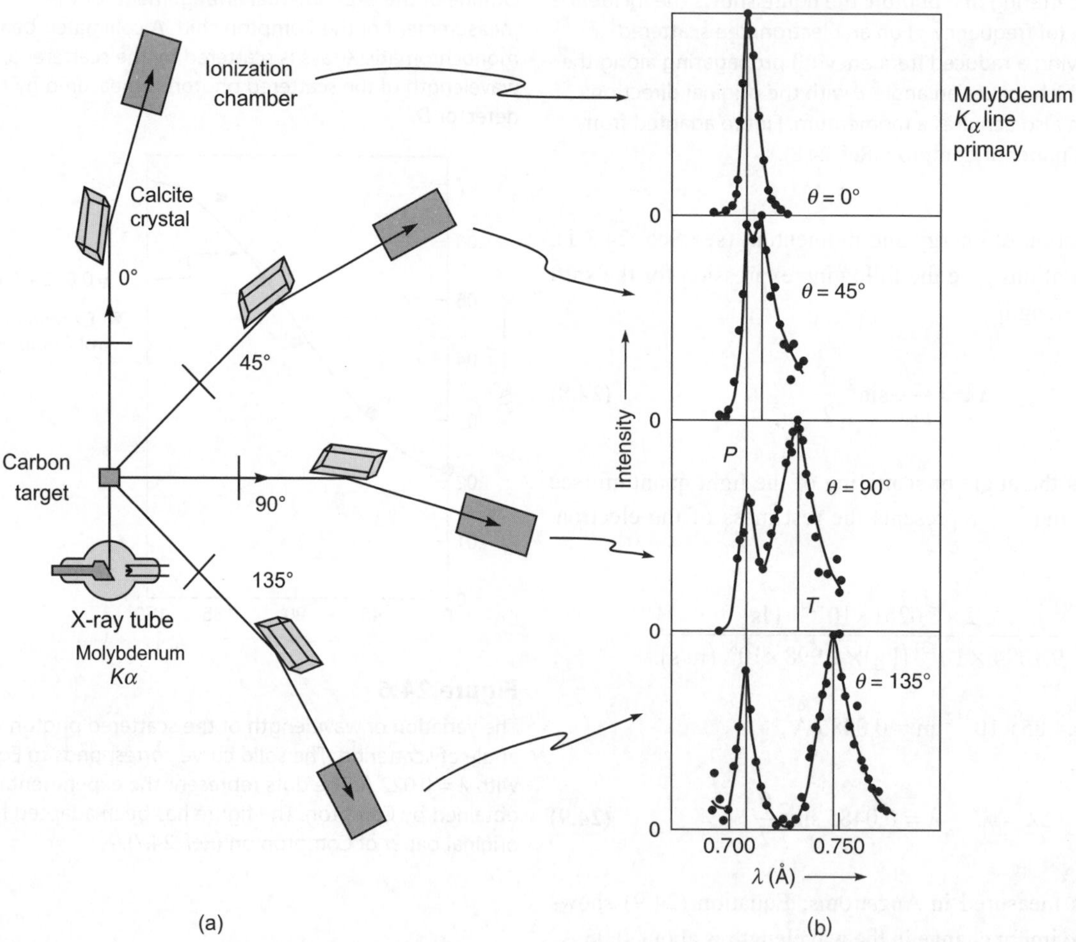

Figure 24.7
Compton's original experiment used molybdenum K-alpha X-rays, which have a wavelength of 0.711 Å. These were scattered from a block of carbon and observed at different angles with a Bragg spectrometer. The experimental data represents the intensity variation as a function of the wavelength of the scattered photon. The vertical line (on the left marked as *P*) corresponds to the unmodified wavelength $\lambda = 0.711$ Å. The second vertical line (marked *T*) corresponds to the wavelength as predicted by Eq. (24.5). The diagram corresponding to the experimental arrangement has been adapted from the original paper of A.H. Compton (Ref. 24.8) and also a diagram created by Professor Rod Nave at Georgia State University [Ref. http://hyperphysics.phy-astr.gsu.edu/hbase/hframe.html].

off an electron. Compton was awarded the 1927 Nobel Prize in Physics *for his discovery of the effect named after him*.

Further evidence of the validity of the above theory was provided by experiments carried out by Compton and Simon who studied the scattering of X-rays through supersaturated water vapour. In the scattering process, the recoil electrons formed tracks of condensed droplets; however, the light quantum did not leave any track. Now, if the light quantum undergoes another Compton scattering then from the track of the second recoil electron one can determine the path of the light quantum by simply joining the line of the starting points of the two recoil electrons. Although there was considerable uncertainty in the analysis of the experimental data (because of the presence of many tracks) Compton and Simon could establish agreement between theoretical results and experimental data.

24.3.1 Kinematics of Compton Scattering

We next consider the scattering of a photon by an electron as shown in Fig. 24.4. The scattered photon is assumed to have a frequency ν'. Conservation of energy leads to

$$h\nu = h\nu' + E_k \tag{24.10}$$

where E_k represents the kinetic energy imparted to the electron. Conserving the x and y components of the momentum, we have

$$\frac{h\nu}{c} = \frac{h\nu'}{c}\cos\theta + p\cos\phi \tag{24.11}$$

and

$$0 = \frac{h\nu'}{c}\sin\theta - p\sin\phi \tag{24.12}$$

where p represents the momentum of the electron after collision, θ and ϕ represent the angles made by the scattered photon and the electron with the original direction of the photon (see Fig. 24.4). It will be shown that for a measurable Compton effect, the frequency ν should be in the X-ray or in the γ-ray region (for X-rays $\lambda \le 1\text{Å}$ and $h\nu \ge 10^4$ eV). For such high energy photons, the velocity imparted to the electron is comparable to the speed of light and one must use proper relativistic expressions for E_k and p. Now, according to the special theory of relativity, the kinetic energy E_k of the scattered electron would be given by (see Sec. 31.4):

$$E_k = E - m_0c^2 = mc^2 - m_0c^2 = \frac{m_0c^2}{\sqrt{1-\beta^2}} - m_0c^2 \tag{24.13}$$

where $\beta = v/c$, m_0 represents the rest mass of the electron, v the speed of the electron and c the speed of light in free-space; the quantities E and m_0c^2 are known as the *total energy* and the *rest mass energy* of the electron. Further, the relativistic momentum of the electron is given by

$$p = mv = \frac{m_0 v}{\sqrt{1-\beta^2}} \tag{24.14}$$

Now,

$$p^2c^2 + m_0^2c^4 = \frac{m_0^2v^2c^2}{1-v^2/c^2} + m_0^2c^4 = \frac{m_0^2c^4}{1-v^2/c^2} = \left(mc^2\right)^2$$

or, $p^2c^2 + m_0^2c^4 = E^2$

$$= \left(E_k + m_0c^2\right)^2 = E_k^2 + m_0^2c^4 + 2E_km_0c^2$$

Thus, $E_k^2 + 2E_km_0c^2 = p^2c^2$

Substituting for E_k from Eq. (24.10), we get

$$h^2(\nu-\nu')^2 + 2h(\nu-\nu')m_0c^2 = p^2c^2 \tag{24.15}$$

Further, Eqs. (24.11) and (24.12) can be rewritten in the form

$$p\cos\phi = \frac{h\nu}{c} - \frac{h\nu'}{c}\cos\theta \tag{24.16}$$

and

$$p\sin\phi = \frac{h\nu'}{c}\sin\theta \tag{24.17}$$

In order to eliminate ϕ, we square and add to obtain

$$p^2 = \left(\frac{h\nu}{c}\right)^2 + \left(\frac{h\nu'}{c}\right)^2 - \frac{2h^2\nu\nu'}{c^2}\cos\theta \tag{24.18}$$

Substituting in Eq. (24.15) we obtain

$$h^2\left(\nu^2 - 2\nu\nu' + \nu'^2\right) + 2h(\nu-\nu')m_0c^2$$

$$= h^2\nu^2 + h^2\nu'^2 - 2h^2\nu\nu'\cos\theta$$

or

$$\frac{2h(\nu-\nu')m_0c^2}{2\nu\nu'} = h^2(1-\cos\theta)$$

Thus, $\Delta\lambda = \lambda' - \lambda = \left(\frac{c}{\nu'} - \frac{c}{\nu}\right) = \frac{h}{m_0c}(1-\cos\theta)$

Thus,

$$\Delta\lambda = \frac{2h}{m_0c}\sin^2\frac{\theta}{2} \tag{24.19}$$

which gives us the Compton shift*.

* In the derivation of the Compton shift, we have assumed that the electron is free, although we know that the electrons are bound to the atoms. The assumption of a free electron is justified because the binding energy (≈ few eV) is usually very much smaller in comparison to the photon energy (> 1000 eV).

24.4 Angular Momentum of a Photon

LO3

We had discussed Jones vectors in Sec. 21.14. We represent the x and y polarized photons by the (normalized) Jones vectors

$$|x\rangle = \begin{pmatrix}1\\0\end{pmatrix} \text{ and } |y\rangle = \begin{pmatrix}0\\1\end{pmatrix} \qquad \mathbf{(24.20)}$$

We define the polarization rotation operator $R_z(\theta)$ which would rotate the state of polarization (about the z-axis) by an angle θ in the clockwise direction; thus (see Fig. 24.8)

$$R_z(\theta)|x\rangle = |\theta\rangle = \cos\theta|x\rangle + \sin\theta|y\rangle = \begin{pmatrix}\cos\theta\\ \sin\theta\end{pmatrix} = |x'\rangle \qquad \mathbf{(24.21)}$$

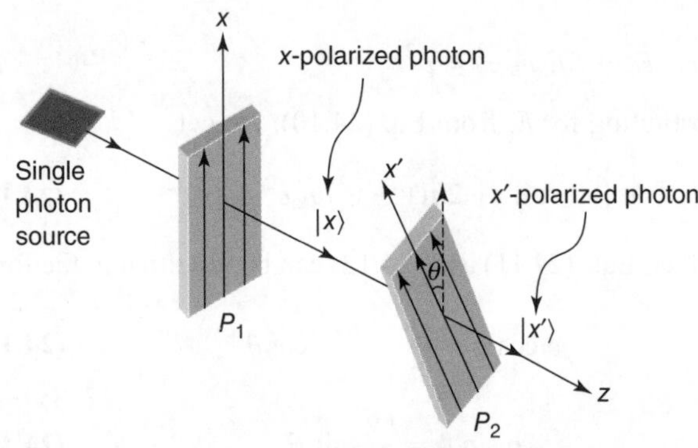

Figure 24.8
The probability that the polarized photon (coming out of the polaroid P_1 whose pass axis is along the x-axis) will pass through the second polaroid P_2 (whose pass axis makes an angle θ with the x-axis) is $\cos^2\theta$

Similarly, $R_z(\theta)|y\rangle = \left|\frac{\pi}{2}+\theta\right\rangle = -\sin\theta|x\rangle + \cos\theta|y\rangle$

or,
$$R_z(\theta)|y\rangle = \begin{pmatrix}-\sin\theta\\ \cos\theta\end{pmatrix} = |y'\rangle \qquad \mathbf{(24.22)}$$

If we represent the polarization rotation operator $R_z(\theta)$ by a 2×2 matrix

$$R_z(\theta) = \begin{pmatrix}a & b\\ c & d\end{pmatrix}$$

then
$$R_z(\theta)|x\rangle = \begin{pmatrix}a & b\\ c & d\end{pmatrix}\begin{pmatrix}1\\0\end{pmatrix} = \begin{pmatrix}a\\c\end{pmatrix}$$

Comparing the above equation with Eq. (24.21) we get

$$a = \cos\theta \text{ and } c = \sin\theta$$

Similarly,
$$R_z(\theta)|y\rangle = \begin{pmatrix}a & b\\ c & d\end{pmatrix}\begin{pmatrix}0\\1\end{pmatrix} = \begin{pmatrix}b\\d\end{pmatrix}$$

Comparing the above equation with Eq. (24.22) we get

$$b = -\sin\theta \text{ and } d = \cos\theta$$

Thus, the matrix representation of the polarization rotation operator $R_z(\theta)$ will be

$$R_z(\theta) = \begin{pmatrix}\cos\theta & -\sin\theta\\ \sin\theta & \cos\theta\end{pmatrix} \qquad \mathbf{(24.23)}$$

One can easily see that

$$R_z(\theta)|\phi\rangle = \begin{pmatrix}\cos(\theta+\phi)\\ \sin(\theta+\phi)\end{pmatrix} = |\theta+\phi\rangle \qquad \mathbf{(24.24)}$$

showing the rotation of the polarization state of the photon. If $|R\rangle$ and $|L\rangle$ are the unit vectors representing the right circularly polarized photon and the left circularly polarized photon, respectively, then

$$|R\rangle = \frac{1}{\sqrt{2}}\begin{pmatrix}1\\i\end{pmatrix} = \frac{1}{\sqrt{2}}[|x\rangle + i|y\rangle] \qquad \text{(RCP)}\ \mathbf{(24.25)}$$

$$|L\rangle = \frac{1}{\sqrt{2}}\begin{pmatrix}1\\-i\end{pmatrix} = \frac{1}{\sqrt{2}}[|x\rangle - i|y\rangle] \qquad \text{(LCP)}\ \mathbf{(24.26)}$$

(see Sec. 21.4). Operating $R_z(\theta)$ on $|R\rangle$, we get

$$R_z(\theta)|R\rangle = \begin{pmatrix}\cos\theta & -\sin\theta\\ \sin\theta & \cos\theta\end{pmatrix}\frac{1}{\sqrt{2}}\begin{pmatrix}1\\i\end{pmatrix} = e^{-i\theta}\frac{1}{\sqrt{2}}\begin{pmatrix}1\\i\end{pmatrix}$$

Thus,
$$R_z(\theta)|R\rangle = e^{-i\theta}|R\rangle \qquad \mathbf{(24.27)}$$

Similarly,
$$R_z(\theta)|L\rangle = e^{+i\theta}|L\rangle \qquad \mathbf{(24.28)}$$

Equations (24.27) and (24.28) are known as *eigenvalue equations*; thus, the right and left circularly polarized states are said to be the eigenstates of $R_z(\theta)$; the corresponding eigenvalues are $e^{-i\theta}$ and $e^{+i\theta}$. Now, in quantum mechanics, if $R_z(\theta)$ represents the rotational operator corresponding to a rotation about the z-axis through an angle θ, then (see, e.g., References 24.11–24.13):

$$R_z(\theta) = \exp\left[-\frac{i}{\hbar}\theta J_z\right] \qquad \mathbf{(24.29)}$$

where $\hbar = \frac{h}{2\pi}$, h being the Planck's constant and J_z represents the z-component of the angular momentum operator. Thus,

$$\exp\left[-\frac{i}{\hbar}\theta J_z\right]|R\rangle = R_z(\theta)|R\rangle = e^{-i\theta}|R\rangle \quad \textbf{(24.30)}$$

Now, the exponential of an operator O is defined by

$$e^O \equiv 1 + \frac{O}{1!} + \frac{OO}{2!} + \frac{OOO}{3!} + \ldots \quad \textbf{(24.31)}$$

We expand the exponential on both sides of Eq. (24.30), and if we use the fact that Eq. (24.30) has to be valid for all values of θ, we must have*

$$J_z|R\rangle = +\hbar|R\rangle \quad \textbf{(24.32)}$$

If we carry out a similar analysis for the left circularly polarized light, we obtain

$$J_z|L\rangle = -\hbar|L\rangle \quad \textbf{(24.33)}$$

Equations (24.32) and (24.33) are *eigenvalue equations*; thus, the right and left circularly polarized states are said to be the *eigenstates* of J_z; the corresponding eigenvalues are $+\hbar$ and $-\hbar$, respectively. According to quantum mechanics, if we measure J_z of a right circularly polarized light photon, we will always obtain the value $+\hbar$; similarly, if we measure J_z of a left circularly polarized photon, we will obtain the value $-\hbar$. For an arbitrary state of polarization, if we measure J_z, we will obtain one of the eigenvalues; i.e., we will obtain either the value $+\hbar$ or the value $-\hbar$. To obtain the probabilities of finding $+\hbar$ and $-\hbar$, the state should be expressed as a superposition of the eigenstates, which are the right circularly polarized state and the left circularly polarized state. For example, a x-polarized state can be represented as

$$|x\rangle = \begin{pmatrix}1\\0\end{pmatrix} = \frac{1}{\sqrt{2}}\left[|R\rangle + |L\rangle\right] \quad \textbf{(24.34)}$$

Thus, if we make a measurement of J_z on a x-polarized (or on a y-polarized) state, then there will be half probability of obtaining $+\hbar$ and half probability of obtaining $-\hbar$; one can never predict the precise outcome of an experiment. As another example, for a left elliptically polarized state (see Sec. 21.14):

$$|\text{LEP}> = \frac{1}{2}\begin{pmatrix}1\\-i\sqrt{3}\end{pmatrix} = a|R> + b|L>$$

$$= \frac{a}{\sqrt{2}}\begin{pmatrix}1\\-i\end{pmatrix} + \frac{b}{\sqrt{2}}\begin{pmatrix}1\\+i\end{pmatrix}$$

Simple manipulations will give $a \approx -0.2588$ and $b \approx +0.9659$. Thus, if we make a measurement of J_z on such an elliptically polarized state, we obtain one of the eigenvalues—the probability of obtaining $+\hbar$ will be about 0.0670, and the probability of obtaining $-\hbar$ will be about 0.933.

24.5 Optical Tweezers** LO4

Optical tweezer owes its origin to the seminal work by Arthur Ashkin who showed that a focused laser beam could be used to trap and manipulate individual microscopic objects (see References 24.14–24.16). Indeed, as mentioned in the Prologue of this book, Arthur Ashkin was awarded half of the 2018 Nobel Prize for

"optical tweezers and their application to biological systems"

In order to understand the working of the optical tweezer***, we consider a ball hitting a heavy object sitting on a frictionless surface (like maybe a train on a frictionless railway track!). As shown in Fig. 24.9(a), the momentum vector associated with the ball will change direction imparting a small momentum to the heavy object in the forward direction. Using the law of conservation of momentum, we will have

$$\mathbf{p}_i = \mathbf{p}_r + \mathbf{P}_h \quad \textbf{(24.35)}$$

where $\mathbf{p}_i$ is the momentum vector associated with the incident ball, $\mathbf{p}_r$ is the momentum vector associated with the reflected ball and $\mathbf{P}_h$ is the momentum vector associated with the heavy object; they are all vector quantities, hence they are in bold. There is also conservation of energy; however, because the object is very heavy (in comparison to the mass of the incident ball), very little energy is transferred to the heavy object and the energy of the reflected ball will almost be the same as that of the incident ball. Now, in Sec. 22.9 we had discussed experiments which demonstrated that there is momentum associated with an electromagnetic wave. Indeed as discussed earlier in this chapter, a photon has momentum given by

* Thus, for example $J_z^3|R\rangle = J_zJ_zJ_z|R\rangle = +\hbar^3|R\rangle$

** The author thanks Professor Pradeep Gupta (Formerly at RRCAT, Indore and now at IIT Delhi) for his help in writing this section.

*** You may like to see the following videos https://www.youtube.com/watch?v=UAmdoOX3870 and https://www.youtube.com/watch?v=XjXLJMUrNBo&t=302s; you go to https://www.youtube.com/ and search for videos on "optical tweezers".

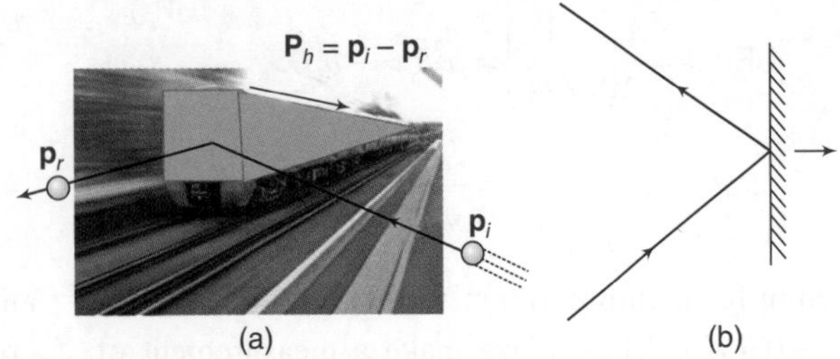

Figure 24.9

(a) A ball (moving at a high speed) hitting a train on a frictionless railway track; the momentum vector associated with the ball will change direction imparting a small momentum to the train. (b) Similarly, if a photon strikes a mirror at an angle, the momentum vector (associated with the reflected photon) will be in a different direction and the mirror will get pushed in the forward direction.

$$p = \frac{h\nu}{c} \tag{24.36}$$

Thus if a photon strikes a mirror at an angle, the momentum vector (associated with the reflected photon) will be in a different direction and using the law of conservation of momentum, the mirror will pick up a small amount of momentum in the forward direction [Fig 24.9(b)]. Thus the mirror will get pushed in the forward direction.

We next consider a laser beam falling just on the upper portion of a lens. As shown in Fig 24.10(a), the beam will change direction and hence the momentum vector associated with the light beam will change direction imparting a small momentum (to the lens) in the upward direction as shown by an arrow at the top of the diagram. Similarly, if a laser beam falls just on the lower portion of the lens, it will impart a small momentum in the downward direction. However, if we have two laser beams falling on the lens [see Fig. 24.10(b)], each will impart momentum in opposite directions and the net force on the lens will be almost zero. Thus if a lens is illuminated uniformly (see Fig. 24.11), the upper portion will try to make it move upward and the lower portion will try to make it move downward and the resultant force will be almost zero.

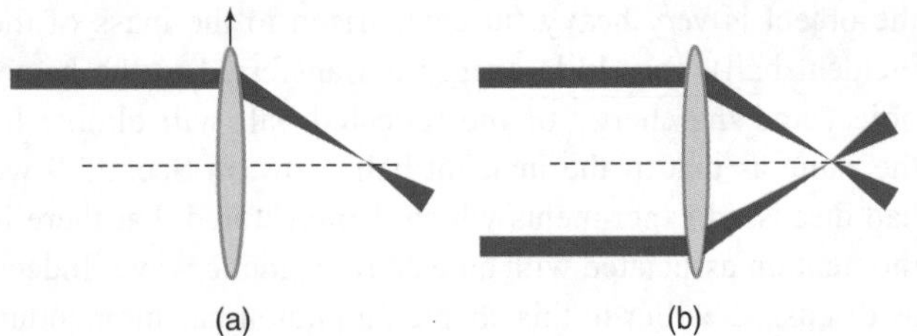

Figure 24.10

(a) When a laser beam falls just on the upper portion of a lens, the beam will change direction imparting a small momentum (to the lens) in the upward direction (b) if we have two laser beams falling on the lens, each will impart momentum in opposite directions and the net force on the lens will be almost zero.

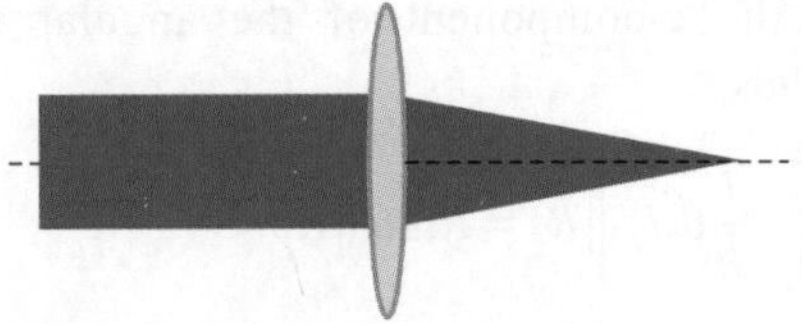

Figure 24.11

When a light beam falls uniformly, no momentum will be transferred to the lens.

Many laser beams have a transverse intensity distribution which is Gaussian (see Sec. 17.4). If such a laser beam is incident normally on a bead as shown in Fig. 24.12(a), then from what has been discussed above, the resultant force will be almost zero and the bead will not move. On the other hand, if the beam is incident at a distance from the axis [see Fig. 24.12(b)], the light ray 2 is brighter than light ray 1 and the force to the right is stronger; this will make the bead move towards the right. Thus the bead will always move back towards the middle of the beam and, if the laser beam is strong enough, the sphere will be trapped inside the laser beam and can be moved from one place to the other. If it tries to drift away, there is a kind of a "restoring force" which will hold it near the center of the beam. This is the basic principle behind the "optical tweezer".

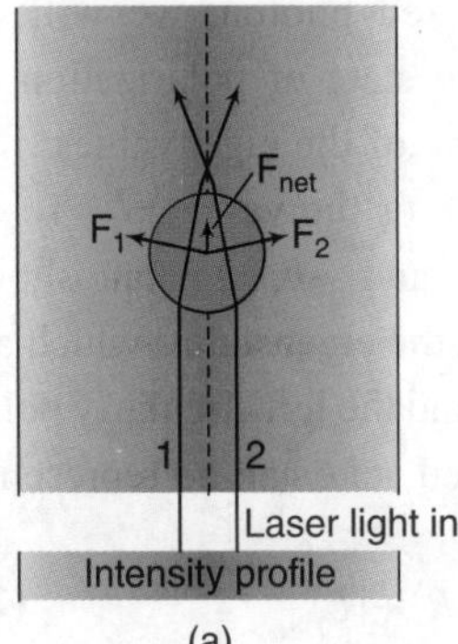

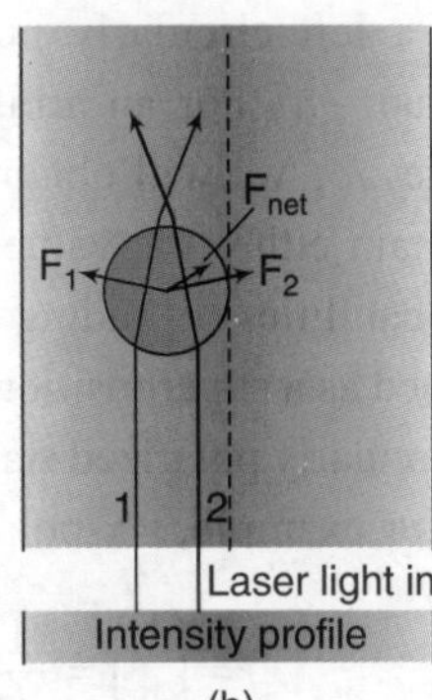

Figure 24.12

The optical tweezer: When the diameter of a trapped particle is significantly greater than the wavelength of light, the trapping phenomenon can be explained using ray optics. As shown in (a), individual rays of light emitted from the laser will be refracted as it enters and exits the dielectric bead. As a result, the ray will exit in a direction different from which it originated. Since light has a momentum associated with it, this change in direction indicates that its momentum has changed. (b) When the bead is displaced from the beam center, the larger momentum change of the more intense rays cause a net force to be applied back toward the center of the laser; thus the bead is held near the center of the laser beam. [*Writeup and photographs courtesy Dr. Ronald Koebler; used with his kind permission*].

There is one more effect: A portion of the light beam gets absorbed by the bead; as such there is a tendency for the bead to get pushed in the direction of the propagation of the beam. One way to circumvent the problem is to have the laser light push the bead in the upward direction so that gravity will try to balance it. A better method is to use a microscope lens which will result in a large momentum associated with the output beam [see Fig. 24.13].

Optical tweezers are finding widespread applications in biological research and technology because unlike mechanical micro tools, the optical trap is gentle and absolutely sterile and can be used to capture, move and position single cells or subcellular particles without direct contact. It is also pertinent to note that Steven Chu, who was also an author of this pioneering work (see Ref. 24.14) later made use of these optical forces for cooling and trapping of neutral atoms, the work for which he got the 1997 Nobel Prize in Physics along with Claude Cohen-Tannoudji and William D. Phillips.

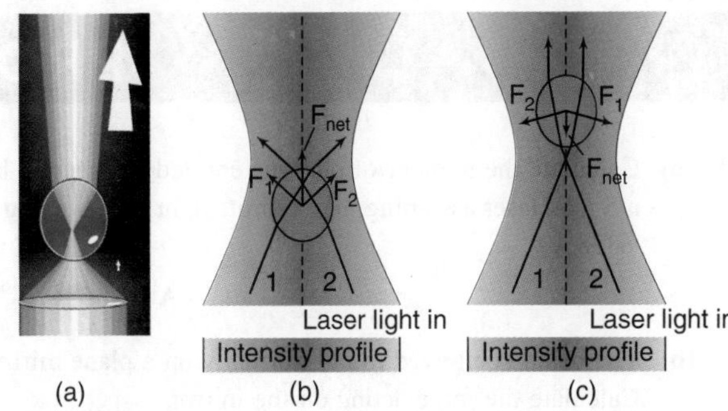

Figure 24.13

(a) A focussed laser beam is made to fall on the sphere.
(b) The focussed laser beam, in addition to keeping the bead in the center of the laser, also keeps the bead in a fixed axial position. The momentum change of the focused rays causes a force towards the laser focus, both when the bead is in front (b) or behind (c) the laser focus. The bead will stay slightly behind the focus. Standard tweezers work with the trapping laser propagating in the direction of gravity.
[*Writeup and drawings in (b) and (c) courtesy Dr. Ronald Koebler; used with his kind permission; (a) adapted from https://www.youtube.com/watch?v=XjXLJMUrNBo&t=302s*].

SUMMARY

- In 1887, while receiving the electromagnetic waves in coil with a spark gap. Hertz found that the maximum spark length was reduced when the apparatus was put in a black box; this is due to what is now known as the photoelectric effect and the box absorbed the ultraviolet radiation which helped the electrons in jumping across the gap. Hertz reported the observations but did not pursue further and also did not make any attempt to explain them. In 1897, J J Thomson discovered electrons and in 1899 he showed that electrons are emitted when light falls on a metal surface; these are now known as photoelectrons and the phenomenon is known as the *photoelectric effect*.
- There are certain peculiarities associated with the photoelectric effect which cannot be explained on the basis of wave theory. For example, a faint violet light would eject electrons of greater kinetic energy than an intense yellow light although the latter would produce a larger number of electrons. In 1905, Einstein provided a simple explanation of the peculiarities by assuming that light consisted of quanta of energy $h\nu$ (where ν is the frequency) and that the emission of a photoelectron was the result of the interaction of a single quantum (i.e. of the photon) with an electron. In his 1905 paper, Einstein wrote *Monochromatic radiation behaves as if it consists of mutually independent energy quanta of magnitude* $h\nu$.
- In 1923, Compton reported his studies on the scattering of X-rays by solid materials (mainly graphite) and showed that the shift of the wavelength of the scattered photon could be explained by assuming the photon to have momentum equal to $h\nu/c$. Compton effect provided an unambiguous example of a process in which a quantum of radiation carrying energy as well as momentum scatters off an electron. The kinematics of the scattering process gives the following for the shift in the wavelength

$$\Delta\lambda = \frac{2h}{m_0 c}\sin^2\frac{\theta}{2} \approx 0.0485\,\sin^2\frac{\theta}{2}$$

where θ is the angle of scattering of the light quantum, m_0 represents the rest mass of the electron and $\Delta\lambda$ is measured in Angstroms. Compton found the above formula to be in agreement with his experimental measurements of $\Delta\lambda$.

PROBLEMS

24.1 **(a)** Calculate the number of photons emitted per second by a 5 mW laser assuming that it emits light of wavelength 6328 Å.

$$\left[\textbf{Ans}: 1.6\times10^{16}\right]$$

(b) The beam is allowed to fall normally on a plane mirror. Calculate the force acting on the mirror.

$$\left[\textbf{Ans}: 3.3\times10^{-11}\,\text{N}\right]$$

24.2 Assume a 40 W sodium lamp ($\lambda \approx 5869$ Å) emitting light in all directions. Calculate the rate at which the photons cross a unit placed normally to the beam at a distance of 10 m from the source.

$$\left[\textbf{Ans}: \approx 10^{17}\ \text{photons/m}^2-\text{s}\right]$$

24.3 In the photoelectric effect, a photon is completely absorbed by the electron. Show that the laws of conservation of energy and momentum cannot be satisfied simultaneously if a free electron is assumed to absorb the photon. (Thus the electron has to be bound to an atom and the atom undergoes a recoil when the electron is ejected. However, the mass of the atom is much larger than that of the electron, hence the atom picks up only a small fraction of the energy, this is somewhat similar to the case of a tennis ball hitting a heavy object, the momentum of the ball is reversed with its energy remaining almost the same.)

24.4 In the Compton scattering experiment, show that the fractional loss of energy of the photon increases with decrease in the wavelength. Calculate the maximum value of this fractional loss for $\lambda \approx 0.711$ Å and $\lambda \approx 0.022$ Å; the former corresponds to the Molybdenum K_α X-ray line and the later to the γ -rays emitted from RaC.

24.5 If photoelectrons are emitted from a metal surface by using blue light, can you say for sure that photoelectric emission will take place with yellow light and with violet light?

24.6 Show that

$J_z|x\rangle = i\hbar|y\rangle$ and $J_z|y\rangle = -i\hbar|x\rangle$

Thus, if we write $|x\rangle = |1\rangle$, $|y\rangle = |2\rangle$ and $(J_z)_{ij} = \langle i|J_z|j\rangle$ then we obtain the following representation of J_z

$$J_z = \hbar\begin{pmatrix} 0 & -i \\ i & 0 \end{pmatrix}$$

24.7 Using the above representation of J_z, obtain the eigenvalues and normalized eigenfunctions of J_z and show that they are consistent with the result in Sec. 24.4

CHAPTER

25

But it is necessary to insist more strongly than usual that what I am putting before you is a model—the Bohr model atom—because later I shall take you to a profounder level of representation in which the electron instead of being confined to a particular locality is distributed in a sort of probability haze all over the atom.

— Arthur Eddington*

Bohr Atom and Line Spectra of Atoms

LEARNING OBJECTIVES

After reading this chapter, the reader should be able to:

LO 1: *discuss the Bohr model for hydrogen atom and hydrogen like one electron atoms*

LO 2: *discuss the discovery of Helium*

LO 3: *discuss Fraunhofer lines*

Important Milestones

1868: The French astronomer Jules Janssen discovered Helium while studying the spectrum of the chromosphere of the Sun during a total solar eclipse in Guntur (in South India).

1885: The Swiss mathematical physicist Johann Balmer (1825–1898) discovered an empirical formula representing the wavelengths of the spectral lines of hydrogen; this formula is now known as the Balmer series.

1913: The Danish physicist Niels Bohr (1885–1962) formulated what is now known as the ***Bohr model for the hydrogen atom*** which could explain the line spectrum of the hydrogen atom. Bohr was awarded the 1922 Nobel Prize in Physics ***for his services in the investigation of the structure of atoms and of the radiation emanating from them.***

* As quoted in Ref. 25.1.

Above Image: Extremely important spectroscopic data are obtained during total solar eclipse shown above. Diagram courtesy: McGraw Hill Digital Access Library.

1932: Harold Urey, George Murphy and Ferdinand Brickwedde jointly published a paper in 1932 announcing the discovery of what we now call deuterium. Urey was awarded the 1934 Nobel Prize in Chemistry ***for his discovery of heavy hydrogen***. Harold Urey's daughter Mary Alice was about to be born, because of which he could not attend the Nobel ceremony in Stockholm.

25.1 Introduction

Light coming out from a hydrogen lamp is quite different in color from the light coming out of a sodium lamp (see Figs. 25.1 and 25.2). The emission (and the absorption) spectrum of each atom is unique and can be considered as its signature. Spectroscopy is the branch of science which investigates measurement and analysis of spectra from atoms and molecules. Spectroscopy has very important applications in many diverse areas and one of the very important application is in astrophysics where many properties of a star are determined from the analysis of spectra obtained by viewing the star. In this chapter, we will discuss the emission and absorption spectra of simple atoms.

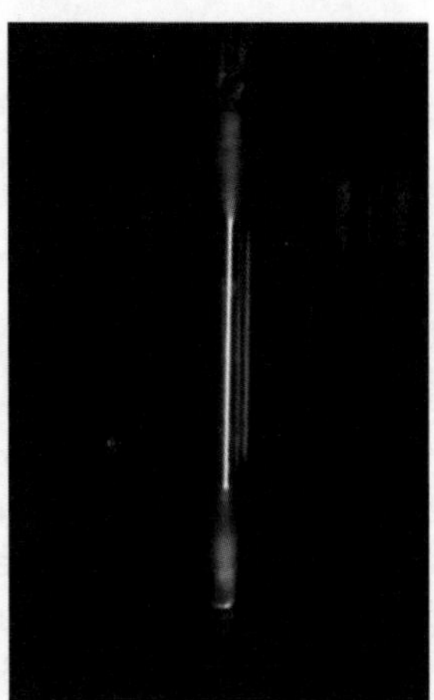

Figure 25.1
Light from a hydrogen lamp.

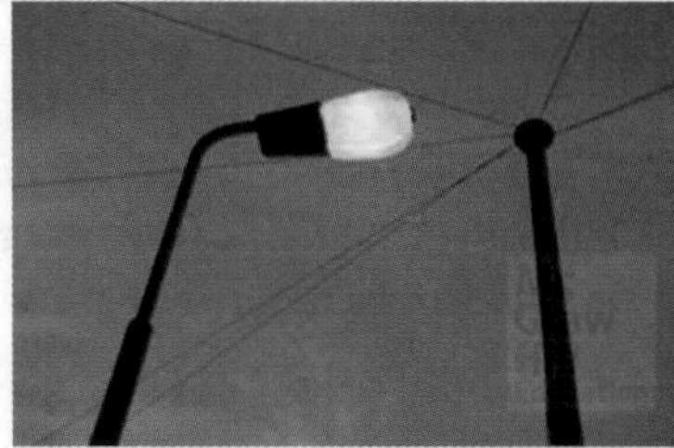

Figure 25.2
Light from a sodium lamp.

25.2 Energy Levels of Hydrogen Like Atoms

LO1

The hydrogen atom consists of a proton (of charge q) and an electron, and a hydrogen like atom consists of a nucleus of charge Zq and one electron where

$Z = 1$ for the hydrogen atom,
$Z = 1$ for the deuterium atom,
$Z = 2$ for the single ionized Helium atom (He^+),
$Z = 3$ for the doubly ionized Lithium ion (Li^{++}),
$Z = 4$ for the triply ionized Beryllium ion (Be^{+++}), etc.

The deuterium ion, the singly ionized Helium ion, the doubly ionized Lithium ion etc. are all single electron systems; they are usually referred to as hydrogen-like atoms. We will assume the mass of the electron to be extremely small in comparison to that of the nucleus so that we may assume the nucleus to remain at rest. Later we will modify the formulae to take into account the finite mass of the nucleus.

In 1913, Niels Bohr put forward a simple model of a hydrogen-like atom (i.e., having just one electron); he assumed the electron to rotate around the nucleus in discrete circular orbits (see Fig. 25.3). In his 1913 paper (published in the July issue of Philosophical Magazine; see Ref. 25.2), Bohr wrote

> *General evidence indicates that an atom of hydrogen consists simply of a single electron rotating round a positive nucleus of charge e.*

Bohr further assumed that the angular momentum of the electron is an integral multiple of $\hbar$:

$$m_e vr = n\hbar; \qquad n = 0, 1, 2, 3 \tag{25.1}$$

where v represents the speed of the electron, r represents the radius of the (circular) orbit,

$$m_e = 9.1093897\ 10^{-31}\ \text{kg} \tag{25.2}$$

represents the mass of the electron, and

$$\hbar \equiv h/2\pi = 1.05457266 \times 10^{-34}\ \text{Js} \tag{25.3}$$

h being the Planck's constant. Further, for the electron rotating around the nucleus (like the earth rotating around the sun), the centripetal force ($= m_e v^2/r$) must be equal to the Coulomb force between the electron and the nucleus ($= Zq^2/4\pi\varepsilon_0 r^2$)*:

* For the Earth rotating around the Sun in a circular orbit, with velocity v, we would have $\frac{M_E v^2}{r} = \frac{GM_E M_S}{r^2}$ where G is the Gravitational constant, M_E and M_S represent the mass of the earth and of the Sun, respectively.

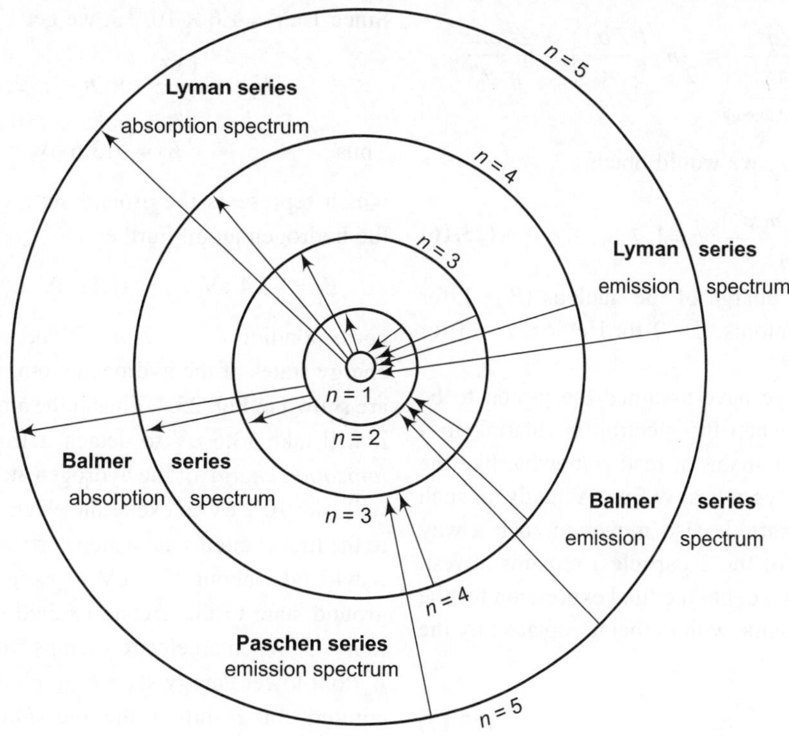

Figure 25.3
The discrete orbits of the hydrogen atom as predicted by Bohr's theory.

$$\frac{m_e v^2}{r} = \frac{Zq^2}{4\pi\varepsilon_0 r^2} \Rightarrow v^2 = \frac{Zq^2}{4\pi\varepsilon_0 m_e r} \quad \textbf{(25.4)}$$

where $q = 1.60217733 \times 10^{-19}$ C **(25.5)**

represents the charge of the electron, and

$$\varepsilon_0 = 8.8542 \times 10^{-12}\ \text{C}^2\ \text{N}^{-1}\ \text{m}^{-2} \quad \textbf{(25.6)}$$

is the dielectric permittivity of free space. Thus from Eqs. (25.1) and (25.4), we get

$$m_e^2 v^2 r^2 = n^2\hbar^2 \Rightarrow m_e^2 \frac{Zq^2}{4\pi\varepsilon_0 m r} r^2 = n^2\hbar^2 \quad \textbf{(25.7)}$$

Simplifying, we get the following expression for the radii of different orbits are given by

$$r = r_n = n^2 \frac{a_0}{Z};\ n = 1, 2, 3 \ldots \quad \textbf{(25.8)}$$

where
$$a_0 = \frac{4\pi\varepsilon_0\hbar^2}{m_e q^2} = \frac{\hbar}{m_e c\alpha} \quad \textbf{(25.9)}$$

is known as the Bohr radius,

$$c = 2.99792458 \times 10^8\ \text{m/s} \quad \textbf{(25.10)}$$

is the speed of light in free space, and

$$\alpha = \frac{q^2}{4\pi\varepsilon_0\hbar c} \approx \frac{1}{137.036} \quad \textbf{(25.11)}$$

is known as the fine structure constant. If we substitute the numerical values, we would obtain

$$a_0 = \frac{\hbar}{m_e c\alpha} \approx \frac{(1.05\times10^{-34}\ \text{J·s})}{(9.11\times10^{-31}\ \text{kg})(3\times10^8\ \text{m/s})(1/137)} \approx 0.529\times10^{-10}\ \text{m} \quad \textbf{(25.12)}$$

Thus the radii of different discrete orbits of the electron for the hydrogen atom ($Z = 1$) are

$$0.529\ \text{Å},\ 2.116\ \text{Å},\ 4.761\ \text{Å},\ \ldots \quad \textbf{(25.13)}$$

where 1 Å (1 Angstrom) ≡ 10^{-10} m. The radii in Fig. 25.3 are also in that ratio. Now,

$$v^2 = \frac{Zq^2}{4\pi\varepsilon_0 m_e r} \Rightarrow v = \frac{Zq^2}{4\pi\varepsilon_0(m_e vr)} \Rightarrow v = \frac{Z\alpha\hbar c}{(n\hbar)} \quad \textbf{(25.14)}$$

In the nth orbit, the velocity of the electron will therefore be

$$v = v_n = \frac{Z\alpha c}{n};\ n = 1, 2, 3, \ldots \quad \textbf{(25.15)}$$

Since $\alpha \approx 1/137$, the velocity of the electron is very small in comparison to c. The total energy of the atom will be the sum of kinetic energy $\left(= \frac{1}{2} m_e v^2\right)$ and potential energy $(= -Zq^2/4\pi\varepsilon_0 r)$:

$$E = \underbrace{\frac{1}{2}m_e v^2}_{\text{Kinetic Energy}} \underbrace{-\frac{Zq^2}{4\pi\varepsilon_0 r}}_{\text{Potential Energy}} = \frac{1}{2}m_e\left(\frac{Z\alpha c}{n}\right)^2 - \frac{Z^2\alpha\hbar c}{n^2 a_0}$$

If we use Eq. (25.9) for a_0, we would obtain

$$E = E_n = -\frac{Z^2\alpha^2(m_e c^2)}{2n^2};\ n = 1, 2, 3, \ldots \quad \textbf{(25.16)}$$

where Zq represents the charge of the nucleus (Z = 1 for hydrogen and deuterium atoms, Z = 2 for He^+ ion, Z = 3 for Li^{++} ion etc.).

In the above model, we have assumed the proton to be infinitely heavy so that when the electron is rotating in a circular orbit, the proton remains at rest; somewhat like the earth rotating around the (very heavy) Sun. Actually, in such a situation, the heavier particle also moves in such a way that the center of mass (of the 2 particles) remains at rest. The analysis is a bit involved, but the final expression for the total energy remains the same with m_e being replaced by the reduced mass μ given by

$$\mu = \frac{m_e M_N}{m_e + M_N} \quad \textbf{(25.17)}$$

with m_e and M_N representing the mass of the electron and that of the nucleus, respectively. Thus the energy levels of the hydrogen-like atom is given by

$$E = E_n = -\frac{Z^2\alpha^2(\mu c^2)}{2n^2};\ n = 1, 2, 3, \ldots \quad \textbf{(25.18)}$$

We may mention here that the Bohr's model is based on a classical description of the motion of the electron in which we assume that the electron rotates (around the nucleus) in discrete circular orbits. This is not a correct description of the atom. According to quantum mechanics, one has to solve what is known as the Schrödinger equation. However, Bohr's model is still studied as it gives an expression for the discrete energy levels of the hydrogen-like atoms [namely Eq. (25.18)] which is exactly the same as given by rigorous quantum mechanics; see, e.g., Refs. 25.3 and 25.4. Indeed Niels Bohr was awarded the 1922 Nobel Prize in Physics *for his services in the investigation of the structure of atoms and of the radiation emanating from them.*

Now, for the hydrogen atom, Z = 1 and

$$M_N = m_p = 1.6726219 \times 10^{-27}\ \text{kg} \quad \textbf{(25.19)}$$

giving $$\mu = \mu_H = \frac{m_e m_p}{m_e + m_p} \approx 9.1045 \times 10^{-31}\ \text{kg} \quad \textbf{(25.20)}$$

where we have used Eq. (25.2) for m_e. Substituting the numerical values in Eq. (25.18), we get

$$E_n \approx -\frac{2.17 \times 10^{-18}\ \text{J}}{n^2};\ n = 1, 2, 3, \ldots \quad \textbf{(25.21)}$$

Since 1 eV ≈ 1.6 × 10^{-19} J, we get

$$E_n \approx -\frac{13.6}{n^2}\ \text{eV};\ n = 1, 2, 3, \ldots \quad \textbf{(25.22)}$$

Thus $$E_1 \approx -13.6\ \text{eV} \quad \textbf{(25.23)}$$

which represents the ground state energy corresponding to the hydrogen atom. Further,

$$E_2 \approx -3.4\ \text{eV},\ E_3 \approx -1.51\ \text{eV},\ E_4 \approx -0.85\ \text{eV} \quad \textbf{(25.24)}$$

corresponding to n = 2, n = 3 and n = 4, respectively . The energy states of the hydrogen atom, as given by Eq. (25.22), are shown in Fig. 25.4. Thus if the atom is in the ground state, it will take 13.6 eV to detach it from the atom; this is the *ionization energy* of the hydrogen atom. On the other hand, it will take 10.2 eV to excite the electron from the ground state to the first excited state which corresponds to n = 2; similarly, it will take about 12.1 eV to excite the electron from the ground state to the second excited state which corresponds to n = 3. When an electron jumps from a higher energy state E_m to a lower energy state E_n, a photon of energy $E_m - E_n$ is emitted; this results in the ***emission spectrum of the atom***. Conversely, when a photon of energy $E_m - E_n$ is absorbed by the atom, the electron jumps from a lower energy state E_n to a higher energy state E_m; this results in the ***absorption spectrum of the atom***. Now, for the $m \rightarrow n$ transition, the wavelength of the emitted radiation is given by

$$\frac{1}{\lambda} = \frac{\nu}{c} = \frac{E_m - E_n}{hc} = Z^2 R\left[\frac{1}{n^2} - \frac{1}{m^2}\right] \quad \textbf{(25.25)}$$

where $$R = \frac{2\pi^2\mu}{ch^3}\left(\frac{q^2}{4\pi\varepsilon_0}\right)^2 = \frac{\mu c\alpha^2}{2h} \quad \textbf{(25.26)}$$

is known as the Rydberg constant. Now, for the deuterium atom

$$m_N = m_D \approx 3.3436 \times 10^{-27}\ \text{kg}$$

giving $$\mu_D \approx 9.1070 \times 10^{-31}\ \text{kg}$$

Values of the Rydberg constant for different (one electron) hydrogen like atoms are given below

R = 109677.58 cm^{-1}	(for the hydrogen atom)	
109707.56 cm^{-1}	(for the deuterium atom)	**(25.27)**
109722.40 cm^{-1}	(for the He^+-atom)	
109728.90 cm^{-1}	(for the Li^{++}-atom)	

The slight difference in the values is because of the difference in the values of the reduced mass μ. [see Eq. (25.17)]. As mentioned earlier, the solution of the Schrödinger equation for the hydrogen-like atoms gives the same expression for the energy levels.

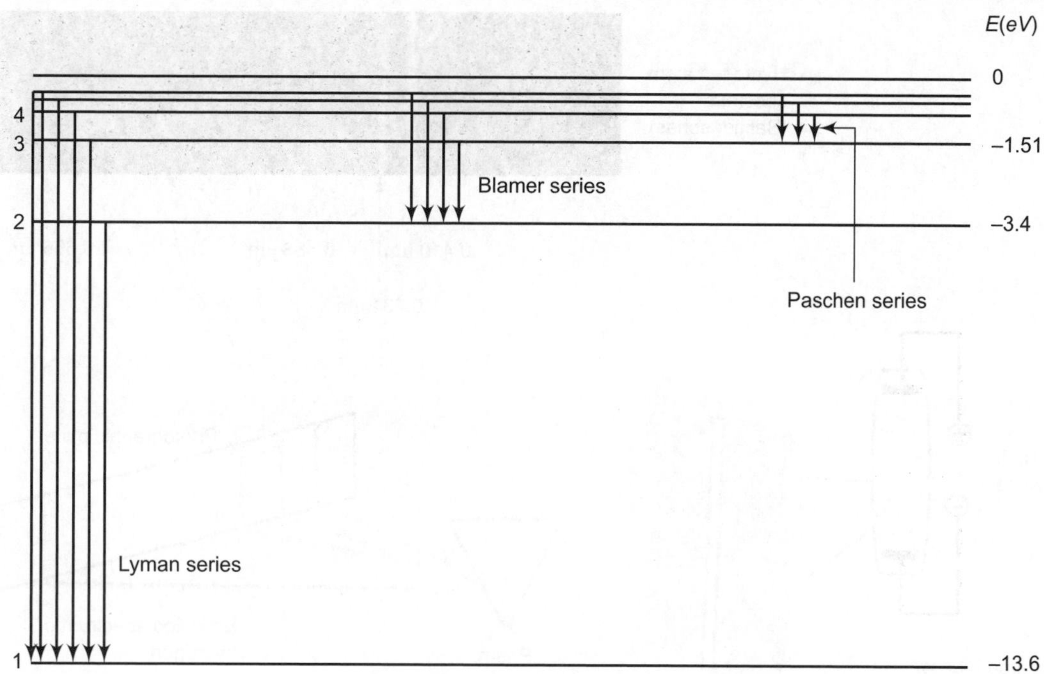

Figure 25.4
The discrete energy levels of the hydrogen atom as predicted by Bohr's theory.

25.2.1 Spectrum of the Hydrogen Atom

We consider the hydrogen atom for which $Z = 1$. For the $m \to 2$ ($m = 3, 4, 5, \ldots, n = 2$) transitions, the wavelength of the emitted radiation will be 0.656 μm

0.656 μm (which is in the red region of the spectrum) for the $3 \to 2$ transition

0.486 μm (which is in the blue region of the spectrum) for the $4 \to 2$ transition

0.434 μm (which is in the violet region of the spectrum) for the $5 \to 2$ transition and

0.4103 μm (which is also in the violet region of the spectrum) for the $6 \to 2$ transition.

The $m \to 2$ ($m = 3, 4, 5, \ldots; n = 2$) transitions given above are referred to as the Balmer series, the corresponding spectral lines are in the visible region of the spectrum. The $m \to 1$ ($m = 2, 3, 4, 5, \ldots, n = 1$) transitions give rise to what is known as the Lyman series, the corresponding spectral lines are in the ultraviolet region; for example, the $2 \to 1$ transition gives rise to wavelength of 0.1217 μm which is in the ultraviolet region; we may recall that the violet end of the visible spectrum has a wavelength of about 0.35 μm. Similarly, the $m = \to 3$ ($m = 4, 5, 6, \ldots; n = 3$) transitions give rise to what is known as the Paschen series, the corresponding spectral lines are in the infra-red region. Each wavelength is a characteristic of the hydrogen atom and is referred to as the "emission spectrum" which is obtained by having a discharge in a gas of hydrogen atoms and allowing a collimated beam to fall on a prism (see Fig. 25.5). The electric discharge gets the hydrogen atom excited to higher energy states and when the atoms (in the higher energy state) make a transition to the lower energy state, we obtain the characteristic lines of the hydrogen atom. This is known as the emission spectrum which is kind of a signature of the atoms (or molecules) in the gas. The emission spectrum of the hydrogen atom (in the visible region of the spectrum) is shown in Fig. 25.5.

25.2.2 Comparison of the Spectrum of the Hydrogen Atom with that of Deuterium

For deuterium, the values of the reduced mass (and hence of the Rydberg constant) are slightly different. For the $n = 3 \to n = 2$ transition, the wavelength of the emitted radiation comes out to be

0.65652 μm for the hydrogen atom

and

0.65634 μm for the deuterium atom,

respectively. The corresponding wavelengths for the $n = 4 \to n = 2$ transition is

0.48631 μm and 0.48617 μm

for the hydrogen atom and the deuterium atom, respectively. Such small differences in wavelength (which is due to the difference in the reduced mass μ) was first observed by Urey in 1932 which led to the discovery of deuterium. Indeed Harold

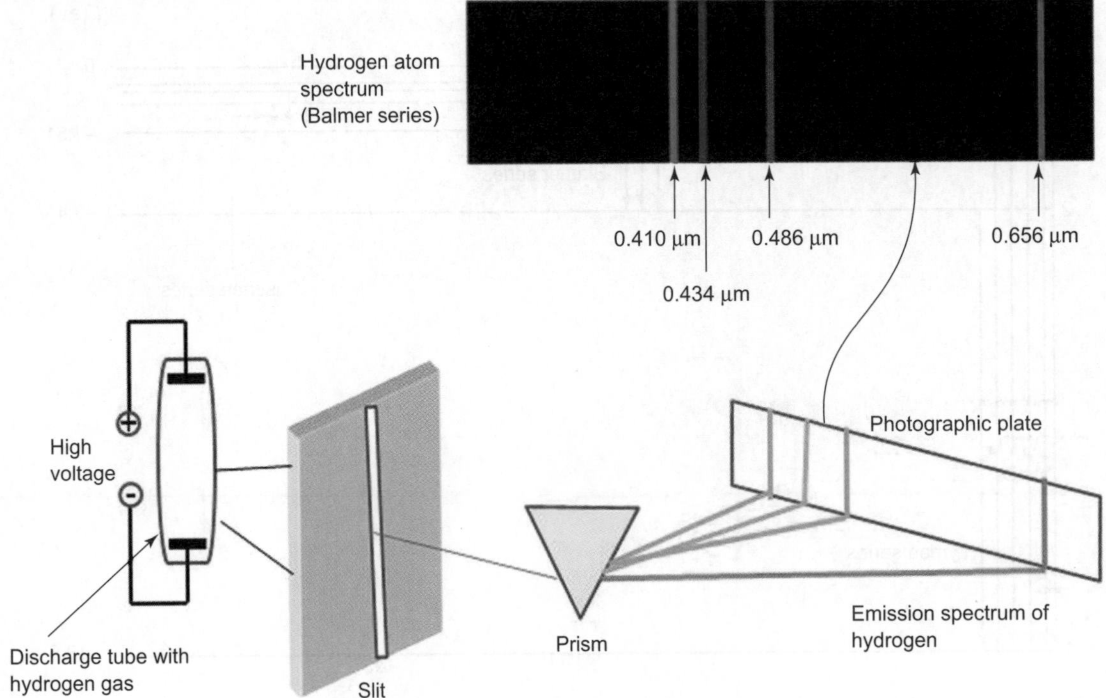

Figure 25.5

The emission spectrum of the hydrogen atom.

Urey* was awarded the 1934 Nobel Prize in Chemistry *for his discovery of heavy hydrogen.*

One can see the power of spectroscopy: careful measurement of the wavelength of the spectral lines leads to great discoveries.

25.2.3 Spectrum of Other Atoms

LO2

The spectra of the helium atom or of the lithium atom are quite different from that of hydrogen. Figure 25.6 shows the emission spectrum of hydrogen, helium, lithium and oxygen. The most important point is

The emission (and the absorption) spectrum of each atom is unique and can be considered as its signature. By studying in detail a measured spectrum, one can determine the elements present in the gas. In fact, spectroscopy is one of the most important tools to determine the gases present in the stars.

In Fig. 25.6 we see a strong yellow line in the spectrum of helium. Indeed on August 18, 1868, during a total solar eclipse in Guntur (in South India), the French astronomer Jules Janssen saw a yellow line in the spectrum of the chromosphere of the Sun†. Initially it was thought to be that from

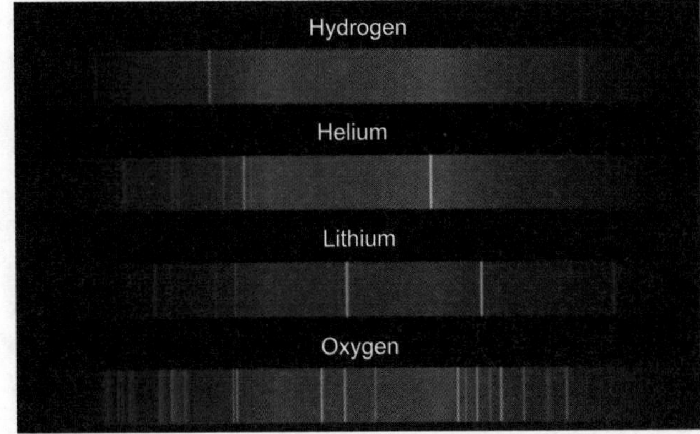

Figure 25.6

The emission spectrum of hydrogen, helium, lithium and oxygen. The emission (and the absorption) spectrum of each atom is unique and can be considered as its signature. By studying in detail a measured spectrum, one can determine the elements present in the gas. In fact, spectroscopy is one of the most important tools to determine the gases present in the stars. The above photograph has been adapted from http://www.thunderbolts.info/forum/phpBB3/viewtopic.php?f=3&t=14811; photograph in the public domain.

* Harold Urey, George Murphy and Ferdinand Brickwedde jointly published a paper in 1932 announcing the discovery of what we now call deuterium. However, only Urey was awarded the 1934 Nobel Prize in Chemistry ***for his discovery of heavy hydrogen.***

† Georges Rayet, C. T. Haig, Norman R. Pogson and John Herschel are also credited with the discovery of helium from the observations made during the total solar eclipse on August 18, 1868; see https://en.wikipedia.org/wiki/Helium.

sodium which gave rise to 2 yellow lines of wavelengths 0.5890 μm and 0.5896 μm (these are the well-known D_1 and D_2 lines of sodium). However, careful measurements showed that the wavelength of the observed yellow line was 0.5875 μm (see Fig. 25.6) which was different from that of sodium. Thus it was surmised that the wavelength was due to an element which was not yet detected on earth. The English chemist Edward Frankland named it helium element deriving it from the word '*helios*' – the Greek word for the Sun. Once again we see the power of spectroscopy and this time it is the spectroscopy of the light coming from the Sun.

Although the spectra of the helium atom or of the lithium atom are quite different from that of hydrogen, the spectra of the He^+ ion (i.e., singly ionized helium atom) or of the Li^{++} (doubly ionized lithium atom) are similar to that of the hydrogen atom because both He^+ ion and Li^{++} ion are single electron ions. However,

> *the corresponding wavelengths are smaller by a factor of about 4 for the He^+ ion and by a factor of about 9 for the Li^{++} ion;*

this is because of the Z^2 term in the expression of energy levels and also because of the slight difference in the values of the reduced mass. For example, for the $n = 4 \rightarrow n = 3$ transition, the wavelength of the emitted radiation comes out to be

1.8756 μm (which is in the far infra-red region) for the hydrogen atom

and

0.4687 μm (which is in the visible region) for the He^+ ion,

respectively.

25.3 Fraunhofer Lines LO3

If we have a white light source (like an incandescent light bulb), we will have a continuous spectrum on the photographic plate as shown in Fig. 25.7. All colors between red and blue will be present. If we put a glass container of hydrogen gas between the white light source and the slit (see Fig. 25.8), then certain frequencies will be absorbed by the hydrogen atom and will result in the atom getting excited to higher energy states; the subsequent emission will, in general,

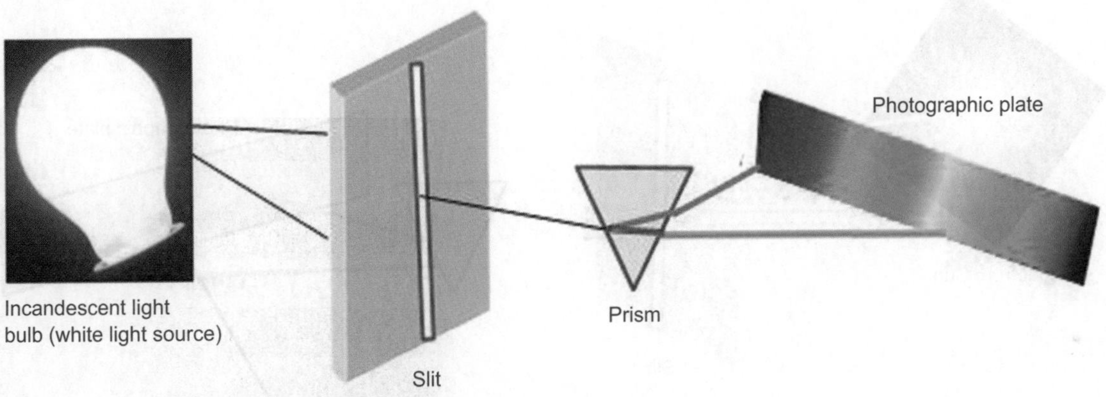

Figure 25.7
If we have a white light source (like an incandescent light bulb), we will have a continuous spectrum on the photographic plate. All colors between red and blue will be present.

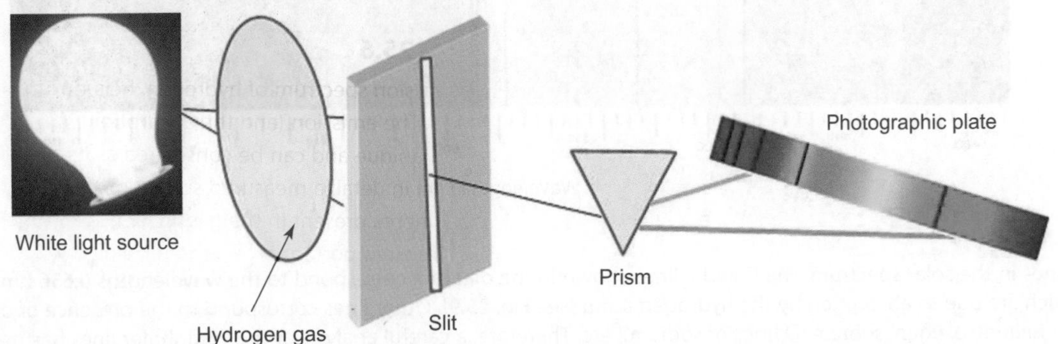

Figure 25.8
If we put a glass container of hydrogen gas between the white light source and the slit, then certain frequencies will be absorbed by the hydrogen atom and will result in the atom getting excited to higher energy states; the subsequent emission will, in general, be in different directions. This will result in the black lines – exactly at wavelengths where we had the emission spectrum. This is the absorption spectrum of the element (in this case, hydrogen).

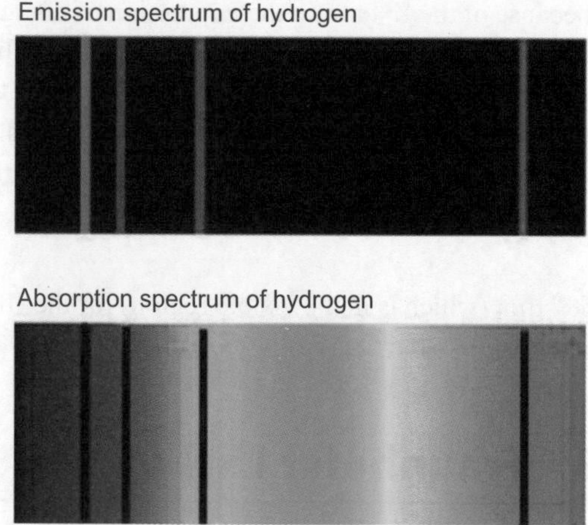

Figure 25.9
Emission and absorption spectrum of the hydrogen atom.

be in different directions. This will result in the black lines – exactly at wavelengths where we had the emission spectrum. This is the absorption spectrum of the element (in this case, hydrogen). Figure 25.9 shows the emission (and the absorption) spectrum of the hydrogen atom. Notice that the dark lines occur exactly at the same wavelength as that of the emission spectrum. In the emission spectrum, a photon of a particular frequency is emitted as the atom makes a transition from an excited state to another state (associated with a smaller energy). On the other hand, in the absorption spectrum, a photon of a particular frequency is absorbed as the atom makes a transition from a lower energy state to an excited state.

Now, instead of the incandescent bulb, if we have sunlight illuminating the slit (see Fig. 25.10), we will have many dark lines superimposed on the continuous spectrum. These dark lines were first observed by W.H. Wollaston in 1802. In 1814, Fraunhofer independently discovered this and carefully measured the wavelengths corresponding to the various dark lines and therefore the dark lines are usually referred to as Fraunhofer lines. Later, in 1845, Kirchhoff and Bunsen carefully compared the measured wavelengths of the dark lines with the emission spectrum of various atoms and concluded that the dark lines coincide with the emission spectrum of different atoms and therefore they occur because of absorption

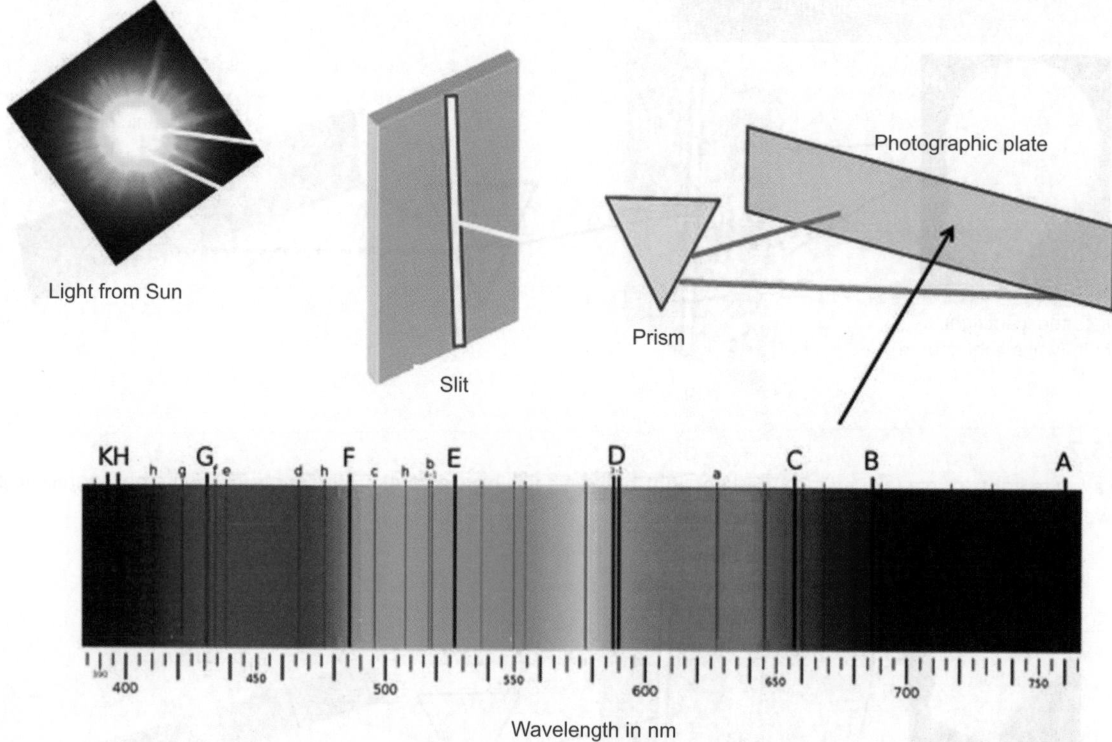

Figure 25.10
Fraunhofer lines in the solar spectrum. The C and F lines shown in the diagram correspond to the wavelengths 0.656 μm and 0.486 μm which are due to absorption by the hydrogen atom [see Fig. 25.9]. Other lines correspond to the presence of other elements like helium, oxygen, sodium (D lines of sodium), etc. Therefore, a careful analysis of the Fraunhofer lines has tremendous applications in astrophysics as it allows us to determine the gases present in the atmosphere of various stars. The lower photograph (in public domain) adapted from http://upload.wikimedia.org/wikipedia/commons/2/2f/Fraunhofer_lines.svg

by different elements present in the atmosphere of the Sun. Thus the C and F lines shown in Fig. 25.10 correspond to the wavelengths 0.656 μm and 0.486 μm which are due to absorption by the hydrogen atom [see Fig. 25.9]. Other lines correspond to the presence of other elements like helium, oxygen, sodium, etc. Therefore, a careful analysis of the Fraunhofer lines has tremendous applications in astrophysics as it allows us to determine the gases present in the atmosphere of various stars. Three kinds of spectra are shown in Fig. 25.11.

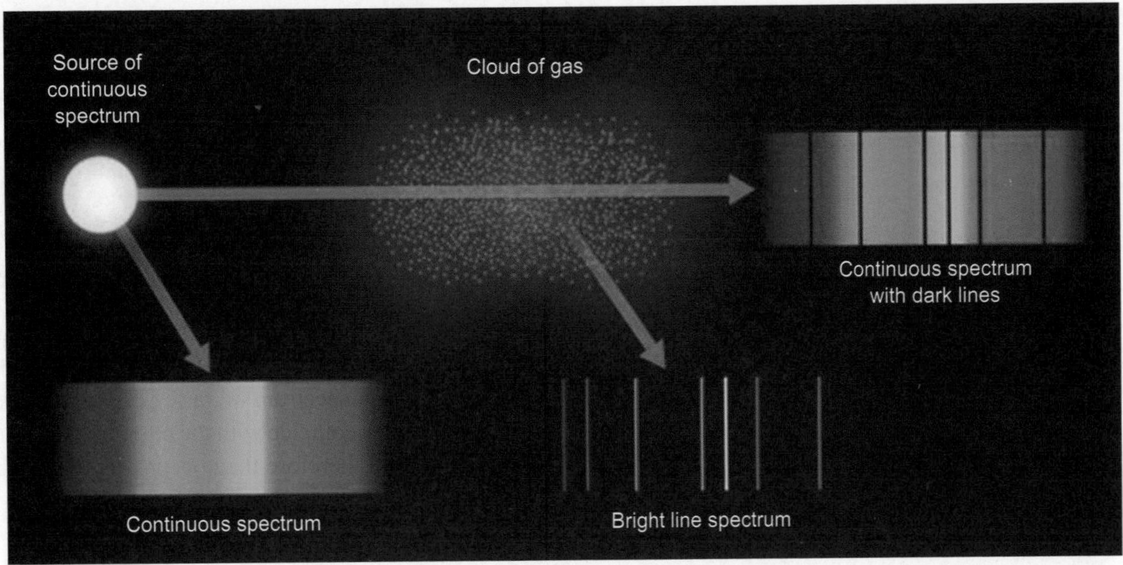

Figure 25.11
Three kinds of spectra. When we see a light bulb or other source of continuous radiation, all the colors are present. When the continuous spectrum is seen through a gas cloud, the cloud's atoms absorb certain wavelengths and produce the Fraunhofer lines. When the excited cloud is seen without the continuous source behind it, its atoms produce emission lines. Spectra created by: OpenStax CNX.
Adapted from https://courses.lumenlearning.com/astronomy/chapter/formation-of-spectral-lines/; photograph in the public domain.

PROBLEMS

Note: Use accurate values of various parameters as given in this chapter.

25.1 For the $n = 3 \rightarrow n = 2$ transition, calculate the wavelength of the emitted radiation from hydrogen atom, deuterium atom, He^+ ion and Li^{++} ion.

25.2 For the $n = 4 \rightarrow n = 2$ transition, calculate the wavelength of the emitted radiation from hydrogen atom, deuterium atom, He^+ ion and Li^{++} ion.

25.3 The Rydberg constant for the deuterium atom is given by

$$R_D \approx 109707.56 \text{ cm}^{-1}$$

Use accurate values of various parameters and determine the mass of the deuterium nucleus (which is known as the deuteron) and the binding energy of the deuteron in MeV.

25.4 The Rydberg constant for the He^+ atom is given by

$$R_{He+} \approx 109722.40 \text{ cm}^{-1}$$

Use accurate values of various parameters and determine the mass of the nucleus (which is known as the alpha particle) and the total binding energy of the alpha particle in MeV.

CHAPTER

26

I remember discussions with Bohr which went through many hours till very late at night and ended almost in despair; and when at the end of the discussion I went alone for a walk in the neighboring park I repeated to myself again and again the question: Can nature possibly be as absurd as it seemed to us in these atomic experiments?

—Werner Heisenberg*

Quantum Theory and Entanglement

LEARNING OBJECTIVES

After reading this chapter, the reader should be able to:

LO 1: *discuss experiments with a beam splitter, polarization beam splitter and a Polaroid.*

LO 2: *understand wave-particle duality.*

LO 3: *solve Schrödinger's equation for a free particle in one dimension.*

LO 4: *understand quantum mechanically single slit diffraction pattern and double slit interference patterns.*

LO 5: *analyse EPR paradox and Bell's inequality.*

Important Milestones

1865: James Clerk Maxwell showed that the speed of electromagnetic waves (as predicted by the laws of electricity and magnetism) was the same as the measured speed of light from which he concluded that light is an electromagnetic wave.

1905: Albert Einstein, in his Year of Miracles, wrote that a propagating light beam *consists of a finite number of energy quanta, localized in space, which move without being divided and which can be absorbed or emitted only as a whole.* Thus wave particle duality was first put forward by Einstein in 1905.

1924: de Broglie proposed that just as light exhibited wave-like and corpuscular behavior; electrons, protons must also show wavelike behavior with its wavelength given by $\lambda = h/p$.

1926: Heisenberg and Schrödinger put forward quantum theory. The 1932 Nobel Prize in Physics was awarded jointly to Heisenberg "for the creation of quantum mechanics, the application of which has, inter alia, led to the discovery of the allotropic forms of hydrogen." The 1933 Nobel Prize in Physics

* Werner Heisenberg in *Physics and Philosophy: The Revolution in Modern Science* p. 42, (1958).

Above Image: Extremely important spectroscopic data are obtained during total solar eclipse shown above. Diagram courtesy: McGraw Hill Digital Access Library.

was awarded jointly to Schrödinger and Dirac "for the discovery of new productive forms of atomic theory."

1927: Clinton Davisson and Lester Germer (in New York) and George Thomson (in Aberdeen, Scotland) carry out experiments demonstrating diffraction of an electron beam. The 1937 Nobel Prize in Physics was awarded jointly to CJ Davisson and GP Thomson *"for their experimental discovery of the diffraction of electrons by crystals"*; Germer missed out on the Prize!

1964: John Bell puts forward his famous theorem which is now known as Bell's theorem.

26.1 Introduction

The three most important concepts in quantum theory are: the indeterminateness in measurement, the principle of superposition and the collapse of the wave function. In this chapter we will discuss a few experiments which would enable us to understand these important concepts. We will also discuss simple solutions of the Schrödinger equation and also the concept of entanglement.

26.2 Experiments with a Beam Splitter

LO1

We assume that light from a single photon source is incident on a beam splitter [see Fig. 26.1]. By a single photon source, we imply that in the beam splitter experiment, the detectors D_1 and D_2 almost never click simultaneously and by 'almost never click simultaneously' we mean that the probability of simultaneous clicks of D_1 and D_2 (or simultaneous arrival of two or more photon at the beam splitter) is less than about 0.005. Of course simultaneous clicks will happen when the photons appear within the resolution time (dead time) of the detectors (which can be about 20–50 ns). In an ideal situation, where we have a truly single-photon source and perfect detectors, the detectors will never click simultaneously. Also, an ideal beam splitter is a partially silvered glass plate such that 50% of light is reflected and 50% of light is transmitted. We have two single-photon detectors D_1 and D_2. Quantum theory tells us that before the photon gets detected (either by the detector D_1 or by the detector D_2), the photon is in both the beams. The photon is indivisible; it does not split into two halves but when the photon gets detected, it collapses from being in both the beams, to being detected by one of

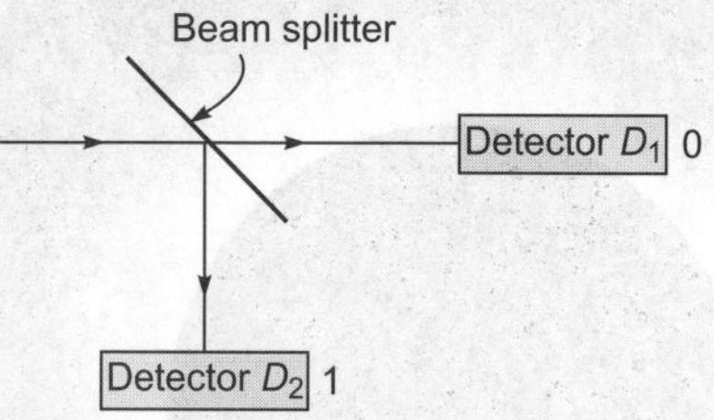

Figure 26.1
A light beam splits into 2 beams by a beam splitter. D_1 and D_2 are single photon detectors. Whenever the detector D_1 clicks, we generate the number 0 and whenever the detector D_2 clicks, we generate the number 1 and thereby generate a set of random numbers [(see Fig. 1.19(b)].

the detectors. This "collapsing" is unique to quantum theory. Dirac, in his very famous book *The Principles of Quantum Mechanics* (Ref. 26.1) writes:

> *we describe the photon as going partly into each of the two components into which the incident beam is split. The photon is then, as we may say, in a translational state given by the superposition of the two translational states associated with the two components. … For a photon to be in a definite translational state it need not be associated with one single beam of light, but may be associated with two or more beams of light, which are the components into which one original beam has been split. … In the accurate mathematical theory, each translational state is associated with one of the wave functions of ordinary wave optics, which may describe either a single beam or two or more beams into which one original beam has been split.*

The photon gets detected either by the detector D_1 or by D_2 and never by both; both detectors having 50% probability of detecting a photon.

No one can predict beforehand as to which detector will detect the photon. To quote from Ref. 26.2, *this fundamental indeterminateness of the universe has not really been integrated into our world view yet*. In fact we can use this indeterminateness to generate random numbers (see Sec. 1.11).

26.3 Experiments with a Polaroid

LO1

In Sec. 21.2, we had discussed that if a linearly polarized light (coming out of the Polaroid P_1) is incident on another Polaroid P_2, then by rotating the Polaroid P_2(about the z-axis) one will observe variation of intensity given by $I = I_0 \cos^2\theta$ which is known as Malus' Law; here θ is the angle that the pass axis of the Polaroid P_2 makes with the pass axis of the Polaroid P_1(see Fig. 21.7). We assume that light from a

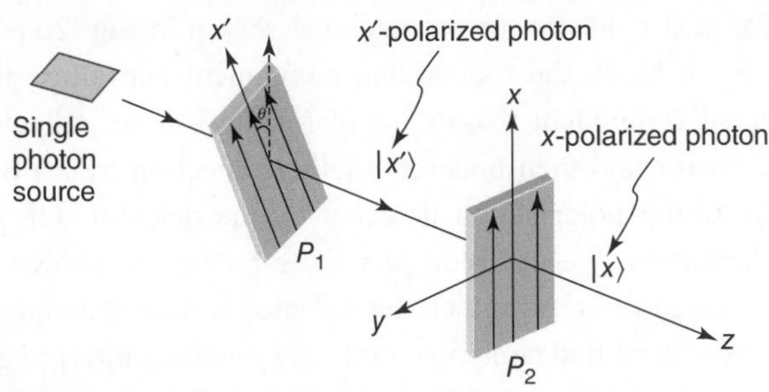

Figure 26.2
The probability that the polarized photon (coming out of the polaroid P_1 (whose pass axis makes an angle θ with the *x*-axis) will pass through the second polaroid P_2 (whose pass axis is along the *x*-axis) is $\cos^2\theta$.

single photon source falls on a Polaroid P_1, whose pass axis is at an angle of θ with the *x*-axis (see Fig. 26.2). Quantum theory tells us that the probability for a photon polarized at an angle θ (with respect to the *x*-axis) to pass through the second polaroid (whose pass axis is along the *x*-axis) is $\cos^2\theta$ and if the experiment is conducted with *N* photons (and if *N* is very large) then about $N\cos^2\theta$ photons will pass through; one cannot predict the fate of an individual photon. Now, an *x*-polarized photon (and a *y*-polarized photon) are described by the (normalized) Jones vectors

$$|x\rangle = \begin{pmatrix} 1 \\ 0 \end{pmatrix} \quad \text{and} \quad |y\rangle = \begin{pmatrix} 0 \\ 1 \end{pmatrix} \tag{26.1}$$

Also, a photon (polarized along the x' -axis) is described by the (normalized) Jones vector [see Sec. 24.4]:

$$|x'\rangle = \begin{pmatrix} \cos\theta \\ \sin\theta \end{pmatrix} = \cos\theta|x\rangle + \sin\theta|y\rangle \tag{26.2}$$

Thus, the photon is in a superposed state; this concept of 'superposition' (along with the concept of indeterminateness) are two very important concepts in quantum theory. The absolute square of the amplitude (= $\cos^2\theta$) represents the probability of detecting *x*-polarized photon. Thus the probability for the photon to pass through the second Polaroid (whose pass axis is along the *x*-axis) is $\cos^2\theta$ and if the experiment is conducted with *N* photons (and if *N* is very large) then about *N* $\cos^2\theta$ photons will pass through; one cannot predict the fate of an individual photon. For example, if $\theta = 45°$, we will have

$$|45^\circ\rangle = \frac{1}{\sqrt{2}}|x\rangle + \frac{1}{\sqrt{2}}|y\rangle \tag{26.3}$$

Thus, approximately half the photons will pass through the Polaroid P_2 and the remaining half will be absorbed by the Polaroid (see Fig. 21.7). It is *not* possible to answer the question as to why a particular photon is absorbed and an identical photon passes through.

26.4 Experiments with a Polarization Beam Splitter

LO1

We next consider a device known as the polarization beam splitter which is usually abbreviated as PBS; it consists of two prisms (made of certain type of crystals) cemented together. An unpolarized light beam incident on a PBS splits in two mutually orthogonal linearly polarized beams as shown in Fig. 26.3. The light reflected by the PBS is *s*-polarized; i.e., the electric field is perpendicular to the plane of incidence. The transmitted light is *p*-polarized; i.e., the electric field is in the plane of incidence. For a commercially available PBS*, the transmission efficiency of the *p*-polarization $T_p > 95\%$ and the reflection efficiency of the *s*-polarization $R_s > 99.9\%$. Thus, according to classical wave theory, if a *s*-polarized light wave is incident on the PBS, it will be totally reflected and if a *p*-polarized light wave is incident on the PBS, it will be totally transmitted [see Figs. 26.4(a) and 26.4(b)]. On the other hand, if a 45° polarized light wave falls on a PBS, half the intensity will be reflected and the remaining half will be transmitted (see Fig. 26.5). Now, what will happen if 45° polarized single photons fall on the PBS?? Once again, a photon is indivisible and it cannot split in two halves. Quantum theory tells us that the photon is in both beams and in a state which is a superposition of two polarizations

$$|45^\circ\rangle = \frac{1}{\sqrt{2}}|s\rangle + \frac{1}{\sqrt{2}}|p\rangle \tag{26.4}$$

where $|45^\circ\rangle$ describes a 45° polarized photon, $|s\rangle$ describes *s*-polarized photon and $|p\rangle$ describes a *p*-polarized photon.

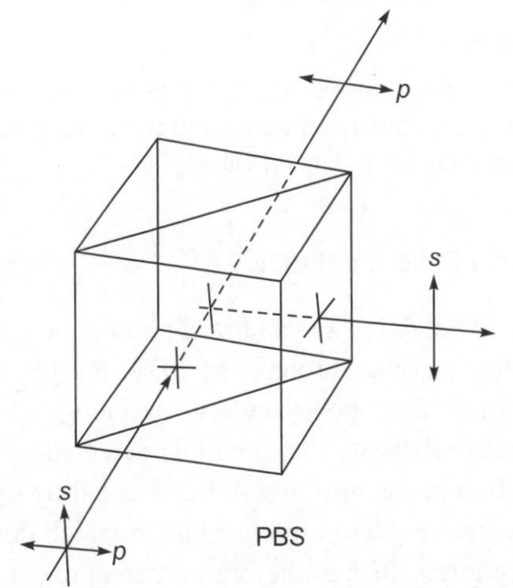

Figure 26.3
A Polarization Beam Splitter (usually abbreviated as PBS); an unpolarized light beam incident on a PBS splits in two mutually orthogonal linearly polarized beams.

* See, for example, www.chinasupply.net/optical/product/optics/beamsplitters/BBPBSC.html

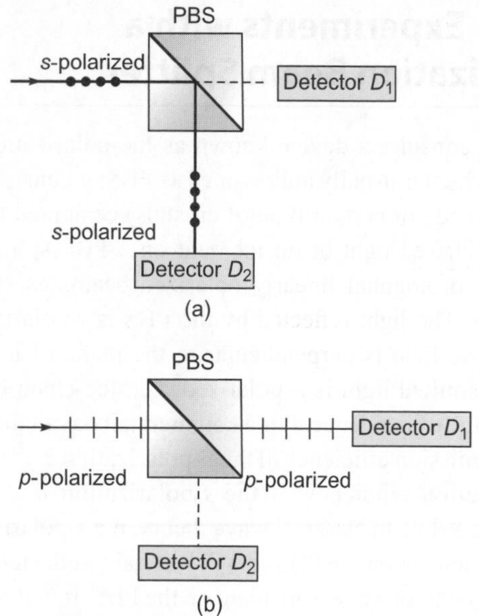

Figure 26.4

A *s*-polarized light incident on the PBS is totally reflected and a *p*-polarized light incident on the PBS will be totally transmitted.

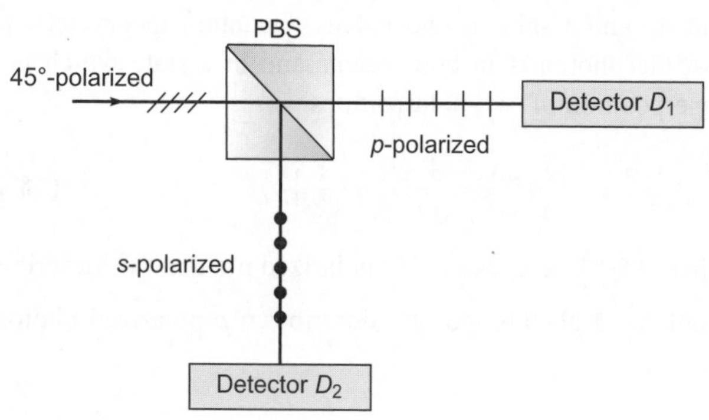

Figure 26.5

If a 45° polarized light wave falls on a PBS, half the intensity will be reflected (as a *s*-polarized wave) and the remaining half will be transmitted (as a *p*-polarized wave).

The square of the amplitude $\left|\frac{1}{\sqrt{2}}\right|^2 \left(=\frac{1}{2}\right)$ represents the probability of detecting a *s*-polarized photon, or a *p*-polarized photon. After passing through the PBS, the photon is in a superposition of the *s*-polarized state and a *p*-polarized state. There is half probability that it will be detected by the detector D_1 and half probability it will be detected by the detector D_2. No one can predict beforehand as to which detector will detect the photon. In fact, before its detection, it is in both the beams (at the same time)–but the process of detection makes it "collapse" to being either detected by D_1 or by the detector D_2. We can also use this arrangement to generate a set of random numbers as we had discussed in Sec. 1.11 (see Ref. 26.3).

We next consider the arrangement shown in Fig. 26.6(a) where we block the transmitted component and allow the reflected component (having *s*-polarization) to get reflected by a mirror and then undergo another reflection by a PBS; the resulting polarization detected by the detector will be *s*-polarization. We next consider the arrangement shown in Fig. 26.6(b) where we block the reflected component and allow the transmitted component (having *p*-polarization) to get reflected by a mirror and then undergo another transmission by a PBS; the resulting polarization detected by the detector will be *p*-polarization.

We next consider the arrangement shown in Fig. 26.7 where we allow both the transmitted and the reflected components to get reflected by mirrors and then incident on the second PBS; if the mirrors are properly adjusted, we would

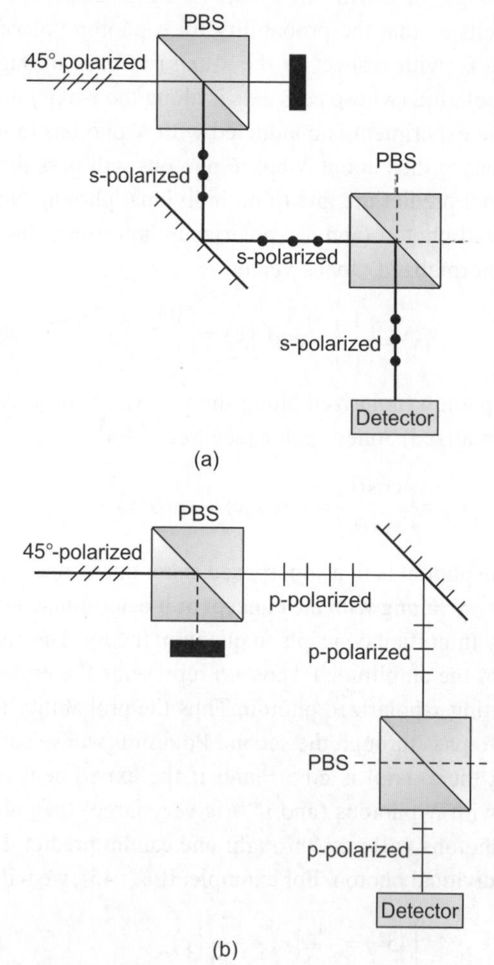

Figure 26.6

(a) If a 45° polarized photon is incident on a PBS, and only the reflected beam is allowed to fall on the second PBS, then the photon detected by the detector will be *s*-polarized. (b) If a 45° polarized photon is incident on a PBS, and only the transmitted beam is allowed to fall on the second PBS, then the photon detected by the detector will be *p*-polarized.

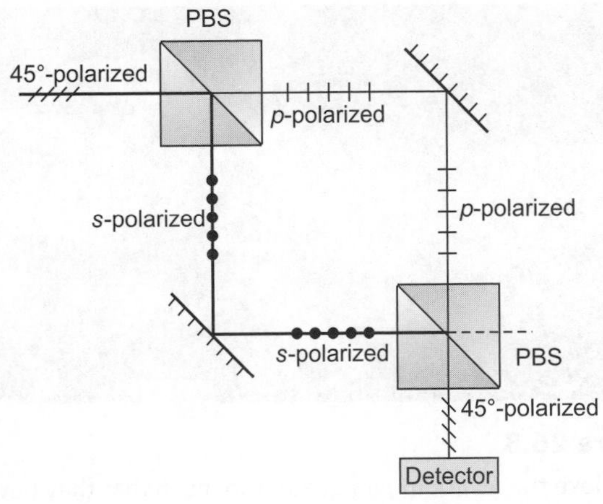

Figure 26.7
If a 45° polarized photon is incident on a PBS, and both the reflected and transmitted beams are allowed to fall on the second PBS, then (if the distances are properly adjusted) the beam coming out of the second PBS will be 45° degree polarized; this can happen only if the photon is in both the paths; diagram adapted from Ref. 26.2.

obtain a photon polarized at 45°; **this can only happen if the photon is in a state of superposition of being in both paths** as described by Eq. (26.4). John Wheeler, the famous American physicist, said (quoted from Ref. 26.2):

> *The photon takes both paths, but it takes only one path.*

We will discuss a similar situation when a light beam is propagating through a doubly refracting crystal–see Sec. 26.11.1.

26.5 Wave-Particle Duality LO2

As mentioned in Chapter 24, Einstein, in his Year of Miracles (1905), had put forward his famous theory according to which light consisted of mutually independent quanta of energy $E = h\nu$, here ν is the frequency and h is the Planck's constant; these quanta of energy were later called photons. Einstein also said that the photon momentum would be given by (see Sec. 24.1):

$$p = \frac{h\nu}{c} = \frac{h}{\lambda} \tag{26.5}$$

Around 1923, Arthur Compton carried out the scattering experiments of high energy photons by electrons and showed that the scattering experiments could only be explained if the energy and momentum of the photon are assumed to be given by the above equations (see Sec. 24.3). In 1924, de Broglie wrote his PhD thesis in which he proposed that just as light exhibited wave-like and corpuscular-like behavior, matter (like electrons, protons, ...) must show wavelike behavior also. He argued that the relation

$$\lambda = \frac{h}{p} \tag{26.6}$$

should be applied for electrons, protons, alpha particles ... as well. Now, in the Bohr model of the hydrogen atom (see Chapter 25), the electron rotates in discrete circular orbits which are defined by the condition that the angular momentum is an integral multiple of $h/2\pi$:

$$mvr = \frac{nh}{2\pi};\ n = 0, 1, 2, 3, \ldots \text{ which implies } 2\pi r = \frac{nh}{p} = n\lambda$$

de Broglie argued that the circumference of each Bohr orbit contains an integral number of wavelengths. de Broglie was awarded the 1929 Nobel Prize in Physics *for his discovery of the wave nature of electrons*. In the presentation speech (on December 12, 1929), the Chairman of the Nobel Committee for Physics said:

> *Louis de Broglie had the boldness to maintain that not all the properties of matter can be explained by the theory that it consists of corpuscles .... At a time when no single known fact supported this theory, Louis de Broglie asserted that a stream of electrons which passed through a very small hole in an opaque screen must exhibit the same phenomena as a light ray under the same conditions.... The experimental results obtained have fully substantiated Louis de Broglie's theory. Hence there are not two worlds, one of light and waves, one of matter and corpuscles. There is only a single universe.*

Later, de Broglie wrote [quoted from p. 58 of Ref. 26.4]:

> *I was convinced that the wave-particle duality discovered by Einstein in his theory of light quanta was absolutely general and extended to all of the physical world, and it seemed certain to me, therefore, that the propagation of a wave is associated with the motion of a particle of any sort—photon, electron, proton or any other.*

The electron was discovered in 1897 by JJ Thomson. The mass and charge of the electron is known to a tremendous degree of accuracy:

$$m_e = 9.1093897 \times 10^{-31}\ \text{kg}$$

$$\text{and} \quad q_e = -1.60217733 \times 10^{-19}\ \text{C} \tag{26.7}$$

The electron can be deflected by an electric (or a magnetic) field. Thus, on the back of our mind, we picture the electron as a tiny particle with definite mass and charge. However, after the prediction made by deBroglie, Davisson and Germer (in 1927), studied the diffraction of electrons from single crystals of nickel and showed that the diffraction patterns could be explained only if the electrons were assumed to have a wavelength given by the de Broglie relation $\lambda = h/p$. In Figs. 1.12(a) and (b), we have shown the diffraction pattern of aluminum foil produced by X-rays and by electrons; one can see the similarity in the diffraction patterns. The experiments by Davisson and Germer and later experiments by G.P. Thomson firmly established the wave nature of electrons – but this was after the amazing prediction of de Broglie.

26.6 The Schrödinger Equation

LO3

The obvious question arises: Is the electron (or a proton or an alpha particle) a wave or a particle? The answer is [to quote Feynman (Ref. 26.5)]:

It is neither a wave nor a particle.

According to quantum theory, it is described by the wave function Ψ which depends on the position and contains all information that is known about the system and determines the time evolution of Ψ and hence of probability of finding the particle in a small volume element. In the non-relativistic domain, the wave function satisfies what is known as the Schrödinger equation

$$i\hbar\frac{\partial\Psi(\mathbf{r},t)}{\partial t} = -\frac{\hbar^2}{2m}\nabla^2\Psi(\mathbf{r},t) + V(\mathbf{r})\Psi(\mathbf{r},t) \quad (26.8)$$

where m represents the mass of the particle, $V(\mathbf{r})$ is the potential energy distribution, and

$$\nabla^2\Psi(\mathbf{r},t) = \left(\frac{\partial^2}{\partial x^2}+\frac{\partial^2}{\partial y^2}+\frac{\partial^2}{\partial z^2}\right)\Psi(\mathbf{r},t) \quad (26.9)$$

According to Feynman (Chapter 15 of Ref. 26.5)

> *Where did we get that [the Schrödinger equation] from? Nowhere. It is not possible to derive it from anything you know. It came out of the mind of Schrödinger, … invented in his struggle to find an understanding of the experimental observations of the real world ….*

Of course Schrödinger had some reasoning to get to this equation. In Appendix C, we have given a heuristic derivation of the Schrödinger equation, and as you will see, the derivation lacks rigor. In spite of the fact that it is not possible to have a rigorous derivation of the Schrödinger equation, it readily got accepted because its solutions agreed extremely well with experimental data. The Schrödinger equation is so much popular that people have painted and tattooed the equation on their body (see Fig. 26.8). In 1926, Max Born gave the following physical interpretation of ψ (this is discussed in almost all books on quantum mechanics; see, e.g., Ref. 26.6, 26.7, 26.8 and also Appendix C):

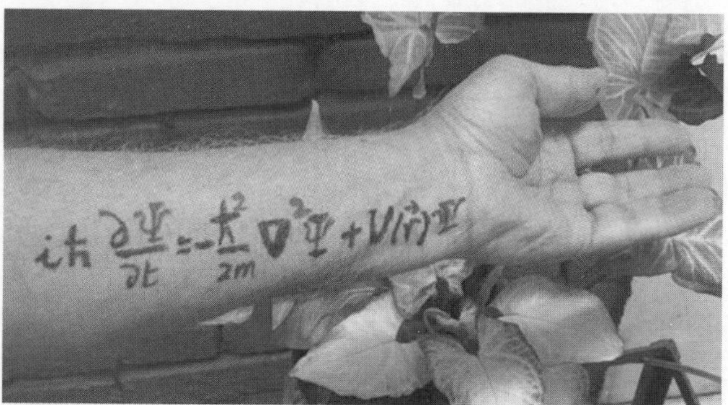

Figure 26.8

Many love the Schrödinger equation so much that they have tattooed the equation on them.

$|\Psi|^2\,dV$ is the probability of finding the particle in the volume element dV **(26.10)**

Thus
$$\iiint|\Psi|^2\,dV = 1 \quad (26.11)$$

where the integration is over the entire space. The above equation (known as the normalization condition) follows from the fact that the particle has to be found somewhere in the universe.

26.7 Free Particle in One Dimension

LO3

We consider the one dimensional case; i.e., assume no dependence of the wave function on y and z. For a free particle (for which the potential energy is zero everywhere), the Schrödinger equation takes the form:

$$i\hbar\frac{\partial\Psi(x,t)}{\partial t} = -\frac{\hbar^2}{2m}\frac{\partial^2\Psi(x,t)}{\partial x^2} \quad (26.12)$$

which is referred to as the one dimensional time-dependent Schrödinger equation for a free particle. Using the method of separation of variables, the solution of Eq. (26.12) would be given by (see Appendix C):

$$\Psi(x,t) = \text{constant}\times\exp\left[\frac{i}{\hbar}\left(p_x x - \frac{p_x^2}{2m}t\right)\right]; \quad -\infty < p_x < +\infty \quad (26.13)$$

where p_x can take any (real) value from $-\infty$ to $+\infty$. Thus, the most general solution of Eq. (26.12) would be a superposition of plane waves (corresponding to different momenta) given by

$$\Psi(x,t)=\frac{1}{\sqrt{2\pi\hbar}}\int_{-\infty}^{+\infty} a(p_x)\exp\left[\frac{i}{\hbar}\left(p_x x-\frac{p_x^2}{2m}t\right)\right]dp_x \quad \textbf{(26.14)}$$

where the factor $1/\sqrt{2\pi\hbar}$ is introduced so that the Fourier transform pair will have symmetric forms as will be shown below. Now, in Sec. 8.4 we had obtained the following integral representation of the Dirac delta function

$$\delta(x-x')=\frac{1}{2\pi}\int_{-\infty}^{+\infty} e^{\pm ik(x-x')}dk$$

$$=\frac{1}{2\pi\hbar}\int_{-\infty}^{+\infty}\exp\left[\frac{i}{\hbar}p_x(x-x')\right]dp_x \quad \textbf{(26.15)}$$

where we have defined $p_x \equiv \hbar k$. Thus

$$\psi(x)=\int_{-\infty}^{+\infty}\delta(x-x')\psi(x')\,dx'$$

$$=\frac{1}{2\pi\hbar}\int_{-\infty}^{+\infty}\int_{-\infty}^{+\infty}\exp\left[\frac{i}{\hbar}p_x(x-x')\right]\psi(x')dx'dp_x \quad \textbf{(26.16)}$$

Using the above equation we may write

$$\psi(x)=\frac{1}{\sqrt{2\pi\hbar}}\int_{-\infty}^{+\infty} a(p_x)\exp\left[\frac{i}{\hbar}p_x x\right]dp_x \quad \textbf{(26.17)}$$

$$\text{where } a(p_x)=\frac{1}{\sqrt{2\pi\hbar}}\int_{-\infty}^{+\infty}\psi(x')\exp\left[-\frac{i}{\hbar}p_x x'\right]dx'$$

$$=\frac{1}{\sqrt{2\pi\hbar}}\int_{-\infty}^{+\infty}\psi(x)\exp\left[-\frac{i}{\hbar}p_x x\right]dx$$

At $t = 0$, Eq. (26.14) becomes

$$\Psi(x,0)=\frac{1}{\sqrt{2\pi\hbar}}\int_{-\infty}^{+\infty} a(p_x)\exp\left[\frac{i}{\hbar}p_x x\right]dp_x \quad \textbf{(26.18)}$$

$$\text{Therefore } a(p_x)=\frac{1}{\sqrt{2\pi\hbar}}\int_{-\infty}^{+\infty}\Psi(x,0)\exp\left[-\frac{i}{\hbar}p_x x\right]dx \quad \textbf{(26.19)}$$

Since the Schrödinger equation is linear (any multiple of the solution is also a solution), we may choose the multiplicative constant such that

$$\int_{-\infty}^{+\infty}\left|\Psi(x,t)\right|^2 dx=1 \quad \textbf{(26.20)}$$

and the wave function is said to be normalized with $|\Psi(x, t)|^2\, dx$ representing the probability of finding the particle's position between x and $x + dx$. Equation (26.14) describes what is known as a localized wave packet with

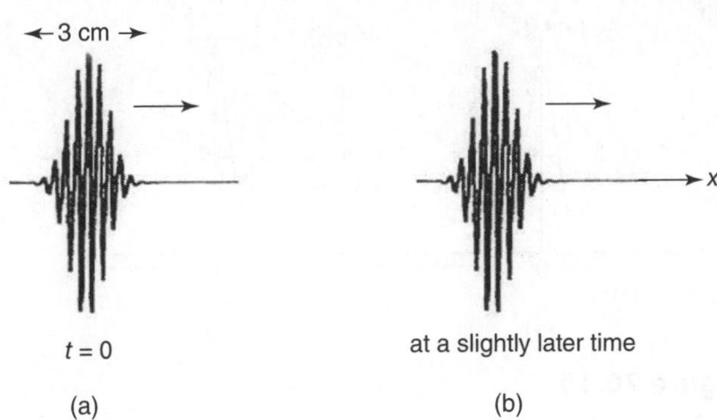

Figure 26.9
Propagation of a 0.1 ns (3 cm long) Gaussian light pulse in vacuum in the +x direction.

$|a(p_x)|^2\, dp_x$ = Probability of finding the (x-component of the) particle's momentum to lie between p_x and $p_x + dp_x$ **(26.21)**

The above physical interpretation of $|a(p_x)^2|$ is also discussed in almost all books on quantum mechanics; see, for example, Ref. 26.7 and also Appendix C. What is a localized wave packet? You know when you switch on a laser pointer and switch it off within a very short time, you create a localized wave packet. If the duration of the pulse is about 0.1 ns ($= 10^{-10}$ s) then we form a localized wave packet whose length is about 3 cm ($= c \times 10^{-10}$ s) and this packet propagates through space (see Fig. 26.9). Thus, if we know $\Psi(x, 0)$, we can determine $a(p_x)$ by using Eq. (26.19) and if we substitute this expression for $a(p_x)$ in Eq. (26.14), we would get the time evolution of the wave packet; that is what we are going to do for a Gaussian wave packet.

26.7.1 The Gaussian Wave Packet

Let us assume that at $t = 0$, the electron is described by a Gaussian wave packet:

$$\Psi(x,0)=\frac{1}{\left(\pi\sigma_0^2\right)^{1/4}}e^{-x^2/2\sigma_0^2}\exp\left[\frac{i}{\hbar}p_0 x\right] \quad \textbf{(26.22)}$$

Thus at $t = 0$, the probability of finding the particle between x and $x + dx$ will be given by

$$P(x)dx=\left|\Psi(x,0)\right|^2 dx=\frac{1}{\sqrt{\pi\sigma_0^2}}e^{-x^2/\sigma_0^2}dx \quad \textbf{(26.23)}$$

Equation (26.23) tells us that at $t = 0$ the particle is located around the origin $x = 0$ localized within a region of about σ_0; i.e., $\Delta x \approx \sigma_0$; see Fig. 26.10(a); [The FWHM is $\approx 1.67\,\sigma_0$ – see Example 8.1]. Further, it can be readily seen that

$$\int_{-\infty}^{+\infty}P(x)\,dx=\int_{-\infty}^{+\infty}\left|\Psi(x,0)\right|^2 dx=\frac{1}{\sqrt{\pi\sigma_0^2}}\int_{-\infty}^{+\infty}e^{-x^2/\sigma_0^2}dx=1 \quad \textbf{(26.24)}$$

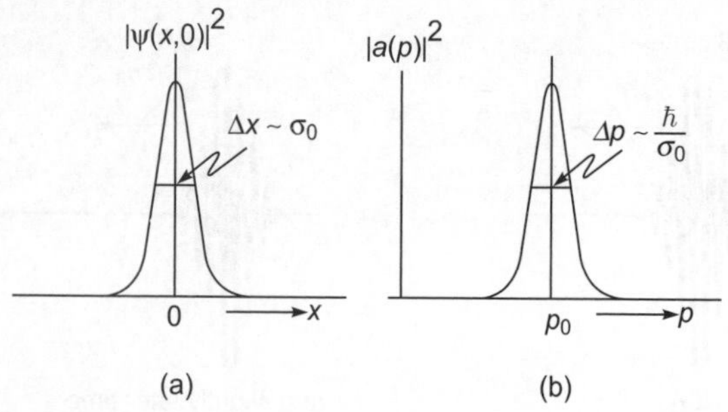

Figure 26.10

(a) The probability distribution function at $t = 0$ showing that the particle is localized around the point $x = 0$ with an uncertainty given by

$$\Delta x \sim \sigma_0.$$

(b) The momentum distribution function showing that the particle's momentum is localized around $p = p_0$ with an uncertainty given by

$$\Delta p \sim \frac{\hbar}{\sigma_0}.$$

which implies that the particle has to be found somewhere!!! If we substitute for $\Psi(x, 0)$ from Eq. (26.19) in Eq. (26.16), and carry out the integration, we would get

$$a(p_x) = \frac{1}{\sqrt{2\pi\hbar}} \frac{1}{\left(\pi\sigma_0^2\right)^{1/4}} \int_{-\infty}^{+\infty} e^{-x^2/2\sigma_0^2} \exp\left[-\frac{i}{\hbar}(p_x - p_0)x\right] dx$$

$$= \left(\frac{\sigma_0^2}{\pi\hbar^2}\right)^{1/4} \exp\left[-\frac{(p_x - p_0)^2 \sigma_0^2}{2\hbar^2}\right] \qquad \textbf{(26.25)}$$

where we have used results in Appendix A. Thus the probability of finding the (x-component of the) particle's momentum between p_x and $p_x + dp_x$ will be given by

$$P(p_x)dp_x = |a(p_x)|^2 \, dp_x$$

$$= \left(\frac{\sigma_0^2}{\pi\hbar^2}\right)^{1/2} \exp\left[-\frac{(p_x - p_0)^2 \sigma_0^2}{\hbar^2}\right] dp_x \qquad \textbf{(26.26)}$$

One can readily see that $\int_{-\infty}^{+\infty} |a(p_x)|^2 \, dp_x = 1$. The FWHM (Full Width at Half Maximum) of $P(p_x)$ is denoted by Δp_x which will be given by (see Example 8.1):

$$\text{FWHM} = \Delta p_x = 2\sqrt{\ln 2}\,\frac{\hbar}{\sigma_0} \approx \frac{1.67\hbar}{\sigma_0}$$

Thus the x-component of the particle's momentum is about p_0 with an uncertainty given by $\Delta p_x \approx \frac{\hbar}{\sigma_0}$ see Fig. 26.10(b). Thus

$$\Delta x \Delta p_x = \hbar \qquad \textbf{(26.27)}$$

The above equation shows that **the uncertainty principle is contained in the solution of the Schrödinger equation.** If we substitute for $a(p_x)$ from Eq. (26.26) in Eq. (26.14) and carry out the integration (which is straight forward but a bit cumbersome), we would obtain the expression for $\Psi(x, t)$ from which we would obtain

$$P(x,t) = |\Psi(x,t)|^2 = \frac{1}{\sqrt{\pi}\,\sigma(t)} \exp\left[-\frac{\left(x - v_g t\right)^2}{\sigma^2(t)}\right] \qquad \textbf{(26.28)}$$

where

$$v_g = \frac{1}{m} p_0 \qquad \textbf{(26.29)}$$

and

$$\sigma(t) = \sigma_0 \sqrt{1 + \frac{\hbar^2}{m^2 \sigma_0^4} t^2} \qquad \textbf{(26.30)}$$

Equation (26.28) tells us that the center of the wave packet moves with the velocity v_g which represents the group velocity of the wave packet (see Example 26.1). Further, Eq. (26.30) tells us that, as the wave packet propagates, the width of the packet (i.e., Δx) increases with time. This broadening is due to the fact that the $\omega - k$ relationship is non-linear: $\omega = \frac{\hbar k^2}{2m}$ (see Example 26.1). This leads to dispersion (see Sec. 11.3.2). However Δp_x remains the same! At all times, $\int_{-\infty}^{+\infty} |\Psi(x,t)|^2 \, dx = 1$. If we introduce the dimensionless variables,

$$X = \frac{x}{\sigma_0}, \quad \tau = \frac{\hbar}{m\sigma_0^2} t \quad \text{and} \quad \alpha = \frac{p_0 \sigma_0}{\hbar} = \frac{m v_g \sigma_0}{\hbar} \qquad \textbf{(26.31)}$$

we would get

$$|\Psi(X,\tau)|^2 = \frac{1}{\sigma_0 \sqrt{\pi}\,\sqrt{1+\tau^2}} \exp\left[-\frac{(X - \alpha\tau)^2}{(1+\tau^2)}\right] \qquad \textbf{(26.32)}$$

In Fig. 26.11, we have plotted $|\Psi(X, \tau)|^2$ as a function of X at different times for $\alpha = 15$. Thus at $\tau = 0$, 0.5, 1.0 and 1.5 the particle is localized around $X = 0$, 7.5, 15.0 and 22.5 respectively. At all times

$$\Delta p \approx \frac{\hbar}{\sigma_0}. \qquad \textbf{(26.33)}$$

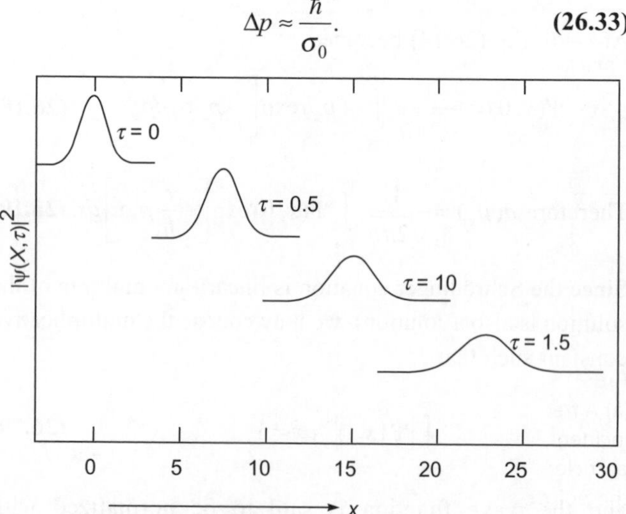

Figure 26.11

Propagation (and broadening) of a Gaussian wave packet. Notice that at $\tau = 0$, 0.5, 1.0 and 1.5 the particle is localized around the points $X = 0$, 7.5, 15.15 and 22.5, respectively.

We next consider a particle (like an electron or an alpha particle or even a fullerene molecule)—described by a wave packet approaching a potential barrier–see Fig. 26.12(a), which results in certain probability of reflection and certain probability of it tunnelling through the barrier. This is similar to the beam splitter experiment (see Fig. 26.1) in which a photon incident on a beam splitter is partially reflected and partially transmitted). Quantum theory tells us that, at a later time, there is a reflected wave packet and a transmitted wave packet—see Fig. 26.12(b). Thus, one electron is described by two wave packets one localized around the point A (moving towards the left) and the other localized around the point B and moving towards the right. Thus, the particle is at both places (which may be hundreds of kilometres apart)—does that mean it has split in two halves?? The answer is no—but it is at both places! If we try to make a measurement of the particle, we will find it either around the point A or around the point B; the particle being at both places collapses to being around A or around B. This collapse of the wave function is similar to the double hole interference experiment in which the electron (or the photon) passes through the two holes simultaneously—but if we tried to measure which hole did it actually pass through then we will find that it passed either through hole # 1 or hole # 2. This collapse of the wave packet is an extremely important characteristic of quantum theory.

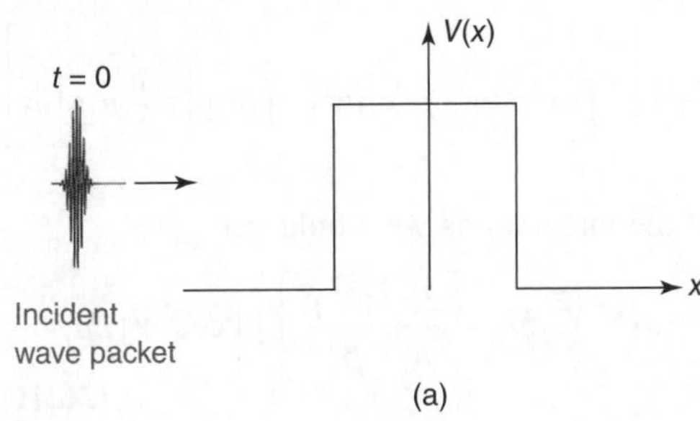

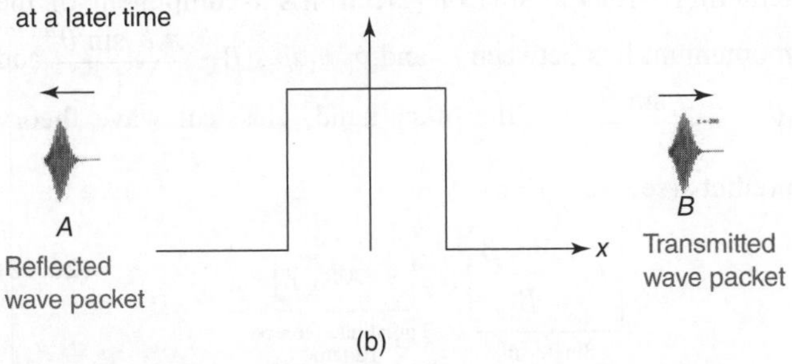

Figure 26.12
(a) A free particle (described by a Gaussian wave packet) incident on a potential barrier. (b) At a slightly later time, the particle is described by 2 wave packets – one localized around the point A and the other localized around the point B. If we make a measurement, then the wave function collapses to being either around the point A or around the point B.

EXAMPLE 26.1 Group Velocity

We have $\lambda = \dfrac{h}{p} \Rightarrow p = \dfrac{h}{2\pi}\dfrac{2\pi}{\lambda} = \hbar k$

where $k = \dfrac{2\pi}{\lambda}$. Now

$$E = \frac{p^2}{2m} \Rightarrow \hbar\omega = \frac{\hbar^2 k^2}{2m} \Rightarrow \frac{dk}{d\omega} = \frac{m}{\hbar k} = \frac{m}{p}$$

In Sec. 9.2 we had shown the group velocity to be given by

$$\frac{1}{v_g} = \left.\frac{dk}{d\omega}\right|_{\omega=\omega_0}$$

Thus $v_g = \dfrac{p_0}{m}$ consistent with Eq. (26.29).

26.8 Diffraction by a Single Slit

LO4

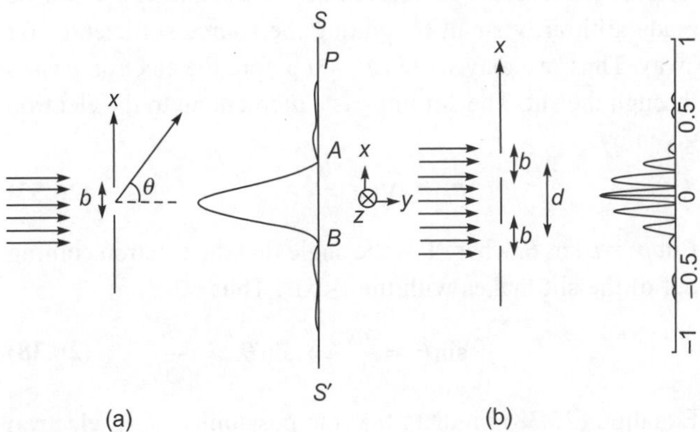

Figure 26.13
(a) Diffraction of an electron by a narrow slit of width b.
(b) Diffraction of an electron by 2 narrow slits, each of width b and separated by d.

We next consider a wave-packet (propagating in the y-direction) incident on a single slit of width b [see Fig. 26.13(a)]. For such a situation we may assume

$$\left.\begin{aligned}\Psi(x,0) &= \frac{1}{\sqrt{b}} \qquad & |x| < \frac{b}{2} \\ &= 0 & |x| > \frac{b}{2}\end{aligned}\right\} \tag{26.34}$$

We substitute the above expression for $\Psi(x, 0)$ in Eq. (26.19) to obtain

$$a(p_x) = \frac{1}{\sqrt{2\pi\hbar}}\frac{1}{\sqrt{b}}\left[\int_{-\frac{b}{2}}^{+\frac{b}{2}} \exp\left[-\frac{i}{\hbar}p_x x\right]dx\right]$$

Carrying out the integration we would get

$$|a(p_x)|^2\, dp_x = P(p_x)\, dp_x = \frac{b}{h}\frac{\sin^2\beta}{\beta^2}\, dp_x \quad \textbf{(26.35)}$$

where $P(p_x)\,dp_x$ is the probability that (after interacting with the slit) the electron's x-component of the momentum lies between p_x and $p_x + dp_x$; the electron acquires this x-component of the momentum from the slit. In the above equation,

$$\beta = \frac{\pi\, b\, p_x}{h} = \frac{\pi\, b\, p \sin\theta}{h} = \frac{\pi\, b \sin\theta}{\lambda} \quad \textbf{(26.36)}$$

Now, one can always choose the electron source to be so far away that (before entering the slit), p_x can be assumed to have an arbitrarily small value. Thus, the electrons approaching the slit can be assumed to have momentum only in the y-direction. The expression for $P(p_x)dp_x$ tells us that by making the electron pass through a slit of width b, the slit imparts a momentum in the x-direction which is $\approx \frac{h}{b}$. It may be pointed out that *before* the electron entered the slit, p_x (and hence Δp_x, which represents the spread in p_x) can be made arbitrarily small by putting the source sufficiently far away. Thus, we may write $\Delta p_x \approx 0$ before the electron passes through the slit. The slit imparts a momentum to the electron given by

$$|p_x| \approx \Delta p_x \approx \frac{h}{b} \quad \textbf{(26.37)}$$

But $p_x = p \sin\theta$, where θ is the angle that the electron coming out of the slit makes with the y-axis. Thus

$$p \sin\theta = \frac{h}{b} \Rightarrow \sin\theta = \frac{h}{pb} \quad \textbf{(26.38)}$$

Equation (26.38) predicts that the possibility of an electron travelling at an angle θ with the y-direction is inversely proportional to the width of the slit; i.e., smaller the value of b, greater is the value of θ and greater is the possibility of the electron to reach deep inside the geometrical shadow. This is indeed the diffraction phenomenon (and also the uncertainty principle); thus everything is contained in the solution of the Schrödinger equation! Further, the intensity distribution as predicted by the classical wave theory is given by (see Sec. 17.2)

$$I = I_0 \frac{\sin^2\beta}{\beta^2} \quad \textbf{(26.39)}$$

where $\beta = \frac{\pi\, b \sin\theta}{\lambda}$ which is the same as given in Eq. (26.36).

Thus the solution of the Schrödinger equation does not predict where exactly the electron will land up; it only predicts a probability distribution – but this probability distribution is the same as the intensity distribution given by the classical wave theory. Thus according to quantum theory, we cannot predict where exactly the electron will be detected on the screen but if we carry out the experiment with millions of electrons, the intensity distribution (as predicted by the wave theory) will slowly build up. Richard Feynman says (in his famous Messenger Lecture) that "electrons arrive in lumps – just like tiny bullets; however, the probability of arrival of the electrons is the same as predicted by the wave theory".

EXAMPLE 26.2 Using Eq. (26.35) show that

$$\int_{-\infty}^{+\infty} P(p_x)\, dp_x = 1 \quad \left[\text{Use the relation } \int_{-\infty}^{+\infty} \frac{\sin^2 x}{x^2}\, dx = \pi\right]$$

and interpret the result physically.

26.9 The Double Slit Interference Pattern

LO4

We next consider the diffraction of an electron beam by two slits each of width b and separated by a distance d [see Fig. 26.13(b)]; thus

$$\Psi(x,0) = \begin{cases} \dfrac{1}{\sqrt{2b}} & \dfrac{d-b}{2} < |x| < \dfrac{d+b}{2} \\ = 0 & \text{elsewhere} \end{cases} \quad \textbf{(26.40)}$$

We substitute the above expression for $\Psi(x, 0)$ in Eq. (26.16) to obtain

$$a(p_x) = \frac{1}{\sqrt{2\pi\hbar}}\frac{1}{\sqrt{2b}}\left[\int_{-\frac{d+b}{2}}^{-\frac{d-b}{2}} \exp\left[-\frac{i}{\hbar}p_x x\right]dx + \int_{\frac{d-b}{2}}^{\frac{d+b}{2}} \exp\left[-\frac{i}{\hbar}p_x x\right]dx\right]$$

If we carry out the integrations we would get

$$p(p_x)\,dp_x = |a(p_x)|^2\, dp_x = \left[\frac{2b}{h}\frac{\sin^2\beta}{\beta^2}\right][4\cos^2\gamma]\, dp_x \quad \textbf{(26.41)}$$

where, as before, $P(p_x)dp_x$ is the probability that (after interacting with the slit) the electron's x-component of the momentum lies between p_x and $p_x + dp_x$, $\beta = \frac{\pi\, b \sin\theta}{\lambda}$ and $\gamma = \frac{\pi\, d \sin\theta}{\lambda}$. On the other hand, classical wave theory predicts (see Sec. 17.6)

$$I = \underbrace{\left[I_0 \frac{\sin^2\beta}{\beta^2}\right]}_{\text{Single-slit diffraction-pattern}} \underbrace{\left[4\cos^2\gamma\right]}_{\text{2 point interference pattern}} \quad \textbf{(26.42)}$$

Thus, once again, the solution of the Schrödinger equation does not predict where exactly the electron will land up, it only predicts a probability distribution - but this probability distribution is the same as the intensity distribution given by the wave theory.

From above we can say the following: The corpuscular nature of the electron is evident from its detection in the form of a single electron and never a fraction of an electron.

Quantum theory tells us that an electron passes through both slits (S_1 and S_2) simultaneously. This is not the splitting of the electron into two halves but only implies that if we did the experiment (for example, by putting a powerful microscope) to find out which slit the electron passed, then half the time it will be found to have passed through the slit S_1 and half the time through S_2. If we do find out which slit the electron has gone through, the interference pattern will not be observed. In the absence of such a measurement, we cannot say that the electron passes through either S_1 or through S_2 which is what we would expect classically. The electron is in a state which is a superposition of two states, one corresponding to the disturbance emanating from the slit S_1 and the other to the one emanating from hole S_2. The superposed state will give rise to a probability distribution of arrival of the electrons which is similar to the intensity distribution obtained by considering the superposition of two waves. Thus according to quantum theory, the electron passes through both slits and we cannot predict where exactly the electron will be detected on the screen; however, if we carry out the experiment with millions of electrons, the intensity distribution will be almost the same as predicted by the wave theory.

David Bohm, who is considered as one of the outstanding quantum physicists has said

> *The most fundamental theory now available is probabilistic in form, and not deterministic ..*

Thus there is a conceptual difference between classical physics (which is deterministic) and quantum physics, which is probabilistic.

The obvious question is: how can a single electron (or, a proton) which has very accurately determined mass and charge pass through both slits simultaneously??? How can we physically understand that??? In 1966, Richard Feynman delivered 6 Messenger Lectures at Cornell University on ***The Character of Physical Law***; in the 6th and final lecture, he spoke on ***Probability and Uncertainty*** in which he said:

> *Electrons do not behave just like particles, they do not behave just like waves. Electrons in orbits are not somewhat like a cloud or fog of some sort surrounding the nucleus, It behaves like nothing that you have seen before. Well there is one simplification at least electrons behave exactly the same way as photons.*

In the same lecture he had also said

> *I think I can safely say that nobody understands quantum mechanics*

I would urge all students to listen to the Messenger Lectures; go to You Tube and look for Feynman's Messenger Lecture on ***Probability and Uncertainty.***

Recently Nairz and his colleagues have carried out a beautiful experiment (see Ref. 26.10) in which they allowed (almost) mono-energetic fullerene molecules to fall on a multiple slit arrangement and they were able to obtain the interference pattern. Figure 26.14 shows the distribution of the count rates as a function of the detector position; the distribution agrees with the calculated interference pattern using wave theory. Thus what we have tried to say for electrons is also valid for the fullerene molecule C60 consisting of 60 carbon atoms; the molecule is said to form the smallest natural soccer ball.

Thus according to quantum theory, we cannot predict where exactly the electron will be detected on the screen but if we carry out the experiment with millions of electrons, the intensity distribution (as predicted by the wave theory) will slowly build up – see Figs. 1.14, 1.17 and 1.18.

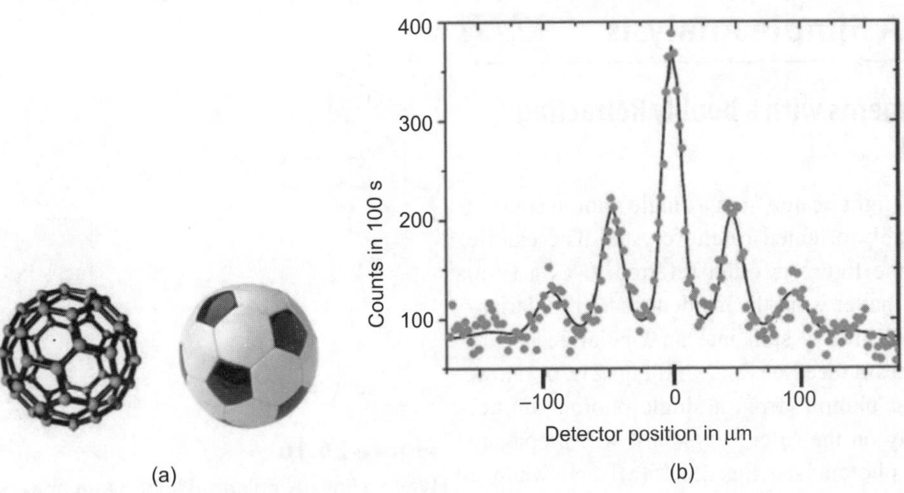

Figure 26.14
Monoenergetic fullerene molecules [see (a)] fall on a multiple slit arrangement and produce the interference pattern. The diagram shows the distribution of the count rates as a function of the detector position; the distribution agrees with the calculated interference pattern using wave theory. Diagram adapted from Ref. 26.10.

26.10 The Equation for the Photon

LO4

For the photon, the rest mass energy is zero and we therefore have the relation (see Sec. 33.3)

$$E^2 = p^2c^2 \tag{26.43}$$

[We may recall that for the free electron or proton, the corresponding relation is $E = p^2/2m$]. If we neglect absorption and emission of photons, then using a procedure very similar to that used in Appendix C, we will obtain the following (one dimensional) equation describing the propagation of the photon

$$-\hbar^2 \frac{\partial^2 \Psi}{\partial t^2} = -\hbar^2 c^2 \frac{\partial^2 \Psi}{\partial x^2} \Rightarrow \frac{\partial^2 \Psi}{\partial x^2} = \frac{1}{c^2}\frac{\partial^2 \Psi}{\partial t^2} \tag{26.44}$$

Considering waves propagating along the $+x$ direction, the most general solution of the above equation will be [cf. Eq. (26.14)]

$$\Psi(x, t) = \frac{1}{\sqrt{2\pi\hbar}} \int_{-\infty}^{+\infty} a(p_x) \exp\left[\frac{i}{\hbar} p_x (x - ct)\right] dp_x \tag{26.45}$$

Once again

$$a(p_x) = \frac{1}{\sqrt{2\pi\hbar}} \int_{-\infty}^{+\infty} \Psi(x, 0) \exp\left[-\frac{i}{\hbar} p_x x\right] dp_x \tag{26.46}$$

which is the same as Eq. (26.19) Thus we will obtain same expressions for the single slit and double slit diffraction patterns. We may note that because of Eq. (26.45), the propagation will be distortionless (see Fig. 11.5). Thus, whereas for an electron (or proton), free space is highly dispersive; for a photon free space is non-dispersive.

26.11 EPR Paradox and Bell's Inequality: A Simple Analysis

LO5

26.11.1 Experiments with a Doubly Refracting Crystal

We next consider a light beam (from a single photon source) incident on a suitably oriented calcite crystal. The calcite crystal shown in the figure is often referred to as a (*x*-*y*) device because no matter what the incident state of polarization may be, it will always split into an *x*-polarized beam and a *y*-polarized beam (see Sec. 21.5 and Fig. 21.20). Now, when a *x*-polarized photon (from a single photon source) is incident normally on the calcite crystal, it will propagate as an *x*-polarized photon [see Fig. 26.15(a)] and when a *y*-polarized photon is incident normally on the crystal, it will propagate as a *y*-polarized photon [see Fig. 26.15(b)]. What will happen if a 45° polarized photon is incident on the calcite crystal (see Fig. 26.16)? We can express a 45° polarized photon by the vector:

$$\left|\text{LP } 45^\circ\right\rangle = \begin{pmatrix}\cos 45^\circ \\ \sin 45^\circ\end{pmatrix} = \frac{1}{\sqrt{2}}|x\rangle + \frac{1}{\sqrt{2}}|y\rangle \tag{26.47}$$

The photon gets detected either by the detector D_1 or by D_2 (never by both); there is half probability of it getting detected by the detector D_1 and half by the detector D_2. No one can predict beforehand as to whether it will be detected by D_1 or by the detector D_2. In fact before detection, the photon is in a state of superposition of being in both paths as described by the above equation.

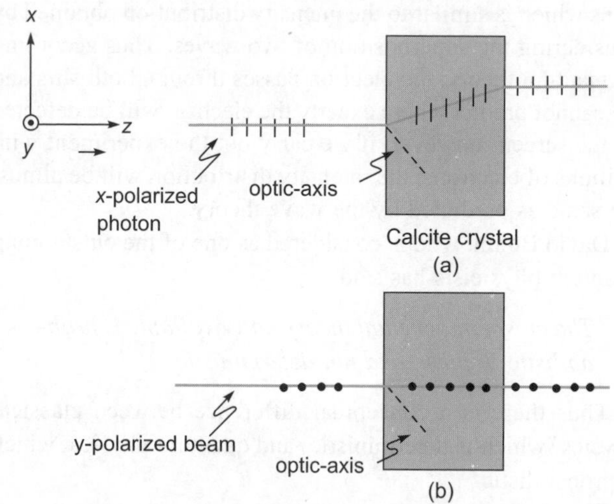

Figure 26.15
(a) when a *x*-polarized photon is incident normally on a suitable oriented calcite crystal, it will propagate as an *x*-polarized photon and (b) when a *y*-polarized photon is incident normally on the crystal, it will propagate as a *y*-polarized photon.

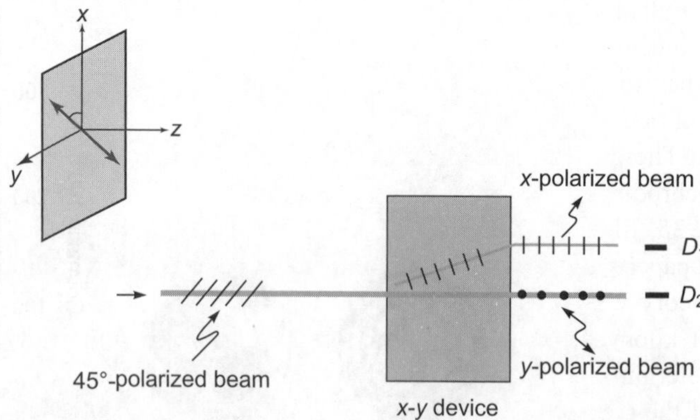

Figure 26.16
When a linearly polarized light beam (making an angle θ with the *x*-axis) is incident on a (suitably oriented) calcite crystal, it would, in general, split up into an *x*-polarized beam and a *y*-polarized beam. In the figure we have assumed $\theta = 45°$.

If we rotate the calcite crystal, as shown in Fig. 26.17, we will obtain an (u-v) device where the u-v axes are obtained by rotating the x-y axes as shown in Fig. 26.17. Thus when an arbitrarily polarized photon is incident normally on the (u-v) device, there will be a certain probability of detecting an u-polarized photon and a certain probability of detecting a v polarized photon.

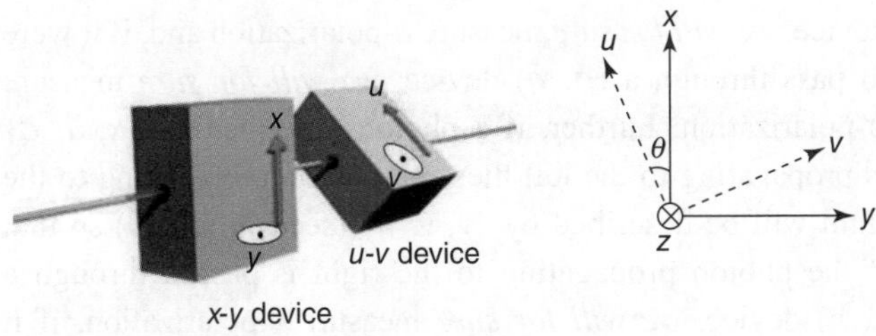

Figure 26.17

By rotating the (x-y) device by a certain angle about the z-axis, we obtain an (u-v) device. Adapted from http://www.upscale.utoronto.ca/PVB/Harrison/BellsTheorem/BellsTheorem.html

26.11.2 What is Entanglement?

There are atoms which emit two photons in quick succession and the two photons are of different frequencies propagating in opposite directions. There are actual transitions where the two photons are characterized by the property that the polarization of one is always orthogonal to that of the other. Thus if the photon travelling to the left is passed through a x-y device and if the photon is found to be x-polarized then the photon travelling to the right will surely be y-polarized (see Fig. 26.18); the two photons are said to be "entangled". This can be seen by making what is known as "coincidence" measurements. Thus in Fig. 26.18, there are events when the detector D_1 on the left and the detector D_4 on the right click simultaneously; such simultaneous measurements are called "coincidence" measurements. However, there are no events when the detector D_1 on the left and the detector D_3 on the right click simultaneously.

The word "entanglement" was introduced by Erwin Schrödinger in a paper published in 1935 (Ref. 26.11). In 1935, Einstein (along with Podolsky and Rosen) published a paper (Ref. 26.12) in which they argued that if quantum theory was correct, then two particles (which are millions of kilometers apart) can be entangled in the sense that by determining a property of one of the particles, the property of the second particle can be instantaneously changed. And special theory of relativity forbids the transmission of any signal faster than the speed of light. This came to be known as *The EPR Paradox*. About thirty years later, experiments confirmed the predictions of quantum mechanics, namely, Einstein's impossible proposition was in fact correct: instantaneous changes in widely separated systems did occur.

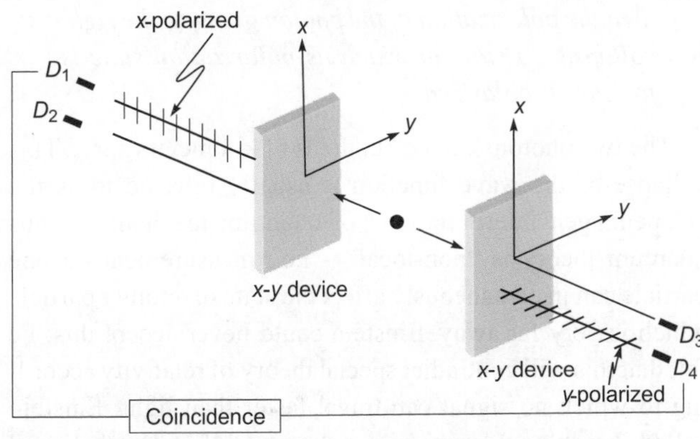

Figure 26.18

Two photons (emitted by the same atom) propagating in opposite directions are characterized by the property that the polarization of one is always othogonal to the other; the polarization of the photon (traveling to the left – or to the right) is not known before one of them is measured. If the photon travelling to the left is passed through a x-y device and if the photon is found to be x-polarized then the photon travelling to the right will be y-polarized; we know the polarization of the photon moving to the right without measuring it.

The EPR paper was so important that main findings of the paper appeared in New York Times on May 4, 1935 (see Fig. 26.19).

The New York Times.

NEW YORK, SATURDAY, MAY 4, 1935. TWO CENTS

EINSTEIN ATTACKS QUANTUM THEORY

Scientist and Two Colleagues Find It Is Not 'Complete' Even Though 'Correct.'

Figure 26.19

Results from the EPR paper was discussed in the May 4, 1935 issue of New York Times.

26.11.3 Non-Locality of Quantum Theory

According to quantum theory,

> *the polarization of the photon (traveling to the left – or to the right) is not known before one of them is measured; and, if the polarization of the photon going to the left is measured as x-polarized then the polarization of the photon going to the right collapses to state in which its polarization state is y-polarized. Similarly, if the polarization of the photon going to the left is measured as u-polarized*

then the polarization of the photon going to the right collapses to state in which its polarization state is for sure v-polarized.

The two photons can be hundreds of kilometers apart. This collapse of the wave function is usually referred to as the "Copenhagen interpretation" of quantum mechanics. Thus quantum theory is "non-local" – i.e., measurement on one particle can instantaneously affect the state of another particle which is very far away. Einstein could never accept this; he felt that this will contradict special theory of relativity according to which no signal can travel faster than light. Einstein called this "Spooky action at a distance". Einstein believed in "locality"; i.e., measuring the state of one particle will not affect the other. Einstein believed that if one could predict the polarization of the second photon by measuring the polarization of the first photon, then both photons had definite states of polarization all the time. Thus associated with the photons are "hidden variables" so that the polarization of the photons are known before the measurements are carried out. In their 1935 paper (Ref. 26.12), EPR wrote:

if without in any way disturbing a system, we can predict with certainty (i.e., with probability equal to unity) the value of a physical quantity, then the second particle must have possessed the measured property before the measurement was carried out.

Einstein had also written (p. 85 in Ref. 26.13; see also Ref. 26.14).

But on one supposition we should, in my opinion, absolutely hold fast: the real factual situation of the system S_2 is independent of what is done with the system S_1, which is spatially separated from the former.

According to Alan Aspect *"Einstein therefore argued for what he felt was the only reasonable description: that each particle in the pair carries a property, decided at the moment of separation, which determines the measurement results. But since entangled particles are not described separately in the quantum formalism, Einstein concluded the formalism was incomplete"*. In his 1964 paper (Ref. 26.14), John Bell wrote

It is the requirement of locality, or more precisely that the result of a measurement on one system be unaffected by operations on a distant system with which it has interacted in the past, that creates the essential difficulty.

26.11.4 Hidden Variables

As mentioned above, Einstein had written that "… the second particle must have possessed the measured property before the measurement was carried out…". Assuming this, we construct a theory based on "hidden variables" so that we know the number of photon pairs which have their own independent attributes when passed through a (x, y) device or a (u, v) device or a (σ, η) device; the (x, y) axes, (u, v) axes and (σ, n) axes are defined in Fig. 26.20. Thus we can assign values of all observables of a system *before* the measurement is carried out. For example, if a photon described by $\{x, u, \sigma\}$ is passed through a (x, y) device, *we will for sure* measure x-polarization, if it were to pass through a (u, v) device, *we will for sure* measure u-polarization and, if it were to pass through a (σ, η) device, *we will for sure* measure σ-polarization. Further, if a photon described by $\{x, u, \sigma\}$ is propagating to the left then the photon propagating to the right will be described by $\{y, v, \eta\}$ (see Fig. 26.20) so that if the photon propagating to the right is passed through a (x,y) device, *we will for sure* measure y-polarization, if it is passed through a (u, v) device, *we will for sure* measure v-polarization and if it is passed through a (σ, η) device, *we will for sure* measure η-polarization.

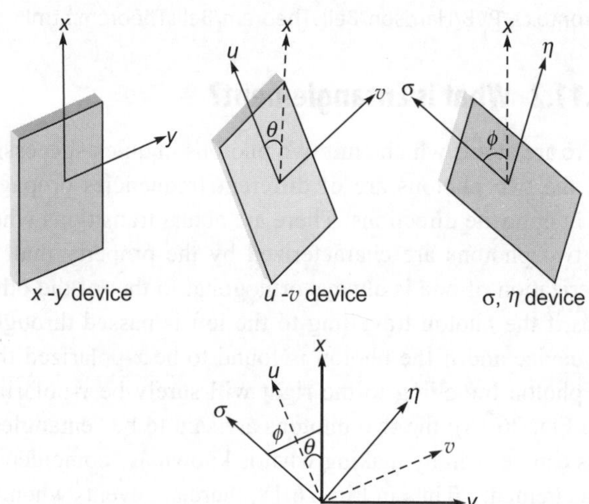

Figure 26.20
The (u,v) axes are obtained by rotating the (x,y) axes by an angle θ similarly the (σ, η) axes are obtained by rotating the (x,y) axes by an angle ϕ.

Let there be

N_1 photons (going to the left) characterized by $\{x, u, \sigma\}$ and equal number of photons (going to the right) characterized by $\{y, v, \eta\}$

Similarly, we may have

N_2 photons (going to the left) characterized by $\{x, u, \eta\}$ and equal number of photons (going to the right) characterized by $\{y, v, \sigma\}$

Obviously, we can have 8 possible pairs as listed in Table 26.1. If $P(x, u)$ represents the probability that the photon (going to the left) is x-polarixed and the photon (going to the right) is u-polarized (see Fig. 26.21) then from Table 26.1 it is obvious that

TABLE 26.1 **Possible hidden variable pairs**

	Photons going to the left	*Photons going to the right*
N_1 pairs characterized by	$\{x, u, \sigma\}$	$\{y, v, \eta\}$
N_2 pairs characterized by	$\{x, u, \eta\}$	$\{y, v, \sigma\}$
N_3 pairs characterized by	$\{x, v, \sigma\}$	$\{y, u, \eta\}$
N_4 pairs characterized by	$\{x, v, \eta\}$	$\{y, u, \sigma\}$
N_5 pairs characterized by	$\{y, u, \sigma\}$	$\{x, v, \eta\}$
N_6 pairs characterized by	$\{y, u, \eta\}$	$\{x, v, \sigma\}$
N_7 pairs characterized by	$\{y, v, \sigma\}$	$\{x, u, \eta\}$
N_8 pairs characterized by	$\{y, v, \eta\}$	$\{x, u, \sigma\}$

$$P(x, u) = \frac{N_3 + N_4}{N} \tag{26.48}$$

where

$$N = N_1 + N_2 + N_3 + N_4 + N_5 + N_6 + N_7 + N_8 \tag{26.49}$$

Similarly, if $P(x, \sigma)$ represents the probability that the photon (going to the left) is x-polarized and the photon (going to the right) is σ-polarized then (again from Table 26.1)

$$P(x, \sigma) = \frac{N_2 + N_4}{N} \tag{26.50}$$

Similarly, if $P(\sigma, u)$ represents the probability that the photon (going to the left) is σ-polarized and the photon (going to the right) is u-polarized then (again from Table 26.1)

$$P(\sigma, u) = \frac{N_3 + N_7}{N} \tag{26.51}$$

Thus $P(x, \sigma) + P(\sigma, u) = \dfrac{N_2 + N_4 + N_3 + N_7}{N}$

Since $N_3 + N_4 \le N_2 + N_4 + N_3 + N_7$

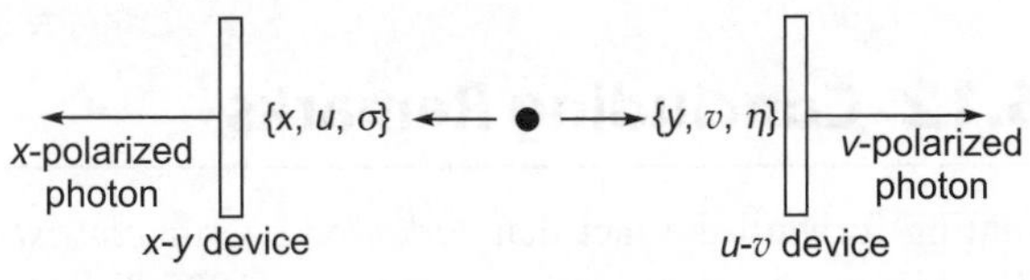

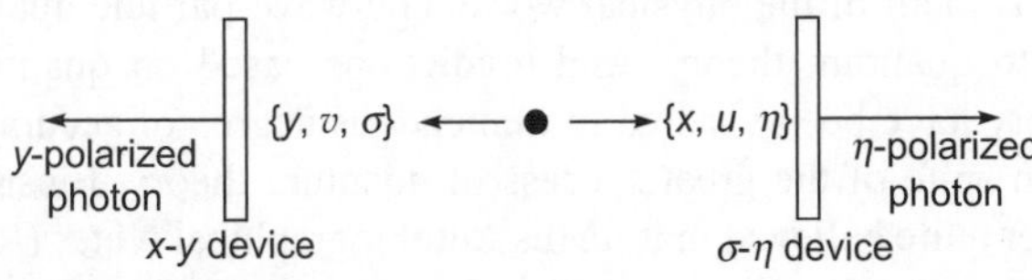

Figure 26.21
We assume that the photon must carry all the information; thus there must exist "hidden variables" so that we can assign values of all observables of a system.

we will have

$$P(x, u) \le P(x, \sigma) + P(\sigma, u) \tag{26.52}$$

This is a simple form of Bell's inequality. In 1964, John Bell published his famous theorem (now referred to as Bell's theorem) in a paper entitled "On the Einstein-Podolsky-Rosen Paradox" (Ref. 26.14). Many experiments have shown that above inequality is violated. The theorem was a revolutionary contribution to the understanding of quantum mechanics.

26.11.5 Results from Quantum Theory

We will now calculate expressions for $P(x, u)$, $P(x, \sigma)$ and $P(\sigma, u)$ using simple quantum theory. If N represents the total number of photons (going to the left) then $N/2$ photons will appear x-polarized. The corresponding photon going to the right will appear y-polarized. Thus, the probability that the photon (going to the left) is x-polarized and the photon (going to the right) is u-polarized (see Fig. 26.22) will be given by:

$$P(x, u) = \frac{1}{2}\cos^2\left(\frac{\pi}{2} + \theta\right) = \frac{1}{2}\sin^2\theta$$

where the angle θ is defined in Figs. 26.20 and 26.22. Similarly

$$P(x, \sigma) = \frac{1}{2}\sin^2\phi$$

Figure 26.22
The entangled photons are made to pass through an (x-y) device an d a (u-v) device.

where the angle ϕ is defined in Fig. 26.20. Similarly

$$P(\sigma,u)=\frac{1}{2}\sin^2(\phi-\theta)$$

Thus, if Bell's inequality is consistent with quantum theory, we must have

$$\sin^2\theta \le \sin^2\phi + \sin^2(\phi-\theta)$$

If we assume $\theta = 2\phi$, the above inequality takes the form

$$\sin^2 2\phi \le 2\sin^2\phi$$

which is violated for $\phi = \frac{\pi}{6}$. Thus, quantum theory and Bell's inequality are not compatible which implies that either quantum theory is right or theory based on hidden variables, but not both. Many have carried out experiments which are always in agreement with quantum theory and against the results obtained by using hidden variables (see References 26.15, 26.16 and other references in Ref. 26.17). Figure 26.23 shows the experimental set up of Aspect and his co-workers (see Ref. 26.17) for performing Bell test. The photon v_1 after passing through the (*x-y*) device will emerge as *x*-polarized or, as *y*-polarized. Similarly, the photon v_2 after passing through the (*u-v*) device will emerge as *u*-polarized or, as *v*-polarized. In Ref. 26.17, Aspect et. al write:

"The linear-polarization correlation of pairs of photons emitted in a radiative cascade of calcium has been measured. The new experimental scheme, using two-channel polarizers (i.e., optical analogs of Stern-Gerlach filters), is a straightforward transposition of Einstein-Podolsky-Rosen-Bohm *gedanken experiment*. The present results, in excellent agreement with the quantum mechanical predictions, lead to the greatest violation of generalized Bell's inequalities ever achieved."

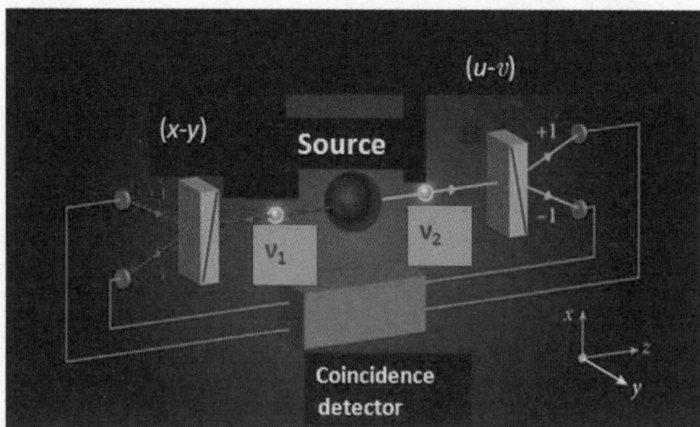

Figure 26.23

An apparatus for performing Bell test. The photon v_1 after passing through the (*x-y*) device will emerge as *x*-polarized or, as *y*-polarized. Similarly, the photon v_2 after passing through the (*u-v*) device will emerge as *u*-polarized or, as *v*-polarized. Adapted from Ref. 26.17.

John Bell has written:

> *It seems to me then beyond dispute that there was at least one Einstein, that of the EPR paper and the Schilpp volume* [Ref. 26.13], *who was fully committed to the view that quantum mechanics was incomplete and should be completed – which is the hidden variable program.*

Bell's theorem proved that the above view (of Einstein) is incorrect!

26.11.6 Correlation Function

We define a correlation function C

$$C = P(x, v) + P(y, u) - P(x, u) - P(y, v)$$

Now, according to quantum theory

$$P(x,u) = \frac{1}{2}\sin^2\theta$$

Similarly,

$$P(x,v) = \frac{1}{2}\cos^2\theta,\ P(y,u) = \frac{1}{2}\cos^2\theta$$

and $$P(y,v) = \frac{1}{2}\sin^2\theta$$

Thus, according to quantum theory, the correlation function *C* is given by

$$C = P(x,v)+P(y,u)-P(x,u)-P(y,v) = \cos^2\theta - \sin^2\theta$$
$$= \cos 2\theta$$

The above variation of the correlation function *C* with θ was verified very accurately by experiments carried out by Freedman and Clauser in 1972 (Ref. 26.15).

26.12 Concluding Remarks

In putting forward the fact that *radiation energy consists of indivisible quanta of energy* .... , Einstein in 1905 discovered wave-particle duality; this was extended by de Broglie (in 1924) to all of the physical world, and wave-particle duality led to quantum theory. And predictions based on quantum theory have been verified to tremendous degree of accuracy.

In spite of the great success of quantum theory, Einstein never quite believed in it; in his Autobiographical Notes (Ref. 26.13, page 51) Einstein (when he was about 67 years old) wrote

> *This double nature of radiation (and of material corpuscles) is a major property of reality, which*

has been interpreted by quantum mechanics in an ingenious and amazingly successful fashion. This interpretation, which is looked upon as essentially final by almost all contemporary physicists, appears to me as only a temporary way out.....

Classical physics tells us that an event at a particular place cannot affect the outcome of another event taking place at a far away point because no signal can travel faster than speed of light. Also, even if measurements are not made, a system will have a definite property at all times; this is usually referred to as "realism". Quantum mechanics does not obey either locality or realism. According to Amir Aczel (Ref. 26.20)

Whatever happened to one particle would thus immediately affect the other particle, wherever in the universe it maybe. Einstein called this "Spooky action at a distance"; in German Einstein called this "Spukhafte Fernwirkung"

In 1962, John Bell put forward his famous theorem which is considered (to quote from Ref. 26.2)

...as one of the most profound discoveries since Copernicus... Bell delivered a death blow to the local realistic picture of the world. .. many experiments have demonstrated that the predictions of quantum mechanics for entangled particles are fully correct ... and the world is really as "crazy" as predicted by quantum mechanics.

Nobel Laureate Brian Josephson remarked that Bell's inequality is the most important recent advance in physics. John Bell's response was "I would say that's probably a bit exaggerated. But if you are primarily concerned with the philosophy of physics, I can see the point" (as quoted in Ref. 26.19, page 30).

SUMMARY

- Wave particle duality led to the development of quantum mechanics.
- The three most important concepts in quantum theory are: the indeterminateness in measurement, the principle of superposition and the collapse of the wave function. These are discussed in detail along with experiments which demonstrate them.
- A heuristic derivation of the Schrödinger equation has been given and its solutions are used to interpret various experiments like the single (and double) slit interference patterns,
- Finally the concept of entanglement has been discussed along with the famous EPR Pardox and Bell's inequality

PROBLEMS

26.1 An atom emits two (entangled) photons in quick succession of different frequencies propagating in opposite directions. The two photons are characterized by the property that the polarization of one is always orthogonal to that of the other. The photon travelling to the left is passed through a (x-y) device and is found to be y-polarized. If the photon (propagating to the right) is passed through a (u-v) device where the u-axis makes an angle of 30° with the x-axis, what will be the probability of finding it u-polarized?

[**Ans:** 0.75]

26.2 Consider a particle of mass μ in a one-dimensional infinitely deep potential well characterized by the following potential energy variation

$$V(x) = 0 \text{ for } 0<x<a$$
$$= \infty \text{ for } x<0 \text{ and for } x>a$$

Since the particle is inside an infinitely deep potential well, it is always confined in the region $0 < x < a$ and, therefore, ψ must vanish for $x < 0$ and $x > L$; and for ψ to be continuous, we must have $\psi(x = 0) = \psi(x = a) = 0$. Solve the one-dimensional Schrödinger equation in the region $0 < x < a$ and use the above boundary conditions to obtain the energy eigenvalues and the corresponding (normalized) eigenfunctions.

[**Ans:** $E = E_n = \dfrac{\pi^2 n^2 \hbar^2}{2\mu a^2}$; $n = 1,2,...$; $\psi_n(x) = \sqrt{\dfrac{2}{a}} \sin\left(\dfrac{n\pi}{a}x\right)$ for $0<x<a$;
$= 0$ everywhere else]

26.3 (a) We next consider the square well potential for which

$$V(x) = 0 \text{ for } -\frac{a}{2}<x<\frac{a}{2}$$
$$= V_0 \text{ for } |x|>\frac{a}{2}$$

(see Sec. 29.6). Assume $E < V_0$. Write the symmetric and antisymmetric solutions of the Schrödinger equation and use the continuity of $\psi(x)$ and $d\psi/dx$ at $x = a/2$ to derive the following transcendental equations determining the energy eigenvalues of the problem:

$$\eta \tan \eta = \sqrt{\alpha^2 - \eta^2} \quad \text{(symmetric states)}$$

$$-\eta \cot \eta = \sqrt{\alpha^2 - \eta^2} \quad \text{(antisymmetric states)}$$

where

$$\eta = \frac{ka}{2} = \left(\frac{2\mu E a^2}{4\hbar^2}\right)^{1/2} \quad \text{and} \quad \alpha = \left(\frac{2\mu V_0 a^2}{4\hbar^2}\right)^{1/2}$$

The transcendental equations are identical to the ones we had obtained in Sec. 29.2 while discussing the modes of a planar waveguide.

(b) Show by using a graphical method (see Fig. 29.2) that for $0 < \alpha < \pi/2$, there will be only one symmetric state; for $\pi/2 < \alpha < \pi$, there will be one symmetric state and one antisymmetric state;
for $\pi < \alpha < 3\pi/2$, there will be two symmetric states and one antisymmetric state; etc.

26.4 In continuation of the above problem, write short programs (may be using software like MATLAB) to solve the transcendental equations in the previous problem for the following cases:

(a) Assume $\alpha = 2$ and show that the solution of the transcendental equations would give the following eigenvalues:

$\eta = 1.02987$ for the symmetric state and

$\eta = 1.89549$ for the antisymmetric state

(b) Consider a proton (with $m_p = 1.672 \times 10^{-27}$ kg) in a potential well characterized by $V_0 = 1$ eV $\approx 1.6 \times 10^{-19}$ J and $a = 0.5$ Å $= 0.5 \times 10^{-10}$ m. Calculate the value of α and solve the transcendental equations to obtain the energy eigenvalues.

[Ans: $E_1 \approx 0.0585$ eV, $E_2 \approx 0.2316$ eV, $E_3 \approx 0.5101$ eV and $E_4 \approx 0.8623$ eV]

26.5 For the linear harmonic oscillator problem,

$$V(x) = \frac{1}{2}\mu\omega^2 x^2$$

Show that the one-dimensional Schrödinger equation can be written in the form

$$\frac{d^2\psi}{d\xi^2} + \left[\Lambda - \xi^2\right]\psi(x) = 0$$

where $\xi = \gamma x$, $\gamma = \sqrt{\frac{\mu\omega}{\hbar}}$ and $\Lambda \equiv \sqrt{\frac{2E}{\hbar\omega}}$. Show that for the wave function not to blow up at $x = \pm\infty$ (which represents the boundary condition), Λ must be equal to an odd integer (see Sec. 29.5 and Appendix D); i.e.

$$\Lambda = (2m+1) \Rightarrow E = E_m = \left(m + \frac{1}{2}\right)\hbar\omega; \quad m = 0,1,2,3,....$$

which are the eigenvalues of the problem. The corresponding eigenfunctions are the Hermite Gauss functions discussed in Sec. 29.5 and Appendix D.

26.6 Show that the free particle wave function [see Sec. 26.7]

$$\psi_p(x) = \frac{1}{\sqrt{2\pi\hbar}}\left[\frac{i}{\hbar}px\right]; \quad -\infty < p < +\infty$$

satisfy the following equations (for convenience, we have removed the subscript x on p – see Sections 8.4 and 26.7):

$$\int_{-\infty}^{+\infty} \psi_p^*(x)\psi_{p'}(x)dx = \delta(p - p') \quad \text{and}$$

$$\int_{-\infty}^{+\infty} \psi_p^*(x)\psi_p(x')dp = \delta(x - x')$$

which represent the orthonormality condition and the completeness condition, respectively.

PART 4

LASERS & FIBER OPTICS

This part consists of four chapters (Chapters 27–30). Chapter 27 is on Lasers–the discovery of which in 1960 has led to numerous applications in many diverse areas; see the Prologue to this book. The chapter discusses the basic physics of lasers along with their special characteristics. The next three chapters are on fiber optics and waveguide theory–an area which has, during the last 40 years, revolutionized communications. Today, making an overseas video call has become almost free is because of the fiber optics revolution.

CHAPTER

27

Lasers: An Introduction

In The War of Worlds, written before the turn of the century, H.G. Wells told a fanciful story of how Martians invaded and almost conquered the earth. Their weapon was a mysterious 'sword of heat', from which flickered 'a ghost of a beam of light', it felled men in their tracks, made lead run like water and flashed anything combustible into masses of flame. Today Wells' sword of heat comes close to reality in the laser...

—Thomas Meloy

LEARNING OBJECTIVES

After reading this chapter, the reader should be able to:

LO 1: *describe the main components of the laser and lasing action.*

LO 2: *explain fiber laser, Ruby laser and He-Ne laser.*

LO 3: *discuss optical resonators and their working.*

LO 4: *discuss Einstein coefficients and optical amplifications.*

LO 5: *describe typical forms of the line-shape function, g(ω).*

LO 6: *calculate typical parameters for a ruby laser.*

LO 7: *discuss monochromaticity of a laser beam.*

LO 8: *discuss Raman laser and Raman amplification.*

Important Milestones

1917: The theory of stimulated emission was put forward by Albert Einstein.

1924: Richard Tolman suggested optical amplification through stimulated emission of radiation.

1954: The phenomenon of stimulated emission was first used by Charles Townes in 1954 in the construction of a microwave amplifier device called the maser which is an acronym for **M**icrowave **A**mplification by **S**timulated **E**mission of **R**adiation. At about the same time, a similar device was also proposed by Prochorov and Basov in USSR.

1958: The maser principle was later extended to the optical frequencies by Schawlow and Townes in 1958, which led to the realization of the device now known as the laser. Townes, Basov and Prochorov were awarded the 1964 Nobel Prize in physics for their fundamental work in the field of Quantum Electronics, which has led to the construction of oscillators and amplifiers based on the laser–maser principle.*

* The Nobel lectures of Townes, Basov and Prochorov [Refs 27.1–27.3] give a nice perspective of the field; these are reprinted in Ref. 27.4.

Above Image: Laser beam in a laboratory. You can see the laser beam because of scattering (of the light beam) by air molecules and also by dust particles; if it was an evacuated chamber, you would not be able to see the propagating laser beam!. Photograph courtesy McGraw Hill Digital Access Library.

1960 The first successful operation of a laser device ($\lambda \sim 0.6943\ \mu m$) was demonstrated by Theodore Maiman in 1960 using a ruby crystal.

1961 Within a few months of the operation of the ruby laser, Ali Javan and his associates constructed the first gas laser ($\lambda \sim 0.6328\ \mu m$), namely the helium-neon laser.

1961 The first fiber laser (barium crown glass doped with Nd^{3+} ions) was fabricated by Elias Snitzer.

1962 Semiconductor laser (which are now extensively used in fiber-optic communication systems) was discovered by four independent groups.

1963 C.K.N. Patel discovered the CO_2 laser ($\lambda \sim 10.6\ \mu m$).

1964 W. Bridges discovered the Ar-ion laser ($\lambda \sim 0.515\ \mu m$);

J.E. Geusic and his co-workers discovered the Nd:YAG laser ($\lambda \sim 1.064\ \mu m$).

Since then, laser action has been obtained in a large variety of materials including liquids, ionized gases, dyes, semiconductors, etc.

27.1 Introduction

LO1

LASER is an acronym for **L**ight **A**mplification by **S**timulated **E**mission of **R**adiation. The light emitted from a laser often possesses some very special characteristics—some of these are:

(a) Directionality: The divergence of the laser beam is usually limited by diffraction (see Sec. 17.4) and the actual divergence can be less than 10^{-5} radians (see Fig. 17.15); this leads to the application of the laser in surveying, remote sensing, lidar, etc.

(b) High Power: Continuous wave lasers having power levels $\sim 10^5$ W and pulsed lasers having a total energy $\sim 50{,}000$ J can have applications in welding, cutting, laser fusion, etc.

(c) Tight Focusing: Because of highly directional properties of the laser beams, they can be focused to areas ~ few $(\mu m)^2$ – this leads to applications in surgery, material processing, compact discs, etc. Laser pulses with very small cross sectional area can be guided through special fibers leading to very interesting non linear effects (see Sec. 11.4 and Fig. 11.12).

(d) Spectral Purity: Laser beams can have an extremely small spectral width because of which they find applications in holography, optical communications, spectroscopy, etc.

Because of such unique properties of the laser beam, it finds important applications in many diverse areas and indeed one can say that after the discovery of the laser, optics has become an extremely important field of study. For example, in Example 17.5, we had shown that a 2 mW diffraction limited laser beam incident on the eye can produce an intensity of about $10^6\ W/m^2$ at the retina—this would certainly damage the retina. Thus, whereas it is quite safe to look at a 500 W bulb, it is very dangerous to look directly into a 5 mW laser beam. Indeed, because a laser beam can be focused to very narrow areas, it has found applications in areas like eye surgery, laser cutting, etc.

The basic principle involved in the lasing action is the phenomenon of stimulated emission, which was predicted by Einstein in 1917 [Ref. 27.5]*. In Sec. 27.1.1 we will discuss spontaneous and stimulated transitions, which will be followed by brief discussions of the main components of a laser and the underlying principle as to how the laser works. In Sec. 27.2, we will briefly discuss the working of a fiber laser and in Sec. 27.3, we will discuss the working of the ruby laser, which was the first laser to be fabricated. In Sec 27.4, we will discuss the working of the helium-neon laser. In Sec. 27.5, we will have a slightly more detailed account of resonators and in Sec. 27.6, we will discuss Einstein coefficients and optical amplification. In Sec. 27.7, we will discuss the line shape function and finally in Sec. 27.8, we will discuss the monochromaticity of the laser beam.

27.1.1 Spontaneous and Stimulated Emissions

Atoms are characterised by discrete energy states. According to Einstein, there are three different ways in which an atom can interact with electromagnetic radiation:

(a) Spontaneous emission: Atoms in the energy state E_2 can make a (spontaneous) transition to the energy state E_1 with the emission of radiation of frequency

$$\omega = \frac{E_2 - E_1}{\hbar} \quad \textbf{(27.1)}$$

where
$$\hbar = \frac{h}{2\pi} \approx 1.0546 \times 10^{-34}\ \text{Js}$$

and h ($\approx 6.626 \times 10^{-34}$ Js) is known as the **Planck's constant**. Since this process can occur even in the absence of any radiation, this is called **spontaneous emission** [see Fig. 27.1(a)]. The rate of spontaneous emission is proportional to the number of atoms in the excited state.

(b) Stimulated emission: As put forward by Einstein, when an atom is in the excited state, it can also make a transition to a lower energy state through what is known as

* The original paper of Einstein is reprinted is Ref. 27.6.

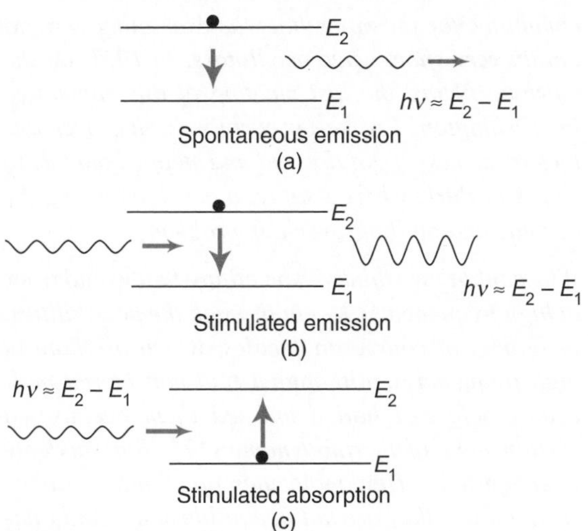

Figure 27.1
(a) Spontaneous emission. (b) Stimulated emission. (c) Stimulated absorption.

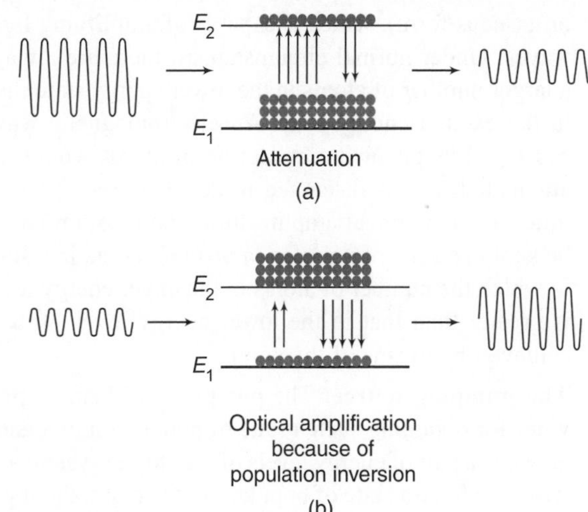

Figure 27.2
(a) Larger number of atoms in the lower state result in the attenuation of the beam. (b) Larger number of atoms in the upper state (which is known as population inversion) result in the amplification of the beam. Drawing courtesy: Professor K Thyagarajan.

stimulated emission in which an incident signal of appropriate frequency triggers an atom in an excited state to emit radiation—this results in the amplification of the incident beam [see Fig. 27.1(b)]. The rate of stimulated emission depends both on the intensity of the external field and also on the number of atoms in the excited state.

(c) Stimulated absorption: Stimulated absorption (or simply absorption) is the process in which the electromagnetic radiation of an appropriate frequency (corresponding to the energy difference of the two atomic levels) can pump the atom to its excited state [see Fig. 27.1(c)]. The rate of stimulated absorption depends both on the intensity of the external field and also on the number of atoms in the lower energy state.

Einstein also showed that the probability of stimulated emission is the same as that of stimulated absorption (because $B_{12} = B_{21}$ – see Sec. 27.6); however, although the phenomenon of stimulated emission was predicted by Einstein in 1917, it was only in 1924 that Richard Tolman suggested optical amplification through stimulated emission. In a paper published in Physical Review, he wrote:

> ...*The possibility arises ... that molecules in the upper quantum state may return to the lower quantum state in such a way as to reinforce the primary beam by "negative absorption"* ... (which) *would presumably be of such a nature as to reinforce the primary beam.*

This was the first hint of the possibility of optical amplification. Now when the atoms are in thermodynamic equilibrium, there are larger number of atoms in the lower state implying that the number of absorptions exceeds the number of stimulated emissions; this results in the attenuation of the beam [see Fig. 27.2(a)]. On the other hand, if we are able to create a state of population inversion in which there are larger number of atoms in the upper state then the number of stimulated emissions would exceed the number of absorptions resulting in the (optical) amplification of the beam [see Fig. 27.2(b)]. The amplification process due to stimulated transitions is *phase coherent*, i.e., *the energy delivered by the molecular system has the same field distribution and frequency as the stimulating radiation* (quoted from Ref. 27.1).

27.1.2 Main Components of the Laser

The three main components of any laser are (see Fig. 27.3):

(a) The active medium: The active medium consists of a collection of atoms, molecules or ions (in solid, liquid

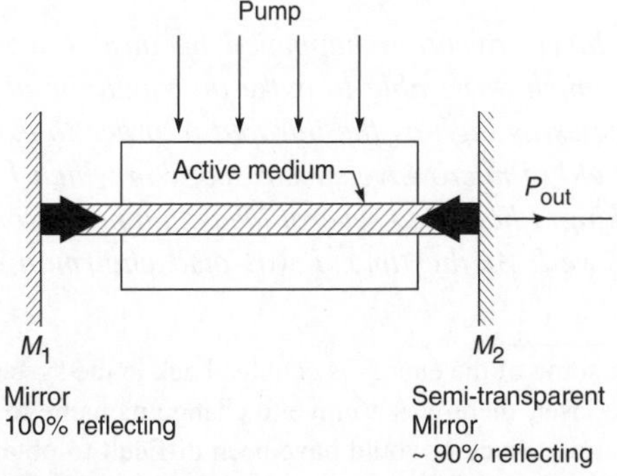

Figure 27.3
The three basic components of a laser are (i) the active medium (which provides amplification), (ii) the optical resonator (which provides frequency selection and optical feedback), and (iii) the pump (which supplies power to the active medium to achieve population inversion).

or gaseous form), which is capable of amplifying light waves. Under normal circumstances, there are always a larger number of atoms in the lower energy state than in the excited energy state. An electromagnetic wave passing through such a collection of atoms would get attenuated; this is discussed in detail in Sec. 27.6. In order to have optical amplification, the medium has to be kept in a state of *population inversion*, i.e., in a state in which the number of atoms in the upper energy level is greater than that in the lower energy level—this is achieved by means of the pump.

(b) The pumping source: The pumping mechanism provides for obtaining such a state of population inversion between a pair of energy levels of the atomic system and when we have a state of population inversion, the input light beam can get amplified by stimulated emission (see Fig. 27.4).

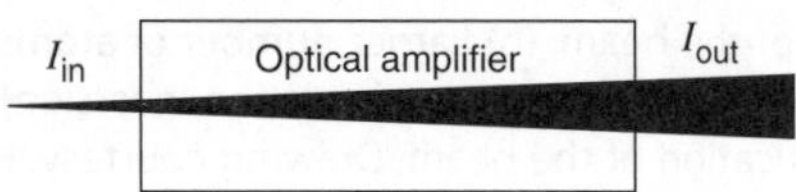

Figure 27.4

The active medium essentially consists of a collection of atoms in a state of population inversion which can amplify the input light beam (or spontaneously emitted light) by stimulated emission. This is known as optical amplification.

(c) The optical resonator: A medium with population inversion is capable of amplification; however, in order that it acts as an oscillator, a part of the output energy must be fed back into the system.* Such a feedback is brought about by placing the active medium in a resonator; the resonator could just be a pair of mirrors facing each other.

We may mention here that although Einstein had proposed the theory of stimulated emission in 1917, the concept of population inversion to amplify the light beam came much much later. According to Charles Townes**:

> *The laser invention happened because I wanted very much to be able to make an oscillator at frequencies as high as the infrared in order to extend the field of microwave spectroscopy in which I was working. I had tried several ideas, but none worked very well. At the time, I was also chairman of a committee for the navy that was examining ways to obtain very short-wave oscillators. In 1951, on the morning before the last meeting of this committee in Washington, I woke up early worrying over our lack of success. I got dressed and stepped outside to Franklin Park, where I sat on a bench admiring the azaleas and mulling over our problem.*
>
> *Why couldn't we think of something that would work at high frequencies? I went through the possibilities, including, of course, molecules, which oscillate at high frequencies. Although I had considered molecules before, I had dismissed them because of certain laws of thermodynamics***. But suddenly I recognized, "Hey, molecules don't have to obey such a law if they are not in equilibrium". And I immediately took a piece of paper out of my pocket and wrote equations to see if selection of excited molecules by molecular beam methods could produce enough molecules to provide a feedback oscillator. Wow! It looked possible.*
>
> *I went back to my hotel and told Art Schawlow about the idea, since he was staying at the same place. … Its extension to waves as short as light came a few years later, after much excitement over the maser and as a result of my continued collaboration with Schawlow, then at Bell Labs. An essential element in this discovery, I believe, was my experience in both engineering and physics: I knew both quantum mechanics and the workings and importance of feedback oscillators.*

27.1.3 Understanding Optical Amplification: The EDFA

Perhaps the easiest way to understand optical amplification is to discuss the working principle of an EDFA (Erbium Doped Fiber Amplifier), which is shown in Fig. 27.5. The EDFA essentially consists of about 20–40 meters of a silica optical fiber the core of which is doped with erbium oxide (Er_2O_3)—we will have a detailed discussion on the optical fiber in Chapters 28 and 30, it may suffice here to say that light is guided through the optical fiber because of total internal reflections (see Figs. 28.2 and 28.7). The radius of the core of the optical fiber is typically about 2–3 μm. The erbium concentration is about 10^{25} ions/m^3. Figure 27.6 shows

* Since some of the energy is coupled back to the system, it is said to act as an oscillator. Indeed, in the early stages of the development of the laser, there was a move to change its name to LOSER which is an acronym for **L**ight **O**scillation by **S**timulated **E**mission of **R**adiation. Since it would have been difficult to obtain a research grant for LOSERs, it was decided to retain the name LASER.

** *Lasers and Fiber Optics*, Essay by Charles H. Townes, Ref. http://www.greatachievements.org/?id=3717

*** In his Nobel lecture (reprinted in Ref. 27.4) Townes writes 'Why not use the atomic and molecular oscillators already built for us by nature? This had been one recurring theme which was repeatedly rejected. Thermodynamic arguments tell us that the interaction between electromagnetic waves and matter at any temperature cannot produce amplification'. However, Townes realized that if population inversion is somehow achieved then the radiation can be amplified. Quoting Townes again 'This condition is of course one of non-equilibrium for the group of molecules, which hence successfully obviates the limits set by blackbody radiation'.

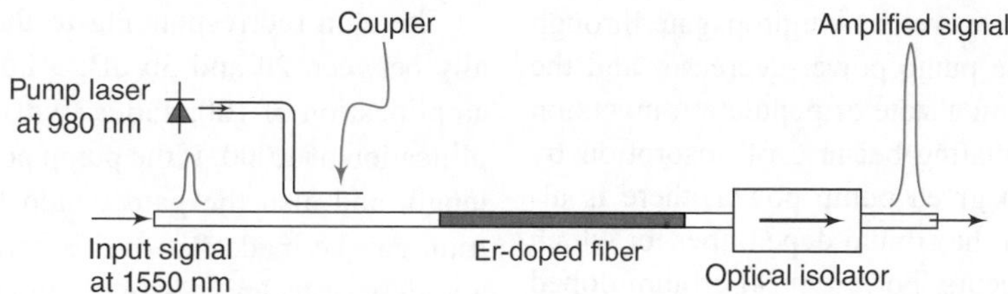

Figure 27.5

The EDFA (Erbium Doped Fiber Amplifier). The core of the optical fiber (which has a diameter of about 10 μm) is doped with erbium. The coupler couples the 980 nm pump laser beam to the Er doped fiber and creates a population inversion. Input optical pulses (at 1550 nm) get amplified when propagating through the erbium doped fiber. Drawing courtesy: Professor K Thyagarajan.

the first three energy levels of Er^{3+} ion in silica host glass. Actually, each level shown in the diagram consists of a large number of very closely spaced levels—but to keep the analysis simple we have shown them as single levels. The energy difference between E_1 (the ground state) and E_3 corresponds to a wavelength of about 980 nm and the energy difference between E_1 and E_2 corresponds to a wavelength of about 1530 nm; thus $E_3 - E_1 \approx 1.3$ eV and $E_2 - E_1 \approx 0.81$ eV.

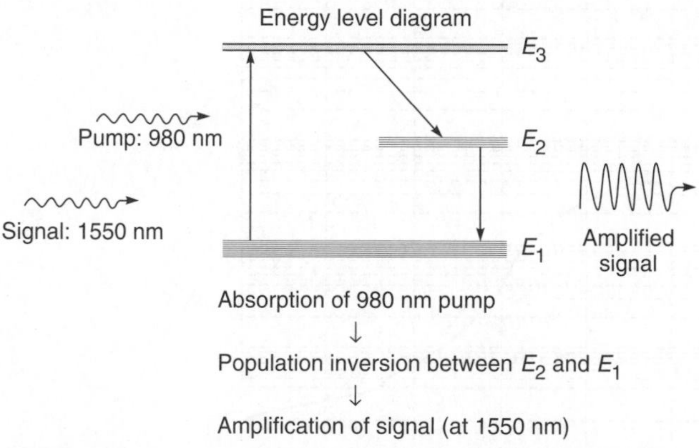

Figure 27.6

The energy level diagram of the erbium atom in host silica.

Now, when a laser beam corresponding to the wavelength 980 nm is coupled into the erbium doped fiber (see Fig. 27.5), the erbium atoms in the ground state E_1 absorb this radiation and get excited to the energy state E_3. This laser beam is usually referred to as a *pump* because it pumps the atoms to the higher energy state E_3. The atom in the energy state E_3 makes an almost immediate non-radiative transition to state E_2; in a non-radiative transition, a photon is not emitted—the energy released could, for example, add to the vibrational energy of the host medium, resulting in its heating. The state E_2 is a metastable state characterized by a long lifetime (~ few milliseconds). Thus, although the erbium atom in the state E_2 can undergo a spontaneous transition to the state E_1; however, since the lifetime is large the atom would *sit* in the excited state for a long period of time before it makes a transition to the state E_1. Now if the pump power is high, the rate at which the erbium atom goes over to the state E_2 can be so high that we may have a state of population inversion between E_1 and E_2; i.e., the number of erbium atoms in the state E_2 is greater than that in E_1. When this happens, a signal beam at 1550 nm can get amplified by stimulated emission of radiation—this is the underlying principle of optical amplification which is nothing but *light amplification through stimulated emission of radiation* [see Fig. 27.2(b)]. [We are considering the signal wavelength to be 1550 nm because most optical communication systems operate around 1550 nm where the fiber loss is minimum (see Sec. 28.8)]. Conversely, if the population of the level E_2 is less than that of the level E_1 the number of stimulated absorptions will exceed stimulated emission resulting in the attenuation of the signal beam at 1550 nm. The variation of the pump and signal powers with distance along the doped fiber is shown schematically in Fig. 27.7. We notice that because of absorption by erbium atoms, the pump power gets attenuated as it propagates through the erbium doped fiber. Because of this absorption, the erbium atoms are in a state of population inversion and the signal at

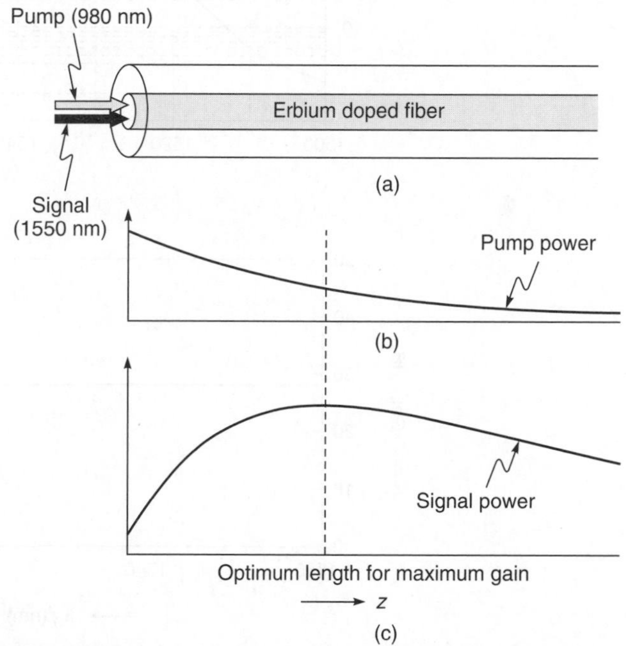

Figure 27.7

(a) The pump (corresponding to 980 nm wavelength) and the signal (corresponding to 1550 nm wavelength) propagates in the core of an erbium doped fiber. (b) and (c) represent the schematic variation of the pump and signal power as the two beams propagate through the erbium doped fiber.

1550 nm gets amplified. However, as we propagate through the erbium doped fiber, the pump power decreases and the erbium atoms are no more in a state of population inversion and the signal starts attenuating because of absorption by erbium atoms. Thus, for a given pump power, there is always an optimum length of the erbium doped fiber for which maximum amplification occurs. For a typical erbium doped fiber, we may have

Er^{3+} concentration $\approx 7 \times 10^{24}$ ions/m^3, Pump power $\approx$ 5 mW, and, the optimum length of the erbium doped fiber $\approx$ 7m

A more detailed theory of EDFA is given in Ref. 27.7. A typical gain spectrum of an EDFA (using a 50 mW pump at 980 nm) is shown in Fig. 27.8(a). The gain is usually measured in dB which is defined as

$$\text{Gain in dB} = 10 \log_{10} \frac{P_{\text{output}}}{P_{\text{input}}}$$

The gain (corresponding to the optimum length) is usually between 20 and 30 dB; a 20 dB gain implies a power amplification of 100; and a 30 dB gain implies a power amplification of 1,000. If the pump power is higher, the optimum length and also the gain would be higher. The gain spectrum can be made flat over a certain wavelength region by a variety of techniques (e.g., by putting an appropriate filter after the EDFA). Figure 27.8(b) shows an almost flat gain (of about 28 dB) of an EDFA for wavelengths lying between 1530 nm and 1560 nm; a 28 dB gain corresponds to a power amplification of about 631. The wavelength region 1530 nm $< \lambda <$ 1560 nm is extremely important for optical communications (see Chapter 28); for more details on EDFA, you may look up Refs 27.7 and 27.8.

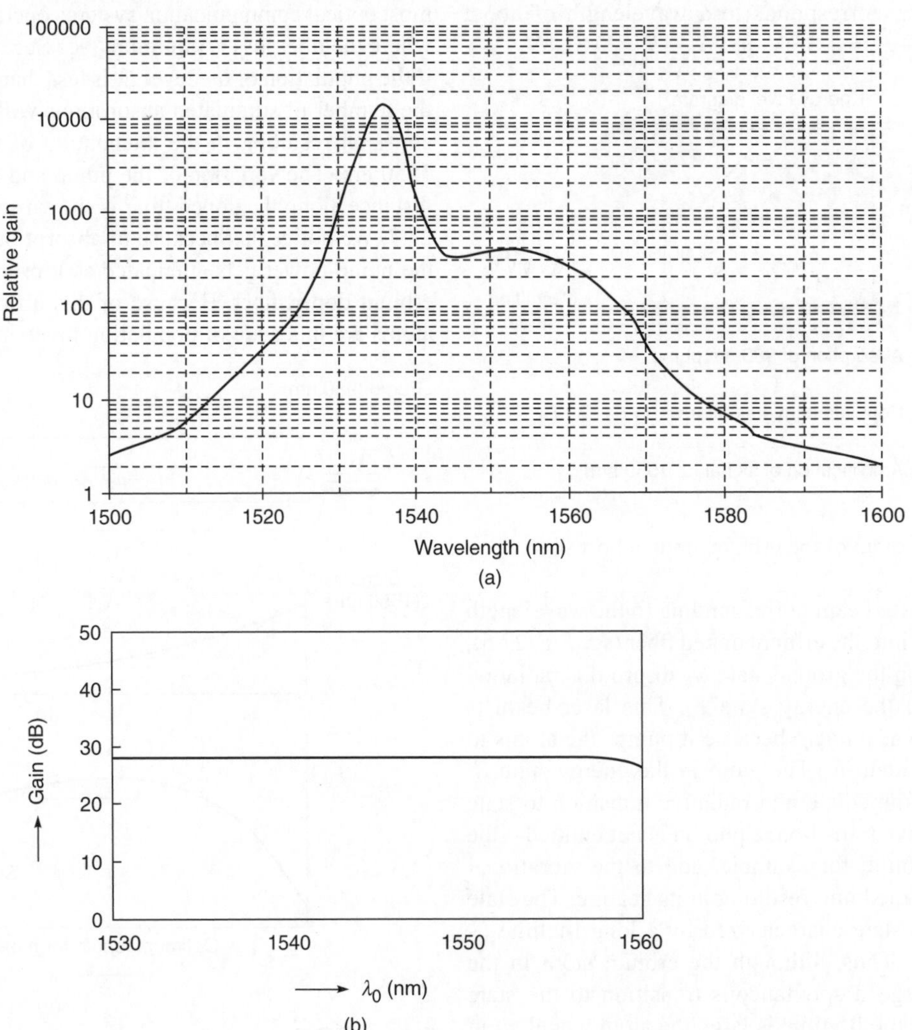

Figure 27.8
(a) The gain spectrum of a typical erbium doped fiber amplifier using a 50 mW pump at 980 nm [*Adapted from Ref. 27.10*].
(b) Through various mechanisms, the gain spectrum of an EDFA can be made almost flat. The above figure corresponds to an EDFA which has an almost flat gain (of about 28 dB) in the wavelength region 1530 nm to 1560 nm [*Adapted from Ref. 27.11*].

We may mention here that there can be two laser diodes providing the pump power for the erbium-doped fiber (see Fig. 27.9). A commercially available EDFA, along with its main characteristics, is shown in Fig. 27.10.

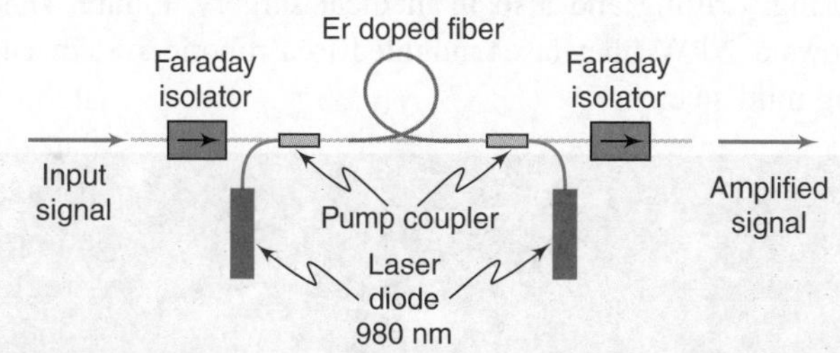

Figure 27.9
Schematic set-up of a simple erbium doped fiber amplifier with two laser diodes (LDs) providing the pump power for the erbium-doped fiber. [*Figure adapted from http://www.rpphotonics.com/erbium_doped_fiber_amplifiers. html*].

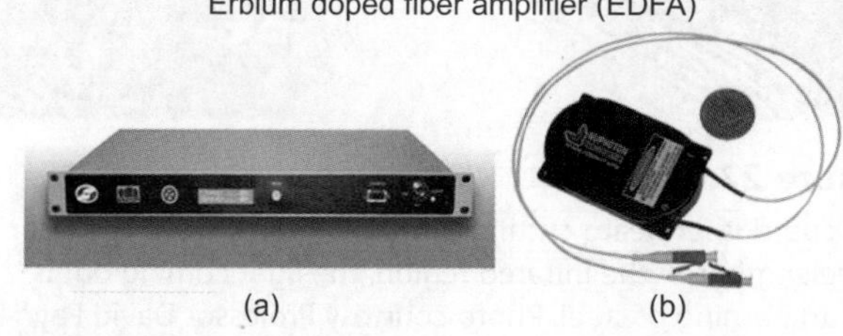

Figure 27.10
(a) An EDFA for telecommunication application developed jointly by CGCRI, Kolkata and NeST, Cochin. The main characteristics are: 32 wavelengths can be simultaneously amplified in the wavelength region from 1532 nm to 1565 nm. The input power (of each channel) can be between –4 dBm (≈ 0.4 mW) to + 3 dBm (≈ 2 mW) and the output power is always 18 dBm (≈ 63 mW) with a gain flatness of ± 0.5 dB. Photograph courtesy: Dr Shyamal Bhadra of CGCRI, Kolkata and Dr Suresh Nair of NeST, Cochin]. (b) A compact EDFA manufactured by NUPHOTON Technologies. It provides up to 16dBm output power and has a 70mm x 43mm x 12mm footprint; the size can be estimated by the 25 cent coin on the side. The unit works at 3.3V with a power consumption < 1.5W. Photograph courtesy: Dr Ramadas Pillai of NUPHOTON Technologies.

27.1.4 The Resonator

As mentioned earlier, a medium with population inversion is capable of amplification but in order that it acts as an oscillator, a part of the output energy must be fed back into the system. Such a feedback is brought about by placing the active medium between a pair of mirrors facing each other (see Fig. 27.3). Such a system formed by a pair of mirrors is referred to as a resonator, a slightly more detailed account of which will be given in Sec. 27.5. The sides of the cavity are usually open and hence such resonators are also referred to as open resonators. A resonator is characterized by various modes of oscillation with different field distributions and frequencies; for more details, see Refs. 27.4 and 27.9. One can visualise a mode as a wave having a well-defined transverse amplitude distribution which forms a standing wave pattern. The transverse intensity distribution of the fundamental mode is usually a Gaussian [see Eq. (27.13)]. Because of the open nature of the resonator, all modes have a finite loss due to the diffraction spillover of energy at the mirrors. In addition to this basic loss, scattering from the laser medium, absorption at the mirrors and output coupling at the mirrors also contribute to the cavity loss. In an actual laser, the modes that keep oscillating are those for which the gain provided by the laser medium compensates for the losses. When the laser oscillates in steady state, the losses are exactly compensated for by the gain. Since the gain provided by the medium depends on the extent of population inversion, for each mode there is a critical value of population inversion (known as the threshold population inversion) below which that particular mode would cease to oscillate in the laser (see Sec. 27.6).

27.1.5 The Lasing Action

The onset of oscillations in a laser cavity can be understood as follows: Through a pumping mechanism, one creates a state of population inversion in the laser medium placed inside the resonator system. Thus the medium is prepared to be in a state in which it is capable of coherent amplification over a specified band of frequencies. The spontaneous emission occurring inside the resonator cavity excites the various modes of the cavity. For a given population inversion, each mode is characterised by a certain amplification coefficient due to the gain and a certain attenuation coefficient due to the losses in the cavity. The modes for which the losses in the cavity exceed the gain die out. On the other hand, the modes whose gain is higher than the losses get amplified by drawing energy from the laser medium. The amplitude of the mode increases rapidly until the upper level population reaches a value when the gain equals the losses, and the mode oscillates in steady state. When the laser oscillates in the steady state, the losses are exactly compensated for by the gain provided by the medium, and the wave coming out of the laser can be represented as a continuous wave.

27.2 The Fiber Laser

If we put the doped fiber between two mirrors (which act as a resonator)—then with an appropriate pump we would have a fiber laser (see Fig. 27.11). Indeed in 1961, Elias Snitzer wrapped a flashlamp around a glass fiber (having a 300 μm core doped with Nd^{3+} ions clad in a lower index glass) and when suitable feedback was applied, the first fiber laser was born [Ref. 27.12]. Thus the fiber laser was fabricated within

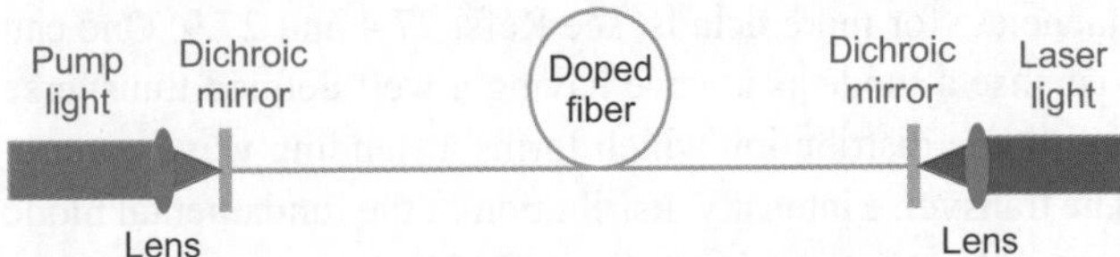

Figure 27.11

Set-up of a simple fiber laser. Pump light is launched from the left side through a dichroic mirror into the core of the doped fiber. The generated laser light is extracted on the right side. [*Figure adapted from http://www.rp-photonics.com/fiber_lasers.html*].

a year of the demonstration of the first ever laser by Theodore Maiman. These days fiber lasers are commercially available in the market which have applications in many diverse areas because of their flexibility and high power levels. The lower curve in Fig. 27.12 corresponds to the output spectrum of an EDFA just before it starts lasing. As we increase the pump

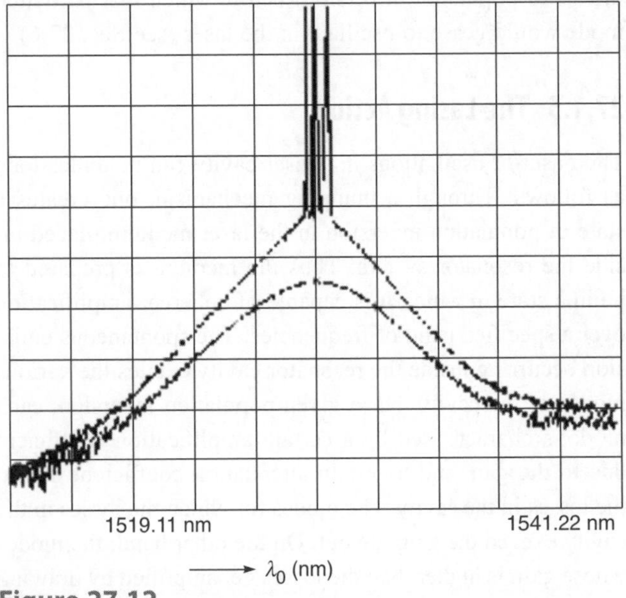

Figure 27.12

The lower and upper curves show the output of an EDFA just before and after it starts lasing. [*Photograph courtesy: Professor Thyagarajan and Mr. Mandeep Singh*].

power, the EDFA starts lasing and the spikes correspond to the various resonator modes; the ends of the fiber act as the resonator. A detailed theory of fiber lasers can be found in Ref. 27.4.

Fiber lasers now find widespread applications in welding, cutting, drilling and also in medical surgery. Figure 27.13 shows a 2 kW fiber laser mounted to a robotic system cutting mild steel.

Figure 27.13

A focused laser beam cutting through 4″ thick steel. The laser wavelength is in the infrared region, the light coming out is due to burning of steel. Photo courtesy Professor David Payne, University of Southampton.

27.2.1 MOPA*

The term **master oscillator power amplifier** (MOPA) refers to a configuration consisting of a master laser (or seed laser) and an optical amplifier to boost the output power. A special case is the master oscillator fiber amplifier (MOFA), where the power amplifier is a fiber device. Although a MOPA configuration is in principle more complex than a laser which directly produces the required output power, the MOPA concept can have the advantage of the ease to achieve the required performance e.g., in terms of line-width, beam

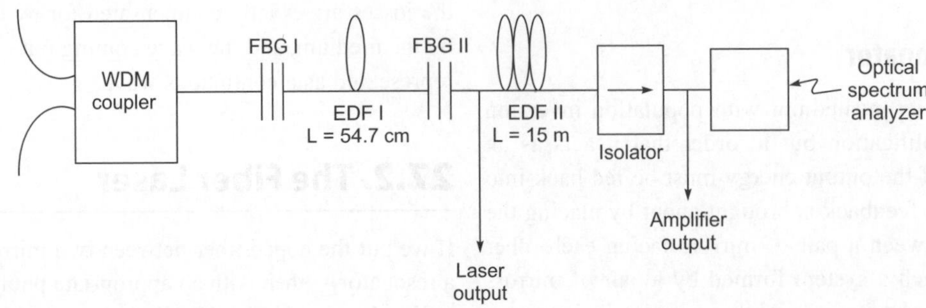

Figure 27.14

Schematic of the Master Oscillator Power Amplifier (MOPA) configuration.

* May be, skipped at the first reading; the writeup for this section along with Figs. 27.14–27.16 have been kindly provided by Mr. Mrinmay Pal and Mr. Kamal Dasgupta, CGCRI, Kolkata. You may like to go through Sec. 14.6 (on Fiber Bragg Gratings) before going through Sec. 27.2.1.

quality or pulse duration if the required power is very high. In the MOPA configuration (shown in Fig. 27.14), the seed laser consists of a 54.7 cm length of EDF (Erbium Doped Fiber) comprising of two high reflective FBGs (Fiber Bragg Gratings) written directly on the both ends of the EDF; we had discussed FBGs in Sec. 14.6 and had shown that they are characterized with high reflectivity at a particular wavelength with a very small bandwidth; thus the two FBGs form a resonator. The important characteristics of both the gratings are given in the Table 27.1. The EDF has a 0.18 NA and 500 ppm Er-ion in the fibre core; NA is defined in Sec. 28.7. EDF in the cavity is pumped through a WDM coupler by a 976 nm laser diode of pump power 100 mW. Lasing emission starts at the peak wavelength when the threshold is achieved. Since, there is a small off-set in the peak wavelengths of the two FBGs, FBG-II is slightly stretched to match the peak wavelength with that of the FBG-I. When these two wavelengths coincide, laser emission is obtained from the FBG-II with maximum output power and very good beam quality. In this MOPA, seed laser at 1549.45 nm of output power 1 mW is generated (shown in Fig. 27.15). To amplify the laser output power, an extra length of 15 m EDF is spliced to the cavity. This extra EDF is pumped by the residual pump power of 976 nm laser diode. An optical isolator is placed after the amplifier to prevent the back reflection which otherwise degrades the noise figure; optical isolator is discussed in Sec. 21.15.1. In the output, 16.05 dBm (≈40 mW) of laser power is obtained (shown in Fig. 27.16). This power can be further enhanced by increasing the pump power.

TABLE 27.1 Characteristics of the two Fiber Bragg Gratings used in MOPA

Parameters	*FBG-I*	*FBG-II*
Peak wavelength (nm)	1549.456	1549.168
3-dB bandwidth	0.344nm	0.216nm
Reflectivity	99%	90%

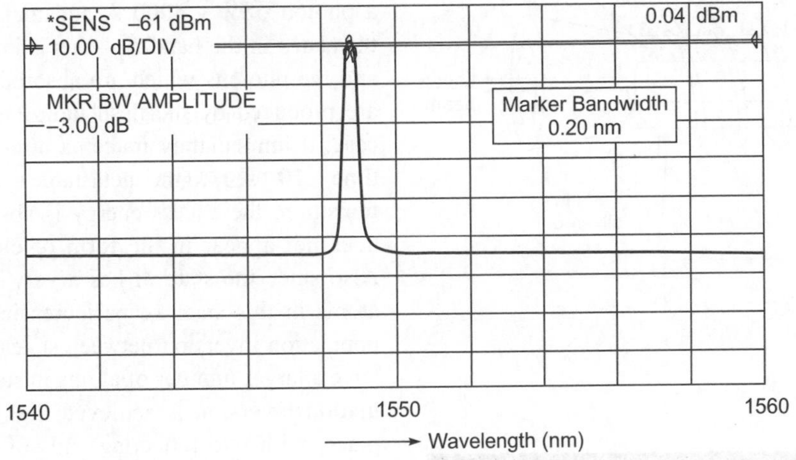

Figure 27.15
Spectrum of the seed laser. The peak wavelength is 1548.73 nm with peak power of –0.05 dBm and bandwidth of 0.225 nm. [*Figure courtesy: Mr. Mrinmay Pal and Mr. Kamal Dasgupta, CGCRI, Kolkata*]

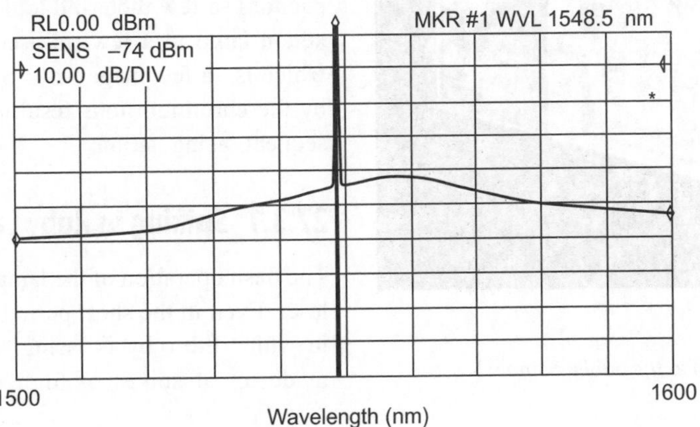

Figure 27.16
Laser output spectrum from MOPA configuration.

27.3 The Ruby Laser

LO2

In the first laser fabricated by Maiman in 1960 [Ref. 27.13], the population inversion was achieved in the following manner. It was made from a single cylindrical crystal of ruby whose ends were flat, with one of the ends completely silvered and the other partially silvered (see Figs 27.17 and 27.18). Ruby consists of Al_2O_3 with some of the aluminum atoms replaced by chromium.* The energy states of the chromium ion are shown in Fig. 27.19. The chief characteristic of the energy levels of a chromium ion is the fact that the bands labeled E_1 and E_2 have a lifetime of $\sim 10^{-8}$ s whereas the state marked M has a lifetime of $\sim 3 \times 10^{-3}$ s —the lifetime represents the average time an atom spends in an excited state before making a transition to a lower energy state. A state characterized by such a long lifetime is termed a metastable state.

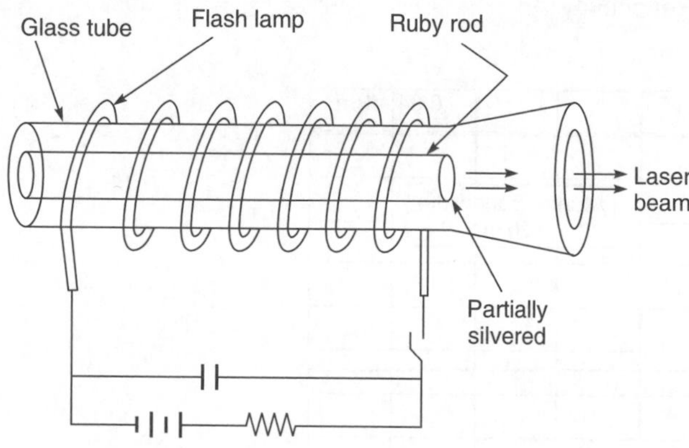

Figure 27.17
The ruby laser.

Figure 27.18
The first ruby laser. [*Photograph in the public domain.*]

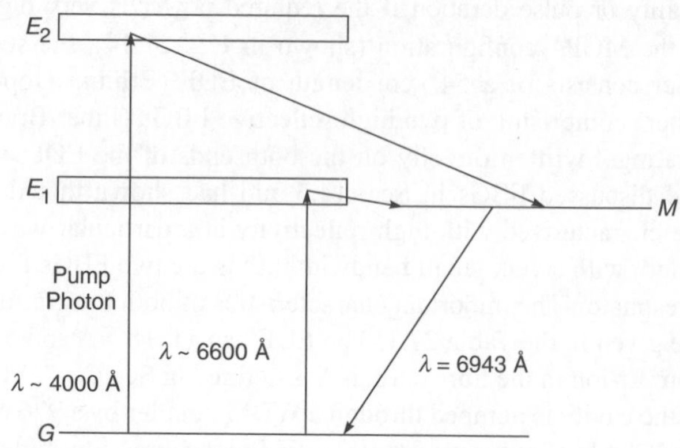

Figure 27.19
The energy levels of the chromium ion; *G* and *M* represent the ground and metastable states, respectively.

The chromium ion in its ground state can absorb a photon (whose wavelength is around 6600 Å) and make a transition to one of the states in the band E_1; it could also absorb a photon of $\lambda \sim 4000$ Å and make a transition to one of the states in the band E_2—this is known as optical pumping and the photons which are absorbed by the chromium ions are produced by the flash lamp (see Fig. 27.17). In either case, it immediately makes a non-radiative transition (in a time $\sim 10^{-8}$ sec) to the metastable state M—in a non-radiative transition, the excess energy is absorbed by the lattice and does not appear in the form of electromagnetic radiation. Also since the state M has a very long life, the number of atoms in this state keeps increasing and one may achieve population inversion between states M and G. Thus we may have a larger number of atoms in states M and G. Once population inversion is achieved, light amplification can take place, with two reflecting ends of the ruby rod forming a cavity. The ruby laser is an example of a three level laser.

In the original set-up of Maiman, the flashlamp (filled with xenon gas) was connected to a capacitor (see Fig. 27.17) which was charged to a few kilovolts. The energy stored in the capacitor (~a few thousand joules) was discharged through the xenon lamp in a few milliseconds. This results in a power which is ~a few megawatts. Some of this energy is absorbed by the chromium ions resulting in their excitation and subsequent lasing action.

27.3.1 Spiking in Ruby Laser

The flash operation of the lamp leads to a pulsed output of the laser. Even in the short period of a few tens of microseconds in which the ruby is lasing, one finds that the emission is made up of spikes of high intensity emissions as shown

*The Al_2O_3 crystal which serves as a medium to suspend the chromium ions is known as the host crystal. The characteristics of the host crystal affect the laser action and also the broadening of the energy levels of the activator atoms which in this case is chromium. For a good lasing action, the ruby crystal consists of about 0.05% (by weight) of chromium; however, higher concentrations of chromium have also been used. For a detailed discussions of host crystals, see Ref. 27.14.

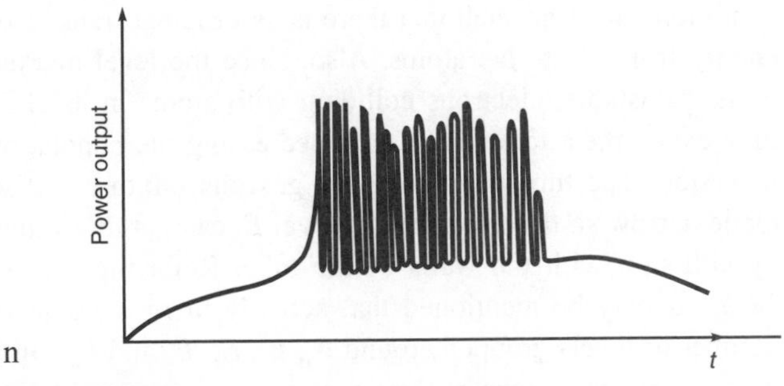

in

Figure 27.20
The characteristic spiking of a ruby laser.

Fig. 27.20. This phenomenon is known as **spiking** and can be understood as follows. When the pump is suddenly switched on to a value much above the threshold, the population inversion builds up and crosses the threshold value, as a consequence of which the photon number builds up rapidly to a value much higher that the steady state value. Since the photon number is higher than the steady state value, the rate at which the upper level depletes (because of stimulated transitions) is much higher than the pump rate. Consequently, the inversion becomes below threshold and the laser action ceases. Thus the emission stops for a few microseconds, within which time the flashlamp again pumps the ground state atoms to the upper level, and laser oscillations begin again. This process repeats itself till the flashlamp power falls below the threshold value and the lasing action stops (see Fig. 27.20).

27.4 The He–Ne Laser 

We will now briefly discuss the He–Ne laser which was first fabricated by Ali Javan and his coworkers at Bell Telephone Laboratories in USA [see Ref. 27.15]. This was also the first gas laser to be operated successfully.

The He–Ne laser consists of a mixture of He and Ne in a ratio of about 10:1, placed inside a long narrow discharge tube (see Figs 27.21 and 27.22). The pressure inside the tube is about 1 Torr.* The gas system is enclosed between a pair of plane mirrors or a pair of concave mirrors so that a resonator system is formed. One of the mirrors is of very high reflectivity while the other is partially transparent so that energy may be coupled out of the system.

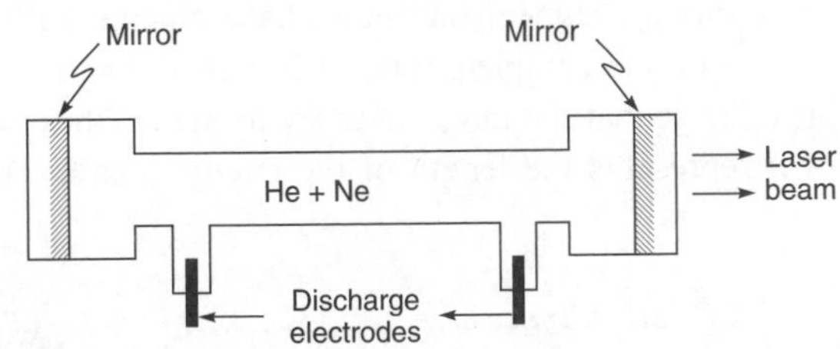
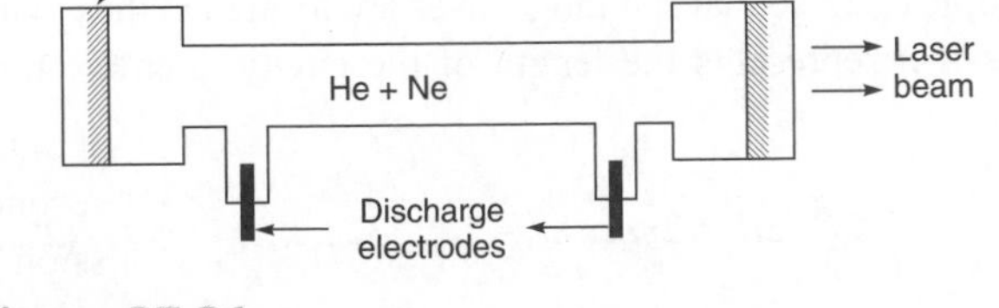

Figure 27.21
The helium–neon laser.

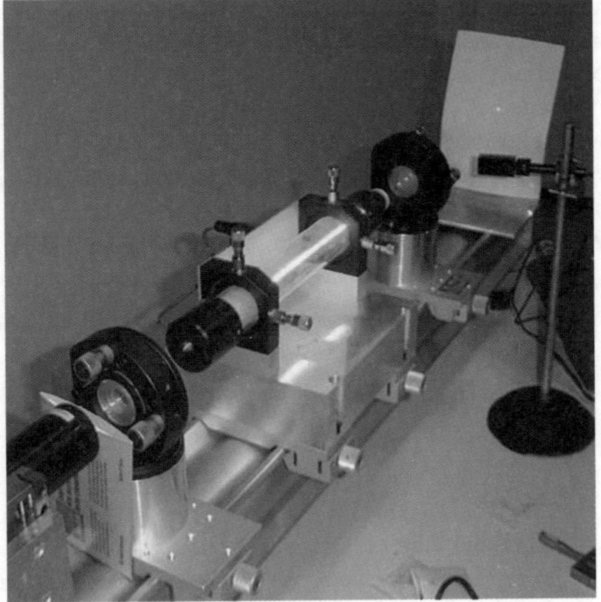

Figure 27.22
A helium-neon laser demonstration at the Kastler-Brossel Laboratory at Univ. Paris 6. The glowing ray in the middle is an electric discharge producing light in much the same way as a neon light. It is the gain medium through which the laser passes, *not* the laser beam itself, which is visible there. The laser beam crosses the air and marks a red point on the screen to the right. [*Photograph by Dr. David Monniaux; used with kind permission of Dr. Monniaux.*].

The first few energy levels of He and Ne atoms are shown in Fig. 27.23. When an electric discharge is passed through the gas, the electrons traveling down the tube collide with the He

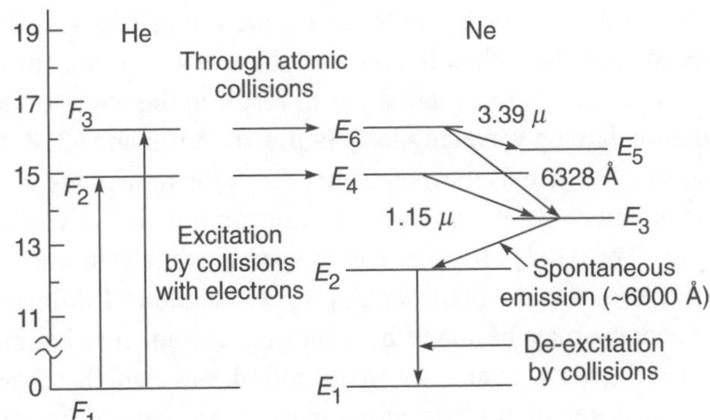

Figure 27.23
Relevant energy levels of helium and neon.

*1 Torr = 1 mm of Hg = 133 Pascal ≈ 133 × 10^{-5} N/m^2; the unit 'Torr' is named after Torricelli, the seventh-century Italian mathematician who invented the mercury manometer.

atoms and excite them (from the ground state F_1) to the levels marked F_2 and F_3. These levels are metastable, i.e., He atoms excited to these states stay in these levels for a sufficiently long time before losing energy through collisions. Through these collisions, the Ne atoms are excited to the levels marked E_4 and E_6 which have nearly the same energy as the levels F_2 and F_3 of He. Thus, when the atoms in levels F_2 and F_3 collide with unexcited Ne atoms, they raise them to the levels E_4 and E_6, respectively. Thus, we have the following two step process:

(a) Helium atom in the ground state F_1 + collision with electron

→ Helium atom in the excited state (F_2 or F_3) + electron with lesser kinetic energy.

(b) The excited states of He (F_2 or F_3) are metastable*—they would not readily lose energy through spontaneous emissions (the radioactive life time of these excited states would be about one hour). However, they can readily lose energy through collisions with Ne atoms:

He atom in the excited state F_3 + Ne atom in the ground state

→ He atom in the ground state + Ne atom in the excited state E_6.

Similarly,

He atom in the excited state F_2 + Ne atom in the ground state

→ He atom in the ground state + Ne atom in the excited state E_4.

This results in a sizeable population of the levels E_4 and E_6. The population in these levels happens to be much more than those in the lower levels E_3 and E_5. Thus a state of population inversion is achieved and any spontaneously emitted photon can trigger laser action in any of the three transitions shown in Fig. 27.23. The Ne atoms then drop down from the lower laser levels to the level E_2 through spontaneous emission. From the level E_2 the Ne atoms are brought back to the ground state through collision with the walls. The transition from E_6 to E_5, E_4 to E_3 and E_6 to E_3 result in the emission of radiation having wavelengths 3.39 μm, 1.15 μm and 6328 Å, respectively. It may be noted that the laser transitions corresponding to 3.39 μm and 1.15 μm are not in the visible region. The 6328 Å transition corresponds to the well-known red light of the He–Ne laser. A proper selection of different frequencies may be made by choosing end mirrors having high reflectivity over only the required wavelength range. The pressures of the two gases must be so chosen that the condition of population inversion is not quenched. Thus, the conditions must be such that there is an efficient transfer of energy from He to Ne atoms. Also, since the level marked E_2 is metastable, electrons colliding with atoms in level E_2 may excite them to level E_3, thus decreasing the population inversion. The tube containing the gaseous mixture is also made narrow so that Ne atoms in level E_2 can get de-excited by collision with the walls of the tube. Referring to Fig. 27.23, it may be mentioned that actually there are a large number of levels grouped around E_2, E_3, E_4, E_5 and E_6. Only those levels are shown in the figure which correspond to the important laser transitions.**

Gas lasers are, in general, found to emit light, which is more directional and more monochromatic. This is because of the absence of such effects as crystalline imperfection, thermal distortion and scattering, which are present in solid-state lasers. Gas lasers are capable of operating continuously without need for cooling.

27.5 Optical Resonators

LO3

In Sec. 27.1, we had briefly discussed that a light beam passing through a suitable medium with population inversion may be amplified. In order to construct an oscillator, which can supply light energy and act as a source of light, one must couple a part of the output back into the medium. This can be achieved by placing the active medium between two mirrors which reflect most of the **output energy** back to the system—see Fig. 27.3. Such a system of two mirrors represents a *resonant cavity*.

Now, in order to obtain an output beam, one of the mirrors is made partially reflecting. Thus, imagine a wave that starts from one of the mirrors and travels towards the other. In passing through the active medium, it gets amplified. If the second mirror is partially reflecting, then the wave is partially transmitted and the rest reflected back towards the first mirror. In traveling to the first mirror, it again gets amplified and returns to the position it has started from. Thus, in between the two mirrors, we have waves propagating along both directions. For resonance, it is necessary that when a wave returns after one round trip, it is in phase with the existing wave. For this to happen, the total phase change suffered by the wave in one complete round trip must be an integral multiple of 2π so that standing waves are formed in the cavity. Thus if d represents the length of the cavity, then we may write

$$\frac{2\pi}{\lambda} 2d = 2m\pi;\ m = 1, 2, 3, \ldots\ldots \tag{27.2}$$

*The spectroscopic states corresponding to the states F_1, F_2 and F_3 are 1^1S_0, 2^3S_1 and 2^1S_0, respectively.

**Further details on He–Ne Laser can be found in Refs. 27.16 and 27.17.

where λ is the wavelength of the radiation in the medium enclosed by the cavity; if n_0 represents the refractive index of the medium enclosed by the cavity then

$$\lambda = \frac{\lambda_0}{n_0} \tag{27.3}$$

If we put $\lambda_0 = c/v$, Eq. (27.2) gives

$$v = v_m = m\frac{c}{2n_0 d} \tag{27.4}$$

which gives the discrete frequencies of oscillation of the modes. If we assume

$$n_0 \approx 1$$

(like in a He–Ne laser), Eq. (27.4) simplifies to

$$v = v_m = m\frac{c}{2d} \tag{27.5}$$

Different values of m lead to different oscillation frequencies, which constitute the longitudinal modes of the cavity; for further details and for reasons why they are known as longitudinal modes the reader is referred to any textbook on lasers*. The frequency difference between adjacent longitudinal modes is given by

$$\delta v = \frac{c}{2d} \tag{27.6}$$

Returning to Eq. (27.4), we would like to mention that for a practical optical resonator, m is a very large number. For example, for an optical resonator of length $d \approx 60$ cm operating at an optical frequency of $v \approx 5 \times 10^{14}$ Hz (corresponding to $\lambda \approx 6000$ Å), we obtain

$$m \approx \frac{5\times10^{14}\times 2\times 60}{3\times10^{10}} = 2 \times 10^6$$

Equation (27.4) tells us that the cavity will support only those frequencies for which the round trip phase shift is an integral multiple of 2π. We may mention here that an open resonator consisting of two plane mirrors facing each other is nothing but the Fabry–Perot interferometer discussed in Sections 15.3 and 15.4; the main difference is that in a Fabry–Perot interferometer, the spacing between the mirrors is small compared to the transverse dimension of the mirrors while in an optical resonator, the converse is true. Now, in Sec. 15.3, we had shown that for a light beam incident normally on a Fabry–Perot interferometer, transmission resonances occur when

$$\delta = \frac{4\pi d}{\lambda_0} = 2m\pi \text{ ; } m = 1, 2, 3, \ldots\ldots \tag{27.7}$$

where we have assumed $n_0 = 1$ and $\cos\theta = 1$ since we have assumed normal incidence. Comparing Eqs. (27.2) and (27.7) we readily observe that transmission resonances occur for the modes of the cavity.

*See, e.g., Refs. 27.4, 27.9, 27.14, 27.16 and 27.17.

EXAMPLE 27.1 Consider a light beam of central frequency $v = v_0 = 6 \times 10^{14}$ Hz and a spectral width of 7000 MHz incident normally on a resonator as shown in Fig. 27.24 with $n_0 = 1$, $d = 10$ cm. The spacing of two adjacent modes will be

$$\delta v = \frac{c}{2d} = 1500 \text{ MHz} \tag{27.8}$$

Thus the output beam will have frequencies

$$v_0 - 2\delta v,\ v_0 - \delta v,\ v_0,\ v_0 + \delta v \text{ and } v_0 + 2\delta v \tag{27.9}$$

corresponding to

$$m = 399998, 399999, 400000, 400001 \text{ and } 400002 \tag{27.10}$$

respectively. In the above example, if the reflectivity of one of the mirrors $R = 0.95$ and if output power corresponding to one of the modes is 1 mW, then the corresponding power *inside* the cavity will be = 1 mW/(1 – 0.95) = 20 mW.

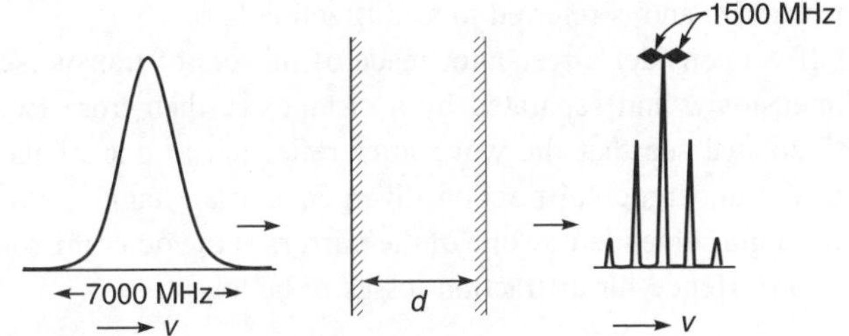

Figure 27.24
A light beam of central frequency $v = v_0 = 6\times10^{14}$ Hz and a spectral width of 7000 MHz is incident normally on a resonator. The output beam corresponds to the resonant frequencies of the optical cavity.

Figure 27.25 shows the output of a typical multilongitudinal mode (MLM) laser. The wavelength spacing of two adjacent modes is about 0.005 μm.

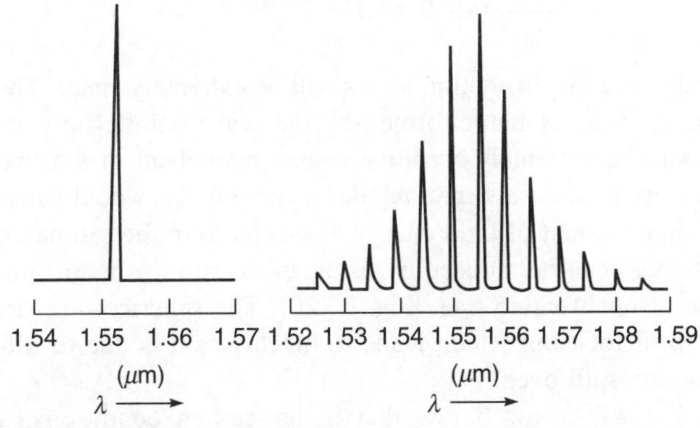

Figure 27.25
The output of a single longitudinal mode laser (a) and of a typical multilongitudinal mode (MLM) laser. (b) [*Adapted from Ref. 27.18*].

In obtaining Eq. (27.4) for the various oscillating frequencies, we have assumed that a plane wave can propagate to and fro unmodified inside the resonator. This would not be true in practice since the mirrors of any practical resonator system have finite transverse dimensions and hence only that portion of the wave which strikes the mirror would get reflected; the portion of the wave lying outside the transverse dimension of the mirror would be lost from the resonator. The wave which travels back to the first mirror has now finite transverse dimensions, determined by the transverse dimensions of the mirror. As we have seen in Chapters 17 and 19, a beam with a finite transverse dimension diffracts as it propagates. Thus, when the beam comes back to the first mirror, it would have a larger transverse dimension than the mirror. Further, since only that portion of the wave that is intercepted by the mirror would be reflected; the remaining portion lying outside the mirror would be lost. This loss constitutes a basic loss mechanism and is referred to as diffraction loss.

If we consider a resonator made of mirrors of transverse dimension a and separated by a distance d, then from Eq. (17.26) we see that the wave after reflection at one of the mirrors undergoes diffraction divergence at an angle $\sim \lambda/a$. The angle subtended by one of the mirrors at the other mirror is $\sim a/d$. Hence for diffraction losses to be low,

$$\frac{\lambda}{a} << \frac{a}{d}$$

or

$$\frac{a^2}{\lambda d} >> 1 \qquad \textbf{(27.11)}$$

The quantity $a^2/\lambda d$ is known as the Fresnel number. As an example, if the resonator mirrors have transverse dimension of 1 cm and are separated by 60 cm, then for a wavelength of 5000 Å, we have

$$\frac{a^2}{\lambda d} \approx 330 >> 1$$

and hence the diffraction losses will be extremely small. The losses in a resonator formed by the plane parallel mirrors would be extremely sensitive to the parallelism of the two mirrors because a slight angular misalignment would cause a large amount of light energy to escape from the resonator. The loss can be reduced by using spherical mirrors to form the resonant cavity (see Fig. 27.26). The spherical mirrors help in focusing which leads to much less loss due to diffraction spill over.

We will show below that under certain conditions, a Gaussian beam with the appropriate spot size will resonate between the mirrors of the resonator system shown in Fig. 27.26. This is known as a (transverse) mode of the cavity; for more details see Chapter 7 of Ref. 27.4.

We consider a general spherical resonator consisting of two mirrors of radii of curvatures R_1 and R_2 separated by a distance d (see Fig. 27.26). The radius of curvature is

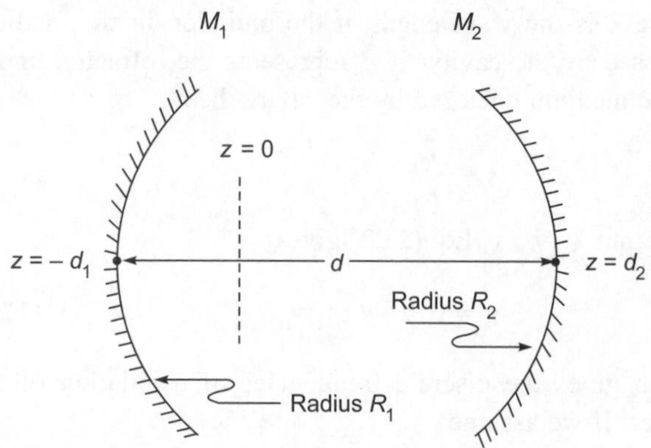

Figure 27.26
A resonator consisting of two spherical mirrors.

assumed to be positive if the mirror is concave towards the resonator and negative if it is convex towards the resonator. We will now derive the condition for the resonator to be stable or unstable.

We consider a Gaussian beam propagating along the z-direction and whose amplitude distribution on the plane $z = 0$ is given by

$$u(x,y,0) = a \exp\left[-\frac{x^2+y^2}{w_0^2}\right] \qquad \textbf{(27.12)}$$

Thus the phase front is plane at $z = 0$. In Sec. 19.5 (and Appendix B), we have shown that as the Gaussian beam propagates along the z-direction, the intensity distribution remains Gaussian:

$$I(x, y, z) = \frac{I_0}{\left(1+\frac{z^2}{\alpha}\right)} \exp\left[-\frac{2(x^2+y^2)}{w^2(z)}\right] \qquad \textbf{(27.13)}$$

$$\text{where} \quad w(z) = w_0\sqrt{1+\frac{z^2}{\alpha}} \quad \text{and} \quad \alpha = \frac{\pi^2 w_0^4}{\lambda^2} \qquad \textbf{(27.14)}$$

Also as the beam propagates, the radius of curvature of the wavefront is given by (see Sec. 19.5 and Appendix B):

$$R(z) = z + \frac{\alpha}{z} \qquad \textbf{(27.15)}$$

Let the poles of the mirrors M_1 and M_2 be at $z = z_1 = -d_1$ and at $z = z_2 = +d_2$, respectively. We are assuming the origin somewhere between the mirrors so that both d_1 and d_2 are positive quantities. Thus, the distance between the two mirrors is given by

$$d = d_1 + d_2$$

Now, for the Gaussian beam to resonate between the two mirrors, the radii of the phase front (at the mirrors) should be equal to the radii of curvatures of the mirrors:

$$-R_1 = -d_1 - \frac{\alpha}{d_1} \quad \text{and} \quad R_2 = d_2 + \frac{\alpha}{d_2}$$

In such a case, the Gaussian beam would be normally incident on the mirrors and hence will retrace its path to the other mirror where it is normally incident. Thus such a Gaussian beam can resonate in the resonator and would form a mode of the resonator.

With the sign convention mentioned earlier, for the type of mirrors shown in Fig. 27.26, both R_1 and R_2 are positive. Thus,

$$\alpha = d_1(R_1 - d_1) = d_2(R_2 - d_2)$$

If we use the relation $d_2 = d - d_1$, we would readily get

$$d_1 = \frac{(R_2 - d)d}{R_1 + R_2 - 2d} \quad \text{and} \quad d_2 = \frac{(R_1 - d)d}{R_1 + R_2 - 2d}$$

We define

$$g_1 = 1 - \frac{d}{R_1} \quad \text{and} \quad g_2 = 1 - \frac{d}{R_2} \tag{27.16}$$

From the above equations we may write $R_1 = \frac{d}{1 - g_1}$ and $R_2 = \frac{d}{1 - g_2}$ and we obtain

$$d_1 = \frac{g_2(1 - g_1)d}{g_1 + g_2 - 2g_1g_2} \quad \text{and} \quad d_2 = \frac{g_1(1 - g_2)d}{g_1 + g_2 - 2g_1g_2} \tag{22.17}$$

Thus,

$$\alpha = d_1(R_1 - d_1) = \frac{g_1g_2 d^2(1 - g_1g_2)}{(g_1 + g_2 - 2g_1g_2)^2} \tag{27.18}$$

Since $\alpha = \frac{\pi^2 w_0^4}{\lambda^2}$, we get for the spot size at the waist

$$w_0^2 = \frac{\lambda d}{\pi |g_1 + g_2 - 2g_1g_2|} \sqrt{g_1g_2(1 - g_1g_2)} \tag{27.19}$$

For w_0 to be real we must have $0 \le g_1g_2 \le 1$, or

$$0 \le \left(1 - \frac{d}{R_1}\right)\left(1 - \frac{d}{R_2}\right) \le 1 \tag{27.20}$$

where R_1 and R_2 are the radii of curvatures of the mirrors. The above equation represents the stability condition for a resonator consisting of two spherical mirrors. Figure 27.27 shows the stability diagram and the shaded region correspond to stable resonator configurations. Figure 27.28 shows different resonator configurations.

The spot sizes of the Gaussian beam at the two mirrors are given by

$$w^2(z_1) = \frac{\lambda d}{\pi} \sqrt{\frac{g_2}{g_1(1 - g_1g_2)}} \tag{27.21}$$

and

$$w^2(z_2) = \frac{\lambda d}{\pi} \sqrt{\frac{g_1}{g_2(1 - g_1g_2)}} \tag{27.22}$$

Since most of the energy in a Gaussian beam is contained within a radius of about twice the beam width, if the transverse dimensions of the mirrors are large compared to the spot sizes at the mirrors, then most of the energy is reflected back and the loss due to diffraction spill over from the edges of the mirrors is small. It can be easily seen from Eqs. (27.21) and (27.22) that when $g_1g_2 \to 0$ or $g_1g_2 \to 1$, $w(z_1)$ or $w(z_2)$ or both become very large and our analysis would not remain valid.

EXAMPLE 27.2 We consider a simple resonator configuration consisting of a plane mirror and a spherical mirror separated by a distance d (see Fig. 27.29); indeed such a configuration is used to produce a single transverse mode oscillation in a ruby laser. Thus $R_1 = \infty$ and $R_2 = R$ giving $g_1 = 1$ and $g_2 = 1 - d/R$. Simple manipulation of the above equation gives

$$w_0^2 = \frac{\lambda d}{\pi} \sqrt{\left(\frac{R}{d} - 1\right)} \tag{27.23}$$

Thus,

$$R = d\left(1 + \frac{\pi^2 w_0^4}{\lambda^2 d^2}\right) \tag{27.24}$$

EXAMPLE 27.3 For a typical He-Ne laser (λ = 0.6328 µm) we may have d = 50 cm and R = 100 cm (see Fig. 27.29), giving $g_1 = 1$ and $g_2 = 0.5$, and the resonator configuration is well within the shaded region of Fig. 27.27 and is very much stable. Further, $g_1g_2 = 0.5$ and w_0 = 0.32 mm. If we increase R to 200 cm, we will get w_0 = 0.38 mm. For $R < d$, w_0 will become imaginary and the resonator will become unstable.

EXAMPLE 27.4 We next consider another resonator configuration consisting of two spherical mirrors separated by a distance d = 150 cm with R_1 = 100 cm and R_2 = 75 cm, giving $g_1 = -0.5$, $g_2 = -1.0$ and $g_1g_2 = 0.5$. Thus the values of g_1 and g_2 are such that the resonator configuration is well within the shaded region of Fig. 27.27 and is very much stable. For λ = 1 µm one can readily show that w_0 = 0.31 mm.

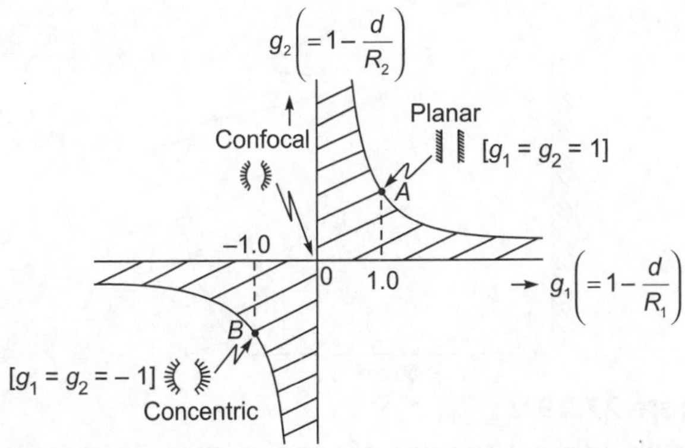

Figure 27.27
The stability diagram for optical resonators. The shaded region corresponds to stable configurations.

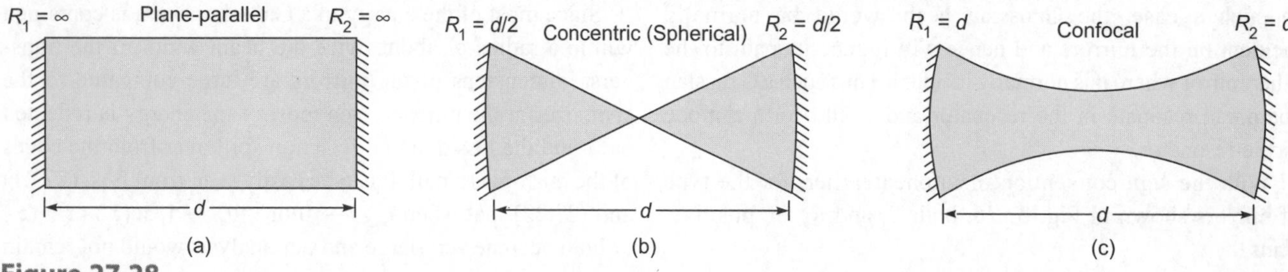

Figure 27.28

Different configurations of the optical resonator.

EXAMPLE 27.5 When $g_1 = g_2 = g$, Eq. (27.19) simplifies to

$$w_0^2 = \frac{\lambda d}{2\pi}\sqrt{\frac{1+g}{1-g}} \quad (27.25)$$

The symmetric concentric resonator will correspond to $R_1 = R_2 = d/2$ so that the centers of curvature of both mirrors are at the center [see Fig. 27.28]. Thus $g_1 = g_2 = -1$ and $g_1g_2 = 1$ and w_0 becomes zero! The symmetric confocal resonator will correspond to $R_1 = R_2 = d$ and $g_1 = g_2 = 0$. Thus $g_1g_2 = 0$ and

$$w_0 = \sqrt{\frac{\lambda d}{\pi}} \quad (27.26)$$

Finally, for plane parallel mirrors $R_1 = R_2 = \infty$, $g_1 = g_2 = 1$ and w_0 becomes infinity!!! All three configurations discussed above (concentric, confocal and planar) lie on the boundary of the stability diagram so that a small variation of the parameters can make the system unstable and will have very large loss.

If one chooses a closed resonator system, then the number of modes (which can get amplified and which can oscillate in a resonator of practical dimensions) becomes so large that the output would be far from monochromatic. In order to overcome this problem, one uses open resonators where the number of modes (which can oscillate) is only a few and even single mode oscillation is possible; furthermore, the open sides of the resonator can be used for optical pumping as in ruby lasers. Because of the open nature of the resonator, all modes have a finite loss due to the diffraction spillover of energy at the mirrors. In addition to this basic loss, scattering from the laser medium, absorption at the mirrors and output coupling at the mirrors also contribute to the cavity loss. One can visualize a mode as a wave having a well-defined transverse amplitude distribution which forms a standing wave pattern. In an actual laser, the modes that keep oscillating are those for which the gain provided by the laser medium compensates for the losses. When the laser oscillates in steady state, the losses are exactly compensated for by the gain. Since the gain provided by the medium depends on the extent of population inversion, for each mode there is a critical value of population inversion (known as the *threshold population inversion*) below which that particular mode would cease to oscillate in the laser.

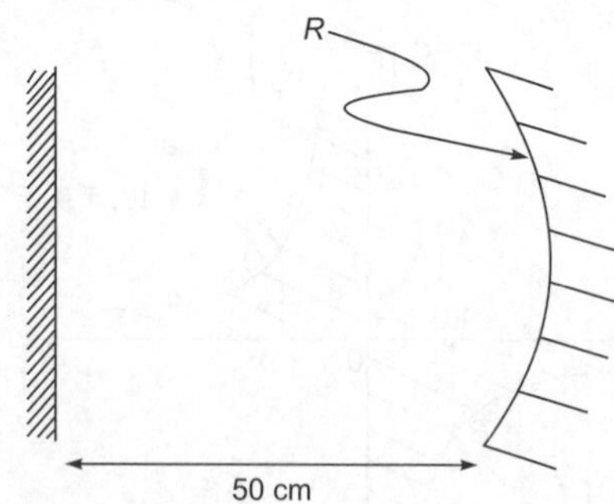

Figure 27.29

A simple resonator consisting of a plane mirror and a concave mirror of radius R [see Eq. (27.24)].

27.6 Einstein Coefficients and Optical Amplification

LO4

The consideration which led Einstein to the prediction of stimulated emission was the description of thermodynamic equilibrium between atoms and the radiation field. Consider an atom having two states. Let N_1 and N_2 be the number of atoms (per unit volume) in states 1 and 2, respectively; the levels correspond to energies E_1 and E_2 (see Fig. 27.30). As mentioned earlier, an atom in the lower energy level

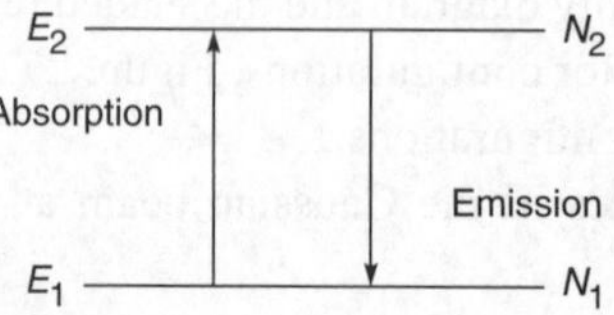

Figure 27.30

E_1 and E_2 represent the energy levels of an atom. N_1 and N_2 represent the number of atoms (per unit volume) in the energy levels E_1 and E_2, respectively.

can absorb radiation and get excited to the level E_2. This excitation process can occur only in the presence of radiation. The rate of absorption depends on the density of radiation at the particular frequency corresponding to the energy separation of the two levels. Thus, if

$$E_2 - E_1 = \hbar\omega \quad \textbf{(27.27)}$$

then the absorption process depends on the energy density of radiation at the frequency ω; this energy density is denoted by $u(\omega)$ and is defined such that

$u(\omega)\,d\omega$ = Radiation energy per unit volume within the frequency interval ω and $\omega + d\omega$.

The rate of absorption is proportional to N_1 and also to $u(\omega)$. Thus, we may write

$$\text{Number of absorptions per unit volume per unit time} = N_1 B_{12}\, u(\omega) \quad \textbf{(27.28)}$$

where B_{12} is the coefficient of proportionality and is a characteristic of the energy levels.

Let us now consider the reverse process namely the emission of radiation at a frequency ω when the atom de-excites from the level E_2 to E_1. As mentioned in Sec. 27.1, an atom in an excited level can make a radiative transition to a lower energy level either through spontaneous emission or through stimulated emission. In spontaneous emission, the probability per unit time of the atom making a downward transition is independent of the energy density of the radiation field and depends only on the levels involved in the transition. The rate of spontaneous transitions (per unit volume) from level E_2 to E_1 is proportional to N_2 and thus

$$\frac{dN_2}{dt} = -A_{21}N_2 = -\frac{N_2}{t_{sp}} \quad \textbf{(27.29)}$$

where A_{21} represents the coefficient of proportionality and is known as the **Einstein *A* coefficient** and depends on the energy level pair and

$$t_{sp} = \frac{1}{A_{21}} \quad \textbf{(27.30)}$$

represents the spontaneous emission lifetime of the upper level. The solution of Eq. (27.29) is given by

$$N_2(t) = N_2(0)\, e^{-\frac{t}{t_{sp}}} \quad \textbf{(27.31)}$$

implying that the population of level 2 reduces by $1/e$ in a time t_{sp}. For example, for the $2P \rightarrow 1S$ transition in hydrogen atom $A \approx 6 \times 10^8\ \text{s}^{-1}$ giving a mean lifetime ($\approx 1/A$) of about 1.6×10^{-9} s.* In the case of stimulated emission, the rate of transition to the lower energy level is directly proportional to the number of atoms in the upper energy level as well as to the energy density of the radiation at the frequency ω. Thus,

$$\text{Number of stimulated emissions (per unit time per unit volume)} = N_2 B_{21}\, u(\omega)$$

with B_{21} representing the corresponding proportionality constant. The quantities A_{21}, B_{12} and B_{21} are known as Einstein coefficients and are determined by the atomic system. At thermal equilibrium, the number of upward transitions must be equal to the number of downward transitions. Thus, we may write (at thermal equilibrium):

$$N_1B_{12}u(\omega) = N_2A_{21} + N_2B_{21}u(\omega)$$

or

$$u(\omega) = \frac{A_{21}}{\dfrac{N_1}{N_2}B_{12} - B_{21}} \quad \textbf{(27.32)}$$

Now according to a fundamental principle in thermodynamics, at thermal equilibrium, we have the following expression for the ratio of the populations of two levels:

$$\frac{N_1}{N_2} = \exp\left[\frac{E_2 - E_1}{k_BT}\right] = \exp\left[\frac{\hbar\omega}{k_BT}\right] \quad \textbf{(27.33)}$$

where k_B ($= 1.38 \times 10^{-23}$ J/K) represents the Boltzmann constant and T represents the absolute temperature. Equation (27.23) is known as the **Boltzmann's law**. Thus, we may write

$$u(\omega) = \frac{A_{21}}{B_{12}e^{\hbar\omega/(k_BT)} - B_{21}} \quad \textbf{(27.34)}$$

Now, at thermal equilibrium, the radiation energy density is given by Planck's law:

$$u(\omega) = \frac{\hbar\omega^3 n_0^3}{\pi^2c^3}\frac{1}{e^{\hbar\omega/(k_BT)} - 1} \quad \textbf{(27.35)}$$

where n_0 represents the refractive index of the medium. Comparing Eqs. (27.34) and (27.35), we obtain

$$B_{12} = B_{21} = B \quad \text{(say)} \quad \textbf{(27.36)}$$

and

$$\frac{A_{21}}{B_{21}} = \frac{\hbar\omega^3 n_0^3}{\pi^2c^3} \quad \textbf{(27.37)}$$

Notice that if we had not assumed the presence of stimulated emission we would not have been able to arrive at an expression for $u(\omega)$; Einstein in 1917 had predicted the existence of stimulated emission which was later confirmed by rigorous quantum theory. (see, e.g., Chapters 28 and 29 of Ref. 27.19).

It may be noted that at thermal equilibrium the ratio of the number of spontaneous to stimulated emissions is given by

$$\frac{A_{21}}{B_{21}\,u(\omega)} = e^{\hbar\omega/(k_BT)} - 1 \quad \textbf{(27.38)}$$

* See, e.g., Chapters 28 and 29 of Ref. 27.19.

We may note the following two important points:

(a) For normal optical source, $T \sim 10^3$ K with $\omega \approx 3 \times 10^{15}$ s^{-1} (corresponding to $\lambda \approx 6000$ Å) we have

$$\frac{\hbar\omega}{k_B T} \approx \frac{1.054\times10^{-34}\,(\text{J}-\text{s})\times3\times10^{15}\,\text{s}^{-1}}{1.38\times10^{-23}\,(\text{J/°K})\times10^{3}\,(\text{K})} \approx 23$$

giving

$$\frac{A_{21}}{B_{21}\,u(\omega)} = 10^{10}$$

Thus, when the atoms are in thermal equilibrium, the emission (at optical frequencies) is predominantly due to spontaneous transitions and hence the emission from ordinary light sources is incoherent.

(b) From Eq. (27.37), one can see that the coefficient B_{21} is inversely proportional to ω^3 implying that laser action would become more difficult as we go to higher frequencies.

27.6.1 Population Inversion

In the previous section, we had assumed that the atom is capable of interacting with radiation of a particular frequency ω. However, if one observes the spectrum of the radiation due to spontaneous emissions from a collection of atoms, one finds that the radiation is not monochromatic but is spread over a certain frequency range. This would imply that energy levels have widths and atoms can interact over a range of frequencies. As an example, in Fig. 27.31, we have shown that the 2*P* level of hydrogen atom has a certain width $\Delta E\,(= \hbar\Delta\omega)$ so that the atom can absorb/emit radiation over a range of frequencies $\Delta\omega$. For the $2P \rightarrow 1S$ transition

$$\Delta E \approx 4\times10^{-7}\ \text{eV} \quad \Rightarrow \quad \Delta\omega \approx 6\times10^{8}\ \text{s}^{-1}$$

Since $\omega_0 \approx 1.55\times10^{16}$ s^{-1} (see Sec. 25.2), we get

$$\frac{\Delta\omega}{\omega_0} \approx 4\times10^{-8}$$

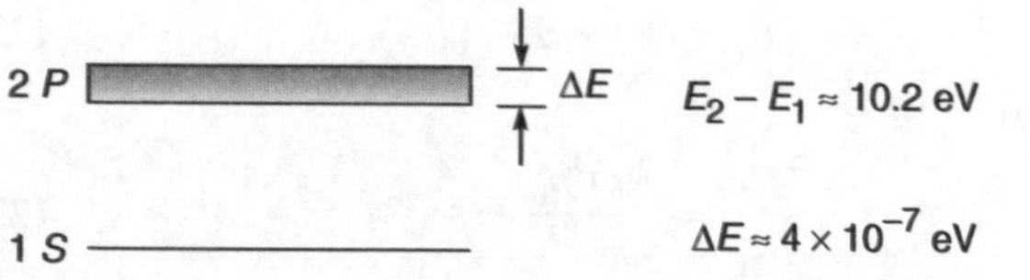

Figure 27.31
The 2*P* level of hydrogen atom has a certain width $\Delta E\,(= \hbar\Delta\omega)$ so that the atom can absorb/emit radiation over a range of frequencies $\Delta\omega$.

Thus, in general, $\Delta\omega << \omega_0$ showing the spectral purity of the source. We introduce the normalized line shape function $g(\omega)$ such that

Number of spontaneous emissions/unit time/unit volume so that the emitted frequency lies between ω and $\omega + d\omega$

$$= N_2 A_{21}\, g(\omega)\, d\omega$$

Similarly,

Number of stimulated emissions/unit time/unit volume so that the emitted frequency lies between ω and $\omega + d\omega$

$$= N_2 B_{21} u(\omega)\, g(\omega)\, d\omega$$

Number of stimulated absorptions/unit time/unit volume so that the absorbed frequency lies between ω and $\omega + d\omega$

$$= N_1 B_{12} u(\omega)\, g(\omega)\, d\omega$$

Thus, the total number of stimulated emissions/unit time/unit volume will be given by

$$W_{21} = N_2 \int_0^\infty B_{21}\, u(\omega)\, g(\omega)\, d\omega$$

$$= N_2 \frac{\pi^2 c^3}{\hbar t_{sp} n_0^3} \int_0^\infty \frac{u(\omega)}{\omega^3}\, g(\omega)\, d\omega$$

where we have used Eqs. (27.37) and (27.30). Now, for a near monochromatic radiation field (as it is indeed the case for the laser), $u(\omega)$ is very sharply peaked at a particular value of ω (say ω') and in carrying out the above integration, $g(\omega)/\omega^3$ can be assumed to be essentially constant over the region where $u(\omega)$ is appreciable to give

$$W_{21} \approx N_2 \frac{\pi^2 c^3}{\hbar t_{sp} n_0^3} \frac{g(\omega')}{\omega'^3} U \qquad (27.39)$$

where $g(\omega')$ represents the value of the line–shape function evaluated at the radiation frequency ω' and U represents the energy density associated with the radiation field:*

$$U = \int_0^\infty u(\omega)\, d\omega \qquad (27.40)$$

Now the energy density U and the intensity I_ω are related through the following equation** [sec See. 23.5]

$$I_\omega = vU = \frac{c}{n_0} U \qquad (27.41)$$

where $v\ (= c/n_0)$ represents the velocity of the radiation field in the medium, n_0 being its refractive index. [The quantity I_ω

*The argument essentially implies

$$u(\omega) \approx U\,\delta(\omega - \omega')$$

where $\delta(\omega - \omega')$ represents the Dirac–delta function.

**This is analogous to the equation $J = \rho v$, where ρ represents the number of particles per unit volume (all propagating with velocity v) and J represents the number of particles crossing a unit area perpendicular to the direction of propagation per unit time. This can be easily seen from the fact that the number of particles crossing a unit area per unit time would be those contained in a cylinder of length v units with unit area of crosssection.

represents energy per unit area per unit time, the MKS units of I_ω would therefore be $Jm^{-2}s^{-1}$; we may mention that the quantity U is denoted by $\langle u \rangle$ in Sec. 22.6]. Thus, the total number of stimulated emissions/unit time/unit volume will be given by

$$W_{21} = N_2 \frac{\pi^2 c^2}{\hbar t_{sp} n_0^2} \frac{g(\omega)}{\omega^3} I_\omega \tag{27.42}$$

where we have dropped the prime on ω. Similarly, the number of stimulated absorptions per unit time per unit volume would be given by

$$W_{12} = N_1 \frac{\pi^2 c^2}{\hbar t_{sp} n_0^2} \frac{g(\omega)}{\omega^3} I_\omega \tag{27.43}$$

We next consider a collection of atoms and let a near monochromatic beam of frequency ω be propagating through it along the z-direction. In order to obtain an expression for the rate of change of the intensity of the beam as it propagates, we consider two planes of area S perpendicular to the z-direction at z and $z + dz$ (see Fig. 27.32). The volume of the medium between planes P_1 and P_2 is $S\,dz$ and hence the number of stimulated absorptions per unit time is $W_{12}\,S\,dz$. Since each photon has an energy $\hbar\omega$, the energy absorbed per unit time in the volume element $S\,dz$ is

$$W_{12}\,\hbar\omega S\,dz$$

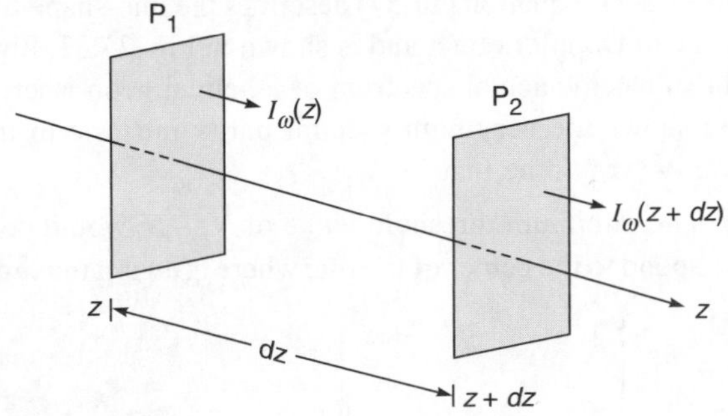

Figure 27.32
Electromagnetic wave propagating along the z-direction through a collection of atoms.

Similarly the corresponding energy gain (because of stimulated emissions) is

$$W_{21}\,\hbar\omega S\,dz$$

where we have neglected the radiation arising out of spontaneous emissions, because such radiations propagate in random directions and are, in general, lost from the beam. Thus, the net amount of energy absorbed per unit time in the volume element $S\,dz$ is

$$(W_{12} - W_{21})\,\hbar\omega S\,dz$$

If $I_\omega(z)$ represents the intensity of the beam in the plane P_1, then the total energy entering the volume element $S\,dz$ per unit time is

$$I_\omega(z)S$$

Similarly, if $I_\omega(z + dz)$ represents the intensity in the plane P_2, then the total energy leaving the volume element per unit time is

$$I_\omega(z + dz)S = I_\omega(z)S + \frac{\partial I_\omega}{\partial z}\,dz\,S$$

Hence, the net amount of energy leaving the volume element per unit time is

$$\frac{\partial I_\omega}{\partial z}\,dz\,S$$

This must be equal to the negative of the energy absorbed by the medium between z and $z + dz$. Thus,

$$\frac{\partial I_\omega}{\partial z} S\,dz = -(W_{12} - W_{21})\,\hbar\omega S\,dz$$

$$= -\frac{\pi^2 c^2}{\hbar t_{sp}\,\omega^3 n_0^2}\, g(\omega) I_\omega \hbar\omega S\,dz\,(N_1 - N_2)$$

or

$$\frac{1}{I_\omega}\frac{\partial I_\omega}{\partial z} = \gamma \tag{27.44}$$

where

$$\gamma = \frac{\pi^2 c^2}{\omega^2 t_{sp}\, n_0^2}(N_2 - N_1) g(\omega) \tag{27.45}$$

Since the line shape function $g(\omega)$ is very sharply peaked (see Sec. 27.7), the function γ is also a sharply peaked function. Equation (27.44) can be readily integrated to give*

$$I_\omega(z) = I_\omega(0)\, e^{\gamma z} \tag{27.46}$$

Thus if $N_1 > N_2$, γ is negative and the intensity of the beam decreases exponentially with z; the intensity decreasing to $1/e$ of its value at $z = 0$ in a distance $1/|\gamma|$. Hence at thermal equilibrium, since the number of atoms in the lower level is greater than that in the upper level, the intensity of the beam (as it propagates through the medium) decreases exponentially. On the other hand, if there are more atoms in the higher energy level than in the lower level, (i.e., if there is a population inversion) then $\gamma > 0$ and there would be an exponential increase in intensity of the beam; this is known as **light amplification**.

27.6.2 Cavity Lifetime

In an actual laser system, the active medium (which is capable of amplification) is placed between a pair of mirrors forming what is known as a *resonator* (see Sec. 27.5). In order that

* In obtaining Eq. (27.47) from Eq. (27.44), it has been assumed that $N_1 - N_2$ (and hence γ) is independent of I_ω. Such an approximation is valid only for small values of I_ω. For intense light beams (when I_ω becomes very large) saturation of the levels set in and the attenuation is linear rather than exponential (see, for example, Ref. 27.4, Secs. 4.2 and 4.3).

oscillations be sustained in the cavity, it is essential that the net losses suffered by the beam be compensated for by the gain of the medium. At threshold and under steady state operation, the two are exactly compensated. In order to obtain the threshold condition, we first calculate the passive cavity lifetime t_c which is the time in which the energy $W(t)$ in the (passive) cavity decreases by a factor $1/e$ in the absence of the amplifying medium:

$$W(t) = W(0) \exp[-t/t_c] \tag{27.47}$$

Let d represent the length of the active medium. In one round trip, the beam traverses a distance $2d$ through the active medium and gets attenuated by a factor

$$R_1R_2 \exp[-2\alpha_c d]$$

where R_1 and R_2 are the reflectivities of the mirrors at the two ends of the resonator and the term $\exp[-2\alpha_c d]$ represents losses caused by absorption, scattering, diffraction, etc. Now the time taken for one round trip is given by

$$t = \frac{2d}{c/n_0}$$

Thus

$$\exp\left[-\frac{2d}{(c/n_0)t_c}\right] = R_1R_2 \exp[-2\alpha_c d] \tag{27.48}$$

giving the following expression for the passive cavity lifetime:

$$\frac{1}{t_c} = \frac{c/n_0}{2d}[2\alpha_c d - \ln(R_1R_2)] \tag{27.49}$$

It can be easily seen that the cavity lifetime can also be expressed as

$$t_c = \frac{2n_0 d}{c \ln\left(\frac{1}{1-x}\right)} \tag{27.50}$$

where

$$x = 1 - R_1R_2 e^{-2\alpha_c d} \tag{27.51}$$

is the fractional loss per round trip.

27.6.3 Threshold Condition

Now, because of population inversion, in one round trip, the beam gets amplified by a factor $\exp(2\gamma d)$ and therefore, for the laser oscillation to begin, we must have

$$e^{2\gamma d}\left[R_1R_2 e^{-2\alpha_c d}\right] \geq 1 \tag{27.52}$$

which can be rewritten in the form

$$e^{2\gamma d} \cdot \exp\left[-\frac{2d}{(c/n_0)t_c}\right] \geq 1$$

or

$$\gamma \geq \frac{1}{(c/n_0)t_c} \tag{27.53}$$

Substituting for γ from Eq. (27.45), we get

$$(N_2 - N_1) \geq \frac{\omega^2 n_0^3 t_{sp}}{\pi^2 c^3 t_c g(\omega)} \tag{27.54}$$

The equality sign in the above equation gives the threshold population inversion required for the oscillation of the laser. Thus, for the frequency ω, the threshold population inversion is given by

$$(N_2 - N_1)_{th} = \frac{\omega^2 n_0^3 t_{sp}}{\pi^2 c^3 t_c g(\omega)} \tag{27.55}$$

Now, as we will show in the next section, for a He–Ne laser, $g(\omega)$ is given by

$$g(\omega)d\omega = \frac{2}{\Delta\omega_D}\left(\frac{\ln 2}{\pi}\right)^{\frac{1}{2}} \exp\left[-4\ln 2\frac{(\omega-\omega_0)^2}{(\Delta\omega_D)^2}\right]d\omega \tag{27.56}$$

where $$\Delta\omega_D = 2\omega_0\left(\frac{2k_BT}{Mc^2}\ln 2\right)^{\frac{1}{2}} \tag{27.57}$$

represents the FWHM of the line; i.e.,

$$g\left(\omega = \omega_0 \pm \frac{1}{2}\Delta\omega_D\right) = \frac{1}{2}g(\omega_0)$$

[see Example 8.1]. In Eq. (27.57), T represents the absolute temperature of the gas and M represents the mass of the atom responsible for the lasing transition (neon in the case of a He–Ne laser). Equation (27.57) describes the line-shape function due to Doppler effect and is shown in Fig. 27.33. Figure 27.34 shows the actual spectrum of a helium neon laser; the figure shows the very high spectral purity intrinsic to most lasers. We may note that

(a) The minimum threshold value of $N_2 - N_1$ would correspond to the center of the line where $g(\omega)$ is a maximum

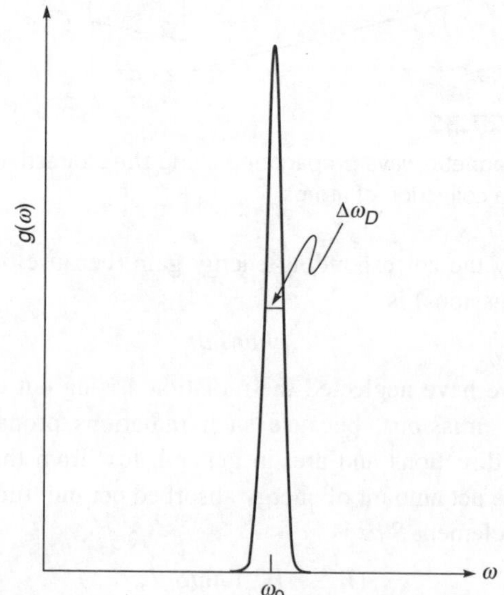

Figure 27.33
The Gaussian line-shape function corresponding to a He–Ne laser; $\Delta\omega_D$ represents the FWHM and usually $\Delta\omega/\omega_0$ <<< 1.

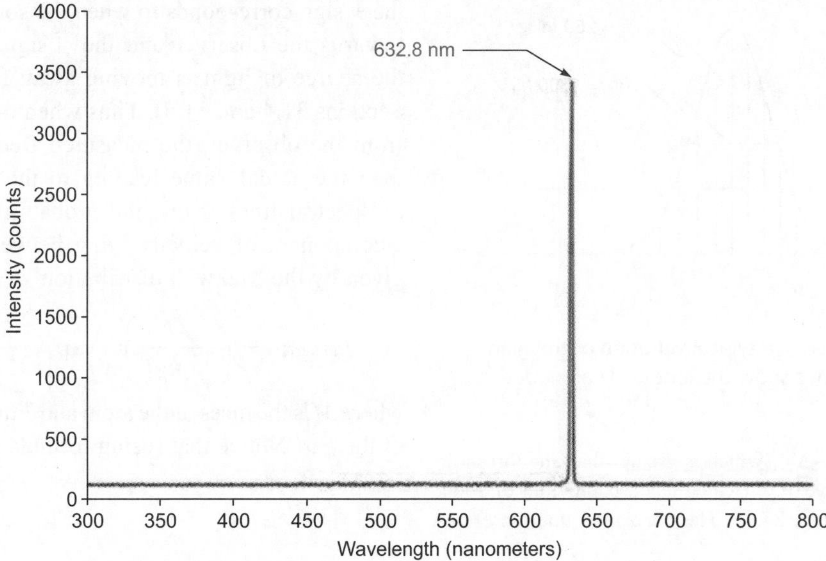

Figure 27.34
Spectrum of a helium neon laser showing the very high spectral purity intrinsic to most lasers. [*Figure adapted from http://en.wikipedia.org/wiki/Helium-neon_laser*].

and for the case of Doppler broadening the maximum value is given by:

$$g(\omega_0) = \frac{2}{\Delta\omega_D}\left(\frac{\ln 2}{\pi}\right)^{\frac{1}{2}} \quad \textbf{(27.58)}$$

Thus, smaller values of $\Delta\omega_D$ will give rise to smaller threshold value of $N_2 - N_1$. Further, as the laser medium is pumped harder and harder, the population inversion between the two levels goes on increasing. The mode that lies nearest to the resonance frequency of the atomic system reaches threshold first and begins to oscillate. As the pumping is further increased, the nearby modes may also reach the threshold and start oscillating.

(b) From Eq. (27.55) it also follows that for smaller values of the threshold population inversion $N_2 - N_1$, one must have a small value of t_{sp} implying strongly allowed transitions; however, for strongly allowed transitions larger pumping power will be required. In general, for a large value of t_{sp}, population inversion is more easily obtained.

EXAMPLE 27.6 Typical parameters for a He–Ne laser

We consider a He–Ne laser; we assume $T \approx 300°$ K. Thus, for the $\lambda_0 \approx 6328$ Å radiation

$$\Delta\omega_D = \frac{2\omega_{21}}{c}\left[\frac{2k_BT}{M}\ln 2\right]^{\frac{1}{2}}$$

$$= \frac{4\pi}{\lambda_0}\left[\frac{2\times 1.38\times 10^{-23}\,(\text{JK}^{-1})\times 300\,(\text{K})\times 0.693}{20\times 1.67\times 10^{-27}\,(\text{kg})}\right]^{\frac{1}{2}}$$

$$\approx 8230 \text{ MHz}$$

implying $$\Delta\nu_D = \frac{\Delta\omega_D}{2\pi} \approx 1310 \text{ MHz}$$

where we have assumed

$$M_{\text{Ne}} \approx 20\, M_H \approx 3.34 \times 10^{-26} \text{ kg}$$

The frequency variation of $g(\omega)$ is shown in Fig. 27.33. We may mention that for $\lambda_0 = 6328$ Å

$$\omega = \frac{2\pi c}{\lambda_0} \approx 2.98 \times 10^{15} \text{ s}^{-1}$$

Thus, $$\frac{\Delta\omega_D}{\omega} \approx 2.8 \times 10^{-6}$$

showing that the line–shape function is usually a very sharply peaked function. Further,

$$g(\omega_0) = \frac{2}{\Delta\omega_D}\left(\frac{\ln 2}{\pi}\right)^{\frac{1}{2}} \approx 1.1 \times 10^{-10} \text{ s} \quad \textbf{(27.59)}$$

(In Sec. 27.7.4, we will show that for a He–Ne laser, the Doppler broadening dominates over natural broadening and collisional broadening). If we assume a cavity with the following values of various parameters

$$d = 60 \text{ cm},\ n_0 \approx 1,\ R_1 \approx 1,\ R_2 \approx 0.98,\ \alpha_c \approx 0$$

we would get $t_c \approx 20 \times 10^{-8}$ s. Further, for the He–Ne laser

$$t_{sp} \approx 10^{-7} \text{ s};\ n_0 \approx 1;\ \lambda_0 \approx 6328 \text{ Å}$$

giving [Using Eq. (27.55)]

$$(N_2 - N_1)_{\text{th}} \approx 1.5 \times 10^{8} \text{ cm}^{-3}$$

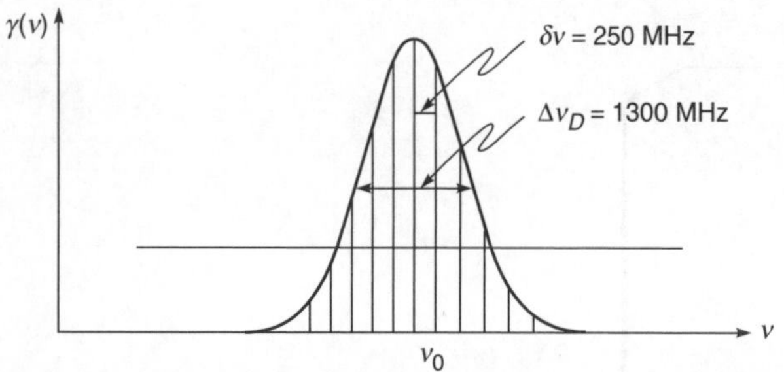

Figure 27.35
For a given value of $(N_2 - N_1)$, a typical variation of the gain curve $\gamma(\nu)$. The vertical lines show the longitudinal modes of the cavity.

For a given value of $(N_2 - N_1)$ (which is greater than the threshold value), a typical gain curve $\gamma(\nu)$ (which has a bandwidth of about 1300 MHz) is shown in Fig. 27.35. The horizontal line represents the value of

$$\frac{1}{(c/n_0)t_c} \tag{27.60}$$

For $n_0 \approx 1$, $t_c \approx 2 \times 10^{-7}$ s the above value is $\approx 1.7 \times 10^{-4}$ cm^{-1}. If we assume a 60 cm long He–Ne laser then the longitudinal mode spacing would be given by

$$\delta\nu = \frac{c}{2d} \approx 250 \text{ MHz} \tag{27.61}$$

and, as shown in Fig. 27.35, there will be seven longitudinal modes for which gain will exceed loss and which will oscillate. On the other hand, if d was only 10 cm then

$\delta\nu$ would be 1500 MHz

and we will have single mode oscillation; the value of t_c and hence the position of the horizontal line in Fig. 27.35 would have changed slightly. More examples can be found in Ref. 27.24.

27.7 The Line-Shape Function LO5

Since the line-shape function $g(\omega)$ determines the threshold population inversion [see Eq. (27.55)], we digress here to discuss some of the typical forms of $g(\omega)$ corresponding to different conditions.

We first consider the Doppler broadening which is due to the thermal motion of gas atoms. Also, in the He–Ne laser (which is probably the most popular laser), the line broadening mechanism is mainly due to Doppler broadening.

27.7.1 Doppler Broadening

In astronomy, we can determine how fast the stars or galaxies are moving (either directly away or directly towards us) by measuring the Doppler shift of spectral lines. For $v/c \ll 1$,

$$\omega - \omega_0 = \pm\omega_0 \frac{v}{c}; \tag{27.62}$$

the + sign corresponds to when the source of light is moving towards the observer and the – sign corresponds to when the source of light is moving away from the observer [see Sections 31.4 and 31.5]. Thus when the star is moving away from the observer, the measured frequency is slightly less than the actual value leading to the well-known *red shift* of spectral lines. Now, the probability that an atom has a z-component of velocity lying between v_z and $v_z + dv_z$ is given by the Maxwell distribution

$$P(v_z)dv_z = \left(\frac{M}{2\pi k_B T}\right)^{1/2} \exp\left(-\frac{Mv_z^2}{2k_B T}\right) dv_z \tag{27.63}$$

where M is the mass of the atom and T the absolute temperature of the gas. Notice that (using formula given in Appendix A):

$$\int_{-\infty}^{+\infty} P(v_z)\, dv_z = 1$$

as it indeed should be. Now, the probability $g(\omega)d\omega$ that the transition frequency lies between ω and $\omega + d\omega$ is equal to the probability that the z-component of the velocity of the atom lies between v_z and $v_z + dv_z$ where

$$v_z = \frac{(\omega - \omega_0)}{\omega_0} c \tag{27.64}$$

Thus,

$$g(\omega)d\omega = \frac{c}{\omega_0}\left(\frac{M}{2\pi k_B T}\right)^{1/2} \exp\left[-\frac{Mc^2}{2k_B T}\frac{(\omega - \omega_0)^2}{\omega_0^2}\right] d\omega \tag{27.65}$$

which corresponds to a Gaussian distribution. The line-shape function is peaked at ω_0, and the FWHM is given by

$$\Delta\omega_D = 2\omega_0\left(\frac{2k_B T}{Mc^2}\ln 2\right)^{1/2} \tag{27.66}$$

where the subscript D implies that we are considering Doppler broadening. In terms of $\Delta\omega_D$ Eq. (27.66) can be written as

$$g(\omega)d\omega = \frac{2}{\Delta\omega_D}\left(\frac{\ln 2}{\pi}\right)^{1/2} \exp\left[-4\ln 2 \frac{(\omega - \omega_0)^2}{(\Delta\omega_D)^2}\right] d\omega \tag{27.67}$$

and it satisfies Eq. (27.73). A typical plot of the Gaussian line–shape function corresponding to the He–Ne laser is shown in Fig. 27.33.

27.7.2 Natural Broadening

The frequency spectrum associated with spontaneous emission is described by the Lorentzian line shape function

$$g(\omega) = \frac{1}{2\pi t_{sp}} \cdot \frac{1}{(\omega - \omega_0)^2 + \dfrac{1}{4t_{sp}^2}} \tag{27.68}$$

where $$t_{sp} = \frac{1}{A_{21}} \tag{27.69}$$

represents the spontaneous emission lifetime. The derivation of Eq. (27.68) [and of (27.74)] are given at many places, see, e.g. Sec. 8.8 of Ref. 27.20. The FWHM of the Lorentzian is

$$\Delta\omega = \frac{1}{t_{sp}} = A_{21} \tag{27.70}$$

Thus, in terms of $\Delta\omega$, Eq. (27.68) can be written in the form

$$g(\omega) = \frac{\Delta\omega}{2\pi} \frac{1}{(\omega - \omega_0)^2 + \left(\frac{\Delta\omega}{2}\right)^2} \tag{27.71}$$

giving

$$g(\omega_0) = \frac{2}{\pi(\Delta\omega)} \quad \text{and} \quad g\left(\omega_0 \pm \frac{1}{2}\Delta\omega\right) = \frac{1}{2} g(\omega_0) \tag{27.72}$$

Further, $$\int_0^{\infty} g(\omega)\, d\omega \approx \int_{-\infty}^{+\infty} g(\omega)\, d\omega = 1 \tag{27.73}$$

27.7.3 Collisional Broadening

In a gas, random collisions occur between the atoms. In such a collision process, when the atoms are very close to each other, the energy levels of the atoms change due to their mutual interaction. This leads to a Lorentzian line shape function given by

$$g(\omega) = \frac{\tau_0}{\pi} \frac{1}{1 + (\omega - \omega_0)^2 \tau_0^2} \tag{27.74}$$

where τ_0 represents the mean time between collisions; The FWHM will be

$$\Delta\omega_c = \frac{2}{\tau_0}$$

In a typical gas laser $\tau_0 \sim 10^{-6}$ s giving

$$\Delta\omega_c \approx 2 \text{ MHz} \Rightarrow \Delta\nu_c \approx 0.3 \text{ MHz}$$

For the He–Ne laser, the Doppler line width is about 1300 MHz (see Example 27.3); on the other hand, the natural broadening is about 20 MHz and the collision broadening at 0.5 Torr is about 0.64 MHz. Thus, for He–Ne laser parameters, the Doppler broadening dominates over natural broadening and collision broadening.

The various line broadening mechanisms can be broadly classified under homogeneous and inhomogeneous broadening. Certain line broadening mechanisms, such as collision broadening or natural broadening, act to broaden the response of each atom in an identical fashion; such broadening mechanisms come under the class of homogeneous broadening. On the other hand, Doppler broadening or broadening produced due to local inhomogeneties in a crystal lattice act to shift the central frequency of the response of individual atoms by different amounts and thereby lead to an overall broadening of the response of the atomic system. Such a form of broadening is referred to as inhomogeneous broadening. If the effects which cause the inhomogeneous broadening are random in origin, then the broadened line is Gaussian in shape. In contrast, homogeneous broadening in general results in a Lorentzian line shape.

We return to Eq. (27.55) and notice that in order to have a low threshold value of population inversion:

(a) The value of t_c should be large, i.e., the losses in the cavity must be small.

(b) The value of $g(\omega)$ at the centre of the line is $\approx 0.64/\Delta\omega$ for a Lorentzian line and $\approx 0.94/\Delta\omega$ for a Gaussian line (see Eqs. 27.72 and 27.58). Thus, smaller the value of $\Delta\omega$ (the width of the line), smaller will be the threshold population inversion.

(c) Smaller values of t_{sp} (i.e., strongly allowed transitions) also lead to smaller values of threshold inversion. It must be noted here that, for shorter relaxation rates, larger pumping power is required to maintain a given amount of population inversion. In general, population inversion is more easily obtained on transitions which have longer relaxation times.

(d) The value of $g(\omega)$ at the center of the line is inversely proportional to $\Delta\omega$, which, for example, in the case of Doppler broadening is proportional to ω [see Eq. (27.57)]. Thus, the threshold population inversion increases approximately in proportion to the third power of ω (apart from the frequency dependence of the other terms). Hence, it is much easier to obtain laser action at infrared wavelengths than in the ultraviolet region.

27.8 Typical Parameters for a Ruby Laser

LO6

In order to get an idea of the magnitude of population inversion required for oscillation, we consider a ruby laser (see Sec. 27.3). Let us consider the laser to be oscillating at the frequency corresponding to the peak of the emission line. We assume a concentration of 0.05 % of Cr^{3+} ions in the crystal; this corresponds to a population of

$$N = 1.6 \times 10^{19} \text{ Cr}^{3+} \text{ ions/cm}^3$$

For the case of ruby, the line is homogeneously broadened and the value of $g(\omega)$ at the peak of the line is $2/(\pi\Delta\omega)$. Hence the threshold population inversion density is

$$(N_2 - N_1)_{\text{th}} = \frac{\omega^2 n_0^3 t_{sp}}{\pi^2 c^3 t_c g(\omega)}$$

$$= \frac{4\pi^2 n_0^3}{\lambda_0^3} \cdot \frac{\Delta\omega}{\omega} \cdot \frac{t_{sp}}{t_c} \quad \textbf{(27.75)}$$

where λ_0 is the free space wavelength, t_{sp} is the spontaneous relaxation time of the upper laser level and t_c is the cavity lifetime. For ruby laser transition, one has

$$\lambda_0 = 6943 \text{ Å} \;\Rightarrow\; \omega \approx 2.715 \times 10^{15} \text{ s}^{-1}$$

$$\Delta\omega \approx 9.4 \times 10^{11} \text{ s}^{-1};$$

$$t_{sp} \approx 3 \times 10^{-3} \text{ s} ; n_0 \approx 1.76$$

where n_0 (= 1.76) represents the refractive index of ruby. If we assume a cavity length of 5 cm and a loss per round trip of 10 % then $x = 0.1$ and using Eq. (27.50) we get

$$t_c \approx 6 \times 10^{-9} \text{ s}$$

Substituting all these values in Eq. (27.75) we get for the threshold population inversion density

$$(N_2 - N_1)_{\text{th}} \approx 1.1 \times 10^{17} \text{ Cr}^{3+} \text{ ions/cm}^3$$

Since the total density of Cr^{3+} ions in ruby is about 1.6×10^{19} cm^{-3}, the fractional excess population required is very small.

We will next calculate approximately the minimum power required to maintain population inversion. Since t_{sp} represents the spontaneous relaxation time of the upper laser level, the number of atoms decaying per unit time from the upper laser level is approximately N_2/t_{sp}. For each atom lifted to level 2, one has to supply at least an amount of energy given by $h\nu_p$ where ν_p represents the average pump frequency. Hence in order to maintain N_2 atoms in the level 2, the minimum power P to be spent (per unit volume of the active material) would be given by

$$P = \frac{N_2 h\nu_p}{t_{\text{sp}}} \quad \textbf{(27.76)}$$

Now, since $(N_2 - N_1)_{\text{th}} << N$ (where N represents the total number of atoms per unit volume), we may write

$$N_2 \approx \frac{N}{2} \quad \textbf{(27.77)}$$

Thus, the minimum pumping power per unit volume required to maintain population inversion in a three level laser system is

$$P_{th} \approx \frac{N}{2} \frac{h\nu_p}{t_{\text{sp}}} \quad \textbf{(27.78)}$$

Taking the average pumping frequency as

$$\nu_p \approx 6.25 \times 10^{14} \text{ Hz}$$

(which is averaged over the green and violet absorption bands), we obtain

$$P_{\text{th}} \approx \frac{(1.6 \times 10^{19})}{2} \times \frac{6.6 \times 10^{-34} \times 6.25 \times 10^{14}}{3 \times 10^{-3}}$$

$$\approx 1100 \text{ W/cm}^3$$

If we assume that the efficiency of the pumping source is 25% and also that only 25% is absorbed in passage through the ruby rod, then the electrical threshold power comes out to be about 18 kW/cm³ of the active material. This is consistent with the threshold powers determined experimentally.

The threshold power calculation is particularly simple for the ruby laser where only three levels are involved. In general, in order to calculate the steady state population difference between the actual levels involved in the laser transition (for a given pumping rate) and also to know whether an inversion of population is achievable in a transition and if so, what would be the minimum pump power required to maintain a steady population inversion for continuous wave operation of the laser, it is necessary to solve equations which govern the rate at which populations of various levels change under the action of a pump and in the presence of laser radiation. These equations are referred to as 'rate equations' and have been discussed at many places; see, for example, Refs. 27.4, 27.9, 27.16 and 27.17. We should mention that even for a three-level laser system the equation $N_2 = N/2$ [see Eq. (27.77)] is only approximately valid and in order to obtain a more accurate expression, it is necessary to solve the rate equations.

27.9 Monochromaticity of the Laser Beam

LO7

Figure 27.36 shows the various linewidths associated with a laser. The broad solid curve represents the spectral width due to Doppler broadening of the laser medium. As an example if we consider the He–Ne laser operating at 6328 Å, the Doppler broadened linewidth is about 1,300 MHz. Inside the broad curve are shown the cavity modes as sharp peaks. The frequency separation between two adjacent cavity modes is $c/2d$ [see Eqs. (27.6) and (27.61)] which for a typical laser cavity 60 cm long corresponds to 250 MHz; this is much less than the Doppler width (see Example 27.6). As we have discussed earlier, the cavity modes are also broadened due to the various losses in the cavity. Thus, for a 60 cm long cavity specified by a fractional loss per round trip of 4×10^{-2}, the width of the cavity mode is about 1.5 MHz. This is much smaller than the spacing between adjacent cavity modes. When the losses in the cavity are compensated for by the active medium placed inside the cavity, the resultant emission becomes extremely narrow and is limited due to

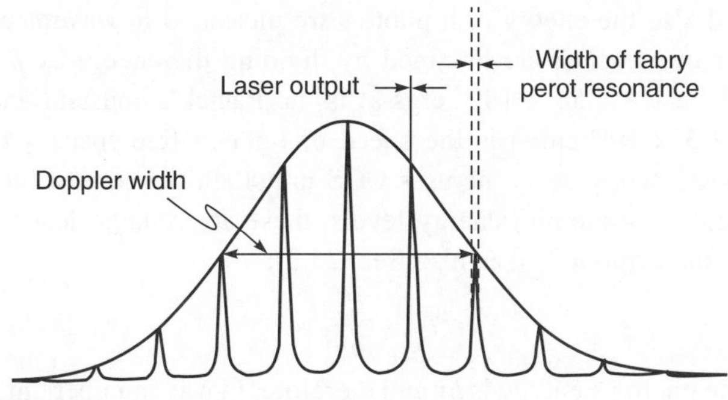

Figure 27.36

The solid curve represents a typical Doppler broadened spectral line. The closely spaced cavity modes are shown as narrow peaks inside the curve. The sharp line represents the output of the laser (Ref. 27.21).

the presence of spontaneous emission (which are random) and the fluctuations in the resonator parameters. The ultimate linewidth of an oscillating laser is determined solely by random spontaneous emissions can be shown to be given by (See., e.g., Ref. 27.22).

$$(\delta\nu)_{\text{sp}} \approx \frac{2\pi(\Delta\nu_p)^2\, h\nu_0}{P^\circ}$$

where ν_0 is the frequency of oscillation, P° is the output power and

$$\Delta\nu_p = \frac{1}{2\pi t_c}$$

is known as the **passive cavity linewidth**, t_c being the cavity lifetime (see Sec. 27.6.2). The subscript '*sp*' refers to the fact that the linewidth is due to spontaneous emissions. The decrease in $(\delta\nu)_{sp}$ with increase in power output is due to the fact that for a given mirror transmittance, increase in P° corresponds to increase in laser power inside the resonator cavity, and this leads to the dominance of stimulated emissions over spontaneous emission.

As a typical example, $\Delta\nu_p \approx 1$ MHz, $P^\circ = 1$ mW $= 10^{-3}$ W, $h\nu = 2\times10^{-19}$ J (corresponding to the red region of the spectrum) so that $(\delta\nu)_{\text{sp}} \approx 10^{-3}$ Hz—an extremely small quantity indeed! Thus, the ultimate monochromaticity is determined by the spontaneous emissions occurring inside the cavity because the radiation coming out due to spontaneous emission is incoherent. However, in practice, the monochromaticity is limited by external factors like temperature fluctuations, mechanical vibrations of the optical cavity, etc. For example, if we assume the oscillation frequency of a mode is given by Eq. (27.4) then, the change in frequency $\Delta\nu$ caused by a change in length Δd is given by

$$\frac{\Delta\nu}{\nu} = \frac{\Delta d}{d}$$

Thus for $d \approx 50$ cm, if we assume a stability of $\Delta d \approx 1$ Å then for $\nu \approx 5 \times 10^{14}$ Hz

$$\Delta\nu \approx 10^5 \text{ Hz}$$

which is much much larger than $(\delta\nu)_{\text{sp}}$. We may mention here that $\Delta\nu \approx 10^5$ Hz correspond to $\Delta\lambda \approx 10^{-6}$ Å . Indeed, for a single moded He–Ne laser, we can have $\Delta\nu \approx 10^5$ Hz. On the other hand, for a multimoded He–Ne laser $\Delta\lambda \sim 0.02$ Å implying a coherence length of about 20 cm. ($L \approx \lambda^2/\Delta\lambda$; see Sec. 16.2).

27.10 Raman Amplification and Raman Laser

LO8

We will first discuss the physics of Raman effect. When a monochromatic light beam gets scattered by a transparent substance, one of the following may occur:

(a) Over 99% of the scattered radiation has the same frequency as that of the incident light beam; this is known as **Rayleigh scattering** which has been discussed in Sec. 6.6. The sky looks blue because of Rayleigh scattering and the light that comes out from the side of the optical fiber (see Fig. 28.2) is also due to Rayleigh scattering.

(b) A very small portion of the scattered radiation has a frequency different from that of the incident beam – this may arise due to one of the following three processes:

(i) The incident radiation may lead to translatory motion of the molecules – this would result in shift of frequency which is usually very small and difficult to measure. This is known as **Brillouin scattering***.

(ii) A part of the energy $h\nu$ of the incident photon is taken over by the molecule in the form of rotational (or vibrational) energy and the scattered photon has a smaller energy $h\nu'$. This leads to what are known as **Raman–Stokes lines** [see Figs. 27.37(a) and 27.38].

(iii) On the other hand, the photon can undergo scattering by a molecule which is already in an excited state. The molecule can de-excite to one of the lower energy states and in the process, the incident photon can take up this excess energy and come out with a higher frequency. This leads to

*The shift in frequency is usually denoted by $\Delta\bar{\nu}$ and is measured in wavenumber units which is defined later in this section. In Brillouin scattering, $\Delta\bar{\nu} \lesssim 0.1$ cm^{-1}. On the other hand, in Raman scattering $\Delta\bar{\nu} \lesssim 10^4$ cm^{-1}.

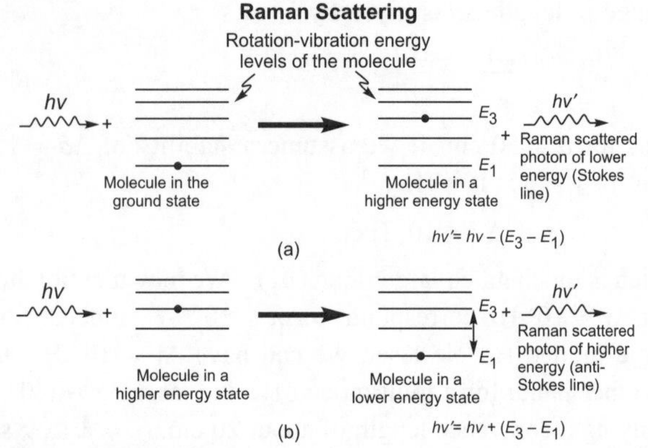

Figure 27.37

The generation of the Raman Stokes and the Raman anti-Stokes lines.

what are known as **Raman anti-Stokes lines** [see Figs. 27.37(b) and 27.38].

The difference energy, which is $(h\nu - h\nu')$ for the Raman Stokes line and $(h\nu' - h\nu)$ for the Raman anti-Stokes line, would therefore correspond to the energy difference between the rotational (or vibrational) energy levels of the molecule and would therefore be a characteristic of the molecule itself.

The quantity $(h\nu - h\nu')$ or $(h\nu' - h\nu)$ is usually referred to as the "Raman-shift" [see Fig. 27.38] and is independent of the frequency of the incident radiation. Through a careful analysis of the Raman spectra, one can determine the structure of molecules; there lies the tremendous importance of Raman effect. The intensity distribution of a typical Raman spectrum for the CCl_4 molecule is shown in Fig. 27.38.

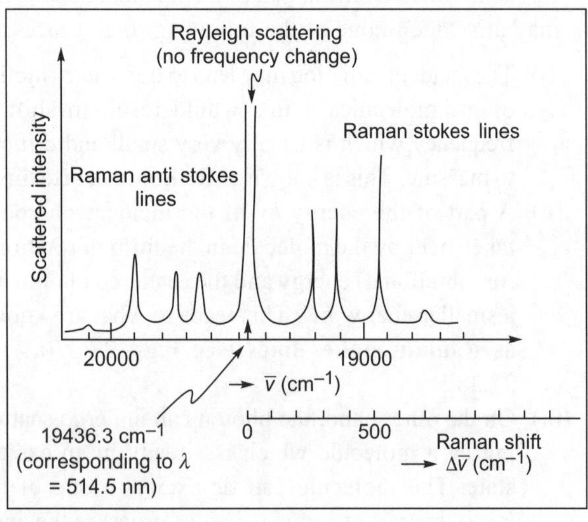

Figure 27.38

Raman spectra of CCl_4 excited by 514.5 nm line of an Argon-ion laser. [*Adapted from http://epsc.wustl.edu/Haskin-group/Raman/faqs.htm*]

In spectroscopy, the energy levels of atoms or molecules and also the energy of a photon are measured in wavenumber units which are obtained by dividing the energy by hc, where $h(\approx 6.56 \times 10^{-27}$ ergs-s) is the Planck's constant and $c(\approx 3 \times 10^{10}$ cm/s) is the speed of light in free space – in spectroscopy everyone uses CGS units!! In the case of molecular (or atomic) energy levels, these are usually denoted by the symbol T_n (see also Sec. 25.2):

$$T_n = \frac{E_n}{hc}$$

The photon's energy is $h\nu$ and therefore, in wavenumber units

$$\frac{h\nu}{hc} = \frac{\nu}{c} = \frac{1}{\lambda}$$

is just the inverse of the wavelength and is usually denoted by the symbol $\bar{\nu}$.Thus,

$$\bar{\nu} = \frac{1}{\lambda}$$

Now, the energy levels of the hydrogen atom in wavenumber units are given by

$$T_n = \frac{E_n}{hc} = -\frac{R}{n^2}; \; n = 1, 2, 3, ...$$

where R (≈ 109678 cm^{-1}) is known as the **Rydberg constant** and n (= 1, 2, 3, …) is the total quantum number of the state. Thus corresponding to the $n = 3$ to $n = 2$ transition (one of the lines of the Balmer series) we will get a photon of wavenumber (see Sec. 25.2)

$$\bar{\nu} = -R\left(\frac{1}{9} - \frac{1}{4}\right) = \frac{5}{36} \times 109678 \approx 15233 \text{ cm}^{-1}$$

The inverse of the above number ($\approx 6.56 \times 10^{-5}$ cm) represents the wavelength of the emitted photon.

Figure 27.38 shows the intensity distribution of the Raman spectrum of CCl_4 molecule* when the incident radiation corresponds to the Argon-ion laser line having a wavelength of 5.145×10^{-5} cm; in wavenumber units the value is 19436.3 cm^{-1}. The central peak in the figure corresponds to this wavelength and is due to Rayleigh scattering. The Raman shift for the Stokes lines is the same as for the anti-Stokes lines although the latter is much weaker. This is due to the fact that at room temperature, the number of molecules in the ground state is much larger than the molecules present in excited states. This leads to very low intensities of the Raman anti-Stokes lines. The actual Raman spectrum of the CCl_4 molecule for the 4046 Å lines of mercury lamp is shown in Fig. 27.39. The photograph is adapted from the 1930 Nobel lecture of C.V. Raman. It may be of interest to mention that on 28th February 1928, K.S. Krishnan and C.V. Raman observed "Raman effect" in several organic vapours like pentane — which they called "the new scattered radiation". Raman made a newspaper announcement on 29th

*The Raman spectrum from a mixture of hydrogen and deuterium molecules (when the mixture is illuminated by a laser beam at l = 488 nm) is discussed in Chapter 9 of Ref. 27.23.

Figure 27.39

The observed Raman spectra of CCl_4 for the 4046 Å and 4358 Å lines of mercury lamp. The photograph is adapted from the 1930 Nobel lecture of C.V. Raman.

February and on 8th March 1928, he communicated a paper entitled "A Change of Wavelength in Light Scattering" to *Nature*; the paper was published on 21st April 1928. Although in the paper, he acknowledged that the observations were made by K.S. Krishnan and himself, the paper had Raman as the author and therefore the phenomenon came to be known as Raman effect although many scientists (particularly in India) kept on referring it as the Raman–Krishnan effect. Subsequently, there were several papers written by Raman and Krishnan. Raman got the Nobel prize in 1930 for "his work on the scattering of light and for the discovery of the effect named after him". At about the same time, Landsberg and Mandel′shtam (in Russia) were also working on light scattering and according to Mandel′shtam, they observed the "Raman-lines" on February 21, 1928. But the results were presented in April 1928 and it was only on 6th May 1928 that Landsberg and Mandel′shtam communicated their results to the journal *Naturwissenschaften*. But by then it was too late! Much later, scientists from Russia kept calling Raman scattering as Mandel′shtam-Raman scattering. For a very nice historical account of Raman effect, we refer the reader to a book by G. Venkataraman on "Journey into Light: Life and Science of C.V. Raman" published by Penguin Books (1994).

In 1958, thirty years after the discovery of the Raman effect, Raman wrote an article on "Raman effect" in Encyclopaedia Britannica. In that article, he wrote "The rotations of the molecules in gases give more readily observable effects, viz., a set of closely spaced but nevertheless discrete Raman lines located on either side of the incident line. In liquids, only a continuous wing or band is usually observed in the same region, indicating that the rotations in a dense fluid are hindered by molecular collisions. The internal vibrations of the molecules, on the other hand, give rise in all cases to large shifts of wave length. The Raman lines attributed to them appear well separated from the parent line and are therefore easily identified and measured."

In stimulated Raman emission, the radiation emitted in the ordinary Raman effect is made to stimulate further Raman emission. This can lead to what is usually referred to as the "Raman amplification" of the beam.

Now, in fused silica, because of interaction between adjacent SiO_2 molecules, the vibrational bands are very broad; this leads to a very broad Raman shift lying between 430 cm^{-1} to 470 cm^{-1} [this corresponds to a Raman frequency shift between 13 and 14 THz (1 THz = 10^{12} Hz)]. Thus, if we have a pump laser at 1450 nm ($\bar{\nu}$ = 6897 cm^{-1}) then an incoming beam at 1550 nm ($\bar{\nu}$ = 6452 cm^{-1}) will get amplified by stimulated Raman scattering [$\Delta\bar{\nu}$ = 445 cm^{-1}] as shown in Fig. 27.40(a). In an actual commercially available single mode fiber of length about 30 km, one can obtain a Raman gain of about 15 dB (i.e., a power amplification by a factor of about 30) by using a pump laser of 500 mW power.

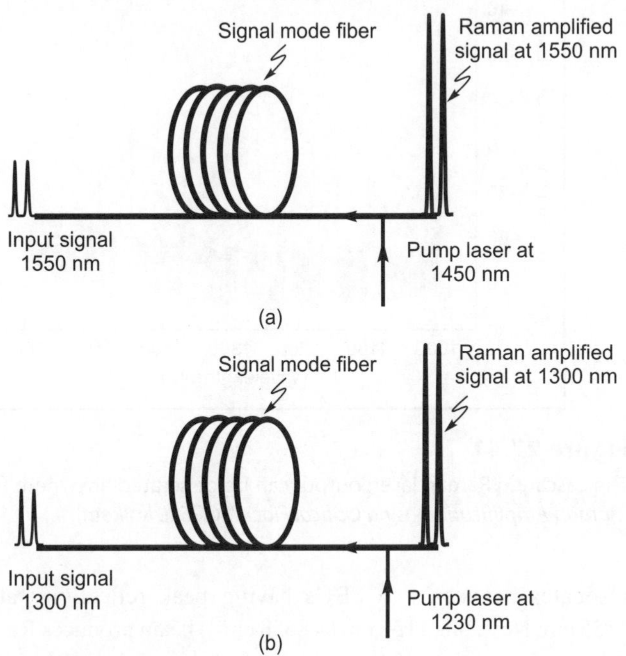

Figure 27.40

Raman fiber amplifiers at 1550 nm and 1300 nm wavelengths. [*Figure adapted from Ref. 27.23*].

Similarly, if we want to amplify an incoming beam at 1300 nm ($\bar{\nu}$ = 7692 cm^{-1}) then we must use a pump laser at about 1230 nm wavelength ($\bar{\nu}$ = 8130 cm^{-1}) as shown in Fig. 27.40(b). This is the great advantage of the Raman fiber amplifier. One can amplify signal at *any* wavelength provided we choose the pump laser frequency separated by about 13.5 THz (equivalent to a wavenumber shift of about 450 cm^{-1}). On the other hand, as we may recall, in Erbium Doped Fiber Amplifiers (EDFAs), one can amplify signals only around 1550 nm wavelength; however, the laser power required is much smaller.

The above principle can be used to build the cascaded Raman laser (see Fig. 27.41). The vertical bars represent FBGs (Fiber Bragg Gratings) which are strongly reflecting at the wavelengths written on the top (see Sec. 14.6.1 for a brief account on FBGs). Thus, the input wavelength of 1100 nm (≈ 9091 cm^{-1}) produces Raman scattered line at 1155 nm (≈ 8658 cm^{-1} implying a Raman shift of about 433 cm^{-1}); this

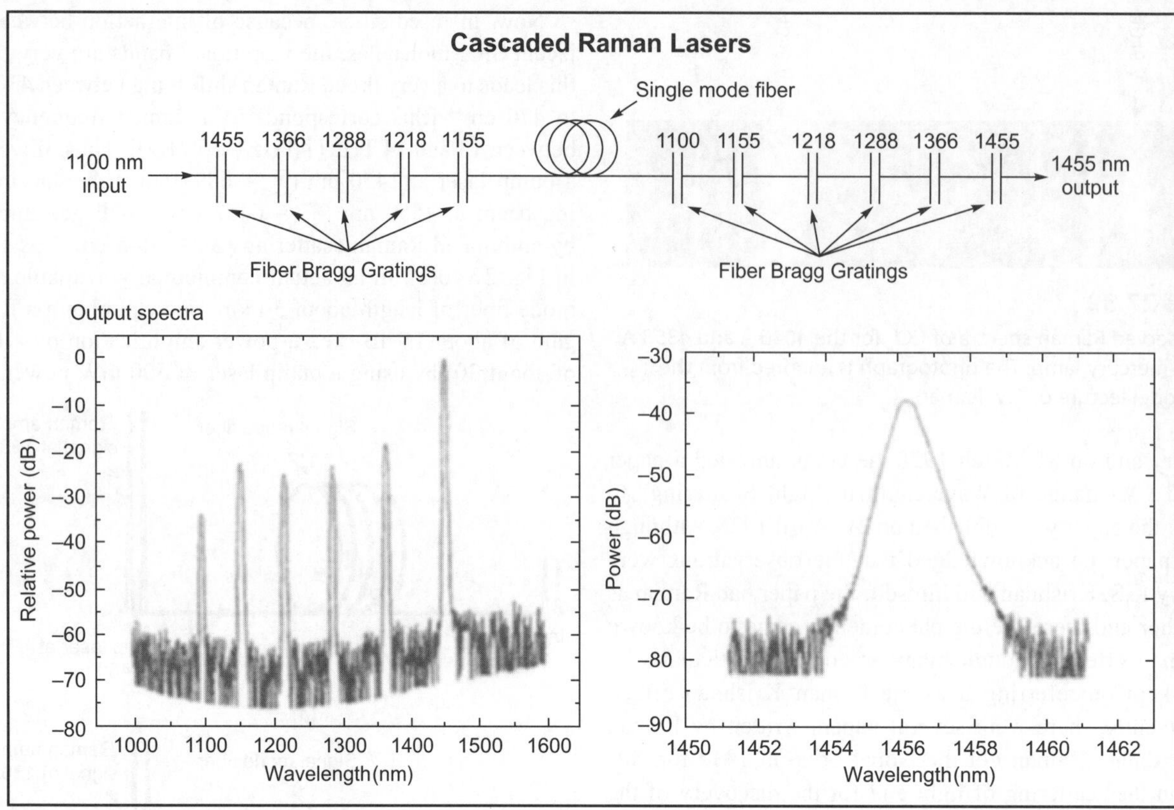

Figure 27.41

The cascaded Raman laser; output can be generated anywhere from 1100 - 1600 nm. [*Adapted from the lecture notes of K. Rottwitt on "Raman Amplification using Optical Fibers", CGCRI, Kolkata*].

resonates between two FBGs having peak reflectivity at 1155 nm. Now, this 1155 nm ($\approx$ 8658 cm^{-1}) beam produces Raman scattered line at 1218 nm ($\approx$ 8210 cm^{-1} implying a Raman shift of about 448 cm^{-1}) which resonates between two FBGs having peak reflectivity at 1218 nm, etc. This way laser output can be generated anywhere from 1100–1600 nm [see Fig. 27.41].

SUMMARY

- Laser is an acronym for Light Amplification by Stimulated Emission of Radiation. The light emitted from a laser often possesses some very special characteristics – some of these are (a) **Directionality:** because of which a laser beam can be focused to areas ~ few (μm)^2 leading to applications in surgery, material processing, compact discs, etc. (b) **High power:** continuous wave lasers having power levels ~ 10^5 W and pulsed lasers having a total energy ~ 50000 J have applications in welding, cutting, laser fusion, etc., and (c) **Spectral purity:** Laser beams can have an extremely small spectral width $\Delta\lambda$, because of which lasers find applications in holography, optical communications, spectroscopy, etc.
- As put forward by Einstein, when an atom is in the excited state then, in addition to the spontaneous emission, it can also make a transition to a lower energy state by what is known as stimulated emission in which an incident signal of appropriate frequency triggers an atom in an excited state to emit radiation – this results in the amplification of the incident beam. If we are able to create a state of population inversion in which there are larger number of atoms in the upper state then the number of stimulated emissions would exceed the number of stimulated absorptions resulting in the (optical) amplification of the beam.
- The three main components of any laser are
  (i) The active medium which consists of a collection of atoms, molecules or ions (in solid, liquid or gaseous form), which is capable of amplifying light waves,
  (ii) The pumping mechanism which allows us to obtain a state of population inversion between a pair of energy levels of the atomic system, and
  (iii) The optical resonator, which provides the feedback.

- Through a pumping mechanism, one creates a state of population inversion in the laser placed inside the resonator system. The spontaneous emission occurring inside the resonator cavity excites the various modes of the cavity. The modes for which the gain is higher than the losses get amplified by drawing energy from the laser medium. The amplitude of the mode increases rapidly until the upper level population reaches a value when the gain equals the losses and the mode oscillates in steady state.
- Two mirrors facing each other form a resonant cavity. The discrete frequencies of the resonator modes are given by $\nu = \nu_m = m\dfrac{c}{2d}$. Different values of m lead to different oscillation frequencies, which constitute the longitudinal modes of the cavity. For example, for an optical resonator of length $d \approx 60$ cm operating at an optical frequency of $\nu \approx 5 \times 10^{14}$ Hz (corresponding to $\lambda \approx 6000$ Å), we obtain $m \approx 2 \times 10^6$.
- The first successful operation of a laser device ($\lambda \sim 0.6943\ \mu$m) was demonstrated by Theodore Mainman in 1960 using a ruby crystal. Within a few months of the operation of the ruby laser, Ali Javan and his associates constructed the first gas laser ($\lambda \sim 0.6328\ \mu$m), namely the helium–neon laser.
- If we put a fiber (doped with Erbium or Neodymium) between two mirrors (which act as a resonator)—then with an appropriate pump we would have a fiber laser. In 1961, the first fiber laser (barium crown glass doped with Nd^{+3} ions) was fabricated by Elias Snitzer.
- The threshold population inversion required for the oscillation of the laser is given by

$$(N_2 - N_1)_{\text{th}} = \frac{\omega^2 n_0^3 t_{sp}}{\pi^2 c^3 t_c g(\omega)}$$

where t_{sp} is the spontaneous emission life time, t_c is the passive cavity life time and $g(\omega)$ is the line shape function. For a He–Ne laser

$$g(\omega) = \frac{2}{\Delta\omega_{\text{D}}}\left(\frac{\ln 2}{\pi}\right)^{\frac{1}{2}} \exp\left[-4\ln 2\frac{(\omega-\omega)^2}{\Delta\omega_{\text{D}}}\right]$$

where $\Delta\omega_{\text{D}} = 2\omega_0\left(\dfrac{2k_BT}{Mc^2}\ln 2\right)^{\frac{1}{2}}$ represent the FWHM (Full Width at Half Maximum) of the line k_B the Boltzmann constant, T represents the absolute temperature of the gas and M represents the mass of the atom responsible for the lasing transition (neon in the case of a He–Ne laser). Notice that the minimum threshold value of $N_2 - N_1$ would correspond to the center of the line where $g(\omega)$ is a maximum and for He–Ne laser at $T = 300$ K, $\Delta\omega_{\text{D}} \approx 8230$ MHz giving $g(\omega_0) \approx 1.1 \times 10^{-10}$ s. Assuming $M = 20\ M_{\text{H}} \approx 3.3 \times 10^{-23}$ g, $t_c \approx 10^{-7}$ s $\approx t_{sp}$, $n_0 \approx 1$, we get $(N_2 - N_1)_{\text{th}} \approx 4 \times 10^8$ cm^{-3}.

PROBLEMS

27.1 Determine the MKS units of $u(\omega)$, u_ω, A and B.

[**Ans.** J s m^{-3}; J m^{-3}; s^{-1}; m^3 J^{-1} s^{-2}].

27.2 For the $2P \rightarrow 1S$ transition in the hydrogen atom calculate ω. Assuming the spontaneous emission lifetime of the $2P$ state to be 1.6 ns, calculate the Einstein B coefficient. Assume $n_0 \approx 1$.

[**Ans:** $\omega \approx 1.55 \times 10^{16}$ Hz, $B_{21} \approx 4.2 \times 10^{20}$ m^3 J^{-1} s^{-2}]

27.3 **(a)** Consider a He–Ne laser with cavity life time $t_c \approx 5 \times 10^{-8}$ s. If $R_1 = 1.0$ and $R_2 = 0.98$, calculate the cavity length d; assume $n_0 \approx 1$.

(b) Calculate $\Delta\nu_p$ and compare with the longitudinal mode spacing $\delta\nu$.

[**Ans:** (a) $d \approx 15$ cm (b) $\Delta\nu_p \approx 3.2$ MHz; $\delta\nu \approx 1$ GHz]

27.4 In a typical He–Ne laser ($\lambda = 6328$ Å) we have $d \approx 20$ cm, $R_1 \approx R_2 \approx 0.98$, $\alpha_c \approx 0$, $t_{sp} \approx 10^{-7}$ s, $\Delta\nu_{\text{D}} \approx 1.3 \times 10^9$ Hz and $n_0 = 1$. Calculate t_c and $(N_2 - N_1)_{th}$.

[**Ans:** 33 ns; 8.8×10^8 cm^{-3}]

27.5 Consider the D_1 line of Na ($\lambda \approx 5890$ Å)

(a) The spontaneous emission lifetime $t_{sp} \approx 16$ ns. Calculate $\Delta\nu_N$ and $\Delta\lambda_N$.

(b) Assume $T = 500$ K. Calculate $\Delta\nu_D$ and $\Delta\lambda_D$.

[$k_B \approx 1.38 \times 10^{-23}$ J/ K; $M_{\text{Na}} \approx 23\ M_H$; $M_H \approx 1.67 \times 10^{-27}$ kg].

[**Ans:** $\Delta\lambda_N \approx 10^{-4}$ Å; $\Delta\lambda_D \approx 0.02$ Å]

27.6 In a CO_2 laser ($\lambda_0 \approx 10.6\ \mu$m), the laser transition occurs between the vibrational states of the CO_2 molecule. At $T \approx 300$ K, calculate the Doppler linewidth $\Delta\nu_D$ and $\Delta\lambda_D$ [$M_{\text{CO2}} \approx 44\ M_H$].

[**Ans:** $\Delta\nu_D \approx 53$ MHz; $\Delta\lambda_D \approx 0.2$ Å]

27.7 Consider a light beam of all frequencies lying between $\nu = \nu_0 = 5.0 \times 10^{14}$ Hz to $\nu = 5.00002 \times 10^{14}$ Hz incident normally on a resonator (see Fig. 27.24) with $R = 0.95$, $n_0 = 1$ and $d = 25$ cm. Calculate the frequencies (in the above frequency range) and the corresponding mode number which will correspond to transmission resonances.

[**Ans:** $\nu = \nu_0 + 400$ MHz ($m = 833{,}334$), $\nu_0 + 1000$ MHz ($m = 833{,}335$) and $\nu_0 + 1600$ MHz ($m = 833{,}336$)]

27.8 Referring to Fig. 27.26, if $d = 2R_1 = 2R_2$ show that all rays passing through the common center of curvature of the mirrors will retrace their path and hence be trapped inside the cavity.

27.9 Consider a He–Ne laser ($\lambda_0 = 0.6328$ μm) with $d = 30$ cm, $n_0 \approx 1$, $R_1 \approx 1$, $R_2 \approx 0.99$. Calculate the passive cavity linewidth $\Delta\nu_p$ and the passive cavity life time t_c. You may assume $\alpha_c \approx 0$.

[**Ans:** 0.8 MHz, 0.2 μs]

27.10 **(a)** For the He–Ne laser described in Problem 27.9, if the power level is 0.5 mW, calculate the ultimate linewidth $(\delta\nu)_{sp}$.

(b) Discuss the stability of the mirror position Δd to obtain the ultimate linewidth.

[**Ans:** (a) $\approx$ 0.0025 Hz, (b) $\Delta d \approx 1.6 \times 10^{-16}$ m]

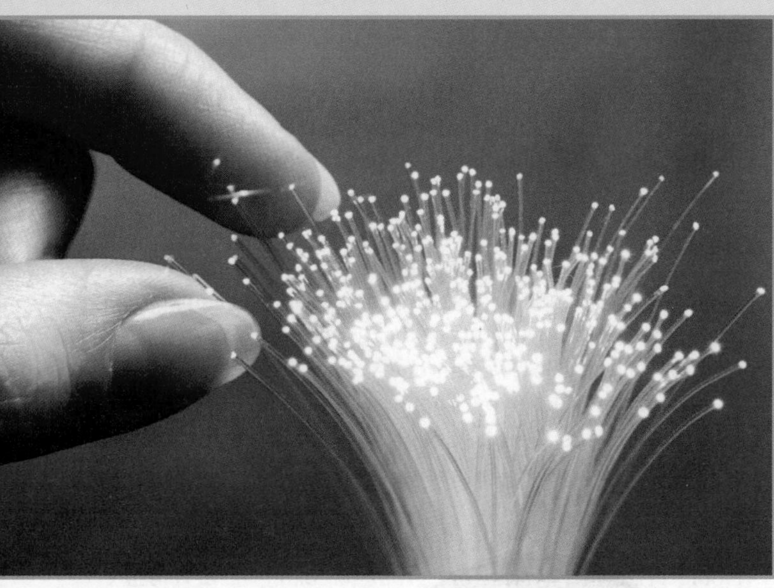

CHAPTER

28

"I have heard a ray of light laugh and sing. We may talk by light to any visible distance without any conducting wire".

—Alexander Graham Bell (1880)

[After succeeding in transmitting a voice signal over 200 metres using light as the signal carrier.]

Fiber Optics I: Basics Using Ray Optics

LEARNING OBJECTIVES

After reading this chapter, the reader should be able to:

LO 1: *know about Graham Bell's photophone experiment.*

LO 2: *understand light guidance by total internal reflection.*

LO 3: *describe various types of optical fibers.*

LO 4: *examine why glass fibers are used in sensors and telecommunications.*

LO 5: *know about coherent bundle and their various applications.*

LO 6: *understand numerical aperture of an optical fiber and its measurement.*

LO 7: *analyse attenuation and dispersion as important characteristics of an optical fiber.*

LO 8: *discuss multimode optical fibers and pulse dispersion.*

LO 9: *relate pulse dispersion to maximum bit rate estimation.*

LO 10: *express ray dispersion corresponding to power law profile.*

LO 11: *understand basic principles behind a few fiber optic sensors.*

Important Milestones*

1841 Daniel Colladon demonstrates (in Geneva) light guiding in water jets.

1842 Jaques Babinet demonstrates (in Paris) light guiding in water jets and also in bent glass rods.

1854 John Tyndall demonstrates light guiding in water jets, duplicating but not acknowledging Babinet.

1880 Alexander Graham Bell invents Photophone in Washington.

1926 C.W. Hansell outlines the principles of fiber-optic imaging bundle.

1930 Heinrich Lamm, a medical student in Munich, first assembled a bundle of transparent fibers to transmit an image.

1954 van Heel in Netherlands and Hopkins and Kapany in UK suggest cladding will improve transmission characteristics.

1960 Maiman fabricates the first laser.

1961 Snitzer publishes the theory of single mode fibers and also fabricates the first fiber

* A nice historical account on the development of the optical fiber has been given in Ref. 28.1 — some of the dates given above are as given in References 28.1 and 28.2.

Above Image: A bundle of optical fibers. Photograph courtesy McGraw Hill Digital Access Library.

laser (barium crown glass doped with Nd^{3+} ions).

1966 Kao and Hockham predict that if it was possible to produce optical fibers with attenuation less than 20 dB/km, it could compete effectively with the conventional communication systems.

1970 Schulz, Keck and Maurer (at Corning Glass in USA) are successful in producing silica fibers with a loss of about 17 dB/km.

1970 Alferov in Leningrad and Panish and Hayashi at Bell Labs demonstrate room temperature operation of Semiconductor Lasers.

1975 Continuous-wave semiconductor laser operating at room temperature commercially available.

1975 Payne and Gambling show very small pulse dispersion at 1.27 μm.

1976 Bell Labs tests parabolic index fiber-optic communication system transmitting 45 Mbits/s.

1978 NTT (Japan) transmits 32 Mbits/s through 53 km of parabolic index fibers at 1.3 μm.

1987 Payne, Mears and Reekie (at University of Southampton) and Desurvire, Becker and Simpson (at AT&T Bell Laboratories) develop EDFAs (Erbium Doped Fiber Amplifiers) operating at 1.55 μm.

1988 First transatlantic fiber cable, using single mode fibers was made operative at 1.3 μm.

1996 Fujitsu, NTT Labs and Bell Labs independently report sending over 1 Tbit/s through one single mode fiber using WDM techniques.

28.1 Introduction

Optics is today responsible for many revolutions in science and technology. This has been primarily brought about by the invention of the laser in 1960 and subsequent development in realizing extremely wide variety of lasers. One of the most important applications of lasers with its direct impact on our lives has been in communications. Use of electromagnetic waves in communication is quite old and the development of the laser gave communication engineers a source of electromagnetic waves with extremely high frequency compared to microwaves and millimeter waves. The development of low loss optical fibers and also EDFAs (Erbium Doped Fiber Amplifiers) led to phenomenal growth in fiber optic communication systems. Today more than 10 terabits of information can be transmitted per second through one hair thin optical fiber; this amount of information is equivalent to simultaneous transmission of about 150 million telephone calls – this is certainly one of the very important technological achievements of the 20th century. We may also mention that in 1961, within one year of the demonstration of the first ever laser by Theodore Maiman, Elias Snitzer fabricated the first fiber laser which is now finding extremely important applications in many diverse areas from defense to sensor physics.

In 2009, Professor Charles Kao was awarded half of the Nobel Prize in Physics for "*groundbreaking achievements concerning the transmission of light in fibers for optical communication*". This is truly a very apt recognition of an area which has touched almost everyone. While awarding the Nobel Prize, the Chair of the Nobel Committee said

> *Charles Kao's discovery made in 1966 led to a breakthrough in Fiber Optics .... and revolutionized the way in which information can be transmitted globally*

The plan of this chapter is as follows: Following a historical introduction, we will use ray optics to discuss the basic principle of light guidance in an optical fiber. This will be followed by a brief discussion in the use of optical fibers in medical endoscopy and also use of plastic fibers in solar lighting. The most important application of optical fibers is in the field of telecommunications and the two important characteristics of the optical fiber (used in telecommunications) are attenuation and pulse dispersion. We will discuss both attenuation and dispersion in what are known as multimode fibers. Although multimode fibers were being used in earlier communication systems, today most fiber based communication systems use single mode fibers and to understand propagation in single mode fibers, it is necessary to use the concept of modes which we will discuss in the following two chapters. Fiber amplifiers and fiber lasers have been briefly discussed in the previous chapter. Other applications of the optical fiber can be found in Refs. 28.3, 28.4, and 28.5.

28.2 Some Historical Remarks LO1

Communication implies transfer of information from one point to another. When it is required to transmit some information such as speech, images, data, etc., over a distance, one generally uses the concept of carrier wave communication. In such a system, the information to be sent modulates an electromagnetic wave such as radio wave, or microwave which acts as a carrier. This modulated wave is then transmitted to the receiver through a channel and the receiver receives the modulated wave and demodulates it to retrieve the signal. For example, the AM broadcast band usually ranges from about 600 kHz to about 2 MHz (the abbreviation AM wave stands for an amplitude modulated wave). If we assume that the highest frequency associated with music is about 20 kHz (= 0.02 MHz), then at a carrier frequency of 1.5 MHz, the spectral range of the AM wave must vary between 1.48 MHz to 1.52 MHz – a bandwidth of 40 kHz. Thus in the entire AM broadcast range from about 600 kHz to about 2 MHz, we can have at most about 30 channels; indeed we will have less number of channels if we use more bandwidth for each channel. On the other hand, in TV transmission since we have to scan pictures, more information needs to be sent and we require much greater bandwidth (about 5 MHz) – necessitating higher carrier frequency; the carrier frequencies associated with the TV broadcast range from about 500 MHz to about 900 MHz.

Since optical beams have frequencies in the range of $10^{14} – 10^{15}$ Hz, the use of such beams as carrier would imply a tremendously large increase in the information transmission capacity of the system as compared to systems employing radio waves or microwaves. It is this large information-carrying capacity of a light beam that has generated interest amongst communication engineers to develop a communication system using light waves as carrier waves.

The idea of using light waves for communication can be traced to as far back as 1880 when Alexander Graham Bell invented the photophone (see Fig. 28.1) shortly after he invented the telephone* in 1876. In this remarkable experiment, speech was transmitted by modulating a light beam, which traveled through air to the receiver. The transmitter consisted of a flexible reflecting diaphragm which could be activated by sound and which was illuminated by sunlight. The reflected light was collimated by a lens and the reflected beam was received by a parabolic reflector placed at a distance. The parabolic reflector concentrated the light on a photoconducting selenium cell, which forms a part of a circuit with a battery and a receiving earphone. Sound waves present in the vicinity of the diaphragm vibrate the diaphragm which leads to a consequent variation of the light reflected by the diaphragm. The variation of the light falling on the selenium cell changes the electrical conductivity of the cell, which in turn changes the current in the electrical circuit. This changing current reproduces the sound on the earphone. To quote from http://en.wikipedia.org/wiki/ Photophone:

> *The* **photophone** *was invented jointly by Alexander Graham Bell and his assistant Charles Sumner Tainter on February 19, 1880. … The device allowed for the transmission of sound on a beam of light. On June 3, 1880, Bell transmitted the first wireless telephone message on his newly-invented photophone. The photophone used crystalline selenium cells as the receiver. This material's electrical resistance varies inversely with the illumination, i.e., its resistance is higher when it is in the dark, and lower when it is lighted. ... The modulation of the light beam was done by a vibrating mirror …. The photophone functioned similarly to the telephone, except the photophone used light as a means of projecting the information, while the telephone relied on electricity.*

To quote from Ref. 28.7

> *In 1880 he* (Graham Bell) *produced his 'photophone' which to the end of his life, he insisted was* **"... the greatest invention I have ever made, greater than the telephone ..."** *Unlike the telephone, it had no commercial value.*

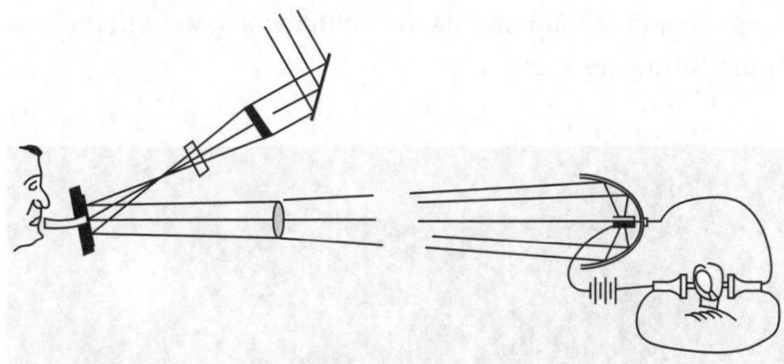

Figure 28.1
The diagram of the Photophone; this has been taken from Alexander Graham Bell's 1880 paper "On the Production and Reproduction of Sound by Light", *American Journal of Sciences*, Third Series, vol. XX, #118, pp. 305–324, October 1880. In this system, sunlight was modulated by a diaphragm and transmitted through a distance of about 200 meters in air to a receiver containing a selenium cell connected to the earphone. Figure adapted from http://en.wikipedia.org/wiki/Image:Photophone.jpg

* Actually according to recent reports (published in June 2002), an Italian immigrant Antonio Meucci, was the inventor of telephone. According to this report, Antonio Meucci demonstrated his "teletrfono" in New York in 1860. Alexander Graham Bell took out his patent 16 years later; some details can be found in http://en.wikipedia.org/wiki/Antonio_Meucci.

The modern impetus for telecommunications with carrier waves at optical frequencies owes its origin to the discovery of the laser in 1960. Earlier, there was no suitable light source available that could reliably be used as the information carrier. We may mention here that although incoherent sources like light emitting diodes (LED) are also often used in present-day optical communication systems, it was discovery of the laser, which triggered serious interest, for the first time, in the development of optical communication systems. The advent of lasers thus immediately triggered a great deal of investigations aimed at examining the possibility of building optical analogues of conventional communication systems. The very first such modern optical communication experiments involved laser beam transmission through the atmosphere. However, it was soon realized that laser beams could not be sent in open atmosphere through reasonably long distances to carry signals unlike, for example, microwave or radio systems operating at longer wavelengths. This is due to the fact that a light beam (of wavelength about 1 μm) is severely attenuated and distorted owing to scattering and absorption by the atmosphere. Thus for reliable light wave communication, it would be necessary to provide a transmission medium that can protect the signal carrying light beam from the vagaries of the terrestrial atmosphere. This guiding medium is the optical fiber (having core diameters from a few μm to about 50 μm) which guides the light beam from one place to another (see Fig. 28.2); the guidance of the light beam through the optical fiber takes place because of the phenomenon of total internal reflection which we will discuss in the following section.

Figure 28.2
A step-index multimode fiber illuminated by HeNe laser with bright output light spot. The light coming out of the optical fiber is primarily due to Rayleigh scattering. [The fiber was produced at the fiber drawing facility at CGCRI, Kolkata. *Photograph courtesy: Dr Shyamal Bhadra and Ms. Atasi Pal*].

In addition to the capability of carrying a huge amount of information, optical fibers fabricated with recently developed technology are characterized by extremely low losses (< 0.25 dB/km) as a consequence of which the distance between two consecutive repeaters (used for amplifying and reshaping the attenuated signals) could be as large as 250 km; the attenuation is usually measured in dB (decibels) – we will define this in Sec. 28.8. We may mention here that a loss of 0.25 dB/km would imply that the power will decrease by a factor of 2 in traversing a distance of about 12 km. It was the important paper of Kao and Hockham in 1966 (Ref. 28.9) which suggested that optical fibers based on silica glass could provide the necessary transmission medium if metallic and other impurities could be removed. To quote from the 1966 paper of Kao and Hockham:

> *Theoretical and experimental studies indicate that a cladded glass fiber with a core diameter of about λ_0 and an overall diameter of about 1000 λ_0 represents a possible practical optical waveguide with important potential as a new form of communication medium. The refractive index of the core needs to be about 1% higher than that of cladding. However, the attenuation should be around 20 dB/km which is much higher than the lower limit of loss figure imposed by fundamental mechanisms.*

Indeed this 1966 paper triggered the beginning of serious research in purifying silica and developing low loss optical fibers. In 1970, Kapron, Keck and Maurer (at Corning Glass in USA) were successful in producing silica fibers with a loss of about 17 dB/km at a wavelength of 0.633 μm (Ref. 28.10). Since then, the technology has advanced with tremendous rapidity. By 1985 glass fibers were routinely produced with extremely low losses (< 0.25 dB/km). Figure 28.3 shows the

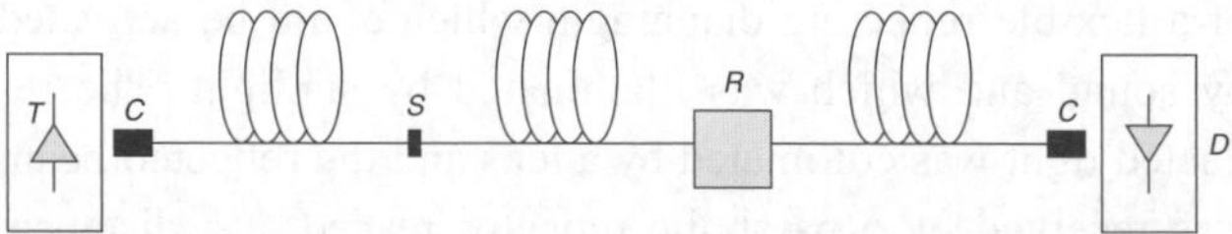

Figure 28.3
Typical optical fiber communication system. It consists of a transmitter *T* which could be either a laser diode or an LED, the light from which is coupled into an optical fiber by means of a connector *C*. Along the path of the optical fiber, there are splices (denoted by *S*) which are permanent joints between sections of fibers and also repeaters (denoted by *R*) which boost the signal and correct any distortion that may have accumulated along the path of the fiber. At the end of the link, a coupler *C* is used to couple the light to a photo detector *D* and processed to retrieve the signal.

basic layout of a typical optical fiber communication system. It consists of a transmitter which could be either an LED or a laser diode, the light from which is coupled into an optical fiber. Along the path of the optical fiber, there are splices which are permanent joints between sections of fibers and also repeaters which boost the signal and correct any distortion that may have accumulated along the path of the fiber. At the end of the link, the light is detected by a photodetector and electronically processed to retrieve the signal.

28.3 Total Internal Reflection LO2

At the heart of an optical communication system is the optical fiber that acts as the transmission channel carrying the light beam loaded with information; and as mentioned earlier, the guidance of the light beam (through the optical fiber) takes place because of the phenomenon of total internal reflection (often abbreviated as TIR). Now, if a ray is incident at the interface of a rarer medium ($n_2 < n_1$) then the ray will bend away from the normal [see Fig. 28.4(b)]. The angle of incidence, for which the angle of refraction is 90°, is known as the critical angle and is denoted by ϕ_c. Thus, when

$$\phi_1 = \phi_c = \sin^{-1}\left(\frac{n_2}{n_1}\right) \tag{28.1}$$

the angle of refraction $\phi_2 = 90°$. When the angle of incidence exceeds the critical angle (i.e., when $\phi_1 > \phi_c$), there is no refracted ray and we have what is known as total internal reflection see Fig. 28.4(b). We may mention here that for $\phi_1 > \phi_c$, energy does penetrate into the rarer medium resulting in what is known as an evanescent wave (see Sec. 23.6); however, the reflection coefficient is unity.

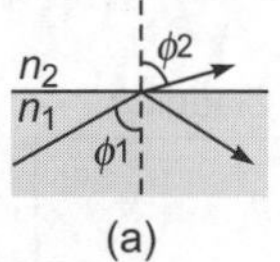

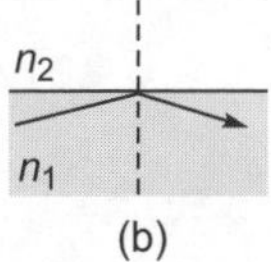

Figure 28.4

(a) For a ray incident on a rarer medium ($n_2 < n_1$), the angle of refraction is greater than the angle of incidence, (b) if the angle of incidence is greater than critical angle, it will undergo total internal reflection.

EXAMPLE 28.1 For the glass-air interface, $n_1 = 1.5$, $n_2 = 1.0$ and the critical angle is given by $\phi_c \approx 41.8°$. On the other hand, for the glass-water interface, $n_1 = 1.5$, $n_2 = 1.33$ and $\phi_c \approx 62.7°$

The phenomenon of total internal reflection can be very easily demonstrated through a simple experiment as shown in Fig. 28.5. When the angle of incidence (at the water-air interface) exceeds the critical angle ($\approx 62.7°$), the laser beam undergoes total internal reflection. If you do this experiment in your laboratory, then in order to see the laser beam propagating through water, you may have to add a few drops of milk.

Although the phenomenon of total internal reflection has been known for hundreds of years, light guidance by total internal reflection was first carried out by Daniel Colladon in 1841 as shown in Fig. 28.6; light undergoes total internal reflection at the water-air interface and travels along the curved path of water emanating from an illuminated vessel. Later Colladon wrote:

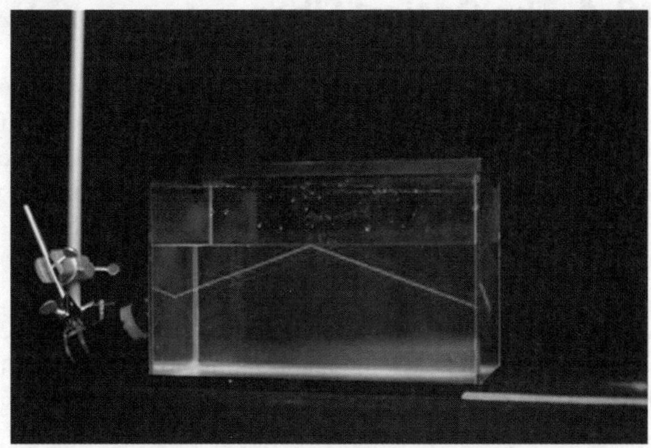

Figure 28.5

Total internal reflection of a laser beam at the interface of water and air. Photograph adapted from http://ecphysicsworld.blogspot.in/2012/03/total-internal-reflection.html.

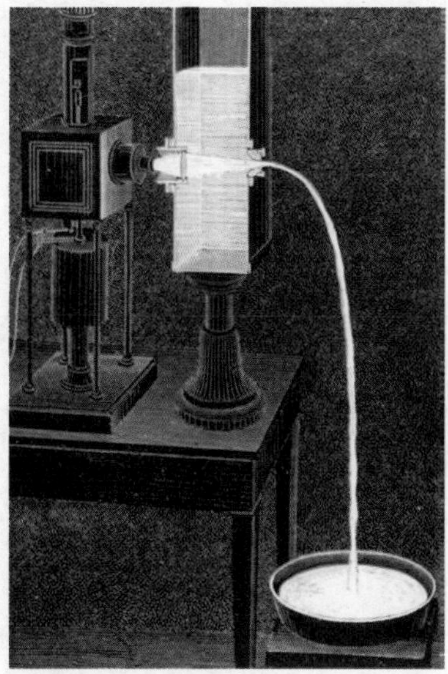

Figure 28.6

Diagram from Colladon's original paper; [Adapted from http://en.wikipedia.org/wiki/ Optical_fiber#mediaviewer/File:Danielcoll- adon%27s_lightfountain_or_Light-fountain_or_Lightpipe, LaNature (magazine, 1884.JPG)]

I managed to illuminate the interior of a stream in a dark space. I have discovered that this strange arrangement offers .... one of the most beautiful, and most curious experiments that one can perform in a course on Optics.

As mentioned by Johnston (Ref. 28.16) "For many decades, the pioneers of fiber optics development erroneously assigned the credit for light guiding phenomenon to the charismatic Tyndall instead of to Daniel Colladon". For a nice historical survey, we refer the reader to Ref. 28.1 and 28.17.

28.4 The Optical Fiber

LO3

Figure 28.7(a) shows an optical fiber, which consists of a (cylindrical) central dielectric core cladded by a material of slightly lower refractive index. The corresponding refractive index distribution (in the transverse direction) is given by

$$\left.\begin{aligned} n &= n_1 \quad 0 < r < a \\ &= n_2 \quad r > a \end{aligned}\right\} \tag{28.2}$$

where n_1 and $n_2(< n_1)$ represent respectively the refractive indices of core and cladding and a represents the radius of the core. We define a parameter Δ through the following equations:

$$\Delta \equiv \frac{n_1^2 - n_2^2}{2n_1^2} \tag{28.3}$$

When $n_1 \approx n_2$, i.e., when $\Delta << 1$ (as is true for most silica fibers)

$$\Delta = \frac{n_1 - n_2}{n_1}\frac{n_1 + n_2}{2n_1} \approx \frac{n_1 - n_2}{n_2} \approx \frac{n_1 - n_2}{n_1} \tag{28.4}$$

For a typical (multimoded) fiber, $a \approx 25$ μm, $n_2 \approx 1.45$ (pure silica) and $\Delta \approx 0.01$ giving a core index of $n_1 \approx 1.465$. The cladding is usually pure silica while the core is usually silica doped with germanium; doping by germanium results in an increase of refractive index.

Now, for a ray entering the fiber, if the angle of incidence (at the core-cladding interface) is greater than the critical angle ϕ_c, then the ray will undergo TIR at that interface. Thus, for TIR to occur at the core-cladding interface.

$$\phi > \phi_c = \sin^{-1}\left(\frac{n_2}{n_1}\right) \tag{28.5}$$

Further, because of the cylindrical symmetry in the fiber structure, the ray will suffer TIR at the lower interface also and therefore get guided through the core by repeated total internal reflections. Even for a bent fiber, light guidance can occur through multiple total internal reflections. Figure 28.2 shows the actual guidance of a light beam as it propagates through a long optical fiber; in the photograph, the light emerging from the side of the fiber is mainly due to Rayleigh scattering, the same phenomenon that is responsible for the blue color of the sky and the red color of the rising or the setting sun (see Sec. 6.6).

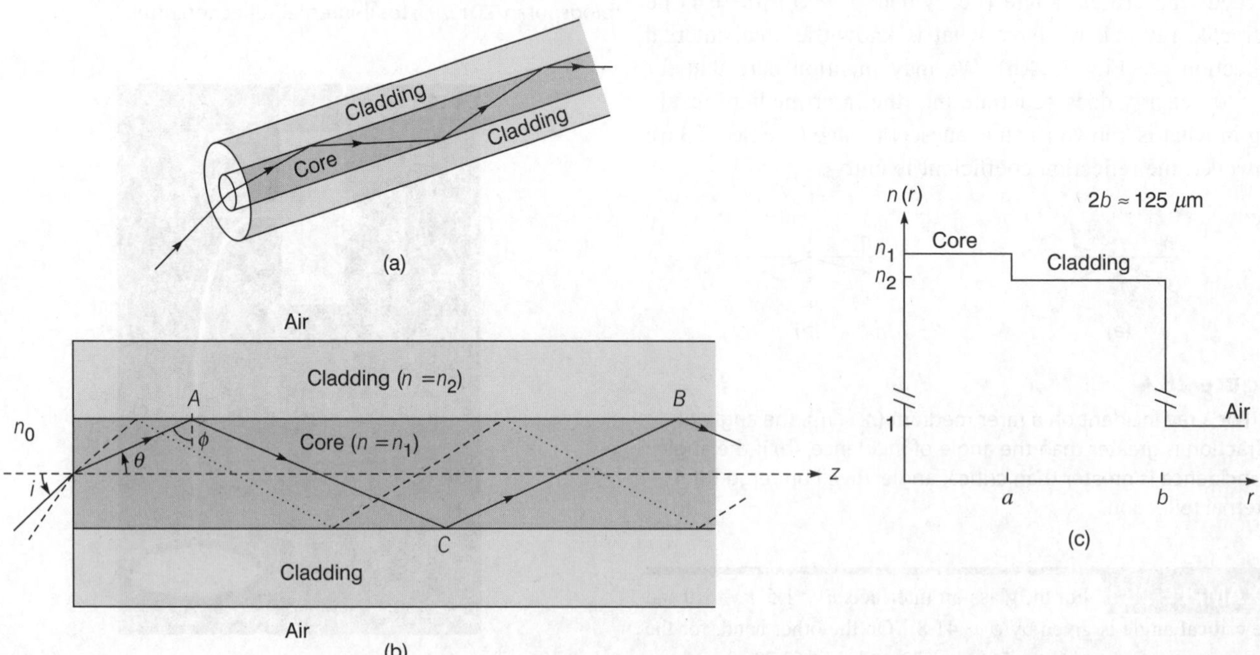

Figure 28.7
(a) A glass fiber consists of a cylindrical central core cladded by a material of slightly lower refractive index. (b) Light rays incident on the core-cladding interface at an angle greater than the critical angle are trapped inside the core of the fiber. (c) Refractive index distribution for a step-index fiber. The diameter of the cladding is almost always 125 μm. For multimode fibers, the core diameters are usually in the range of 25–50 μm. For single-mode fibers, the core diameters are usually between 5 and 10 μm.

The necessity of a cladded fiber (Fig. 28.7) rather than a bare fiber i.e., without a cladding, was felt because of the fact that for transmission of light from one place to another, the fiber must be supported, and supporting structures may considerably distort the fiber thereby affecting the guidance of the light wave. This can be avoided by choosing a sufficiently thick cladding. Further, in a fiber bundle, in the absence of the cladding, light can leak through from one fiber to another. The idea of adding a second layer of glass (namely, the cladding) came in 1955 from Hopkins and Kapany in the UK; however, during that time the use of optical fibers was mainly in image transmission rather than in communications. Indeed, the early pioneering works in fiber optics (in the 50's) were by Hopkins and Kapany in the UK and by Van Heel in Holland; these works led to the use of the fiber in optical devices (see Ref. 28.18).

The retina of the human eye consists of a large number of rods and cones which have the same kind of structure as the optical fiber, i.e. they consist of dielectric cylindrical rods surrounded by another dielectric of slightly lower refractive index (see Fig. 28.8). The core diameters are in the range of a few microns. The light absorbed in these "light guides" generates electrical signals, which are then transmitted to the brain through various nerves.

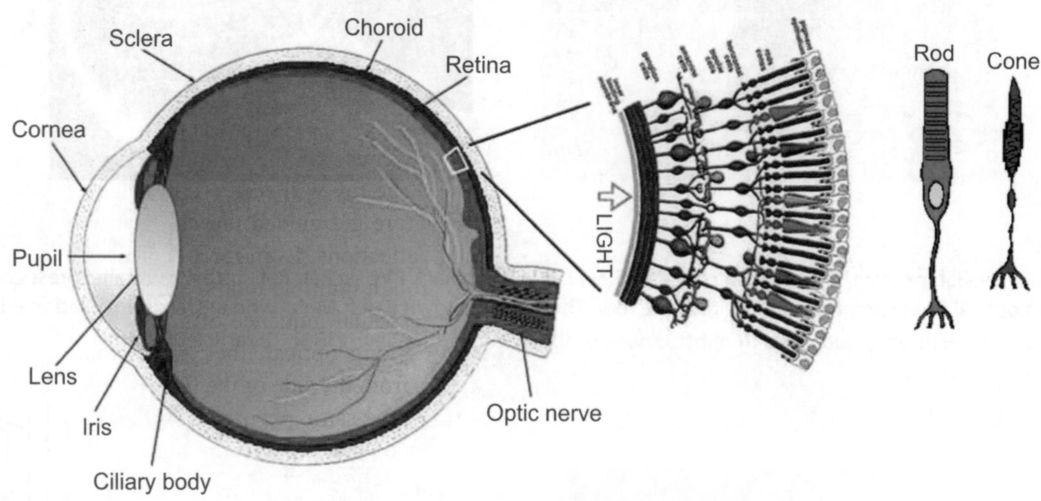

Figure 28.8

The rods and cones of the eye; adapted from http://www.biologymad.com/NervousSystem/eyenotes.htm and http://faculty.washington.edu/chudler/retina.html

28.4.1 Large Diameter Plastic Fibers

We should mention that Plastic Optical Fibers [see Fig. 28.9(a)] are now extensively used by many companies in bringing in sunlight inside the rooms. In Fig. 28.9(b) we have shown Jeff Muhs surrounded by the light carrying optical fiber, who at Oak Ridge National Laboratory developed this solar technology. Figure 28.10(a) shows the basic layout for using sunlight to illuminate dark rooms, Fig. 28.10(b) shows the Patent describing light gathering techniques and Fig. 28.10(c) shows the light collectors on the roof top. Figure 28.11(a) shows optical fibers bringing sunlight to rooms. Unfortunately the losses in such fibers are quite high; Fig. 28.11(b) shows that there is 50% decrease in power in traversing a distance of only about 50 feet. Quoting from an article entitled Letting The Sunshine In (Ref. 28.19)

> *A rooftop hybrid solar lighting (HSL) system collects, concentrates, and transmits sunlight through optical fibers to hybrid light fixtures inside the building, which also contain high-efficiency fluorescent lighting. When the transmitted sunlight completely illuminates each room, the electric lights stay off…*

Plastic Optical Fibers are briefly discussed in Sec. 28.13.

28.5 Why Glass Fibers? LO4

In telecommunications and also in sensors, one always uses glass fibers. Why glass fibers? Quoting Professor W.A. Gambling, who is one of the pioneers in the field of fiber optics (Ref. 28.2): *We note that glass is a remarkable material which has been in use in 'pure' form for at least 9000 years. The compositions remained relatively unchanged for millennia and its uses have been widespread. The three most important properties of glass which makes it of unprecedented value are:*

1. *First, there is a wide range of accessible temperatures where its viscosity is variable and can be well controlled unlike most materials, like water and metals which remain liquid until they are cooled down to their freezing temperatures and then suddenly become solid. Glass, on*

the other hand, does not solidify at a discrete freezing temperature but gradually becomes stiffer and stiffer and eventually becoming hard. In the transition region, it can be easily drawn into a thin fiber.

(a)

(b)

Figure 28.9

(a) Commercially available 8 mm/11 mm solid core end glow cable with black PVC jacket. Ref. http://www.aliexpress.com.
(b) Wrapped in optical fiber carrying sunlight from the roof. The person shown is Jeff Muhs who at Oak Ridge National Laboratory developed this solar technology; adapted from http://web.ornl.gov/info/ornlreview/v38_1_05/article09.shtml

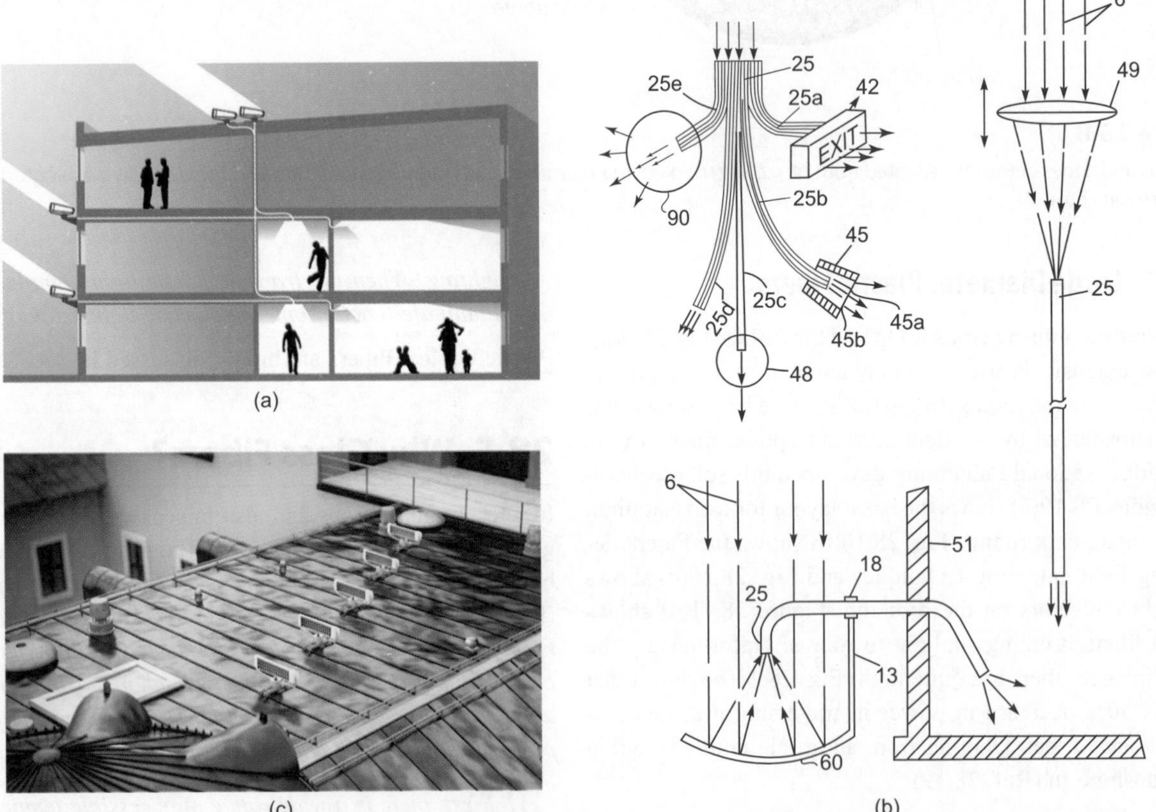

Figure 28.10

(a) Basic layout for using sunlight to illuminate dark rooms. (b) An US Patent describing light gathering techniques. (c) Collectors on the roof top. Diagrams adapted from *http://www.parans.com/eng/sp3*; used with permission.

2. *The second most important property is that highly pure silica is characterized with extremely low-loss; i.e., it is highly transparent. Today in most commercially available silica fibers 96% of the power gets transmitted after propagating through 1 km of optical fiber. This indeed represents a truly remarkable achievement.*
3. *The third most remarkable property is the intrinsic strength of glass. Its strength is about 2000,000 lb/in² so that a glass fiber of the type used in the telephone network and having a diameter (125 μm) of twice the thickness of a human hair, can support a load of 40 lb.*

(a)

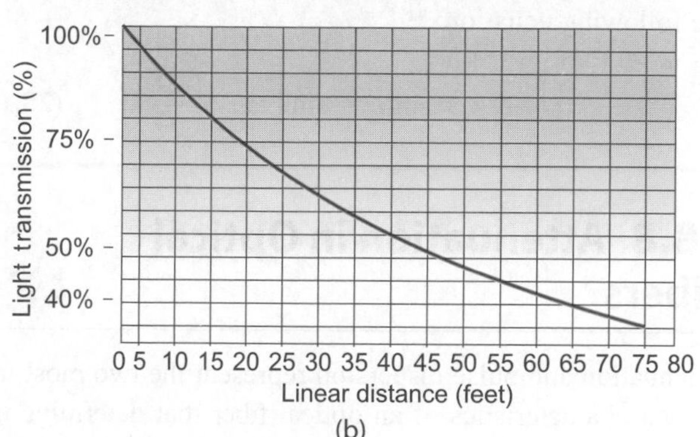

(b)

Figure 28.11

(a) Optical fibers transporting sunlight into a room. (b) Typical loss curve for a plastic optical fiber. Diagrams adapted from *http://parans.com/eng/sp3/L1_luminaire.cfm*; used with permission.

28.6 The Coherent Bundle

LO5

If a large number of fibers are put together, it forms what is known as a bundle. If the fibers are not aligned, i.e. they are all jumbled up, the bundle is said to form an incoherent bundle. However, if the fibers are aligned properly, i.e., if the relative positions of the fibers in the input and output ends are the same, the bundle is said to form a coherent bundle. Now, if a particular fiber is illuminated at one of its ends, then there will be a bright spot at the other end of the same fiber; thus a coherent bundle will transmit the image from one end to another (see Fig. 28.12).

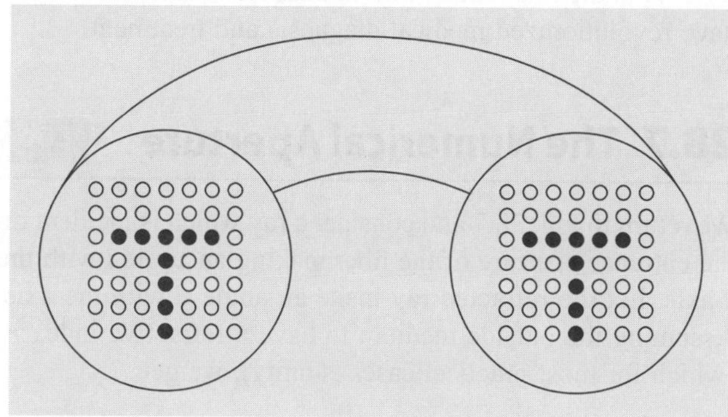

Figure 28.12

A bundle of aligned fibers. A bright (or dark) spot at the input end of the fiber produces a bright (or dark) spot at the output end. Thus an image will be transmitted (in the form of bright and dark spots) through a bundle of aligned fibers.

In an incoherent bundle the output image will be scrambled. Incoherent bundles are used in illumination such as in traffic lights or road signs. They can also be used as cold light sources by removing the heat radiation using a filter at the input to the fiber bundle. The light emerging from the bundle is also free from UV radiation and is suitable for illumination of paintings etc. in museums.

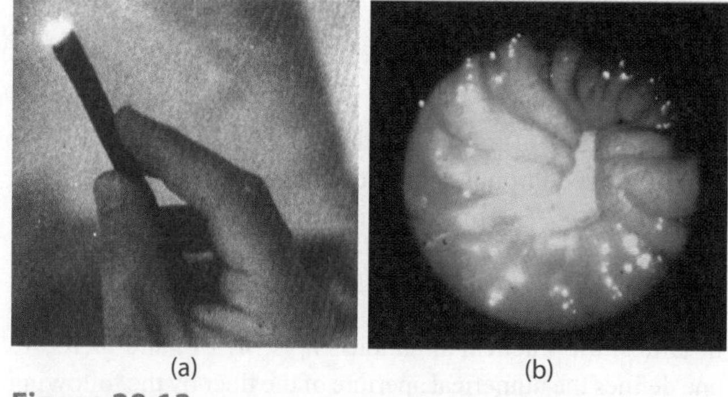

(a) (b)

Figure 28.13

(a) An optical fiber medical probe called an endoscope enables doctors to examine the inner parts of the human body, and (b) a stomach ulcer as seen through an endoscope. [*Photographs courtesy: United States Information Service, New Delhi*].

Perhaps the most important application of a coherent bundle is in a fiber-optic endoscope where it can be put inside a human body and the interior of the body can be viewed from outside, thus avoiding invasive surgery. In an endoscope; for illuminating the portion that is to be seen, the bundle is enclosed in a sheath of fibers which carry light from outside to the interior of the body (see Fig. 28.13). An incoherent bundle is often used to illuminate the area under investigation. And, a coherent bundle is used to transmit back the image. A typical fiber endoscope can have about 10000 fibers which would form a bundle of about 10 mm in diameter. Fiber endoscopes have revolutionized medical diagnosis and treatment.

28.7 The Numerical Aperture

LO6

We return to Fig. 28.7 and consider a ray which is incident on the entrance aperture of the fiber making an angle i with the z-axis. Let the refracted ray make an angle θ with the axis. Assuming the outside medium to have a refractive index n_0 (which for most practical cases is unity), we get

$$\frac{\sin i}{\sin \theta} = \frac{n_1}{n_0} \tag{28.6}$$

Obviously, if this ray has to suffer total internal reflection at the core-cladding interface,

$$\sin \phi (= \cos \theta) > \frac{n_2}{n_1} \tag{28.7}$$

or

$$\sin\theta < \sqrt{1-\left(\frac{n_2}{n_1}\right)^2} \Rightarrow \sin i < \sqrt{\frac{\left(n_1^2 - n_2^2\right)}{n_0^2}} \tag{28.8}$$

In most cases, the outside medium is air, i.e.; $n_0 = 1$, and therefore the maximum value of sin i for a ray to be guided is given by

$$\sin i_m = \begin{cases} \sqrt{n_1^2 - n_2^2} & \text{if} \quad n_1^2 < n_2^2 + 1 \\ 1 & \text{if} \quad n_1^2 < n_2^2 + 1 \end{cases} \tag{28.9}$$

Thus, if a cone of light is incident on one end of the fiber, it will be guided through it provided the semi-angle of the cone is less than i_m. The quantity sin i_m is known as the numerical aperture (NA) of the fiber and is a measure of the *light gathering power of the fiber.*

In almost all practical situations, $n_1^2 < n_2^2 + 1$, and therefore one defines the numerical aperture of the fiber by the following equation:

$$\text{NA} = \sqrt{n_1^2 - n_2^2} \tag{28.10}$$

EXAMPLE 28.2 For a typical step-index (multimode) fiber with $n_1 \approx 1.45$ and $\Delta \approx 0.01$, we get

$$\sin i_m \approx 0.205 \Rightarrow i_m \approx 12°$$

Now, in a short length of an optical fiber, if all rays between i = 0 and i_m are launched, then, the light coming out of the fiber will also appear as a cone of semi-angle i_m emanating from the fiber end. If we now allow this beam to fall normally on a white paper (see Fig. 28.14) and measure its diameter we can easily calculate the NA of the fiber. This allows us to estimate the NA of the optical fiber by a very simple experiment. The procedure is as follows:

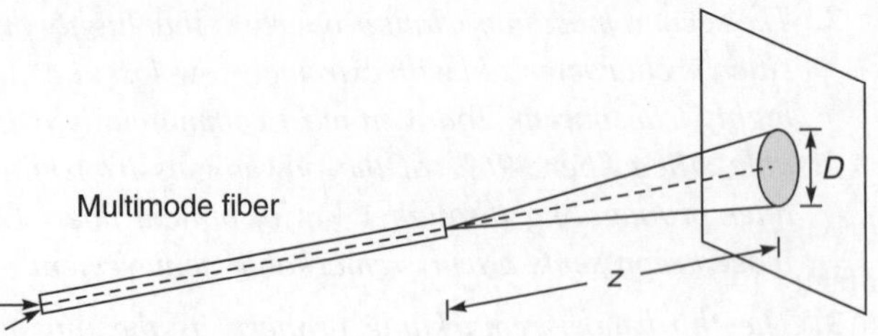

Figure 28.14

Measurement of the diameter D of the spot on a screen placed at a far-field distance z from the output end of a multimode fiber can be used to measure the NA of the fiber.

Several concentric circles of increasing radii-say, starting from 0.5 cm to 1.5 cm, are drawn on a small paper screen and the screen is positioned in the far field such that the axis of the fiber, at the output end, passes perpendicularly through the center of these circles on the screen. The fiber end, which is mounted on a *XYZ*-stack, is moved slightly towards or away from the screen so that one of the circles just circumscribes the far-field radiation spot. The distance z between the fiber-end and the screen, and the diameter D of the coinciding circle are measured accurately. The NA is calculated using the following equation:

$$\text{NA} = \sin i_m = \sin\left[\tan^{-1}\left(\frac{D}{2z}\right)\right] \tag{28.11}$$

28.8 Attenuation in Optical Fibers

LO7

Attenuation and pulse dispersion represent the two most important characteristics of an optical fiber that determine the information carrying capacity of a fiber-optic communication system. Obviously, lower the attenuation (and similarly lower the dispersion), greater will be the required repeater spacing and therefore lower will be the cost of the communication system. Pulse dispersion will be discussed in the next section, while in this section, we will briefly discuss the various attenuation mechanisms in an optical fiber.

The attenuation of an optical beam is usually measured in decibels (dB). If an input power P_{input} results in an output power P_{output}, then the loss in decibels is given by

$$\text{Loss (dB)} = 10 \log_{10}\left(\frac{P_{\text{input}}}{P_{\text{output}}}\right) \tag{28.12}$$

Thus,

if the output power is the same as the input power, then the loss is = 0 dB;

if the output power is only one tenth of the input power, then the loss is = 10 dB;

if the output power is only one hundredth of the input power, then the loss is = 20 dB; and

if the output power is only one thousandth of the input power, then the loss is = 30 dB; etc.

Also, in a typical fiber amplifier, a power amplification by a factor of 100 implies a power gain of 20 dB and a gain of 30 dB would imply a power amplification by a factor of 1000.

EXAMPLE 28.3 If the output power is only half of the input power, then the loss is 10 log 2 ≈ 3 dB. On the other hand, if 96% of the light is transmitted through the fiber, the loss is

$$10 \log \left(\frac{1}{0.96}\right) \approx 0.18 \text{ dB}.$$

Figure 28.15 shows the variation of the loss coefficient (i.e., loss per kilometer length of the optical fiber) as a function of wavelength of a typical silica optical fiber. One can notice two important low loss windows around 1.3 μm and 1.55 μm. Typical losses at these wavelengths are about 0.8 dB/km and about 0.25 dB/km respectively. This is the reason why most fiber optic systems operate either in the 1.3 μm window or 1.55 μm window. The latter window has become extremely important in view of the availability of optical amplifiers (see Sec. 27.1.3).

The losses are caused due to various mechanisms such as Rayleigh scattering, absorption due to metallic impurities and water and due to intrinsic absorption of silica molecule itself. Even 1 ppm (part per million) of iron can cause a loss of about 0.68 dB/km around 1.1 μm. Similarly a concentration of 1 ppm of OH^- ion can cause a loss of 4 dB/km at 1.38 μm. This shows the level of purity that is required to achieve very low loss optical fibers. In Fig. 28.15 the two peaks are due to traces of water (and other impurities) present in the fiber. However, with sophisticated fabrication techniques it is possible to remove these impurities and one can obtain very low loss in the wavelength region 1.2 μm to 1.65 μm– see Fig. 28.16.

It is possible to demonstrate the wavelength dependence of Rayleigh scattering using a long optical fiber. White light (from a lamp such as a tungsten halogen lamp) is coupled into approximately a 1 km long multimode optical fiber and we look into the output and notice the color of the light. Next, we cut the fiber leaving about 1 m from the input end of the fiber and repeat the experiment with this 1 m of the fiber. One would see that in the former case, the emerging light looks reddish while in the latter case it looks white. This difference is due to the decrease of loss with increase in wavelength due to Rayleigh scattering; light wavelengths toward the blue region have suffered greater scattering out of the fiber than those of the red region. Thus although at the input end all wavelengths are coupled, there is more power in the red part at the output giving it a reddish color.

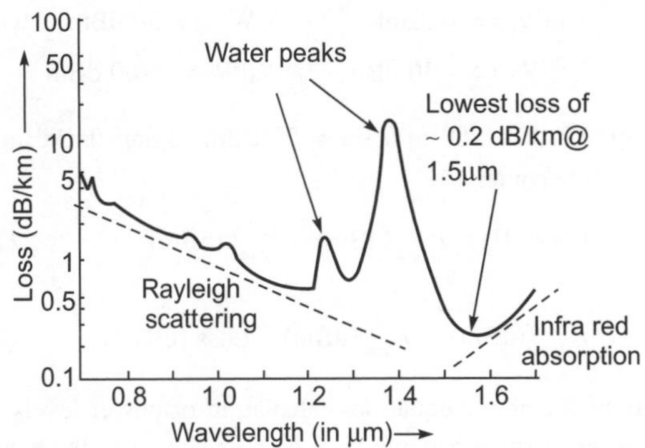

Figure 28.15

Typical wavelength dependence of loss for a silica fiber. The peaks in the attenuation curve in the wavelength regions 1.25 μm and 1.40 μm are due to the presence of minute amount of water and other impurities. Notice that the lowest loss occurs at 1.55 μm. [Adapted from Ref. 28.14].

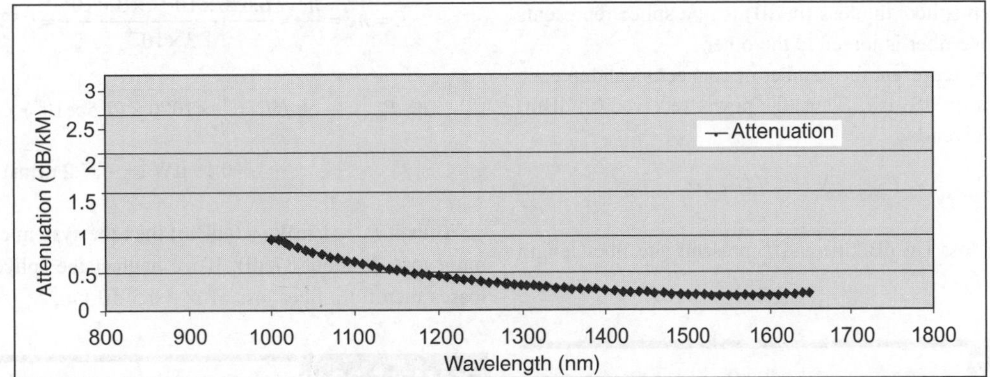

Figure 28.16

Using sophisticated techniques, it is possible to remove the trace amount of water and other impurities. The loss is less than 0.4 dB/km in the entire wavelength range from 1250 nm to 1600 nm. The diagram corresponds to a fiber fabricated by Sterlite Industries at Aurangabad and provided to the author by Mr S Bhatia of Sterlite Industries.

EXAMPLE 28.4 Calculation of losses using dB scale becomes very easy. For example, if we have a 40 km fiber link (with a loss of 0.4 dB/km) having 3 connectors in its path and if each connector has a loss of 1.8 dB then the total loss will be 0.4 dB/km × 40 km + 3 × 1.8 dB = 21.4 dB.

EXAMPLE 28.5 Let us assume that the power of a 5 mW laser beam decreases to 30 μW after traversing through 40 km of an optical fiber. The attenuation of the fiber is therefore

$$\frac{1}{40}\left[10 \log\left(\frac{5 \text{ mW}}{0.03 \text{ mW}}\right)\right] = 0.56 \text{ dB/km}$$

It is often very convenient to measure the power level in dBm which is defined as

$$P(\text{dBm}) = 10 \log_{10} P(\text{mW}) \quad \textbf{(28.13)}$$

Thus,

1 mW ⇔ 0 dBm	1 W ⇔ 30 dBm
1 μW ⇔ −30 dBm	1 nW ⇔ −60 dBm

Similarly, 0.2 W = 200 mW ⇔ ≈ 23 dBm. Using the dBm scale Eq. (28.12) becomes

$$\text{Loss(dB)} = P_{\text{input}}(\text{dBm}) - P_{\text{output}}(\text{dBm}) \quad \textbf{(28.14)}$$

or,

$$P_{\text{output}}(\text{dBm}) = P_{\text{input}}(\text{dBm}) - \text{Loss (dB)} \quad \textbf{(28.15)}$$

Because of the above equation, calculation of power levels losses using the dBm scale become very easy as shown in the examples below.

EXAMPLE 28.6 Consider a 5 mW laser beam passing through a 40 km fiber link of loss 0.5 dB/km. The total loss is 20 dB. Since the input power of 5 mW corresponds to 6.99 dBm, the power at the output would be –13.01 dBm which is equal to 0.05 mW.

Between a source and a detector, let N_s represent the number of splices and in each splice, the loss (in dB) is l_s; a splice represents the point where one fiber is joined to the other.

Similarly, let N_c represent the number of connectors and in each connector the loss (in dB) is l_c. Thus, the power received (in dBm) at the detector is given by

$$P_{\text{received}} = P_{\text{input}} - N_c l_c - N_s l_s - L\alpha$$

where α = Fiber loss (in dB/km) and L presents the fiber length in km.

EXAMPLE 28.7 Let P_{input} = 1 mW ⇔ 0 dBm; l_c = 1 dB/connector, N_c = 2; l_s = 0.5 dB/splice, N_s = 4; α = 0.5 dB/km, L = 40 km. Thus the loss in the fiber is 20 dB and

$$P_{\text{received}} = 0 - 2 - 2 - 20 = -24 \text{ dBm} \Leftrightarrow \approx 4 \,\mu\text{W}$$

EXAMPLE 28.8 In a typical optical communication system, let the available components be as given below:

Laser Output	1.5 mW (⇔ 1.76 dBm)	
Laser Wavelength	1300 nm	
Fiber Loss	1 dB/km	
Required Length of Link	20 km	
Loss in Fiber	20 × 1 dB/km	20 dB
Splice (every 5 km) Loss	0.5 dB/splice	
Splices 3 × 0.5 dB		1.5 dB
Laser to Fiber Coupling Loss		8 dB
Fiber to Detector Loss		2 dB
	Total Loss	31.5 dB

Since the laser power is 1.76 dBm, the power available at the detector is –29.74 dBm (≈ 1.06 μW) and if the Detector Margin is –40 dBm [i.e., the detector is able to detect –40 dBm of power (= 0.1 μW)], then there is an excess power margin of 10.26 dBm at the detector. The above represents a typical power budget calculation.

28.8.1 The Attenuation Limit

Let N_p represent the minimum number of photons (per bit of information) required for the pulse to be detected. The corresponding average optical power received by the detector would be given by

$$P_{\min} = \frac{1}{2} N_p BE \quad \textbf{(28.16)}$$

where $E = h\nu$ = energy of each photon and B represents the bit rate (the number of bits per second) in the communication system. Typically $N_p \approx 1000$ and $B \approx 2.5$ G bits/s.

EXAMPLE 28.9 For λ_0 = 1.3 μm,

$$E = h\nu = \frac{hc}{\lambda_0} \approx \frac{6.626 \times 10^{-34} \times 3 \times 10^8}{1.3 \times 10^{-6}} \approx 1.53 \times 10^{-19} \text{ J}$$

$$\Rightarrow P_{\min} = \frac{1}{2} N_P B E \approx \frac{1}{2} \times 1000 \times (2.5 \times 10^9) \times (1.53 \times 10^{-19})$$

$$\approx 0.19 \,\mu\text{W} \; (= -37.2 \text{ dBm})$$

Thus if $P_{in} \approx$ 1 mW (= 0 dBm) then the system can have a maximum loss of about 37 dB. If we neglect the splice and connector losses then for a fiber loss of α = 0.5 dB/km, $L_{\max} \approx$ 70 km.

EXAMPLE 28.10 For $\lambda_0 \approx$ 155 μm,

$$E = h\nu = \frac{hc}{\lambda_0} \approx \frac{6.626 \times 10^{-34} \times 3 \times 10^8}{1.55 \times 10^{-6}} \approx 1.28 \times 10^{-19} \text{ J}$$

$$\Rightarrow P_{min} = \frac{1}{2} N_P B E \approx \frac{1}{2} \times 1000 \times (2.5 \times 10^9) \times (1.28 \times 10^{-19})$$

$$\approx 0.16 \, \mu\text{W} \; (\approx -38 \text{ dBm})$$

Thus if $P_{in} \approx 1$ mW (= 0 dBm) then the system can have a maximum loss of about 38 dB. If we neglect the splice and connector losses then for a fiber loss of $\alpha = 0.2$ dB/km, $L_{max} \approx 190$ km.

28.9 Multimode Fibers

LO8

In the next section we will discuss broadening of an optical pulse as it passes through a multimode optical fiber. The obvious question that arises is as to what do we understand by a multimode optical fiber? The concept of modes will be discussed in the following two chapters – it will suffice here to say that if we solve Maxwell's equations for an optical waveguide then we obtain discrete modes which represent *transverse field distributions that suffer only a phase change as they propagate through the waveguide along z*. Each mode has a specific transverse field distribution and also a specific group velocity [see Sections 29.5 and 30.5]. Now, while studying the propagation of rays in an optical fiber [see Fig. 28.7(b)], we had assumed that all rays characterized by $\theta > \theta_c$ will be guided through the optical fiber. In Sec. 29.3, we will show by solving Maxwell's equations that each mode of the waveguide may be assumed to correspond to a 'discrete' value of θ which would imply discrete ray paths; thus, qualitatively speaking, we may say that only discrete values of θ are possible. When the number of such discrete ray paths becomes very large, we have what is known as a multimode fiber and may assume the validity of geometrical optics.

28.9.1 Power Law Profile

A broad class of *multimoded* graded index fibers can be described by the following refractive index distribution (see Fig. 28.17):

$$n^2(r) = n_1^2 \left[1 - 2\Delta \left(\frac{r}{a} \right)^q \right]; \quad 0 < r < a \qquad \textbf{(28.17)}$$

$$= n_2^2 = n_1^2(1 - 2\Delta); \qquad r > a$$

where r corresponds to a cylindrical radial coordinate, n_1 represents the value of the refractive index on the axis (i.e., at $r = 0$), n_2 represents the refractive index of the cladding and a represents the radius of the core. Equation (28.17) describes what is usually referred to as a power law profile or a *q*-profile; $q = 1$, $q = 2$ and $q = \infty$ correspond to the linear, parabolic, and step-index profiles, respectively (see Fig. 28.17). One defines the normalized waveguide parameter

$$V = \frac{2\pi}{\lambda_0} a \sqrt{n_1^2 - n_2^2} \qquad \textbf{(28.18)}$$

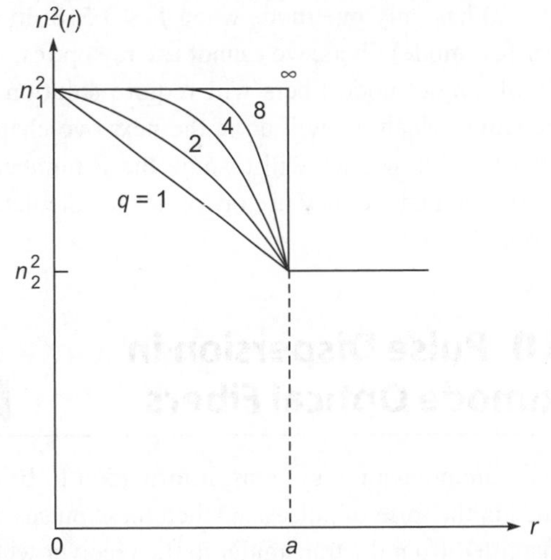

Figure 28.17

Power law profiles for the refractive index distribution given by (Eq. 28.17).

where λ_0 is the wavelength of operation. The waveguide parameter V is an extremely important parameter describing the optical fiber and will be discussed in the next two chapters. The total number of modes in a highly multimoded graded index optical fiber characterized by Eq. (28.17) are approximately given by (see, e.g., Ref. 28.15).

$$N \approx \frac{q}{2(2+q)} V^2 \qquad \textbf{(28.19)}$$

Thus, a parabolic index fiber ($q = 2$) with $V = 10$ will support approximately 25 modes. Similarly, a step-index fiber ($q = \infty$) with $V = 10$ will support approximately 50 modes. When the fiber supports such a large number of modes, the fiber is said to be a multimoded fiber. Each mode travels with a slightly different group velocity leading to what is known as *intermodal dispersion*. In References 28.15 and 28.22 it has been shown that for a highly multimoded graded index optical fiber, the value of intermodal dispersion is very nearly the same as obtained from ray analysis. Thus in highly multimoded fibers ($V \geq 10$), one is justified to use the ray-optics result for *intermodal (or ray) dispersion*. We may note that for a given fiber (i.e., for given values of n_1, n_2 and a), the value of V depends on the operating wavelength λ_0; thus, as the wavelength becomes smaller, the value of V (and hence the number of modes) increases and in the limit of the operating wavelength becoming very small, we have the geometric optics limit. Also, as will be shown in Chapter 30, a step-index fiber ($q = \infty$) has only one mode when $V < 2.4048$ and we have what is known as a single mode fiber. For a given step-index fiber, the wavelength at which V becomes equal to 2.4045 is known as the "cut-off wavelength" and for all wavelengths greater than the "cut-off wavelength" the fiber is said to be single moded (see Sec. 30.3.1). A parabolic fiber ($q = 2$) has only one mode when $V < 3.518$. In single-mode (or few mode) fibers, we cannot use ray optics; indeed, analysis of single mode fibers will require solution of the wave equation which we will do in the next two chapters.

In all what follows, we will assume the V number to be large (≥ 10), so that we may use ray optics to calculate pulse dispersion.

28.10 Pulse Dispersion in Multimode Optical Fibers

LO8

In digital communication systems, information to be sent is first coded in the form of pulses and then these pulses of light are transmitted from the transmitter to the receiver where the information is decoded. Larger the number of pulses that can be sent per unit time and still be resolvable at the receiver end, larger would be the transmission capacity of the system. A pulse of light sent into a fiber broadens in time as it propagates through the fiber; this phenomenon is known as pulse dispersion and occurs primarily because of the following mechanisms:

1. In multimode fibers, different rays take different times to propagate through a given length of the fiber. We will discuss this for a step-index fiber and for a parabolic index fiber in this and the following sections. In the language of wave optics, this is known as *intermodal dispersion* because it arises due to different modes traveling with different velocities.
2. Any given light source emits over a range of wavelengths and, because of the intrinsic property of the material of the fiber, different wavelengths take different amounts of time to propagate along the same path. This is known as material dispersion and obviously, it is present in both single mode and multimode fibers.
3. On the other hand, in single-mode fibers since there is only mode, there is no intermodal dispersion; however, we have what is known as waveguide dispersion which is due to the geometry of the fiber. We will discuss single-mode fibers and waveguide dispersion in Chapter 30. Obviously, waveguide dispersion is present in multimode fibers also but the effect is very small and can be neglected.

28.10.1 Ray Dispersion in Multimode Step-Index Fibers

We first consider ray paths in a step-index fiber as shown in Fig. 28.7. As can be seen, rays making larger angles with the axis (those shown as dotted rays) have to traverse a longer optical path length and therefore take a longer time to reach the output end.

We will now derive an expression for the intermodal dispersion for a step-index fiber. Referring back to Fig. 28.7, for a ray making an angle θ with the axis, the distance AB is traversed in time

$$t_{AB} = \frac{AC + CB}{c/n_1} = \frac{AB/\cos\theta}{c/n_1} = \frac{n_1 AB}{c\cos\theta} \qquad \textbf{(28.20)}$$

where c/n_1 represents the speed of light in a medium of refractive index n_1, c being the speed of light in free space. Since the ray path will repeat itself, the time taken by a ray to traverse a length L of the fiber would be

$$t_L = \frac{n_1 L}{c\cos\theta} \qquad \textbf{(28.21)}$$

The above expression shows that the time taken by a ray is a function of the angle θ made by the ray with the z-axis, which leads to pulse dispersion. If we assume that all rays lying between $\theta = 0$ and $\theta = \theta_c = \cos^{-1}(n_2/n_1)$ are present [see Eq. (28.7)], then the time taken by these extreme rays for a fiber of length L would be given by

$$t_{\min} = \frac{n_1 L}{c} \quad \text{corresponding to } \theta = 0 \qquad \textbf{(28.22)}$$

$$t_{\max} = \frac{n_1^2 L}{c n_2} \quad \text{corresponding to } \theta = \theta_c = \cos^{-1}(n_2/n_1) \qquad \textbf{(28.23)}$$

Hence, if all the input rays were excited simultaneously, the rays would occupy a time interval at the output end of duration

$$\Delta\tau_i = t_{\max} - t_{\min} = \frac{n_1 L}{c}\left[\left(\frac{n_1}{n_2}\right) - 1\right] \qquad \textbf{(28.24)}$$

or

$$\boxed{\Delta\tau_i \cong \frac{n_1 L}{c}\Delta = \frac{L}{2n_1 c}(\text{NA})^2} \qquad \textbf{(28.25)}$$

The above equation represents the intermodal dispersion in multimode SIF where Δ has been defined earlier [see Eqs. (28.3) and (28.4)] Assuming the validity of ray optics, Eq. (28.24). is exact; however, in writing Eq. (28.25) we have assumed $\Delta \ll 1$, which is true for almost all commercially available silica fibers. The quantity $\Delta\tau_i$ represents the pulse dispersion due to different rays taking different times in propagating through the fiber which, in wave optics, is nothing but the intermodal dispersion and hence the subscript i. Note that the pulse dispersion is proportional to the square of NA. Thus, to have a smaller dispersion, one must have a smaller NA which of course reduces the acceptance angle and hence, the light gathering power. Now, if at the input end of the fiber, we have a pulse of width τ_1 then after propagating through a length L of the fiber, the pulse would have a width τ_2 given approximately by

$$\tau_2^2 = \tau_1^2 + \Delta\tau_i^2 \qquad \textbf{(28.26)}$$

Consequently, the pulse broadens as it propagates through the fiber (see Fig. 28.18). Hence, even though two pulses may be well resolved at the input end, because of the broadening of the pulses they may not be so at the output end.

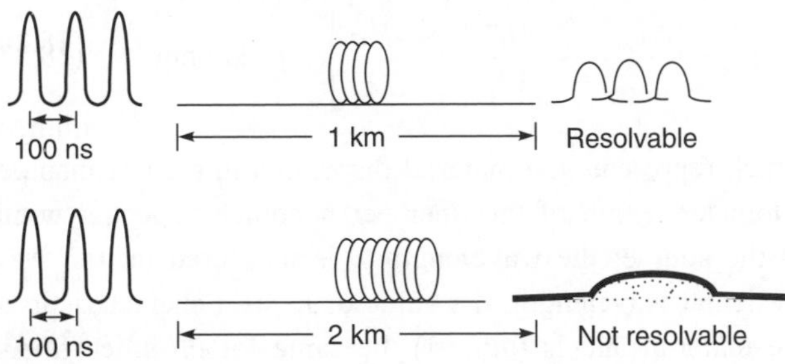

Figure 28.18
Pulses separated by 100 ns, at the input end would be resolvable at the output end of 1 km of the fiber. The same pulses would not be resolvable at the output end of 2 km of the same fiber. Figure adapted from Ref. 28.13.

EXAMPLE 28.11 For a typical (multimoded) step-index fiber, if we assume $n_1 = 1.5$, $\Delta = 0.01$, $L = 1$ km, we would get

$$\Delta\tau_i = \frac{1.5\times 1000}{3\times 10^8}\times 0.01 = 50 \text{ ns/km} \tag{28.27}$$

i.e., a pulse after traversing through the fiber of length 1 km will be broadened by 50 ns. Thus, two pulses separated by, say, 500 ns at the input end would be quite resolvable at the end of 1 km of the fiber. However, if consecutive pulses are separated by, say, 10 ns at the input end, they would be absolutely unresolvable at the output end. Hence in a 1 Mbit/s fiber optic system, where we have one pulse every 10^{-6} s, a 50 ns/km dispersion would require repeaters to be placed every 3–4 km. On the other hand, in a 1 Gbit/s fiber optic communication system, which requires the transmission of one pulse every 10^{-9} s, a dispersion of 50 ns/km would result in intolerable broadening even within 50 meters or so which would be highly inefficient and uneconomical from a system point of view.

Where the output pulses are not resolvable, no information can be retrieved. Thus, smaller the pulse dispersion, greater will be the information carrying capacity of the system.

From the discussion in the above example, it follows that for a very high information carrying system, it is necessary to reduce the pulse dispersion; two alternative solutions exist—one involves the use of near parabolic index fibers and the other involves single mode fibers. We will discuss parabolic index fibers in this chapter, single mode fibers will be discussed in Chapter 30.

28.10.2 Parabolic-Index Fibers (PIF)

In a step-index fiber, such as that pictured in Fig. 28.7, the refractive index of the core has a constant value. By contrast, in a parabolic-index fiber, (often abbreviated as PIF) the refractive index in the core decreases continuously (in a quadratic fashion) from a maximum value at the center of the core to a constant value at the core-cladding interface. (see Fig. 28.17 corresponding to $q = 2$). The refractive index variation given by

$$n^2(r) = n_1^2\left[1 - 2\Delta\left(\frac{r}{a}\right)^2\right] \qquad 0 < r < a \quad \text{core} \tag{28.28}$$
$$= n_2^2 = n_1^2(1 - 2\Delta) \qquad r > a \quad \text{cladding}$$

with Δ as defined in Eq. (28.4). In Sec. 2.4.1 we had shown that the ray paths in a parabolic waveguide are sinusoidal [see Fig. 28.19]. For a typical (multimode) parabolic-index silica fiber $\Delta \approx 0.01$, $n_2 \approx 1.45$ and $a \approx 25$ μm.

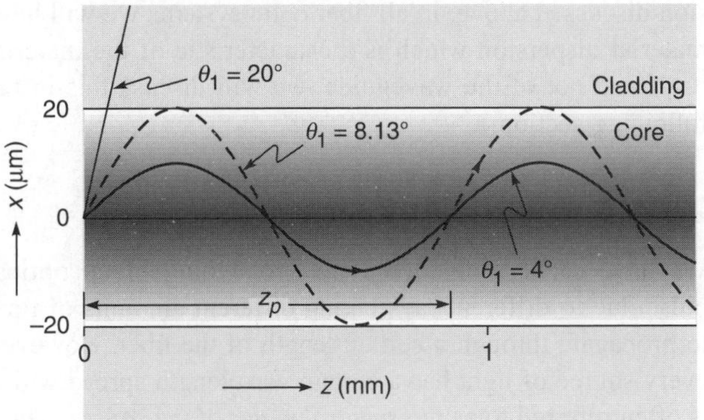

Figure 28.19
Ray paths in a parabolic index fiber.

Now, even though rays making larger angles with the axis traverse a larger path length, they do so now in a region of lower refractive index (and hence greater speed). The longer path length is almost compensated for by a greater average speed such that all rays take approximately the same amount of time in traversing the fiber. In Sec. 2.4.2, we had made a detailed calculation of determining the time taken by a particular ray to propagate through a parabolic index waveguide; the final result for the intermodal dispersion is given by (see also Sec. 28.12):

$$\Delta\tau_i = \frac{n_2 L}{2c}\left(\frac{n_1 - n_2}{n_2}\right)^2 \quad \text{Pulse dispersion in multimode PIF} \tag{28.29}$$

(In Sec. 28.12 we have given the general expression for pulse dispersion corresponding to the power law profile). When $\Delta << 1$, the above equation can be written as

$$\Delta\tau_i \approx \frac{n_2 L}{2c}\Delta^2 \approx \frac{L}{8cn_1^3}(\text{NA})^4 \tag{28.30}$$

Note that as compared to a step-index fiber, the pulse dispersion is proportional to the square of Δ. For a typical (multimode parabolic index) fiber with $n_2 \approx 1.45$ and $\Delta \approx 0.01$, we would get

$$\Delta\tau_i \approx 0.25 \text{ ns/km} \tag{28.31}$$

Comparing with Eq. (28.27) we find that for a parabolic index fiber the pulse dispersion is reduced by a factor of about 200 in comparison to the step-index fiber. It is because of this reason that first and second generation optical communication systems used near parabolic index fibers. In order to further decrease the pulse dispersion, it is necessary to use single mode fibers because there will be no intermodal dispersion. We must mention that although in almost all long distance fiber optic communication systems one uses single mode fibers; nevertheless, in many local area communication systems (like intra office networks), one still uses parabolic index multimode fibers. One of the main advantages of using multimode fibers (in communication networks) is the fact that they have very large core diameters allowing easy splicing at joints. Now, in addition to the intermodal dispersion discussed above, in all fiber optic systems we will have material dispersion which is a characteristic of the material itself and not of the waveguide; we will discuss this in the following section.

28.10.3 Material Dispersion

We have earlier considered the broadening of an optical pulse due to different rays taking different amounts of time to propagate through a certain length of the fiber. However, every source of light has a certain wavelength spread which is often referred to as the *spectral width of the source*. Thus, a white light source (like the sun) would have a spectral width of about 300 nm; on the other hand, an LED would have a spectral width of about 25 nm and a typical laser diode (LD) would have a spectral width of about 2 nm or less. In Chapter 11 we had discussed that the refractive index of the medium (and hence the group velocity v_g) depends on the wavelength. Thus, each wavelength component (of the pulse) will travel with a slightly different group velocity through the fiber, resulting in a broadening of a pulse. In Sec. 11.2 we had shown that the pulse broadening (due to wavelength dependence of the refractive index) is given by

$$\Delta\tau_m = -\frac{L\Delta\lambda_0}{\lambda_0 c}\left[\lambda_0^2\frac{d^2n}{d\lambda_0^2}\right] \tag{28.32}$$

where L is the length of the fiber, $\Delta\lambda_0$ is the spectral width of the source and c the speed of light in free space; the subscript m in Eq. (28.32) refers to the fact that we are considering material dispersion. We assume $\Delta\lambda_0$ = 1 nm = 10^{-9} m and L = 1 km = 1000 m so that

$$\Delta\tau_m = -\frac{L\Delta\lambda_0}{\lambda_0 c}\left[\lambda_0^2\frac{d^2n}{d\lambda_0^2}\right]$$

$$= -\frac{(1000\text{ m})\times(10^{-9}\text{ m})}{\left[\lambda_0(\mu\text{m})\times(10^{-6})\right]\times(3\times10^8\text{ m/s})}\left[\lambda_0^2\frac{d^2n}{d\lambda_0^2}\right]\text{ s}$$

$$= -\frac{10^{-8}}{3\lambda_0(\mu\text{m})}\times10^{12}\left[\lambda_0^2\frac{d^2n}{d\lambda_0^2}\right]\text{ ps}$$

where 1 ps = 10^{-12} s, λ_0 is measured in μm and the quantity inside the square brackets is dimensionless. Thus, we may define the material dispersion coefficient (which is measured in ps/km.nm):

$$D_m = \frac{\Delta\tau_m}{L\Delta\lambda_0} = -\frac{10^4}{3\lambda_0}\left[\lambda_0^2\frac{d^2n}{d\lambda_0^2}\right]\text{ ps/km.nm} \tag{28.33}$$

which represents the material dispersion in picoseconds per kilometer length of the fiber per nanometer spectral width of the source; the wavelength λ_0 is measured in μm. At a particular wavelength, the value of D_m is a characteristic of the material and is (almost) the same for *all* silica fibers. The values of D_m for different wavelengths (for pure silica) are tabulated in Table 11.1. When D_m is negative, it implies that the longer wavelengths travel faster; similarly, a positive value of D_m implies that shorter wavelengths travel faster.

EXAMPLE 28.12 The LED's used in the earlier optical communication systems had a spectral width $\Delta\lambda_0$ of about 20 nm around λ_0 = 850 nm (=0.85 μm); at this wavelength (see Table 11.1)

$$\frac{d^2n}{d\lambda_0^2} \approx 0.0297\ (\mu\text{m})^{-2}$$

$$\Rightarrow \left[\lambda_0^2\frac{d^2n}{d\lambda_0^2}\right] \approx 0.85\times0.85\times0.0297 \approx 0.02146$$

Thus,

$$D_m \approx -\frac{10^4}{3\lambda_0}\left[\lambda_0^2\frac{d^2n}{d\lambda_0^2}\right] \approx -\frac{10^4}{3\times0.85}\times0.02146 \approx -84.2\text{ ps/km.nm}$$

Thus a pulse will broaden by (disregarding the sign)

$$\Delta\tau_m = (D_m)\times(L)\times(\Delta\lambda_0) = (84.2\text{ ps/km.nm})\times(1\text{ km})\times(20\text{ nm})$$

$$\approx 1700\text{ ps} = 1.7\text{ ns}$$

in traversing 1 km length of the fiber. On the other hand, if we carry out a similar calculation around $\lambda_0 \approx$ 1300 nm (where $D_m \approx$ 2.4 ps/km.nm), we will obtain a much smaller value of $\Delta\tau_m$:

$$\Delta\tau_m = (D_m)\times(L)\times(\Delta\lambda_0)$$

$$= (2.4\text{ ps/km.nm})\times(1\text{ km})\times(20\text{ nm}) \approx 0.05\text{ ns}$$

in traversing 1 km length of the fiber. The very small value of $\Delta\tau_m$ is due to the fact that v_g (and hence n_g) is approximately constant around $\lambda_0 \approx$ 1300 nm, as shown in Fig. 11.3. Indeed the wavelength $\lambda_0 \approx$ 1270 nm is usually referred to as the zero material dispersion wavelength, and it is because of such low material dispersion that in early 80's, the optical communication systems shifted their operation to around $\lambda_0 \approx$ 1300 nm.

EXAMPLE 28.13 In the optical communication systems that are in operation today, one uses LD's (Laser Diodes) with $\lambda_0 \approx$ 1550 nm having a spectral width of about 2 nm. At this wavelength,

$D_m \approx 21.5$ ps/km.nm (see Table 11.1). Thus, for a 1 km length of the fiber, the material dispersion $\Delta\tau_m$ becomes

$$\Delta\tau_m = (D_m) \times (L) \times (\Delta\lambda_0)$$
$$= (21.5 \text{ ps/km.nm}) \times (1 \text{ km}) \times (2 \text{ nm}) \approx 43 \text{ ps}$$

the positive sign indicating that higher wavelengths travel slower than lower wavelengths. [Notice from Table 11.1 that for $\lambda_0 \geq 1300$ nm, n_g increases with λ_0].

28.11 Dispersion and Maximum Bit Rates

LO9

We may mention here briefly that in a digital communication system employing light pulses, pulse broadening would result in an overlap of pulses, resulting in loss of resolution and leading to errors in detection. Thus, pulse broadening is one of the mechanisms (other than attenuation) that limits the distance between two repeaters in a fiber optic link. It is obvious that larger the pulse broadening, smaller would be the number of pulses per second that can be sent down a link. There are different criteria based on slightly different considerations that are used to estimate the maximum permissible bit rate (B_{max}) for a given pulse dispersion. However, it is always of the order of $1/\Delta\tau$. In one type of extensively used coding [known as NRZ (Non Return to Zero)] we have

$$B_{max} \approx \frac{0.7}{\Delta\tau} \tag{28.34}$$

The above formula takes into account (approximately) only the limitation imposed by the pulse dispersion in the fiber. In an actual link the source and detector characteristics should also be taken into account while estimating the maximum bit rate. It should also be pointed out that in a fiber, the pulse dispersion is caused, in general by intermodal dispersion, material dispersion and waveguide dispersion. However, waveguide dispersion is important only in single mode fibers and may be neglected in carrying out analysis for multimode fibers. Thus, (considering multimode fibers), if $\Delta\tau_i$ and $\Delta\tau_m$ are the dispersion due to intermodal and material dispersions respectively, then the total dispersion is given by

$$\Delta\tau = \sqrt{(\Delta\tau_i)^2 + (\Delta\tau_m)^2} \tag{28.35}$$

EXAMPLE 28.14 We consider a step-index multimode fiber with $n_1 \approx 1.46$, $\Delta \approx 0.01$ operating at 850 nm. For such a fiber, the intermodal dispersion (for a 1 km length of the fiber) is

$$\Delta\tau_i = \frac{n_1 L\Delta}{c} \approx \frac{1.46 \times 1000 \times 0.01}{3 \times 10^8} \approx 49 \text{ ns}$$

which is usually written as

$$\Delta\tau_i \approx 49 \text{ ns/km}$$

If the source is an LED with $\Delta\lambda_0 = 20$ nm, then using Table 11.1 the material dispersion $\Delta\tau_m$ is 1.7 ns/km [see Example 28.12]. Thus, in step-index multimode fibers, the dominant pulse broadening mechanism is intermodal dispersion and the total dispersion is given by

$$\Delta\tau = \sqrt{(\Delta\tau_i)^2 + (\Delta\tau_m)^2} = 49 \text{ ns/km} = 49 \times 10^{-9} \text{ s/km}$$

Using Eq. (28.35), this gives a maximum bit rate of about

$$B_{max} \approx \frac{0.7}{\Delta\tau} = \frac{0.7}{49 \times 10^{-9}} \text{ bits-km/s} \approx 14 \text{ M bit-km/s}$$

Thus, a 10 km link can at most support only 1.4 Mbit/s.

EXAMPLE 28.15 Let us now consider a parabolic index multimode fiber with $n_1 = 1.46$, $\Delta = 0.01$ operating at 850 nm with an LED of spectral width 20 nm. For such a fiber, the intermodal dispersion, using Eq. (28.28), is

$$\Delta\tau_i = \frac{n_1}{2c}\Delta^2 L \approx 0.24 \text{ ns/km}$$

The material dispersion is again 1.7 ns/km. Thus, in this case, the dominant mechanism is material dispersion rather than intermodal dispersion. The total dispersion is

$$\Delta\tau = \sqrt{0.24^2 + 1.7^2} \approx 1.72 \text{ ns/km}$$

This gives a maximum bit rate of about

$$B_{max} \approx \frac{0.7}{1.72 \times 10^{-9}} \text{ bits-km/s} \approx 400 \text{ Mbits-km/s}$$

giving a maximum permissible bit rate of 20 Mbit/s for a 20 km link.

EXAMPLE 28.16 If we now shift the wavelength of operation to 1300 nm and use the parabolic index fiber of the previous example, we see that the intermodal dispersion remains the same as 0.24 ns/km while the material dispersion (for an LED of $\Delta\lambda_0 = 20$ nm) becomes 0.05 ns /km (see Example 27.11). The material dispersion is now negligible in comparison to intermodal dispersion. Thus, the total dispersion and maximum bit rate are respectively given by

$$\Delta\tau = \sqrt{0.24^2 + 0.05^2} \approx 0.25 \text{ ns/km} \Rightarrow B_{max} \approx 2.8 \text{ Gbit-km/s}$$

Indeed, the fiber optic communication systems operating (around 1981) at 1300 nm used parabolic-index multimode fibers and had a bit rate of 45 Mbits/s with repeater spacing of 30 km implying 1.35 Gbit - km/s. We should reiterate that in the examples discussed above the maximum bit rate has been estimated by considering the fiber only. In an actual link, the temporal response of the source and detector must also be taken into account.

We end this section by mentioning that around 1977, we had the first generation optical communication systems which used graded index multimode fibers and the source used was the LED operating at 850 nm wavelength; the loss was $\approx$ 3dB/km, the repeater spacing was $\approx$ 10 km and the bit rate was $\approx$ 45 Mbits/s. Around 1981, we had the second generation optical communication systems which again used graded index multimode fibers but now operating at 1300 nm wavelength (so that the material dispersion is very small); the bit rate was almost the same ($\approx$45 Mbits/s) but since the loss was ≈ 1 dB/km and the dispersion was also less, the repeater spacing increased to ≈ 30 km. The third and fourth generation optical communication systems used single-mode fibers operating at 1300 nm and at 1550 nm wavelengths, respectively.

28.12 General Expression for Ray Dispersion Corresponding to a Power Law Profile

LO10

The time taken to propagate through a length L of a multimode fiber described by a q-profile (see Eq. 28.17) is given by

$$\tau(\tilde{\beta}) = \left(A\tilde{\beta} + \frac{B}{\tilde{\beta}}\right)L \tag{28.36}$$

where $$A = \frac{2}{c(2+q)}; \quad B = \frac{qn_1^2}{c(2+q)} \tag{28.37}$$

and for rays guided by the fiber $n_2 < \tilde{\beta} < n_1$; see Sec. 2.4.1. In the ray optics approximation, Eq. (28.36) is rigorously correct [see References 28.15 and 28.22 for derivation of Eq. (28.36)]. Using the above equations, we can calculate the ray dispersion in fibers with different q values. For the step profile, $q = \infty$ and

$$A = 0; \text{ and } B = \frac{n_1^2}{c} \Rightarrow \tau(\tilde{\beta}) = \frac{n_1^2}{c\tilde{\beta}}L \tag{28.38}$$

Thus,

$$\tau_{\max} = \tau(\tilde{\beta} = n_2) = \frac{n_1^2}{cn_2}L \text{ and } \tau_{\min} = \tau(\tilde{\beta} = n_1) = \frac{n_1}{c}L \tag{28.39}$$

giving $$\Delta\tau = \tau_{\max} - \tau_{\min} = \frac{n_1}{c}\frac{(n_1 - n_2)}{n_2}L \tag{28.40}$$

which is the same expression as given by Eq. (28.24). For the parabolic profile, $q = 2$ and

$$A = \frac{1}{2c}; \text{ and } B = \frac{n_1^2}{2c} \Rightarrow \tau(\tilde{\beta}) = \left(\frac{\tilde{\beta}}{2c} + \frac{n_1^2}{2c\tilde{\beta}}\right)L \tag{28.41}$$

Thus, $$\tau_{\max} = \tau(\tilde{\beta} = n_2) = \frac{1}{2c}\left[n_2 + \frac{n_1^2}{n_2}\right]L$$

and $$\tau_{\min} = \tau(\tilde{\beta} = n_1) = \frac{n_1}{c}L \tag{28.42}$$

giving $$\Delta\tau = \tau_{\max} - \tau_{\min} = \frac{n_2}{2c}\left(\frac{n_1 - n_2}{n_2}\right)^2 L \tag{28.43}$$

which is the same expression as given by Eq. (28.29). The calculation of the optimum value of q (which would give minimum ray dispersion) requires a plot of $\tau(\tilde{\beta})$ as a function of $\tilde{\beta}$ for different values of q. The details are given in Reference 28.15 and the minimum dispersion occurs for $q \approx 2–2\Delta$ where the pulse dispersion is given by

$$\Delta\tau(\text{optimum profile}) = \frac{n_1}{8c}\left(\frac{n_1 - n_2}{n_2}\right)^2 L \tag{28.44}$$

However, because of the fact that in a given fiber the profile itself depends on wavelength (because the refractive changes slightly with wavelength) most graded index fibers used in optical communication systems correspond to $q \approx 2$.

28.13 Plastic Optical Fibers

We had briefly mentioned about plastic optical fibers (usually abbreviated as POFs) in Sec. 28.4.1. POFs are fibers made from plastic materials such as PMMA (poly methyl methacrylate) ($n = 1.49$), polystyrene ($n = 1.59$), polycarbonates ($n = 1.5–1.57$), fluorinated polymers etc. These fibers share the same advantages as glass optical fibers in terms of insensitivity to electromagnetic interference, small size and weight, low cost and potentially capable of carrying information at high rates. The most important attribute of POFs is their large core diameters of around 1 cm as compared to glass fibers with core diameters around 50 μm. Such a large diameter (in POF's) results in easy alignments at joints. They are also more durable and flexible than glass fibers. In addition, they usually have a large numerical aperture and therefore much larger light gathering power. Thus, coupling to a POF is much easier than for a normal silica based optical fiber. One of the major disadvantages of the POFs is their having much higher losses as compared to silica-based fibers. The low loss windows of POFs are around 570 nm, 650 nm and 780 nm. For example, a graded-index PMMA fiber would have a loss of about 110 dB/km around the wavelength of 650 nm. This value is much larger than for silica fibers. Because of such high losses, POFs are never used in long distance communication systems but are being used in intra office communication systems where one requires only a few hundred meters of the fiber. Thus, although silica-based optical fibers dominate the long-distance optical communication systems, POFs are providing low cost solutions to short distance applications such as Local Area Networks (LAN), high-speed internet access, etc.

28.14 Fiber Optic Sensors*

LO11

Sensors that exploit the optical properties and light guiding capabilities of fibers are called fiber-optic sensors (FOS). In the recent past, there has been tremendous interest in the development of fiber-optic sensors; this is due to high immunity of the optical fiber to electromagnetic interference, applicability to remote sensing, etc. another important attribute is the possibility of having distributed sensing geometries.

* This section was kindly written by Dr. Tarun Gangopadhyay of CSIR-CGCRI, Kolkata.

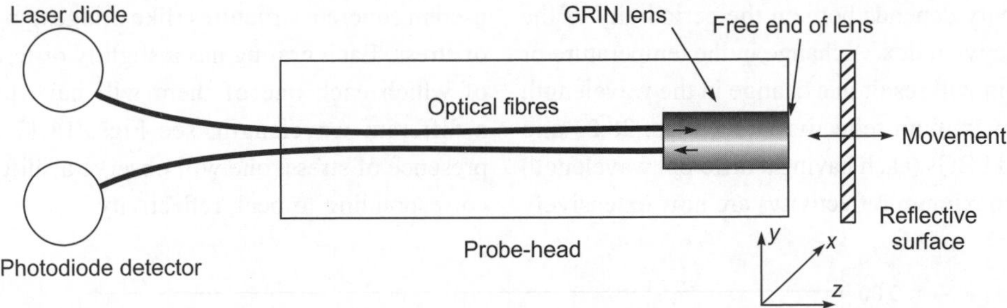

Figure 28.20

Intensity-based displacement sensor using two multimode fibers. [Adapted from Refs. 28.23 and 28.25.]

Fiber-optic sensors can be broadly classified into two categories: extrinsic and intrinsic. In the case of extrinsic sensors, the optical fiber simply acts as a device to transmit and collect light from a sensing element, which is external to the fiber. The sensing element responds to the external perturbation and the change in the characteristics of the sensing element is transmitted by the return fiber for analysis. The optical fiber here plays no role other than that of transmitting the light beam. On the other hand, in the case of intrinsic sensors, the physical parameter to be sensed directly alters the properties of the optical fiber, which in turn leads to changes in a characteristic such as intensity, polarization, phase etc. of the light beam propagating in the fiber.

We give below descriptions of a few fiber-optic sensors.

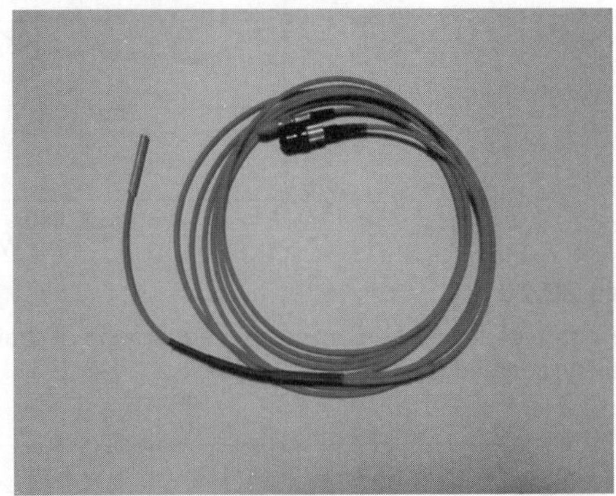

Figure 28.21

Typical cabled probe used for displacement measurement. [*Photpgraph courtesy: Dr Tarun Gangopadhyay, CSIR-CGCRI, Kolkata.*]

28.14.1 Precision Displacement Sensor

An extrinsic type intensity-based displacement sensor arrangement is shown in Fig. 28.20. As shown in the diagram a GRIN lens is butted with two multimode optical fibres in a *Y*-splitting configuration. Two 50/125 µm fibres enter the probe-head, with one attached to a 680 nm laser-diode source and the other attached to a photodiode detector. In a typical setup, the probe-head is pencil-shaped, 5 mm in diameter and 35 mm in length. A movable reflective surface is used as the transducing device, while a GRIN lens efficiently guides the light between the multimode fibers. The setting-up procedure includes butting the GRIN lens against the fibre ends and aligning the reflective surface with the *y*-axis of the probe. The lens is manipulated within the *x*-*y* plane for maximum detected light, and bonded to the fibre ends using epoxy. Translation and displacement of the reflective surface were allowed along the *z*-axis. A photograph of a typical fiber-optic displacement sensor (cabled) probe is shown in Fig. 28.21.

In Fig. 28.22 we have shown a typical variation of the detector output with displacement using both plane mirror and polished steel reflectors. The reflector has been moved forward and backward along *z*-axis using translation stage. The detected optical intensity increases to a maximum value at about 1 mm displacement (the beam waist position) and decreases thereafter giving a usable monotonic displacement-measurement range of at most from about 1 mm to 5.5 mm, indicating a practical working range of some 4.5 mm.

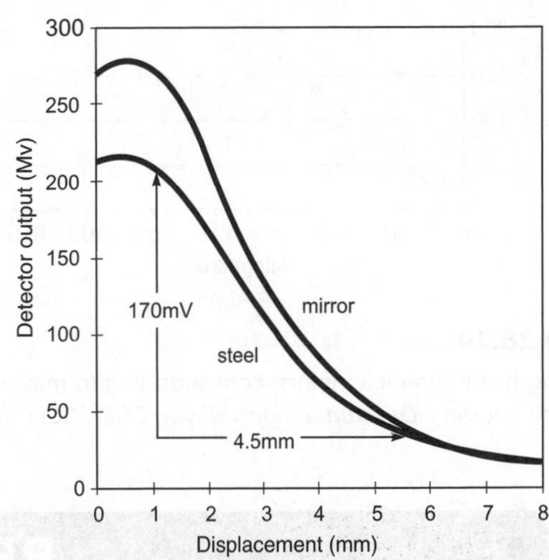

Figure 28.22

Displacement measurement using the plane mirror and polished steel reflectors; figure adapted from Ref. 28.24.

28.14.2 FBG-Based Sensors

We had discussed Fiber Bragg Gratings (FBGs) in Sec. 14.6. As discussed there, the wavelength corresponding to maximum reflectivity depends both on the periodicity of the FBG and the refractive index. A change in the temperature or application of strain will result in a change in the wavelength corresponding to maximum reflectivity (see Figs. 28.23 and 28.24). Distributed FBGs (each having a different wavelength corresponding to maximum reflectivity) are now extensively used in concrete structures (like bridges) to study the variation of stress. Each grating has a slightly different period because of which each one of them will have peak reflectivity at a different wavelength; see Figs. 14.17 and 14.18. In the presence of stress, one will observe a shift in the wavelength corresponding to peak reflectivity.

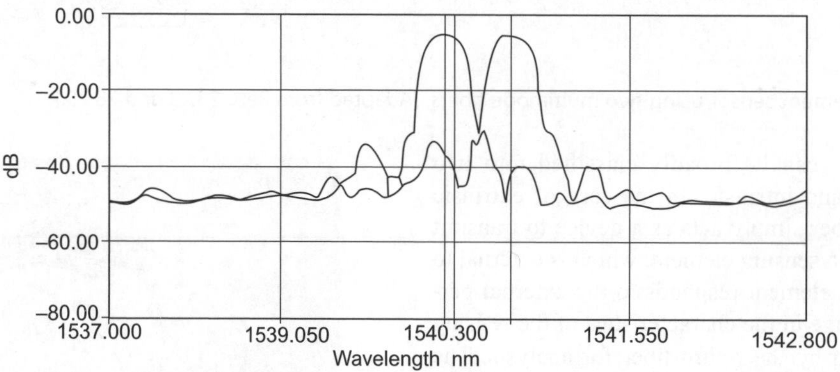

Figure 28.23

The response of an FBG before and after application of strain. Notice the shift in the wavelength corresponding to maximum reflectivity; adapted from Ref. 28.27.

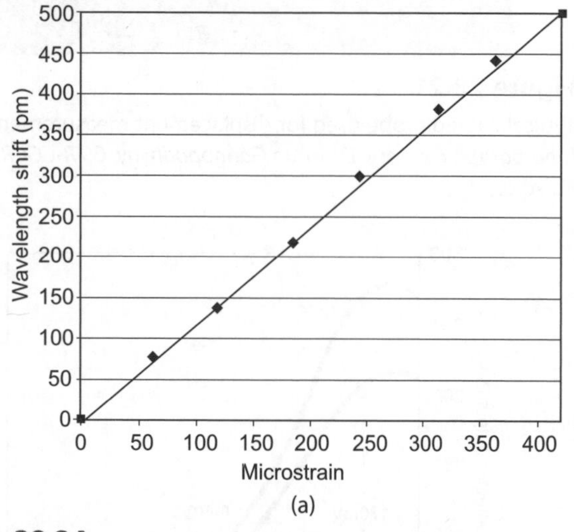

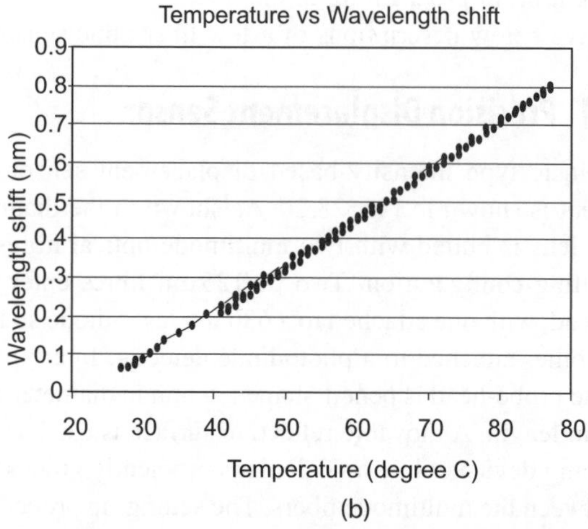

Figure 28.24

Wavelength shift (in pico meters) corresponding to maximum reflectivity of a FBG sensor with (a) applied strain (b) temperature. [*Diagrams courtesy: Dr Tarun Gangopadhyay, CSIR-CGCRI, Kolkata.*]

PROBLEMS

28.1 Consider a step index fiber with $n_1 = 1.5$, $\Delta = 0.015$ and $a = 25$ μm placed in air. Calculate n_2 and the maximum acceptance angle (i_m). If the fiber tip is immersed in water ($n = 1.33$), calculate the maximum acceptance angle (i_m).

[**Ans:** 1.477; 0.26; 15°; 11.3°]

28.2 A step index optical fiber with $n_1 = 1.46$, $n_2 = 1.44$, and core radius $a = 50$ μm is placed in air. Calculate the maximum acceptance angle. If the fiber is now immersed in water ($n = 1.33$), calculate the maximum acceptance angle.

[**Ans.** 13.9°; 10.4°]

28.3 A step-index fiber with $n_1 = 2$, $n_2 = \sqrt{3}$ is placed in air; what is the maximum angle an incident ray can make with the axis of the fiber at the input end in air, so that it is guided after entering the fiber.

[**Ans.** 90°]

28.4 Consider a bare fiber with: $n_1 = 1.46$ (pure silica), $n_2 = 1.0$ (air) and core radius $a = 30$ μm.

(a) Show that all rays (inside the core) making an angle $\theta < 46.77°$ with the z-axis will be guided through the fiber.

(b) Assume $\theta = 30°$ and calculate the number of reflections that will occur in propagating through 1 km length of the fiber. Assume only 0.01% decrease in power at each reflection; calculate the power loss at each reflection and also in propagating through 1 km length of the fiber.

[**Ans.** 9.6×10^6, 4.34×10^{-4} dB; 4179 dB/km]

28.5 The power of a 2 mW laser beam decreases to 15 μW after traversing through 25 km of a single mode optical fiber. Calculate the attenuation of the fiber.

[**Ans:** 0.85 dB/km]

28.6 A 5 mW laser beam passes through a 26 km fiber of loss 0.2 dB/km. Calculate the power at the output end.

[**Ans:** 1.5 mW]

28.7 Consider a 15 mW laser beam passing through a 40 km fiber link of loss 0.5 dB/km. Calculate the output power in dBm and then in mW.

[**Ans:** 0.15 mW]

28.8 The power of a 10 mW laser beam decreases to 40 μW after traversing through 40 km of an optical fiber. Calculate the attenuation of the fiber in dB/km.

[**Ans:** 0.6 dB/km]

28.9 Consider a 50 km fiber link (with a loss of 0.25 dB/km) having 4 connectors in its path and if each connector has a loss of 1.8 dB then calculate the total loss. The loss at the source to the fiber is 2 dB and the loss from the fiber to the detector is 2.5 dB. The input laser power is 10 mW; calculate the output power in dBm and also in mW.

28.10 (a) Consider a step-index fiber with $n_1 = 1.46$, $n_2 = 1.44$, and $a = 50$ μm. Assume that the operating wavelength $\lambda_0 = 0.85$ μm, calculate the V value and show that it is a multimoded fiber. Calculate the ray dispersion in ns/km.

(b) Next consider a bare step-index fiber with $n_1 = 1.46$, $n_2 = 1.0$ and $a = 50$ μm. Assume that the operating wavelength $\lambda_0 = 0.85$ μm, calculate the V value and show that it is a multimoded fiber. Calculate the ray dispersion.

[**Ans: (a)** 67.6 ns/km **(b)** 2239 ns/km]

28.11 In Sec. 28.9.1 we had discussed the power law profile. The time taken for a ray (characterized by $\tilde{\beta}$) to propagate through a length L of a multimode fiber described by a q-profile [see Eq. (28.17)] is given by:

$$\tau(\tilde{\beta}) = \left(A\tilde{\beta} + \frac{B}{\tilde{\beta}}\right)L$$

where all symbols have been defined in Sections 28.9.1 and 28.12. Assume $n_1 = 1.46$, $n_2 = 1.44$, $a = 50$ μm and $L = 1$ km. Calculate Δ and plot $\tau(\tilde{\beta})$ for $q = \infty$, $q = 2$ and $q = 2 - 2\Delta$ for $n_2 < \tilde{\beta} < n_1$ and hence calculate the ray dispersion in each case and compare your results with that obtained in Sec. 28.12.

28.12 In the following problem assume that the material dispersion coefficient D_m is given by

$$D_m = \frac{\Delta\tau_m}{L\Delta\lambda_0} = -\frac{10^4}{3\lambda_0}\left[\lambda_0^2 \frac{d^2n}{d\lambda_0^2}\right] \text{ ps/km.nm}$$

where λ_0 is measured in μm. For silica fibers $\frac{d^2n}{d\lambda_0^2} \approx 0.0297$ $(\mu m)^{-2}$ at $\lambda_0 = 0.85$ μm; ≈ 0.0120 $(\mu m)^{-2}$ at $\lambda_0 = 1.0$ μm; ≈ -0.00055 $(\mu m)^{-2}$ at $\lambda_0 = 1.30$ μm and ≈ -0.00416 $(\mu m)^{-2}$ at $\lambda_0 = 1.55$ μm

(a) At $\lambda_0 = 0.85$ μm, 1.0 μm, 1.30 μm and 1.55 μm, calculate the material dispersion [in ns/km] when $\Delta\lambda_0$ (the spectral width of source) is 50 nm (LED) and 2.5 nm (LD) respectively.

(b) Consider a SIF with $n_1 = 1.5$, $a = 40$ μm and $\Delta = 0.015$ operating at 850 nm with a spectral width of 50 nm. Is this a single mode fiber or a multimode fiber? Calculate the material dispersion, ray dispersion, the total pulse dispersion and hence the maximum bit rate.

(c) Next, consider a parabolic index fiber with $n_1 = 1.5$, $a = 40$ μm and $\Delta = 0.015$ operating at 850 nm with a spectral width of 50 nm. Is this a single mode fiber or a multimode fiber? Calculate the material dispersion, ray dispersion, the total pulse dispersion and hence the maximum bit rate.

(d) Finally, consider a parabolic index fiber with $n_1 = 1.5$, $a = 40$ μm and $\Delta = 0.015$ operating at 1300 nm with a spectral width of 50 nm. Calculate the material dispersion, ray dispersion, the total pulse dispersion and hence the maximum bit rate.

[**Ans. (b)** 4.2 ns/km, 75 ns/km, 75.1 ns/km
(c) 4.2 ns/km, 0.6 ns/km, 4.2 ns/km]

CHAPTER 29

Fiber Optics II: Basic Waveguide Theory and Concept of Modes

LEARNING OBJECTIVES

After reading this chapter, the reader should be able to:

LO 1: *understand the concept of modes in planar optical waveguides.*

LO 2: *derive TE modes of a symmetric step index planar waveguides.*

LO 3: *provide a physical understanding of modes.*

LO 4: *derive TM modes of a symmetric step index planar waveguides.*

LO 5: *derive TE modes of a parabolic index planar waveguide.*

LO 6: *discuss the relationship between waveguide theory and quantum mechanics.*

Above Image: A bundle of optical fibers. Photograph courtesy McGraw Hill Digital Access Library.

29.1 Introduction

LO1

In the design of an optical communication system, it is necessary to have a good understanding of the propagation characteristics of the optical fiber. In the previous chapter, we had used ray optics to understand the propagation characteristics of the optical fiber. Such an analysis is valid when the fiber supports a large number of modes. However, today, single mode fibers are extensively used in optical communication systems. In single mode fibers, ray optics is not applicable at all and one has to solve Maxwell's equations to determine the modes of the waveguide. Thus, the first thing to do would be to understand the concept of modes, which we plan to do in this chapter. In order to understand the concept of modes, it is probably best to consider the simplest planar optical waveguide that consists of a thin dielectric film sandwiched between materials of slightly lower refractive indices and is characterized by the following refractive index variation (see Fig. 29.1):

$$n(x) = \begin{cases} n_1; & |x| < \dfrac{d}{2} \\ n_2; & |x| > \dfrac{d}{2} \end{cases} \qquad \textbf{(29.1)}$$

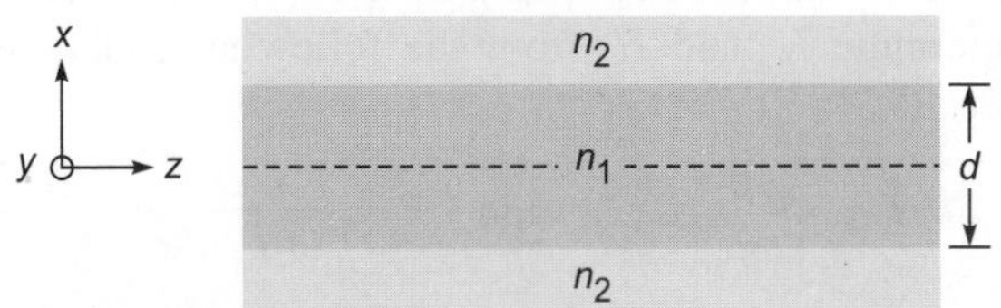

Figure 29.1
A planar dielectric waveguide of thickness d (along x direction) but infinitely extended along the y direction. Light propagates along the z direction.

with $n_1 > n_2$. Equation (29.1) describes what is usually referred to as a *step-index profile*. The waveguide is assumed to extend to infinity in the y and z directions. To start with, we will first consider a more general case of the refractive index depending only on the x coordinate:

$$n^2 = n^2(x) \tag{29.2}$$

When the refractive index variation depends only on the x coordinate, we can always choose the z-axis along the direction of propagation of the wave and we may, *without any loss of generality*, write the solutions of Maxwell's equations in the form

$$\mathcal{E} = \mathbf{E}(x)e^{i(\omega t-\beta z)} \tag{29.3}$$

$$\mathcal{H} = \mathbf{H}(x)e^{i(\omega t-\beta z)} \tag{29.4}$$

The above equations *define* the modes of the system. Thus,

> *modes represent transverse field distributions that suffer only a phase change as they propagate through the waveguide along z.*

The transverse field distributions described by $\mathbf{E}(x)$ and $\mathbf{H}(x)$ do not change as the field propagates through the waveguide. The quantity β represents the propagation constant of the mode. If we substitute the above solutions in Maxwell's equations, we will obtain two independent sets of equations (see Sec. 29.7). The first set of equations correspond to non-vanishing values of E_y, H_x and H_z with E_x, E_z and H_y vanishing, giving rise to what are known as **TE modes** because the electric field has only a transverse component. The second set of equations correspond to non-vanishing values of E_x, E_z and H_y with E_y, H_x and H_z vanishing, giving rise to what are known as **TM modes** because the magnetic field now has only a transverse component.

For TE modes, we have shown in Sec. 29.7 that $E_y(x)$ satisfies the following differential equation:

$$\frac{d^2E_y}{dx^2} + [k_0^2 n^2(x) - \beta^2]E_y = 0 \tag{29.5}$$

where

$$k_0 = \omega\sqrt{\varepsilon_0\mu_0} = \frac{\omega}{c} \tag{29.6}$$

is the free space wave number and $c \left(= \frac{1}{\sqrt{\varepsilon_0\mu_0}}\right)$ is the speed of light in free space. Once $E_y(x)$ is known, we can determine H_x and H_z from the following equations (see Sec. 29.7):

$$H_x = -\frac{\beta}{\omega\mu_0}E_y(x) \quad \text{and} \quad H_z = \frac{i}{\omega\mu_0}\frac{dE_y}{dx} \tag{29.7}$$

We may mention here that whenever the refractive index distribution depends only on the x coordinate, the above equations are rigorously correct.

29.2 TE Modes of a Symmetric Step Index Planar Waveguide* LO2

Until now our analysis has been valid for an arbitrary x-dependent profile. We now assume that the refractive index variation is given by Eq. (29.1) [see Fig. 29.1]. Substituting for $n(x)$ in Eq. (29.5) we obtain

$$\frac{d^2E_y}{dx^2} + (k_0^2n_1^2 - \beta^2)E_y = 0; \ |x| < \frac{d}{2} \quad \text{film} \tag{29.8}$$

$$\frac{d^2E_y}{dx^2} + (k_0^2n_2^2 - \beta^2)E_y = 0; \ |x| > \frac{d}{2} \quad \text{cover} \tag{29.9}$$

We will solve Eqs. (29.8) and (29.9) subject to the appropriate boundary and continuity conditions. Since E_y and H_z represent tangential components on the planes $x = \pm d/2$, they must be continuous at $x = \pm d/2$ and since H_z is proportional to dE_y/dx [see Eq. (29.7)], we must have

$$E_y \text{ and } \frac{dE_y}{dx} \text{ continuous at } x = \pm d/2 \tag{29.10}$$

The above represents the continuity conditions that have to be satisfied; the very fact that E_y satisfies Eq. (29.5) also implies that E_y and dE_y/dx are continuous unless $n^2(x)$ has an infinite discontinuity. This follows from the fact that if dE_y/dx is discontinuous, then d^2E_y/dx^2 will be a delta function (see Problem 8.2) and Eq. (29.5) will lead to an inconsistent equation.

Now, guided modes are those modes that are mainly confined to the film and hence their field should decay in the cover, i.e., the field should decay in the region $|x| > \frac{d}{2}$, so that most of the energy associated with the modes lies inside the film. Thus, we must have

$$\beta^2 > k_0^2n_2^2 \tag{29.11}$$

When $\beta^2 < k_0^2n_2^2$, the solutions are oscillatory in the region $|x| > \frac{d}{2}$ and they correspond to what are known as *radiation modes* of the waveguide. These radiation modes correspond to rays that undergo refraction (rather than total internal reflection) at the film-cover interface and when these are excited, they quickly leak away from the core of the waveguide. Furthermore, we must also have $\beta^2 < k_0^2n_1^2$, otherwise the boundary conditions cannot be satisfied** at $x = \pm d/2$. Thus, for guided modes we must have

$$n_2^2 < \frac{\beta^2}{k_0^2} < n_1^2 \qquad \textbf{GUIDED MODES} \tag{29.12}$$

---

*More details about waveguide modes can be found in Refs. 29.1–29.4.

**It is left as an exercise for the reader to show that if we assume $\beta^2 > k_0^2n_1^2$ and also assume decaying fields in the region $|x| > \frac{d}{2}$, then the boundary conditions at $x = +d/2$ and at $x = -d/2$ can never be satisfied simultaneously.

At this point, we recall our discussion in Sec. 2.4 where we said that for an optical waveguide, guided rays correspond to

$$n_2 < \tilde{\beta} < n_1 \qquad \textbf{GUIDED RAYS} \tag{29.13}$$

and refracting rays correspond to $\tilde{\beta} < n_2$; further, there cannot be any ray with $\tilde{\beta} > n_1$. Thus, $\tilde{\beta}$ (in ray optics) corresponds to β/k_0 in wave optics:

$$\tilde{\beta} \Leftrightarrow \frac{\beta}{k_0} \tag{29.14}$$

Using Eq. (29.12), we write Eqs. (29.8) and (29.9) in the form

$$\frac{d^2E_y}{dx^2} + \kappa^2 E_y = 0; \quad |x| < \frac{d}{2} \quad \text{film} \tag{29.15}$$

$$\frac{d^2E_y}{dx^2} - \gamma^2 E_y = 0; \quad |x| > \frac{d}{2} \quad \text{cover} \tag{29.16}$$

where
$$\kappa^2 = k_0^2 n_1^2 - \beta^2 \tag{29.17}$$
and
$$\gamma^2 = \beta^2 - k_0^2 n_2^2 \tag{29.18}$$

Now, when the refractive index distribution is symmetric about $x = 0$; that is, when

$$n^2(-x) = n^2(x) \tag{29.19}$$

the solutions are either symmetric or antisymmetric functions of x (see, Problem 29.8). Thus, we must have

$$E_y(-x) = E_y(x) \quad \text{symmetric modes} \tag{29.20}$$
$$E_y(-x) = -E_y(x) \quad \text{antisymmetric modes} \tag{29.21}$$

For the symmetric mode, we must have

$$E_y(x) = \begin{cases} A\cos\kappa x; & |x| < \dfrac{d}{2} \\ Ce^{-\gamma|x|}; & |x| > \dfrac{d}{2} \end{cases} \tag{29.22}$$

where we have neglected the exponentially amplifying solution in the region $|x| > \frac{d}{2}$. Continuity of $E_y(x)$ and dE_y/dx at $x = \pm d/2$ gives us

$$A\cos\left(\frac{\kappa d}{2}\right) = Ce^{-\frac{\gamma d}{2}} \tag{29.23}$$

and

$$-\kappa A\sin\left(\frac{\kappa d}{2}\right) = -\gamma Ce^{-\frac{\gamma d}{2}} \tag{29.24}$$

respectively. Dividing Eq. (29.24) by Eq. (29.23) we get

$$\xi\tan\xi = \frac{\gamma d}{2} \tag{29.25}$$

where
$$\xi \equiv \frac{\kappa d}{2} \tag{29.26}$$

Now, if we add Eqs. (29.17) and (29.18), we would get

$$(\kappa^2 + \gamma^2)\frac{d^2}{4} = \frac{1}{4}[k_0^2 d^2(n_1^2 - n_2^2)] = \frac{1}{4}V^2 \tag{29.27}$$

where

$$V = k_0 d\sqrt{n_1^2 - n_2^2} \tag{29.28}$$

is known as the **dimensionless waveguide parameter** which is an extremely important parameter in waveguide theory. Thus

$$\frac{\gamma d}{2} = \sqrt{\frac{1}{4}V^2 - \xi^2} \tag{29.29}$$

and Eq. (29.25) can be put in the form

$$\xi\tan\xi = \sqrt{\frac{1}{4}V^2 - \xi^2} \tag{29.30}$$

Similarly, for the antisymmetric mode, we have

$$E_y(x) = \begin{cases} B\sin\kappa x; & |x| < \dfrac{d}{2} \\ De^{-\gamma x}; & x > \dfrac{d}{2} \\ -De^{\gamma x}; & x < -\dfrac{d}{2} \end{cases} \tag{29.31}$$

and following an exactly similar procedure, we get

$$-\xi\cot\xi = \sqrt{\frac{1}{4}V^2 - \xi^2} \tag{29.32}$$

Thus, we have

$$\xi\tan\xi = \sqrt{\left(\frac{V}{2}\right)^2 - \xi^2} \quad \text{for symmetric modes} \tag{29.33}$$

and

$$-\xi\cot\xi = \sqrt{\left(\frac{V}{2}\right)^2 - \xi^2} \quad \text{for antisymmetric modes} \tag{29.34}$$

Since the equation

$$\eta = \sqrt{\left(\frac{V}{2}\right)^2 - \xi^2} \tag{29.35}$$

(for positive values of ξ) represents a circle (of radius $V/2$) in the first quadrant of the $\xi - \eta$ plane*, the numerical evaluation of the allowed values of ξ (and hence of the propagation constants) is quite simple. In Fig. 29.2, we have plotted the functions $\xi\tan\xi$ (solid curve) and $-\xi\cot\xi$ (dashed curve) as a function of ξ. For a given value of V, the points of intersection of these curves with the quadrant of the circle would determine the allowed (discrete) values of ξ. The two circles in Fig. 29.2 correspond to $V/2 = 2$ and $V/2 = 5$. Obviously,

* This follows from the fact that if we square Eq. (29.35), we would get $\eta^2 + \xi^2 = \left(\frac{V}{2}\right)^2$ which represents a circle of radius $V/2$.

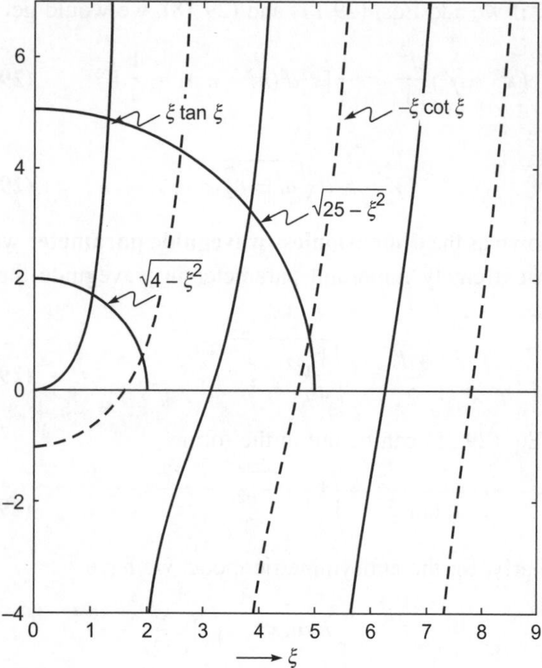

Figure 29.2
Variation of $\xi \tan \xi$ (solid curve) and $-\xi \cot \xi$ (dashed curve) as a function of ξ. The points of intersection of these curves with the quadrant of a circle of radius $V/2$ determine the discrete propagation constants of the waveguide.

as can be seen from the figure, for $V = 4$, we will have one symmetric and one antisymmetric mode and for $V = 10$, we will have two symmetric and two antisymmetric modes*.

It is often very convenient to define the dimensionless propagation constant

$$b \equiv \frac{\beta^2/k_0^2 - n_2^2}{n_1^2 - n_2^2} \tag{29.36}$$

Thus,

$$b = \frac{\beta^2 - k_0^2 n_2^2}{k_0^2\left(n_1^2 - n_2^2\right)} = \frac{\gamma^2 d^2}{V^2}$$

giving

$$\frac{\gamma d}{2} = \frac{1}{2} V \sqrt{b} \tag{29.37}$$

Further, using Eqs. (29.27) and (29.38), we can write

$$\xi = \frac{\kappa d}{2} = \sqrt{\left(\frac{1}{4}V^2 - \frac{\gamma^2 d^2}{4}\right)}$$

$$= \frac{1}{2} V \sqrt{1-b} \tag{29.38}$$

Thus Eqs. (29.33) and (29.34) can be written in the form

$$\left(\frac{1}{2}V\sqrt{1-b}\right)\tan\left(\frac{1}{2}V\sqrt{1-b}\right) = \frac{1}{2}V\sqrt{b} \quad \text{for symmetric modes} \tag{29.39}$$

$$-\left(\frac{1}{2}V\sqrt{1-b}\right)\cot\left(\frac{1}{2}V\sqrt{1-b}\right) = \frac{1}{2}V\sqrt{b} \quad \text{for antisymmetric modes} \tag{29.40}$$

Obviously, because of Eq. (29.12), for guided modes we will have

$$0 < b < 1 \tag{29.41}$$

For a given value of V, solutions of Eqs. (29.39) and (29.40) will give us discrete values of b; the mth solution ($m = 0, 1, 2, 3, \ldots$) is referred to as the TE_m mode. In Table 29.1, we have tabulated the discrete values of b for various values of V; these discrete values have been obtained by using the software in Ref. 29.7. The universal curves describing the dependence of b on V are shown in Fig. 29.3. For any given (step index) waveguide, we just have to calculate V, and then obtain the corresponding value of b either by solving Eqs. (29.39) and (29.40) or by using Table 29.1. A numerical method for solving Eqs. (29.39) and (29.40) is discussed in Ref. 29.11. From the values of b, one can obtain the propagation constants by using the following equation [see Eq. (29.36)]:

$$\frac{\beta}{k_0} = \sqrt{[n_2^2 + b(n_1^2 - n_2^2)]} \tag{29.42}$$

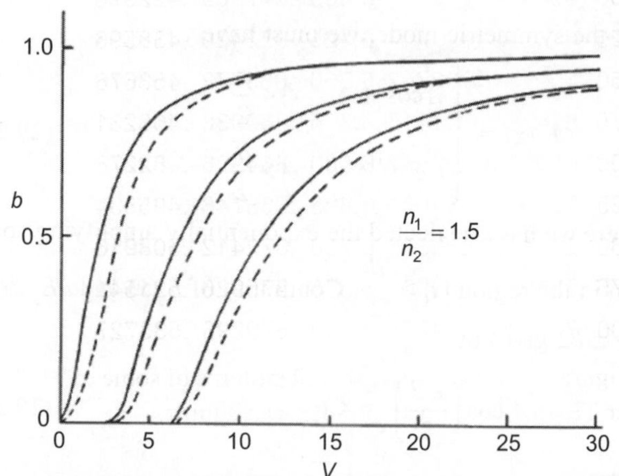

Figure 29.3
Dependence of b on V for a step index planar waveguide. For the TE modes (shown as solid curves), the $b - V$ curves are universal; however, for the TM modes (shown as dashed curves), the $b - V$ curves require the value of n_1/n_2. *[Adapted from Ref. 29.2.]*

*Those who are familiar with basic quantum mechanics will notice that the procedure for determining the discrete TE modes in a planar waveguide is almost identical to the one used in obtaining the discrete energy eigenvalues of the one-dimensional Schrödinger equation. Similarly, the modal analysis of the parabolic index planar waveguide is almost identical to the linear harmonic oscillator problem in quantum mechanics (see Sec. 29.6).

TABLE 29.1 Values of the normalized propagation constant (corresponding to TE modes) for a symmetric planar waveguide.

The values are generated by using the software in Ref. 29.7. Notice that for $V < \pi$, we will have only one TE mode which will be symmetric in x and for $\pi < V < 2\pi$, we will have 2 TE modes-one of them will be symmetric in x and the other antisymmetric in x.

V	b(TE$_0$)	b(TE$_1$)	V	b(TE$_0$)	b(TE$_1$)	b(TE$_2$)
1.000	.189339		4.000	.734844	.101775	
1.125	.225643		4.125	.745021	.123903	
1.250	.261714		4.250	.754647	.146349	
1.375	.297049		4.375	.763756	.168864	
1.500	.331290		4.500	.772384	.191259	
1.625	.364196		4.625	.780563	.213390	
1.750	.395618		4.750	.788321	.235151	
1.875	.425479		4.875	.795686	.256461	
2.000	.453753		5.000	.802683	.277265	
2.125	.480453		5.125	.809335	.297523	
2.250	.505616		5.250	.815663	.317210	
2.375	.529300		5.375	.821689	.336310	
2.500	.551571		5.500	.827429	.354817	
2.625	.572502		5.625	.832902	.372731	
2.750	.592169		5.750	.838123	.390056	
2.875	.610649		5.875	.843107	.406800	
3.000	.628017		6.000	.847869	.422976	
3.125	.644344		6.125	.852420	.438596	
3.250	.659701	.002702	6.250	.856772	.453676	
3.375	.674151	.011415	6.375	.860938	.468231	.001845
3.500	.687758	.024612	6.500	.864926	.482278	.008819
3.625	.700579	.041077	6.625	.868748	.495834	.019189
3.750	.712667	.059875	6.750	.872412	.508916	.031806
3.875	.724073	.080292	6.875	.875926	.521541	.045942
4.000	.734844	.101775	7.000	.879298	.533727	.061106

Figure 29.4 shows typical field patterns of some of the low order TE_m modes of a step index waveguide.

EXAMPLE 29.1 We consider a step index planar waveguide with $d = 3$ μm, $n_1 = 1.5$ and $n_2 = 1.49153$. The value of n_2 is chosen such that $\sqrt{n_1^2 - n_2^2} = \dfrac{1}{2\pi}$ so that $V = \dfrac{2\pi}{\lambda_0} d\sqrt{n_1^2 - n_2^2} = \dfrac{d}{\lambda_0} = \dfrac{3}{\lambda_0}$ (where λ_0 is measured in μm) and

$$\frac{\beta}{k_0} = \sqrt{\left[n_2^2 + \frac{b}{4\pi^2}\right]}.$$

For $\lambda_0 = 1.5$ μm, V is equal to 2.0 and from Table 29.1, we see that there will be only one TE mode with $b = 0.453753$; the corresponding value of $\beta/k_0 \approx 1.49538$. The same waveguide operating at $\lambda_0 = 1.0$ μm will have $V = 3.0$ and from Table 29.1, we see that there will be again only one TE mode with $b = 0.628017$; the corresponding value of $\beta/k_0 \approx 1.49686$. However, for $\lambda_0 = 0.6$ μm, $V = 5.0$ and there will be two TE modes with $b = 0.802683$ (the TE_0 mode) and the other with $b = 0.277265$ (the TE_1 mode). The corresponding values of $\beta/k_0 \approx 1.49833$ and 1.49389. Finally, for $\lambda_0 = 0.4286$ μm, $V = 7.0$ and there will have 3 TE modes with $b = 0.879298$ (TE_0), 0.533727 (TE_1) and 0.061106 (TE_2). The corresponding values of β/k_0 are ≈ 1.4990, 1.49606 and 1.49205, respectively. Notice that all values of β/k_0 lie between n_1 and n_2. We must mention here that, in each case, the waveguide will support equal number of TM modes (see Sec. 29.5). Further, as the wavelength is made smaller, the waveguide will support larger number of modes and in the limit of the wavelength tending to zero, we will have a continuum of modes which is nothing but the ray-optics limit.

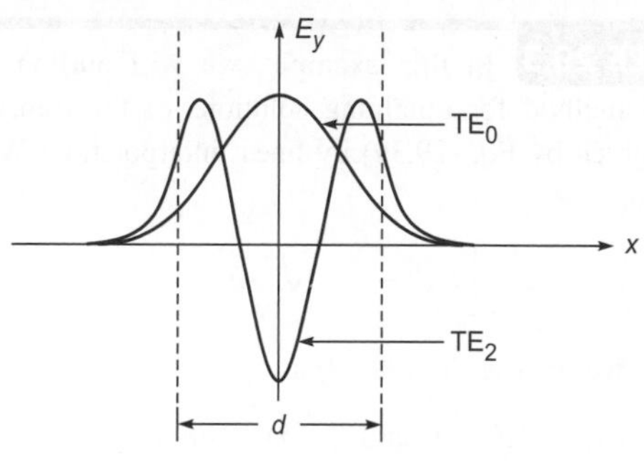

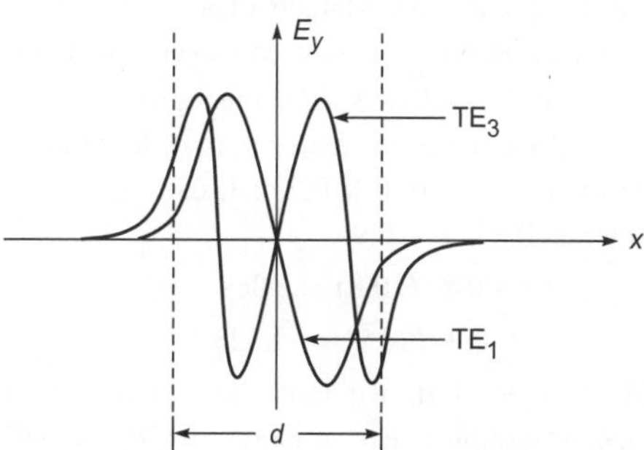

Figure 29.4

Typical mode field distributions for TE modes in a step index planar waveguide; TE_0 and TE_2 modal patterns are symmetric in x and are known as *even* modes, while TE_1 and TE_3 modal patterns are anti-symmetric in x and are known as *odd* modes.

EXAMPLE 29.2 We next consider a step index planar waveguide with $d = 2.5$ μm, $n_1 = 1.5$ and $n_2 = 1.47$. Assuming the operating wavelength $\lambda_0 = 1.0$ μm, we get $V = 4.6888$. If we carry out linear interpolation we would obtain for the TE_0 mode

$$b = 0.780563 + \frac{0.788321 - 0.780563}{0.125} \times 0.0638 \approx 0.78452$$

We therefore get $\dfrac{\beta}{k_0} \approx 1.49359$. Similarly for the TE_1 mode.

$$b = 0.213390 + \frac{0.235151 - 0.213390}{0.125} \times 0.0638 \approx 0.22450$$

and the corresponding value of $\dfrac{\beta}{k_0}$ will be ≈ 1.47679.

EXAMPLE 29.3 In this example, we will outline a simple numerical method for obtaining solutions of the transcendental equation given by Eq. (29.39) by linear interpolation. We assume $V = 6$. Thus

$$\xi = \frac{1}{2} V \sqrt{1-b} = 3\sqrt{1-b}$$

For $V = 6$, we rewrite Eq. (29.39) as

$$F(b) = 3\sqrt{1-b}\tan(3\sqrt{1-b}) - 3\sqrt{b} = 0$$

You can use a software like Mathematica to find the roots of the above equation; alternatively you can even use EXCEL to list $F(b) = 3\sqrt{1-b}\tan(3\sqrt{1-b}) - 3\sqrt{b}$ in the region $0 < b < 1$ and look for the values of b when $F(b)$ crosses 0. In order to do it manually, we evaluate $F(b)$ for $b = 0, 0.1, 0.2, 0.3, 0.4, 0.5, \ldots$ and find that it crosses 0 when $0.8 < b < 0.9$:

For $b = 0.8$, $F(0.8) \simeq 3.069$

and for $b = 0.9$, $F(0.9) = -1.523$

Since $F(b)$ changes sign, we must have a root in the region $0.8 < b < 0.9$. Assuming linear variation of $F(b)$ we will have

$$F(b) = F(b = 0.8) + \frac{F(b = 0.9) - F(b = 0.8)}{0.9 - 0.8}(b - 0.8)$$

$$F(b) = 3.069 + \frac{-1.523 - 3.069}{0.1}(b - 0.8)$$

Notice that if we substitute $b = 0.8$ in the above equation, we will get 3.069 and if we substitute $b = 0.9$ we will get -1.523. Simplifying, we get

$$F(b) = 3.069 - 45.92(b - 0.8)$$

Thus $F(b) = 0$ when $b \simeq 0.8 + \dfrac{3.069}{45.92} \simeq 0.866$

In order to get a more accurate value, we see that $F(b)$ changes sign when $0.84 < b < 0.85$:

$b = 0.84$ for which $F(0.84) = 0.337$

and $b = 0.85$ for which $F(0.85) = -0.0845$

Once again, since $F(b)$ changes sign, we must have a root in the region $0.84 < b < 0.85$. Again assuming a linear variation of $F(b)$ we will have

$$F(b) = F(b = 0.84) + \frac{F(b = 0.85) - F(b = 0.84)}{0.85 - 0.84}(b - 0.84)$$

or $$F(b) = 0.337 - 42.15(b - 0.84)$$

Thus, $F(b) = 0$ when $b \simeq 0.84 + \dfrac{0.337}{42.15} \simeq 0.8480$

which compares very well with the exact value of $b \simeq 0.8479$ (see Table 29.1).

EXAMPLE 29.4 For antisymmetric modes, we rewrite Eq. (29.40) in the form

$$G(b) \equiv 3\sqrt{1-b}\cot(3\sqrt{1-b}) + 3\sqrt{b} = 0$$

If we evaluate $G(b)$ for $b = 0, 0.1, 0.2, 0.3, 0.4, 0.5, \ldots$, we will find that $G(b)$ changes sign between $b = 0.4$ and $b = 0.5$. We may then proceed in a way as outlined in Example 29.3.

29.3 Physical Understanding of Modes

LO3

To have a physical understanding of modes, we consider the electric field pattern inside the film ($-d/2 < x < d/2$). For example, for a symmetric TE mode, this is given by [see Eq. (29.22)] $E_y(x) = A \cos \kappa x$. Thus the complete field inside the film is given by

$$\mathcal{E}_y(x, z, t) = A \cos \kappa x\, e^{i(\omega t - \beta z)}$$

$$= \frac{1}{2} A e^{i(\omega t - \beta z - \kappa x)} + \frac{1}{2} A e^{i(\omega t - \beta z + \kappa x)} \quad (29.43)$$

Now,

$$\exp[i(\omega t - \mathbf{k.r})] = \exp[i(\omega t - k_x x - k_y y - k_z z)]$$

represents a wave propagating along the direction of **k** whose x, y, and z components are k_x, k_y and k_z, respectively. Thus, for the two terms on the RHS of Eq. (29.43) we will have

$$k_x = \kappa,\ k_y = 0,\ k_z = \beta \quad (29.44)$$

and $$k_x = -\kappa,\ k_y = 0,\ k_z = \beta \quad (29.45)$$

which represent plane waves with propagation vectors parallel to the x-z plane making angles $+\theta$ and $-\theta$ with the z-axis (see Fig. 29.5) where

$$\tan\theta = \frac{k_x}{k_z} = \frac{\kappa}{\beta}$$

or $$\cos\theta = \frac{\beta}{\sqrt{\beta^2 + \kappa^2}} = \frac{\beta}{k_0 n_1} \quad (29.46)$$

Thus, a guided mode can be considered to be

a superposition of two plane waves propagating at angles $\pm \cos^{-1}\dfrac{\beta}{k_0 n_1}$ *with the z-axis*

(see Fig. 29.5). Referring to the waveguide discussed in Example 29.1, at $\lambda_0 = 0.6\ \mu$m, V will be 5.0 and we will have 2 TE modes with $\beta/k_0 \approx 1.49833$ and 1.49389. Since $n_1 = 1.5$, the values of $\cos\theta$ will be 0.99889 and 0.99593 and therefore

$$\theta \approx 2.70° \text{ and } 5.17°$$

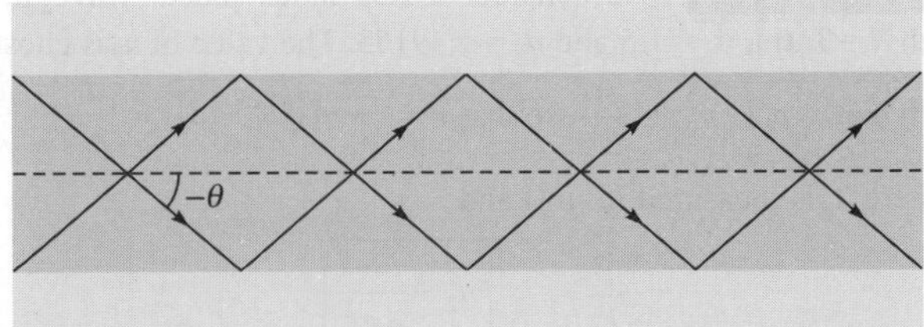

Figure 29.5
A guided mode in a step index waveguide corresponds to the superposition of two plane waves propagating at particular angles $\pm\theta$ with the z-axis.

corresponding to the symmetric TE_0 mode and the antisymmetric TE_1 mode, respectively. Each mode is therefore characterized by a discrete angle of propagation θ_m. We may mention here that, according to ray optics, the angle θ could take *all* possible values from 0 (corresponding to a ray propagating parallel to the *z*-axis) to $\cos^{-1}(n_2/n_1)$ (corresponding to a ray incident at the critical angle on the core-cladding interface). However, we now find that according to wave optics, only discrete values of θ are allowed and each 'discrete' ray path corresponds to a mode of the waveguide. This is the basic principle of the prism film-coupling technique for determining the (discrete) propagation constants of an optical waveguide (see Fig. 29.6). The method consists of placing a prism (whose refractive index is greater than that of the film) close to the waveguiding film. In the presence of the prism, the rays undergo refraction and leaks away from the waveguide. The direction at which the light beam emerges from the prism is directly related to θ_m. From the measured values of θ_m, one can obtain the discrete values of the propagation constant β by using the following formula:

$$\beta = k_0 n_1 \cos\theta \tag{29.47}$$

For a given waveguide, if λ_0 is made to go to 0, the value of V would become very large and the waveguide will support a very large number of modes. In this limit, we can assume all values of θ to be allowed and it will be quite appropriate to use ray optics in studying the propagation characteristics of the waveguide.

From Fig. 29.3, we can derive the following conclusions about TE modes (similar discussion can be made for TM modes, which are discussed in the next section):

(a) If $0 < V/2 < \pi/2$ – that is, when

$$0 < V < \pi \tag{29.48}$$

we have only one discrete (TE) mode of the waveguide and this mode is symmetric in x. When this happens, we refer to the waveguide as a *single-moded waveguide*. In Example 29.1, the waveguide will be single moded for $\lambda_0 > 0.955$ μm; this wavelength (for which V becomes equal to π) is referred to as the cutoff wavelength. Actually for $V < \pi$, the waveguide will support one TE and one TM mode (see Sec. 29.5) and when n_1 has a value very close to n_2, the two modes will have very nearly the same propagation constants.

(b) From Fig. 29.2, it is easy to see that if $\pi/2 < V/2 < \pi$ (or $\pi < V < 2\pi$), we will have one symmetric and one antisymmetric TE mode. In general, if

$$2m\pi < V < (2m + 1)\pi \tag{29.49}$$

we will have $(m + 1)$ symmetric modes and m antisymmetric modes, and if

$$(2m + 1)\pi < V < (2m + 2)\pi \tag{29.50}$$

we will have $(m + 1)$ symmetric modes and $(m + 1)$ antisymmetric modes where $m = 0, 1, 2, \ldots$. **Thus, the total number of modes will be the integer closest to (and greater than)** V/π.

(c) When the waveguide supports many modes (i.e., when $V >> 1$), the points of intersection (in Fig. 29.2) will be very close to $\xi = \pi/2, 3\pi/2, \ldots$. Thus, the propagation constants corresponding to the first few modes can be approximately determined by the following equation:

$$\xi = \xi_m = \sqrt{k_0^2 n_1^2 - \beta_m^2}\,\frac{d}{2} \approx (m+1)\frac{\pi}{2}\,;\ V >> 1 \tag{29.51}$$

where

$m = 0, 2, 4, \ldots$ correspond to symmetric modes

and

$m = 1, 3, 5, \ldots$ correspond to antisymmetric modes.

29.4 TM Modes of a Symmetric Step Index Planar Waveguide

LO4

In the above discussion, we considered the TE modes of the waveguide. A very similar analysis can also be performed

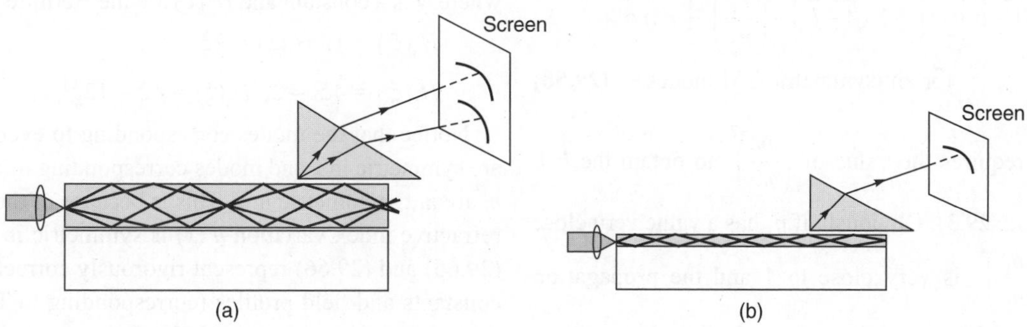

Figure 29.6
The prism film-coupling technique for determining the (discrete) propagation constants of an optical waveguide.

for the TM modes. In Sec. 29.7 we have shown that for TM modes $H_y(x)$ satisfies the following equation:

$$n^2(x)\frac{d}{dx}\left[\frac{1}{n^2(x)}\frac{dH_y}{dx}\right]+\left[k_0^2n^2(x)-\beta^2\right]H_y(x)=0 \quad \textbf{(29.52)}$$

For a step index waveguide [see Eq. (29.1)], $n^2(x)$ will be constant in each region and therefore $H_y(x)$ will also satisfy Eqs. (29.15) and (29.16) in the regions $|x| < \frac{d}{2}$ and $|x| > \frac{d}{2}$ respectively. Now $H_y(x)$ is a tangential component and hence it will be continuous at the core-cladding interface. Further, since

$$E_z = \frac{1}{i\omega\varepsilon_0 n^2(x)}\frac{dH_y}{dx} \quad \textbf{(29.53)}$$

[see Eq. (29.110)] and since $E_z(x)$ is a tangential component, the continuity conditions are now

$$H_y \text{ and } \frac{1}{n^2}\frac{dH_y}{dx} \text{ continuous at } x = \pm d/2 \quad \textbf{(29.54)}$$

If we incorporate these continuity conditions and use the same procedure as in Sec. 29.2, we would get the following transcendental equations

$$\xi \tan \xi = \left(\frac{n_1}{n_2}\right)^2\sqrt{\left(\frac{V}{2}\right)^2-\xi^2}$$

for symmetric TM modes **(29.55)**

A similar derivation gives us

$$-\xi \cot \xi = \left(\frac{n_1}{n_2}\right)^2\sqrt{\left(\frac{V}{2}\right)^2-\xi^2}$$

for antisymmetric TM modes **(29.56)**

where ξ and V have been defined earlier. One can again use a graphical method to determine the discrete propagation constants for TM modes. In terms of the parameters b and V, we have

$$\left(\frac{1}{2}V\sqrt{1-b}\right)\tan\left(\frac{1}{2}V\sqrt{1-b}\right)=\left(\frac{n_1}{n_2}\right)^2\frac{1}{2}V\sqrt{b}$$

for symmetric TM modes **(29.57)**

$$-\left(\frac{1}{2}V\sqrt{1-b}\right)\cot\left(\frac{1}{2}V\sqrt{1-b}\right)=\left(\frac{n_1}{n_2}\right)^2\frac{1}{2}V\sqrt{b}$$

for antisymmetric TM modes **(29.58)**

One now requires the value of $\left(\frac{n_1}{n_2}\right)^2$ to obtain the b-V curves (see Fig. 29.3). Obviously if n_1 has a value very close to n_2 then $\left(\frac{n_1}{n_2}\right)^2$ is very close to 1 and the propagation constants for TM modes will be very close to the propagation constants for TE modes—this is known as the weakly guiding approximation.

29.5 TE Modes of a Parabolic Index Planar Waveguide

LO5

As another example, we consider parabolic variation of refractive index (see Sec. 2.4.1)

$$n^2(x) = n_1^2 - \gamma^2x^2 \quad \textbf{(29.59)}$$

Thus Eq. (29.5) takes the form

$$\frac{d^2E_y}{dx^2} + [(k_0^2n_1^2 - \beta^2) - k_0^2\gamma^2x^2]\,E_y = 0 \quad \textbf{(29.60)}$$

which can be written in the form

$$\frac{d^2E_y}{d\xi^2} + [\Lambda - \xi^2]\,E_y = 0 \quad \textbf{(29.61)}$$

where $\xi = \alpha x$ and we have chosen $\alpha = \sqrt{k_0\gamma}$. Further,

$$\Lambda = \frac{k_0^2n_1^2-\beta^2}{\alpha^2} = \frac{k_0^2n_1^2-\beta^2}{k_0\gamma} \quad \textbf{(29.62)}$$

For the wave function not to blow up at $x = \pm\infty$ (which represents the boundary condition), Λ must be equal to an odd integer (see Appendix D); i.e.,

$$\Lambda = \frac{k_0^2n_1^2-\beta^2}{k_0\gamma} = (2m+1); \quad m = 0, 1, 2, 3, \ldots \quad \textbf{(29.63)}$$

[Equation (29.61) is identical to the one obtained while solving the one-dimensional Schrödinger equation for the linear harmonic oscillator problem (see, e.g., Refs. 29.5 and 29.6)]. Equation (29.63) would give us the following expression for the discrete propagation constants:

$$\beta = \beta_m = k_0n_1\left[1-\frac{(2m+1)\gamma}{k_0n_1^2}\right]^{1/2}; \; m = 0, 1, 2, 3, \ldots \quad \textbf{(29.64)}$$

The corresponding modal patterns are Hermite–Gauss functions:

$$E_y(x) = NH_m(\xi)\exp\left(-\frac{1}{2}\xi^2\right); \; m = 0, 1, 2, 3, \ldots \quad \textbf{(29.65)}$$

where N is a constant and $H_m(\xi)$ are the Hermite polynomials:

$$H_0(\xi) = 1, \; H_1(\xi) = 2\xi,$$

$$H_2(\xi) = 4\xi^2 - 2, \; H_3(\xi) = 8\xi - 12\xi^3, \ldots \quad \textbf{(29.66)}$$

Notice that the modes corresponding to even values of m are symmetric in x and modes corresponding to odd values of m are anti-symmetric in x. This is because of the fact that the refractive index variation $n^2(x)$ is symmetric in x. Equations (29.65) and (29.66) represent rigorously correct propagation constants and field profiles (corresponding to TE modes) in an infinitely extended parabolic index medium; of course the refractive index distribution is itself unrealistic. A more realistic distribution is given by (see Sec. 2.4.1)

$$n^2(x)\, x = n_1^2\left[1 - 2\Delta\left(\frac{x}{a}\right)\right]^2, \quad |x| < a \qquad \text{Core}$$

$$= n_2^2 = n_1^2(1 - 2\Delta), \qquad |x| > a \qquad \text{Cladding} \tag{29.67}$$

The region $|x| < a$ is known as the **core** of the waveguide and the region $|x| > a$ is referred to as the cladding. Thus,

$$\gamma = \frac{n_1\sqrt{2\Delta}}{a} \tag{29.68}$$

The waveguide parameter is given by

$$V = k_0 a\sqrt{n_1^2 - n_2^2} = k_0 a n_1\sqrt{2\Delta} \tag{29.69}$$

In a typical parabolic index medium,

$$n_1 \approx 1.5,\ \Delta \approx 0.01,\ a \approx 20\ \mu\text{m} \tag{29.70}$$

giving $n_2 \approx 1.485$ and $\gamma \approx 1.0607 \times 10^4\ \text{m}^{-1}$. For discrete guided modes we must have

$$n_2^2 < \frac{\beta^2}{k_0^2} < n_1^2 \tag{29.71}$$

and therefore the maximum value of m will correspond to $\beta = \beta_m = \beta_{min} = k_0 n_2$. Indeed when the waveguide supports a very large number of modes, the low order modes would be accurately given by Eq. (29.64). Now when $\dfrac{\gamma}{k_0 n_1^2} \ll 1$ and for not too large values of m, we may carry out a binomial expansion in Eq. (29.64) to obtain

$$\beta = \beta_m \approx k_0 n_1 - \left(m + \frac{1}{2}\right)\frac{\gamma}{n_1}$$

$$\approx \frac{\omega}{c} n_1 - \left(m + \frac{1}{2}\right)\frac{\gamma}{n_1};\ m = 0, 1, 2, 3, \ldots \tag{29.72}$$

Thus, the group velocity v_g of the mode will be given by

$$\frac{1}{v_g} = \frac{d\beta}{d\omega} \approx \frac{n_1}{c} \tag{29.73}$$

independent of the mode number !!!! [In writing the above equation, we have neglected material dispersion, i.e., dependence of n_1 on ω.] Thus, in this approximation, all modes travel with the same group velocity. Indeed, using ray optics, we had shown in Sec. 2.4 that *all* rays take approximately the same time to propagate through a certain distance of a parabolic index waveguide. It is for this reason that parabolic index waveguides are often used in fiber-optic communication systems.

For a cladded waveguide, if we assume the validity of Eq. (29.63), we can easily calculate the total number of modes. Since the minimum value of β is $k_0 n_2$ we will have

$$\frac{k_0^2(n_1^2 - n_2^2)}{k_0\gamma} = (2m_{max} + 1) \tag{29.74}$$

where m_{max} represents the maximum value of m. Thus the total number of modes is given by

$$N \approx 2m_{max} \approx V \tag{29.75}$$

where we have used Eqs. (29.68) and (29.69) and the fact that there would be an equal number of TM modes. For the parameters given by Eq. (29.70) we obtain $N \approx 27$.

29.6 Waveguide Theory and Quantum Mechanics

LO6

In Sec. 29.3, we had shown that for a given waveguide, if λ_0 is made to go to 0, the value of V would become very large and the waveguide will support a very large number of modes. In this limit, we can assume all values of θ to be allowed and it will be quite appropriate to use ray optics to study the propagation characteristics of the waveguide.

In this section, we will show that for a given quantum well structure, if $\hbar$ is made to go to 0, the quantum well structure will have a very large number of bound states and in this limit, we can assume all values of energy to be allowed and it will be quite appropriate to use classical mechanics. Further, the one dimensional Schrödinger equation is very similar to the wave equation for TE modes; the former leads to the bound states of a quantum mechanical problem and the latter leads to guided modes of a waveguide problem. Obviously, the methodology of solving either of the equations is the same. Indeed the modal analysis of the step-index planar waveguide is almost identical to the procedure used for solving the one dimensional Schrödinger equation corresponding to the symmetric potential well. Similarly, the modal analysis of the parabolic index planar waveguide is almost identical to the linear harmonic oscillator problem in quantum mechanics (see, e.g., Refs. 29.5 and 29.6). Thus, it is often easier to understand a concept in quantum mechanics through fiber optics and vice versa. Further, we can say that

The relationship between geometric and wave optics is very similar to the relation between classical and quantum mechanics. In the limit of $\lambda_0 \to 0$, wave optics goes over to ray optics and in the limit of $\hbar \to 0$, quantum mechanics goes over to classical mechanics.

Now, for a particle of mass μ the one-dimensional Schrödinger equation is given by

$$\frac{d^2\psi}{dx^2} + \frac{2\mu}{\hbar^2}[E - V(x)](\psi) = 0 \tag{29.76}$$

We consider a potential energy function given by the following equation [cf. Eq. (29.1)]

$$V(x) = \begin{cases} 0; & |x| < \frac{d}{2} \\ V_0; & |x| > \frac{d}{2} \end{cases} \tag{29.77}$$

(see Fig. 29.7). Thus, the Schrödinger equation can be written in the form

$$\frac{d^2\psi}{dx^2} + \kappa^2\psi(x) = 0;\ |x| < \tfrac{d}{2} \tag{29.78}$$

$$\frac{d^2\psi}{dx^2} - \gamma^2\psi(x) = 0;\ \ |x| > \tfrac{d}{2} \tag{29.79}$$

where $$\kappa^2 = \frac{2\mu E}{\hbar^2} \tag{29.80}$$

and $$\gamma^2 = \frac{2\mu}{\hbar^2}[V_0 - E] \tag{29.81}$$

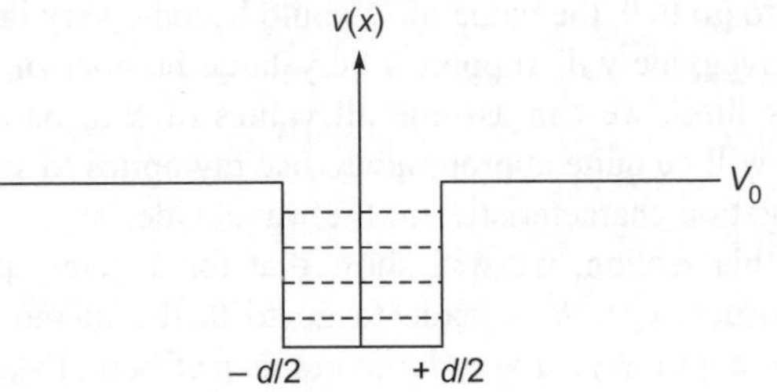

Figure 29.7
The potential energy variation as given by Eq. 29.75, the dashed horizontal lines represent the discrete energy states—similar to the discrete bound states in a planar optical waveguide.

As in the waveguide problem, we will solve Eqs. (29.78) and (29.79) subject to the appropriate boundary and continuity conditions. The continuity conditions are

$$\psi \text{ and } \frac{d\psi}{dx} \quad \text{continuous at } x = \pm d/2 \tag{29.82}$$

Now, for a bound state, the wave function is mainly confined to the film and hence their field should decay in the region $|x| > \frac{d}{2}$, so that there is a large probability of finding the particle inside the well. Thus, we must have

$$E < V_0$$

When $E > V_0$, the solutions are oscillatory in the region $|x| > \frac{d}{2}$ and they correspond to what are known as scattering states. Furthermore, E cannot be less than the minimum value of $V(x)$ (in this case the minimum value is zero) otherwise the boundary conditions cannot be satisfied at $x = \pm d/2$. Thus, for bound states we must have

$$0 < E < V_0 \quad \text{Bound States} \tag{29.83}$$

Now, when the potential energy variation is symmetric about $x = 0$; that is, when

$$V(-x) = V(x) \tag{29.84}$$

the solutions are either symmetric or antisymmetric functions of x (see Problem 29.8; see also pp. 126–127 of Ref. 29.2); thus we must have

$$\psi(-x) = \psi(x) \quad \text{Symmetric states} \tag{29.85}$$

$$\psi(-x) = -\psi(x) \quad \text{Antisymmetric states} \tag{29.86}$$

Carrying out an analysis identical to that in Sec. 29.2, we will find that the wave function for symmetric states will be given by Eq. (29.22) and the wave function for antisymmetric states will be given by Eq. (29.31). Continuity of ψ and $\frac{d\psi}{dx}$ at $x = \pm d/2$ will give us the following equations

$$\xi \tan \xi = \sqrt{\alpha^2 - \xi^2} \quad \text{for symmetric states} \tag{29.87}$$

$$-\xi \cot \xi = \sqrt{\alpha^2 - \xi^2} \quad \text{for antisymmetric states} \tag{29.88}$$

where

$$\xi = \sqrt{\frac{2\,\mu E_0 d^2}{4\hbar^2}} \quad \text{and} \quad \alpha = \sqrt{\frac{2\,\mu V_0 d^2}{4\hbar^2}} \tag{29.89}$$

For a given value of α, the solutions of Eqs. (29.87) and (29.88) will give the bound states for the potential well problem given by Eq. (29.77). Obviously, for $\alpha < \pi/2$ we will have only bound state – similar to the condition we had for a single mode waveguide. For given values of V_0, μ and d, as $\hbar \to 0$, the value of α will become large and we will have a continuum of states implying that all energy levels are possible. Thus in the limit of $\hbar \to 0$, we have the results of classical mechanics.

Now, when $E < V_0$ there is a finite probability of finding the particle in the region $|x| > d/2$, this region is forbidden in classical mechanics because the total energy E is less than the potential energy ($= V_0$) and therefore the kinetic energy will be negative. Similarly, in the waveguide problem the ray undergoes total internal reflection at the core cladding interface and a geometrical ray is not possible in the rarer medium; on the other hand, while solving Eq. (29.16) we had the evanescent wave in the region $|x| > d/2$. Indeed when a light beam is incident on a layer of lower refractive index at an angle of incidence greater than the critical angle, then a part of the beam "tunnels through" the rarer medium and appears in the third medium as shown in Fig. 29.8(a) and (b); this phenomenon is known as **frustrated total internal reflection** (usually abbreviated as FTIR) and is a consequence of the evanescent wave present in the rarer medium. (The tunneling coefficient can be calculated using a procedure similar to that discussed in Sec. 23.10). Such a tunneling is not allowed in geometrical optics because the beam will undergo total internal reflection at the first interface. An almost identical situation arises in quantum mechanics when a particle of energy $E(< V_0)$, incident on a potential barrier (of height V_0), has a finite probability of tunneling through as shown in Fig. 29.8(c); [see also Sec. 26.7 and Fig. 26.12]. Such a tunneling is not possible in classical mechanics and, as shown in almost all text books in quantum mechanics; the tunneling probability will go to zero when $\hbar \to 0$.

We may mention here that in 1897, Professor Jagadish Chandra Bose was the first to demonstrate optical tunneling

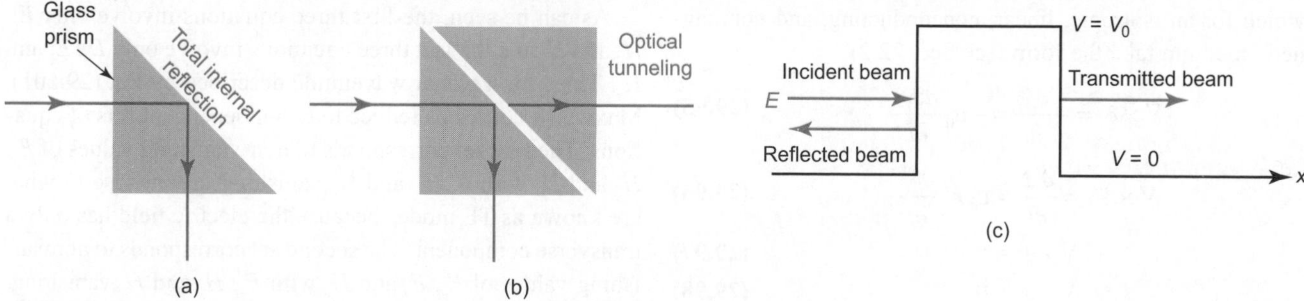

Figure 29.8

(a) When a light beam is incident on a medium of lower refractive index at an angle of incidence greater than the critical angle, it undergoes total internal reflection. (b) When a light beam is incident on a layer of lower refractive index at an angle of incidence greater than the critical angle; a part of the beam tunnels through to the third medium; this phenomenon is known as FTIR (Frustrated Total Internal Reflection) and is a consequence of the evanescent wave present in the rarer medium. (c) A particle of energy $E(< V_0)$ incident on a potential barrier (of height V_0), has a finite probability of tunneling through the potential barrier.

using microwaves. His apparatus is shown in Figs. 29.9 and 29.10; the two prisms shown are right-angled isosceles prisms. Microwaves were incident normally on a 45° prism and underwent total internal reflection at the second face of the prism [see Figs. 29.8(a) and (b)]. In the presence of the second prism, optical tunneling was observed. There was a small air-gap between the two prisms. For detailed discussions on this, see Refs. 29.8–29.10.

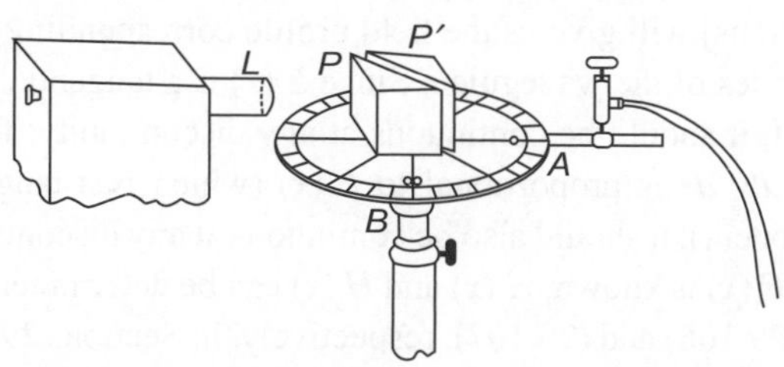

Figure 29.9

Layout of J C Bose's experiment demonstrating FTIR (Frustrated Total Internal reflection); *P* and *P′* are the right angled isosceles prisms, *A* and *B* are two positions of the receiver. [*Adapted from Ref. 29.10.*]

Figure 29.10

One of J.C. Bose's original double-prism attenuators, with adjustable air gap. [*Adapted from Ref. 29.9.*]

Finally we consider the linear harmonic oscillator problem in quantum mechanics where the potential energy function is given by

$$V(x) = \frac{1}{2}\mu\omega^2 x^2 \tag{29.90}$$

and the Schrödinger equation [Eq. (29.76)] would become

$$\frac{d^2\psi}{d\xi^2} + [\Lambda - \xi^2]\psi = 0 \tag{29.91}$$

where $\xi = \alpha x$ and we have chosen

$$\alpha = \frac{d^2\psi}{d\xi^2} \quad \text{so that} \quad \Lambda \equiv \frac{2E}{\hbar\omega} \tag{29.92}$$

For the wave function not to blow up at $x = \pm\infty$ (which represents the boundary condition), Λ must be equal to an odd integer (see Appendix D); i.e.,

$$\Lambda = \frac{2E}{\hbar\omega} = (2m + 1); \quad m = 0, 1, 2, 3, \ldots \tag{29.93}$$

The above equation would give us the following expression for the discrete energy eigenvalues:

$$E = E_m = \left(m + \frac{1}{2}\right)\hbar\omega; \quad m = 0, 1, 2, 3, \ldots \tag{29.94}$$

The relationship of the quantum mechanical oscillator with classical oscillator is discussed in detail in Ref. 29.6 and the relationship of ray optics in a parabolic index waveguide with the results obtained in modal theory is discussed in Ref. 29.2.

29.7 TE and TM Modes in Planar Waveguides

In this section we will derive the equations which we had used earlier in the chapter to carry out the modal analysis of a planar waveguide. We start with Maxwell's equations, which for an isotropic, linear, nonconducting, and nonmagnetic medium take the form (see Sec. 22.2)

$$\nabla \times \mathcal{E} = -\frac{\partial \mathcal{B}}{\partial t} = -\mu_0 \frac{\partial \mathcal{H}}{\partial t} \quad (29.95)$$

$$\nabla \times \mathcal{H} = \frac{\partial \mathcal{D}}{\partial t} = \varepsilon_0 n^2 \frac{\partial \mathcal{E}}{\partial t} \quad (29.96)$$

$$\nabla \cdot \mathcal{D} = 0 \quad (29.97)$$

$$\nabla \cdot \mathcal{B} = 0 \quad (29.98)$$

where we have used the constitutive relations

$$\mathcal{B} = \mu_0 \mathcal{H} \quad (29.99)$$

$$\mathcal{D} = \varepsilon \mathcal{E} = \varepsilon_0 n^2 \mathcal{E} \quad (29.100)$$

in which $\mathcal{E}$, $\mathcal{D}$, $\mathcal{B}$ and $\mathcal{H}$ represent the electric field, electric displacement, magnetic induction and magnetic intensity, respectively, ε (= $\varepsilon_0 n^2$) represents the dielectric permittivity of the medium, and n, the refractive index. For a planar waveguide, the refractive index varies only in the x-direction – that is

$$n^2 = n^2(x) \quad (29.101)$$

For such planar waveguides, we can always choose the z-axis along the direction of propagation of the wave and we may, without any loss of generality, write the solutions of Eqs. (29.95) and (29.96) in the form

$$\mathcal{E} = \mathbf{E}(x) e^{i(\omega t - \beta z)} \quad (29.102)$$

$$\mathcal{H} = \mathbf{H}(x) e^{i(\omega t - \beta z)} \quad (29.103)$$

where β is known as the propagation constant. Equations (29.102) and (29.103) define the modes of the system. Thus modes represent transverse field distributions that suffer a phase change only as they propagate through the waveguide along z; the transverse field distributions described by $\mathbf{E}(x)$ and $\mathbf{H}(x)$ do not change as the field propagates through the waveguide. The quantity β represents the propagation constant of the mode. We rewrite the components of Eqs. (29.102) and (29.103):

$$\mathcal{E}_j = E_j(x) e^{i(\omega t - \beta z)}; \quad j = x, y, z \quad (29.104)$$

$$\mathcal{H}_j = H_j(x) e^{i(\omega t - \beta z)}; \quad j = x, y, z \quad (29.105)$$

Substituting the above expressions for the electric and magnetic fields in Eqs. (29.95) and (29.96) and taking their x, y and z components we would obtain

$$i\beta E_y = -i\omega\mu_0 H_x \quad (29.106)$$

$$\frac{\partial E_y}{\partial x} = -i\omega\mu_0 H_z \quad (29.107)$$

$$-i\beta H_x - \frac{\partial H_z}{\partial x} = i\omega\varepsilon_0 n^2(x) E_y \quad (29.108)$$

$$i\beta H_y = i\omega\varepsilon_0 n^2(x) E_x \quad (29.109)$$

$$\frac{\partial H_y}{\partial x} = i\omega\varepsilon_0 n^2(x) E_z \quad (29.110)$$

$$-i\beta E_x - \frac{\partial E_z}{\partial x} = -i\omega\mu_0 H_y \quad (29.111)$$

As can be seen, the first three equations involve only E_y, H_x and H_z and the last three equations involve only E_x, E_z and H_y. Thus, for a planar waveguide described by Eq. (29.101), Maxwell's equations reduce to two independent sets of equations. The first set corresponds to non-vanishing values of E_y, H_x and H_z with E_x, E_z and H_y vanishing, giving rise to what are known as TE modes because the electric field has only a transverse component. The second set corresponds to nonvanishing values of E_x, E_z and H_y with E_y, H_x and H_z vanishing, giving rise to what are known as TM modes because the magnetic field now has only a transverse component. Thus the propagation of waves in planar waveguides may be described in terms of TE and TM modes. In what follows, we will discuss the TE and TM modes of a symmetric step index planar waveguide.

29.7.1 TE Modes

We first consider TE modes: we substitute for H_x and H_z from Eqs. (29.106) and (29.107) in Eq. (29.108) to obtain

$$\frac{d^2 E_y}{dx^2} + [k_0^2 n^2(x) - \beta^2] E_y = 0 \quad (29.112)$$

For a given refractive index profile $n^2(x)$, the solution of Eq. (29.112) [subject to appropriate boundary and continuity conditions] will give us the field profile corresponding to the TE modes of the waveguide. Since $E_y(x)$ is a tangential component, it should be continuous at any discontinuity; further since dE_y/dx is proportional to $H_z(x)$ (which is a tangential component), it should also be continuous at any discontinuity. Once $E_y(x)$ is known, $H_x(x)$ and $H_z(x)$ can be determined from Eqs. (29.106) and (29.107), respectively. In Sections 29.2 and 29.4 we have solved Eq. (29.112) for a symmetric step-index waveguide and for a parabolic index waveguide, respectively.

29.7.2 TM Modes

For the TM modes, which are characterized by field components H_x and H_z [see Eqs. (29.109)–(29.110)], we substitute for E_x and E_z from Eqs. (29.109) and (29.110) in Eq. (29.111) we will get

$$n^2(x) \frac{d}{dx}\left[\frac{1}{n^2(x)} \frac{dH_y}{dx}\right] + [k_0^2 n^2(x) - \beta^2] H_y(x) = 0 \quad (29.113)$$

The above equation is of a form that is somewhat different from the equation satisfied by E_y for TE modes [see Eq. (29.112)]; however, for the step index waveguide shown in Fig. 29.1, the refractive index is constant in each region we will have

$$\frac{d^2 H_y}{dx^2} + [k_0^2 n_i^2 - \beta^2] H_y(x) = 0; \quad (29.114)$$

However at each discontinuity

$$H_y \text{ and } \frac{1}{n^2}\frac{dH_y}{dx} \tag{29.115}$$

should be continuous. This follows from the fact that since $H_y(x)$ is a tangential component, it should be continuous at any discontinuity; further since dE_y/dx is proportional to $E_z(x)$ (which is a tangential component), it should also be continuous at any discontinuity.

PROBLEMS

29.1 Consider a symmetric step-index waveguide [see Eq. (29.1)] with $n_1 = 1.50$, $n_2 = 1.46$, $d = 4$ μm operating at $\lambda_0 = 0.6328$ μm. Calculate the number of TE and TM modes.

29.2 Consider TE modes in a step index planar waveguide with $d = 2.0$ μm, $n_1 = 1.5$ and the value of n_2 is chosen such that $\sqrt{n_1^2 - n_2^2} = \frac{1}{\pi}$. For $\lambda_0 = 1$ μm, 0.8 μm and 0.66667 μm calculate (using Table 29.1) the values of b and the corresponding value of β/k_0. Show that the values of β/k_0 lie between n_1 and n_2.

29.3 Consider now a parabolic index waveguide [see Eq. (29.67)] with $n_1 = 1.50$, $n_2 = 1.46$, $a = 2$ μm operating again at $\lambda_0 = 0.6328$ μm. Assuming the validity of Eq. (29.64) and that for discrete guided modes we must have $n_2 < \frac{\beta}{k_0} < n_1$, calculate the maximum value of m and the total number of TE modes.

29.4 Consider a step index symmetric waveguide with $n_1 = 1.50$, $n_2 = 1.48$ operating at $\lambda_0 = 0.6328$ μm. Calculate the value of d so that $V = 6$. Using Table 29.1 calculate the values of b, the corresponding propagation constants $\frac{\beta}{k_0}$ and the angles that the component waves make with the z-axis.

[**Ans:** $d = 2.4752$ μm]

29.5 We consider the same waveguide as in the previous problem. At what wavelength will the value of V be equal to 3. Using Table 29.1 calculate the value of b and the corresponding propagation constant $\frac{\beta}{k_0}$.

29.6 **(a)** Consider a symmetric step-index waveguide [see Eq. (29.1)] with $n_1 = 1.49$, $n_2 = 1.46$, $d = 4$ μm operating at $\lambda_0 = 0.6328$ μm. Solve Eqs. (29.39) and (29.40) numerically (see Ref. 29.11) to calculate the values of $\frac{\beta}{k_0}$.

(b) Calculate the corresponding values of θ_m.

[**Ans: (a)** The values of $\frac{\beta}{k_0}$ are 1.4885, 1.4839,1.4765 and 1.4668

(b) $\theta_1 \approx 2.6°$; $\theta_2 \approx 5.2°$; $\theta \approx 7.7°$; $\theta_4 \approx 10.1°$]

29.7 **(a)** Consider a step index symmetric waveguide with $n_1 = 1.503$, $n_2 = 1.500$ and $d = 4$ μm. For $\lambda_0 = 1$ μm, calculate the value of V and use linear interpolation of the numbers given in Table 29.1 to calculate the value of $\frac{\beta}{k_0}$.

(b) If the operating wavelength is changed to 0.5 μm, show that $V = 4.771$ and by linear interpolation of the numbers given in Table 29.1 calculate the discrete values of $\frac{\beta}{k_0}$ and the corresponding angles that the waves make with the z-axis.

[**Ans: (a)** $\frac{\beta}{k_0} \approx 1.5016$ **(b)** $\frac{\beta}{k_0} \approx 1.5024$ and 1.5007]

29.8 In Eq. (29.5), make the transformation $x \to -x$ and assuming $n^2(-x) = n^2(x)$ show that $E_y(-x)$ satisfies the same equation as $E_y(x)$; hence we must have $E_y(-x) = \lambda E_y(x)$. Make the transformation $x \to -x$ again to prove that the solutions are either symmetric or antisymmetric functions of x [i.e., prove Eqs. (29.20) and (29.21)].

CHAPTER 30

Fiber Optics III: Single Mode Fibers

A new era is dawning in the West, the era of light. Under city streets and beneath oceans, in commercial skyscrapers ..., a host of new technologies based on lasers, ultrapure glass fibers and exotic new materials are challenging the wonders of conventional electronic gadgetry .... With growing speed, the new technology promises to turn the electronic age into the age of optics, in which gadgetry built around beams of light becomes virtually indispensable.

—TIME Magazine, October 6, 1986

LEARNING OBJECTIVES

After reading this chapter, the reader should be able to:

LO 1: *understand the modes of an optical fiber.*

LO 2: *derive basic equations which give us the modes of a step index fiber.*

LO 3: *discuss the propagation characteristics of a single mode step index fiber.*

LO 4: *describe pulse dispersion in single-mode fibers.*

LO 5: *discuss dispersion compensating fibers.*

Above Image: A bundle of optical fibers. Photograph courtesy McGraw Hill Digital Access Library.

30.1 Introduction

At the heart of an optical communication system is the optical fiber that acts as the transmission channel propagating the light beam carrying the information. According to ray optics, the light beam gets guided through the optical fiber due to the phenomenon of total internal reflection (often abbreviated as TIR); we had discussed this in Chapter 28. However, for a single mode fiber (which are now extensively used in optical communication systems), the core diameter is very small (few microns) and ray optics does not remain valid. Here, one has to use Maxwell's electromagnetic theory to study the propagation characteristics of the (single mode) fiber. In the previous chapter, we had carried out modal analysis of planar waveguides which enabled us to understand the concept of modes. In this chapter, we will carry out modal analysis of the step index fiber that would help us in the design of a fiber optic communication system.

30.2 Basic Equations LO1

The simplest refractive index variation is that of a step index fiber which is characterized by the following refractive index distribution (see Fig. 30.1):

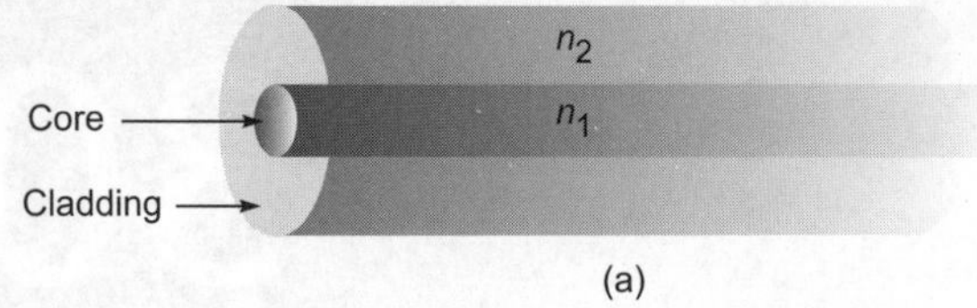

(a)

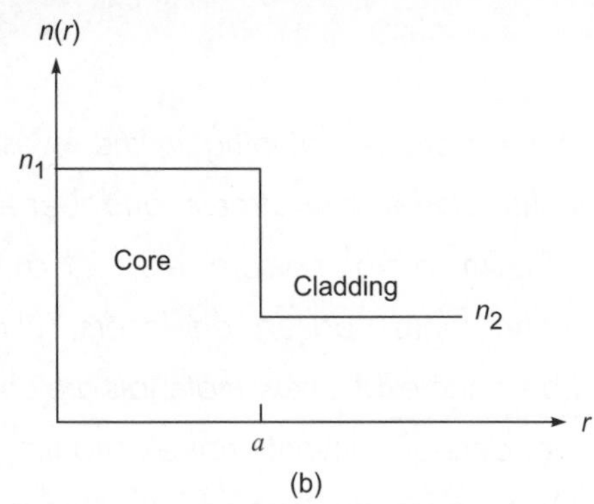

(b)

Figure 30.1
(a) A step index fiber is a cylindrical structure in which the refractive index is n_1 for $0 < r < a$ and n_2 for $r > a$. (b) The refractive index variation of a step index fiber.

$$\begin{aligned} n(r) &= n_1 \quad 0 < r < a \quad \text{core} \\ &= n_2 \quad r > a \quad \text{cladding} \end{aligned} \tag{30.1}$$

where we are using the cylindrical system of coordinates (r, ϕ, z). In actual fibers

$$\frac{n_1 - n_2}{n_2} \le 0.01 \tag{30.2}$$

and this allows use of the so-called scalar wave approximation (also known as the *weakly guiding approximation**). In this approximation, the modes are assumed to be nearly transverse and can have an arbitrary state of polarization. Thus, the two independent sets of modes can be assumed to be x-polarized and y-polarized, and in the weakly guiding approximation, they have the same propagation constants. These are usually referred to as LP modes (LP stands for linearly polarized). We may compare this with the discussion in Sec. 29.4 where we showed that when $n_1 \approx n_2$, the modes are nearly transverse and the propagation constant of the TE and TM modes are almost equal. In the weakly guiding approximation, the transverse component of the electric field (E_x or E_y) satisfies the scalar wave equation

$$\nabla^2\Psi = \varepsilon_0\mu_0 n^2 \frac{\partial^2\Psi}{\partial t^2} = \frac{n^2}{c^2}\frac{\partial^2\Psi}{\partial t^2} \tag{30.3}$$

where $c \left(= \frac{1}{\sqrt{\varepsilon_0\mu_0}}\right) \approx 3 \times 10^8$ m/s is the speed of light in free space. In most practical fibers n^2 depends only on the cylindrical coordinate r and therefore it is convenient to use the cylindrical system of coordinates (r, ϕ, z) and write the solution of Eq. (30.3) in the form

$$\Psi(r, \phi, z, t) = \psi(r, \phi)e^{i(\omega t - \beta z)} \tag{30.4}$$

where ω is the angular frequency and β is known as the **propagation constant**. The above equation defines the modes of the system. Since $\psi(r, \phi)$ depends only on the transverse coordinates r and ϕ,

> *the modes represent transverse field configurations that do not change as they propagate through the optical fiber except for a phase change.*

In the cylindrical system of coordinates (r, ϕ, z) we have

$$\nabla^2\Psi = \frac{\partial^2\Psi}{\partial r^2} + \frac{1}{r}\frac{\partial\Psi}{\partial r} + \frac{1}{r^2}\frac{\partial^2\Psi}{\partial\phi^2} + \frac{\partial^2\Psi}{\partial z^2} \tag{30.5}$$

Now, from Eq. (30.4) it readily follows that

$$\frac{\partial^2\Psi}{\partial t^2} = -\omega^2\,\Psi = -\omega^2\,\psi(r, \phi)e^{i(\omega t - \beta z)} \tag{30.6}$$

and

$$\frac{\partial^2\Psi}{\partial z^2} = -\beta^2\,\Psi = -\beta^2\,\psi(r, \phi)e^{i(\omega t - \beta z)} \tag{30.7}$$

Substituting Eq. (30.4) in Eq. (30.3) and using Eqs. (30.5)–(30.7), we obtain

$$\frac{\partial^2\psi}{\partial r^2} + \frac{1}{r}\frac{\partial\psi}{\partial r} + \frac{1}{r^2}\frac{\partial^2\psi}{\partial\phi^2} + [k_0^2 n^2(r) - \beta^2]\psi = 0 \tag{30.8}$$

where $\quad k_0 = \frac{\omega}{c} = \frac{2\pi}{\lambda_0}$

is the free space wave number. Because the medium has cylindrical symmetry, i.e., n^2 depends only on the cylindrical coordinate r, we can solve Eq. (30.8) by the method of separation of variables:

$$\psi(r, \phi) = R(r)\,\Phi(\phi)$$

On substituting and dividing by $\psi(r, \phi)/r^2$, we obtain

$$\frac{r^2}{R}\left(\frac{d^2R}{dr^2} + \frac{1}{r}\frac{dR}{dr}\right) + r^2[n^2(r)k_0^2 - \beta^2] = -\frac{1}{\Phi}\frac{d^2\Phi}{d\phi^2} = l^2 \tag{30.9}$$

Thus the variables have separated out and we have set each side equal to a constant ($= l^2$). Solving the equation depending only on ϕ, we find that the ϕ dependence will be of the form $\cos l\phi$ or $\sin l\phi$ and for the function to be single valued [i.e., for $\Phi(\phi + 2\pi) = \Phi(\phi)$] we must have

$$l = 0, 1, 2, \ldots, \text{etc.}$$

* For more details about the weakly guiding approximation see, e.g., Refs. 30.1 and 30.2.

Negative values of l correspond to the same field distribution. Thus the complete transverse field is given by

$$\Psi(r, \phi, z, t) = R(r)e^{i(\omega t-\beta z)}\begin{pmatrix}\cos l\phi \\ \sin l\phi\end{pmatrix}; l = 0, 1, 2, \ldots \quad \textbf{(30.10)}$$

where $R(r)$ satisfied the radial part of the equation

$$r^2\frac{d^2R}{dr^2} + r\frac{dR}{dr} + \{[k_0^2 n^2(r) - \beta^2]r^2 - l^2\}R = 0 \quad \textbf{(30.11)}$$

Since for each value of l, there can be two independent states of polarization, modes with $l \geq 1$ are four-fold degenerate (corresponding to two orthogonal polarization states and to the ϕ dependence being cos $l\phi$ or sin $l\phi$). Modes with $l = 0$ are ϕ independent and have two-fold degeneracy. The word 'degeneracy' means that for the same value of the propagation constant, there are more than one field profiles. For $l = 0$, we will have two independent state of polarization. Thus, the mode is said to be two-fold degenerate. On the other hand, for $l = 1, 2, 3, \ldots$ the mode will be four-fold degenerate because (for the same value of β^2) we will have two field profiles: one proportional to cos $l\phi$ and the other to sin $l\phi$ and for each field profile, we will again have two independent states of polarization.

We may mention here that on the right hand side of Eq. (30.9) we cannot set it equal to a negative constant, because then the ϕ dependence of the field will not be single valued. In the next section, we have given the solution of Eq. (30.11) for a step index profile. However, for an arbitrary cylindrically symmetric profile having a refractive index that decreases monotonically from a value n_1 on the axis to a constant value n_2 beyond the core-cladding interface $r = a$ [see Fig. 30.2], we can make the general observation that the solutions of Eq. (30.11) can be divided into two distinct classes [compare with the discussions in Sec. 29.2]; the first class of solutions correspond to

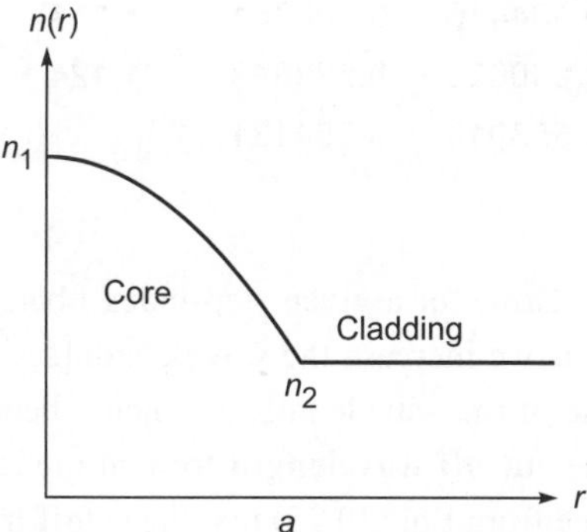

Figure 30.2
A cylindrically symmetric refractive index profile having a refractive index that decreases monotonically from a value n_1 on the axis to a constant value n_2 beyond the core-cladding interface $r = a$.

$$n_2^2 < \frac{\beta^2}{k_0^2} < n_1^2 \quad \textbf{GUIDED MODES} \quad \textbf{(30.12)}$$

For β^2 lying in the above range, the field $R(r)$ are oscillatory in the core and decay in the cladding and β^2 assumes only discrete values. These are known as the **guided modes of the waveguide**. For a given value of l, there will be a finite number of guided modes, these are designated as LP_{lm} modes ($m = 1, 2, 3, \ldots$). The second class of solutions correspond to

$$\beta^2 < k_0^2 n_2^2 \quad \textbf{RADIATION MODES} \quad \textbf{(30.13)}$$

For such β values, the field are oscillatory even in the cladding and β can assume a continuum of values. These are known as the **radiation modes***.

We will discuss in detail the guided modes of a step index fiber.

30.3 Guided Modes of a Step Index Fiber

LO2

In this section, we obtain the modal fields and the corresponding propagation constants for guided modes in a step index fiber for which the refractive index variation is given by Eq. (30.1). For such a fiber, for guided modes [for which $n_2^2 < \frac{\beta^2}{k_0^2} < n_1^2$], Eq. (30.11) can be written in the form

$$r^2\frac{d^2R}{dr^2} + r\frac{dR}{dr} + \left(U^2\frac{r^2}{a^2} - l^2\right)R = 0; \quad 0 < r < a \quad \textbf{(30.14)}$$

and

$$r^2\frac{d^2R}{dr^2} + r\frac{dR}{dr} - \left(W^2\frac{r^2}{a^2} + l^2\right)R = 0; \quad r > a \quad \textbf{(30.15)}$$

where $$U \equiv a\sqrt{k_0^2 n_1^2 - \beta^2} \quad \textbf{(30.16)}$$

and $$W \equiv a\sqrt{\beta^2 - k_0^2 n_2^2} \quad \textbf{(30.17)}$$

Because of Eq. (30.12), both U and W are real. The normalized waveguide parameter V is defined by

$$V = \sqrt{U^2 + W^2} = k_0 a\sqrt{n_1^2 - n_2^2} \quad \textbf{(30.18)}$$

In terms of the wavelength

$$V = \frac{2\pi}{\lambda_0}a\sqrt{n_1^2 - n_2^2} \quad \textbf{(30.19)}$$

The waveguide parameter V is an extremely important quantity characterizing an optical fiber. It is convenient to define the normalized propagation constant

* For more details about radiation modes and also excitation of leaky modes, see, e.g. Refs. 30.1 and 30.3.

$$b = \frac{\frac{\beta^2}{k_0^2} - n_2^2}{n_1^2 - n_2^2} = \frac{W^2}{V^2} \tag{30.20}$$

Thus $$W = V\sqrt{b} \tag{30.21}$$

and $$U = V\sqrt{1-b} \tag{30.22}$$

From Eq. (30.12) we find that for guided modes $0 < b < 1$. The two independent solutions of Eq. (30.14) are $J_l(Ur/a)$ and $Y_l(Ur/a)$ [see, e.g., Refs. 30.4–30.6]. However, the solution $Y_l(Ur/a)$ has to be rejected since it diverges as $r \to 0$. The solutions of Eq. (30.15) are the modified Bessel functions $K_l(Wr/a)$ and $I_l(Wr/a)$; the solution $I_l(Wr/a)$ has to be rejected since it diverges as $r \to \infty$. Thus, for guided modes, the transverse dependence of the modal field is given by

$$\psi(r,\phi) = \begin{cases} \dfrac{A}{J_l(U)} J_l\left(\dfrac{Ur}{a}\right)\begin{bmatrix}\cos l\phi \\ \sin l\phi\end{bmatrix}; & r < a \\ \dfrac{A}{K_l(W)} K_l\left(\dfrac{Wr}{a}\right)\begin{bmatrix}\cos l\phi \\ \sin l\phi\end{bmatrix}; & r > a \end{cases} \tag{30.23}$$

where A is a constant and we have assumed the continuity of ψ at the core-cladding interface ($r = a$). Continuity of $\partial\psi/\partial r$ at $r = a$ and use of identities involving Bessel functions [see, e.g., Ref. 30.3] give us the following transcendental equations which determine the allowed discrete values of the normalized propagation constant b of the guided LP_{lm} modes:

$$V(1-b)^{1/2}\frac{J_{l-1}[V(1-b)^{1/2}]}{J_l[V(1-b)^{1/2}]} = -Vb^{1/2}\frac{K_{l-1}[Vb^{1/2}]}{K_l[Vb^{1/2}]};\ l \ge 1 \tag{30.24}$$

and

$$V(1-b)^{1/2}\frac{J_1[V(1-b)^{1/2}]}{J_0[V(1-b)^{1/2}]} = Vb^{1/2}\frac{K_1[Vb^{1/2}]}{K_0[Vb^{1/2}]};\ l = 0 \tag{30.25}$$

The solution of the above transcendental equations will give us universal curves describing the dependence of b (and therefore of U and W) on V. For a given value of l, there will be a finite number of solutions and the mth solution ($m = 1, 2, 3, \ldots$) is referred to as the LP_{lm} mode. The variation of b with V form a set of universal curves, which are plotted in Fig. 30.3. Table 30.1 gives the numerical values of b (corresponding to the LP_{01} mode) for values of V lying between 1.0 and 2.5.

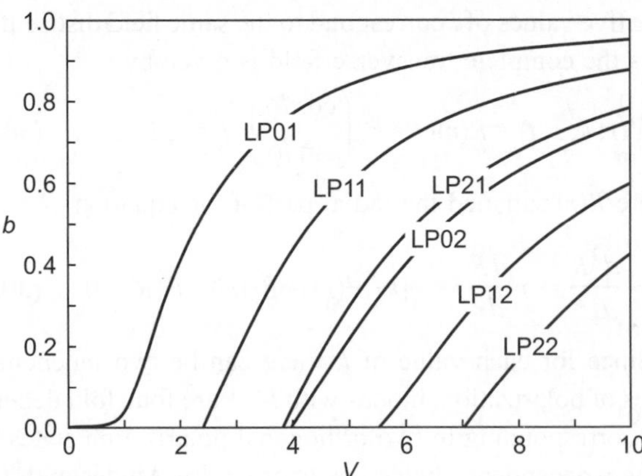

Figure 30.3
Variation of the normalized propagation constant b with normalized waveguide parameter V corresponding to a few lower order modes. *[Adapted from Ref. 30.2.]*

TABLE 30.1 Values of b, $(bV)'$ and $V(bV)''$ vs V for a step index fiber; the values in the second, fourth and fifth columns are generated by solving Eq. (30.25) for a step index fiber using the software given in Refs. 30.7 and 30.8.

V	b	b [using Eq. (30.30)]	$\frac{d}{dV}(bV)$	$V(bV)''$
1.5	0.229248	0.229249	0.849	1.063
1.6	0.270063	0.270712	0.913	0.919
1.7	0.309467	0.310157	0.965	0.785
1.8	0.347068	0.347471	1.006	0.664
1.9	0.382660	0.382653	1.039	0.556
2.0	0.416163	0.415767	1.065	0.462
2.1	0.447581	0.446911	1.086	0.380
2.2	0.476969	0.476200	1.102	0.309
2.3	0.504416	0.503754	1.114	0.248
2.4	0.530026	0.529693	1.124	0.195
2.5	0.553915	0.554131		

30.3.1 Cut-Off Frequencies

From Fig. 30.3, we see that the value of b decreases as we decrease the value of V. For every mode, there is a value of V when b becomes zero (i.e., when β/k_0 becomes equal to n_2) and the mode ceases to be a guided mode. The value of V for which b becomes zero is known as the **cut-off frequency** of the mode. Now, for a given step-index fiber, the value of V decreases as we increase the wavelength [see Eq. (30.19)] and the value of the wavelength at which b becomes zero is known as the **cut-off wavelength** for that mode.

We can see from Eq. (30.25) that the cutoff frequencies of the LP_{0m} modes will occur at the zeroes of $J_1(V)$, i.e., when $V = 0$ (LP_{01}), 3.8317 (LP_{02}), 7.0156 (LP_{03}), 10.1735 (LP_{04}),…. Similarly, we can see from Eq. (30.24) that the cutoff frequencies of the LP_{1m} modes will occur at the zeroes of $J_0(V)$, i.e., when $V = 2.4048$ (LP_{11}), 5.5201 (LP_{12}), 8.6537 (LP_{13}), 11.7915 (LP_{14}),…;

cut-off frequencies of the LP_{2m} modes occur at the zeroes of $J_1(V)$ (excluding the value $V = 0$), i.e., when $V = 3.8317$ (LP_{21}), 7.0156 (LP_{22}), 10.1735 (LP_{23}), ….

For $l \geq 1$, cut-off frequencies of the LP_{lm} modes will occur at the zeroes of $J_{l-1}(V)$ (excluding the value $V = 0$); thus*

cut-off frequencies of the LP_{3m} modes occur when $V = 5.1356$ (LP_{31}), 8.4172 (LP_{32}), 11.6198 (LP_{33}), ….

cut-off frequencies of the LP_{4m} modes occur when $V = 6.3802$ (LP_{41}), 9.7610 (LP_{42}), 13.015 (LP_{43}), ….

cut-off frequencies of the LP_{5m} modes occur when $V = 7.5883$ (LP_{51}), 11.0647 (LP_{52}),….

cut-off frequencies of the LP_{6m} modes occur when $V = 8.7715$ (LP_{61}), 12.3386 (LP_{62}),,…

Thus, as can also be seen from the figure:

For $0 < V < 2.4048$ we will only have the LP_{01} mode (which is referred to as the fundamental mode); $V = 2.4048$ represents the cut-off of the LP_{11} mode where (for the LP_{11} mode) b becomes 0, i.e., β/k_0 becomes equal to n_2.

For $2.4048 < V < 3.8317$ we will only have LP_{01} and LP_{11} modes; $V = 3.8317$ represents the cut-off of the LP_{02} and the LP_{21} modes where (for the LP_{02} and the LP_{21} modes) b becomes 0, i.e., β/k_0 becomes equal to n_2.

For $3.8317 < V < 5.1356$ we will only have LP_{01}, LP_{02}, LP_{11} and LP_{21} modes; $V = 5.1356$ represents the cutoff of the LP_{31} mode.

Thus at a particular V value, the fiber can support only a finite number of modes [see Eq. (30.26)]. We must mention here that each LP_{0m} mode is two-fold degenerate; i.e., there are two independent modes with the same value of b, corresponding to two independent states of polarization. Further each LP_{lm} mode ($l > 1$) is four-fold degenerate; i.e., there are four independent modes with the same value of b, corresponding to ϕ-dependence of $\cos l\phi$ and $\sin l\phi$ with each mode having two independent states of polarization.

EXAMPLE 30.1 We consider a step index fiber with $n_1 = 1.5$, $n_2 = 1.49$ and the core radius $a = 3.0$ μm. Thus,

$$V = \frac{2\pi}{\lambda_0} a\sqrt{n_1^2 - n_2^2} = \frac{3.2594}{\lambda_0}$$

where λ_0 is measured in μm. Thus the cut-off wavelength of the LP_{11} mode will be 1.355 μm, cut-off wavelengths of the LP_{21} and LP_{02} modes will be 0.8506 μm, cut-off wavelength of the LP_{31} mode will be 0.6347 μm, ….

The LP_{01} mode has no cutoff. Thus for $\lambda_0 > 1.355$ μm, we will only have the LP_{01} mode and for $0.8506\ \mu\text{m} < \lambda_0 < 1.355\ \mu\text{m}$, we will have LP_{01} and LP_{11} modes. For $0.6347\ \mu\text{m} < \lambda_0 < 0.8506\ \mu\text{m}$, we will have LP_{01}, LP_{11}, LP_{21} and LP_{02} modes.

A manufacturer would always specify the cut-off wavelength of the fiber; that cut-off wavelength would correspond to that of the LP_{11} mode. In Example 30.1, the cut-off wavelength would be 1.355 μm because for all wavelengths *greater* than this, the fiber will be single moded supporting only the LP_{01} mode. Thus,

> **the minimum wavelength for which we will have only the LP_{01} mode (which, for a step-index fiber will correspond to $V = 2.4048$)** is known as the *cut-off wavelength* and is denoted by λ_c.**

It is λ_c that is almost always mentioned in the data sheet of a silica fiber [see. e.g., Ref. 30.11].

EXAMPLE 30.2 We consider a step index fiber with $n_1 = 1.5$, $n_2 = 1.48$ and core radius $a = 6.0$ μm. Assuming the operating wavelength $\lambda_0 = 1.3$ μm, we get $V = 7.0796$. Thus we will have two each of LP_{01}, LP_{02} and LP_{03} modes, four each of LP_{11}, LP_{12}, LP_{21}, LP_{22}, LP_{31} and LP_{41} modes and we will have a total of 30 modes. Now the total number of modes in a highly multi-moded ($V \geq 10$) step index fiber is approximately given by

$$N \approx \frac{1}{2}V^2 \tag{30.26}$$

For $V = 7.0796$, we get $N \approx 25$. For higher value of V, the values given by Eq. (30.26) will become closer to the exact value (see Problem 30.5).

30.3.2 Power Law Profile

We may mention here that a broad class of *multi-moded* graded index fibers can be described by the following refractive index distribution (see Fig. 28.17):

$$\begin{aligned} n^2(r) &= n_1^2\left[1 - 2\Delta\left(\frac{r}{a}\right)^q\right]; \qquad 0 < r < a \\ &= n_2^2 = n_1^2(1 - 2\Delta); \qquad r > a \end{aligned} \tag{30.27}$$

where r corresponds to a cylindrical radial coordinate, n_1 represents the value of the refractive index on the axis (i.e., at $r = 0$), and n_2 represents the refractive index of the cladding. Equation (30.27) describes what is usually referred to as a power law profile or a q-profile; $q = 1$, $q = 2$ and $q = \infty$ correspond to the linear, parabolic, and step index profiles, respectively (see Fig. 28.17). The total number of modes in a highly multimoded graded index optical fiber characterized by Eq. (30.27) are approximately given by (see Appendix C of Ref. 30.3).

$$N \approx \frac{q}{2(2+q)}V^2 \tag{30.28}$$

Thus, a parabolic index fiber ($q = 2$) with $V = 10$ will support approximately 25 modes. Similarly, a step index fiber

* The values of the zeros of the Bessel functions are taken from Ref. 30.9.

** For a graded index fiber with parabolic variation of refractive index in the core, the cut-off wavelength will correspond to $V = 3.518$ (Ref. 30.10).

($q = \infty$) with $V = 10$ will support approximately 50 modes. When the fiber supports such a large number of modes, then use of ray optics to calculate pulse dispersion would give accurate results. Now, in multimode fibers, in addition to the material dispersion (see Sec. 28.10.3) we also have *intermodal dispersion* which arises due to different modes traveling with different group velocities. In Ref. 30.12 (see also Ref. 30.3), it has been shown that for a highly multimoded graded index optical fiber, the value of intermodal dispersion is very nearly the same as obtained from ray analysis. In Chapter 28, we had used ray optics to calculate intermodal dispersion in step index and parabolic index fibers. Such an analysis will give accurate results for a highly multimoded fiber with $V \geq 10$.

30.4 Single-Mode Step Index Fiber

LO3

The LP_{01} mode (for which $l = 0$ and $m = 1$) is known as the **fundamental mode**. As mentioned earlier, for a step index fiber when $0 < V < 2.4048$, we will only have the fundamental mode. When this happens, the fiber is referred to as a single-mode fiber which are extensively used in optical fiber communication systems. For the fundamental mode, the actual numerical values of b for various values of V are tabulated in Table 30.1. Thus for a given step index fiber operating at a particular wavelength, we just have to calculate the value of V and then use simple interpolation to calculate the value of b from Table 30.1. From the value of b, one can obtain the corresponding propagation constant by using the following equation [see Eq. (30.20)]:

$$\frac{\beta}{k_0} = \sqrt{[n_2^2 + b(n_1^2 - n_2^2)]} \approx n_2\sqrt{1+(2\Delta)b} \qquad \textbf{(30.29)}$$

where in the last step we have assumed $n_1 \approx n_2$.

EXAMPLE 30.3 We consider a step index fiber with $n_2 = 1.447$, $\Delta = 0.003$ and $a = 4.2$ µm giving $V = 2.958/\lambda_0$, where λ_0 is measured in µm. Thus for $\lambda_0 > 1.23$ µm, the fiber will be single moded. The cut-off wavelength λ_c (for which $V = 2.4045$) is 1.23 µm. We assume the operating wavelength $\lambda_0 = 1.479$ µm so that $V = 2.0$ and therefore (from Table 30.1)

$$b \approx 0.4162 \quad \Rightarrow \quad \frac{\beta}{k_0} \approx n_2\sqrt{1+(2\Delta)b} \approx 1.4488$$

$$\Rightarrow \quad \beta \approx 6.1549 \times 10^6 \text{ m}^{-1}$$

EXAMPLE 30.4 In continuation of the previous problem, we consider the same step index fiber [$n_2 = 1.447$, $\Delta = 0.003$ and $a = 4.2$ µm] now operating at $\lambda_0 = 1.55$ µm. Thus, $V \approx 1.908$ and we again have a single mode fiber. Using Table 30.1 and linear interpolation, we get

$$b \approx 0.382660 + \frac{0.416163 - 0.382660}{0.1} \times 0.008$$

$$\approx 0.38534$$

$$\Rightarrow \quad \frac{\beta}{k_0} \approx n_2\sqrt{1+(2\Delta)b} \approx 1.4487$$

$$\Rightarrow \quad \beta \approx 5.8725 \times 10^6 \text{ m}^{-1}$$

EXAMPLE 30.5 For reasons that will be discussed later, the fibers used in IV generation optical communication systems (operating at 1.55 µm) have a small value of core radius and a large value of Δ. A typical fiber (operating at $\lambda_0 \approx 1.55$ µm) would have $n_2 = 1.444$, $\Delta = 0.0075$ and $a = 2.3$ µm. Thus, at $\lambda_0 = 1.55$ µm

$$V = \frac{2\pi}{1.55} \times 2.3 \times 1.444 \times \sqrt{0.015} \approx 1.649$$

The fiber will be single moded at 1.55 µm and

$$b \approx 0.270063 + \frac{0.309467 - 0.270063}{0.1} \times 0.049 = 0.28937$$

$$\Rightarrow \quad \frac{\beta}{k_0} \approx n_2\sqrt{1+(2\Delta)b} \approx 1.44713$$

Further, for the given fiber, we may write

$$V = \frac{2.556}{\lambda_0}$$

and therefore the cut-off wavelength will be

$$\lambda_c = 2.556/2.4045 \approx 1.06 \text{ µm}.$$

30.4.1 Empirical Formula for the Normalized Propagataion Constant

For a single mode step index fiber, a convenient empirical formula for $b(V)$ is given by

$$b(V) = \left(A - \frac{B}{V}\right)^2; \quad 1.5 \lesssim V \lesssim 2.5 \qquad \textbf{(30.30)}$$

with $A \approx 1.1428$ and $B \approx 0.996$. The above formula gives values of b which are within about 0.2% of the exact values (see Table 30.1).

30.4.2 Spot Size of the Fundamental Mode

As mentioned earlier, a single mode fiber supports only one mode that propagates through the fiber; this is also referred to as the fundamental mode of the fiber. The transverse field distribution associated with the fundamental mode of a single mode fiber is an extremely important quantity and it determines various important parameters like splice loss at joints, launching efficiencies, bending loss, etc. For a step index fiber, one has analytical expression for the fundamental field distribution in terms of Bessel functions (see Sec. 30.3). For most single mode fibers, the fundamental mode field distributions can be well approximated by a Gaussian function, which may be written in the form

$$\psi(x, y) = A\, e^{-\frac{x^2+y^2}{w^2}} = A\, e^{-\frac{r^2}{w^2}} \quad \textbf{(30.31)}$$

where w is referred to as the **spot size** of the mode field pattern and $2w$ is called the **mode field diameter** (MFD). MFD is a very important characteristic of a single mode optical fiber. For a step index fiber, one has the following empirical expression for w (see Ref. 30.13):

$$\frac{w}{a} \approx 0.65 + \frac{1.619}{V^{3/2}} + \frac{2.879}{V^6}; \quad 0.8 \le V \le 2.5 \quad \textbf{(30.32)}$$

where a is the core radius. Many single mode fibers used in optical communication systems do not have a step variation of refractive index; in fact, they often have very special refractive index distribution. Nevertheless, the modal field is very nearly Gaussian and one usually describes the fiber though the MFD. We may mention here that the light coming out of a He-Ne laser (or of a laser pointer) has a transverse intensity distribution very similar to that coming out from a single mode fiber except that the spot size is much larger.

EXAMPLE 30.6 Consider a step index fiber (operating at 1300 nm) with $n_2 = 1.447$, $\Delta = 0.003$ and $a = 4.2$ μm (see Example 30.2). Thus $V \approx 2.28$ giving $w \approx 4.8$ μm. The same fiber will have a V value of 1.908 at $\lambda_0 = 1550$ nm giving a value of the spot size ≈ 5.5 μm. *Thus, the spot size increases with wavelength.*

EXAMPLE 307 For a step index fiber (operating at 1550 nm) with $n_2 = 1.444$, $\Delta = 0.0075$ and $a = 2.3$ μm (see Example 30.5). Thus $V \approx 1.65$ giving $w \approx 3.6$ μm. The same fiber will have a V value of 1.97 at $\lambda_0 = 1300$ nm giving a value of the spot size ≈ 3.0 μm.

30.4.3 Splice Loss Due to Transverse Misalignment

The most common misalignment at a joint between two similar fibers is the transverse misalignment similar to that shown in Fig. 30.4. Corresponding to a transverse misalignment of u the loss in decibels is given by (see Problem 30.15)

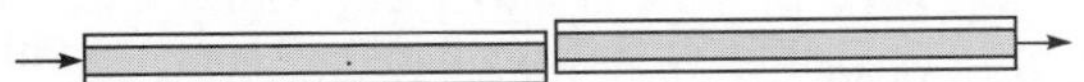

Figure 30.4

A transverse alignment between two fibers would result in a loss of the optical beam.

$$\alpha(\text{dB}) \approx 4.34\, (u/w)^2 \quad \textbf{(30.33)}$$

Thus, a larger value of w will lead to a greater tolerance to transverse misalignment. For $w \approx 5$ μm, and a transverse offset of 1 μm the loss at the joint will be approximately 0.17 dB; on the other and, for $w \approx 3$ μm, a transverse offset of 1 μm will result in a loss of about 0.5 dB.

EXAMPLE 30.8 For a single mode fiber operating at 1300 nm, $w = 5$ μm, and if the splice loss is to be below 0.1 dB, then from Eq. (30.18) we obtain $u < 0.76$ μm. Thus, for a low-loss joint, the transverse alignment is very critical and connectors for single-mode fibers require precision matching and positioning for achieving low loss.

Many data sheets describing a commercially available single mode fiber would not always give the actual refractive index profile. They would instead give the MFD may be at more than one wavelength. They would also give the cutoff wavelength (see for example Ref. 30.11). For example, the standard single mode fiber designated as G.652 fiber when operating at 1.3 μm has a MFD of 9.2 ± 0.4 μm; the same fiber when operating at 1.55 μm has a MFD of 10.4 ± 0.8 μm.

EXAMPLE 30.9 We assume $V = 8$ and $l = 0$. Using a software like Mathematica, if we plot the LHS and RHS of Eq. (30.25) as a function of b, we will get Fig. 30.5. The points of intersection will give the discrete values of the normalized propagation constant b which we find to be $b \simeq 0.9288$ for the LP_{01} mode; $b \simeq 0.6301$ for the LP_{02} mode and $b = 0.1321$ for the LP_{01} mode.

The corresponding values of β/k_0 is obtained by using Eq. (30.29).

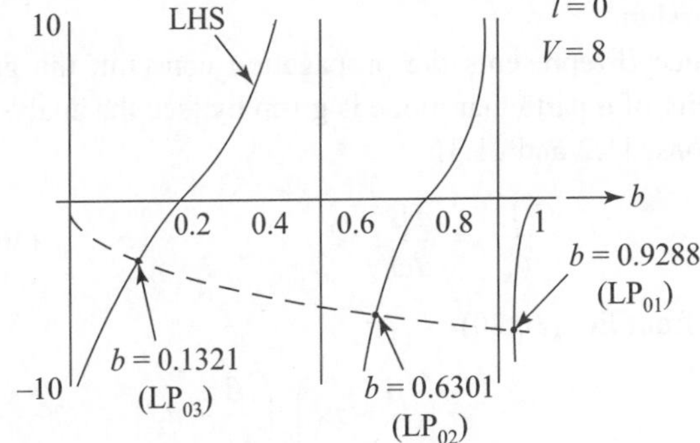

Figure 30.5

Variation of the LHS and RHS of Eq. (30.25) as a function of b; we have assumed $V = 8$ and $l = 0$. The points of intersection will give the discrete values of the normalized propagation constant b.

EXAMPLE 30.10 We assume $V = 8$ and $l = 1$. If we plot the LHS and RHS of Eq. (30.24) with $l = 1$ as a function of b, we will get Fig. 30.6. The points of intersection will give the discrete values of the normalized propagation constant b which we find to be $b \simeq 0.82$ for the LP_{11} mode and $b \simeq 0.41$ for the LP_{12} mode.

The corresponding values of β/k_0 is obtained by using Eq. (30.29).

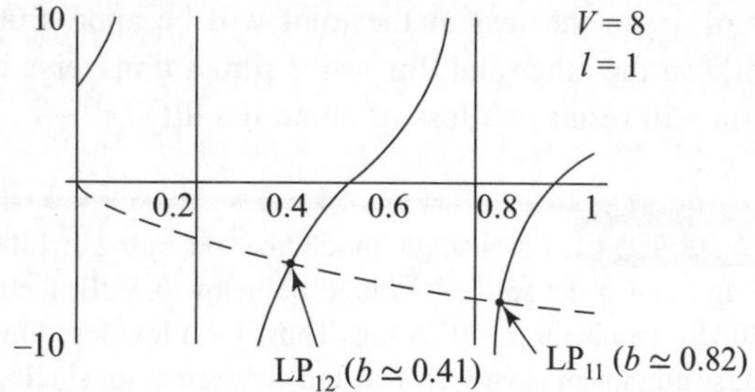

Figure 30.6
Variation of the LHS and RHS of Eq. (30.24) as a function of *b*; we have assumed $V = 8$ and $l = 1$. The points of intersection will give the discrete values of the normalized propagation constant *b*.

30.5 Pulse Dispersion in Single-Mode Fibers

LO4

In single-mode fibers, there is only one mode and there is no intermodal dispersion. However, we have (in addition to material dispersion) waveguide dispersion which is characteristic of the transverse refractive index variation*. In Sec. 28.10.3 we have discussed material dispersion. In this section, we will show that even if n_1 and n_2 are independent of wavelength (i.e., even if there is no material dispersion), the group velocity of a particular mode will depend on the wavelength. This leads to what is known as the **waveguide dispersion**.

Since β represents the propagation constant, the group velocity of a particular mode is given by [see the analysis in Sections. 11.2 and 11.3]:

$$\frac{1}{v_g} = \frac{d\beta}{d\omega} \tag{30.34}$$

Now from Eq. (30.20)

$$b = \frac{\left(\frac{\beta}{k_0} - n_2\right)}{(n_1 - n_2)} \frac{\left(\frac{\beta}{k_0} + n_2\right)}{(n_1 + n_2)} \tag{30.35}$$

Since for a guided mode β/k_0 lies between n_1 and n_2, and since for all practical single mode fibers n_1 is very close to n_2 (see Examples 30.6 and 30.7), we may write the above equation as

$$b = \frac{\frac{\beta}{k_0} - n_2}{n_1 - n_2} \tag{30.36}$$

Thus,
$$\beta = \frac{\omega}{c}[n_2 + (n_1 - n_2)b(V)] \tag{30.37}$$

We will assume that n_1 and n_2 are independent of ω and calculate group velocity:

$$\frac{1}{v_g} = \frac{d\beta}{d\omega} = \frac{1}{c}[n_2 + (n_1 - n_2)b(V)] + \frac{\omega}{c}(n_1 - n_2)\frac{db}{dV}\cdot\frac{dV}{d\omega} \tag{30.38}$$

Now,
$$V = \frac{2\pi}{\lambda_0} a\sqrt{n_1^2 - n_2^2} = \frac{\omega}{c} a\sqrt{n_1^2 - n_2^2} \tag{30.39}$$

Thus,
$$\frac{dV}{d\omega} = \frac{V}{\omega} \tag{30.40}$$

implying

$$\frac{1}{v_g} = \frac{1}{c}[n_2 + (n_1 - n_2)b(V)] + \frac{1}{c}(n_1 - n_2)V\frac{db}{dV} \tag{30.41}$$

or
$$\frac{1}{v_g} = \frac{n_2}{c} + \frac{n_1 - n_2}{c}\left[\frac{d}{dV}(bV)\right] \tag{30.42}$$

Thus, the time taken by a pulse to traverse length L of the fiber is given by

$$\tau = \frac{L}{v_g} = \frac{L}{c} n_2\left[1 + \Delta\frac{d}{dV}(bV)\right] \tag{30.43}$$

where
$$\Delta \equiv \frac{n_1^2 - n_2^2}{2n_1^2} \approx \frac{n_1 - n_2}{n_2} \tag{30.44}$$

and we have assumed $n_1 \approx n_2$. From Eq. (30.43) we see that even if n_1 and n_2 are independent of wavelength (i.e., if there is no material dispersion), the group velocity (and hence τ) will depend on ω because, as obvious from Fig. 30.3 [and also Eq. (30.30)] b depends on V. This leads to what is known as the **waveguide dispersion**. Physically this arises due to the fact that the spot size depends on the wavelength (see Examples 30.6 and 30.7). For a source having a spectral width $\Delta\lambda_0$, the corresponding waveguide dispersion is given by

$$\Delta\tau_w = \frac{d\tau}{d\lambda_0}\Delta\lambda_0 \cong \frac{L}{c} n_2\Delta\frac{d^2}{dV^2}(bV)\frac{dV}{d\lambda_0}\Delta\lambda_0 \tag{30.45}$$

From Eq. (30.39) we find

$$\frac{dV}{d\lambda_0} = -\frac{V}{\lambda_0} \tag{30.46}$$

* At very high bit rates, we also have what is known as polarization mode dispersion (abbreviated as PMD). This may arise due to many factors, for example, if there is slight ellipticity in the core of the fiber, then the two states of polarization travel with slightly different group velocities leading to what is known as PMD. However, this phenomenon becomes important at very high bit rates – above 40 Gb/s. For a nice overview of PMD, see Ref. 30.14; for more details see references therein.

Thus, $$\Delta\tau_w = -\frac{L n_2 \Delta}{c} f(V) \Delta\lambda_0 \qquad \textbf{(30.47)}$$

where $$f(V) \equiv V \frac{d^2}{dV^2}(bV) \qquad \textbf{(30.48)}$$

For a step index fiber, b as a function of V is an universal curve; in fact this is true for a fiber with a power law profile given by Eq. (30.27). Therefore, the variation of $f(V)$ with V will also be universal (see Table 30.1). A convenient empirical formula for a step index fiber is given by [Ref. 30.15]

$$f(V) \approx 0.080 + 0.549(2.834 - V)^2;\ 1.3 < V < 2.4 \qquad \textbf{(30.49)}$$

A comparison between the above empirical values with the exact values have been made in Ref. 30.3. Thus,

$$\Delta\tau_w = -\frac{L}{c} n_2\Delta[0.080 + 0.549(2.834 - V)^2]\frac{\Delta\lambda_0}{\lambda_0}$$

$$\text{for } 1.3 < V < 2.4 \qquad \textbf{(30.50)}$$

As in Sec. 28.10.3, we assume $\Delta\lambda_0 = 1$ nm $= 10^{-9}$ m and $L = 1$ km $= 1000$ m, and define the dispersion coefficient as (see Sec. 28.10.3):

$$D_w \equiv \frac{\Delta\tau_w}{L\Delta\lambda_0} \approx -\frac{n_2\Delta}{3\lambda_0} \times 10^7 \times [0.080 + 0.549(2.834 - V)^2] \text{ ps/km.nm} \qquad \textbf{(30.51)}$$

where λ_0 is measured in nanometers and we have assumed $c = 3 \times 10^{-4}$ m/ps [meters per picosecond]. The quantity D_w is referred as the waveguide dispersion coefficient (because it is due to the waveguiding properties of the fiber) and hence the subscript w on D. In the single-mode regime, the quantity within the bracket in Eq. (30.51) is usually positive. Hence the waveguide dispersion is negative indicating that longer wavelengths travel faster. Since the sign of material dispersion depends on the operating wavelength region, it is possible that the two effects namely, material and waveguide dispersions cancel each other at a certain wavelength. Such a wavelength, which is a very important parameter of single-mode fibers, is referred to as the zero-dispersion wavelength (λ_{ZD}).

The total dispersion is given by the sum of material and waveguide dispersions*:

$$D_{tot} = D_m + D_w \qquad \textbf{(30.52)}$$

Let us consider the two single mode fibers discussed in Examples 30.6 and 30.7.

30.5.1 Conventional Single Mode (G 652) Fibers

We consider the fiber discussed in Example 30.6 for which $n_2 = 1.447$, $\Delta = 0.003$ and $a = 4.2$ μm so that $V = 2958/\lambda_0$, where λ_0 is measured in nanometers. Substituting in Eq. (30.51), we get

$$D_w = -\frac{1.447 \times 10^4}{\lambda_0} \times \left[0.080 + 0.549\left(2.834 - \frac{2958}{\lambda_0}\right)^2\right] \text{ ps/km.nm}$$

Elementary calculations show that at $\lambda_0 \approx 1300$ nm, $D_w = -2.8$ ps/km.nm. The variations of D_m, D_w and D_{tot} with λ_0 are shown in Fig. 30.7; the variation of D_m is calculated by using Eq. (28.33) and Table 11.1. The total dispersion passes through zero around $\lambda_0 \approx 1300$ nm which is the *zero total dispersion wavelength* and represents an extremely important parameter. Such fibers which have zero dispersion around $\lambda_0 \approx 1300$ nm are known as **conventional single mode** (or G 652) fibers and are extensively used in optical communication systems.

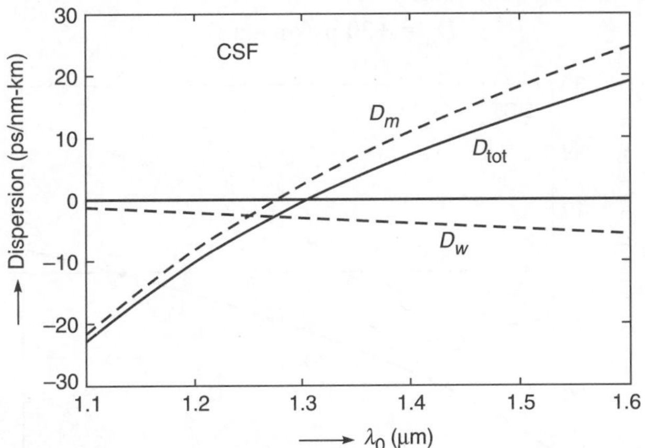

Figure 30.7

The wavelength dependence of D_m, D_w and D_{tot} for a typical conventional single mode fiber (CSF) with parameters as given in Example 30.6. The total dispersion passes through zero around $\lambda_0 \approx 1300$ nm which is known as zero dispersion wavelength.

30.5.2 Dispersion Shifted (G 653) Fibers

As mentioned at the end of Sec. 28.11, the wavelength of operation for the second and third generation optical communication systems was 1300 nm because at that wavelength, the material dispersion is very small (see Sec. 28.10.3 and Table 11.1). Indeed the third generation optical communication systems used conventional single mode (or G 652) fibers discussed in Sec. 30.5.1 operating at a wavelength around 1300 nm. Now, one could significantly increase the transmission capacity of these system by shifting the operating wavelength to 1550 nm where the loss is extremely small (see Sec. 28.8) and we can have the added advantage of using EDFAs (Erbium Doped Fiber Amplifiers) for optical amplification at this wavelength. If the operating wavelength is

* Strictly speaking, material and waveguide dispersions are not additive. For a given variation of $n^2(r)$, one really should solve Eq. (30.11) at different wavelengths taking into account the wavelength dependence of the refractive index and determine β as a function of λ_0. This is indeed done in the software developed in Ref. 30.8.

shifted to 1550 nm, we must tailor the refractive index profile such that we have very small dispersion at 1550 nm. In order to achieve this we consider the fiber discussed in Example 30.7 for which $n_2 = 1.444$, $\Delta = 0.0075$ and $a = 2.3$ µm, so that $V = 2556/\lambda_0$, where, once again, λ_0 is measured in nanometers. Substituting in Eq. (30.51), we get

$$D_w = -\frac{3.61\times10^4}{\lambda_0}\times\left[0.080+0.549\left(2.834-\frac{2556}{\lambda_0}\right)^2\right]\text{ ps/km.nm}$$

Thus at $\lambda_0 \approx 1550$ nm,

$$D_w = -20 \text{ ps/km.nm}$$

On the other hand, the material dispersion at this wavelength is given by [see Table 11.1]

$$D_m = +20 \text{ ps/km.nm}$$

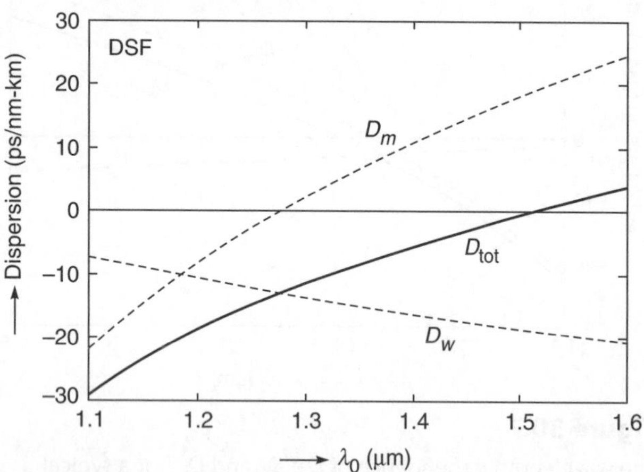

Figure 30.8

The wavelength dependence of D_m, D_w and D_{tot} for a typical dispersion shifted fiber (DSF) with parameters as given in Example 30.7. The zero dispersion wavelength is around 1550 nm.

We therefore see that the two expressions are of opposite sign and almost cancel each other. Physically, because of waveguide dispersion, longer wavelengths travel faster than shorter wavelengths and because of material dispersion, longer wavelengths travel slower than shorter wavelengths– the two effects compensate each other resulting in zero total dispersion around 1550 nm. The corresponding variation of D_m, D_w and D_{tot} with wavelength is shown in Fig. 30.8. As can be seen from the figure, we have been able to shift the zero dispersion wavelength by changing the fiber parameters; these are known as the **dispersion shifted fibers**. Thus dispersion shifted fibers are those fibers whose total dispersion becomes zero at a shifted wavelength. We should mention here that dispersion shifted fibers (which are abbreviated as DSF and referred to as G 653 fibers) usually do not have a step variation of refractive index.

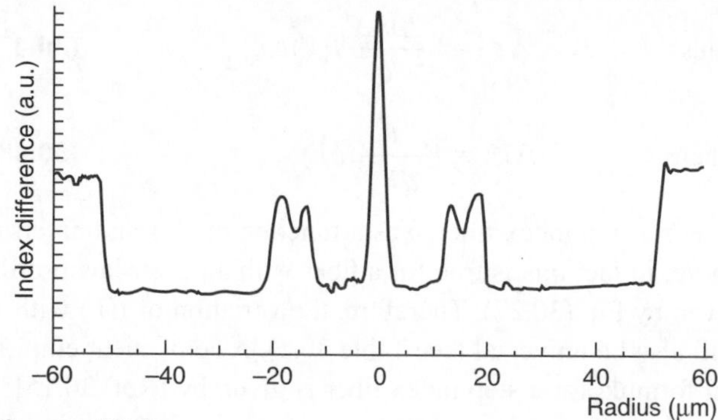

Figure 30.9

The refractive index profile of a typical dispersion compensating fiber (DCF) characterized by $D_{tot} \approx -200$ ps/km.nm at 1550 nm. *[Adapted from Ref. 30.16.]*

30.6 Dispersion Compensating Fibers

LO5

In many countries, there already exist millions of kilometers of conventional single mode fibers (of the type discussed in Example 30.6) in the underground ducts operating at 1310 nm. As mentioned in Sec. 30.5.1, these fibers have very low dispersions around 1310 nm. One could significantly increase the transmission capacity of these system by operating these fibers at 1550 nm (where the loss is extremely small) and we can have the added advantage of using EDFA (Erbium Doped Fiber Amplifiers) for optical amplification in this wavelength range (see Sec. 27.1.3). However, if we operate the conventional single mode fibers at 1550 nm, we will have a significant residual dispersion; and as discussed in Sec. 30.5.1, this residual dispersion would be about 20 ps/km.nm. Such a large dispersion would result in significant decrease in the information carrying capacity of the communication system. On the other hand, replacing the existing conventional single mode fibers by dispersion shifted fibers (DSF's) would involve huge costs. As such, in recent years there has been considerable amount of work in upgradation of the installed 1310 nm optimized optical fiber links for operation at 1550 nm. This is achieved by developing fibers with very large negative dispersion coefficients, a few hundred meters to a kilometer of which can be used to compensate for dispersion over tens of kilometers of the fiber in the link.

In Secs. 30.5.1 and 30.5.2, we have seen that by changing the refractive index profile, we can alter the waveguide dispersion and hence the total dispersion. Indeed, it is possible to have specially designed fibers whose dispersion coefficient (D_{tot}) is large and negative at 1550 nm. A typical refractive index profile, which is characterized by $D_{tot} \approx -1800$ ps/km.nm at 1550 nm, is shown in Fig. 30.9 [Ref. 30.16]*. These types of fibers are known as dispersion compensating fibers (DCF's). A short length of DCF can be used in conjunction with the 1310 nm optimized fiber link so as to have small total dispersion value at the end of the link (see Fig. 30.10).

* The refractive index variation used in Ref. 30.16 is based on the refractive index profile suggested in Ref. 30.17.

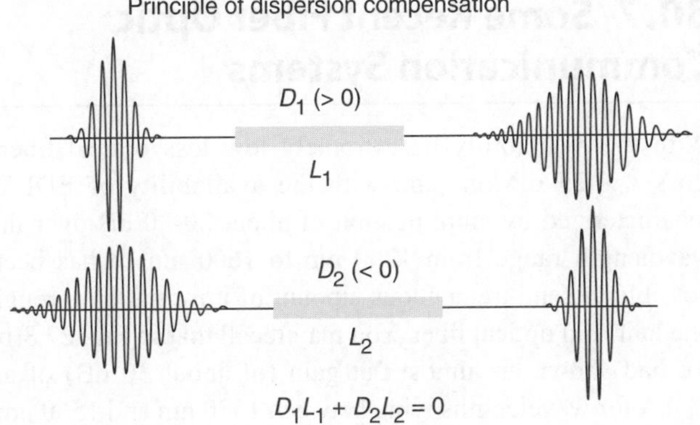

Figure 30.10

A short length of a DCF can be used in conjunction with the conventional single mode fiber (CSF) so as to have small dispersion value at the end of the link.

In order to understand this phenomenon, we have plotted in Fig. 30.11 (as a solid curve) a typical variation of the group velocity v_g with wavelength for a conventional single mode fiber (CSF) with zero dispersion around 1300 nm wavelength. As can be seen from the figure, v_g attains a maximum value at the zero dispersion wavelength and on either side, it monotonically decreases with wavelength. Thus, if the central wavelength of the pulse is around 1550 nm, then the red components of the pulse (i.e., longer wavelengths) will travel slower than the blue components (i.e., smaller wavelengths) of the pulse. Because of this, the pulse will get broadened and chirped (see Sec. 11.3, Figures 11.7 and 11.8). Now, after propagating through a CSF for a certain length L_1, the pulse is allowed to propagate through a length L_2 of the DCF in which the group velocity v_g varies as shown by the dashed curve in Fig. 30.11. The red components (i.e. longer wavelengths)

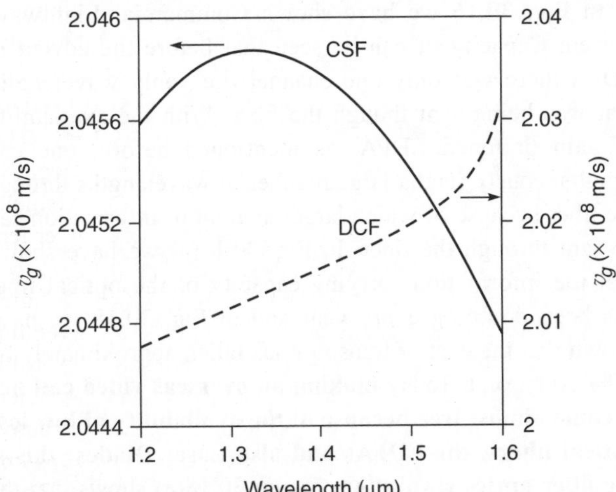

Figure 30.11

The wavelength variation of group velocity for a typical dispersion compensating fiber and a typical conventional single-mode fiber.

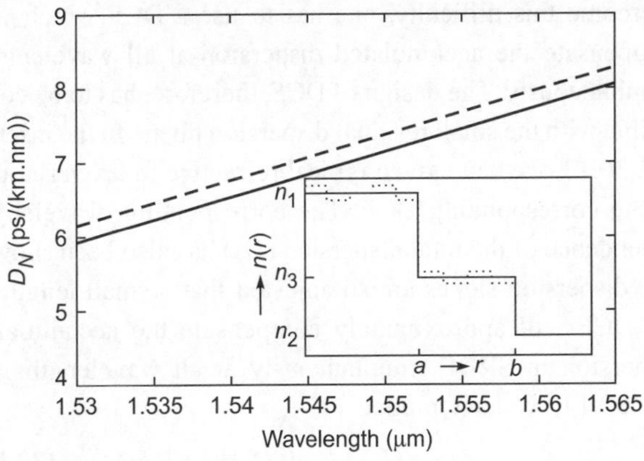

Figure 30.12

Variation of the total dispersion (D_N) of the SRDF as a function wavelength. The solid and dashed curves correspond to the proposed and the perturbed refractive index profiles (shown schematically in inset), respectively [*Figure adapted from Ref. 30.18*].

will now travel faster than the blue components and the pulse will tend to reshape itself into its original form. Indeed if the lengths of the two fibers (L_1 and L_2) are such that

$$D_1 L_1 + D_2 L_2 = 0 \tag{30.53}$$

then the pulse emanating from the second fiber will be almost identical to the pulse entering the first fiber as shown in Fig. 30.10.

We may mention here that the latest trend in optical communication has been to use DWDM (Dense Wavelength Division Multiplexed) systems in which many closely spaced wavelengths (in the wavelength region 1530–1565 nm) are simultaneously propagated and amplified by Erbium Doped Fiber Amplifiers (EDFA). Now, if the fiber is operated at the zero dispersion wavelength then all nearby wavelengths will travel with the same group velocity because of which they interact with each other to create new frequencies – this is known as **four wave mixing**, usually abbreviated as FWM. To overcome this difficulty, the use of small dispersion fiber has been suggested, where the dispersion is typically in the range 2–8 ps/(km.nm). Because of this, different wavelengths travel with different velocities and the unwanted frequencies are not generated. In the inset of Fig. 30.12, we have given typical refractive index variations of a small dispersion fiber named as **Small Residual Dispersion Fiber** (SRDF). The figure also shows the corresponding total dispersion (D_N) as a function wavelength; the tolerance of the dispersion characteristics on the refractive index profile are shown by dotted lines. However, if one wants repeaterless transmission over very large distances, the residual dispersion (2–8 ps/(km. nm)) in these fibers will go on accumulating and will limit the number of bits that can be sent at each wavelength. To overcome this difficulty, one has to use a DCF which will compensate the accumulated dispersion at all wavelengths simultaneously. The design of DCF, therefore, has to be compatible with the small residual dispersion fibers. In the inset of Fig. 30.13, we have given typical refractive index variations of the corresponding DCF. The corresponding wavelength dependence of the total dispersion (D_C) has also been shown. The dispersion slopes are so adjusted that a small length of the DCF will approximately compensate the accumulated dispersion in SRDF simultaneously at all wavelengths. In Fig. 30.14, we have plotted

$$D_E = (L_1 D_N + L_2 D_C)/(L_1 + L_2) \qquad \textbf{(30.54)}$$

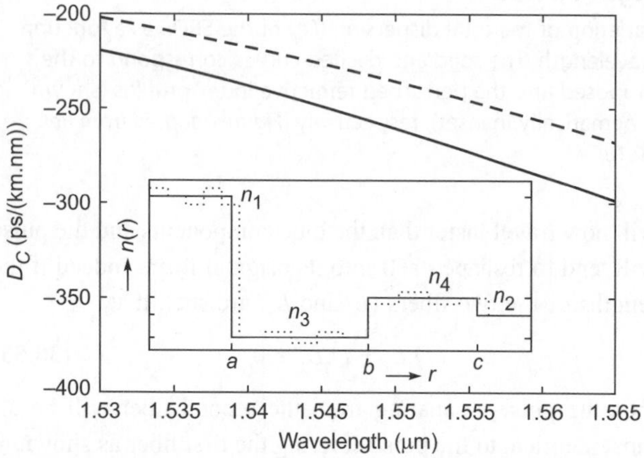

Figure 30.13

Variation of the total dispersion (D_C) of the DCF as a function wavelength. The solid and dashed curves correspond to the proposed and the perturbed refractive index profiles (shown schematically in inset), respectively. [*Figure adapted from Ref. 30.18.*]

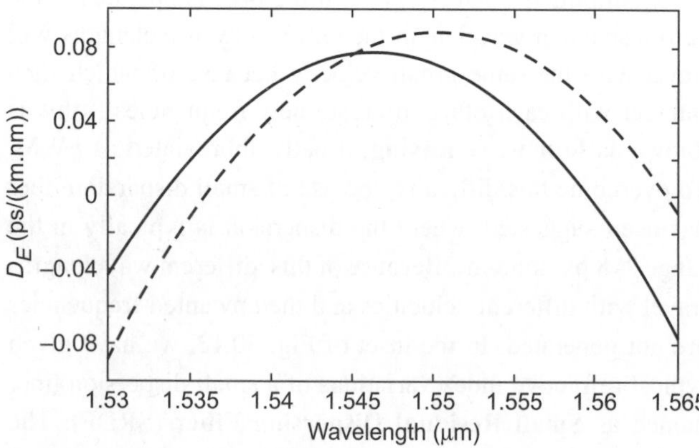

Figure 30.14

Variation of the effective dispersion (D_E) of the system as a function wavelength. [*Figure adapted from Ref. 30.18.*]

for $L_1 = 36.74\ L_2$, where D_N and D_C represent the dispersions associated with the SRDF and DCF, respectively. It may be noted that the maximum value of the effective dispersion, is less than 0.08 ps/(km.nm).

30.7 Some Recent Fiber Optic Communication Systems

With the availability of extremely low loss optical fibers (loss < 0.25 dB/km) and with the availability of EDFAs (characterized by amplification of about 20-30 dB over the wavelength range from 1200 nm to 1600 nm) it has been possible to send tremendous amount of information through one hair thin optical fiber. You may recall that in Fig. 27.8(b) we had shown an almost flat gain (of about 30 dB) of an EDFA for wavelengths lying between 1530 nm and 1560 nm. The wavelength region 1530 nm $< \lambda <$ 1560 nm is extremely important for optical communications; thus we can now simultaneously send information by using a large number of wavelengths propagating through one optical fiber; all optical pulses get simultaneously amplified by the EDFA. In 2001, a French company propagated simultaneously 256 wavelength channels through one optical fiber sending 10.2 Tb/s of information; 10.2 Tb/s of information implies 150 million telephone channels through one hair thin optical fiber !! This was a great technological achievement. Many other companies also achieved similar information carrying capacity and during the past 10 years or so there has been a remarkable increase in the information carrying capacity. This has led to what is usually referred to as the fiber optic revolution. Figure 30.15 shows the layout of a typical wavelength division multiplexed (usually abbreviated as WDM) fiber optic system with each wavelength carrying an independent channel. The capacity of each channel can be ~ 10 Gigabits/s and if we have 100 channels, it will result in a total capacity of the link ~1 terabit/s. The pulses are amplified periodically by EDFAs and the dispersion is compensated by DCFs.

In Fig. 30.16 we have shown Commercial Lightwave System Capacity; it can be seen that before the advent of EDFA there was only one channel (i.e., only wavelength) that was being sent though the fiber. With the availability of gain flattened EDFA, as mentioned before, one can simultaneously send a large number of wavelengths through the fiber because of which larger amount of information can be sent through the fiber. In Fig. 30.17(a) we have shown that the information carrying capacity of the optical fiber has been doubling every year and in Fig. 30.18 we have shown that the cost of transport has fallen approximately by 35% every year. Today **making an overseas video call has become almost free because of the availability of low loss optical fibers, the EDFAs and also Laser Diodes; this is the fiber optics revolution.** Figure 30.18(a) shows that the fiber connects us across the oceans through undersea fiber optic systems and (b) shows that most major cities in India are connected through fiber optic links. Figure 30.20 shows worldwide deployment of silica fibers which in 2019 had an annual market worth 2 billion US dollars.

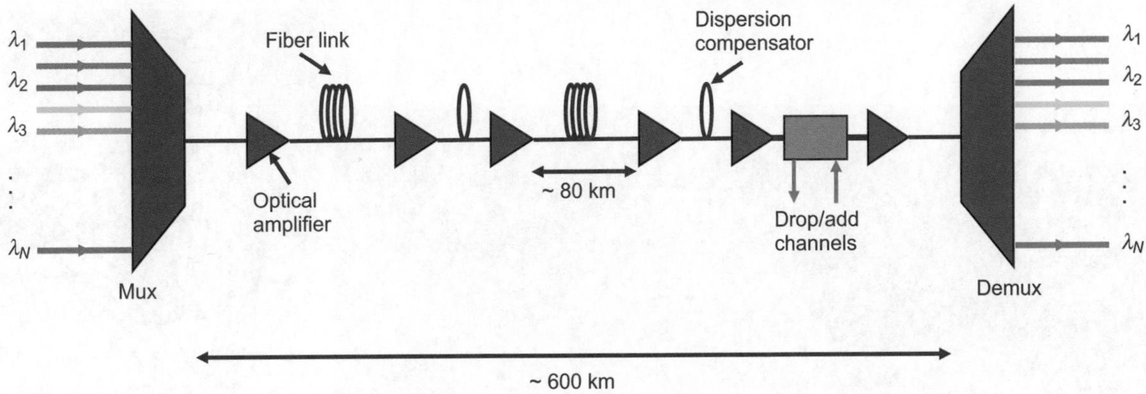

Figure 30.15

A typical WDM fiber optic system with each wavelength carrying an independent channel. The capacity of each channel can be ~ 10 Gigabits/s and if we have 100 channels, it will result in a total capacity of the link ~1terabit/s. [*Diagram courtesy Prof K Thyagarajan.*]

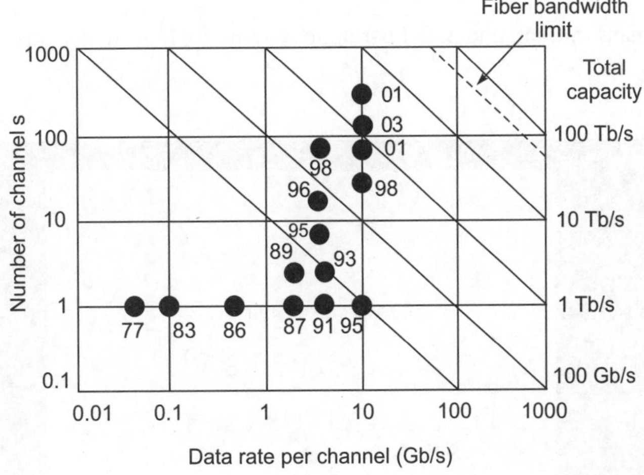

Figure 30.16

Commercial Lightwave System Capacity; adapted from lecture notes of Dr. Atul Srivastava.

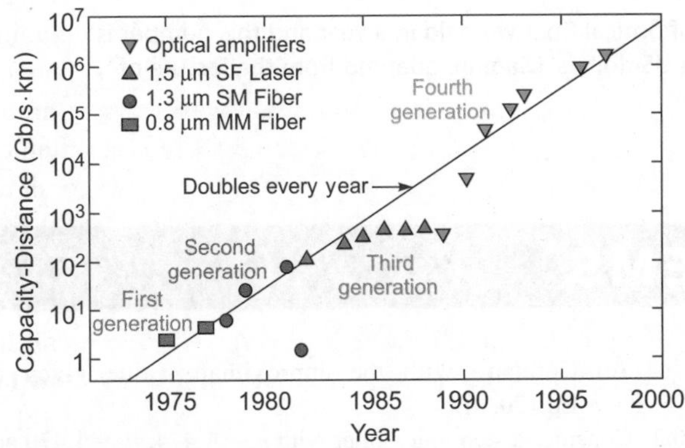

Figure 30.17(a)

The information carrying capacity of the optical fiber has been doubling every year. [*Diagram Courtesy: Dr Atul Srivastava; the original slide was by H. Kogelnik of Bell Labs.*]

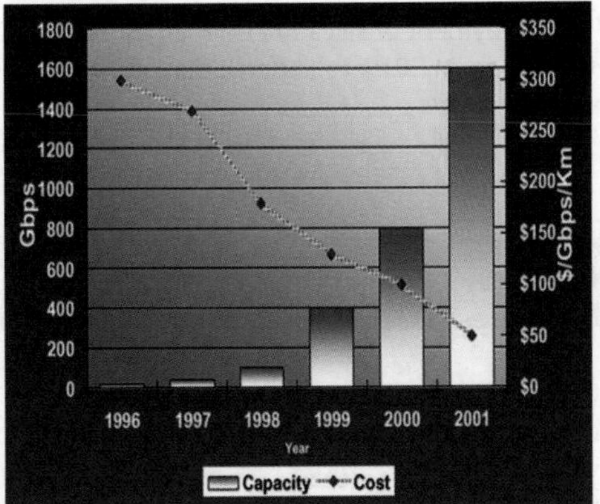

Figure 30.18

Cost of transport has fallen approximately by 35% every year. Reference: Gawrys (AT &T) NFOEC 2001; [*slide courtesy: Dr. Atul Srivastava*].

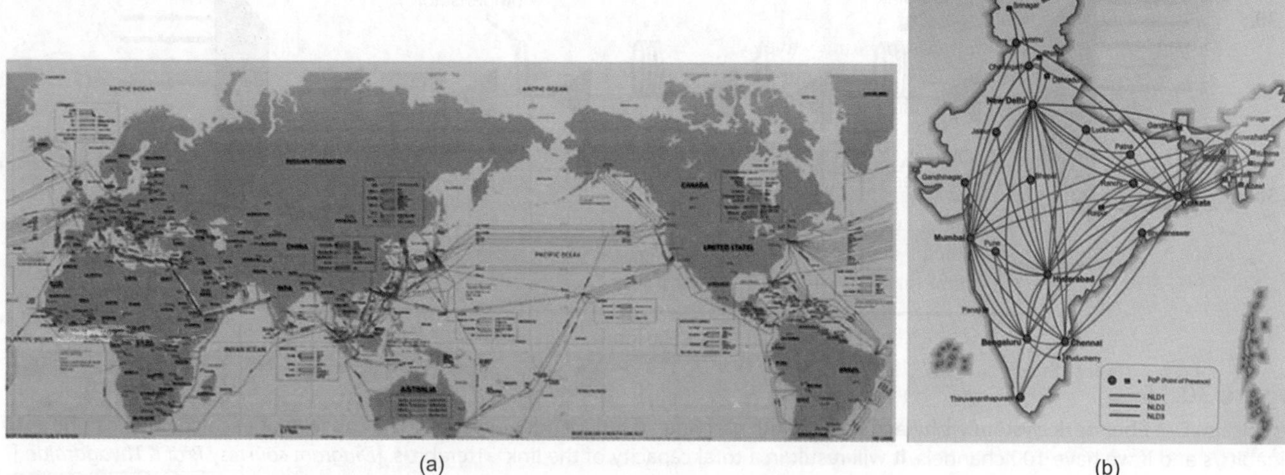

Figure 30.19
(a) Fiber connects us across the oceans through undersea fiber optic systems. (b) Most major cities in India are connected through fiber optic links.

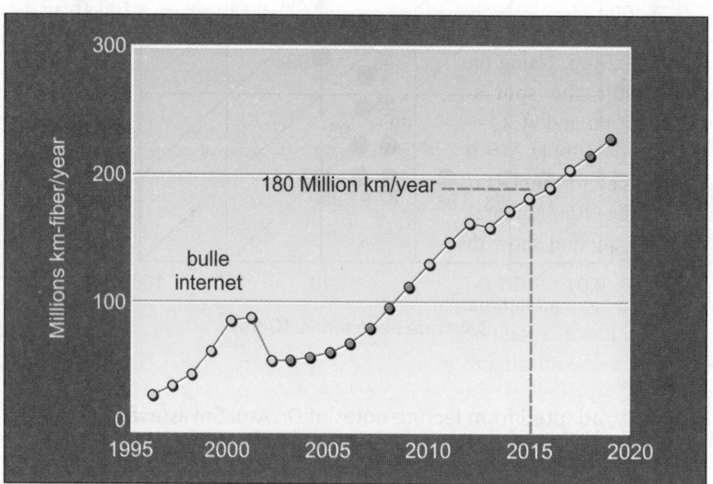

Figure 30.20
Worldwide deployment of silica fibers. In 2015, 180 million kilometers of optical fiber was laid in a year and this number is steadily increasing. In 2019, the annual market has been worth 2 billion US dollars. Diagram adapted from the lecture of Professor David Payne.

PROBLEMS

30.1 Consider a step index fiber with $n_1 = 1.474$, $n_2 = 1.470$ and having a core radius $a = 4.5\ \mu$m. Determine the cutoff wavelength.

30.2 Consider a step index fiber with $n_1 = 1.5$, $n_2 = 1.48$ and having a core radius $a = 6.0\ \mu$m.

(a) Determine the operating wavelength λ_0 for which $V=8$,

(b) Calculate the total number of modes for $V = 8$, and

(c) Compare with the approximate value given by Eq. (30.26).

30.3 Consider a step index fiber with $n_1 = 1.474$, $n_2 = 1.470$ and having a core radius $a = 3.0\,\mu$m operating at a wavelength $0.889\,\mu$m. Calculate the spot size of the fundamental mode.

30.4 We consider a step index fiber with $n_1 = 1.5$, $n_2 = 1.48$ and the core radius $a = 3.0\ \mu$m. Calculate the range of the values of λ_0 for which LP_{01}, LP_{11}, LP_{21} and LP_{02} modes will exist.

30.5 Consider a step index fiber with $n_1 = 1.5$, $n_2 = 1.48$ and core radius $a = 7.0\,\mu$m. Assuming the operating wavelength $\lambda_0 = 1.3\,\mu$m calculate (a) the number of modes and (b) compare with that obtained by using the approximate formula [Eq. (30.26)].

[**Ans:** (b) $V = 8.26$; $N \approx 34$

30.6 We consider a step index fiber with $n_2 = 1.447$, $\Delta = 0.003$ and $a = 4.2\,\mu$m. Calculate the domain of single mode operation. Find the value of λ_0 for which $V = 2.0$ and therefore use Table 30.1 to determine b and then the values of β/k_0 and of β.

30.7 In continuation of the previous problem, we consider the same step index fiber [$n_2 = 1.447$, $\Delta = 0.003$ and $a = 4.2\,\mu$m] now operating at $\lambda_0 = 1.55$ μm. Use Table 30.1 and linear interpolation to determine b and then the values of β/k_0 and of β.

30.8 Fibers used in IV generation optical communication systems (operating at 1.55 μm) have a small value of core radius and a large value of Δ. Consider a fiber with $n_2 = 1.447$, $\Delta = 0.0075$ and $a = 2.3\,\mu$m. Assuming the operating wavelength to be $\lambda_0 = 1.55$ μm, calculate the values of b and β/k_0.

30.9 Consider a step index fiber (operating at 1300 nm) with $n_2 = 1.447$, $\Delta = 0.003$ and $a = 4.2$ μm. Using the empirical formula [Eq. (30.32)], calculate the spot size of the fundamental mode at $\lambda_0 = 1300$ nm and at $\lambda_0 = 1550$ nm.

30.10 For a step index fiber with $n_2 = 1.444$, $\Delta = 0.0075$ and $a = 2.3\,\mu$m. Using the empirical formula [Eq. (30.32)], calculate the spot size of the fundamental mode at $\lambda_0 = 1300$ nm and at $\lambda_0 = 1550$ nm and show that the spot size increases with wavelength.

30.11 Assume the single mode fiber to have a Gaussian spot size $w = 4.5$ μm. Calculate the splice loss at a joint between two such identical fibers with a transverse misalignment of 1, 2 and 3 μm.

30.12 Consider a step index fiber with $n_2 = 1.447$, $\Delta = 0.003$ and $a = 4.2$ μm (see Problem 30.7). Calculate and plot D_m, D_w and D_{total} and determine the wavelength corresponding to zero total dispersion.

30.13 We next consider the fiber discussed in Problem 30.9 for which $n_2 = 1.447$, $\Delta = 0.0075$ and $a = 2.3$ μm. Calculate and plot D_m, D_w and D_{total} and determine the wavelength corresponding to zero total dispersion.

30.14 The modal field is said to be normalized if

$$\iint |\psi(x,y)|^2\, dx\, dy = 1$$

Show that the normalized Gaussian field is given by

$$\psi(x,y) = \sqrt{\frac{2}{\pi}}\,\frac{1}{w}\,e^{-\frac{x^2+y^2}{w^2}} = \sqrt{\frac{2}{\pi}}\,\frac{1}{w}\,e^{-\frac{r^2}{w^2}}$$

30.15 Consider two identical single mode fibers joined together with a transverse misalignment of u (along the x-axis). The fractional power that is coupled to the fundamental mode of the second fiber is given by the overlap integral

$$T = \left|\iint \psi_1(x,y)\,\psi_2(x,y)\,dx\,dy\right|^2$$

Assuming a Gaussian spot size [see Eq. (30.32)], show that

$T = \exp\left(-\dfrac{u^2}{w^2}\right)$. Thus

Loss in dB $= 10 \log T = 4.34\left(\dfrac{u}{w}\right)^2$

30.16 Consider a parabolic index fiber characterized by the following refractive index variation

$$n^2(r) = n_i^2\left[1 - 2\Delta\left(\frac{r}{a}\right)^2\right] = n_i^2\left[1 - 2\Delta\frac{x^2+y^2}{a^2}\right] \quad 0 < r < a \text{ core}$$

$$= n_2^2 \qquad r > a \text{ cladding}$$

Using the method of separation of variables and the results in Sec. 29.5, show that the corresponding propagation constants for guided modes are approximately given by

$$\beta_2 = \beta_{mn}^2 \approx k_0^2 n_1^2 - 2(m + n + 1)\gamma k_0;\ m, n = 0, 1, 2, 3, \ldots$$

where $\gamma = \dfrac{n_1\sqrt{2\Delta}}{a}$

(a) Show that the group velocity is approximately independent of the mode number.

(b) Assuming Eq. (30.12), calculate approximately the number of modes for a given value of V.

30.17 Assume $V = 8$ and $l = 2$. Using a software like Mathematica, plot the LHS and RHS of Eq. (30.25) as a function of b, and show that the points of intersection will give $b \simeq 0.678$ for the LP_{21} mode and $b \simeq 0.17$ for the LP_{21} mode. Obtain the corresponding values of β/k_0 by using Eq. (30.29).

PART 5

SPECIAL THEORY OF RELATIVITY

Special theory of relativity is considered as one of the major revolutions of the twentieth century. This part consists of three short chapters (Chapters 31–33). In Chapter 31, we will discuss the mass energy relation: $E = mc^2$ and its applications. In Chapters 32 and 33, we will discuss the postulates and applications of the special theory of relativity; in particular, we will discuss time dilation, length contraction and equations describing Lorentz transformations.

CHAPTER

31

The Mass Energy Relation: $E = mc^2$

The principle of relativity ... requires that mass be a direct measure of the energy contained in a body; ***light carries mass with it****...The argument is amusing and seductive; but for all I know, the Lord might be laughing over it and leading me around the nose.*

—Albert Einstein to his friend Conrad Habicht in his Year of Miracles (1905)

Important Milestone

1905 Einstein derived the equation $E = mc^2$ in his Year of Miracles working in total isolation at the Swiss Patent office. This was experimentally verified by Cockcroft and Walton in 1932 [see the Einstein quote on page 31.6].

LEARNING OBJECTIVES

After reading this chapter, the reader should be able to:

LO 1: *discuss examples for understanding the equation* $E = mc^2$.

LO 2: *discuss the energy liberated by the Sun.*

LO 3: *present a simple derivation of the equation* $E = mc^2$.

LO 4: *present a simple derivation of Doppler shifted frequencies.*

Above Image: The first atomic explosion on July 16, 1945.

31.1 Introduction

The equation $$E = mc^2 \quad \textbf{(31.1)}$$ is probably **the** most famous equation. Figure 31.1 shows a statue of Albert Einstein at Frankfurt airport and below the right hand of Einstein is a book which has the title $E = mc^2$. This tells us the enormous interest of the general public in the equation $E = mc^2$. Figure 31.2 shows the equation $E = mc^2$ in Einstein's own handwriting. Figure 31.3 shows the immense popularity of the equation $E = mc^2$. In fact, David Bodanis has written a book with the title

> $E = mc^2$: *A Biography of the World's Most Famous Equation*

(see Ref. 31.1). In Eq. (31.1), E represents the energy, m the mass and c the velocity of light in free space which is about 300 million meters per second. Equation (31.1) was put forward by Einstein in 1905 (see Ref. 31.2); it tells us about the equivalence of mass and energy and that mass can be converted to energy and vice versa (see Fig. 31.4). Many would like to know what exactly the equation implies. In the next section, by considering a few simple examples, we will try to understand what the equation $E = mc^2$ really implies and then in Sec. 31.3, we will give a simple derivation of the equation.

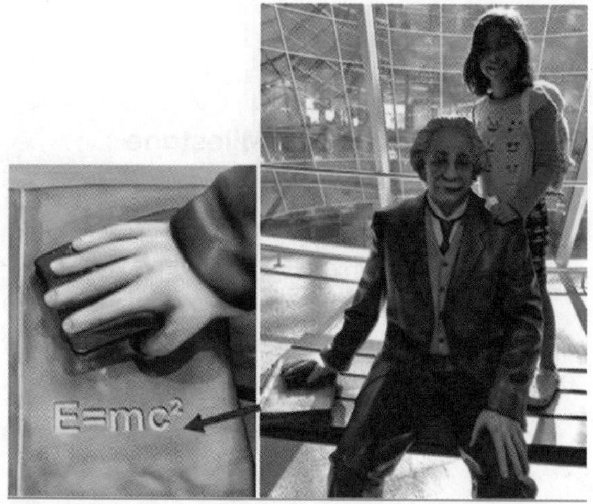

Figure 31.1
A statue of Albert Einstein at Frankfurt airport. Below the right hand of Einstein is a book which has the title $E = mc^2$. Behind Einstein's statue is Ananya who has been wanting to know as to why the equation $E = mc^2$ is so famous. Hopefully, after she goes through this chapter, she will be able to know that. *Photograph courtesy:* Arjun Ghatak.

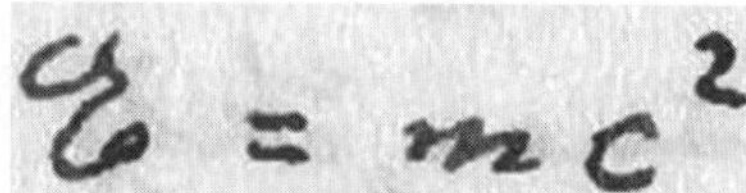

Figure 31.2
The equation $E = mc^2$ as written by Albert Einstein.

Figure 31.3
The $E = mc^2$ sculpture in Berlin, on the occasion of 2006 FIFA World Cup Germany; *Photograph Courtesy:* Mr. Wolf Schneider, Scholz & Friends, Berlin.

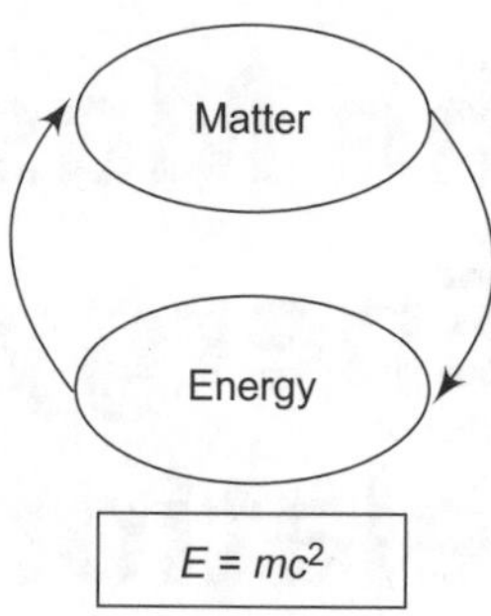

Figure 31.4
Equivalence of that mass can be converted to energy and vice versa.

31.2 Simple Examples to Understand the Equation $E = mc^2$

LO1

EXAMPLE 31.1 We consider two magnets (which are far away) on a frictionless table with the North Pole of one facing the South Pole of the other (see Fig. 31.5). Both magnets will attract one another and when these get stuck together, the mass of the two magnets (stuck together) would be slightly less than the sum of the individual masses of the two magnets (see Fig. 31.5). This is because when the two magnets are far away (say on a frictionless table), they will attract each other and gain kinetic energy and when they get stuck together, a small amount of energy will be released; because of this, the combined mass will be slightly smaller. Conversely,

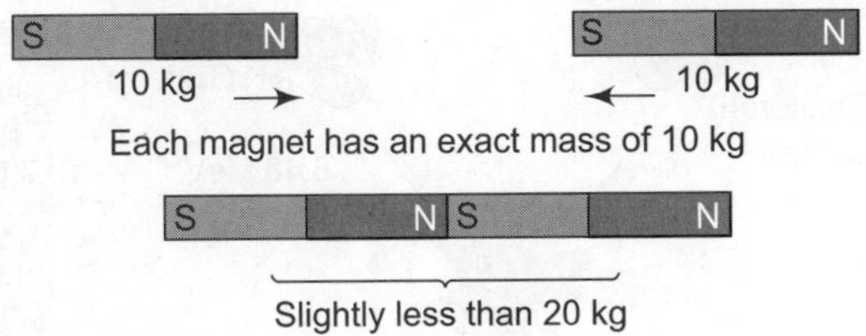

Figure 31.5
When the 2 magnets get stuck together, the mass of the two magnets (stuck together) would be slightly less than the sum of the individual masses of the two magnets.

when we want to separate the two magnets that are stuck together, a small amount of energy has to be supplied and therefore the mass must increase.

Let us suppose that each of the magnets has the exact mass 10 kg. We *assume* that the mass of the two magnets stuck together be

19.9999999999999 kg

implying a loss of mass of 10^{-13} kg (= 10^{-10} g) which is a tenth of a billionth of a gram; with magnets that are available in the market, the loss of mass is even smaller than what has been mentioned above. However, if the loss of mass **is** 10^{-13} kg, then according to Einstein's mass-energy relation

$$\text{Energy released in the process} = \text{Loss of mass} \times c^2 \quad \textbf{(31.2)}$$

where $c \approx 300{,}000{,}000$ m/s is the speed of light in free space. Thus

$$\text{Energy released in the process} = (10^{-13}\ \text{kg}) \times (3 \times 10^8\ \text{m/s})^2 = 9000\ \text{Joules}$$

Just to have a feel for 9000 Joules of energy, we may mention here that a 1000 Watt bulb emits 1000 Joules of energy per second and would therefore emit 9000 Joules of energy in 9 seconds. Also, to lift a 45 kg mass to a height of 20 meters, we would have to spend about 9000 Joules of energy.

Thus if the total mass of the two magnets becomes a 0.1 ng less, it will generate about 9000 Joules of energy when they get stuck together. On the other hand, if we have 2 such magnets stuck together, it would require about 9000 Joules of energy to separate them creating a tiny amount of mass (0.1 ng).

EXAMPLE 31.2 In the Bohr model of the hydrogen atom, the (negatively charged) electron rotates in discrete circular orbits around a (positively charged) proton as shown in Fig. 25.3. Now, when the electron from a higher orbit makes a transition to a lower orbit, radiation is emitted. Since radiation carries energy, the mass of the hydrogen atom decreases by a small amount – ***although the atom consists of one electron and one proton before and after the emission of radiation***. As discussed in Sec. 25.2, for the $(n = 2) \rightarrow (n = 1)$ transition in the hydrogen atom, the wavelength of the emitted radiation is 0.1217 μm; the corresponding frequency will be $\nu \approx 2.47 \times 10^{15}\ \text{s}^{-1}$. The loss of mass of the hydrogen atom will therefore be given by

$$\Delta m = \frac{\text{Energy of the photon}}{c^2} = \frac{h\nu}{c^2}$$

$$= \frac{1.637 \times 10^{-18}\ \text{J}}{(3 \times 10^8\ \text{m/s})^2} \approx 1.8 \times 10^{-35}\ \text{kg}$$

The above analysis justifies what Einstein had said "... *light carries mass with it*" (see the quotation at the beginning of the chapter). The value of Δm calculated above is indeed a very small amount of mass; the mass of the electron ($m_\varepsilon \approx 9.1 \times 10^{-31}$ kg) is about 50,000 times that of Δm calculated above.

EXAMPLE 31.3 **Binding Energy of Deuteron:** As another example, we consider the deuteron nucleus (which is the nucleus of heavy hydrogen ${}_1H^2$); the deuteron nucleus consists of one neutron and one proton held together by nuclear forces. Using the values for m_p (rest mass of proton), m_n (rest mass of neutron) and of m_d (rest mass of the deuteron) as given on page 31.11, we would find that the mass of the deuteron is slightly less than the sum of the mass of a neutron and a proton (see Fig. 31.6) and the loss of mass is given by

$$\text{Loss of mass} = \Delta m = (m_p + m_n) - m_d = 3.9657 \times 10^{-30}\ \text{kg}$$

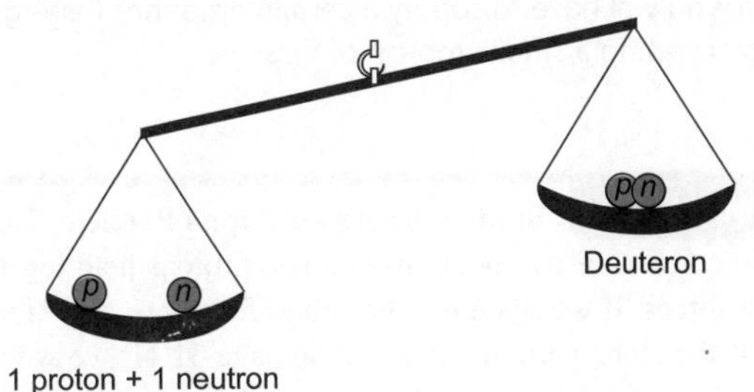

Figure 31.6
The mass of the deuteron (which consists of a proton and a neutron) is slightly less than the sum of the mass of the proton and the neutron.

Thus if you have a neutron and a proton and you put them together to form the deuteron nucleus, the total mass will slightly decrease and the energy that will be released will be given by.

$$\Delta E = (\Delta m)c^2 = 3.9657 \times 10^{-30} \times 9 \times 10^{16} \approx 3.569 \times 10^{-13}\ \text{J} \approx 2.23\ \text{MeV}$$

where we have used the relation 1 MeV ≈ 1.60218×10^{-13} J. Thus it would require about 2.23 MeV of energy to separate the neutron and proton from the deuteron nucleus (this is known as the binding energy of the deuteron); indeed it requires a γ-ray photon of energy about 2.23 MeV to separate the neutron and proton (see Fig. 31.7).

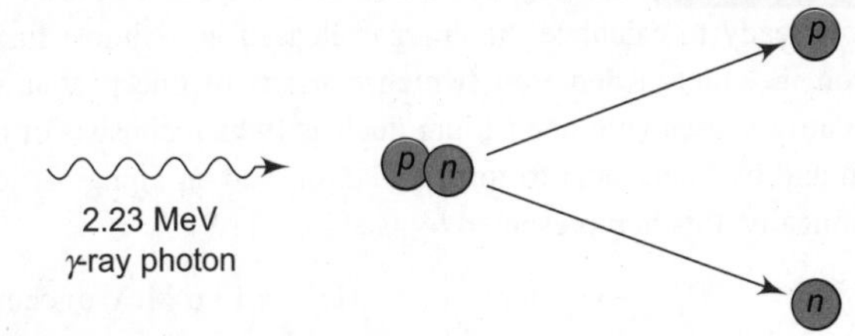

Figure 31.7
It requires a 2.23 MeV γ-ray photon to split the deuteron to a proton and a neutron.

On the other hand, if we put together a neutron and a proton to form the deuteron nucleus, the total mass will slightly decrease and energy will be released. In general, [see Fig. 31.8(a)]:

Whenever a loosely bound system goes over to a tightly bound system, energy is released and there is a small loss of mass.

And, [see Fig. 31.8(b)]:

Certain amount of energy is required when tightly bound system goes over to a loosely bound system and a small loss of mass is created.

Figure 31.8

(a) When a loosely bound system goes over to tightly bound system, certain amount of energy is released. (b) In order to make a tightly bound system to go over to loosely bound system, you will have to supply a certain amount of energy thereby creating a small amount of mass.

EXAMPLE 31.4 **Binding Energy of Alpha Particle:** The alpha particle consists of two neutrons and two protons held together by nuclear forces. If we again use the values for m_p, m_n and of m_α (rest mass of the alpha particle) as given on page 31.11, we would find that the loss of mass is given by

$$\Delta m = (2m_p + 2m_n) - m_\alpha = 5.0481 \times 10^{-30} \text{ kg}$$

Hence the binding energy of the alpha particle will be

$$\Delta E = \Delta m \times c^2 = (5.0481 \times 10^{-30} \text{kg}) \times (3 \times 10^8 \text{m/s})^2$$

$$\approx 4.543 \times 10^{-12} \text{J}$$

or, $$\Delta E \approx \frac{4.543 \times 10^{-12}}{1.60218 \times 10^{-13}} \text{MeV} \approx 28.3 \text{ MeV}$$

implying that about 28.3 MeV of energy is required to separate the 4 particles in the alpha particle and in the process about 5×10^{-30} kg of mass is created.

EXAMPLE 31.5 **Energy Released in a Fusion Process:** We are now ready to calculate the energy released in a simple fusion reaction in which a deuteron (which consists of one proton and one neutron) fuses with one tritium nucleus (which consists of one proton and two neutrons) to form a neutron and an alpha particle. Symbolically, this is represented by (see Fig. 31.9)

$$_1\text{H}^2 + {}_1\text{H}^3 \rightarrow {}_0\text{n}^1 + {}_2\text{He}^4 + 17.6 \text{ MeV of energy}$$

$$\text{Deuteron} + \text{Tritium} \rightarrow \text{neutron} + \alpha\text{-particle}$$

$$(14.1 \text{ MeV}) \quad (3.5 \text{ MeV})$$

Now the binding energies of $_1\text{H}^2$, $_1\text{H}^3$ and $_2\text{He}^4$ are 2.23 MeV, 8.48 MeV and 28.3 MeV, respectively; this would imply that it will require about 8.48 MeV of energy to separate the 3 particles in $_1\text{H}^3$ and about 28.3 MeV of energy to separate the 4 particles in $_2\text{He}^4$ (see Example 31.3 and 31.4); thus, in the nuclear reaction shown above

$$\text{Net gain in binding energy} = 28.3 - (2.23 + 8.48) \text{ MeV}$$

$$= 17.6 \text{ MeV}$$

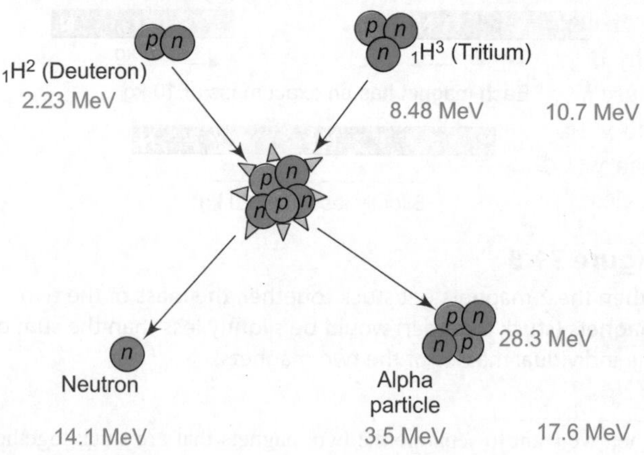

Figure 31.9

A fusion reaction in which the deuteron nucleus fuses with the tritium nucleus to form neutron and a very tightly bound alpha particle producing about 17.6 MeV of heat energy. Such fusion reactions require very high temperature because the deuteron and the tritium nucleus are positively charged and they repel each other.

Thus a "loosely bound" system goes over to a "tightly bound" system and a tiny bit of mass gets converted into 17.6 MeV of energy which appears in the form of heat; i.e., in the form of kinetic energies of the neutron and the alpha particle. The kinetic energies of the neutron and the alpha particle are 14.1 MeV and 3.5 MeV, respectively as shown in Fig. 31.9. Such fusion reactions are responsible for the tremendous amount of energy that we get from the Sun and also the energy released in a fusion bomb.

You go to youtube.com, search for *Einstein explains his famous formula, $E = mc^2$*, you will get the link https://www.youtube.com/watch?v=o7YtbEmRrfs where you can see Einstein explaining the ideas expressed by the equation $E = mc^2$, by saying:

> *It followed from the special theory of relativity that mass and energy are both but different manifestations of the same thing — a somewhat unfamiliar conception for the average mind. Furthermore, the equation $E = mc^2$, in which energy is put equal to mass, multiplied by the square of the velocity of light, showed that very small amounts of mass may be converted into a very large amount of energy and vice versa. The mass and energy were in fact equivalent, according to the formula mentioned before. This was demonstrated by Cockcroft and Walton in 1932, experimentally.*

Einstein also wrote

> *Before the advent of relativity, physics recognized two conservation laws of fundamental importance, namely the law of the conservation of energy and the law of the conservation of mass; these two fundamental laws appeared to be quite independent of each other. By means of the theory of relativity they have been united to one law.*

In continuation of what is quoted above, we may ask as to why did this go unnoticed for such a long time? This is because in most processes the change in mass is extremely small and very hard to detect. As Einstein wrote "It is as though a man who is fabulously rich gives away a cent". Only when nuclear reactions (or radioactive disintegrations) were getting observed, the fractional change in mass became measurable.

31.3 Energy Emitted by the Sun

LO2

The Sun liberates (in one second) approximately

4,000,000,000,000,000,000,000,000,00 Joules

of energy in the form of light – see Fig. 31.10. We can calculate this from the fact that on the earth, we receive from the sun 1.35 kW of radiation on 1 square meter of an area placed normal to the direction of the rays coming from the sun. Thus, on our earth, we receive from the Sun 1350 Joules of energy per square meter every second. The distance between the sun and the earth is about 150 million km — which is equal to 1.5×10^{11} m [which we denote by R]. Thus the total energy emitted by the Sun is approximately

$$(1.35 \times 10^3 \text{ J/m}^2 \text{ per second}) \times (4\pi R^2) = 4 \times 10^{26} \text{ J/s}$$

If we now use Einstein's mass-energy relation, we would get

Loss of mass of the sun

$$\Delta m = \frac{\Delta E}{c^2} = \frac{4\times10^{26}\text{ J/s}}{(3\times10^8\text{ m/s})^2} \approx 4\times10^9\text{kg/s}$$

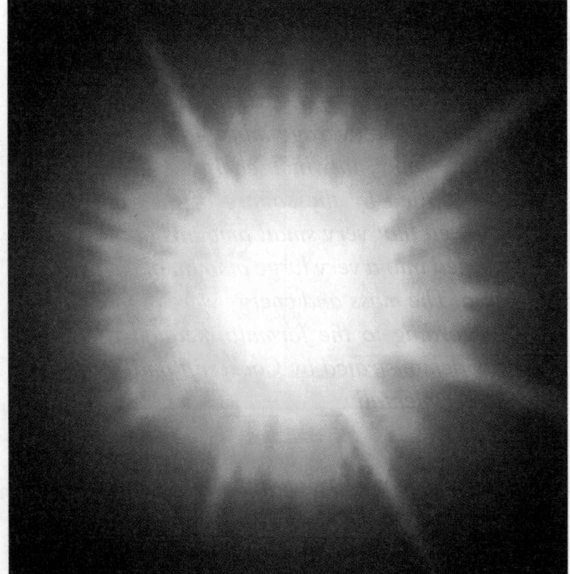

Figure 31.10

The sun is like a 400 trillion trillion Watt light bulb.

Thus in the Sun, every second

about 4 billion kilograms of mass is continuously getting converted into energy

and a very small part of the energy we receive on the surface of the earth. Since 1 year ≈ 3×10^7 s, the mass of the Sun is decreasing by about 120,000 trillion kilograms every year; we do not see that difference because the mass of the sun is very large ≈ 2×10^{30} kg, which is about 16 trillion times of the mass that the Sun loses every year.

EXAMPLE 31.6 **Energy Radiated by the Sun by using Stefan's Law:** We can also calculate the energy radiated by the Sun by using Stefan's law. The temperature on the surface of the Sun is about 5778 °K. According to Stefan's law, the energy radiated by a square meter of the Sun will be σT^4, where $\sigma \approx 5.67 \times 10^{-8}$ W/m²-(°K)$^{-4}$ is the Stefan's constant. Thus the total energy radiated by the sun will be $\sigma T^4 \times (4\pi R_s^2) \approx (5.67\times10^{-8})\times(5778)^4\times(4\pi\times 49\times10^{16}) \approx 4\times10^{26}$ J/s where $R_s \approx 7 \times 10^8$ m is the radius of the Sun.

31.3.1 How was the Sun Created?

It is believed that a huge cloud of gas collapsed under the influence of its own gravity (see Fig. 31.11); the gas was mainly hydrogen and helium. As the gas collapsed, a **loosely bound system went over to a tightly bound system resulting in the release of energy.** Thus, gravitational energy transformed into kinetic energy and the gas would get heated. The temperature of the gas would initially be about few thousand degrees Celsius and it would have a red glow. Eventually, the temperatures at the center of the sphere would be in millions of degrees Celsius and would be so high that "fusion reactions" will start occurring and slowly a "steady state" will be reached when the force due to gravitational attraction will be balanced by the outward pressure due to the gas. Astrophysicists tell us that the Sun is right now in this "steady state" and will keep radiating energy at about the same rate

Evaluation of the Sun

Figure 31.11

Approximate evolution of the sun: in about 5 billion years, the Sun is expected to become a red giant (enveloping the earth!!!) then in another 4 billion years, it will become a white dwarf star. Diagram is similar to that given in https://commons.wikimedia.org/wiki/File:Sun-life-f.gif

for the next 5 billion years. Astrophysicists also tell us that the density of the innermost region of the sun (extending to about 1/5th of the Sun's radius) is about 160 grams/cm^3, the temperature around 15 million degrees Celsius and its pressure about 100,000,000,000 atmospheres; it seems we know much more about the center of the Sun than about the center of our earth … that is the power and beauty of theoretical physics! At such high temperatures and pressures, fusion reactions occur which lead to the production of enormous amount of energy. Eventually (in about 5 billion years), when the nuclear fuel (capable of causing fusion reactions) gets depleted, the sun will cool down and expand and will become a red giant; it will then envelope our earth and life will cease to exist. Much later, the sun will start contracting again and thereby increasing its central density and temperature. This process of contraction cannot continue indefinitely and the electrons become a degenerate gas and we will have what is known as a white dwarf star. The theory of the white dwarf star was given by S Chandrasekhar; he was awarded (half of) the 1983 Nobel Prize in Physics for his theoretical studies in the understanding of evolution of stars.

31.4 Simple Derivation of the Equation $E = mc^2$

LO3

In this section we will carry out a very simple and straightforward derivation of the mass-energy relationship. The analysis is somewhat similar to that given in Ref. 31.3 (see also References 31.4 and 31.5). A_1 and A_2 are in the reference frame S and B is in the reference frame S' which is moving with respect to the reference frame S with velocity u (see Fig. 31.12). An atom is at rest in the reference frame S'. The atom emits two photons (of the same frequency ν_0) in opposite directions as shown in Fig. 31.12. The magnitude of the momentum associated with each photon will be $h\nu_0/c$. Therefore, for the observer inside the train, the momentum associated with each photon would be equal and opposite and the total momentum of the two photons will be

$$\frac{h\nu_0}{c} - \frac{h\nu_0}{c} = 0 \Rightarrow (\Delta p)_{S'} = 0 \quad (31.3)$$

(see Fig. 31.12). Thus, from the law of conservation of momentum, there will be no change in the momentum of the atom and therefore,

the atom (which was initially at rest) will continue to remain at rest inside the train.

The change in the energy of the atom (as observed by B in the reference frame S'), will be given by

$$(\Delta E)_{S'} = 2h\nu_0 \quad (31.4)$$

Now, in order to calculate $(\Delta E)_S$ and $(\Delta p)_S$ in the reference frame S, we have to first know the frequencies of the light beam observed in the reference frame S. For that, we consider the situation when we are standing on the platform of a railway station and a railway engine is approaching the station; the frequency of the whistle that we hear will be higher than its normal frequency. Similarly, when the railway engine leaves the station, the frequency of its whistle will be lower than its normal frequency. This is known as the Doppler effect* and was first suggested by Christian Doppler in 1842 (Ref. 31.6). The shift in the frequency due to the relative motion between the source and the observer is referred to as the Doppler shift. By measuring the change in the frequency (i.e., the Doppler shift) we can determine how fast the source is moving towards us or away from us.

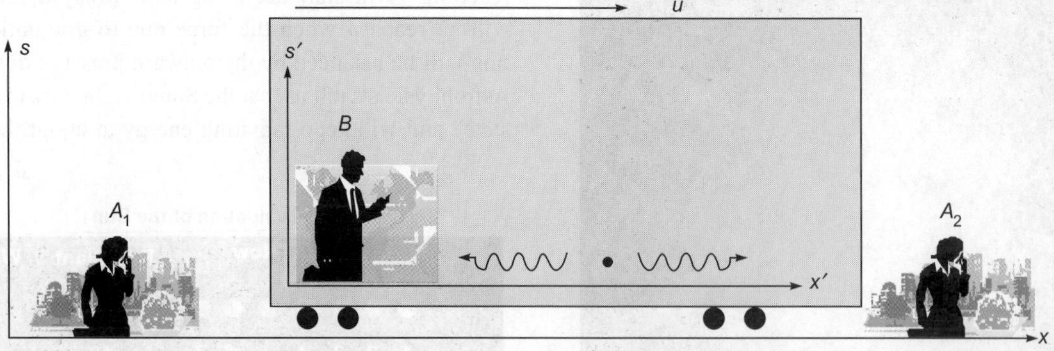

Figure 31.12

A_1 and A_2 are at rest in the reference frame S. B is at rest in the reference frame S' which is moving with speed u with respect to the frame S. In the reference frame S', an atom is at rest and emits two photons of the same frequency ν_0; since the two photons will have equal and opposite momenta, the atom will remain at rest. In the reference frame S, A_1 and A_2 will observe Doppler shifted frequencies.

* In 1842, Christian Doppler — an Austrian physicist — was the first to point out in a treatise (see Ref. 31.6) that the observed frequency of a wave will change if there is a relative motion between the observer and the source. This was verified in 1845 by Buys Ballot when he showed that the observed frequency was higher when the source (emitting sound waves) was moving towards him and conversely, the observed frequency was lower when the sound source was moving away from him.

In astronomy, we can determine how fast the stars or galaxies are moving (either directly away or directly towards us) by measuring the Doppler shift of spectral lines. When the star is moving away from us, the measured frequency is slightly less than the actual value leading to the well-known *red shift* of spectral lines. On the other hand, when the star is moving towards us, the measured frequency is slightly more than the actual value leading to what is known as the *blue shift* of spectral lines. The website https://en.wikipedia.org/wiki/Doppler_effect shows a very nice animation of the Doppler effect (animation created by Mr Wee Loo Kang Lawrence and Mr Fu-kwun Hwang); in Fig. 31.13 we have shown a snap shot of the animation.

Now, both A_1 and A_2 are in the reference frame *S*; for A_1, the atom is moving away from the observer and for A_2 the atom is moving towards the observer. The observers A_1 and A_2 will observe different Doppler shifted frequencies ν_1 and ν_2 which are given by:

$$\nu_1 = \nu_0\sqrt{\frac{1-\frac{u}{c}}{1+\frac{u}{c}}} \quad \text{and} \quad \nu_2 = \nu_0\sqrt{\frac{1+\frac{u}{c}}{1-\frac{u}{c}}} \tag{31.5}$$

[The above expressions have been derived in the next section; see also Sec. 33.4]. Thus, the change in the energy of the atom (as observed in the reference frame *S*) will be given by

$$(\Delta E)_S = h\nu_1 + h\nu_2 = \gamma(2h\nu_0) = \gamma(\Delta E)_{S'} \tag{31.6}$$

where γ is known as the Lorentz factor defined by

$$\gamma = \frac{1}{\sqrt{1-\frac{u^2}{c^2}}} \tag{31.7}$$

As mentioned earlier, in the reference frame S', the atom (after the emission of two photons) will remain at rest. Thus, for an observer in the reference frame *S*, the atom will be moving with same velocity *u* ***before*** **and** ***after*** the emission of photons. In the reference frame *S*, since $\nu_2 < \nu_2$, the momentum of the two photons are different. Therefore if we use the law of conservation of momentum in the reference frame *S*, the atom (which is moving with the *same* velocity *u*) must have a slightly lesser mass given by

$$(\Delta m)_S u = \frac{h\nu_2}{c} - \frac{h\nu_1}{c} = \gamma(2h\nu_0)\frac{u}{c^2} = \frac{(\Delta E)_S u}{c^2} \tag{31.8}$$

Thus we get $\quad (\Delta E)_S = (\Delta m)_S c^2 \quad$ **(31.9)**

The above two equations are independent of the value of *u*. Further, in the above equation, ΔE and Δm need not be infinitesimal amounts. Thus when a hydrogen atom makes a transition from an excited state to the ground state with the emission of a photon, the mass of the hydrogen atom (which still consists of one proton and one electron) will decrease by a small amount (see Example 31.2). In general, whenever a loosely bound system goes over to a tightly bound system a

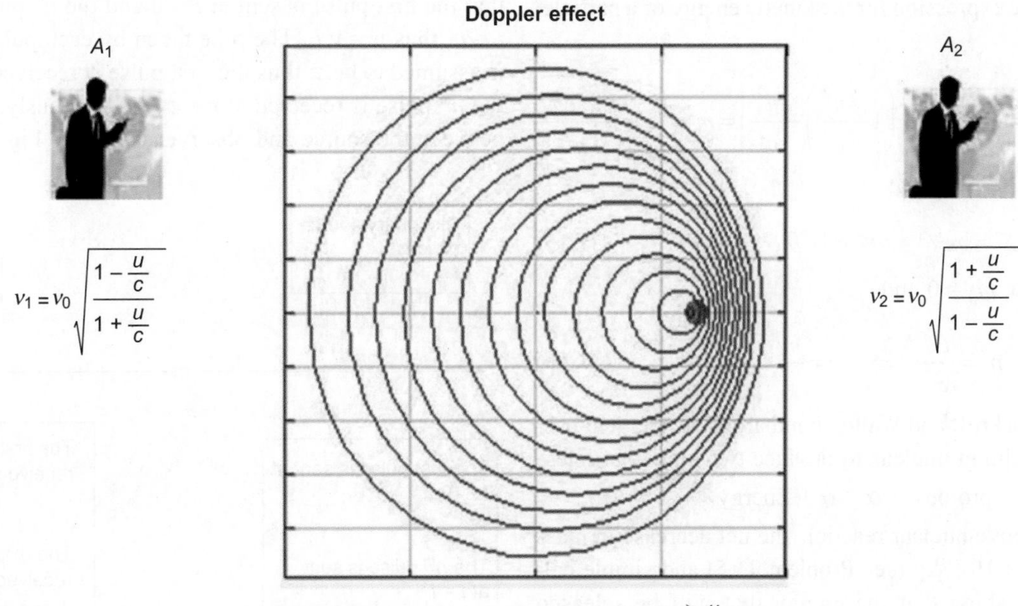

Figure 31.13
A snapshot gf the animation in the website https://en.wikipedia.org/wiki/Doppler_effecte created by Mr Wee Loo Kang Lawrence and Mr Fu-kwun Hwang; used with permission.

small amount of mass gets converted to energy. In his 1905 paper (Ref. 31.2), Einstein wrote:

> *If a body emits the energy L in the form of radiation, its mass decreases by L/V [2].... The mass of a body is a measure of its energy content.*

[The quantity V in Einstein's original paper is now usually denoted by c]. Further, if we write

$$(\Delta E)_{S'} = (\Delta m)_{S'}c^2 \quad \textbf{(31.10)}$$

then using Eqs. (31.6) and (31.9) we get

$$(\Delta m)_S = \gamma(\Delta m)_{S'} \quad \textbf{(31.11)}$$

Thus the mass varies with velocity according to the following equation:

$$m = \gamma m_0 = \frac{m_0}{\sqrt{1-\dfrac{u^2}{c^2}}} \quad \textbf{(31.12)}$$

where we have used Eq. (31.7) and m_0 is the mass of the body when it is at rest and is usually referred to as the "rest mass". The momentum of a body of rest mass m_0 moving with velocity u will be given by

$$p = mu = \gamma m_0 u \quad \textbf{(31.13)}$$

Further the kinetic energy of a particle of rest mass m_0 will be given by

$$T = mc^2 - m_0c^2 = m_0c^2(\gamma - 1) \quad \textbf{(31.14)}$$

When $\frac{u}{c} << 1$, $\gamma \approx 1 + \frac{u^2}{2c^2}$ and $T \approx \frac{1}{2}m_0u^2$ which is the non-relativistic expression for the kinetic energy of a particle. Further

$$E^2 = m^2c^4 = \frac{m_0^2c^4}{\left(1-\dfrac{u^2}{c^2}\right)}\left[\left(1-\frac{u^2}{c^2}\right)+\frac{u^2}{c^2}\right] = m_0^2c^4 + \frac{m_0^2u^2c^2}{\left(1-\dfrac{u^2}{c^2}\right)}$$

Thus $$E^2 = m^2c^4 = m_0^2c^4 + p^2c^2 \quad \textbf{(31.15)}$$

For the photon, $m_0 = 0$ and

$$p^2 = \frac{E^2}{c^2} \Rightarrow p = \frac{h\nu}{c} \quad \textbf{(31.16)}$$

In 1932, Cockroft and Walton bombarded accelerated protons on the Lithium nucleus to produce two alpha particles:

$${}_3Li^7 + \text{proton} \rightarrow \alpha + \alpha + \text{Energy}$$

Now, in the above nuclear reaction, the net decrease in mass will be $\Delta m \approx \times 10^{-27}$ kg (see Problem 31.5) and simple calculations will show that the energy that will be released (in the form of kinetic energies of the alpha particles) will be $(\Delta m)c^2 \approx 2.6 \times 10^{-12}$ J. The experiment of Cockroft and Walton demonstrated the first artificial splitting of a nucleus and also the first experimental proof of Einstein's mass-energy equation; they received the 1951 Nobel Prize in Physics *for their pioneering work on the transmutation of atomic nuclei by artificially accelerated atomic particles.*

EXAMPLE 31.7 Consider a body with rest mass 50 kg. If we have to make it move with a velocity 0.9 c the value of γ will be $\approx$ 2.3 and therefore the kinetic energy will be

$$T \approx (50 \text{ kg}) \times (3 \times 10^8 \text{ m.s})^2 \times 1.3 \approx 6 \times 10^{18} \text{ J.}$$

This is an enormous amount of energy. For example, in 2000 years, a 100 MW power station will generate

$$(100 \times 10^6 \text{ W}) \times (2000 \times 3.1 \times 10^7 \text{ s}) \approx 6 \times 10^{18} \text{ Joules}$$

of energy; we have assumed 1 year $\approx 3.1 \times 10^7$ s. Even if we have to make the mass move with a velocity 0.5 c, the factor 1.3 will be replaced by 0.15 and the kinetic energy will be $T \approx 0.7 \times 10^{18}$ J which is also an enormous amount of energy !! Thus it would require a tremendously large amount of energy to make a spacecraft (which would have a much larger rest mass) move close to the speed of light.

31.5 The Doppler Shift

LO4

In this section we will calculate Doppler shift. We will follow the method put forward by Feynman (see Sec. 34.6 of Ref. 31.8).

Let us consider a light source which is at rest with respect to the observer A. Instead of a continuous wave, we assume that the light source emits ν_0 pulses in a second. We assume that the first pulse is sent at $t = 0$ and the nth pulse is sent at $t = t_1$; thus $n = \nu_0 t_1$. The time taken by each pulse to reach A is assumed to be τ; thus the first pulse is received at $t = \tau$ and the nth pulse is received at $t = \tau + t_1$; obviously, the distance between the source and observer is $c\tau$ (see Fig. 31.14).

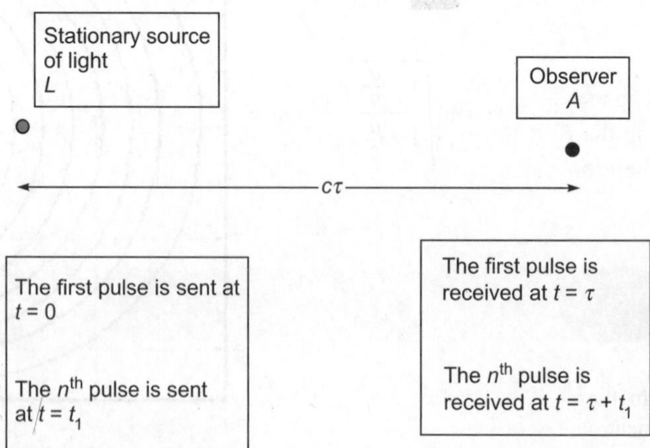

Figure 31.14
L is a stationary light source. Light takes time τ to reach the observer *A*.

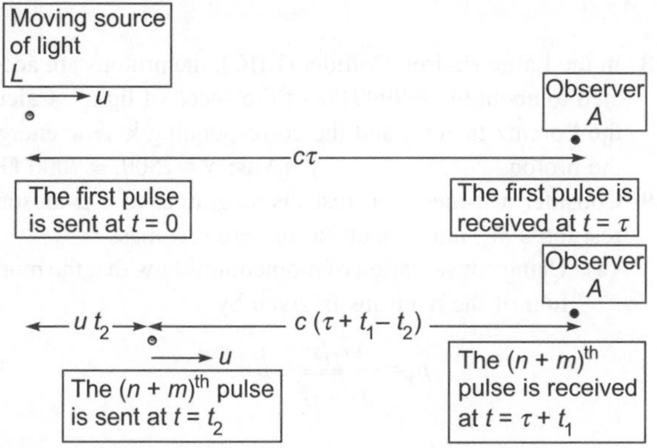

Figure 31.15

The light source L is moving towards the observer A with velocity u. The first pulse is sent at $t = 0$ which is received by A at $t = \tau$. According to A, the $(n + m)^{th}$ pulse is sent at $t = t_2$ which is received by A at $t = \tau + t_1$

We next assume the source to be moving with velocity u towards the observer as shown in Fig. 31.15. In time t_1 the observer A will now receive larger number of pulses because as the source moves towards the observer, the light pulse takes lesser amount of time to reach the observer. If in time t_1 the observer receives $(n + m)$ pulses, and if the source has moved through the distance ut_2 when the source emits the $(n + m)^{th}$ pulse at $t = t_2$ (see Fig. 31.15):

$$c\tau = ut_2 + c(\tau + t_1 - t_2) \quad \Rightarrow \quad \frac{t_1}{t_2} = \left(1 - \frac{u}{c}\right) \qquad \textbf{(31.17)}$$

Both t_1 and t_2 are as measured by the observer A. Now an observer B (who is moving with the source) will observe the duration t_2 as (see Sec. 32.3)

$$t_2' = t_2\sqrt{1 - \frac{u^2}{c^2}} \qquad \textbf{(31.18)}$$

Thus the number of pulses received by the observer A (during the time interval $t = \tau$ and $t = \tau + t_1$) would be $\nu_0 t_2'$ and therefore the observed frequency will be

$$\nu_2 = \frac{\nu_0 t_2'}{t_1} = \nu_0\sqrt{\frac{1 + \frac{u}{c}}{1 - \frac{u}{c}}} \qquad \textbf{(31.19)}$$

where we have used Eqs. (31.17) and (31.18). The above equation (31.19) represents the Doppler shifted frequency observed by A. Thus we may write for the Doppler shifted frequency

$$\nu_{DS} = \nu_0\sqrt{\frac{1 \pm \frac{u}{c}}{1 \mp \frac{u}{c}}} \quad \Rightarrow \quad \lambda_{DS} = \lambda_0\sqrt{\frac{1 \mp \frac{u}{c}}{1 \pm \frac{u}{c}}} \qquad \textbf{(31.20)}$$

where the upper and the lower signs correspond respectively to the source moving towards the observer and away from the observer. Thus, if a star is moving away from us, we must take the lower sign and the wavelength increases—this is known as the *red-shift* of spectral lines. When $u/c << 1$, we get the non-relativistic expressions for the Doppler shift:

$$\lambda_{DS} \approx \lambda_0\left(1 \mp \frac{u}{c}\right) \quad \Rightarrow \quad \frac{\Delta\lambda}{\lambda_0} \approx \mp\frac{u}{c} \qquad \textbf{(31.21)}$$

Equation (31.20), correspond to what is known as the *longitudinal Doppler effect* because the source is moving along the line joining the source and the observer. If the source is moving in a direction perpendicular to the line joining the source and the observer, we have what is known as the *transverse Doppler effect* which we will discuss in Sec. 33.4.

EXAMPLE 31.8 According to Hubble's law, greater the distance of the galaxy greater is the velocity of the galaxy moving away from us. Thus if u represents the velocity of the galaxy then $u \approx HD$, where D is the distance from the galaxy; the parameter H is known as the Hubble parameter and $H \approx 15 - 30$ km/s per million light years; we must mention that there is a lot of controversy on the validity of Hubble's law. However, if we assume $H \approx 20$ km/s, the above equation implies that if a galaxy is about 150 million light years away then it would be moving away from us with a speed of about 3000 km/s and $u/c \approx 0.01$. Thus the fractional increase in the Doppler shifted wavelength will be about 1%.

PROBLEMS

In the problems below assume the rest masses of the proton, neutron, deuteron and alpha particle to be given respectively by: $m_p = 1.6726231 \times 10^{-27}$ kg, $m_n = 1.6749286 \times 10^{-27}$ kg, $m_d = 3.3435860 \times 10^{-27}$ kg, $m_\alpha = 6.644656209 \times 10^{-27}$ kg and $m_{{}_3\text{Li}^7} \approx 1.1626 \times 10^{-26}$ kg.

31.1 As discussed in Chapter 26, for the 2P → 1S transition in the hydrogen atom, the frequency of the emitted radiation is given by $\nu \approx 2.47 \times 10^{-15}$ s^{-1}. (a) Calculate the energy of the emitted photon. (b) Calculate the corresponding loss of mass of the hydrogen atom.

[**Ans:** (a) ≈ 10.2 eV (b) $\Delta m \approx 1.8 \times 10^{-35}$ kg]

* See, e.g., http://en.wikipedia.org/wiki/Large_Hadron_Collider

31.2 The deuteron nucleus consists of one neutron and one proton held together by nuclear forces. Show that the binding energy of the deuteron is about 2.23 MeV. Thus it would require about 2.23 MeV of energy to separate the neutron and proton from the deuteron nucleus.

31.3 The alpha particle consists of two neutron and two protons held together by nuclear forces. Calculate the binding energy of the alpha particle. **[Ans:** 28.3 MeV]

31.4 The rest mass of the tritium nucleus is $\approx 5.0376 \times 10^{-27}$ kg. Calculate the binding energy of the tritium nucleus (which consists of one proton and two neutrons) is 8.482 MeV. **[Ans:** $\approx$ 8.482 MeV]

31.5 Consider the nuclear reaction ${}_3\text{Li}^7 + \text{proton} \rightarrow \alpha + \alpha + \text{Energy}$. Calculate the net decrease in mass and the energy that will be released (in the form of kinetic energies of the alpha particles). Mass of the ${}_3\text{Li}^7$ nucleus $\approx 1.1626 \times 10^{-26}$ kg.

31.6 In nuclear physics, using the equation $E = mc^2$, mass is often measured in energy units. The rest mass of the proton is given by $m_p = 1.6726231 \times 10^{-27}$ kg. Calculate the energy associated with the rest mass of the proton in MeV. **[Ans:** $\approx$ 938 MeV]

31.7 Show that the rest mass energy of the electron is about 0.511 MeV.

31.8 In the Large Hadron Collider (LHC), the protons are accelerated to about 99.9999991% of the speed of light*. Calculate the Lorentz factor γ and the corresponding kinetic energy of the proton. **[Ans:** $\gamma = 7500$, $\approx$ 7000 GeV].

31.9 Consider a π-meson at rest disintegrating to a μ-meson (of rest mass m_0) and a neutrino of zero rest mass.

(a) Using conservation of momentum show that the momentum of the neutrons is given by

$$p_v = \frac{m_0 \beta c}{\sqrt{1-\beta^2}}; \; \beta = \frac{v}{c}$$

where v is the velocity of the μ-meson.

(b) Show by using conservation of total energy

$$\beta = \frac{M_0^2 - m_0^2}{M_0^2 + m_0^2}$$

where M_0 is the rest mass of the π-meson. Further

$$\text{kinetic energy of the } \mu\text{-meson} = \frac{(M_0 - m_0)^2 c^2}{2M_0}$$

CHAPTER

32

Special Theory of Relativity I:

Time Dilation and Length Contraction

The two men (Einstein and his close friend Michele Besso) regularly discussed science and philosophy—including the nature of time. After one such discussion, Einstein came to a sudden realization: **time is not absolute**. *In other words, despite our common perception that a second is always a second everywhere in the universe, the rate at which time flows depends upon where you are and how fast you are traveling. Einstein thanked Besso in his first paper on the Special Theory of Relativity*.*

Important Milestones

1905 Einstein put forward special theory of relativity in his Year of Miracles working in total isolation at the Swiss Patent office. He published this paper in Annalen der Physik. In this paper, he derived equations what are known as Lorentz transformations; however, he did not refer to Lorentz's work. Most probably he was not aware of Lorentz's work.

LEARNING OBJECTIVES

After reading this chapter, the reader should be able to:

LO 1: *understand the concept of time dilation.*

LO 2: *explain mu-meson experiment.*

LO 3: *discuss the concept of length contraction.*

LO 4: *analyze mu-meson experiment with length contraction.*

LO 5: *interpret simultaneity of two events.*

LO 6: *understand the twin paradox.*

LO 7: *explain the Michelson–Morley experiment.*

* Adapted from http://www.amnh.org/exhibitions/einstein/time/index.php; the conversation between Einstein and Besso was just before Einstein's paper on Special Theory of Relativity which was published in 1905 (Ref. 32.1).

Above Image: The first atomic explosion on July 16, 1945.

32.1 Introduction

A train is moving past a platform. For a person on the platform, the train is moving at a speed of say 50 km/hour. I am inside the train and if I throw a tennis ball horizontally (along the length of the train) at a speed of 10 km/hr, then for a person on the platform the ball will move away at a speed of about 60 km/h. I next hold a laser pointer (I am still inside the moving train); for the person on the platform, the laser pointer is also moving with the speed of the moving train. I switch on the laser pointer and quickly switch it off to produce a light pulse. The light pulse emitted by the laser pointer travels with the same speed with respect to me as well as for the observer on the platform. Thus the speed of light in vacuum (which is denoted by c) does not depend on the speed of the source of light. This was the remarkable statement that was made by Albert Einstein in his famous 1905 paper (Ref. 32.1). To quote from the English translation of this paper (reprinted in Ref. 32.2):

> *light always propagates in empty space with a definite velocity V that is independent of the state of motion of the emitting body ....*

[The quantity V in Einstein's original paper is now usually denoted by c]. That the speed of light does not depend on the speed of the source of light has since been verified in many experiments. The most important experiment was carried out by Alvager (and his colleagues) in 1964 (Ref. 32.3). In this experiment, neutral pi mesons traveling with speeds very close to that of light were produced; neutral pi mesons (denoted by π^0) have a mass of about 264 times the mass of an electron and decay (with a mean lifetime of about 8×10^{-17} seconds) to 2 gamma ray photons:

$$\pi^0 \rightarrow \gamma + \gamma$$

The photons (from the decay of very fast moving neutral pi mesons) were found to travel with speed c. The measurement of the speed of the gamma ray photons was difficult, but it was unambiguously established that their speed was equal to c. Why do we require a fast moving π^0 meson as a source of photon? This is because of the fact that it would be extremely difficult (and would require an enormous amount of energy) to make an object like an ordinary light source travel with a speed close to that of light – see Example 31.7.

We will first state the two postulates of the special theory of relativity put forward by Einstein in 1905. However, in order to understand the two postulates, it is necessary to define an inertial system which is defined as

> *An inertial system is one in which Newton's first law holds.*

That raises the question *What is Newton's first law*? Newton wrote his famous laws in his incredible book entitled *Principia.* The book was in Latin and according to the English translation of this book; the first law is (Quoted from Ref. 32.4):

> *Every body perseveres in its state of rest, or of uniform motion in a straight line, unless it is compelled to change that state by forces impressed thereon.*

Feynman writes Newton's first law as (Ref. 32.5):

> *If something is moving, with nothing touching it and completely undisturbed, it will go on forever, coasting at a uniform speed in a straight line. (Why does it keep on coasting? We do not know, but that is the way it is).*

Feynman further writes "Newton modified this idea, saying that the only way to change the motion of a body is to use force. If the body speeds up, a force has been applied in the direction of motion". Any system moving with constant velocity with respect to an inertial system is also an inertial system. And Newton had written that the laws of mechanics (which determine the motion of bodies) are the same in all inertial systems. This implies, for example, that (to quote Feynman)

> *if a space ship is drifting along at a uniform speed, all experiments performed in the space ship will appear the same as if the ship was not moving, provided of course, that one does not look outside. That is the meaning of the principle of relativity.*

Einstein found that for the laws of electricity and magnetism (described by Maxwell's equations) to remain the same in a moving space ship, the speed of light in vacuum should not depend on the speed of the source of light. This led Einstein to put forward (in 1905) the following two postulates of the special theory of relativity:

1. The laws of physics are the same in all inertial systems.
2. The speed of light in vacuum (which is denoted by c) does not depend on the speed of the source of light.

The first postulate was known much before Einstein. Isaac Newton, in one of his corollaries to the laws of motion had written*:

> *The motions of bodies included in a given space are the same among themselves, whether that space is at rest or moves uniformly forward in a straight line.*

The first postulate is also known as the principle of relativity and in 1904 the famous French mathematician Henri Poincare had stated this very precisely**

> *According to the principle of relativity, the laws of physical phenomena must be the same for a fixed*

* The author found this in Ref. 32.5; see also Ref. 32.4.

** The author found this in Ref. 32.5. Poincare was also the first to present the Lorentz transformations in their modern symmetrical form.

observer as for an observer who has a uniform motion of translation relative to him, so that we have not, nor can we possibly have, any means of discerning whether or not we are carried along in such a motion.

32.2 Speed of Light for a Moving Observer

Let us consider two coordinate systems S and S' which are in uniform relative motion along the x axis as shown in Fig. 32.1. We have two persons A and B; A is at rest in the coordinate system S and B is at rest in the coordinate systems S'; thus according to A, B is moving in the $+x$ direction with a constant velocity u. On the other hand, according to B, A is moving in the minus x direction with the same speed u. Figure 32.1 shows A holding a light source (like a laser pointer) and of course, according to A the speed of light is c. Now, according to the observer B, the laser pointer is moving in the minus x direction with speed u and therefore according to the second postulate of Einstein, B must also measure the same speed of light. Thus we infer that

A person moving with respect to a light source measures the same speed of light as the person who is stationary with respect to the light source.

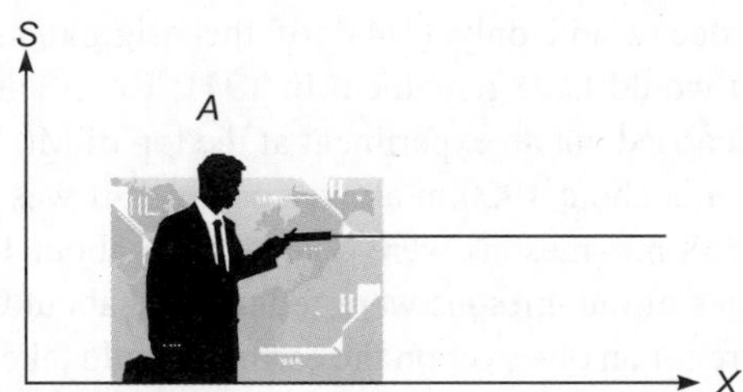

Figure 32.1

A is on the platform and B is inside a train moving with velocity u in the +x direction. According to A, B is moving in the +x direction with a constant velocity u. On the other hand, according to B, A is moving in the minus x direction with the same speed u. A is holding a light source (like a laser) and both A and B measure the same speed of light.

32.3 Time Dilation

LO1

Consider an observer B inside a train moving with speed u on a railway track. Inside the train (which is our reference frame S'), B produces a light pulse (by switching on a bulb and very quickly switching it off), allows the light beam to get reflected by a mirror M (which is right above the bulb) and detects the reflected light by a detector D (see Fig. 32.2). We have therefore two events: the first event is the switching on the bulb producing a light pulse and the second event is its subsequent detection by the detector. B measures the time interval $\Delta t'$ between the two events; this time would obviously be given by

$$\Delta t' = \frac{2H}{c} \tag{32.1}$$

where H is the distance between the floor and the mirror as shown in Fig. 32.2. For an observer A on the platform (which is our reference frame S), the whole train is moving with speed u, and therefore the light beam will take a diagonal path which would be longer than observed by B [see Fig. 32.3]. Since the velocity of light is always the same, the time interval between the two events (as observed by A) will take a longer time by his clock. If Δt represents the time interval measured by A then

$$\Delta t = \frac{PM + MD}{c} = \frac{2}{c}\sqrt{H^2 + \left(\frac{u\Delta t}{2}\right)^2} \tag{32.2}$$

where we have used the fact that the speed of light for the observer outside the train will be the same as observed by the person inside the train. If we substitute for H from Eq. (32.1) in Eq. (32.2), we would obtain

$$\Delta t = \gamma \Delta t' \tag{32.3}$$

where

$$\gamma = \frac{1}{\sqrt{1 - \dfrac{u^2}{c^2}}} \tag{32.4}$$

is known as the **Lorentz factor**. For the observer B on the train, the light bulb and the detector are at the same place so that the two events (switching on the bulb and its subsequent detection by the detector) occur at the same position. The time interval between two events occurring at the same position is known as the *proper time*; thus $\Delta t'$ represents the *proper time* between the two events. To quote from Ref. 32.6

> The *proper time* interval between two events is the time interval measured in the reference frame in which the two events occur at the same position. Time intervals that occur at different positions are called *improper*.

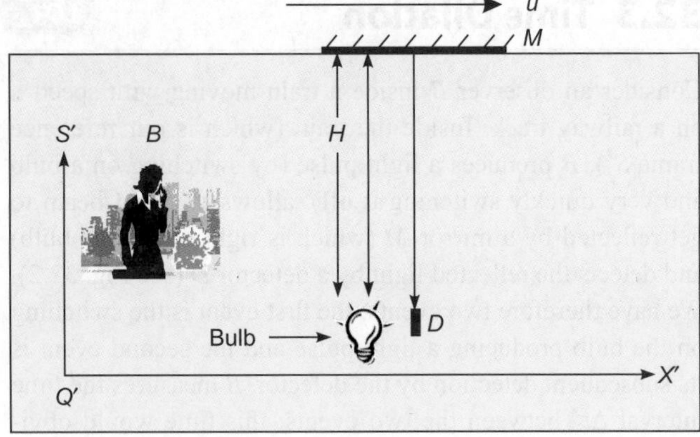

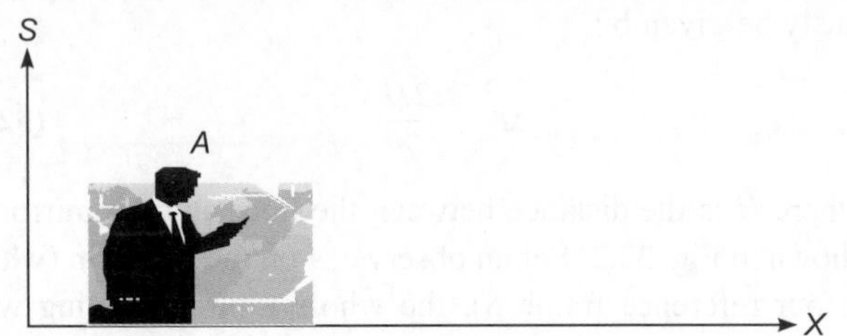

Figure 32.2

An observer *B* is inside a train which is moving with speed *u* on a railway track. Inside the train (which is our reference frame *S*′), *B* switches on a bulb, allows the light beam to get reflected by a mirror *M* (which is right above the bulb) and detects the reflected beam by a detector *D*.

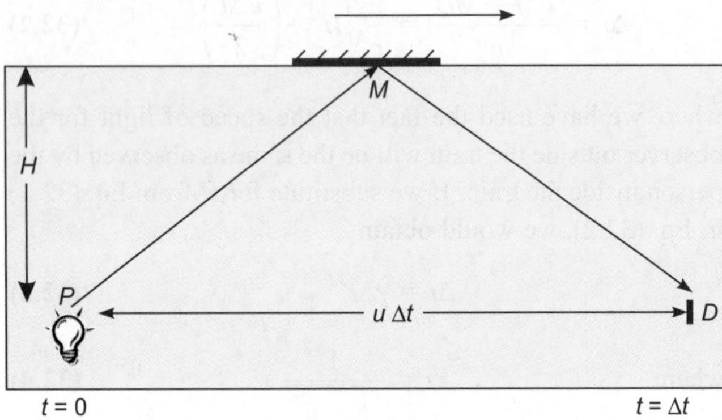

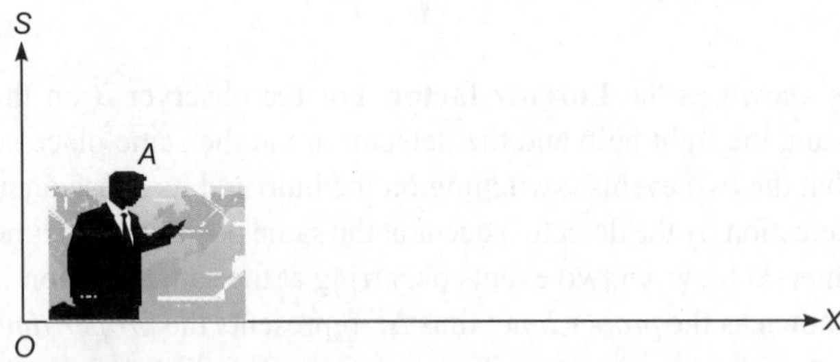

Figure 32.3

According to *A* (who is on the platform), when the light reaches the detector *D* (via the mirror *M*), the detector has moved through a distance $u\Delta t$.

On the other hand, for the observer *A* (outside the train) both the light bulb and the mirror are moving with velocity *u* and the two events occur at different places. Thus Eq. (32.3) represents the important result that

Time interval between the two events in reference frame *S* moving with relative speed *u* with respect to the reference frame *S*′

= $\gamma\times$ Time interval between two events occurring **at the same place** in the reference frame *S*′ (referred to as the *proper time*) **(32.5)**

Since the Lorentz factor γ is always greater than 1, the time interval between two events as seen by any reference frame (which is moving with respect to the frame where the events occur at the same place) gets "dilated".

32.4 The Mu-meson Experiment

LO2

A mu-meson (also known as *muon*) is a negatively charged elementary particle which has exactly the same charge as the electron but has a mass about 207 times the mass of the electron. In 1937, mu-mesons were first detected in cosmic rays by S.H. Neddermeyer and C.D. Anderson. These particles are created at the top of our atmosphere, i.e., at a height of about 5000 meters. It is believed that when high energy protons (from outer space) collide with molecules in the outer region of the atmosphere, many particles (including the mu-mesons) are created. Mu-mesons have also been created in the laboratories. Mu-mesons are radioactive and undergo the following decay

Mu-meson → Electron + Neutrino + Anti-neutrino **(32.6)**

The half life for this decay is about 1.5 μs. This would imply that if initially (in the rest frame of the mu–mesons) there are 1000 mu–mesons then in 1.5 μs about half of them will undergo decay. After 3 μs about 750 mu–mesons would have undergone decay and only (1/4)th of the original number (about 250) would have remained. In 1941, Rossi and Hall (Ref. 32.7) carried out an experiment at the top of Mt. Washington which is about 1920 m above sea level. It was found that about 568 mu–mesons were detected* in about 1 hour. The velocities of mu–mesons were found to be about 0.995*c* and therefore for an observer on the earth, it would take about

$$\frac{1920\text{ m}}{0.995\times 3\times 10^{8}\text{ m/s}} \approx 6.4\ \mu\text{s} \qquad (32.7)$$

to traverse the distance of 1920 meters [see Fig. 32.4(a)]. This traversal time approximately corresponds to 4 half-lives; as

* Numbers taken from http://www.egglescliffe.org.uk/physics/relativity/muons1_.htm

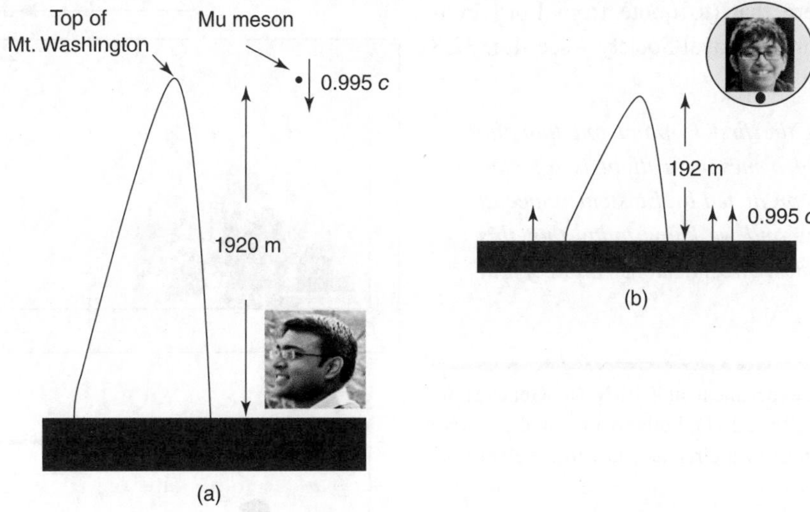

Figure 32.4
(a) For an observer on the earth, a mu-meson (moving with a velocity of about 0.995 *c*) would take about 6.4 μs to traverse the distance of 1920 meters. (b) Inside the space ship, the mu-meson is at rest and an observer inside the spaceship sees the earth moving towards him with a speed 0.995*c* and a contracted distance of 192 meters which is covered in 0.64 μs.

such, after traversing a distance of 1920 meters only $(1/16)^{th}$ of the original number (i.e., about 40) should have remained and about 530 mu–mesons should have undergone decay; a more accurate calculation has been done later in this section. However, when the experiment was performed, it was found that about 412 mu–mesons were detected.

Now, for $u \approx 0.995c$, $\gamma \approx 10$ and if $\Delta t'$ represents the time interval in the reference frame of the mu–meson and Δt represents the time interval in the reference frame of the earth, then in the reference frame of the mu–meson, the two events occur at the same space point, so the time elapsed is the proper time and therefore $\Delta t' \approx 0.1\ \Delta t$ [see Eq. (32.3)]. Thus, although in the reference frame of the earth, the time elapsed is 6.4 μs; in the reference frame of the mu–meson (which is moving at a speed of 0.995*c* with respect to the earth), the time elapsed is only one tenth of that, viz., 0.64 μs and in this time only a very few mu–mesons would have undergone decay. We do the calculation more carefully:

The mean lifetime of the mu–meson decay process [as given by Eq. (32.6)] is about 2.2 μs. Thus, if there are N_0 muons at $t = 0$ (at rest in the laboratory) then at a later time t, the number of mu-mesons which would **not** have undergone decay will be given by

$$N(t) = N_0 e^{-t/\tau} \tag{32.8}$$

where τ ($\approx$ 2.2 μs) represents the mean lifetime of the mu–meson. The quantity

$$t_{1/2} = (\ln 2)\tau \approx 0.693\ \tau$$

represents the half life. For the mu–meson, $t_{1/2} \approx 1.525$ μs. In this time, half the number of mu–mesons would **not** have undergone decay:

$$1000 \exp\left[-\frac{1.525\ \mu\text{s}}{2.2\ \mu\text{s}}\right] \approx 500$$

As mentioned earlier, in the experiment of Rossi and Hall (Ref. 32.7) 568 mu–mesons were detected in about 1 hour at the top of Mt. Washington. For the observer on the earth, it would take about 6.4 μs to traverse the distance of 1920 meters [see Eq. (32.10)]. In this time, the number of mu–mesons that should reach the surface of the earth would be about

$$568 \exp\left[-\frac{6.4\ \mu\text{s}}{2.2\ \mu\text{s}}\right] \approx 568 e^{-2.9} \approx 31$$

Thus in traversing the distance of 1920 m, about 537 mu–mesons should have undergone decay and only 31 of them should have reached the surface of the earth. However, when the experiment was performed, it was found that about 412 mu-mesons were detected. This is because of the fact that in the reference frame of the muon, the time elapsed is only 0.64 μs [see the discussion below Eq. (32.7)], and therefore the number of muons that should reach the surface of the earth would be about

$$568 \exp\left[-\frac{0.64\ \mu\text{s}}{2.2\ \mu\text{s}}\right] \approx 425 \tag{32.9}$$

which agrees well with the observed value. Thus,

> *whereas in the reference frame of the earth, the time elapsed is 6.4* μs*; in the reference frame of the mu–meson (which is moving at a speed of 0.995c with respect to the earth), the time elapsed is only 0.64* μs.

We may mention here that (to quote from Lord Penney's paper in Proceedings of Royal Society – see Ref. 32.8 [reprinted in Ref. 32.9]):

> *Homi Bhabha* was the first to point out that the measured lifetime of a meson in flight is affected by the time dilation predicted by Einstein's Special Theory of Relativity, and we know today that this measurement is the most direct demonstration of that phenomenon …*

EXAMPLE 32.1 In an experiment at CERN (in Geneva) by Bailey and his co-workers (Ref 32.11), both positive and negative mu–mesons were accelerated (in a circular path) to a velocity so that the Lorentz factor

$\gamma \approx 29.33$ which implies $u \approx 0.99942c$. The measured lifetimes were

$\tau^{+} = 64.419 \pm 0.058$ μs for positively charged mu–mesons and

$\tau^{-} = 64.368 \pm 0.029$ μs for negatively charged mu–mesons

Using Eq. (32.3), Bailey and his co-workers (Ref. 32.11) found the mean proper lifetime for negatively charged mu–mesons to be equal to 2.195 μs which represents one of the most accurately determined values of the mu–meson lifetime. Thus if we create two mu–meson twins in the laboratory, one of them remains at rest and the other is accelerated to a speed of 0.9994c, then the mu–meson (moving with a speed of 0.9994c) would come back to find its "twin" has undergone decay long long time back!!!!

We conclude this section by a quote which is often attributed to Einstein

> *When you sit with a nice girl for two hours you think it's only a minute, but when you sit on a hot stove for a minute you think it's two hours. That's relativity.*

Even in National Geographic's documentary on the life of Einstein, Einstein is shown saying a very similar sentence to President Roosevelt. However, it is widely believed that he did not say this himself.

32.5 Length Contraction LO3

We again consider two coordinate systems S and S' which are in uniform relative motion along the x axis as shown in Fig. 32.5. We have two persons A and B; A is at rest in the coordinate system S and B (inside a moving train) is at rest in the coordinate systems S'. Consider a rod RR' (of length L_0) at rest in the reference frame S. Now,

> The length of the rod L_0, measured in an inertial frame in which the rod is at rest, is known as the **proper length**.

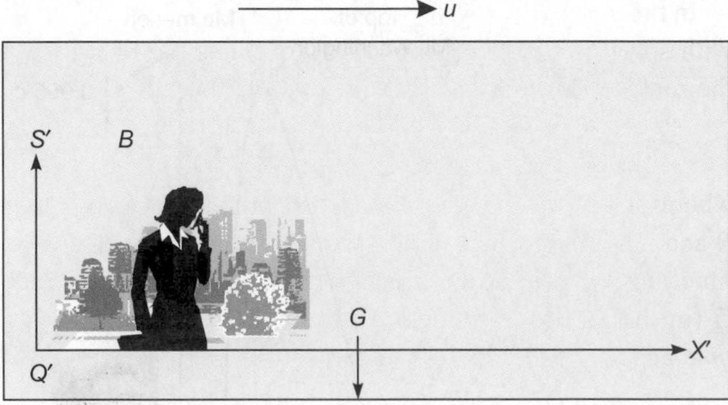

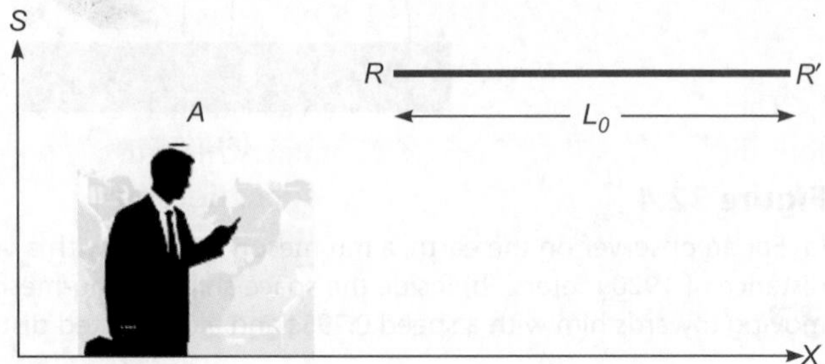

Figure 32.5
A is on the platform and *B* is inside a train moving with velocity *u* in the +*x* direction. A rod *RR'* (of length L_0) is at rest in the reference frame *S*. In the inertial frame *S'* (moving with velocity *u* with respect to the frame *S*), we have an observer *B* and also an arrow *G*.

In the inertial frame S' (moving with velocity u with respect to the frame S), we have an observer B and also an arrow G as shown in Fig. 32.5. We have two events: the first event is when the arrow G is in front of the end R of the rod and the second event is when the arrow G is in front of the end R' of the rod.

The observer A in the inertial frame S sees the arrow move with velocity u and if Δt is the time elapsed (as measured by A) for the arrow to go from the end R of the rod to the end R', then

$$L_0 = u\Delta t \tag{32.10}$$

* In a paper published in 1938 (see Ref. 32.10), Bhabha wrote that positively and negatively charged mesons should spontaneously decay into a positron and electron respectively. He further wrote (quoting from his paper)

> *This disintegration being spontaneous, the U-particle may be described as a 'clock', and hence it follows merely from considerations of relativity that the time of disintegration is longer when the particle is in motion.*

The *U*-particles in Bhabha's paper referred to mesons.

In the inertial frame S', the observer B sees the rod moving with speed u in the minus x direction. Thus the length L of the rod as measured by B would be given by

$$L = u\Delta t' \tag{32.11}$$

where $\Delta t'$ is the time elapsed (as measured by B) as the ends R and R' of the rod cross the arrow. Now, $\Delta t'$ represents the time interval of the two events occurring at the same place G (in the reference frame S') and therefore it is the *proper time* and since $\Delta t = \gamma\,\Delta t'$, we get

$$L = \sqrt{1-\frac{u^2}{c^2}}\;L_0 = \frac{L_0}{\gamma} \tag{32.12}$$

The Lorentz factor γ is always greater than 1, and therefore the observer B measures a contracted length given by the above equation. This is known as **length contraction**.

32.6 Understanding the Mu–meson Experiment via Length Contraction

LO4

We go back to the mu–meson experiment. For the observer A (in the reference frame S at rest on the earth) the mu–meson moves with velocity $u = 0.995c$ and traverses the distance of 1920 m (the height of Mt. Washington) in about 6.4 μs [see Fig. 32.4(a)].

We next consider the mu–meson inside a space ship and the space ship moving with the same velocity as the mu–meson. Thus the mu-meson is at rest inside the space ship [see Fig. 32.4(b)]. For an observer B inside the space ship, the earth is moving towards it with velocity $u = 0.995c$ which implies $\gamma \approx 10$. Now, because of length contraction, for the observer inside the space ship, the distance between the top of Mt. Washington and the earth is not 1920 m but the contracted distance of 192 m. This distance is traversed (by the earth) in only

$$\frac{192\text{ m}}{0.995c} = \frac{192\text{ m}}{0.995\times 3\times 10^{8}\text{ m/s}} = 0.64\ \mu s$$

and in this time, only 43 number of muons will undergo decay [see Eq. (32.9)].

32.7 Length Contraction of a Moving Train

Consider a mirror M placed inside a train (moving with speed u) as shown in Fig. 32.6. A pulse of light emitted from the light source P gets reflected by the mirror and is detected at D. Obviously, the time interval (as measured by the observer B in the moving train) between the emission of light and its subsequent detection will be given by

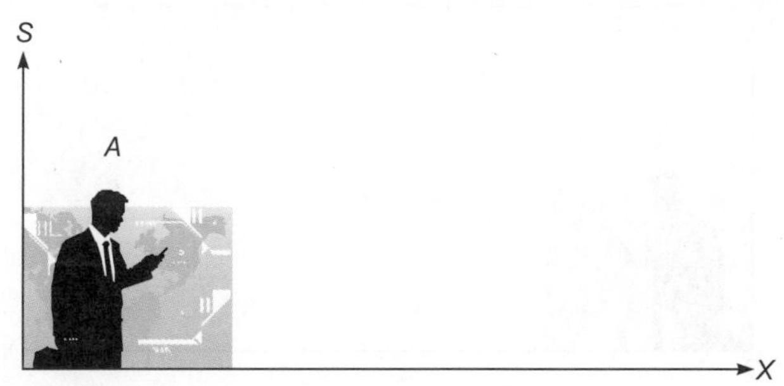

Figure 32.6

A mirror M placed inside a moving train. A pulse of light emitted from the light source P gets reflected by the mirror and is detected at D. For the observer B, the mirror and the source of light are stationary and are at a distance of L_0 from each other.

$$\Delta t' = \frac{2L_0}{c} \tag{32.13}$$

where L_0 is the distance between the light source and the mirror as measured by the observer B in the moving train.

We next consider the events as seen by a person on the platform; for him, the speed of light is the same and we assume that the distance between the point P and the mirror M is L. If Δt_1 represents the time interval (as observed by the person A on the platform) for light to travel to the mirror then

$$\Delta t_1 = \frac{L - u\,\Delta t_1}{c} \;\Rightarrow\; \Delta t_1 = \frac{L}{c\left(1+\dfrac{u}{c}\right)} \tag{32.14}$$

where we have taken into account the fact that in time Δt_1 the mirror has moved through a distance $u\Delta t_1$ (see Fig. 32.7). Similarly, if Δt_2 represents the time interval (as observed by the person A on the platform) for light to travel from the mirror to the detector then (see Fig. 32.8).

$$\Delta t_2 = \frac{L - u\,\Delta t_1 + u(\Delta t_1 + \Delta t_2)}{c} \Rightarrow \Delta t_2 = \frac{L}{c\left(1-\dfrac{u}{c}\right)} \tag{32.15}$$

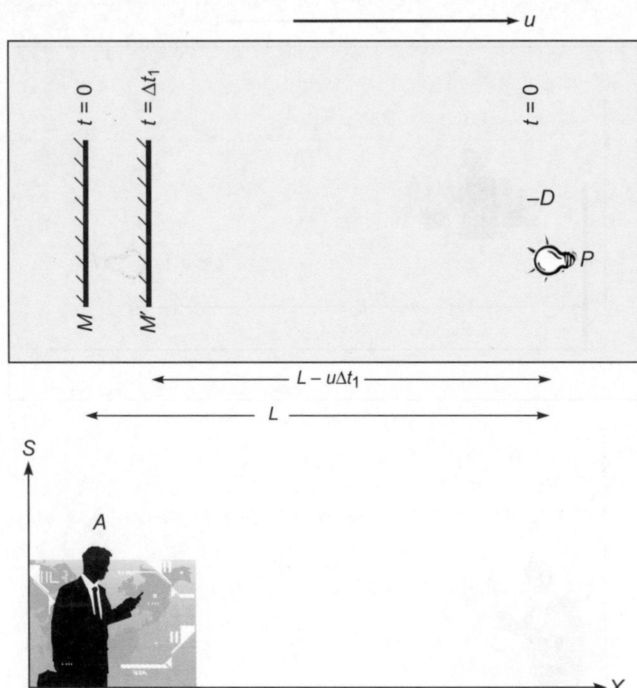

Figure 32.7

The observer A on the platform, sees a contracted distance L between P and the mirror (inside the moving train). The pulse of light emitted from the light source P reaches the mirror at $t = \Delta t_1$ and by then the mirror has moved through the distance $u\,\Delta t_1$.

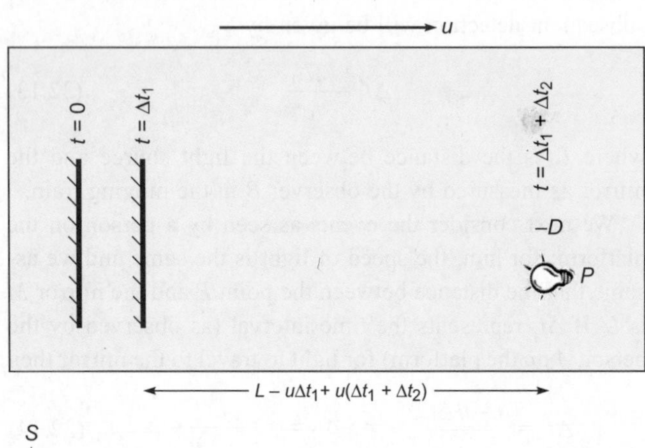

Figure 32.8

For the observer A on the platform, the light beam reflected from the mirror reaches the detector D at $t = \Delta t_1 + \Delta t_2$.

Thus if Δt represents the time interval (as observed by the person on the platform) between the emission of light and its subsequent detection, then it would be given by

$$\Delta t = \Delta t_1 + \Delta t_2 = \frac{2L}{c\left(1 - \frac{u^2}{c^2}\right)} \tag{32.16}$$

Thus

$$\frac{\Delta t}{\Delta t'} = \frac{L}{\left(1 - \frac{u^2}{c^2}\right)L_0} \tag{32.17}$$

But, since $\Delta t'$ represents the time interval between two events occurring *at the same place* inside the moving train, $\Delta t'$ and Δt will be related by the equation

$$\Delta t' = \sqrt{1 - \frac{u^2}{c^2}}\;\Delta t \tag{32.18}$$

Thus

$$L = \sqrt{1 - \frac{u^2}{c^2}}\;L_0 \tag{32.19}$$

Thus because the speed of light is the same in all inertial frames, the observer on the platform will calculate a shorter length of the train.

32.8 Simultaneity of Two Events

LO5

We next consider an atom (at rest in the moving train) emitting simultaneously two photons; the two detectors D_1 and D_2 are at the same distance ($= L_0$) from the atom and therefore for an observer B in the reference frame S', the photons are detected simultaneously (see Fig. 32.9). For the observer A on the platform, let Δt_1 and Δt_2 represent the time taken by the two photons to reach the two detectors D_1 and D_2, respectively. Using the arguments given in the previous section

$$\Delta t_1 = \frac{L}{c\left(1 + \frac{u}{c}\right)} \quad \text{and} \quad \Delta t_2 = \frac{L}{c\left(1 - \frac{u}{c}\right)} \tag{32.20}$$

where L is the contracted distance between the atom and either of the detectors. The difference in the two time intervals will be

$$\Delta t_2 - \Delta t_1 = \gamma^2 \frac{2uL}{c^2} = \gamma \frac{2uL_0}{c^2} \tag{32.21}$$

where γ is the Lorentz factor. Thus whereas the two events are simultaneous in the reference frame S', they are not simultaneous in the reference frame S; we will discuss this again in Sec. 33.2.

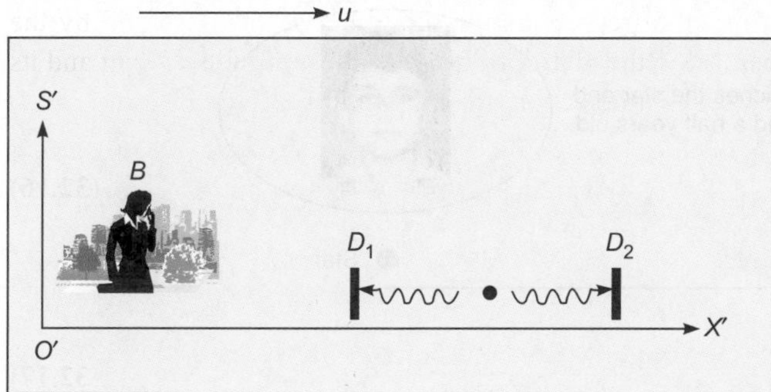

Figure 32.9
For the observer *B* on the moving train, the atom is at rest and emits two photons simultaneously in opposite directions. The two detectors D_1 and D_2 are equidistant from the atom and detect the photons simultaneously; however, the two events are not simultaneous for observer *A*.

EXAMPLE 32.2 We assume $L_0 = 10$ m. For $u \approx 0.995c$, which implies $\gamma \approx 10$ and the time interval between the two events (as observed in the reference frame *S*) will be

$$\gamma \frac{2uL_0}{c^2} \approx 10 \times \frac{2 \times 0.995 \times 10}{3 \times 10^8} \approx 6.7 \times 10^{-7}\ \text{s} = 0.67\ \mu\text{s}$$

On the other hand, for $u = 30$ km/s $= 0.0001c$ (which is about 10 times faster than the fastest aircraft), the Lorentz factor will be $\gamma \approx 1.000000005$ and the time interval between the two events (as observed in the reference frame *S*) will be ≈ 6.7 ps.

32.9 The Twin Paradox

LO6

We illustrate the twin paradox through a few examples. The effect due to general theory of relativity is not taken into account.

EXAMPLE 32.3 We consider a star which is 15 light years away*. Thus a light beam will take about 15 years to travel from earth to this star. Now,

$$1 \text{ year} = 365 \times 24 \times 60 \times 60\,\text{s} \approx 3.15 \times 10^7\,\text{s}$$

(An easy way to remember the above formula is that one year is very nearly equal to $\pi \times 10^7$s). Thus, one light year is about 9.4 trillion kilometers. Thus, we are considering a star which is about 140 trillion kilometers away. We consider the following experiment:

Amitabh and Arjun are twins—they are both five years old (see Fig. 32.10). At $t = 0$, Amitabh gets into a flying spacecraft which is moving (towards the star) with an extremely high speed which is only about 168 kilometers per second less than the speed of light – thus $u \approx 0.99944c$ and the speed of the spacecraft is about 299,832 kilometers per second (we are assuming the speed of light to be 300,000 kilometers per second). The Lorentz factor is given by $\gamma \approx 30$. Amitabh is at rest inside the aircraft. According to Arjun (who is on earth), Amitabh will take about 15 years to reach the star**. Amitabh will see a contracted distance of ≈ 0.5 light years ≈ 4.7 trillion km. Thus according to Amitabh, he will reach the star in about six months which is (1/30)[th] of the time recorded by Arjun (see Fig. 32.11). Amitabh returns to earth at the same speed. On his return journey, he finds that the earth is moving towards him with a

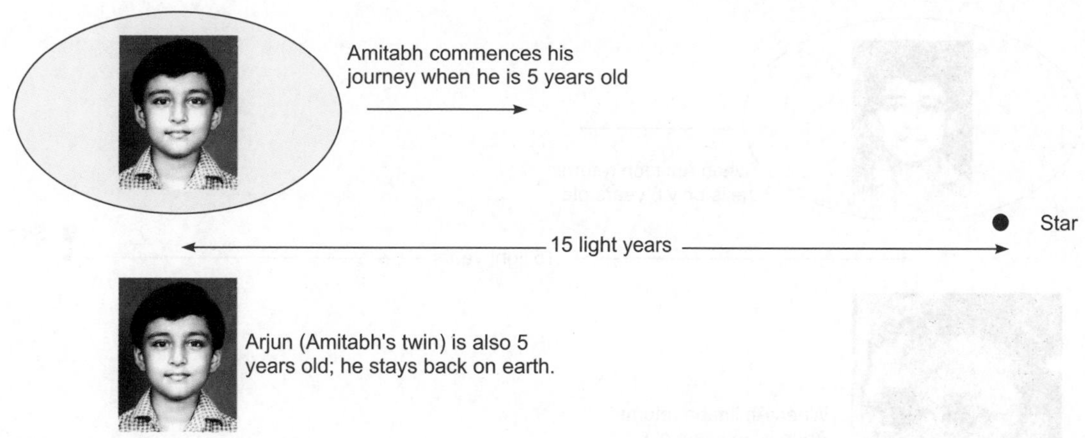

Figure 32.10
Arjun and Amitabh are twins—they are both five years old. Amitabh synchronizes his watch with Arjun and gets into a flying spacecraft which is moving towards the star with an extremely large velocity so that the Lorentz factor $\gamma \approx 30$.

* The star closest to us is Proxima Centauri and it is about 4.2 light years away. There are stars which are thousands of light years away.

** This should be obvious because the star is 15 light years away and the spacecraft is moving with a speed which is very close to the speed of light.

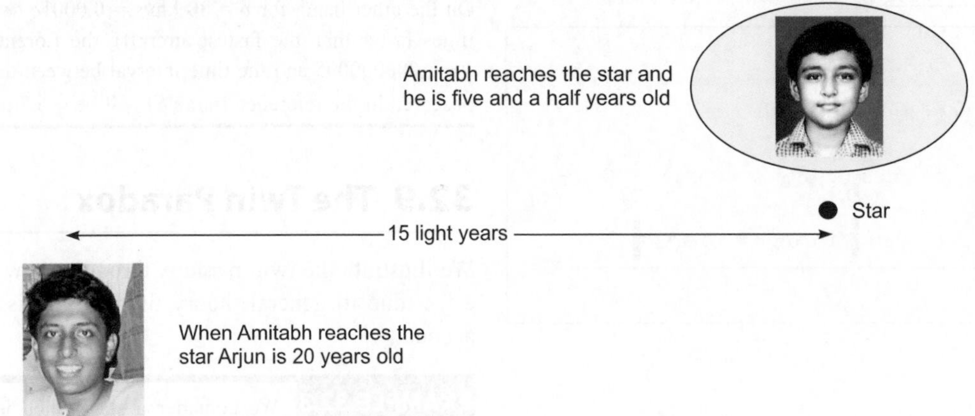

Figure 32.11
When Amitabh's spacecraft reaches the star, he is five and a half years old but Arjun is now 20 years old.

velocity 299,833 km/s and the contracted distance would be covered in ≈ 0.5 light years. When Amitabh's space ship stops, he finds that his clock shows only 1 year whereas Arjun's clock would show 30 years (see Fig. 32.12).

We can understand the above situation from another point of view. The first event corresponds to when the space ship starts moving (with velocity u) from the earth and the second event corresponds to when the space ship reaches the star. In the moving frame (i.e., inside the space ship) both events occur at the same space point. Thus the time interval $\Delta t'$ measured by Amitabh is the "proper time" and would be less than the time measured by Arjun by a factor $(1/\gamma)$ (see the discussion in Sec. 32.2).

EXAMPLE 32.4 In the previous example, we had assumed that the spacecraft was moving with a velocity 299,832 km/s. As shown in Example 31.7, it would require tremendously large amount of energy for a spacecraft to move with such a high velocity. The fastest aircraft moves with a speed less than 3 km/s; let us assume that the speed of the spacecraft to be 100 times of this value; i.e., $u = 300$ km/s. At such speeds $u/c = 0.001$. Now,

$$\Delta t - \Delta t' = \left(1 - \sqrt{1 - \frac{u^2}{c^2}}\right) \Delta t \approx \frac{u^2}{2c^2}\, \Delta t \approx 5 \times 10^{-7}\, \Delta t$$

where we have assumed $u/c \ll 1$. We assume the moon to be at a distance of about 400,000 km from the Earth; thus, for an observer on Earth, for a spacecraft traveling with a speed of 300 km/s, it will take about 1330 s (≈ 22.2 min) to travel from Earth to moon. Thus (for the observer on Earth) the round trip will take about 2660 s ≈ 44.4 min. The astronaut inside the spaceship will record a slightly lesser time, the time difference being

$$5 \times 10^{-7} \times 2660 = 1.33 \times 10^{-3}\,\text{s} = 1.33\ \text{ms}$$

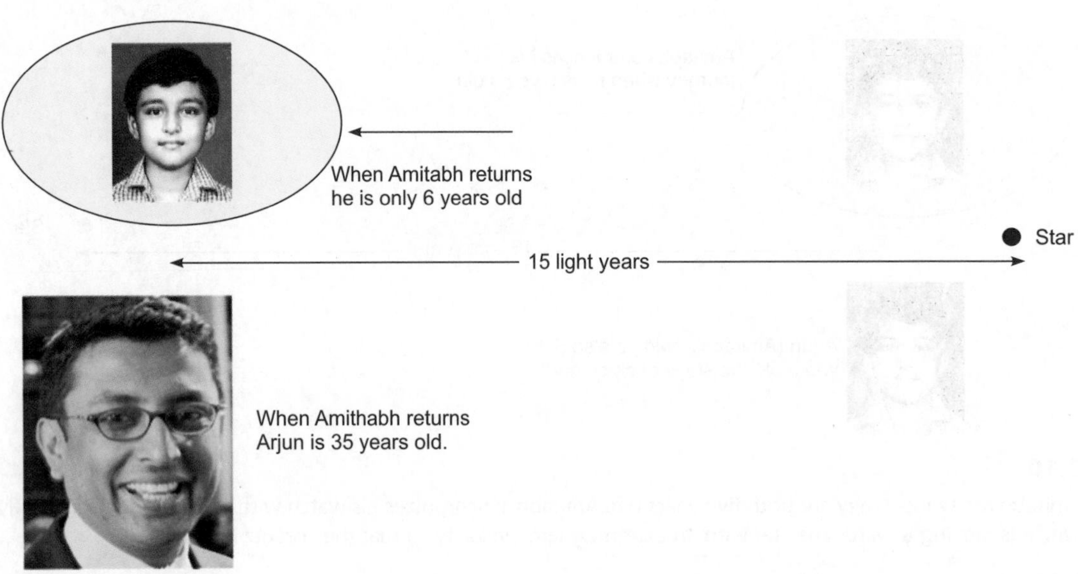

Figure 32.12
When Amitabh returns, he feels that he is only 6 years old whereas Arjun is now 35 years old. This is a consequence of time dilation.

Thus, even for a spacecraft traveling with a speed 100 times that of the fastest aircraft, the time difference will be extremely small.

EXAMPLE 32.5 Consider an aircraft moving around the earth at a speed of 1000 km/hr ($\approx$ 278 m/s). The radius of the earth is about 6400 km, thus the circumference $2\pi r$ is about 4×10^7 m and therefore for the observer on Earth, the round trip will take about 1.44×10^5 s $\approx$ 40 hours. Now $u/c \approx 9.3 \times 10^{-7}$ and

$$\Delta t - \Delta t' \approx \frac{u^2}{2c^2} \Delta t \approx 4.3 \times 10^{-13} \Delta t$$

and the time difference will be about $\approx 6.3 \times 10^{-8}$ s = 63 ns. The time difference is small but measurable; however, in order to compare with experiments one has to take into account the fact that since the aircraft is at a height, it moves at a different gravitational potential – and when this is also taken into account, theoretical predictions agree with experiments.

EXAMPLE 32.6 In continuation of Example 32.2, we consider the case when the star was 45 light years away and the space ship was traveling with the same speed (= 0.99944*c*). Let us assume that, to start with, both Arjun and Amitabh were 5 years old. When Amitabh returns to earth, Arjun would be about 95 years old and Amitabh would be only 8 years old. Thus Arjun would have aged significantly!

The above experiment has led to a lot of controversy – scientists have argued that according to Arjun, Amitabh was moving with a velocity 0.99944*c* and according to Amitabh, Arjun was moving with a velocity 0.99944*c* (in the opposite direction). But there is really no controversy when we consider that we must always be careful to define the "proper time" and when Amitabh returns from his space journey, he *will* be younger to Arjun. Also it is Amitabh who undergoes acceleration (and deceleration) and because of this, the motions of Arjun and Amitabh are not symmetrical.

EXAMPLE 32.7 **Correction due to relativity in GPS satellites:** While using the GPS (Global Positioning System) technology for accurate positioning of objects, it is very necessary to incorporate corrections due to special (and general) theory of relativity. We consider satellites associated with GPS which circle the earth twice a day. Thus the angular velocity of the satellite is

$$\omega = \frac{2\pi}{T} = \frac{2\pi}{12 \times 60 \times 60} \approx 1.454 \times 10^{-4}\ \text{s}^{-1}$$

Now, if the satellite is at a distance R (from the center of the earth) then

$$\frac{G M_e m_s}{R^2} = m_s \omega^2 R \Rightarrow R = \left(\frac{G M_e}{\omega^2}\right)^{1/3}$$

where $G\left(\approx 6.674 \times 10^{-11}\ \text{N.m}^2/\text{kg}^2\right)$ is the gravitational constant, $M_e\left(\approx 5.972 \times 10^{24}\ \text{kg}\right)$ is the mass of the earth and m_s is the mass of the satellite. Substituting the values we get

$$R \approx 2.66 \times 10^7\ \text{m}$$

We could have also used the relation

$$\frac{G M_e m}{R_e^2} = mg \Rightarrow G M_e = g R_e^2$$

where $g(\approx 9.8\ \text{m/s}^2)$ is the acceleration due to gravity at the surface of the earth and $R_e(\approx 6.378 \times 10^6$ m) is the average radius of the earth. From the above equation, we find that the satellite is at a distance of about 26600 km from the center of the earth and hence at a height of about 20200 km from the surface of the earth. Now, the speed of the satellite is

$$v = \omega R \approx 3.868 \times 10^3\ \text{m/s}$$

According to special theory of relativity, the satellite clock will differ from the earth clock by a time interval

$$\Delta t = \sqrt{1 - \frac{v^2}{c^2}}\, \Delta t_e$$

Thus,

$$(\Delta t - \Delta t_e)_{STR} = \left[\sqrt{1 - \frac{v^2}{c^2}} - 1\right] \Delta t_e \approx -\frac{v^2}{2c^2} \Delta t_e$$

For Δt_e = 1 day = 86400 s, the satellite clock will be slower by

$$\approx 7.18\ \mu\text{s}$$

Now, the clock the satellite is at a different gravitational potential with respect to the clock on the earth. According to the general theory of relativity (usually abbreviated as GTR), the clock inside the satellite will be faster; the final result is

$$(\Delta t - \Delta t_e)_{GTR} \approx \frac{g R_e^2}{c^2}\left(\frac{1}{R_e} - \frac{1}{R}\right) \Delta t_e \approx 45.5\ \mu\text{s}$$

Thus the satellite clock will be faster by about 38.2 μs.

32.10 The Michelson–Morley Experiment

LO5

In the beginning of the nineteenth century, a few very beautiful experiments were carried out which demonstrated the interference and diffraction phenomena of light. Both interference and diffraction phenomena could only be explained by assuming a wave model of light. However, it was believed that a wave would always require a medium and since light could propagate through vacuum, the presence of an "all pervasive" medium called the ether was assumed.

If we assume the existence of this "all pervasive" ether, then the observed velocity of light would change if we move with respect to the ether. We know that the earth moves around the sun in an approximately circular orbit with a speed of about 30 km/s (see Fig. 32.13). Thus we should expect that, whatever may be the motion of the solar system, during a certain period of time in a year, the earth will be moving with respect to the ether with a speed of at least

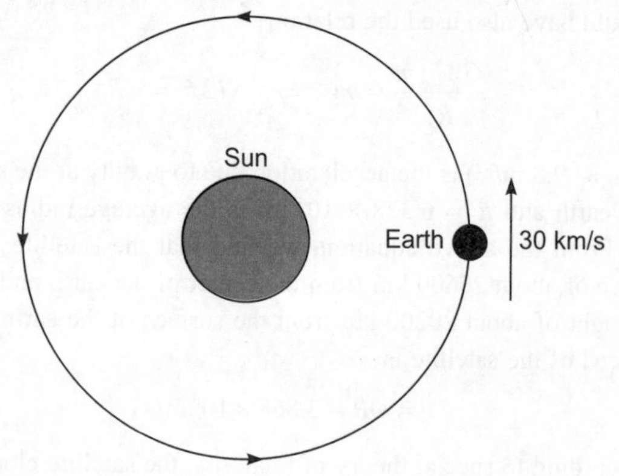

Figure 32.13

The earth rotates around the sun in an approximately circular orbit with a speed of about 30 km/s.

30 km/s and experience what is often referred as "the ether wind".

The experiment involved the famous Michelson interferometer shown in Fig. 32.14 (see also Sec. 14.11). The beam splitter (shown as *BS* in the figure) splits the light beam into two beams traveling at right angles to each other. Subsequently, the beams get reflected by M_1 and M_2 and the beam reflected from M_1 gets reflected by the beam splitter and superposes with the beam reflected from M_2 to form an interference pattern. We assume the positions of the two mirrors to be such that the distance of the beam splitter to each of the mirrors is exactly the same and equal to *L*.

If the whole interferometer is at rest with respect to the ether then the light would travel with the same velocity in all directions and therefore the light reflected by the mirrors M_1 and M_2 would reach the detector *D* at the same time.

We next assume that the apparatus moving through the ether so that with respect to the interferometer, the ether is moving to the left with velocity *u* as shown in Fig. 32.15. Thus as the light beam travels from *P* to *R*, it is opposed by the ether wind and its velocity is $c - u$. On the other hand, when the light beam travels from to *R* to *P*, it is carried by the ether wind* and its velocity is $c + u$. Thus, if t_{PR} and t_{RP} are the time taken for the outward and return trips then

$$t_{PR} = \frac{L}{c-u} \quad \text{and} \quad t_{RP} = \frac{L}{c+u}$$

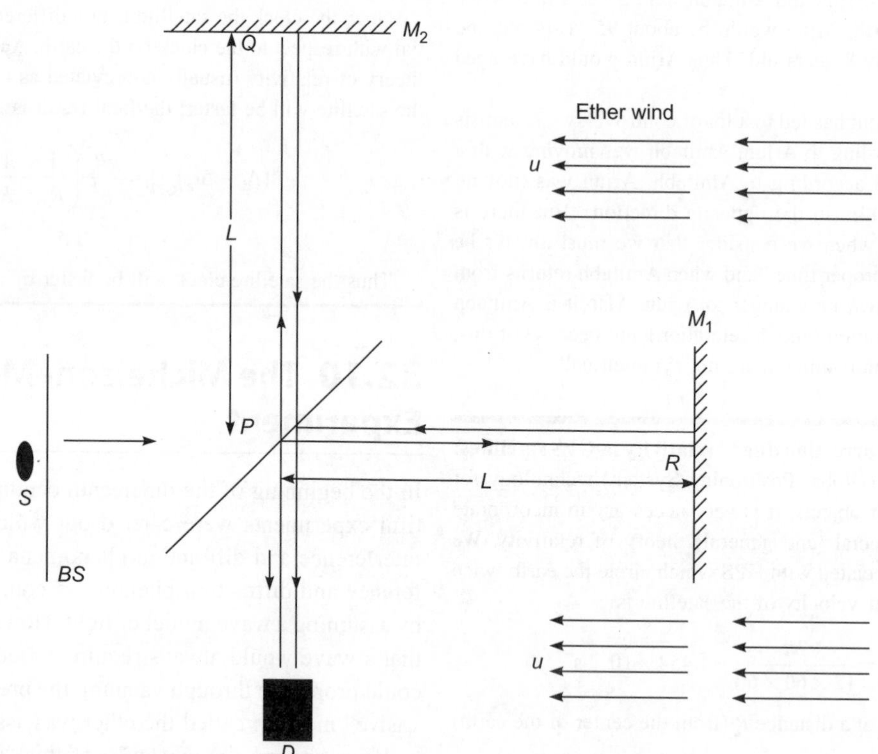

Figure 32.14

The Michelson interferometer arrangement. An observer at rest with the interferometer, experiences the ether wind as shown above.

---

* The easiest way to understand this is to first consider a ship which travels with a certain velocity *V* in still water. We next assume that there is a current in the water moving with speed *u*. If the ship travels along the current, its velocity will increase to $V + u$. On the other hand, if the ship travels against the current, its velocity will decrease to $V - u$.

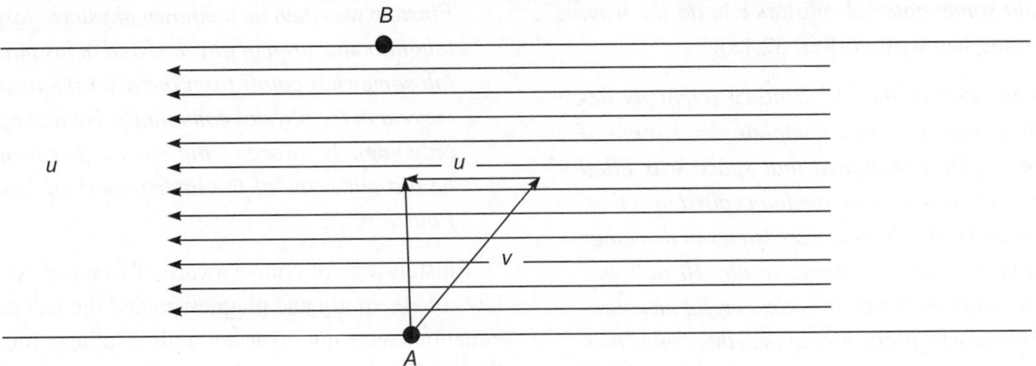

Figure 32.15
There is a current in the river. A swimmer is trying to cross from the point A to the point B. The swimmer must try to swim slightly to the right so that his trajectory is straight.

Therefore, the total time for the light beam to travel from P to R and back will be given by

$$t_1 = t_{PR} + t_{RP} = \frac{2L}{c}\frac{1}{1-\frac{u^2}{c^2}} \tag{32.22}$$

We next consider the light beam reflected by the mirror M_2. This case is similar to a ship trying to cross from the point A to the point B when there is current in the river (see Fig. 32.15). Obviously the ship must point slightly to the right so that its trajectory is straight. In the absence of the current, if the speed was V then the actual speed will be $\sqrt{V^2-u^2}$. Thus, the effective speed of the light beam for the path PQ will be $\sqrt{c^2-u^2}$. Similarly, the effective speed of the light beam for the return path QP will also be $\sqrt{c^2-u^2}$. Thus if t_{PQ} and t_{RP} are the time taken for the outward and return trips then

$$t_{PQ} = \frac{L}{\sqrt{c^2-u^2}} \quad \text{and} \quad t_{QR} = \frac{L}{\sqrt{c^2-u^2}}$$

Therefore, the total time for the light beam to travel from P to Q and back will be given by

$$t_2 = t_{PQ} + t_{QR} = \frac{2L}{\sqrt{c^2-u^2}} = \frac{2L}{c}\frac{1}{\sqrt{1-\frac{u^2}{c^2}}} \tag{32.23}$$

Thus,
$$t_2 = \sqrt{1-\frac{u^2}{c^2}}\; t_1 \tag{32.24}$$

and t_2 will always be less than t_1. The time difference $t_1 - t_2$ will be given by

$$\Delta t = t_1 - t_2 = \frac{2L}{c}\left[\left(1-\frac{u^2}{c^2}\right)^{-1} - \left(1-\frac{u^2}{c^2}\right)^{-\frac{1}{2}}\right] \approx \frac{Lu^2}{c^3} \tag{32.25}$$

where we have assumed $u/c \ll 1$ and made a Binomial expansion of the terms inside the square brackets. This will correspond to a path difference of

$$c\Delta t \approx \frac{Lu^2}{c^2} \tag{32.26}$$

If we now rotate the interferometer by exactly 90°, the two beams will exchange their time of traversals and therefore the fringe shift will correspond to twice the path difference given above. Thus, the effective path difference will be

$$2c\Delta t \approx \frac{2Lu^2}{c^2} \tag{32.27}$$

Now a path difference of λ results in shift of one fringe; thus the fractional fringe shift will be

$$\frac{2c\Delta t}{\lambda} \approx \frac{2Lu^2}{\lambda c^2}$$

In one of the experiments carried by Michelson and Morley $L \approx 11$ m, $\lambda \approx 6 \times 10^{-7}$ m and if we assume that the relative velocity of the ether is at least the velocity of the earth (i.e., $u \approx 3 \times 10^4$ km/s), we get

$$\frac{2Lu^2}{\lambda c^2} \approx \frac{2\times(11\,\text{m})\times(3\times10^4\,\text{m/s})^2}{(6\times10^{-7}\,\text{m})\times(3\times10^8\,\text{m/s})^2} \approx 0.4$$

Thus a shift of about 0.4 fringe should have been observed. During 1881–1887, Professor Michelson (along with his colleague Edward Morley) carried out a series of very careful measurements for different orientations of the interferometer and they always got a null result; their apparatus was capable of detecting 0.01 fringe shift. These came to be known as the famous Michelson–Morley experiments which proved that ether did not exist. David Park (Ref. 32.12) has written "*He* (Michelson) *was 34 when he established that ether cannot be found; he made delicate optical measurements for 44 more years and to the end of his days did not believe there could be a wave without some material substance to do the waving*". Stephen Hawking has written (Ref. 32.13):

> *Towards the end of the 19th century scientists believed they were close to a complete description of the universe. They imagined that space was filled everywhere by a continuous medium called the ether. Light rays and radio signals were waves in this ether just as sound is pressure waves in air. All that was needed to complete the theory was careful measurements of the elastic properties of the ether; once they have those nailed down, everything else would fall into place. Soon, however, discrepancies with the idea of an all pervading ether begin to appear. You would expect light to travel at a fixed speed through the ether. So if you were traveling in the same direction as the light, you would expect that its speed would appear to be lower, and if you were traveling in the opposite direction to the light, that its speed would appear to be higher. Yet a series of experiments failed to find any evidence for differences in speed due to motion through the ether.*

32.11 Brief Historical Remarks

The Michelson–Morley experiments were carried out about 20 years before Einstein's 1905 paper on Special Theory of Relativity. Then why did we put this section at the end? When Einstein wrote the famous five papers in 1905, he was working in Swiss Patent office and did not have much discussion with other physicists – he studied on his own and it appears he was not aware of the Michelson–Morley experiments. Professor R.S. Shankland (of Case Institute of Technology at Cleveland, Ohio) had a series of meetings with Einstein in 1950; subsequently, he published an account of his talks with Einstein in American Journal of Physics (see Refs. 32.14 and 32.15). In his interview on February 4, 1950, Shankland asked Einstein as to how he had learnt about the Michelson–Morley experiments. To quote from Shankland's paper

> *... he (Einstein) told me that he had become aware of it through the writings of H.A. Lorentz, but only after 1905 had it come to his attention! "Otherwise," he (Einstein) said, "I would have mentioned it in my paper".*

Casper and Noer (Ref. 32.6) have made a careful study of the history and they write:

> *Einstein was then an unknown physicist, largely self-taught in this area of physics, and in his patent office job somewhat cutoff from the discussions and ideas current in the physics community. He was apparently only vaguely aware of the ether experiments... and he did not know of the later papers of Lorentz and Poincare. ...*

Einstein was of course aware of Maxwell's equations and laws of electricity and magnetism and the fact that Maxwell's equations were not invariant under Galilean transformation*. Physically this implies that if Galilean transformation was correct then (to quote from Ref. 32.5)

> *in a moving space ship the electrical and optical phenomena should be different from those in a stationary ship. Thus one could use these optical phenomena to determine the speed of the ship; in particular one could determine the absolute speed of the ship by making suitable optical and electrical measurements*

Thus, for Einstein, the fundamental question was (to quote from Ref. 32.1)

> *"Why should the laws of electromagnetism and light, alone among the laws of physics, allow the possibility of detecting the motion of an inertial reference frame?"*

Einstein started his 1905 paper by writing (Ref. 32.1)

> *It is well known that Maxwell's electrodynamics — as usually understood at present — when applied to moving bodies, lead to asymmetries that do not seem to be inherent in the phenomena.*

He further wrote (in the same paper)

> *The same laws of electrodynamics and optics will be valid for all coordinate systems...We shall raise this conjecture to the status of a postulate and shall also introduce another postulate, namely that light always propagates in free space with a definite velocity V that is independent of the state of motion of the emitting body.*

The null result of the Michelson–Morley experiment is consistent with Einstein's postulates. Indeed, Einstein wrote

> *The introduction of a 'light ether' will prove to be superfluous in as much as the view to be developed here will not require a 'space at absolute rest' endowed with special properties.*

* In Appendix E, we have shown that the scalar wave equation is invariant under Lorentz transformation; if instead we use Galilean transformation of coordinates, the wave equation will not have the same form.

PROBLEMS

32.1 At a height of about 3 km above sea level, about 1000 mu–mesons were detected in 1 hour. Calculate the number that will decay before they reach sea level. Assume that the mean lifetime of the mu–meson is about 2.2 μs and that their velocity about $0.9c$.

32.2 At a height of about 1.2 km, about 550 mu–mesons were detected in 1 hour and at the base about 420 mu–mesons were detected in 1 hour. Assuming that the mean lifetime of the mu–meson is about 2.2 μs, calculate their velocity.

[**Ans:** $\approx 0.99c$]

32.3 In an experiment, the measured lifetime of the negatively charged mu–meson was found to be 32 μ*s*. Calculate the velocity of the mu–meson; the mean proper lifetime for the mu–meson may be assumed to be = 2.195 μs.

32.4 A motor car of "proper length" 5 meters is passing by with a speed of 200 km/hr. (a) Calculate the contracted length observed by a person standing on the road. (b) Calculate the contracted length if the velocity of the car was $0.99c$.

32.5 We assume the planet Venus to be at a distance of about 60 million km from the Earth. We assume a spacecraft moving with a speed of 30 km/s. (a) For an observer on Earth, calculate the time that the spacecraft will take for making the roundtrip from earth to Venus and back. (b) The astronaut inside the spaceship will record a slightly lesser time; calculate the time difference.

[**Ans:** (a) 46 days, (b) 0.02 s]

32.6 A and B are twins. B enters a spacecraft (see Fig. 32.10) and synchronizes his watch with $A(t = t' = 0)$. The spacecraft closes and quickly accelerates to a velocity given by

$$u = \sqrt{\frac{15}{16}}\, c \approx 0.9682c$$

The spacecraft goes to a nearby star 10 light years away and promptly returns to earth with the same speed. What will be the age difference between A and B.

32.7 A and B are twins. B enters a spacecraft (see Fig. 32.10) and synchronizes his watch with $A(t = t' = 0)$. The spacecraft closes and quickly accelerates to the same velocity as in the previous problem ($\approx 0.9682c$). The spacecraft goes to moon (which is about 384 000 km away) and promptly returns to earth with the same speed. What will be the age difference between A and B.

32.8 Consider an atom (at rest inside a spaceship moving with velocity 3 km/s) emitting simultaneously two photons; the two detectors D_1 and D_2 are at the same distance (= 10 m) from the atom and therefore for an observer B inside the spaceship, the photons are detected simultaneously (see Fig. 32.9). For the observer A on earth calculate the time difference between the two events.

CHAPTER 33

Special Theory of Relativity II: Lorentz Transformations

In the twentieth century, we have been greatly privileged to witness two major revolutions in our physical picture of the world .... We have come to use the term 'relativity' to encompass the first of these revolutions and 'quantum theory' to encompass the second .... It is particularly remarkable that a single physicist – Albert Einstein – had such extraordinary deep perceptions of the workings of Nature that he laid foundation stones for both of these twentieth century revolutions in the single year of 1905.

—Roger Penrose*

LEARNING OBJECTIVES

After reading this chapter, the reader should be able to:

LO 1: *describe Lorentz transformations.*

LO 2: *calculate relative velocities of two objects, and derive the rule for addition of velocities.*

LO 3: *determine transformation laws for the components of the momentum vector.*

33.1 Introduction

In this chapter, we will derive expressions for what are known as Lorentz transformations. Using the equations describing Lorentz transformations, we will rederive some of the results obtained in previous chapters including time dilation, Doppler shifted frequencies, etc. In Appendix E, we have shown the invariance of the wave equation under Lorentz transformations.

33.2 The Lorentz Transformations

LO1

The observer A is on the platform and the observer B is inside a train which is moving with velocity u in the $+x$ direction with respect to A (see Fig. 33.1). Let t and t' be the times measured by A and B and we assume that the two clocks are synchronized such that at $t = t' = 0$, the origin O coincides with the origin O'.

* Roger Penrose wrote this in the Foreword of the book by John Stachel (Ref. 33.1).

Above Image: The first atomic explosion on July 16, 1945.

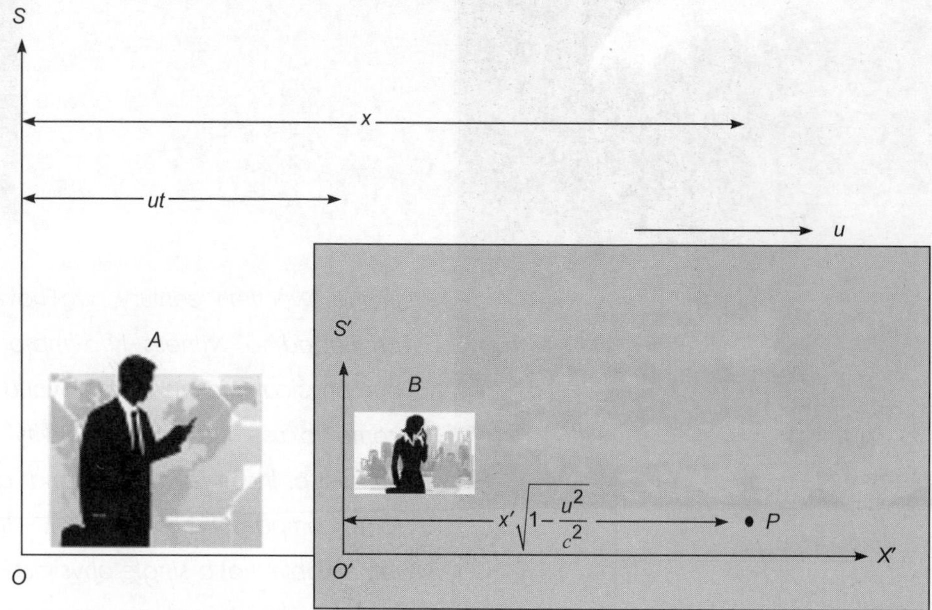

Figure 33.1
An event occurs at the point *P*; for *A*, the event occurs at time *t* at a distance *x* from *O*. For *B*, the event occurs at a distance *x*′ from *O*′ which *A* sees as a contracted distance as shown in the figure.

A certain event occurs at the point *P*; the event could be like the switching on of a light bulb. For *A* the event occurs at time t at a distance of x from the origin (see Fig. 33.1). In this time (according to *A*), O' has moved through a distance ut. Now, according to *B*, the distance of the point *P* from her origin is x', which *A* observes as the contracted distance x'/γ where γ is the Lorentz factor defined in Eq. (32.4). Thus according to *A*

$$x = ut + \frac{x'}{\gamma} \quad \Rightarrow \quad x' = \gamma(x - ut) \qquad \textbf{(33.1)}$$

For *B*, *A* is moving with speed u in the minus x direction and the event occurs at time t' at a distance x' from O'. In this time (according to *B*), the origin O has moved through a distance $-ut'$. Since the distance x is measured by *A*, *B* will measure the contracted distance x/γ. Thus (see Fig. 33.2)

$$x' = \frac{x}{\gamma} - ut' \quad \Rightarrow \quad x = \gamma(x' + ut') \qquad \textbf{(33.2)}$$

In the above equation, we substitute for x' from Eq. (33.1) and simplify to obtain

$$t' = \gamma\left(t - \frac{ux}{c^2}\right) \qquad \textbf{(33.3)}$$

If we substitute for x from Eq. (33.2) in Eq. (33.1), we would obtain

$$t = \gamma\left(t' + \frac{ux'}{c^2}\right) \qquad \textbf{(33.4)}$$

Equations (33.1)–(33.4) along with the equations $y' = y$ and $z' = z$ describe what are known as **Lorentz transformations**. Using these equations, we will derive some of the results that were obtained in Chapter 32.

We consider two events; in the reference frame S the two events occur at (x_1, t_1) and (x_2, t_2) and in the reference frame S' the two events occur at (x_1', t_1') and (x_2', t_2'). Using Eq. (33.1)

$$x_1' = \gamma(x_1 - ut_1) \quad \text{and} \quad x_2' = \gamma(x_2 - ut_2)$$

and therefore

$$\Delta x' = x_2' - x_1' = \gamma(\Delta x - u\Delta t) \qquad \textbf{(33.5)}$$

We consider three cases:

(i) If the two events take place at the same place in the S' frame then $\Delta x' = 0$ [see Fig. 32.2] and therefore $\Delta x = u\Delta t$ [see Fig. 32.3]. Further, using Eq. (33.4)

$$t_1 = \gamma\left(t_1' + \frac{ux_1'}{c^2}\right) \quad \text{and} \quad t_2 = \gamma\left(t_2' + \frac{ux_2'}{c^2}\right)$$

we have

$$\Delta t = t_2 - t_1 = \gamma\left(\Delta t' + \frac{u\Delta x'}{c^2}\right) \qquad \textbf{(33.6)}$$

Since the two events take place at the same place in the S' frame, $\Delta x' = 0$ and we obtain

$$\Delta t = \gamma\Delta t' \qquad \textbf{(33.7)}$$

which expresses time dilation and is the same as Eq. (32.3).

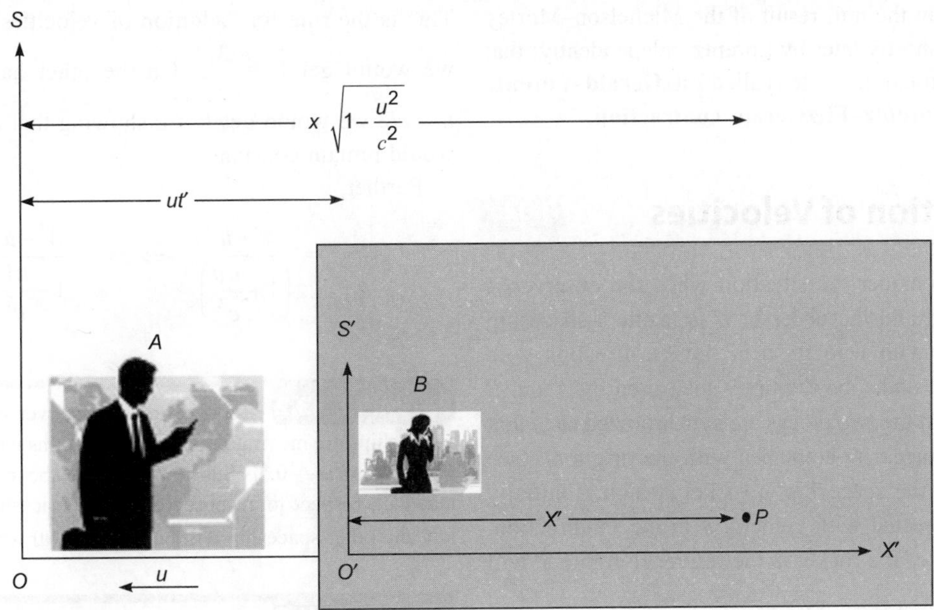

Figure 33.2
For *B*, *A* is moving with speed *u* in the –*x* direction. For *B*, the event occurs at time *t′* at a distance *x′* from *O′*. For *A*, the event occurs at a distance *x* from *O* which *B* sees as a contracted distance as shown in the figure.

(ii) We next consider two events which occur at the same time in the reference frame S' but at points separated by $2L_0$ (see Fig. 32.9). Thus in Eq. (33.6) we must substitute $\Delta t' = 0$ and $\Delta x' = 2L_0$ to obtain

$$\Delta t = \gamma L_0 \frac{2u}{c^2} \tag{33.8}$$

Thus whereas the two events are simultaneous in the reference frame S', they are not simultaneous in the reference frame S. We had obtained the same result in Sec. 32.8.

(iii) We next consider the two events discussed in Sec. 32.5; the two events occur at the same space point G in the S' frame [see Fig. 32.5]. If we use Eq. (33.3), we get

$$\Delta t' = t_2' - t_1' = \gamma\left(\Delta t - \frac{u\Delta x}{c^2}\right) = \gamma\left(\gamma\Delta t' - \frac{u\Delta x}{c^2}\right) \tag{33.9}$$

where we have used Eq. (33.15). Now $\Delta x = L_0$ [see Fig. 32.5] and therefore Eq. (33.9) would give us

$$\gamma \frac{uL_0}{c^2} = (\gamma^2 - 1)\Delta t' = \frac{\frac{u^2}{c^2}}{1-\frac{u^2}{c^2}}\Delta t'$$

$$\Rightarrow \sqrt{1-\frac{u^2}{c^2}}\, L_0 = u\Delta t' = L$$

where $L = u\Delta t'$ represents the length measured in the S' frame. The above equation describes the length contraction that we had derived in Sec. 32.5.

EXAMPLE 33.1 If we use Eqs. (33.2) and (33.4), we readily get

$$x^2 - c^2t^2 = \gamma^2\left[(x' + ut')^2 - c^2\left(t' + \frac{ux'}{c^2}\right)^2\right] = x'^2 - c^2t'^2$$

If we now use the equations $y' = y$ and $z' = z$, we would get

$$x^2 + y^2 + z^2 - c^2t^2 = x'^2 + y'^2 + z'^2 - c^2t'^2 \tag{33.10}$$

Consider a point source of light at the origin in the S frame. If the source of light emits a pulse, the light wave will spread out as a sphere whose radius will be equal to ct; thus the sphere will be described by the equation

$$x^2 + y^2 + z^2 = c^2t^2 \tag{33.11}$$

Because of Eq. (33.10) we will have

$$x'^2 + y'^2 + z'^2 = c^2t'^2 \tag{33.12}$$

which describes a sphere (of radius ct') in the S' frame. Thus, it must be a spreading sphere in the S' frame also; in fact the coordinate transformation in which this condition is satisfied is called the Lorentz transformation.

Equations describing Lorentz transformations were put forward by Lorentz much before Einstein. Lorentz (and later Poincare) had shown that Maxwell's equations are invariant under Lorentz transformations; in Appendix E we have shown the invariance of the wave equation under Lorentz transformations. In his 1905 paper, Einstein (using his two postulates) derived Eqs. (33.1) – (33.4) but he made no mention of Lorentz's work. Many feel that Einstein was probably not aware of the work of Lorentz. Even the length contraction (discussed in Sec. 32.5) was first suggested by FitzGerald in 1889 (to explain the null result of the Michelson–Morley experiment) and shortly later by Lorentz independently; that is why length contraction is often called **FitzGerald–Lorentz contraction or Lorentz–FitzGerald contraction.**

33.3 Addition of Velocities

LO2

Once again we consider the situation when the observer A is on the platform and the observer B is inside a spaceship which is moving with velocity u in the $+x$ direction with respect to A. Let t and t' be the times measured by A and B and we assume that the two clocks are synchronized such that at $t = t' = 0$, the origin O coincides with the origin O' (see Fig. 33.3). Inside the spaceship, a rocket (which is initially at the origin) is ejected with velocity v in the $+x$ direction. The displacement of the rocket in the reference frame S' will be given by

$$x' = vt' \;\Rightarrow\; x = \gamma(v + u)t' \qquad \textbf{(33.13)}$$

where we have used Eq. (33.2). If we now substitute the above equation in Eq. (33.4) we will get

$$t = \gamma\left(1 + \frac{uv}{c^2}\right)t' \qquad \textbf{(33.14)}$$

We divide Eq. (33.13) by Eq. (33.14) to obtain the following expression for the velocity of the rocket as seen by the observer in the reference frame S:

$$V = \frac{x}{t} = \frac{v + u}{\left(1 + \frac{uv}{c^2}\right)} \qquad \textbf{(33.15)}$$

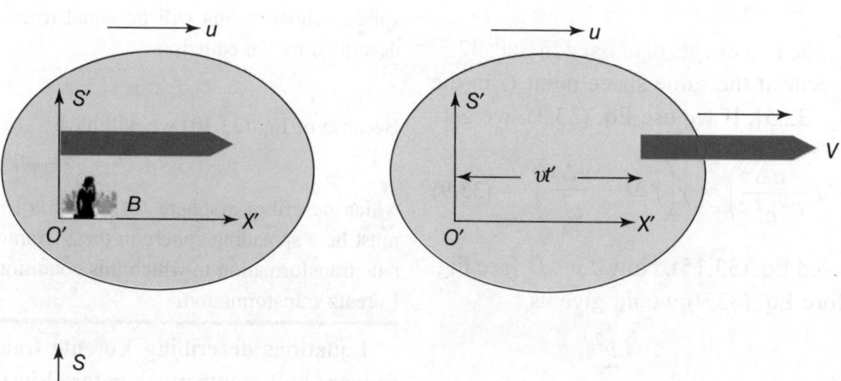

Figure 33.3
A spaceship moving (in the +x direction) with velocity *u* relative to A (the observer on the ground). A rocket is ejected out of the spaceship with velocity v relative to *B* (who is inside the spaceship). Relative to A (the observer on the ground), the velocity of the rocket is *V*.

This is the rule for "addition of velocities". If $v = u = c/3$, we would get $V = \frac{3}{5}c$. On the other hand, if $v = c$ and $u = c/2$ we would get $V = c$ showing that the speed of light would remain constant.

Further,

$$V = \frac{v + u}{\left(1 + \frac{uv}{c^2}\right)} \;\Rightarrow\; v = \frac{V - u}{1 - \frac{uV}{c^2}} \qquad \textbf{(33.16)}$$

EXAMPLE 33.2 Relative to the observer on the ground, two space ships are moving in opposite directions with speed $0.5c$. Thus $V = 0.5c$ and $u = -0.5c$. Substituting in the above equation, we obtain that with respect to an observer in the spaceship moving towards left, the other spaceship will be moving with velocity $0.8c$.

EXAMPLE 33.3 A light beam is propagating (in the $+x$ direction) through glass with velocity c/n. If the whole glass slab is inside a train which is moving with velocity u (in the $+x$ direction), then the velocity of light as measured by an observer on the platform will be

$$V = \frac{\frac{c}{n} + u}{\left(1 + \frac{u}{nc}\right)} \qquad \textbf{(33.17)}$$

When $u/c << 1$, we may carry out a binomial expansion to obtain

$$V = \left(\frac{c}{n} + u\right)\left[1 - \frac{u}{nc} + \left(\frac{u}{nc}\right)^2 + \ldots\right]$$

$$\approx \frac{c}{n} + u\left(1 - \frac{1}{n^2}\right) + \ldots \approx \frac{c}{n}(1 \pm g) \qquad \textbf{(33.18)}$$

where

$$g = \frac{n|u|}{c}\left(1 - \frac{1}{n^2}\right) \tag{33.19}$$

In Eq. (33.18), we must take the positive sign if the light beam is propagating along the motion of the medium and we must take the negative sign if the light beam is propagating in a direction opposite to the motion of the medium.

EXAMPLE 33.4 **The Fizaeu Experiment:** In 1851, the French physicist Hippolyte Fizaeu carried out the experiment to show that the speed of light (in water) is greater when the water flows along the direction of propagation of light in comparison to when the water flows opposite to the direction of propagation of light. A schematic of the apparatus is shown in Fig. 33.4. A beam of monochromatic light is split by a beam splitter (which is nothing but a partially silvered mirror); the beam transmitted through the beam splitter propagates along the flow of water and the beam reflected by the beam splitter propagates in a direction opposite to the flow of water. If V_p represents the velocity of light when it propagates parallel to the flow of water, V_a represents the velocity of light when it propagates anti-parallel to the flow of water and if L represents the length of the moving water column, then the time difference between the two beams will be given by

$$\Delta t \approx \frac{L}{V_a} - \frac{L}{V_p} \approx L\frac{n}{c}\left(\frac{1}{1-g} - \frac{1}{1+g}\right) \approx L\frac{n}{c}2g \tag{33.20}$$

We assume $L = 12$ m, $n = 1.33$ (water), $u = 5$ m/s then $g \approx 10^{-8}$. If we now use the above equation, we would get $\Delta t \approx 10^{-15}$ s. Thus, if the wavelength is $\lambda_0 \approx 6000$ Å $= 6 \times 10^{-7}$ m then the frequency will be $\nu \approx 0.5 \times 10^{15}$ s^{-1} and the phase shift will be $\approx 0.5 \approx \pi/6$ which is measurable.

33.4 Transformation Laws for the Components of the Momentum Vector

LO3

If p_x, p_y and p_z represent respectively the x, y and z components of the photon in the S frame and E the corresponding energy, then since the rest mass of the photon is zero, we have [see Eq. (31.16)]:

$$p_x^2 + p_y^2 + p_z^2 = \frac{E^2}{c^2} \tag{33.21}$$

If p'_x, p'_y and p'_z represent the components of the momentum of the photon in the S' frame and E' the corresponding energy, then

$$p'^2_x + p'^2_y + p'^2_z = \frac{E'^2}{c^2} \tag{33.22}$$

If we compare the above two equations with Eqs. (33.11) and (33.12), we can conclude that for Eqs. (33.21) and (33.22) to remain valid in all inertial frames, p_x, p_y, p_z and E/c^2 must transform in the same way as x, y, z and t. Thus we may replace x, y, z and t by p_x, p_y, p_z and E/c^2 in Eqs. (33.1)–(33.4) to obtain:

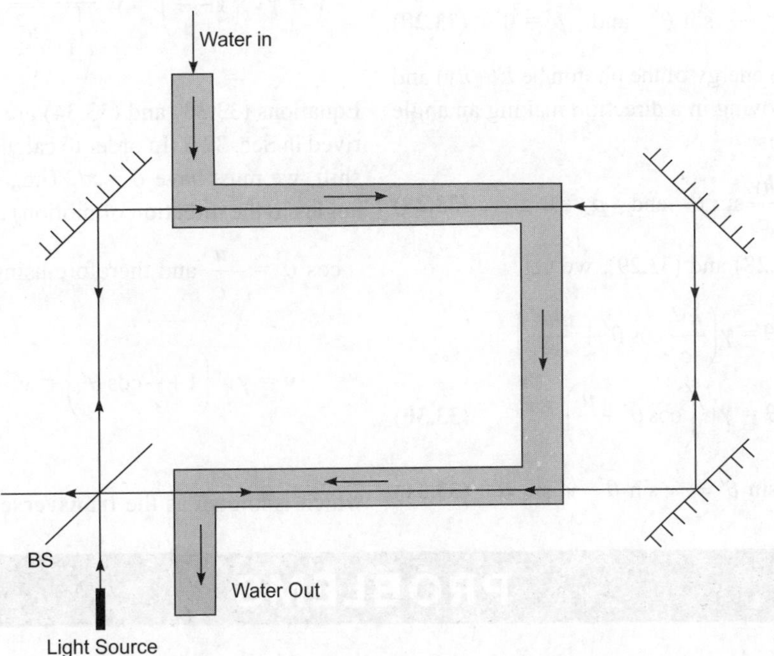

Figure 33.4
An experimental arrangement to determine the speed of light in a moving medium; BS represents a beam splitter. The beam reflected by the beam-splitter travels in a direction opposite to the flow of water. The beam transmitted by the beam-splitter travels in a direction parallel to the flow of water.

$$p'_x = \gamma\left(p_x - \frac{uE}{c^2}\right); \quad (33.23)$$

$$E' = \gamma(E - up_x); \quad (33.24)$$

$$p_x = \gamma\left(p'_x + \frac{uE'}{c^2}\right); \quad (33.25)$$

$$E = \gamma(E' + up'_x); \quad (33.26)$$

We will also have $p'_y = p_y$ and $p'_z = p_z$. Simple manipulations of the above equations will give:

$$p_x^2 + p_y^2 + p_z^2 - \frac{E^2}{c^2} = p'^2_x + p'^2_y + p'^2_z - \frac{E'^2}{c^2} \quad (33.27)$$

$$\Rightarrow p^2c^2 + m_0^2c^4 - E^2 = p'^2c^2 + m_0^2c^4 - E'^2$$

Thus, the relation $E^2 = p^2c^2 + m_0^2c^4$ is valid for all particles in all inertial frames.

33.5 Longitudinal and Transverse Doppler Shift

As before, we assume that the S' frame is moving (relative to the S frame) with velocity u along the $+x$ direction and that the two clocks are synchronized such that at $t = t' = 0$, the origin O coincides with the origin O'. We have a source of light at rest at the origin of the S' frame; let $E'(= h\nu')$ and $p'(= h\nu'/c)$ represent the energy and momentum of the photon moving (in the S' frame) in a direction making an angle of θ' with the x-axis; thus

$$p'_x = \frac{h\nu'}{c}\cos\theta';\ p'_y = \frac{h\nu'}{c}\sin\theta' \text{ and } p'_z = 0 \quad (33.28)$$

In the S frame, let the energy of the photon be $E(= h\nu)$ and momentum $p(= h\nu/c)$ moving in a direction making an angle of θ with the x-axis; thus

$$p_x = \frac{h\nu}{c}\cos\theta;\ p_y = \frac{h\nu}{c}\sin\theta \text{ and } p_z = 0 \quad (33.29)$$

Using Eqs. (33.25), (33.28) and (33.29), we get

$$p_x = \frac{h\nu}{c}\cos\theta = \gamma\left(\frac{h\nu'}{c}\cos\theta' + \frac{uh\nu'}{c^2}\right)$$

$$\Rightarrow \nu\cos\theta = \gamma\nu'\left(\cos\theta' + \frac{u}{c}\right) \quad (33.30)$$

$$p_y = \frac{h\nu}{c}\sin\theta = \frac{h\nu'}{c}\sin\theta' \Rightarrow \nu\sin\theta = \nu'\sin\theta' \quad (33.31)$$

Using Eq. (33.26) we get

$$E = h\nu = \gamma\left(h\nu' + u\frac{h\nu'}{c}\cos\theta'\right)$$

$$\Rightarrow \nu = \gamma\nu'\left(1 + \frac{u}{c}\cos\theta'\right) \quad (33.32)$$

Dividing Eq. (33.30) by Eq. (33.32), we get

$$\cos\theta = \left(\frac{\cos\theta' + \frac{u}{c}}{1 + \frac{u}{c}\cos\theta'}\right) \quad (33.33)$$

Thus when $\theta = 0$, then $\theta' = 0$ [which also follows from Eq. (33.31)], and

$$\nu = \gamma\nu'\left(1 + \frac{u}{c}\right) = \nu'\frac{1 + \frac{u}{c}}{\sqrt{1 - \frac{u^2}{c^2}}} = \nu'\sqrt{\frac{1 + \frac{u}{c}}{1 - \frac{u}{c}}} \quad (33.34)$$

which is the expression for the longitudinal Doppler effect derived in section 31.5; the above corresponds to the source moving towards the observer. For the source moving away from the observer, $\theta = \pi = \theta'$ and we have the red shifted frequency:

$$\nu = \gamma\nu'\left(1 - \frac{u}{c}\right) = \nu'\frac{1 - \frac{u}{c}}{\sqrt{1 - \frac{u^2}{c^2}}} = \nu'\sqrt{\frac{1 - \frac{u}{c}}{1 + \frac{u}{c}}} \quad (33.35)$$

Equations (33.33) and (33.34) are identical to the results derived in Sec. 32.3. In order to calculate the transverse Doppler shift, we must have $\theta = \pi/2$ (i.e., light must be seen at right angles to the direction of motion) and thus using Eq. (33.30):

$\cos\theta' = -\frac{u}{c}$ and therefore using Eq. (33.32), we get

$$\nu = \gamma\nu'\left(1 + \frac{u}{c}\cos\theta'\right) = \nu'\frac{1 - \frac{u^2}{c^2}}{\sqrt{1 - \frac{u^2}{c^2}}} = \nu'\sqrt{1 - \frac{u^2}{c^2}}$$

which is known as the **transverse Doppler shift**.

PROBLEMS

33.1 For an observer on the platform, a train is moving with speed $0.5c$ along the $+x$ direction. Inside the train, an object is moving with speed $0.5c$ along the $+x$ direction. What will be the speed of the object for an observer on the platform?

[**Ans:** $0.8c$]

33.2 A spaceship is moving (in the $+x$ direction) with velocity $0.4c$ relative to the observer on the ground. Another spaceship is moving with velocity $0.3c$ (in the $-x$ direction) relative to the observer on the ground. What would be the speed of the second space ship as observed by the observer inside the first spaceship?

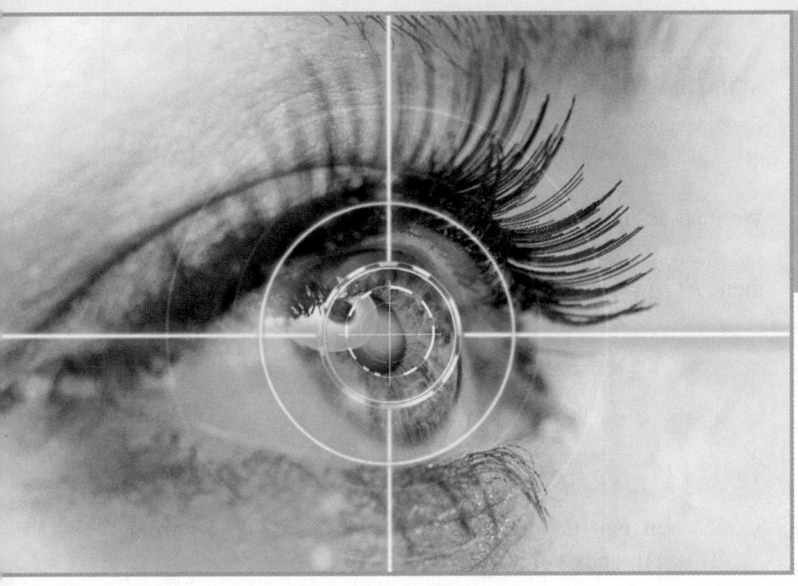

APPENDIX

A

Few Mathematical Formulae

A.1 Gamma Functions and Integrals Involving Gaussian Functions

We will first show that

$$\int_{-\infty}^{+\infty} e^{-\alpha x^2+\beta x} dx = \sqrt{\frac{\pi}{\alpha}} \exp\left[\frac{\beta^2}{4\alpha}\right]; \text{Re}\, \alpha > 0 \quad \textbf{(A.1)}$$

We consider the integral

$$I = \int_{-\infty}^{+\infty} e^{-x^2} dx \quad \textbf{(A.2)}$$

Thus, $$I^2 = \int_{-\infty}^{+\infty} e^{-x^2} dx \int_{-\infty}^{+\infty} e^{-y^2} dy = \int_{-\infty}^{+\infty}\int_{-\infty}^{+\infty} e^{-(x^2+y^2)} dxdy$$

Transforming to polar coordinates we get

$$I^2 = \int_0^{+\infty} e^{-r^2}\, r\, dr \int_0^{2\pi} d\theta = \left[-\frac{1}{2}e^{-r^2}\right]_0^{\infty} \times 2\pi = \pi$$

Thus, $$I = \int_{-\infty}^{+\infty} e^{-x^2} dx = \sqrt{\pi} \quad \textbf{(A.3)}$$

Now, $$\int_{-\infty}^{+\infty} e^{-\alpha x^2+\beta x} dx = \exp\left[\frac{\beta^2}{4\alpha}\right] \int_{-\infty}^{+\infty} \exp\left[-\alpha\left(x - \frac{\beta}{2\alpha}\right)^2\right] dx$$

$$= \exp\left[\frac{\beta^2}{4\alpha}\right] \int_{-\infty}^{+\infty} e^{-\alpha z^2} dz$$

where $z = x - \dfrac{\beta}{2\alpha}$. Using Eq. (A.3) we get

$$\int_{-\infty}^{+\infty} e^{-\alpha z^2} dz = \sqrt{\frac{\pi}{\alpha}} \quad \textbf{(A.4)}$$

using which we obtain Eq. (A.1). We also get

$$\sqrt{\pi} = 2\int_0^{+\infty} e^{-x^2} dx = \int_0^{+\infty} \xi^{-1/2} e^{-\xi}\, d\xi \quad \text{where } \xi \equiv x^2$$

Thus, $$\Gamma\left(\frac{1}{2}\right) = \sqrt{\pi} \quad \textbf{(A.5)}$$

where $\Gamma(z)$ is defined through the equation

$$\Gamma(z) = \int_0^{+\infty} x^{z-1} e^{-x}\, dx \quad \text{Re}\, z > 0 \quad \textbf{(A.6)}$$

For Re $z > 1$, if we integrate by parts we would obtain

$$\Gamma(z) = (z-1)\Gamma(z-1) \quad \textbf{(A.7)}$$

Since $$\Gamma(1) = \int_0^{+\infty} e^{-x}\, dx = 1$$

we obtain $$\Gamma(n+1) = n!; \quad n = 0, 1, 2, \ldots \quad \textbf{(A.8)}$$

Further since $\Gamma\left(\frac{1}{2}\right) = \sqrt{\pi}$, we obtain

$$\Gamma\left(\frac{3}{2}\right)=\frac{1}{2}\Gamma\left(\frac{1}{2}\right)=\frac{1}{2}\sqrt{\pi};\ \Gamma\left(\frac{5}{2}\right)=\frac{3}{2}\Gamma\left(\frac{3}{2}\right)=\frac{3}{2}\cdot\frac{1}{2}\sqrt{\pi};$$
$$\Gamma\left(\frac{7}{2}\right)=\frac{5}{2}\cdot\frac{3}{2}\cdot\frac{1}{2}\sqrt{\pi} \qquad \textbf{(A.9)}$$

etc. Finally for $n = 0, 1, 2, \ldots$

$$\int_{-\infty}^{+\infty} x^{2n}e^{-x^2}dx=\Gamma\left(n+\frac{1}{2}\right)=\frac{1.3.5\ldots(2n-1)\sqrt{\pi}}{2^n} \qquad \textbf{(A.10)}$$

and $$\int_{-\infty}^{+\infty} x^{2n+1}e^{-x^2}dx=0 \qquad \textbf{(A.11)}$$

A.2 Evaluation of the integral $\int_{-\infty}^{+\infty}\frac{\sin gx}{x}dx$

The Laplace transform of a function $f(x)$ is defined by the following equation

$$F(p) = L[f(x)] = \int_0^\infty e^{-px}f(x)dx \qquad \textbf{(A.12)}$$

Now, $\int_s^\infty F(p)dp=\int_s^\infty\int_0^\infty e^{-px}f(x)dx\,dp=\int_0^\infty dx\,f(x)\left[\int_s^\infty e^{-px}dp\right]$

Carrying out the integration over p, we get

$$\int_s^\infty F(p)dp=\int_0^\infty\frac{f(x)}{x}e^{-sx}dx \qquad \textbf{(A.13)}$$

In the limit of $s \to 0$, we obtain

$$\int_0^\infty F(p)dp=\int_0^\infty\frac{f(x)}{x}dx \qquad \textbf{(A.14)}$$

We next assume $f(x) = \sin gx$; $g > 0$

then $$F(p)=\int_0^\infty \sin gx\, e^{-px}dx=\frac{1}{2i}\int_0^\infty[e^{-(p-ig)x}-e^{-(p+ig)x}]dx$$
$$=\frac{1}{2i}\left[\frac{1}{p-ig}-\frac{1}{p+ig}\right]=\frac{g}{p^2+g^2}$$

Thus, $$\int_0^\infty F(p)dp=g\int_0^\infty\frac{dp}{p^2+g^2}=\int_0^\infty\frac{dx}{1+x^2};\ x=\frac{p}{g}$$
$$=\tan^{-1}x\Big|_0^\infty=\frac{\pi}{2};\quad g>0$$

Obviously, for $g < 0$ the above integral is $-\pi/2$. Thus, we get

$$\left.\begin{aligned}\int_0^\infty\frac{\sin gx}{x}dx &= \frac{\pi}{2};\quad g>0\\ &= 0;\quad g=0\\ &= -\frac{\pi}{2};\quad g<0\end{aligned}\right\} \qquad \textbf{(A.15)}$$

The integrand is an even function of x; thus

$$\int_{-\infty}^{+\infty}\frac{\sin gx}{\pi x}dx=\frac{2}{\pi}\int_0^\infty\frac{\sin gx}{x}dx=1;\quad (g>0) \qquad \textbf{(A.16)}$$

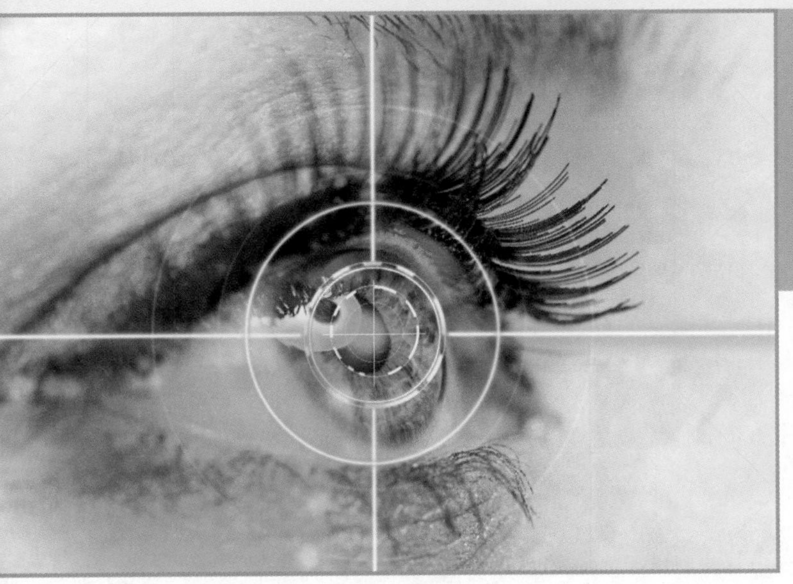

APPENDIX

B

Diffraction of a Gaussian Beam

If the amplitude and phase distribution on the plane $z = 0$ is given by $A(\xi, \eta)$ then the diffraction pattern is given by [see Eq. (20.23)].

$$u(x, y, z) \approx -\frac{i}{\lambda z} \exp(ikz) \iint A(\xi, \eta) \times \exp\left\{+\frac{ik}{2z}[(x-\xi)^2 + (y-\eta)^2]\right\} d\xi\, d\eta \quad \textbf{(B.1)}$$

We consider a Gaussian beam propagating along the z-direction whose amplitude distribution on the plane $z = 0$ is given by

$$A(\xi, \eta) = a \exp\left[-\frac{\xi^2 + \eta^2}{w_0^2}\right] \quad \textbf{(B.2)}$$

implying that the phase front is plane at $z = 0$. Thus at a distance w_0 from the z-axis, the amplitude falls by a factor $1/e$ (i.e., the intensity reduces by a factor $1/e^2$). This quantity w_0 is called the *spot size* of the beam. Substituting Eq. (B.2) in Eq. (B.1), we obtain

$$u(x, y, z) \approx -\frac{ia}{\lambda z} e^{ikz} \int_{-\infty}^{\infty} \exp\left[\frac{ik}{2z}(x-\xi)^2 - \frac{\xi^2}{w_0^2}\right] d\xi \times \int_{-\infty}^{\infty} \exp\left[\frac{ik}{2z}(y-\eta)^2 - \frac{\eta^2}{w_0^2}\right] d\eta$$

or

$$u(x, y, z) \approx -\frac{iae^{ikz}}{\lambda z} e^{\frac{ik}{2z}(x^2+y^2)} \int_{-\infty}^{+\infty} e^{-\alpha\xi^2 + \beta_1\xi} d\xi \times \int_{-\infty}^{+\infty} e^{-\alpha\eta^2 + \beta_2\eta} d\eta \quad \textbf{(B.3)}$$

where

$$\alpha = \frac{1}{w_0^2} - \frac{ik}{2z} = -\frac{ik}{2z}(1 + i\gamma) \quad \textbf{(B.4)}$$

$$\gamma = \frac{\lambda z}{\pi w_0^2} \quad \textbf{(B.5)}$$

$$\beta_1 = -\frac{ikx}{z}, \quad \beta_2 = -\frac{iky}{z}$$

If we now use the integral (see Appendix A)

$$\int_{-\infty}^{+\infty} e^{-\alpha x^2 + \beta x} dx = \sqrt{\frac{\pi}{\alpha}} \exp\left[\frac{\beta^2}{4\alpha}\right] \quad \textbf{(B.6)}$$

we would get

$$u(x, y, z) \approx \frac{a}{(1+i\gamma)} \exp\left[-\frac{x^2+y^2}{w^2(z)}\right] e^{i\Phi} \quad \textbf{(B.7)}$$

where

$$w(z) = w_0[1 + \gamma^2]^{1/2} = w_0\left[1 + \frac{\lambda^2 z^2}{\pi^2 w_0^4}\right]^{1/2} \quad \textbf{(B.8)}$$

and

$$\Phi = kz + \frac{k}{2z}(x^2 + y^2) - \frac{k(x^2+y^2)}{2z(1+\gamma^2)} = kz + \frac{k}{2R(z)}(x^2 + y^2) \quad \textbf{(B.9)}$$

where

$$R(z) \equiv z\left[1 + \frac{1}{\gamma^2}\right] = z\left[1 + \frac{\pi^2 w_0^4}{\lambda^2 z^2}\right] \quad \textbf{(B.10)}$$

A Heuristic Derivation of the Schrödinger Equation and its Physical Interpretations

The simplest type of wave is a plane monochromatic wave described by the wave function

$$\Psi(\mathbf{r},t) = A\exp\left[i(\mathbf{k}\cdot\mathbf{r}-\omega t)\right] \tag{C.1}$$

which represents a disturbance of amplitude A and of wavelength $\lambda = 2\pi/k$ travelling in the direction of its wave vector $\mathbf{k}$ with phase velocity ω/k. If we assume the propagation to be along the x–axis, then $\mathbf{k} = k\hat{\mathbf{x}}$ and we have

$$\Psi(x,t) = A\exp\left[i(kx-\omega t)\right] \tag{C.2}$$

which on using the Einstein equation

$$E = h\nu = \hbar\omega \tag{C.3}$$

and the de-Broglie equation:

$$p = \frac{h}{\lambda} = \hbar k; \quad k = \frac{2\pi}{\lambda} \tag{C.4}$$

takes the form $\Psi(x,t) = A\exp\left[\frac{i}{\hbar}(px - Et)\right]$ (C.5)

Successive differentiation of the above equation (with respect to x) will give us

$$-i\hbar\frac{\partial\Psi}{\partial x} = p\Psi(x,t) \tag{C.6}$$

$$-\frac{\hbar^2}{2m}\frac{\partial^2\Psi}{\partial x^2} = \frac{p^2}{2m}\Psi(x,t) \tag{C.7}$$

Now for a free non-relativistic particle, $E = \dfrac{p^2}{2m}$, and therefore differentiating Eq. (5) with respect to t , we would get

$$i\hbar\frac{\partial\Psi}{\partial t} = E\Psi(x,t) = \frac{p^2}{2m}\Psi(x,t) \tag{C.8}$$

From Eqs. (C.7) and (C.8) we get

$$i\hbar\frac{\partial\Psi}{\partial t} = -\frac{\hbar^2}{2m}\frac{\partial^2\Psi}{\partial x^2} \tag{C.9}$$

which is the one-dimensional time dependent Schrödinger equation for a free particle. In order to solve the above equation we use the method of separation of variables:

$$\Psi(x,t) = \psi(x)T(t) \tag{C.10}$$

Substituting the above solution in Eq. (C.9) and subsequent division by $\psi(x)T(t)$ gives us

$$\frac{i\hbar}{T(t)}\frac{dT(t)}{dt} = -\frac{\hbar^2}{2m}\frac{1}{\psi(x)}\frac{d^2\psi(x)}{dx^2} = E = \frac{p^2}{2m} \quad \textbf{(C.11)}$$

Since the LHS is a function of t alone and the RHS is a function of x alone, each side must be equal to a constant; we have set this constant equal to E; and we have defined $p^2 \equiv 2mE$. Integrating the time dependent part, we readily have

$$T(t) = \text{constant} \times e^{-iEt/\hbar} \quad \textbf{(C.12)}$$

Obviously E has to be real; because if E is complex, the solution will blow up as $t \to +\infty$ or as $t \to -\infty$. From Eq. (C.11) we also have

$$\frac{d^2\psi(x)}{dx^2} + \frac{p^2}{\hbar^2}\psi(x) = 0 \quad \textbf{(C.13)}$$

Integrating the above equation, we get

$$\psi(x) = \text{constant} \times \exp\left(\frac{ipx}{\hbar}\right) \quad \textbf{(C.14)}$$

Obviously E cannot be negative because then p would be imaginary and the solutions will blow up as $x \to +\infty$ or $x \to -\infty$. Thus we must have

(i) $E\left(=\frac{p^2}{2m}\right)$ real and positive, and

(ii) p can take any real value between $-\infty$ and $+\infty$.

We write the solution of Eq. (C.13) as

$$\psi_p(x) = \frac{1}{\sqrt{2\pi\hbar}}\left[\frac{i}{\hbar}px\right] \quad \textbf{(C.15)}$$

which would satisfy [see Eq. (26.15) and Problem 26.6]:

$$\int_{-\infty}^{+\infty} \psi_p^*(x)\psi_{p'}(x)dx = \delta(p-p') \quad \textbf{(C.16)}$$

which represents the orthonormality condition. Thus the complete solution will be

$$\Psi(x,t) = \psi(x)T(t) = \frac{1}{\sqrt{2\pi\hbar}}\exp\left[\frac{i}{\hbar}(px - Et)\right]$$

or
$$\Psi(x,t) = \frac{1}{\sqrt{2\pi\hbar}}\exp\left[\frac{i}{\hbar}\left(px - \frac{p^2}{2m}t\right)\right] \quad \textbf{(C.17)}$$

Since p can take any real value between $-\infty$ and $+\infty$, the most general solution of Eq. (C.9) is

$$\Psi(x,t) = \frac{1}{\sqrt{2\pi\hbar}}\int_{-\infty}^{+\infty} a(p)\exp\left[\frac{i}{\hbar}\left(px - \frac{p^2}{2m}t\right)\right]dp \quad \textbf{(C.18)}$$

We had used the above solution in Chapter 26. If the particle is in a potential field described by the potential energy function $V(x)$, then the total energy will be given by

$$E = \frac{p^2}{2m} + V(x) \quad \textbf{(C.19)}$$

and therefore the equation

$$E\Psi(x,t) = \left[\frac{p^2}{2m} + V(x)\right]\Psi(x,t) \quad \textbf{(C.20)}$$

will give us $$i\hbar\frac{\partial\Psi}{\partial t} = -\frac{\hbar^2}{2m}\frac{\partial^2\Psi}{\partial x^2} + V(x)\Psi(x,t) \quad \textbf{(C.21)}$$

If we use the method of separation of variables to solve Eq. (C.21), we would obtain [cf. Eq. (C.12)]:

$$\Psi(x,t) = \psi(x)e^{-iEt/\hbar} \quad \textbf{(C.22)}$$

where $\psi(x)$ would satisfy the following equation

$$\frac{d^2\psi(x)}{dx^2} + \frac{2m}{\hbar^2}[E - V(x)]\psi(x) = 0 \quad \textbf{(C.23)}$$

which is the time-independent one dimensional Schrödinger equation for a particle in a potential field described by the potential energy function $V(x)$. We have discussed its solutions in Sec. 29.6 for the potential well problem and the linear harmonic oscillator problem.

We can easily extend the analysis to 3 dimensions; instead of Eq. (C.5), we start with Eq. (C.1) and write it in the form

$$\Psi(\mathbf{r},t) = A\exp\left[\frac{i}{\hbar}(\mathbf{p}.\mathbf{r} - Et)\right]$$

$$= A\exp\left[\frac{i}{\hbar}(p_x x + p_y y + p_z z - Et)\right] \quad \textbf{(C.24)}$$

If we follow the same procedure, we will obtain the 3 dimensional time dependent Schrödinger equation for a free particle:

$$i\hbar\frac{\partial\Psi(\mathbf{r},t)}{\partial t} = -\frac{\hbar^2}{2m}\nabla^2\Psi(\mathbf{r},t) \quad \textbf{(C.25)}$$

where $$\nabla^2\Psi = \frac{\partial^2\Psi}{\partial x^2} + \frac{\partial^2\Psi}{\partial y^2} + \frac{\partial^2\Psi}{\partial z^2} \quad \textbf{(C.26)}$$

If the particle is in a potential field described by the potential energy function $V(\mathbf{r})$, then the corresponding Schrödinger equation will be given by

$$i\hbar\frac{\partial\Psi}{\partial t} = -\frac{\hbar^2}{2m}\nabla^2\Psi + V(\mathbf{r})\Psi(\mathbf{r},t) \quad \textbf{(C.27)}$$

The above equation represents the 3-dimensional time dependent Schrödinger equation for a particle in a potential field $V(\mathbf{r})$. We must mention that we have given a very heuristic derivation of the Schrödinger equation - it is far from rigorous! However, results obtained by solving the above equation agree very well with numerous experimental findings. It is for this reason that the Schrödinger equation is widely accepted and has been used to solve (with great success) numerous problems in spectroscopy, nuclear physics, astrophysics, solid state physics etc.

In order to obtain a physical interpretation of the wave function Ψ, we take the complex conjugate of Eq. (C.27) to obtain

$$-i\hbar\frac{\partial\Psi^*}{\partial t} = -\frac{\hbar^2}{2m}\nabla^2\Psi^* + V(\mathbf{r})\Psi^*(\mathbf{r},t) \quad \textbf{(C.28)}$$

where $V(\mathbf{r})$ is assumed to be real. If we multiply Eq. (C.27) by Ψ^* and Eq. (C.28) by Ψ and subtract, we would obtain

$$i\hbar\left[\Psi^*\frac{\partial\Psi}{\partial t} + \Psi\frac{\partial\Psi^*}{\partial t}\right] = -\frac{\hbar^2}{2m}[\Psi^*\nabla^2\Psi - \Psi\nabla^2\Psi^*]$$

$$\text{or, } \frac{\partial}{\partial t}(\Psi^*\Psi) = \frac{i\hbar}{2m}\nabla.[\Psi^*\nabla\Psi - \Psi\nabla\Psi^*]$$

$$= \frac{i\hbar}{2m}\,\text{div}\left[\Psi^*(\text{grad}\,\Psi) - \Psi(\text{grad}\,\Psi^*)\right] \quad \textbf{(C.29)}$$

We can rewrite the above equation in the form

$$\frac{\partial\rho}{\partial t} + \nabla.\mathbf{J} = 0 \quad \textbf{(C.30)}$$

where

$$\rho \equiv \Psi^*\Psi \quad \textbf{(C.31)}$$

$$\nabla.\mathbf{J} = \frac{\partial J_x}{\partial x} + \frac{\partial J_y}{\partial y} + \frac{\partial J_x}{\partial z} \quad \textbf{(C.32)}$$

with

$$J_x = \frac{i\hbar}{2m}\left[\Psi\frac{\partial\Psi^*}{\partial x} - \Psi^*\frac{\partial\Psi}{\partial x}\right];$$

$$J_y = \frac{i\hbar}{2m}\left[\Psi\frac{\partial\Psi^*}{\partial y} - \Psi^*\frac{\partial\Psi}{\partial y}\right] \quad \textbf{(C.33)}$$

and a similar expression for J_z. Equation (C.30) is nothing but the equation of continuity in fluid dynamics where ρ represents the number of particles per unit volume and **J** the current density. Thus we may associate $\Psi^*\Psi$ with *position probability density* in the sense that $\Psi^*\Psi\,d\tau$ will be proportional to the probability of finding the particle in volume element $d\tau$. Now, since the Schrödinger equation is a linear equation, a multiple of Ψ would also be a solution and we may choose the multiplicative constant such that

$$\iiint\Psi^*\Psi\,d\tau = 1 \quad \textbf{Normalization condition} \quad \textbf{(C.34)}$$

where the integration is over the entire space. Equation (C.34) is known as the normalization condition. If the wave function is normalized [i.e. if it satisfies the above equation] then $\Psi^*\Psi\,d\tau$ can be interpreted to represent the probability of finding the particle in the volume element $d\tau$ and Eq. (C.34) implies the fact that the particle has to be found somewhere in space. Further,

$$\mathbf{J} = \frac{i\hbar}{2m}[\Psi\nabla\Psi^* - \Psi^*\nabla\Psi] = \text{Re}\left[\Psi^*\left(\frac{-i\hbar\nabla}{m}\right)\Psi\right]$$

Probability current density (C.35)

By differentiating Eq. (C.24) with respect to x, y and z [and comparing with Eq.(C.6)], one can associate p_x, p_y and p_z with the operators $-i\hbar\frac{\partial}{\partial x}$, $-i\hbar\frac{\partial}{\partial y}$ and $-i\hbar\frac{\partial}{\partial z}$ respectively. Thus we can associate momentum **p** with the operator $-i\hbar\nabla$. Thus the operator $\frac{-i\hbar\nabla}{m}$ can be associated with the velocity **v** of the particle. Now, if ρ represents the density of particles having velocity **v**, the classical expression for the current density would be given by

$$\mathbf{J} = \rho\mathbf{v} \quad \textbf{(C.36)}$$

which is consistent with Eq. (C.35) when we associate the operator $\frac{-i\hbar\nabla}{m}$ with the velocity **v** of the particle.

Finally, Eq. (C.18) gives us

$$\Psi(x,0) = \frac{1}{\sqrt{2\pi\hbar}}\int_{-\infty}^{+\infty} a(p_x)\exp\left[\frac{i}{\hbar}p_x x\right]dp_x \quad \textbf{(C.37)}$$

where we have introduced a subscript x to p to remember that p in Eq. (C.18) represents the x-component of the momentum of the particle. The above equation essentially represents superposition of plane waves with a momentum spread determined by $|a(p_x)|^2$. Further, if $\int_{-\infty}^{+\infty} |\Psi(x,0)|^2\, dx = 1$ then one can easily show that $\int_{-\infty}^{+\infty} |a(p_x)|^2\, dp_x = 1$. This is known as Parseval's theorem – see also Section 26.7.1 and Example 26.2. If we recall the analysis in Sections 8.4 and 26.6, we may infer that if we assume $|\Psi|^2\, dx$ to represent the probability of finding the electron between x and $x + dx$ then, $|a(p_x)|^2\, dp_x$ can be interpreted to represent the probability of finding the (x-component) of the momentum of the electron between p_x and $p_x + dp_x$.

In Sec. 26.7.1 we had discussed the propagation of a Gaussian wave packet for which at (at $t = 0$), the probability of finding the particle between x and $x + dx$ will be given by

$$P(x)dx = |\Psi(x,0)|^2\, dx = \frac{1}{\sqrt{\pi\sigma_0^2}} \exp\left(-\frac{x^2}{\sigma_0^2}\right) dx \tag{C.38}$$

Now $\langle x\rangle = \int_{-\infty}^{+\infty} xP(x)\, dx$

$$= \frac{1}{\sqrt{\pi\sigma_0^2}} \int_{-\infty}^{+\infty} x \exp\left(-\frac{x^2}{\sigma_0^2}\right) dx = 0$$

Further, $\langle x^2\rangle = \int_{-\infty}^{+\infty} x^2 P(x)\, dx$

$$= \frac{1}{\sqrt{\pi\sigma_0^2}} \int_{-\infty}^{+\infty} x^2 \exp\left(-\frac{x^2}{\sigma_0^2}\right) dx = \frac{1}{2}\sigma_0^2$$

Thus $$\Delta x = \sqrt{\langle x^2\rangle - \langle x\rangle^2} = \frac{\sigma_0}{\sqrt{2}} \tag{C.39}$$

Now, in Sec. 26.7.1 we had also calculated $a(p_x)$ and had shown that the probability of finding the (x-component of the) particle's momentum betweenn p_x and $p_x + dp_x$ will be given by

$$P(p_x)dp_x = |a(p_x)|^2\, dp_x$$

$$= \left(\frac{\sigma_0^2}{\delta\hbar^2}\right)^{1/2} \exp\left[-\frac{(p_x - p_0)^2\, \sigma_0^2}{\hbar^2}\right] dp_x \tag{C.40}$$

Thus $\langle p_x\rangle = \int_{-\infty}^{+\infty} p_x P(p_x) dp_x$

$$= \left(\frac{\sigma_0^2}{\pi\hbar^2}\right)^{1/2} \int_{-\infty}^{+\infty} p_x \exp\left[-\frac{(p_x - p_0)^2\, \sigma_0^2}{\hbar^2}\right] dp_x = p_0$$

$$\langle p_x^2\rangle = \int_{-\infty}^{+\infty} p_x^2\, P(p_x) dp_x$$

$$= \left(\frac{\sigma_0^2}{\pi\hbar^2}\right)^{1/2} \int_{-\infty}^{+\infty} p_x^2 \exp\left[-\frac{(p_x - p_0)^2\, \sigma_0^2}{\hbar^2}\right] dp_x$$

$$= p_0^2 + \frac{\hbar^2}{2\sigma_0^2}$$

Therefore $$\Delta p_x = \sqrt{\langle p_x^2\rangle - \langle p_x\rangle^2} = \frac{\hbar}{\sqrt{2}\,\sigma_0} \tag{C.41}$$

Thus we get the uncertainty product $\Delta x\, \Delta p_x = \frac{\hbar}{2}$.

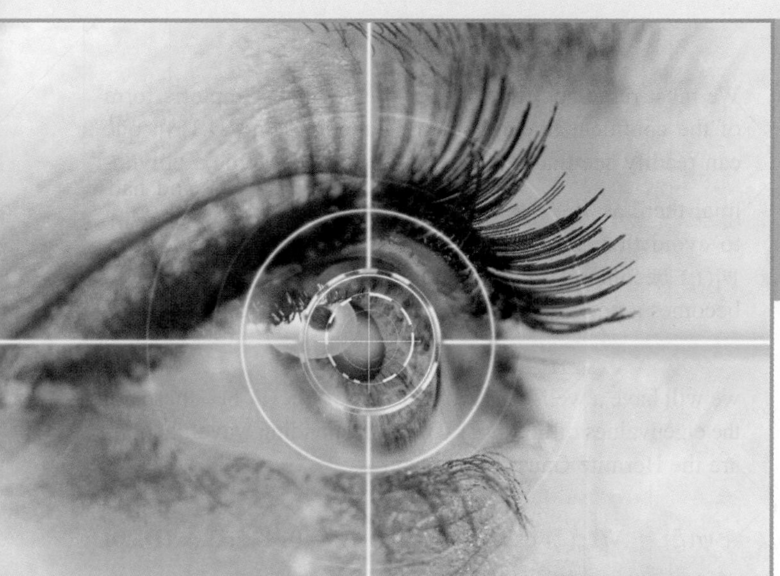

APPENDIX

D

Solution for the Parabolic Index Waveguide

In this appendix, we will show that for the solution of the following equation

$$\frac{d^2\psi}{d\xi^2} + [\Lambda - \xi^2]\psi(\xi) = 0 \quad \textbf{(D.1)}$$

to be well behaved, we must have $\Lambda = 1, 3, 5, 7, ...$; i.e., Λ must be an odd integer. These are the eigenvalues of Eq. (D.1). We introduce the variable

$$\eta = \xi^2 \quad \textbf{(D.2)}$$

Thus,

$$\frac{d\psi}{d\xi} = \frac{d\psi}{d\eta}\frac{d\eta}{d\xi} = \frac{d\psi}{d\eta}2\xi \quad \textbf{(D.3)}$$

and

$$\frac{d^2\psi}{d\xi^2} = 4\eta\frac{d^2\psi}{d\eta^2} + 2\frac{d\psi}{d\eta} \quad \textbf{(D.4)}$$

Substituting in Eq. (D.1), we obtain

$$\frac{d^2\psi}{d\eta^2} + \frac{1}{2\eta}\frac{d\psi}{d\eta} + \left[\frac{\Lambda}{4\eta} - \frac{1}{4}\right]\psi(\eta) = 0 \quad \textbf{(D.5)}$$

In order to determine the asymptotic form, we let $\eta \to \infty$ so that the above equation takes the form

$$\frac{d^2\psi}{d\eta^2} - \frac{1}{4}\psi(\eta) = 0$$

the solution of which would be $e^{\pm\frac{1}{2}\eta}$. This suggests that we try out the following solution

$$\psi(\eta) = y(\eta)\, e^{-\frac{1}{2}\eta} \quad \textbf{(D.6)}$$

Thus,

$$\frac{d\psi}{d\eta} = \left[\frac{dy}{d\eta} - \frac{1}{2}y\right]e^{-\frac{1}{2}\eta} \quad \textbf{(D.7)}$$

and

$$\frac{d^2\psi}{d\eta^2} = \left[\frac{d^2y}{d\eta^2} - \frac{dy}{d\eta} + \frac{1}{4}y(\eta)\right]e^{-\frac{1}{2}\eta} \quad \textbf{(D.8)}$$

Substituting Eqs. (D.7) and (D.8) in Eq. (D.5) we get

$$\eta\frac{d^2y}{d\eta^2} + \left(\frac{1}{2} - \eta\right)\frac{dy}{d\eta} + \frac{\Lambda - 1}{4}y(\eta) = 0 \quad \textbf{(D.9)}$$

Now the confluent hypergeometric equation is given by (see, e.g., Chapter 8 of Ref. 30.6):

$$x\frac{d^2y}{dx^2} + (c - x)\frac{dy}{dx} - a\,y(x) = 0 \quad \textbf{(D.10)}$$

where a and c are constants. For $c \neq 0, \pm1, \pm2, \pm3, \pm4,.....$ the two independent solutions of the above equation are

$$y_1(x) = {}_1F_1(a, c, x) \quad \textbf{(D.11)}$$

and

$$y_2(x) = x^{1-c}\; {}_1F_1(a - c + 1, 2 - c, x) \quad \textbf{(D.12)}$$

where ${}_1F_1(a, c, x)$ is known as the **confluent hypergeometric function** and is defined by the following equation

$$ {}_1F_1(a, c, x) = 1 + \frac{a}{c}\frac{x}{1!} + \frac{a(a+1)}{c(c+1)}\frac{x^2}{2!} + \frac{a(a+1)(a+2)}{c(c+1)(c+2)}\frac{x^3}{3!} + ... \quad \textbf{(D.13)} $$

Obviously, for $a = c$ we will have

$$ {}_1F_1(a, a, x) = 1 + \frac{x}{1!} + \frac{x^2}{2!} + \frac{x^3}{3!} + ... = e^x \quad \textbf{(D.14)} $$

Thus although the series given by Eqs. (D.13) and (D.14) are convergent for all values of x, they would blow up at infinity. Indeed the asymptotic form of ${}_1F_1(a, c, x)$ is given by

$$ {}_1F_1(a, c, x) \underset{x\to\infty}{\rightarrow} \frac{\Gamma(c)}{\Gamma(a)} x^{a-c} e^x \quad \textbf{(D.15)} $$

The confluent hypergeometric series ${}_1F_1(a, c, x)$ is very easy to remember and its asymptotic form is easy to understand. Returning to Eq. (D.9), we find that $y(\eta)$ satisfies the confluent hypergeometric equation with

$$ a = \frac{1-\Lambda}{4} \text{ and } c = \frac{1}{2} \quad \textbf{(D.16)} $$

Thus, the two independent solutions of Eq. (D.1) are

$$ \psi_1(\eta) = {}_1F_1\left(\frac{1-\Lambda}{4}, \frac{1}{2}, \eta\right) e^{-\frac{1}{2}\eta} \quad \textbf{(D.17)} $$

and

$$ \psi_2(\eta) = \sqrt{\eta}\ {}_1F_1\left(\frac{3-\Lambda}{4}, \frac{3}{2}, \eta\right) e^{-\frac{1}{2}\eta} \quad \textbf{(D.18)} $$

We must remember that $\eta = \xi^2$. Using the asymptotic form of the confluent hypergeometric function [Eq. (D.15)], one can readily see that if the series does not become a polynomial then, as $\eta \to \infty$, $\psi(\eta)$ will blow up as $e^{\frac{1}{2}\eta}$. In order to avoid this, the series must become a polynomial. Now $\psi_1(\eta)$ becomes a polynomial for $\Lambda = 1, 5, 9, 13,...$ and $\psi_2(\eta)$ becomes a polynomial for $\Lambda = 3, 7, 11, 15$. Thus, only when

$$ \Lambda = 1, 3, 5, 7, 9,.... \quad \textbf{(D.19)} $$

we will have a well-behaved solution of Eq. (D.1) – these are the eigenvalues of Eq. (D.1). The corresponding wavefunctions are the Hermite Gauss functions:

$$ \psi(\xi) = NH_m(\xi) \exp\left(-\frac{1}{2}\xi^2\right); \quad m = 0, 1, 2, 3,.... \textbf{(D.20)} $$

Indeed

$$ H_n(\xi) = (-1)^{n/2} \frac{n!}{\left(\frac{n}{2}\right)!}\ {}_1F_1\left(-\frac{n}{2}, \frac{1}{2}, \xi^2\right) $$

for $n = 0, 2, 4,....$ **(D.21)**

and

$$ H_n(\xi) = (-1)^{(n-1)2} \frac{n!}{\left(\frac{n-1}{2}\right)!} 2\xi\ {}_1F_1\left(-\frac{n-1}{2}, \frac{3}{2}, \xi^2\right) $$

for $n = 1, 3, 5,....$ **(D.22)**

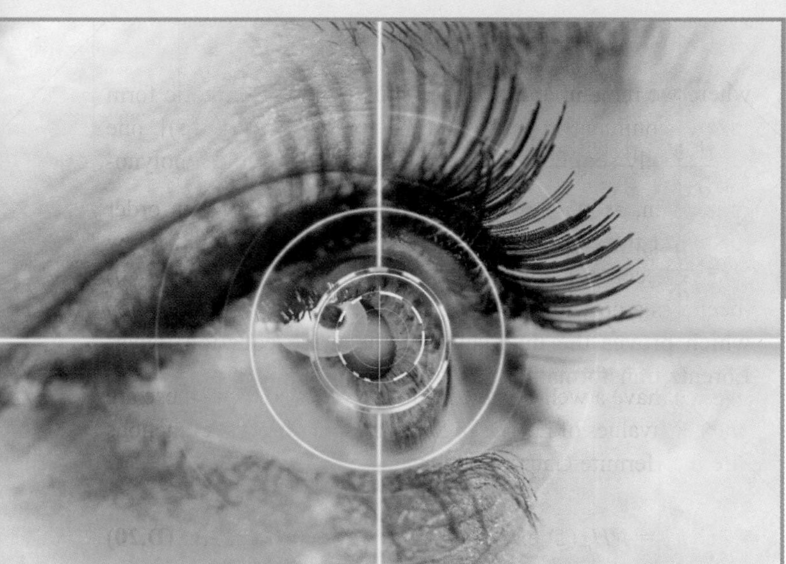

APPENDIX

E

Invariance of the Wave Equation under Lorentz Transformation

In this appendix, we will show that the scalar wave equation

$$\nabla^2 \psi = \frac{1}{c^2}\frac{\partial^2 \psi}{\partial t^2} \quad \textbf{(E.1)}$$

is invariant under Lorentz transformation. In Cartesian coordinates

$$\nabla^2 \psi = \frac{\partial^2 \psi}{\partial x^2} + \frac{\partial^2 \psi}{\partial y^2} + \frac{\partial^2 \psi}{\partial z^2} \quad \textbf{(E.2)}$$

The equations describing Lorentz transformations are given by (see Sec. 33.2)

$$x' = \gamma(x - ut) \quad \textbf{(E.3)}$$

$$t' = \gamma\left(t - \frac{ux}{c^2}\right) \quad \textbf{(E.4)}$$

with $y' = y$ and $z' = z$. In the above equations

$$\gamma = \frac{1}{\sqrt{1 - \dfrac{u^2}{c^2}}} \quad \textbf{(E.5)}$$

is the Lorentz factor. Since $y' = y$ and $z' = z$

$$\frac{\partial^2 \psi}{\partial y^2} = \frac{\partial^2 \psi}{\partial y'^2} \quad \text{and} \quad \frac{\partial^2 \psi}{\partial z^2} = \frac{\partial^2 \psi}{\partial z'^2} \quad \textbf{(E.6)}$$

From Eqs. (E.3) and (E.4)

$$\frac{\partial x'}{\partial x} = \gamma, \quad \frac{\partial t'}{\partial x} = -\frac{\gamma u}{c^2} \quad \textbf{(E.7)}$$

Now,

$$\frac{\partial \psi}{\partial x} = \frac{\partial \psi}{\partial x'}\frac{\partial x'}{\partial x} + \frac{\partial \psi}{\partial y'}\frac{\partial y'}{\partial x} + \frac{\partial \psi}{\partial z'}\frac{\partial z'}{\partial x} + \frac{\partial \psi}{\partial t'}\frac{\partial t'}{\partial x} \quad \textbf{(E.8)}$$

Using Eq. (E.7)

$$\frac{\partial \psi}{\partial x} = \gamma\frac{\partial \psi}{\partial x'} - \frac{\gamma u}{c^2}\frac{\partial \psi}{\partial t'} \quad \textbf{(E.9)}$$

and

$$\frac{\partial^2 \psi}{\partial x^2} = \gamma\left[\frac{\partial^2 \psi}{\partial x'^2}\frac{\partial x'}{\partial x} + \frac{\partial^2 \psi}{\partial x'\partial t'}\frac{\partial t'}{\partial x}\right] - \frac{\gamma u}{c^2}\left[\frac{\partial^2 \psi}{\partial x'\partial t'}\frac{\partial x'}{\partial x} + \frac{\partial^2 \psi}{\partial t'^2}\frac{\partial t'}{\partial x}\right]$$

$$= \gamma^2\frac{\partial^2 \psi}{\partial x'^2} - \frac{2\gamma^2 u}{c^2}\frac{\partial^2 \psi}{\partial x'\partial t'} + \frac{\gamma^2 u^2}{c^4}\frac{\partial^2 \psi}{\partial t'^2} \quad \textbf{(E.10)}$$

From Eqs. (E.3) and (E.4)

$$\frac{\partial x'}{\partial t} = -\gamma u \quad \text{and} \quad \frac{\partial t'}{\partial t} = \gamma \quad \textbf{(E.11)}$$

Thus,

$$\frac{\partial \psi}{\partial t} = \frac{\partial \psi}{\partial x'}\frac{\partial x'}{\partial t} + \frac{\partial \psi}{\partial y'}\frac{\partial y'}{\partial t} + \frac{\partial \psi}{\partial z'}\frac{\partial z'}{\partial t} + \frac{\partial \psi}{\partial t'}\frac{\partial t'}{\partial t}$$

$$= -\gamma u\frac{\partial \psi}{\partial x'} + \gamma\frac{\partial \psi}{\partial t'} \quad \textbf{(E.12)}$$

$$\frac{\partial^2 \psi}{\partial t^2} = -\gamma u\left[\frac{\partial^2 \psi}{\partial x'^2}\frac{\partial x'}{\partial t} + \frac{\partial^2 \psi}{\partial x'\partial t'}\frac{\partial t'}{\partial t}\right] +$$

$$\gamma\left[\frac{\partial^2 \psi}{\partial x'\partial t'}\frac{\partial x'}{\partial t} + \frac{\partial^2 \psi}{\partial t'^2}\frac{\partial t'}{\partial t}\right]$$

$$= +\gamma^2 u^2\frac{\partial^2 \psi}{\partial x'^2} - 2\gamma^2 u\frac{\partial^2 \psi}{\partial x'\partial t'} + \gamma^2\frac{\partial^2 \psi}{\partial t'^2}$$

or, $$\frac{\partial^2 \psi}{\partial x^2} - \frac{1}{c^2}\frac{\partial^2 \psi}{\partial t^2} = \gamma^2\frac{\partial^2 \psi}{\partial x'^2} - \frac{2\gamma^2 u}{c^2}\frac{\partial^2 \psi}{\partial x'\partial t'} + \frac{\gamma^2 u^2}{c^4}\frac{\partial^2 \psi}{\partial t'^2}$$

$$- \frac{\gamma^2 u^2}{c^2}\frac{\partial^2 \psi}{\partial x'^2} + \frac{2\gamma^2 u}{c^2}\frac{\partial^2 \psi}{\partial x'\partial t'} - \frac{\gamma^2}{c^2}\frac{\partial^2 \psi}{\partial t'^2}$$

$$= \frac{\partial^2 \psi}{\partial x'^2} - \frac{1}{c^2}\frac{\partial^2 \psi}{\partial t'^2}$$

where we have used Eq. (E.5). Thus,

$$\frac{\partial^2 \psi}{\partial x^2} + \frac{\partial^2 \psi}{\partial y^2} + \frac{\partial^2 \psi}{\partial z^2} - \frac{1}{c^2}\frac{\partial^2 \psi}{\partial t^2}$$

$$= \frac{\partial^2 \psi}{\partial x'^2} + \frac{\partial^2 \psi}{\partial y'^2} + \frac{\partial^2 \psi}{\partial z'^2} - \frac{1}{c^2}\frac{\partial^2 \psi}{\partial t'^2} \quad \textbf{(E.15)}$$

which proves the invariance of the wave equation under Lorentz transformation.

Multiple-Choice Questions

In this section, a collection of multiple-choice questions from all the topics discussed in this book are presented. Read all the questions carefully and select the correct option. You may use $h \approx 6.6 \times 10^{-34}$ J.s; $c \approx 3 \times 10^8$ m/s; 1 eV $\approx 1.6 \times 10^{-19}$ J

Chapters 1–5

1. The displacement associated with a transverse wave propagating on a string is given by

   $y(x, t) = 0.005 \cos(4\pi x - 200\pi t)$

   where the distances are measured in meters and time in seconds. The velocity of the wave is
   (a) 200 m/s (b) 50 m/s
   (c) 4 m/s (d) 0.02 m/s
2. For an electromagnetic wave propagating in vacuum in the +z direction, the electric field is given by

   $E_x = E_0 \cos[(4 \times 10^6\ \pi)z - \omega t],\ E_y = 0,\ E_z = 0$

   where the distances are measured in meters and time in seconds. The wavelength of the wave (in meters) is
   (a) 0.5×10^{-6} (b) 4×10^6
   (c) 3×10^8 (d) 6×10^{14}
3. For an electromagnetic wave propagating in vacuum in the +z direction, the electric field is given by $E_x = E_0 \cos[(4 \times 10^6\ \pi)z - \omega t]$, $E_y = 0$, $E_z = 0$ where the distances are measured in meters and time in seconds. The frequency ν of the wave (in Hz) is
   (a) 0.5×10^{-6} (b) 4×10^6
   (c) 3×10^8 (d) 6×10^{14}
4. The energy of the photon is given by
   (a) $h\nu$ (b) $h\nu/c$
   (c) ν/c (d) hc/λ
5. The momentum of the photon is given by
   (a) $h\nu$ (b) $h\nu/c$
   (c) ν/c (d) hc/λ
6. The ray paths in a continuously varying refractive index, $n(x)$ are determined by the solution of the ray equation given by

   $$\frac{d^2x}{dz^2} = G\frac{dn^2}{dx}$$

   where the constant G is given by
   (a) $\dfrac{1}{\tilde{\beta}^2}$ (b) $\dfrac{1}{2\tilde{\beta}^2}$
   (c) $2\tilde{\beta}^2$ (d) $2\tilde{\beta}$

   and $\tilde{\beta} = n(x) \cos \theta(x)$ is the invariant of the ray path.
7. For a refractive index variation given by $n^2(x) = n_1^2 - \gamma^2 x^2$, the solution of the ray equation is given by $x(z) = x_0 \sin(\Gamma z)$. The quantity Γ is given by
   (a) $\dfrac{2\gamma}{\tilde{\beta}^2}$ (b) $\dfrac{\gamma}{\tilde{\beta}^2}$
   (c) $\dfrac{\gamma}{\tilde{\beta}}$ (d) $\dfrac{2\gamma}{\tilde{\beta}}$
8. For a refractive index variation given by $n^2(x) = n_1^2 - \gamma^2 x^2$, the solution of the ray equation is given by $x(z) = x_0 \sin(\Gamma z)$. The quantity x_0 is given by
   (a) $\dfrac{1}{\gamma}\sqrt{n_1^2 - \tilde{\beta}^2}$ (b) $\dfrac{\gamma}{\tilde{\beta}^2}$
   (c) $\dfrac{\gamma}{\tilde{\beta}}$ (d) $\dfrac{2\gamma}{\tilde{\beta}}$

Above Image: The moon eclipsing the sun. Photograph courtesy McGraw Hill Digital Access Library.

Chapters 6–23

9. The displacement associated with a wave is given by
$x(z, t) = 0.001 \cos(3x - 600t)$
where the distances are measured in meters and time in seconds. The velocity of the wave is
(a) 200 m/s (b) 50 m/s
(c) 4 m/s (d) 0.02 m/s

10. For an electromagnetic wave propagating in vacuum in the $+z$ direction, the electric field is given by
$$E_x = E_0 \cos[(4 \times 10^6\ \pi)z - \omega t],\ E_y = 0,\ E_z = 0$$
where the distances are measured in meters and time in seconds. The wavelength of the wave (in meters) is
(a) 0.5×10^{-6} (b) 4×10^6
(c) 3×10^8 (d) 6×10^{14}

11. For an electromagnetic wave propagating in vacuum in the $+z$ direction, the electric field is given by
$$E_x = E_0 \cos[(4 \times 10^6 \pi)z - \omega t],\ E_y = 0,\ E_z = 0$$
where the distances are measured in meters and time in seconds. The frequency ν of the wave (in Hz) is
(a) 0.5×10^{-6} (b) 4×10^6
(c) 3×10^8 (d) 6×10^{14}

12. For an electromagnetic wave propagating in vacuum in the $-z$ direction, the electric field is given by
$$E_x = 0,\ E_y = E_0 \cos[kz + (6 \times 10^{14})t],\ E_z = 0$$
where the distances are measured in meters and time in seconds. The wavelength λ of the wave is approximately given by
(a) 0.31 μm (b) 0.5 μm
(c) 3.1 μm (d) 5 μm

13. For an electromagnetic wave propagating in a dielectric in the $+z$ direction, the electric field is given by
$$E_x = E_0 \cos[(2 \times 10^6\ \pi)z - (4 \times 10^{14}\ \pi)],\ E_y = 0,\ E_z = 0$$
where the distances are measured in meters and time in seconds. The refractive index of the dielectric is
(a) 4 (b) 2
(c) 1.5 (d) 1.33

14. Sky appears blue because of
(a) Rayleigh scattering
(b) interference
(c) total internal reflection
(d) atmosphere being a graded-index medium

15. Setting sun is slightly elliptical in shape because of
(a) Rayleigh scattering
(b) interference
(c) total internal reflection
(d) atmosphere being a graded-index medium

16. Setting sun is red in color because of
(a) Rayleigh scattering
(b) interference
(c) total internal reflection
(d) atmosphere being a graded-index medium

17. In the integral representation of the Dirac delta function:
$$\delta(x-a) = K \int_{-\infty}^{+\infty} e^{+ik(x-a)}\, dk$$
The constant K is given by
(a) 2π (b) $\sqrt{2\pi}$
(c) $\dfrac{1}{\sqrt{2\pi}}$ (d) $\dfrac{1}{2\pi}$

18. In the Gaussian representation of the Dirac delta function:
$$\delta(x-a) = K \exp\left(-\frac{(x-a)^2}{2\sigma^2}\right); \sigma > 0$$
The constant K is given by
(a) $\dfrac{1}{\sigma\sqrt{2\pi}}$ (b) $\sqrt{\dfrac{2\pi}{\sigma}}$
(c) $\dfrac{\sigma}{\sqrt{2\pi}}$ (d) $\sigma\sqrt{2\pi}$

19. $H(x-a)$ is the unit step function at $x = a$. $H'(x) =$
(a) $\delta(x)$ (b) $-\delta(x)$
(c) $2\delta(x)$ (d) $-2\delta(x)$

20. Consider a function given by $f(x) = e^{-|x|}$. The value of $\dfrac{d^2 f}{dx^2}$ will be
(a) $f(x)$ (b) $-f(x)$
(c) $f(x) + 2\delta(x)$ (d) $f(x) - 2\delta(x)$

21. Consider a function given by $f(x) = A \exp\left[-\dfrac{x^2}{\sigma^2}\right]$. Its FWHM (Full Width at Half Maximum) is approximately given by
(a) $\approx \dfrac{12}{\sigma}$ (b) $\approx \dfrac{1.2}{\sigma}$
(c) $\approx 12\sigma$ (d) $\approx 1.2\sigma$

22. Assume $n(\lambda_0) = n_0 + A\lambda_0$; the group velocity is given by
(a) $\dfrac{c}{n_0 + A\lambda_0}$ (b) $\dfrac{c}{n_0}$
(c) cn_0 (d) $c(n_0 + A\lambda_0)$

23. The electric fields produced by two point sources are given by $E_1 = E_0 \cos(\omega t)$ and $E_1 = E_0 \cos(\omega t + \phi)$. The intensity distribution is given by
(a) $I = I_0 \cos^2(\phi/2)$ (b) $I = 4I_0 \cos^2(\phi/2)$
(c) $I = 4I_0 \cos^2(\phi)$ (d) $I = I_0 \cos^2(\phi)$
where I_0 is the intensity produced by each of the sources.

24. For a Gaussian pulse, the electric field is given by $E(t) = E_0 \exp\left[-\frac{t^2}{\tau_0^2}\right] e^{+i\omega_0 t}$. Its Fourier transform $A(\omega)$ will be

(a) $K \exp\left[-\frac{1}{4}(\omega - \omega_0)^2 \tau_0^2\right]$

(b) $K \exp\left[-\frac{(\omega - \omega_0)^2}{4\tau_0^2}\right]$

(c) $K \exp\left[-\frac{1}{2}(\omega - \omega_0)^2 \tau_0^2\right]$

(d) $K \exp\left[-\frac{(\omega - \omega_0)^2}{2\tau_0^2}\right]$

25. Consider a pulse for which, the electric field is given by

$E(t) = E_0 \exp(i\omega_0 t)$ for $|t| < \frac{1}{2}\tau$ and zero for $|t| < \frac{1}{2}\tau$

0 for $|t| > \frac{1}{2}\tau$

The frequency spread of the pulse $\Delta\omega$ is approximately given by

(a) $\sim\frac{1}{\tau}$ (b) $\sim\frac{c}{\tau}$

(c) $\sim\omega_0$ (d) $\sim\omega_0\tau$

26. The intensity distribution associated with the single slit Fraunhofer diffraction pattern is given by

$I = I_0 \frac{\sin^2\beta}{\beta^2}$, where

(a) $\beta = \frac{\lambda \sin\theta}{b}$ (b) $\beta = \frac{b \sin\theta}{\lambda}$

(c) $\beta = \frac{\pi\,\lambda \sin\theta}{b}$ (d) $\beta = \frac{\pi\, b \sin\theta}{\lambda}$

(b is the width of the slit and λ is the wavelength)

27. The first zero of $J_1(x)$ occurs at $x = 3.832$. Consider a parallel beam of light focused by a telescope objective of diameter D and focal length f. The first zero of the Airy pattern will occur at

(a) $\sin\theta = \frac{3.832\, D}{\pi\lambda}$ (b) $\sin\theta = \frac{3.832\,\lambda}{\pi D}$

(c) $\sin\theta = \frac{3.832\,\lambda}{\pi f}$ (d) $\sin\theta = \frac{3.832\, f}{\pi\lambda}$

28. Consider two point sources, such as stars being focused by a telescope objective of diameter D and focal length f. Each point source will produce its Airy pattern. According to the Rayleigh criterion for the two objects to be resolved, the angular separation of the two distant objects is given by

(a) $\Delta\theta \approx \frac{\lambda}{D}$ (b) $\Delta\theta \approx \frac{D}{\lambda}$

(c) $\Delta\theta \approx \frac{\lambda}{f}$ (d) $\Delta\theta \approx \frac{f}{\lambda}$

29. One of the Fresnel integrals is given by

$C(x) \equiv \int_0^x \cos\left[\frac{\pi}{2}x^2\right] dx$; $C(-\infty)$ is equal to

(a) $-\infty$ (b) $-\frac{1}{2}$

(c) 0 (d) $\frac{1}{2}$

30. Who discovered X-rays?
(a) Albert Einstein (b) Max Planck
(c) W E Roentgen (d) E Rutherford

31. Who was the first to say that '*light is an electromagnetic wave*?
(a) Albert Einstein (b) Christiaan Huygens
(c) J C Maxwell (d) Thomas Young

32. Who was the first to introduce the concept of displacement current?
(a) Albert Einstein (b) Christiaan Huygens
(c) J C Maxwell (d) Thomas Young

33. An x-polarized electromagnetic wave propagating in vacuum is described by the following equation

$$\mathbf{E} = \hat{\mathbf{x}} E_0 \exp[i(\omega t - 300y + 400z)]$$

The wavelength of the wave is approximately
(a) ≈ 0.126 m (b) $\approx 1.26 \times 20^{-2}$ m
(c) ≈ 500 m (d) $\approx \frac{500}{2\pi}$ m

34. An x-polarized electromagnetic wave propagating in vacuum is described by the following equation

$$\mathbf{E} = \hat{\mathbf{x}} E_0 \exp[i(\omega t - 500z)]$$

The angular frequency ω of the wave is approximately
(a) 24 GHz (b) 240 GHz
(c) 150 GHz (d) 1500 GHz

35. For an x-polarized electromagnetic wave propagating in vacuum $\mathbf{E} = \hat{\mathbf{x}} E_0 \cos(kz - \omega t)$. The corresponding magnetic field is given by $\mathbf{H} = \hat{\mathbf{y}} H_0 \cos(kz - \omega t)$. The value of H_0 is given by

(a) $\sqrt{\frac{\mu_0}{\varepsilon_0}}\, E_0$ (b) $\sqrt{\frac{\varepsilon_0}{\mu_0}}\, E_0$

(c) $\sqrt{\varepsilon_0 \mu_0}\, E_0$ (d) $\frac{1}{\sqrt{\varepsilon_0 \mu_0}} E_0$

36. For an x-polarized electromagnetic wave propagating in vacuum $\mathbf{E} = \hat{\mathbf{x}} E_0 \cos(kz - \omega t)$. The corresponding average of the Poynting vector $\langle \mathbf{S} \rangle$ is given by

(a) $\hat{\mathbf{z}}\frac{1}{2}\sqrt{\frac{\varepsilon_0}{\mu_0}}E_0^2$ (b) $\hat{\mathbf{z}}\sqrt{\frac{\varepsilon_0}{\mu_0}}E_0^2$

(c) $\hat{\mathbf{z}}\frac{1}{2}\sqrt{\frac{\mu_0}{\varepsilon_0}}E_0^2$ (d) $\hat{\mathbf{z}}\sqrt{\frac{\mu_0}{\varepsilon_0}}E_0^2$

37. At $z = 0$, the electric field associated with an electromagnetic wave (propagating in the $+z$ direction) is given by

$$E_x = E_0 \cos \omega t$$

$$E_y = E_0 \sin \omega t$$

If we plot the electric field in the diagram shown above (with z-axis going into the page) the electric field will rotate in the

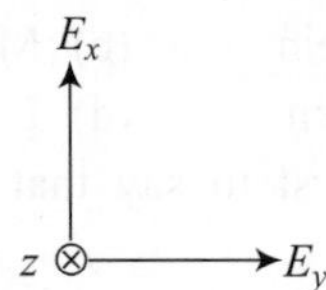

(a) clockwise direction
(b) anti-clockwise direction

38. When an unpolarized light wave is incident on a dielectric at the polarizing angle $\left(\theta_i = \theta_p = \tan^{-1}\frac{n_2}{n_1}\right)$, the reflected light is linearly polarized. The oscillation of the electric field (associated with the reflected light) is
(a) in the plane of incidence
(b) perpendicular to the plane of incidence.

Chapters 24–26

39. The 1921 Nobel Prize in Physics was awarded for "*his services to Theoretical Physics, and especially for his discovery of the law of the photoelectric effect*" to
(a) Albert Einstein (b) Erwin Schrödinger
(c) Niels Bohr (d) Werner Heisenberg

40. The 1922 Nobel Prize in Physics was awarded "*for his services in the investigation of the structure of atoms and of the radiation emanating from them*" to
(a) Albert Einstein (b) Erwin Schrödinger
(c) Niels Bohr (d) Louis de Broglie

41. The 1932 Nobel Prize in Physics was awarded for "*creation of quantum mechanics...*" to
(a) Albert Einstein (b) Louis de Broglie
(c) Max Born (d) Werner Heisenberg

42. A laser beam corresponds to a wavelength of 0.6 μm. The energy of each photon is approximately
(a) 3.3×10^{-19} J (b) 1.3×10^{-18} J
(c) 3.3×10^{-18} J (d) 1.3×10^{-17} J

43. Number of photons emitted per second by a 1 mW laser beam (corresponding to a frequency of 3×10^{14} Hz) is approximately
(a) 5×10^3 (b) 5×10^7
(c) 5×10^{11} (d) 5×10^{15}

44. In the Bohr model of the hydrogen atom, the angular momentum quantization condition is

(a) $m_e vr = nh$ (b) $m_e vr = n\frac{h}{2\pi}$

(c) $\frac{m_e v}{r} = nh$ (d) $\frac{m_e v}{r} = n\frac{h}{2\pi}$

where m_e represents the mass of the electron, v its speed, r represents the radius of the (circular) orbit and $n = 1, 2, 3, \ldots$

45. In the Bohr model of the hydrogen atom, the condition for the centripetal force to be equal to the Coulomb force between the electron and the nucleus is given by

(a) $\frac{m_e v^2}{r} = \frac{Zq^2}{4\pi\varepsilon_0 r^2}$ (b) $\frac{m_e v^2}{r} = \frac{Zq^2}{4\pi\varepsilon_0 r}$

(c) $m_e vr = \frac{Zq^2}{4\pi\varepsilon_0 r^2}$ (d) $\frac{m_e v^2}{r^2} = \frac{Zq^2}{4\pi\varepsilon_0 r}$

46. For the hydrogen atom, for the $n = 3 \rightarrow n = 2$ transition, the wavelength of the emitted radiation is 0.6565 μm. For the Helium ion, the wavelength for the $n = 3 \rightarrow n = 2$ transition will be approximately
(a) 0.1641 μm (b) 0.3282 μm
(c) 1.3130 μm (d) 2.6260 μm

47. The one dimensional time dependent Schrödinger equation is given by

$$i\hbar\frac{\partial\Psi(x,t)}{\partial t} = \qquad\qquad + V(x)\Psi(x,t)$$

The first term on the RHS is

(a) $-i\hbar\frac{\partial\Psi(x,t)}{\partial x}$ (b) $-\frac{\hbar^2}{2m}\frac{\partial\Psi(x,t)}{\partial x}$

(c) $-\hbar^2\frac{\partial^2\Psi(x,t)}{\partial t^2}$ (d) $-\frac{\hbar^2}{2m}\frac{\partial^2\Psi(x,t)}{\partial x^2}$

48. The solution of the one-dimensional time independent Schrödinger equation for a free particle is given by the following wave function: $\psi_p(x) = N\exp(i\,\alpha x)$. The value of α is given by

(a) $\frac{p}{\hbar}$ (b) $\hbar p$

(c) $\frac{\hbar}{p}$ (d) $\frac{p^2}{2m}$

49. The solution of the one-dimensional time independent Schrödinger equation for a free particle is given by the following wave function: $\psi_p(x) = N \exp(i\,\alpha x)$. The value of the normalization constant N is given by

(a) $\dfrac{1}{\sqrt{2\pi}}$ (b) $\dfrac{1}{2\pi}$

(c) $\dfrac{1}{\sqrt{2\pi\hbar}}$ (d) $\dfrac{1}{2\pi\hbar}$

50. The most general solution of the one dimensional time-dependent Schrödinger equation for a free particle is given by

(a) $\int_{-\infty}^{+\infty} a(p_x)\exp\left[\frac{i}{\hbar}\left(p_x x - \frac{2m}{p_x^2}t\right)\right]dp_x$

(b) $\int_{-\infty}^{+\infty} a(p_x)\exp\left[\frac{i}{\hbar}\left(p_x x - \frac{p_x^2}{2m}t\right)\right]dp_x$

(c) $\int_{-\infty}^{+\infty} a(p_x)\exp\left[i\left(p_x x - \frac{2m}{p_x^2}t\right)\right]dp_x$

(d) $\int_{-\infty}^{+\infty} a(p_x)\exp\left[i\left(p_x x - \frac{p_x^2}{2m}t\right)\right]dp_x$

51. The Gaussian function describing a free particle is given by $\Psi(x\cdot 0) = N\exp\left[-\frac{x^2}{2\sigma_0^2}\right]\exp\left[\frac{i}{\hbar}p_0 x\right]$. The normalization constant N is given by

(a) $\left(\dfrac{\pi}{\sigma_0^2}\right)^{1/4}$ (b) $(\pi\sigma_0^2)^{1/4}$

(c) $\dfrac{1}{(\pi\sigma_0^2)^{1/4}}$ (d) $\dfrac{1}{(\pi\sigma_0^2)^{1/2}}$

52. Assume $|\Psi(x, 0)|^2 = |N|^2 \exp\left[-\frac{x^2}{\sigma_0^2}\right]$. The quantity Δx, which represents the FWHM (Full Width at Half Maximum) will be about

(a) $\dfrac{1.67\hbar}{\sigma_0}$ (b) $\dfrac{3.34\sigma_0}{\hbar}$

(c) $\dfrac{1}{2}\hbar$ (d) $1.67\ \sigma_0$

53. Assume $a(p_x) = N\exp\left[-\frac{(p_x - p_0)^2\sigma_0^2}{2\hbar^2}\right]$; $|a(p_x)|^2\,dp_x$ = Probability of finding the (x-component of the) particle's momentum to lie between p_x and $p_x + dp_x$. The value of the normalization constant N is given by

(a) $\left(\dfrac{\sigma_0^2}{\pi\hbar^2}\right)^{1/2}$ (b) $\left(\dfrac{\sigma_0^2}{\pi\hbar^2}\right)^{1/4}$

(c) $\left(\dfrac{\pi\hbar^2}{\sigma_0^2}\right)^{1/4}$ (d) $\left(\dfrac{\pi\hbar^2}{\sigma_0^2}\right)^{1/2}$

54. Assume $|a(p_x)|^2 = N^2\exp\left[-\frac{(p_x - p_0)^2\sigma_0^2}{\hbar^2}\right]$. Without doing any detailed calculations, what will be a rough estimate of $\langle p\rangle$:

(a) $\dfrac{\hbar}{\sigma_0}$ (b) $\dfrac{p_0}{\hbar}$

(c) $\dfrac{p_0^2\sigma_0}{\hbar}$ (d) p_0

55. Assume $|a(p_x)|^2 = N^2\exp\left[-\frac{(p_x - p_0)^2\sigma_0^2}{\hbar^2}\right]$. The quantity Δp, which represents the FWHM (Full Width at Half Maximum) will be about

(a) $\dfrac{1.67\hbar}{\sigma_0}$ (b) $\dfrac{3.34p_0}{\hbar}$

(c) $\dfrac{0.84p_0^2\sigma_0}{\hbar}$ (d) $1.67p_0$

56. When photons are allowed to fall on a beam splitter
(a) The photon will always be in the reflected beam
(b) The photon will always be in the transmitted beam
(c) The photon will be in a superposed state being in the reflected beam as well as in the transmitted beam

57. Electrons are allowed to fall on a 2 hole arrangement to produce an interference pattern on a screen
(a) The electron will always pass through one of the slits
(b) The electron will be in a superposed state passing through both slits.

Chapters 27–30

58. Who was the first scientist to fabricate the laser?
(a) Theodore Maiman (b) Eli Snitzer
(c) C K N Patel (d) Ali Javan

59. Who was the first scientist to fabricate the He-Ne laser?
(a) Theodore Maiman (b) Eli Snitzer
(c) C K N Patel (d) Ali Javan

60. Who was the first scientist to fabricate the fiber laser?
(a) Theodore Maiman (b) Eli Snitzer
(c) C K N Patel (d) Ali Javan

61. Who was the first scientist to put forward the concept of stimulated emission?
(a) Max Planck (b) Niels Bohr
(c) Albert Einstein (d) Richard Tolman

62. Who was the first scientist to put forward the concept of optical amplification by stimulated emission?
(a) Max Planck (b) Niels Bohr
(c) Albert Einstein (d) Richard Tolman

63. A light ray, propagating in a medium of refractive index 1.46, is incident in a medium of refractive index 1.47. TIR (Total Internal Reflection) will occur when the angle of incidence is greater than
(a) 1.454° (b) 41.8°
(c) 83.3° (d) TIR will never occur

64. A light ray, propagating in a medium of refractive index 1.47, is incident in a medium of refractive index 1.46. TIR will occur when the angle of incidence is greater than
(a) 1.454° (b) 41.8°
(c) 83.3° (d) TIR will never occur

65. 1 μW power corresponds to
(a) –60 dBm (b) –30 dBm
(c) 0 dBm (d) 30 dBm
(e) 60 dBm

66. 1 mW power corresponds to
(a) –60 dBm (b) –30 dBm
(c) 0 dBm (d) 30 dBm
(e) 60 dBm

67. 0 dBm power corresponds to
(a) 1 nW (b) 1 μW
(c) 1 mW (d) 1 W

68. 400 mW power corresponds to
(a) 4.6 dBm (b) 23 dBm
(c) 46 dBm (d) 230 dBm

69. An Erbium Doped Fiber Amplifier (EDFA) has a gain of 30 dB. This corresponds to a power amplification of
(a) 30 (b) 60
(c) 100 (d) 1000

70. In a He-Ne laser, it is transition between atomic states of which atom that results in the laser wavelength of 0.6328 μm
(a) He (b) Ne
(c) Chromium ion (d) Erbium ion

71. In a Ruby laser, it is transition between atomic states of which atom that results in the laser wavelength of 0.6943 μm
(a) He (b) Ne
(c) Chromium ion (d) Erbium ion

72. In an Erbium Doped Fiber Amplifier (EDFA), it is transition between atomic states of which atom that results in the amplification of the wavelength of 1.55 μm
(a) He (b) Ne
(c) Chromium ion (d) Erbium ion

73. In a He-Ne laser (operating at a wavelength of 0.6328 μm), the two mirrors are separated by a distance of 60 cm; the frequency spacing between the longitudinal modes will be
(a) 15 MHz (b) 25 MHz
(c) 250 MHz (d) 1500 MHz

74. In a multi-longitudinal mode laser (operating at a wavelength of 1.55 μm) longitudinal modes are separated by a wavelength of about 0.005 μm. The frequency spacing between the longitudinal modes will be about
(a) 62 MHz (b) 620 MHz
(c) 62 GHz (d) 620 GHz

75. The wavelength corresponding to the lowest loss window for silica fiber is
(a) 0.60 μm (b) 0.85 μm
(c) 1.27 μm (d) 1.55 μm

76. What is the wavelength region in which EDFA amplifies optical signals?
(a) 0.60 μm (b) 0.85 μm
(c) 1.27 μm (d) 1.55 μm

77. Zero material dispersion will occur when
(a) $n(\lambda_0) = 1$ (b) $\frac{dn}{d\lambda_0} = 0$
(b) $\frac{d^2n}{d\lambda_0^2} = 0$ (d) $\frac{d^3n}{d\lambda_0^3} = 0$

78. Zero material dispersion wavelength for pure silica is approximately
(a) 0.60 μm (b) 0.85 μm
(c) 1.3 μm (d) 1.55 μm

79. The symmetric modes of a symmetric step index planar waveguide are determined from the following transcendental equation:

$$\xi \tan \xi = \sqrt{\left(\frac{V}{2}\right)^2 - \xi^2}$$

For $V = 8$, the number of symmetric modes will be
(a) 1 (b) 2
(c) 3 (d) 4

80. The anti-symmetric modes of a symmetric step index planar waveguide are determined from the following transcendental equation:

$$-\xi \cot \xi = \sqrt{\left(\frac{V}{2}\right)^2 - \xi^2}$$

For $V = 12$, the number of anti-symmetric modes will be
(a) 1 (b) 2
(c) 3 (d) 4

81. The V number of a step index fiber is given by
(a) $\frac{2\pi}{\lambda_0}a\sqrt{n_1^2 - n_2^2}$ (b) $\frac{2\pi\lambda_0}{a}\sqrt{n_1^2 - n_2^2}$
(c) $\frac{2\pi}{\lambda_0}a(n_1^2 - n_2^2)$ (d) $\frac{2\pi\lambda_0}{a}(n_1^2 - n_2^2)$

82. For a step index fiber with core refractive index $n_1 = 1.5$, cladding refractive index $n_2 = 1.49$ and core radius $a = 6$ μm; the value of the waveguide parameter V will be about
(a) $3.26\ \lambda_0$ (b) $\frac{3.26}{\lambda_0}$
(c) $6.52\ \lambda_0$ (d) $\frac{6.52}{\lambda_0}$
where λ_0 is measured in μm.

83. For a step index fiber [with n_1 and n_2 core and cladding refractive indices, respectively, and core radius a], the cut-off wavelength (λ_c) for single-mode operation given by
(a) $\frac{2\pi}{2.4045a}\sqrt{n_1^2 - n_2^2}$
(b) $\frac{2\pi}{2.4045}a\sqrt{n_1^2 - n_2^2}$
(c) $2\pi \times 2.4045 \times a\sqrt{(n_1^2 - n_2^2)}$
(d) $\frac{2\pi \times 2.4045}{a}(n_1^2 - n_2^2)$

84. For a fiber to work as a single-mode fiber at a wavelength of say, λ_0, the fiber's cut-off wavelength (λ_c) should be
(a) greater than λ_0 (b) less than λ_0

85. In a step index fiber the core radius $a = 4.5$ μm, $n_1 = 1.474$ and $n_2 = 1.470$, where n_1 and n_2 are the core and cladding refractive indices respectively. Calculate the wavelength region for the fiber to be single moded.
(a) $\lambda_0 < 0.65$ μm (b) $\lambda_0 > 0.65$ μm
(c) $\lambda_0 < 1.3$ μm (d) 1.3 μm

Chapters 31–33

86. The 1967 Nobel Prize in Physics was awarded for '*his contributions to the theory of nuclear reactions, especially his discoveries concerning the energy production in stars*' to
(a) Hans Bethe (b) Homi Bhabha
(c) Max Born (d) Albert Einstein

87. Who directed the 'atom bomb' project (also known as the Manhattan project)?
(a) Homi Bhabha (c) Max Born
(c) R Oppenheimer (d) Erwin Schrödinger

88. Who had first suggested that mesons could be used to study time dilation?
(a) Werner Heisenberg (b) Homi Bhabha
(c) Enrico Fermi (d) Erwin Schrödinger

89. The red shift of spectral lines (when atoms are moving away from the observer) is due to
(a) Lorentz contraction (b) Doppler effect
(c) Time dilation (d) Faraday effect

90. The hydrogen atom at rest emits radiation of frequency $\nu_0 = 6 \times 10^{14}$ Hz. If the hydrogen atom is moving towards you with a velocity $0.9c$, the observed frequency ν will approximately be
(a) 0.54×10^{14} Hz (b) 5.4×10^{14} Hz
(c) 6×10^{14} Hz (d) 6.6×10^{14} Hz

91. The hydrogen atom at rest emits radiation of wavelength 0.5 μm. If the hydrogen atom is moving away from you with a velocity $0.9c$, the observed wavelength will approximately be
(a) 0.45 μm (b) 0.5 μm
(c) 0.55 μm (d) 5.5 μm

92. In the nuclear reaction $H^2 + H^3 \rightarrow$ neutron + ??
(a) H^2 (b) H^3
(c) He^3 (d) He^4

93. In the nuclear reaction $Li^7 + H^1 \rightarrow$ alpha particle + ??
(a) H^2 (b) H^3
(c) He^3 (d) He^4

94. $m_p = 1.6726231 \times 10^{-27}$ kg, $m_n = 1.6749286 \times 10^{-27}$ kg and $m_d = 3.3435860 \times 10^{-27}$ kg where m_p, m_n and m_d represent the masses of the proton, neutron and deuteron, respectively; the deuteron consists of one proton and one neutron. The energy required to separate the two particles inside the deuteron nucleus will be approximately
(a) $\approx 4 \times 10^{-18}$ J (b) $\approx 4 \times 10^{-13}$ J
(c) $\approx 4 \times 10^{-8}$ J (d) $\approx 4 \times 10^{-3}$ J

95. $m_p = 1.6726231 \times 10^{-27}$ kg, $m_n = 1.6749286 \times 10^{-27}$ kg and $m_\alpha = 6.644656209 \times 10^{-27}$ kg where m_p, m_n and m_α represent the masses of the proton, neutron and alpha particle, respectively. The energy required to separate the 4 particles inside the alpha particle will be approximately
(a) $\approx 4.5 \times 10^{-18}$ J (b) $\approx 4.5 \times 10^{-15}$ J
(c) $\approx 4.5 \times 10^{-12}$ J (d) $\approx 4.5 \times 10^{-9}$ J

96. For the hydrogen atom, for the $n = 3 \rightarrow n = 2$ transition, the wavelength of the emitted radiation is 0.6565 μm. The loss of mass (when the atom makes the $n = 3 \rightarrow n = 2$ transition) will be
(a) $\approx 1.44 \times 10^{-48}$ kg (b) $\approx 3.35 \times 10^{-42}$ kg
(c) $\approx 3.35 \times 10^{-36}$ kg (d) $\approx 3.35 \times 10^{-42}$ kg

97. The sun emits 4×10^{26} Joules per second of energy. Its mass decreases approximately by
    (a) There is no decrease in mass
    (b) 4×10^{9} kg per second
    (c) 1×10^{18} kg per second
    (d) 4×10^{26} kg per second
98. For an observer on the earth, the mu-meson is moving vertically downwards with velocity $u = 0.995c$ and traverses the distance of 2 km in about 6.4 μs. For an observer moving downwards with the mu-meson (with the same velocity), the distance will be covered in about
    (a) 0.64 μs (b) 3.2 μs
    (c) 6.4 μs (d) 32 μs
99. For an observer on the earth, the mu-meson is moving vertically downwards with velocity $u = 0.995c$ and traverses the distance of 1920 m in about 6.4 μs. For an observer moving downwards with the mu-meson (with the same velocity), the distance 1920 m will appear to be
    (a) $0.5c$ (b) $0.6c$
    (c) $0.8c$ (d) c
100. Relative to the observer on the ground, two spaceships are moving in opposite directions with speed $0.5c$. With respect to an observer in the spaceship moving towards left, what will be the velocity of the other spaceship?
    (a) $0.5c$ (b) $0.6c$
    (c) $0.8c$ (d) c

For additional MCQs and answers to all MCQs, visit www.mheducation.co.in or scan the given QR Code. See inside back cover for more details.

References and Suggested Readings

Chapter 1

1.1 Isaac Newton, *OPTICKS: Or, A Treatise of the Reflexions, Refractions, Inflexions and Colours of Light*; the first edition was published in 1704, the fourth edition was published in 1730 and the Dover reprint was published in 1952. As a part of the Gutenberg project, it is now available on the internet; see http://sirisaacnewton.info/writings/opticks-by-sir-isaac-newton/.

1.2 Cristiaan Huygens, *Treatise On Light In Which Are Explained The Causes Of That Which Occurs In Reflexion, & In Refraction; And Particularly in the Strange Refraction of Iceland Crystal*; this is the English translation of his original book *Traite de la Lumiere* which was published in 1690*. As a part of the Gutenberg project, it is now available on the internet; see http://www.gutenberg.org/files/14725/14725-h/14725-h.htm and also http://www.gutenberg.org/ebooks/14725.

1.3 Thomas Young, *The Bakerian Lecture. Experiments And Calculations Relative To Physical Optics*, Read at the Royal Society of London on November 24, 1803; this lecture can be read at the website https://royalsocietypublishing.org/doi/pdf/10.1098/rstl.1804.0001

1.4 Andrew Robinson, ***The Last Man Who Knew Everything**: Thomas Young, The Anonymous Polymath Who Proved Newton Wrong, Explained How We See, Cured the Sick, and Deciphered the Rosetta Stone, Among Other Feats of Genius*, Oneworld Publications, Oxford (2006).

1.5 James Clerk Maxwell, *A Treatise on Electricity and Magnetism*, Clarendon Press, Oxford (1873). The second edition of this book (published in 1881) can be read at https://books.google.co.in/books/about/A_Treatise_on_Electricity_and_Magnetism.html?id=vltAAAAAIAAJ&printsec=frontcover&source=kp_read_button&redir_esc=y#v=onepage&q&f=false

1.6 A. Einstein, *On a heuristic point of view concerning the production and transformation of light*, Annalen der Physik, 17, 132-148, 1905. The English translation of this paper (and also of other papers published in his Year of Miracles) can be read at https://www.loc.gov/rr/scitech/SciRefGuides/einstein.html

* The translator (S. P. Thomson) in his Preface writes: The Treatise on Light of Huygens has, however, withstood the test of time: and even now the exquisite skill with which he applied his conception of the propagation of waves of light to unravel the intricacies of the phenomena of the double refraction of crystals, and of the refraction of the atmosphere, will excite the admiration of the student of Optics.

1.7 W.B. Joyce and Alice Joyce, *Descartes, Newton and Snell's law*, Journal of Optical Society of America, Vol. 66, pp. 1-8, (1976).

1.8 PSSC: Physical Science Study Committee, *Physics*, D. C. Heath and Co., Boston, Mass., 1967.

1.9 Robert P Crease, *THE PRISM & THE PENDULUM: The Ten Most Beautiful Experiments in Science*, Random House Publishing Company, New York (2003).

1.10 Dennis Gabor, *Holography 1948-1971*, Nobel Lecture (delivered on December 11, 1971); see http://www.nobelprize.org/nobel_prizes/physics/laureates/1971/gabor-lecture.html

1.11 R.P. Feynman, R.B. Leighton and M. Sands, *The Feynman Lectures on Physics*, Vol. III, Addison Wesley Publishing Co., Reading, Mass. (1965).

1.12 R.P. Feynman, R.B. Leighton and M. Sands, *The Feynman Lectures on Physics*, Vol. II, Addison Wesley Publishing Co., Reading, Mass. (1965).

1.13 A. Einstein, *Autobiographical Notes* (Translated from German by Paul Arthur Schilpp) in *Albert Einstein: Philosopher Scientist*, (Editor: Paul Arthur Schilpp), Second Edition, Tudor Publishing Co., New York (1951).

1.14 Max Jammer, *The Conceptual Development of Quantum Mechanics*, McGraw-Hill, New York (1965).

1.15 Victor F. Weisskopf, *What is Quantum Mechanics?*, in *The Privilege of Being a Physicist*, W.H. Freeman and Company, New York (1989); this article has been reprinted in Ref. 1.16.

1.16 Ajoy Ghatak and S. Lokanathan, *Quantum Mechanics: Theory & Applications*, 6th Edition, Trinity Press, Laxmi Publications, New Delhi (2019).

1.17 C.G. Shull, *Neutron Diffraction: A General Tool in Physics* in Current Problems in Neutron Scattering, Proceedings of the Symposium held at CNEN Casaccia Center in September 1968, CNEN, Rome (1970).

1.18 A. Tonomura, J. Endo, T. Matsuda, T. Kawasaki and H. Ezawa, *Demonstration of single-electron build up of an interference pattern*, Am. J. Phys. 57 (2). 117 (1989).

1.19 A. Rose, *Quantum Effects in Human Vision*, Advances in Biological and Medical Physics, Vol. V, Academic Press, (1957).

1.20 A. Zeilinger, *Dance of the Photons: From Einstein to Quantum Teleportation*, Farrar, Straus and Giroux, New York (2010).

1.21 T. Jennewein, U. Achleitner, G. Weihs, H. Weinfurter, and A. Zeilinger, *A Fast and Compact Quantum Random Number Generator*, Rev. Sci. Instr. 71, 1675–1680 (2000).

Chapter 2

2.1 M. Born and E. Wolf, *Principles of Optics*, Pergamon Press, Oxford, UK, 1975.

2.2 A.K. Ghatak and K. Thyagarajan, *Contemporary Optics*, Plenum Press, New York, (1978). [Reprinted by Laxmi Publications, New Delhi.]

2.3 R.P. Feynman, R.B. Leighton and M. Sands, *The Feynman Lectures on Physics*, **I**, Addison-Wesley Publishing Co., Reading, Mass., 1965.

2.4 M.S. Sodha, A.K. Aggarwal and P.K. Kaw, 'Image formation by an optically stratified medium: Optics of mirage and looming', *British Journal of Applied Physics*, **18**, 503, 1967.

2.5 R.T. Bush and R.S. Robinson, 'A Note explaining the mirage', *American Journal of Physics*, **42**, 774, 1974.

2.6 A.B. Fraser and W.H. Mach, 'Mirages', *Scientific American*, January, **234**, 102, 1976.

2.7 E. Khular, K. Thyagarajan and A. K. Ghatak, 'A note on mirage formation', *American Journal of Physics*, **45**, 90, 1977.

2.8 W.J. Humphreys, *Physics of the Air*, McGraw-Hill Book Co., New York, 1920.

2.9 S.K. Mitra, *The Upper Atmosphere*, Second Edition, The Asiatic Society, Calcutta, 1952.

2.10 W.A. Newcomb, 'Generalized Fermat's principles', *American Journal of Physics*, **51**, 338, 1982.

2.11 E. Khular, K. Thyagarajan and A.K. Ghatak, 'Ray tracing in uniaxial and biaxial media', *Optik*, **46**, 297, 1976.

2.12 V. Lakshminarayanan, A. Ghatak and K. Thyagarajan, *Lagrangian Optics*, Kluwer Academic Publishers, 2002.

Chapter 3

3.1 M. Born and E. Wolf, *Principles of Optics,* Pergamon Press, Oxford, 1975.

3.2 R.P. Feynman, R.B. Leighton and M. Sands, *The Feynman Lectures on Physics*, **I**, Addison Wesley Publishing Co., Reading, Mass, 1965.

3.3 A.K. Ghatak and K. Thyagarajan, *Contemporary Optics*, Plenum Press, New York, 1978. [Reprinted by Laxmi Publications, New Delhi.]

3.4 R.H. Penfield, 'Consequences of parameter invariance in geometrical optics', *American Journal of Physics.*, **24**, 19, 1956.

Chapter 4

4.1 J.N. Blaker, *Geometrical Optics: The Matrix Theory,* Marcel Dekker, New York, 1971.

4.2 W. Brouwer, *Matrix Methods in Optical Instrumental Design,* Benjamin, New York, 1964.

4.3 D.M. Eakin, and S.P. Davis, 'An application of matrix optics,' *American Journal of Physics,* **34**, 758, 1966.

4.4 A. Gerrard, and J.M. Burch, *Introduction to Matrix Methods in Optics,* John Wiley & Sons, New York, 1975.

4.5 K. Halbach, 'Matrix representation of Gaussian optics,' *American Journal of Physics,* **32**, 90, 1964.

4.6 A. Nussbaum, *Geometric Optics: An Introduction,* Addison-Wesley Publishing Co., Reading, Mass, 1968.

4.7 J.W. Simmons and M.J. Guttmann, *States, Waves and Photons: A Modern Introduction to Light,* Addison Wesley Publishing Co., Reading, Mass, 1970.

Chapter 5

5.1 M. Born, and E. Wolf, *Principles of Optics,* Pergamon Press, Oxford, 1975.

5.2 M. Cagnet, M. Francon and J.C. Thierr, *Atlas of Optical Phenomena,* Springer-Verlag, Berlin, 1962.

5.3 A. Ghatak and K. Thyagarajan, *Contemporary Optics,* Plenum Press, New York, 1978. [Reprinted by Laxmi Publications, New Delhi.]

5.4 H.H. Hopkins, *Wave Theory of Aberrations,* Oxford University Press, London, 1950.

5.5 C.J. Smith, 'A Degree Physics', Part III, *Optics,* Edward Arnold Publishers, London, 1960.

5.6 W. T. Welford, *Geometrical Optics,* North Holland Publishing Co., Amsterdam, 1962.

5.7 W. T. Welford, *Aberrations of the Symmetrical Optical System,* Academic Press, New York, 1974.

Chapter 6

6.1 C.J.F. Bottcher, *Theory of Electric Polarization*, Elsevier Publishing Co., Amsterdam, 1952.

6.2 H.J.J. Braddick, *Vibrations, Waves and Diffraction*, McGraw-Hill Publishing Co., London, 1965.

6.3 F.S. Crawford, *Waves and Oscillations: Berkeley Physics Course,* **III**, McGraw-Hill Book Co., New York, 1968.

6.4 R.P. Feynman, R. B. Leighton and M. Sands, *The Feynman Lectures on Physics*, **I**, Addison Wesley Publishing Co., Reading, Mass., 1965.

6.5 A.P. French, *Vibrations and Waves*, Arnold-Heineman India, New Delhi, 1973.

6.6 R. Loudon, *The Quantum Theory of Light*, Clarendon Press, Oxford, 1973.

6.7 H.J. Pain, *The Physics of Vibrations and Waves*, John Wiley & Sons, London, 1968.

6.8 R. Resnick and D. Halliday, *Physics*, Part I, John Wiley & Sons, New York, 1966.

6.9 A. Sommerfeld, *Optics*, Academic Press, New York, 1964.

6.10 J.M. Stone, *Radiation and Optics*, McGraw-Hill Book Co., New York, 1963.

Chapter 7

7.1 H.S. Carslaw, *Introduction to the Theory of Fourier Series and Integrals*, Dover Publications, New York, 1950.

7.2 E.C. Titchmarsh, *Introduction to the Theory of Fourier Integrals*, Oxford University Press, New York, 1937.

7.3 A.K. Ghatak, I. C. Goyal and S. J. Chua, *Mathematical Physics*, Laxmi Publications, New Delhi, 1995.

7.4 J. Arsac, *Fourier Transforms and the Theory*, Prentice-Hall, Englewood Cliffs, 1966.

7.5 E.C. Titchmarsh, *Introduction to the Theory of Fourier Integrals*, Clarendon Press, Oxford, (1959).

Chapter 8

8.1 P.A.M. Dirac, *The Principles of Quantum Mechanics*, Oxford University Press, Oxford (1958).

8.2 Ajoy Ghatak, I C Goyal and S J Chua, *Mathematical Physics,* Laxmi Publications, New Delhi (1985).

Chapter 9

9.1 H.J.J. Braddick, *Vibrations, Waves and Diffraction*, McGraw-Hill Publishing Co., London, 1965.

9.2 F.S. Crawford, *Waves and Oscillations, Berkeley Physics Course*, **III**, McGraw-Hill Book Co., New York, 1968.

9.3 C.A. Coulson, *Waves*, Seventh Edition, Oliver & Boyd Ltd., Edinburgh, 1955.

9.4 W.C. Elmore and M.A. Heald, *Physics of Waves*, McGraw-Hill Publishing Co., Maidenhead, 1969.

9.5 G. Joos, *Theoretical Physics* (translated by I. M. Freeman), Blackie & Son Ltd., London, 1955.

9.6 H.J. Pain, *The Physics of Vibrations and Waves*, John Wiley & Sons, London, 1968.

9.7 Physical Science Study Committee, *Physics*, D.C. Heath and Co., Boston, Mass., 1967.

9.8 J.C. Slater and N.H. Frank, *Electromagnetism*, Dover Publications, New York, 1969.

9.9 R.A. Waldson, *Waves and Oscillations*, Van Nostrand Publishing Co., New York, 1964.

Chapter 10

10.1 A.B. Arons, *Development of Concepts in Physics*, Addison-Wesley Publishing Co., Reading, Mass., 1965.

10.2 B.B. Baker and E.J. Copson, *The Mathematical Theory of Huygens' Principle*, Oxford University Press, London, 1969.

10.3 H.J.J. Braddick, *Vibration, Waves and Diffraction*, McGraw-Hill Publishing Co., London, 1965.

10.4 A.J. DeWitte, 'Equivalence of Huygens' principle and Fermat's principle in ray geometry', *American Journal of Physics*, **27**, 293, 1959.

10.5 C. Huygens, *Treatise on Light*, Dover Publications, New York, 1962.

10.6 PSSC, *Physics*, D.C. Heath and Company, Boston, Mass., 1965.

10.7 F.A. Jenkins and H.E. White, *Fundamentals of Optics*, 3rd Ed., McGraw-Hill, 1957, p. 465.

10.8 M. Born and E. Wolf, *Principle of Optics*, Pergamon Press, Oxford, 1975.

Chapter 11

11.1 R. P. Feynman, R. B. Leighton and M. Sands, *The Feynman Lectures on Physics*, Vol. I, Addison-Wesley Publishing Co., Reading, Massachusetts (1964).

11.2 U.C. Paek, G.E. Peterson and A. Carnevale, *Dispersionless single mode light guides with a index profiles, Bell Syst. Tech. J.* 60, 583 (1981).

11.3 S. Ramachandran (Ed.) *Fiber based dispersion compensation*, Springer Verlag (2008).

11.4 Donna Strickland and Gérard Mourou, *Compression of amplified chirped optical pulses*, Optics Communications, Volume 56, Issue 3, Pages 219-221, 1 December 1985.

11.5 G. P. Agrawal, *Nonlinear Fiber Optics*, Academic Press, Boston (1989).

11.6 A. Ghatak and K Thyagarajan, *Introduction to Fiber Optics*, Cambridge University Press, Cambridge, (1998) [reprinted by Cambridge India, New Delhi].

11.7 Akira Hasegawa and Frederick Tappert, *Transmission of stationary nonlinear optical pulses in dispersive dielectric fibers,* Appl. Phys. Lett. 23, 171 (1973);.

11.8 H. Toda, Y. Inada, Y. Kodama and A. Hasegawa, 10 *Gbit/s Optical Soliton Transmission Experiment in a Comb-Like Dispersion Profiled Fiber Loop*, 24th European Conference on Optical Communication (ECOC '98), MoC09, 101 (1998).

11.9 R. W. Boyd and D. J. Gauthier, *Controlling the Velocity of Light Pulses*, Science, 326, p. 1074 (2009).

11.10 ***Donna Strickland gives inside story of her Nobel-prize-winning research*** in ***Physics World***; see https://physicsworld.com/a/donna-strickland-gives-inside-story-of-her-nobel-prize-winning-research/

Chapter 12

See at the end of Chapter 13.

Chapter 13

13.1 F. Graham Smith and T.A. King, *Optics and Photonics: An Introduction*, John Wiley, Chicester (2000).

13.2 R.W. Ditchburn, *Light*, Academic Press, London (1976).

13.3 R.P. Feynman, R.B. Leighton and M. Sands, *The Feynman Lectures on Physics*, **I**, Chapter 52, Addison-Wesley, 1965.

13.4 M. Born and E. Wolf, *Principles of Optics*, Cambridge University Press, Cambridge, 2000.

13.5 E. Hecht and A. Zajac, *Optics*, Addison–Wesley, Reading, Mass., 1974.

13.6 R.S. Longhurst, *Geometrical and Physical Optics*, 2nd Ed. Longman, London, 1973.

13.7 D.E. Bailey and M.J. Welch, 'Moire Fringes', *Proceedings of the Conference and Workshop on the Teaching of Optics* (Edited by: G.I. Opat, D. Booth, A.P. Mazzolini and G. Smith, University of Melbourne, Australia.

13.8 A. Baker, *Modern Physics and Anti Physics*, Chapter 3, Addison–Wesley, Reading, Mass., 1970.s

13.9 PSSC, *Physics*, D.C. Heath & Co. Boston, Mass., 1965.

Chapter 14

14.1 M. Born and E. Wolf, *Principles of Optics*, Pergamon Press, Oxford, 1975.

14.2 M. Cagnet, M. Francon and S. Mallick, *Atlas of Optical Phenomena*, Springer–Verlag, Berlin, 1971.

14.3 E.F. Cave and L.V. Holroyd, 'Inexpensive Michelson interferometer', *Amer. J. Phys*., **23**, 61, 1955.

14.4 A.H. Cook, *Interference of Electromagnetic Waves*, Clarendon Press, Oxford, 1971.

14.5 M. Francon, *Optical Interferometry*, Academic Press, New York 1966.

14.6 A.K. Ghatak and K. Thyagarajan, *Optical Electronics*, Cambridge University Press, London, 1989. [Reprinted by Cambridge India, New Delhi.]

14.7 F.A. Jenkins and H.E. White, *Fundamentals of Optics*, McGraw-Hill Book Co., New York, 1976.

14.8 V. Oppenheim and J.H. Jaffe, 'Interference in an optical wedge' *Amer. J. Phys*., **24**, 610, 1956.

14.9 J. Sladkova, *Interference of Light*, Iliffe Books Ltd., London, 1968.

14.10 W.H. Steel, *Interferometry*, Cambridge University Press, London, 1967.

14.11 S. Tolansky, *An Introduction to Interferometry*, Longmans Green and Co., London, 1955.

Chapter 15

15.1 R. Baierlein, *Newton to Einstein: the Trail of Light,* Cambridge University Press, 1992.

15.2 P. Baumeister and G. Pincus, 'Optical interference coatings', *Scientific American*., **223**, 59, December, 1970.

15.3 M. Born and E. Wolf, *Principles of Optics*, Pergamon Press, Oxford, 1975.

15.4 M. Cagnet, M. Francon and S. Mallick, *Atlas of Optical Phenomena*, Springer–Verlag, Berlin, 1971.

15.5 R.W. Ditchburn, *Light*, Academic Press, London, 1976.

15.6 M. Francon, *Modern Applications of Physical Optics*, Interscience, New York, 1963.

15.7 M. Francon, *Optical Interferometry*, Academic Press, New York, 1966.

15.8 F.A. Jenkins and H.E. White, *Fundamentals of Optics*, McGraw-Hill Book Co., New York, 1976.

15.9 C. Lin, 'Optical communications: Single-mode optical fiber transmission systems', *Optoelectronic Technology and Lightwave Communications Systems*, Ed. C. Lin, Van Nostrand Reinhold, New York, 1989.

15.10 W.H. Steel, *Interferometry*, Cambridge University Press, Cambridge, London, 1967.

15.11 S. Tolansky, *Multiple Beam Interferometry of Surfaces and Films*, Oxford University Press, London, 1948.

15.12 S. Tolansky, *An Introduction to Interferometry*, Longmans Green and Co., London, 1955.

Chapter 16

16.1 D.E. Bailey and M.J. Welch, 'Moiré Fringes', *Proceedings of the Conference and Workshop on the Teaching of Optics*, Ed. G.I. Opat, D. Booth, A.P. Mazzolini and G. Smith, University of Melbourne, 1989.

16.2 J. Beran and G.B. Parrent, *Theory of Partial Coherence*, Prentice–Hall, Englewood Cliffs, N. J., 1964.

16.3 M. Born and E. Wolf, *Principles of Optics*, Pergamon Press, Oxford, 1975.

16.4 M. Francon, *Diffraction: Coherence in Optics*, Pergamon Press, Oxford, 1966.

16.5 A.T. Forrester, 'On Coherence Properties of Light Waves' *American Journal of Physics*, **24**, 192, 1956.

16.6 A.T. Forrester, R.A. Gudmundsen and P.O. Johnson, 'Photoelectric mixing of Incoherent Light', *Physical Review*, **99** (6), 1891, 1955.

16.7 A. Ghatak and K. Thyagarajan, *Contemporary Optics*, Plenum Press, New York, 1978. [Reprinted by Laxmi Publications, New Delhi.]

16.8 E. Hecht and A. Zajac, *Optics*, Addison–Wesley, Reading, Mass., 1974.

16.9 T.S. Jaseja, A. Javan and C.H. Townes, 'Frequency Stability of He–Ne Masers and Measurement of Length', *Physical Review Letters*, **10**, 165, 1963.

16.10 M.V. Klein, *Optics*, John Wiley, New York, 1970.

16.11 M.S. Lipsett and L. Mandel, 'Coherence Time Measurement of light from Ruby Optical Masers', *Nature*, **199**, 553, 1963.

16.12 G.F. Lothian, *Optics and its Uses*, Van Nostrand Reinhold, New York, 1975.

16.13 H.F. Meiners, *Physics Demonstrations and Experiments*, **2**, The Ronald Press Co., New York, 1970.

16.14 D.F. Nelson and R.J. Collins, 'Spatial Coherence in the Output of an Optical Maser', *Journal of Applied Physics*, **32**, 739, 1961.

16.15 A.E. Siegman, *Lasers*, Oxford University Press, 1986.

16.16 B.J. Thompson, *J. Soc. Photo. Inst. Engr.,* **4**, **7**, 1965.

16.17 K. Thyagarajan and A.K. Ghatak, *Lasers: Theory and Applications*, Plenum Press, New York, 1981. [Reprinted by Laxmi Publications, New Delhi.]

16.18 G.A. Vanasse and H. Sakai, *'Fourier Spectroscopy' in Progress in Optics*, **VI**, Ed. E. Wolf, North Holland Pub. Co., Amsterdam, 1967.

16.19 H. Weltin, 'Light Beats', *American Journal of Physics*, **30**, 653, 1962.

16.20 A. Sharma, A.K. Ghatak and H.C. Kandpal, 'Coherence', *Encyclopaedia of Modern Optics* (Ed: R. Guenther, A. Miller, L. Bayvel and J. Midwinter), Elsevier (2005).

Chapter 17

17.1 M. Born and E. Wolf, *Principles of Optics*, Pergamon Press, Oxford, 1975.

17.2 F.A. Jenkin and H.E. White, *Fundamentals of Optics*, McGraw-Hill Book Co., New York, 1957.

17.3 E. Hecht and A. Zajac, *Optics*, Addison-Wesley, Reading, Mass., USA, 1974.

17.4 A. Nussbaum and R.A. Philips, *Contemporary Optics for Scientists and Engineers*, Prentice-Hall, Englewood Cliffs, NJ, 1976.

17.5 K. Thyagarajan and A. Ghatak, *Lasers: Theory and Applications*, Plenum Press, New York, 1981; [Reprinted by Laxmi Publications, New Delhi.]

17.6 A. Ghatak and K. Thyagarajan, *Optical Electronics*, Cambridge University Press, Cambridge, 1989; [Reprinted by Cambridge India, New Delhi.]

17.7 A.R. Verma and O.N. Srivastava, *Crystallography for Solid State Physics*, Wiley Eastern, New Delhi, 1982.

17.8 M.S. Sodha, 'Theory of Nonlinear Refraction: Self Focusing of Laser Beams' *Journal of Physics Education, (India)*, **1 (2)**, **13**, 1973.

17.9 M.S. Sodha, A.K. Ghatak and V.K. Tripathi, *Self-Focusing of Laser Beams in Dielectrics, Plasmas and Semiconductors*, Tata McGraw-Hill, New Delhi, 1974.

17.10 W.K.H. Panofsky and M. Philips, *Classical Electricity and Magnetism*, Addison-Wesley, Reading, Mass., 1962.

17.11 W.G. Wagner, H.A. Haus and J.M. Marburger, 'Large Scale Self-trapping of Optical Beams in Paraxial Ray Approximation' *Physical Review Letters,* **175**, 256, 1968.

17.12 E. Garmire, R.V. Chiao and C.H. Townes, 'Dynamics and Characteristics of the Self-trapping of Intense Light Beams' *Physical Review Letters.*, **16**, 347, 1966.

17.13 J.W. Goodman, *Introduction to Fourier Optics*, McGraw-Hill, New York, 1968.

17.14 C.J. Ball, *An Introduction to the Theory of Diffraction*, Pergamon Press, Oxford, 1971.

17.15 J.M. Cowley, *Diffraction Physics*, North Holland, Amsterdam, 1975.

17.16 M. Francon, *Diffraction, Coherence in Optics*, Pergamon Press, Oxford, 1966.

17.17 H.F. Meiners, *Physics Demonstration Experiments*, **II**, The Ronald Press Co., New York, 1970.

Chapter 18

18.1 M. Born and E. Wolf, *Principles of Optics*, Seventh Edition, Cambridge University Press, Cambridge, UK (1999).

18.2 J.W. Goodman, *Introduction to Fourier Optics*, Third Edition, Roberts & Co., Englewood, Co. USA (2005).

18.3 M.V. Klein and T.E. Furtak, *Optics*, John Wiley, New York (1986).

18.4 A. Ghatak and K. Thyagarajan, *Contemporary Optics*, Plenum Press, New York (1978); reprinted by Laxmi Publications, New Delhi (1981).

18.5 J. Irving and N. Mullineux, *Mathematics in Physics and Engineering*, Academic Press, New York (1959).

18.6 G. Arfken, *Mathematical Methods for Physicists*, Second Edition, Academic Press, New York (1970).

18.7 A.K. Ghatak, I.C. Goyal and S.J. Chua, *Mathematical Physics*, Laxmi Publications, New Delhi (1985).

18.8 E.G. Steward, *Fourier Optics: An Introduction*, Second Edition, Dover Publications, New York (2004).

18.9 B.E.A. Saleh and M.C. Teich, *Fundamentals of Photonics*, John Wiley, New York (1991).

18.10 E. Hecht, *Optics*, Pearson Education, Singapore (2002). http://en.wikipedia.org/wiki/Fourier_optics.

18.11 A. Ghatak and K. Thyagarajan, *Problems and Solutions in Optics and Photonics*, McGraw Hill Education, New Delhi (2011).

Chapter 19

19.1 R. Baierlein, *Newton to Einstein: The Trail of light*, Cambridge University Press, 1992.

19.2 P.M. Rinard, 'Large scale diffraction patterns from circular objects', *American Journal of Physics,* **44**, 70, 1976.

19.3 M. Born and E. Wolf, *Principles of Optics*, Cambridge University Press, 2000.

19.4 A. Ghatak and K. Thyagarajan, *Contemporary Optics*, Plenum Press, New York, 1978.

19.5 M. Abramowitz and I.A. Stegun, *Handbook of Mathematical Functions with Formulas, Graphs and Mathematical Tables*, Applied Mathematics Series, **55**; National Bureau of Standards, Washington (1964).

19.6 A. Ghatak and K. Thyagarajan, *Problems and Solutions in Optics and Photonics*, McGraw Hill Education, (2011).

Chapter 20

20.1 D. Gabor, 'A New Microscopic Principle', *Nature*, **161**, 777, 1948; 'Microscopy by Reconstructed Wavefronts', *Proceedings of the Royal Society* (London), **A197**, 454, 1949.

20.2 K. Thyagarajan and A.K. Ghatak, *Lasers: Theory and Applications*, Plenum Press, New York, 1981 (Reprinted by Laxmi Publications, New Delhi.)

20.3 J.C. Brown and J.A. Harte, 'Holography in the undergraduate optics course', *American Journal of Physics*, **37**, 441, 1969.

20.4 H.J. Caulfield and S. Lu, *The Applications of Holography*, John Wiley & Sons, New York, 1970.

20.5 R.J. Collier, C.B. Burckhardt and L. H. Lin, *Optical Holography*, Academic Press, New York, 1971.

20.6 A.K. Ghatak and K. Thyagarajan, *Contemporary Optics*, Plenum Press, New York, 1978 (Reprinted by Laxmi Publications, New Delhi, 1984.)

20.7 M.P. Givens, 'Introduction to holography', *American Journal of Physics*, **35**, 1056, 1967.

20.8 E.N. Leith and J. Upatnieks, 'Photography by Laser', *Scientific American*, **212**, p. 24, June, 1965.

20.9 A.F. Metheral, 'Acoustical holography', *Scientific American*, **221**, p. 36, October, 1969.

20.10 K.S. Pennington, 'Advances in holography', *Scientific American*, **218**, p. 40, February, 1968.

20.11 H.M. Smith, *Principles of Holography*, Wiley Interscience, New York, 1975.

20.12 D. Venkateshwarulu, 'Holography, theory and applications', *Journal of Scientific and Industrial Research*, **29**, November, 1970.

20.13 B.L. Worsnop and H.T. Flint, *Advanced Practical Physics for Students*, Asia Publishing House, Bombay, 1951.

20.14 C. Sakher and Ajoy Ghatak, 'Holography' *Encyclopaedia of Modern Optics* (Eds. R. Guenther, A. Miller, L. Bayvel and J. Midwinter), Elsevier (2005).

Chapter 21

21.1 W.A. Shurcliff and S.S. Ballard, *Polarized Light*, Van Nostrand, Princeton, New Jersey, USA (1964).

21.2 G.R. Bird and M.P. Parrish, *The wire grid as a near infrared polarizer*, *J. Opt. Soc. Am* (1960), **50**, 886.

21.3 M. Alonso and E.J. Finn, *Physics*, Addison-Wesley, Reading, Massachusetts, USA (1970).

21.4 R.P. Feynman, R.B. Leighton and M. Sands, *The Feynman Lectures on Physics*, **I**, Addison-Wesley, Reading, Mass, USA (1963).

21.5 M. Born and E. Wolf, *Principles of Optics*, Pergamon Press, Oxford, England (1970).

21.6 A.K. Ghatak and K. Thyagarajan, *Optical Electronics*, Cambridge University Press, Cambridge, UK (1989). [Reprinted by Cambridge India, New Delhi]

21.7 F.A. Jenkins and H.E. White, *Fundamentals of Optics*, McGraw-Hill, New York, USA (1976).

21.8 *Polarized Light: Selected Reprints*, American Institute of Physics, New York, USA (1963).

21.9 S. Chandrashekhar, 'Simple model for optical activity', *Amer. J. Phys*, **24**, 503 (1956).

21.10 P. Gay, *An Introduction to Crystal Optics*, Longmans Green and Co, London, England (1967).

21.11 T.H. Waterman, 'Polarized light and animal navigation', *Scien. Amer* (July, 1955).

21.12 E.A. Wood, *Crystals and Light*, Van Nostrand Momentum Book No. 5, Van Nostrand, Princeton, New Jersey, USA (1964).

21.13 L.B. Jeunhomme, *Single-mode Fiber Optics,* Marcel Dekker, New York (1983).

21.14 Arun Kumar and Ajoy Ghatak, *Polarization of Light with Applications in Optical Fibers*, SPIE Tutorial Texts **TT90**, SPIE Press, USA, (2011); also published by Tata McGraw-Hill, New Delhi (2012).

21.15 Ajoy Ghatak and K. Thyagarajan, *Problems and Solutions in Optics & Photonics*, Tata McGraw-Hill, New Delhi, (2011).

21.16 Guy Ropars, Albert Le Flocha and Vasudevan Lakshminarayanan, *The sunstone and polarised skylight: Ancient Viking navigational tools*?, Contemporary Physics, 2014.

Chapter 22

22.1 D.J. Griffiths, *Introduction to Electrodynamics*, Prentice–Hall Inc., Englewood Cliffs, NJ, USA (1999).

22.2 C.S. Liu and V.K. Tripathi, *Electromagnetic Theory for Telecommunications*, Foundation Books, Delhi (2007).

22.3 J.R. Reitz and F.J. Milford, *Foundations of Electromagnetic Theory*, Addison–Wesley Publishing Company Inc., Reading Mass., USA (1967).

22.4 W.H. Hayt and J.A. Buck, *Engineering Electromagnetics*, McGraw–Hill, New York (2001).

22.5 W.K.H. Panofsky and M. Philhips, *Classical Electricity and Magnetism*, Addison-Wesley, Reading) Mass., 1962.

22.6 R.P. Feynman, R.B. Leighton and M. Sands, *The Feynman Lectures on Physics*, **1**, Addison Wesley, Reading, Mass., 1962.

22.7 D.R. Corson and P. Lorrain, *Introduction to Electromagnetic Fields and Waves*, W.H. Freeman and Co., San Francisco, 1962.

Chapter 23

23.1 J.M. Bennett and H.E. Bennett, 'Polarization' in *Handbook of Optics* (Ed. W.J. Driscoll), McGraw-Hill, New York, 1978.

23.2 O. Bryngdahl, 'Evanescent Waves in Optical Imaging', *Progress in Optics* (Ed. E. Wolf), **XI**, North-Holland, Amsterdam, 1973.

23.3 D.R. Corson and P. Lorrain, *Introduction to Electromagnetic Fields and Waves*, W.H. Freeman and Co., San Francisco, 1962.

23.4 R.P. Feynman, R.B. Leighton, and M. Sands, *The Feynman Lectures on Physics*, **I**, Addison–Wesley, Reading, Mass., 1964.

23.5 A. Ghatak, and K. Thyagarajan, *Optical Electronics*, Cambridge University Press, 1989. [Reprinted by Cambridge India, New Delhi].

23.6 J.R. Heirtzler, 'The Largest Electromagnetic Waves', *Scientific American*, **206**, 128, September 1962.

23.7 E.C. Jordon and K.G. Balmain, *Electromagnetic Waves and Radiating Systems*, Prentice-Hall, N.J., USA 1970.

23.8 W.K.H. Panofsky and M. Phillips, *Classical Electricity and Magnetism*, Addison–Wesley, Reading, Mass., 1962.

23.9 J.R. Reitz and F.J. Milford, *Foundations of Electromagnetic Theory*, Addison–Wesley, Reading, Mass., 1962.

23.10 H.S. Sandhu and G.B. Friendmann, 'Change of Phase on Reflection', *American Journal of Physics*, **39**, 388, 1971.

23.11 R.M.A. Azzam and N.M. Bashara, *Ellipsometry and Polarized Light*, North-Holland, Personal Library, (1987).

23.12 M. Beck, *Quantum Mechanics: Theory and Experiment*, Oxford University press, New York (2012).

Chapter 24

24.1 Isaac Newton, *OPTICKS: Or, A Treatise of the Reflexions, Refractions, Inflexions and Colours of Light*; the first edition was published in 1704, the fourth edition was published in 1730 and the Dover reprint was published in 1952. As a part of the Gutenberg project, it is now available on the internet; see http://sirisaacnewton.info/writings/opticks-by-sir-isaac-newton/

24.2 W. H. Cropper, *The Quantum Physicists and an Introduction to their Physics*, Oxford University Press, New York (1970).

24.3 A. Einstein, *Über einen die Erzeugung und Verwandlung des Lichtes betreffenden heuristischen Gesichtspunkt*, Annalen der Physik, Vol. 17, 132-148 (1905); English translation of this paper with the title *On a Heuristic Viewpoint Concerning the Production and Transformation of Light* can be read in the internet; see https://einsteinpapers.press.princeton.edu/vol2-trans/117

24.4 R. A. Millikan, *The Electron and the light-quanta from the experimental point of view*, Nobel Lecture delivered in May 1924, Reprinted in *Nobel Lectures in Physics*, Elsevier Publishing Co., Amsterdam (1965); the lecture can be read at http://nobelprize.org/nobel_prizes/physics/laureates/1923/millikan-lecture.pdf

24.5 R. A. Millikan, *THE ELECTRON: Its isolation and measurements and the determination of some of its properties*, University of Chicago Press, Chicago (1917).

24.6 David Bohm, *Quantum Theory*, Prentice-Hall, Englewood Cliffs, N.J. (1951).

24.7 A. H. Compton, *A Quantum Theory on the Scattering of X-Rays by Light Elements*, Physical Review, Vol. 21, p. 483. (1923). Reprinted in Ref. 24.10.

24.8 A. H. Compton, *The Spectrum of Scattered X-rays*, Physical Review, Vol. 22, p. 409, (1923). Reprinted in Ref. 24.10.

24.9 A. H. Compton, *X-Rays as a Branch of Optics*, Nobel Lecture (1927); see https://www.nobelprize.org/uploads/2018/06/compton-lecture.pdf

24.10 R.S. Shankland (Editor), *Scientific Papers of A. H. Compton: X-ray and Other Studies*, University of Chicago Press, 1975.

24.11 G. Baym, *Lectures on Quantum Mechanics*, W.A. Benjamin, Inc. New York (1969).

24.12 J. Townsend, *A Modern Approach to Quantum Mechanics*, McGraw-Hill Inc., New York (1992).

24.13 Ajoy Ghatak and S. Lokanathan, *Quantum Mechanics: Theory & Applications*, 6th Edition, Trinity Press, Laxmi Publications, New Delhi (2019).

24.14 A. Ashkin, J.M. Dziedzic, J. E. Bjorkholm and S. Chu, *Observation of a single-beam gradient force optical trap for dielectric particles,* Optics Letters, 11, 288-290 (1986).

24.15 A. Ashkin, *Forces of a single-beam gradient laser trap on a dielectric sphere in the ray optics regime, Biophys. J.*, 61, 569-582 (1992).

24.16 Arthur Ashkin, Optical Tweezers and their Application to Biological Systems, Nobel Lecture, see https://www.nobelprize.org/prizes/physics/2018/ashkin/lecture/

Chapter 25

25.1 Arthur Eddington, *New Pathways in Science*, Messenger Lectures (1934).

25.2 Niels Bohr, *On the Constitution of Atoms and Molecules*, *Philosophical Magazine,* Series 6, Volume 26, pp. 1-25, July 1913.

25.3 Ajoy Ghatak and S Lokanathan, *Quantum Mechanics: Theory & Applications*, 6th Edition, Laxmi Publications, New Delhi (2019).

25.4 J L Powell and B Craseman, *Quantum Mechanics*, Addison Wesley Publishing Co., Reading, Mass (1961).

Chapter 26

26.1 P.A.M. Dirac, *The Principles of Quantum Mechanics*, Oxford University Press, Oxford (1958).

26.2 Anton Zeilenger, *Dance of the Photons: From Einstein to Quantum Teleportation*, Farrar, Straus and Giroux, New York (2010).

26.3 W. H. Cropper, *The Quantum Physicists and an Introduction to their Physics*, Oxford University Press, New York (1970).

26.4 T. Jennewein, U. Achleitner, G. Weihs, H. Weinfurter, and A. Zeilinger,A Fast and Compact Quantum Random Number Generator, Rev. Sci. Instr. 71, 1675–1680 (2000).

26.5 W. H. Cropper, *The Quantum Physicists and an Introduction to their Physics*, Oxford University Press, New York (1970).

26.6 R.P. Feynman, R.B. Leighton and M. Sands, *The Feynman Lectures on Physics*, Vol. III, Addison Wesley Publishing Co., Reading, Mass. (1963).

26.7 David Bohm, *Quantum Theory*, Prentice-Hall, Englewood Cliffs, N.J. (1951).

26.8 A. Ghatak, *Basic Quantum Mechanics,* Trinity Press, Laxmi Publications, New Delhi (2005).

26.9 J.L. Powell and B. Craseman, *Quantum Mechanics*, Addison-Wesley, Reading, Mass., (1961).

26.10 Olaf Nairz, Markus Arndt and Anton Zeilinger, Quantum interference experiments with large molecules, American journal of Physics, Am. J Phys. Vol 71, 319-325, April 2003.

26.11 E. Schrodinger, *Discussion of Probability Relations between separated Systems*, Proceedings of the Cambridge Philosophical Society 31, 555-563 (1935); 32, 446-451 (1936).

26.12 A. Einstein, B. Podolsky, and N. Rosen, *Can quantum-mechanical description of physical reality be considered complete?*, Phys. Rev. 47, 777 (1935).

26.13 A. Einstein, *Autobiographical Notes* (Translated from German by Paul Arthur Schilpp) in *Albert Einstein: Philosopher Scientist*, (Editor: Paul Arthur Schilpp), Second Edition, Tudor Publishing Co., New York (1951).

26.14 J.S. Bell, "*On the Einstein-Podolsky-Rosen Paradox*", Physics 1, 195-200 (1964).

26.15 S. J. Freedman and J. F. Clauser, *Experimental Test of Local Hidden-Variable Theories*, Phys. Rev. Lett. 28, 938–941 (1972).

26.16 E. S. Fry and R. C. Thompson, "Experimental Test of Local Hidden-Variable Theories, Phys. Rev. Letts. 37, 465 (1976).

26.17 A. Aspect, *Closing the Door on Einstein and Bohr's Quantum Debate* in *Physics* 8, 123, 16Dec2015; see https://physics.aps.org/articles/v8/123.

26.18 A. Aspect, P. Grangier, and G. Roger, *Experimental Realization of Einstein-Podolsky-Rosen-Bohm Gedankenexperiment: A New Violation of Bell's Inequalities*, Physical Review Letters, Vol. 49, No. 2, pp. 91–94 (1982).

26.19 G. Venkataraman, *Quantum Revolution III: What Is Reality?*, Universities Press India Ltd., (1994).

26.20 Amir D. Aczel, *ENTANGLEMENT: The Unlikely Story of How Scientists, Mathematicians, and Philosophers Proved Einstein's Spookiest Theory*, Plume (Member of Penguin Group), New York (2001).

Chapter 27

27.1 C.H. Townes, 'Production of Coherent Radiation by Atoms and Molecules' in *Nobel Lectures in Physics (1963–1970),* Elsevier Publishing Company, Amsterdam, 1972. (Reprinted in Ref. 27.4).

27.2 N.G. Basov, 'Semiconductor Lasers' in *Nobel Lectures in Physics (1963–1970),* Elsevier Publishing Company, Amsterdam, 1972. (Reprinted in Ref. 27.4).

27.3 A.M. Prochorov, 'Quantum Electronics' in *Nobel Lectures in Physics (1963–1970),* Elsevier Publishing Company, Amsterdam, 1972. (Reprinted in Ref. 27.4).

27.4 K. Thyagarajan and A.K. Ghatak, *Lasers: Fundamentals and Applications*, Second Edition, Springer, New York (2011); Also published by Laxmi Publications, New Delhi (2011).

27.5 A. Einstein, 'On the Quantum Theory of Radiation', *Physikalische Zeitschrift*, **18**, 121, 1917 [Reprinted in Ref. 27.6].

27.6 D. Ter Haar, *The Old Quantum Theory*, Pergamon Press, Oxford, 1967.

27.7 A. Ghatak and K. Thyagarajan, *Introduction to Fiber Optics*, Cambridge University Press, 1998. (Reprinted by Cambridge India).

27.8 E. Desurvire, *Erbium Doped Fiber Amplifiers*, John Wiley, New York, 1994.

27.9 A.E. Siegman, *Lasers*, Oxford University Press, Oxford, 1986.

27.10 W. Johnstone, *Erbium Doped Fiber Amplifiers*, (Unpublished lecture notes).

27.11 S. Yoshida, S. Kuwano and K. Iwashita, 'Gain Flattened EDFA with high Al-concentration for multistage repeated WDM transmission experiments', *Electronics Letters,* **31**, 1765, 1995.

27.12 E. Snitzer, 'Optical Maser Action of Nd^{+3} in a Barium Crown Glass', *Physical Review Letters,* **7**, 444 – 446, 1961.

27.13 T.H. Maiman, 'Stimulated Optical Radiation in Ruby', *Nature*, **187**, 493–494, 1960.

27.14 R. Brown, *Lasers, A Survey of their Performance and Applications*, Business Books, London, 1969.

27.15 A. Javan, W.R. Bennett Jr. and D.R. Herriott, 'Population Inversion and Continuous Optical Maser Oscillation in a Gas Discharge Containing a He–Ne Mixture', *Physical Review Letters*, **6**, 106–110, 1961.

27.16 C.C. Davis, *Lasers and Electro-Optics*, Cambridge University Press, Cambridge, 1996.

27.17 J.T. Verdeyen, *Laser Electronics*, Prentice-Hall, Englewoodcliffs, N. J, 1989.

27.18 C. Lin, 'Optical Communications: single mode optical fiber transmission systems', in *Optoelectronic Technology and Lightwave Communication Systems,* Ed. C. Lin, Van Nostrand Reinhold, New York, 1989.

27.19 A.K. Ghatak and S. Lokanathan, *Quantum Mechanics*, 6th Edition, Laxmi Publications, New Delhi (2019).

27.20 A.K. Ghatak and K. Thyagarajan, *Optical Electronics*, Cambridge University Press, Cambridge, 1989.

27.21 D.R. Herriot, 'Optical Properties of a Continuous He–Ne Optical Maser', *Journal of the Optical Society of America,* USA, **52**, p. 31, 1962.

27.22 A. Maitland and M.H. Dunn, *Laser Physics*, North Holland Publishing Co., Amsterdam, 1969.

27.23 A. Ghatak and K. Thyagarajan, *Fiber Optics & Lasers: The Two Revolutions*, Laxmi Publications, New Delhi (2018).

27.24 A. Ghatak and K. Thyagarajan, *Problems and Solutions in Optics and Photonics*, Tata McGraw-Hill, New Delhi (2011).

Chapter 28

28.1 J. Hecht, *City of Light*, Oxford (1999).

28.2 W.A. Gambling, 'Glass, light, and the information revolution', Ninth W.E.S. Turner Memorial Lecture, Glass Technology **27**(6), 179, (1986).

28.3 S. Bhadra and A. Ghatal (Editors), *Guided Wave Optics and Photonic Device* CRC press, USA (2013).

28.4 B.P. Pal (Ed.), *Guided Wave Optical Components and Devices: Basics, Technology and Applications,* Academic Press (2006).

28.5 K. Porsezian and R. Ganpathy, *Odyssoy of Light in Nonlinear Optical Fibre* Boca Ratan, Florida (2015).

28.6 http://en.wikipedia.org/wiki/Photophone

28.7 D.J.H. Maclean, *Optical Line Systems*, John Wiley, Chichester, 1996.

28.8 A.G. Chynoweth, 'Lightwave Communications: The Fiber Lightguide', *Phys.Today*, **29**(5), 28 (1976).

28.9 C.K. Kao and G.A. Hockham, 'Dielectric-fibre Surface Waveguides for Optical Frequencies', *Proc. IEE,* **113** (7), 1151, (1966).

28.10 F. P. Kapron, D. B. Keck and R. D. Maurer, 'Radiation Losses in Glass Optical Waveguides', *Appl. Phys. Lett.*, **17**, 423 (1970).

28.11 *Schott is lighting the way home*, Fiberoptic Product News, February, 1997, p. 13.

28.12 *Fiber Optic Technology Put to Work-Big time, Photonics Spectra*, August 1994, p. 114.

28.13 A. Ghatak and K. Thyagarajan, *Optical Waveguides and Fibers* in *Fundamentals of Photonics* (Editors: A. Guenther, L. Pedrotti and C Roychoudhuri), Materials developed under project STEP (Scientific and Technology Education in Photonics) by University of Connecticut and CORD, National Science Foundation, USA.

28.14 T. Miya, Y. Terunama, T. Hosaka, and T. Miyashita, 'An Ultimate Low Loss Single Mode Fiber at 1.55 mm,' *Electron. Letts.* **15**, 106 (1979).

28.15 A. Ghatak and K. Thyagarajan, *Introduction to Fiber Optics*, Cambridge University Press, Cambridge (1998). Reprinted by Cambridge India.

28.16 W.K. Johnston III, *The Birth of Fiber Optics*, J. Endourology, **18**(5), June 2004.

28.17 A. Ghatak and K. Thyagarajan, *The Story of the Optical Fiber*, Physics News, July 2010.

28.18 N.S. Kapany, *Fiber Optics: Principles and Applications*, Academic Press, new York (1967).

28.19 Oak Ridge National Laboratory Review, *Letting The Sunshine In,* http://web.ornl.gov/info/ornlreview/v38_1_05/article09.shtml

28.20 B. Culshaw, 'Principles of Fiber Optic Sensors', in *Guided Wave Optical Components and Devices* (Ed. B. P. Pal), Academic Press, Amsterdam (2006).

28.21 B.D. Gupta, *Fiber Optic Sensors: Principles and Applications*, New India Publishing Agency, New Delhi (2006).

28.22 A. Ankiewicz and C. Pask, 'Geoemetric optics Approach to light acceptance and propagation in graded-index fibers', *Optical & Quantum Electronics*, **9**, p. 87 (1977).

28.23 T.K. Gangopadhyay, P.J. Henderson and A.D. Stokes, "Vibration Monitoring using a Dynamic Proximity Sensor with Interferometric Encoding", *Applied Optics,* **36**, No. 22, 1 August, 1997, pp. 5557-5561.

28.24 T.K. Gangopadhyay and P.J. Henderson, "Vibration: history and measurement with an extrinsic Fabry-Perot Sensor with solid-state laser Interferometry", *Applied Optics,* **36**, No. 12, 20 April, 1999, pp. 2471–2477.

28.25 T.K.Gangopadhyay. "Non-contact vibration measurement based on extrinsic Fabry-Perot interferometer implemented using arrays of single-mode fibres", *Measurement Science and Technology (IOP),* **15**, issue 5, May 2004, pp. 911 - 917.

28.26 T.K. Gangopadhyay, G.E. Town and A.D. Stokes, 'Noncontact vibration monitoring technique using a single-mode fibre sensor', Australian Conference on Optical Fibre Technology (ACOFT-99), 4–9 July 1999, Sydney, Australia.

28.27 T.K. Gangopadhyay, M. Majumder, A.K. Chakraborty, A.K. Dikshit and D.K. Bhattacharya, 'Fibre Bragg Grating strain sensor and study of its packaging material for use in critical analysis on steel structure', *Sensors and Actuators A: Physical*, **150** (2009), pp. 78-86.

28.28 Ajoy Ghatak and K. Thyagarajan, *Optical Waveguides and Fibers in Fundamentals of Photonics* (Editors: A. Guenther, L. Pedrotti and C Roychoudhuri), Materials developed under project STEP (Scientific and Technology Education in Photonics) by University of Connecticut and CORD, National Science Foundation, USA.

Chapter 29

29.1 A.W. Snyder and J.D. Love, *Optical Waveguide Theory*, Chapman and Hall, London (1983).

29.2 A. Ghatak and K. Thyagarajan, *Introduction to Fiber Optics*, Cambridge University Press, Cambridge, UK (1998); reprinted in India by Foundation Books, New Delhi.

29.3 D.K. Mynbaev and L.L. Scheiner, *Fiber-Optic Communications Technology*, Prentice Hall, USA (2001).

29.4 B.E.A. Saleh and M.C. Teich, *Fundamentals of Photonics*, John Wiley, New York (1991).

29.5 B.H. Bransen and C.J. Joachain, *Introduction to Quantum Mechanics*, Longman Group, UK (1989).

29.6 A. Ghatak and S. Lokanathan, *Quantum Mechanics: Theory and Applications*, 5th Edition, Laxmi Publications, New Delhi (2004); reprinted by Kluwer academic Publishers, Dordrecht (2004).

29.7 A. Ghatak, I.C. Goyal and R. Varshney, *FIber Optica: A software for characterizing fiber and integrated-optic waveguides*, Viva Books, New Delhi (1999).

29.8 J.C. Bose, 'On the influence of thickness of air-space on total reflection of electric radiation,' *Proceedings of the Royal society* A, **62**, pp. 301–310 (1897).

29.9 D.T. Emerson, *The work of Jagadis Chandra Bose: 100 years of mm-wave research* in http://www.tuc.nrao.edu/~demerson/bose/bose.html

29.10 D. Home, 'J.C. Bose's double-prism experiment using single photon states vis-a-vis wave-particle duality,' *Science & Culture*, **74**, pp. 408–415 (2008).

29.11 A. Ghatak and K. Thyagarajan, *Problems and Solutions in Optics and Photonics*, McGraw-Hill, New Delhi (2011).

Chapter 30

30.1 A.W. Snyder and J.D. Love, *Optical Waveguide Theory*, Chapman & Hall, London (1983).

30.2 D. Gloge, 'Weakly Guiding Fibers,' *Appl. Opt.* **10**, 2252, (1971).

30.3 A. Ghatak and K. Thyagarajan, *Introduction to Fiber Optics*, Cambridge University Press, Cambridge, (1998).

30.4 J. Irving and N. Mullineux, *Mathematics in Physics and Engineering*, Academic Press, New York (1959).

30.5 G. Arfken, *Mathematical Methods for Physicists*, Second Edition, Academic press, New York (1970).

30.6 A.K. Ghatak, I.C. Goyal and S.J. Chua, *Mathematical Physics*, Laxmi Publications, New Delhi (1985).

30.7 A. Ghatak, A. Sharma and R. Tewari, *Fiber Optics on a PC*, Viva Books, New Delhi (1994).

30.8 A. Ghatak, I.C. Goyal and R. Varshney, *Fiber Optica: A software for characterizing fiber and integrated-optic waveguides*, Viva Books, New Delhi (1999).

30.9 M. Abramowitz and I. Stegun, *Handbook of Mathematical Functions*, National Bureau of Standards, Washington DC, (1965).

30.10 T.I. Lukowski and F.P. Kapron, 'Parabolic fiber cutoffs: A comparison of theories', *J. Opt. Soc. Am.* **67**, 1185 (1977).

30.11 D.K. Mynbaev and L.L. Scheiner, *Fiber-Optic Communications Technology*, Prentice Hall, USA (2001).

30.12 D. Gloge and E.A.J. 'Marcatili, Multimode theory of graded-core fibers,' *Bell. Syst. Tech. J.*, **52**, 1563, (1973).

30.13 D. Marcuse, 'Gaussian approximation of the fundamental modes of a graded index fibers', *J. Opt. Soc. Am.* **68**, 103 (1978).

30.14 Arun Kumar, 'Polarization Effects in Single-Mode Optical Fibers,' in *Guided Wave Optics* (Ed: Anurag Sharma), Viva Books, New Delhi (2005).

30.15 D. Marcuse, 'Interdependence of waveguide and material dispersion,' *App. Opt.*, **18**, pp. 2930–2932, (1979).

30.16 J.L. Auguste, R. Jindal, J.M. Blondy, Clapeau J. Marcou, B. Dussardier, G. Monnom, D.B. Ostrowsky, B.P. Pal and K. Thyagarajan, *Electron. Lett.*, **36**, 1689, (2000).

30.17 K. Thyagarajan, R. Varshney, P. Palai, A. Ghatak and I.C. Goyal, 'A novel design of a dispersion compensating fiber', *Photon. Tech. Letts.*, **8**, 1510, (1996).

30.18 I.C. Goyal, R.K. Varshney and A.K. Ghatak, 'Design of a Small Residual Dispersion Fiber and a Corresponding Dispersion Compensating Fiber for DWDM Systems', *Optical Engineering*, **42**, pp 977–980, (2003).

Chapter 31

31.1 D. Bodanis, *E=mc²: A Biography of the World's Most Famous Equation,* Walker & Company, New York (2000).

31.2 A. Einstein, Ist die Trägheit eines Körpers von seinem Energieinhalt abhängig?, Annalen der Physik Vol. 18, 639-641 (1905); English translation of this paper with the title *Does the Inertia of a Body Depend Upon Its Energy Content?* can be read at https://www.fourmilab.ch/etexts/einstein/E_mc2/e_mc2.pdf .

31.3 F. Rohrlich, *An Elementary Derivation of* $E = mc^2$, American Journal of Physics, Vol. 58(4), 348-349, April 1990.

31.4 R. Baierlein, *Newton to Einstein: The trail of light*, Cambridge University Press, UK (1992).

31.5 R. Baierlein, *Does Nature Convert Mass into Energy*?, American Journal of Physics, Vol. 75(4), 320-325, April 2007.

31.6 Christian Doppler, *Über das farbige Licht der Doppelsterne und einiger anderer Gestirne des Himmels* (On the coloured light of the binary stars and some other stars of the heavens) published in 1842; Alac Eden has given an English translation of Doppler's 1842 treatise in his book *The search for Christian Doppler*, Springer-Verlag, Wien (1992).

31.7 B. M. Casper and R. J. Noer, *Revolutions in Physics*, W.W. Norton & Co., New York (1972).

31.8 R.P. Feynman, R.B. Leighton and M. Sands, *The Feynman Lectures on Physics*, Vol. I, Addison Wesley Publishing Co., Reading, Mass (1963).

Chapter 32

32.1 A. Einstein, *Zur Elektrodynamik bewegter Körper*, Annalen der Physik, **17**, 891-921 (1905); English transation of this paper with the title *On the Electrodynamics of Moving Bodies* can be seen in the internet; also reprinted in the book by John Stachel (Ref. 31.2).

32.2 J. Stachel (Editor), *Einstein's Miraculous Year: Five Papers That Changed the face of Physics*, Princeton University Press (1998); reprinted by Srishti Publishers, New Delhi.

32.3 T. Alvager, F.J.M. Farley, J. Kjellman and L. Wallin, 'Test of the Second Postulate of Special Relativity in the GeV region,' *Physics Letters*, **12**, pp. 260–262, October 1, 1964.

32.4 htt://members.tripod.com/~gravitee/axioms.htm

32.5 R.P. Feynman, R.B. Leighton and M. Sands, *The Feynman Lectures on Physics*, **I**, Addison Wesley Publishing Co., Reading, Mass (1963).

32.6 B.M. Casper and R.J. Noer, *Revolutions in Physiscs*, W.W. Norton & Co., New York (1972).

32.7 R. Rossi and D.B. Hall, 'On Muon Time Dilation', *Physical* Review **59**, 223 (1941). In 1963 David Frisch and James Smith repeated the Mt. Washington experiment and reported their measurements in the paper entitled Measurement of the Relativistic Time Dilation Using Mesons, *American Journal of Physics*, **31**, 342 (1963).

32.8 Lord Penney, *Homi Jehangir Bhabha*, in Biographical Memories of Fellows of Royal Society, **13**, 1967.

32.9 D. Ghosh and A.K. Grover (Editors), Special issue on H.J. Bhabha's Birth Centenary, *Physics News*, **39**, No. 1, January 2009.

32.10 H.J. Bhabha, 'Nuclear Forces, Heavy Electrons and the *β Decay'*, *Nature* (London), **141**, pp. 117–118 (1938).

32.11 J. Bailey, K. Borer, F. Combley, H. Drumm, F. Krienen, F. Lange, E. Picasso, W. Von Ruden, F.J.M. Farley, J.H. Field, W. Flegel and P.M. Hattersley, 'Measurements of relativistic time dilatation for positive and negative muons in a circular orbit', *Nature (London)*, **268**, pp. 301–05, 28 July 1977.

32.12 David Park, *The Fire within the Eye: A Historical Essay on the Nature and Meaning of Light*, Princeton University Press (1997).

32.13 Stephen Hawking, *A Brief History of Relativity* in the December 31, 1999 issue of TIME.

32.14 R.S. Shankland, 'Conversations with Albert Einstein', *American Journal of Physics,* **31**, pp. 47–57 (1963).

32.15 R.S. Shankland, 'Conversations with Albert Einstein II,' *American Journal of Physics*, **41**, pp. 895–901 (1973).

Chapter 33

33.1 J. Stachel (Editor), *Einstein's Miraculous Year: Five Papers That Changed the face of Physics*, Princeton University Press (1998); reprinted by Srishti Publishers, New Delhi.

Index

E

F

G

H

I

J

K

L

M

N

O

P

Q

R

S

T

U

V

W

X

Y

Z